GEOLOGY

TWELFTH EDITION

LEON E. LONG

DEPARTMENT OF GEOLOGICAL SCIENCES
THE UNIVERSITY OF TEXAS AT AUSTIN

Cover: The map on the front cover and information on the back cover were provided by the Bureau of Economic Geology, a research entity within the Jackson School of Geosciences at the University of Texas at Austin. Maps and reports published by the Bureau are available for a nominal price. A list of publications is available on request by writing to The University of Texas at Austin, University Station, Box X, Austin, Texas, 78713-8924, or calling (512) 471-1534.

Excerpts taken from:

Exploring Geography
by Shannon O'Dunn and William D. Sill
Copyright © 1986 by Prentice-Hall, Inc.
A Pearson Education Company
Upper Saddle River, New Jersey 07458

Revised material by Leon E. Long

This special edition published in cooperation with Pearson Custom Publishing.

Printed in the United States of America

10 9 8 7 6 5 4 3 2 1

ISBN 0-536-97916-2

2005260030

EH/LS

Please visit our web site at *www.pearsoncustom.com*

PEARSON CUSTOM PUBLISHING
75 Arlington Street, Suite 300, Boston, MA 02116
A Pearson Education Company

Contents

Preface

Our comprehension of nature has always progressed very unevenly. Often while data are patiently gathered for years, even decades, the mysteries that the data are supposed to explain seem only to grow darker. Then some new theory will quickly draw together the information into a pattern that is both reasonable and beautiful. Geology, the science of the composition, structure, and processes of the earth, is now experiencing a golden era.

The turning point began in the 1950s when geologic research suddenly flourished, handsomely supported at that time by government funds. Antarctica, the ocean basins, and other once inaccessible places began to be explored in detail. These investigations led to the theory of plate tectonics, a hypothesis that has given us a profound insight into the internal workings of the earth in space and time. Other dramatic advances include new understandings of the complex causes of climate change and Ice Ages, and of planetary origin through study of Moon and Mars rocks.

Geology is vitally important for another reason. It is the science of an Earth that is home for billions of human beings. Pressures of the population explosion and the rapid consumption of materials and energy have already reached a state of chronic crisis. More resources must be found. Cities remain pleasant living places only if their growth is carefully planned. Supply of clean fresh water sets a limit to development in many places. Hurricane, earthquake, and pollution hazards must be clearly recognized, if not avoided altogether. Demand for geologists equipped to cope with the problems of a technology-based civilization will increase in the future.

In contrast to the frenzied lives led by most of us, changes in the earth continue at an unhurried tempo. Although we may write poetry about the eternal hills, we know that they are not truly eternal. Geology is concerned not only with configuration and process, but also with an interpretation of the long and varied history of this planet. So strong is the historical flavor that the subject has traditionally been taught as separate courses in "physical" and "historical" geology. This book does not make such a distinction. Broadly speaking, geologic time is its unifying theme. Perhaps this reflects my own fascination with antiquity, as my research specialty is to utilize trace amounts of naturally occurring radioactivity in a procedure to tell ages of ancient geologic events.

This book is designed for a one-semester introductory course, GEO 303, based upon classroom lectures, and labs in which smaller groups of students learn minerals, rocks, fossils, geologic maps and structures, and participate in field trips. Lecture and lab material are interwoven throughout. Chapters 1 and 2 examine the origins of the universe, and of the earth and solar system. Chapters 3 through 10 present the minerals and rocks (aggregates of minerals) of which the earth is made. Chapter 11, describing methods to tell geologic time, is preparation for the history of the development of life (Chapters 12 through 15). Chapters 16 through 21 are concerned with geophysics, earth structures, and other items in preparation for the grand synthesis, plate tectonics. The final chapters focus upon sedimentary processes, Ice Ages and climate, and natural resources—aspects of geology important to our civilization and indeed to our survival.

From the outset GEO 303 has been team-taught, by now to approximately 25 thousand students at the University of Texas at Austin. I owe so much to my professor colleagues who have joined me in this endeavor. In recent years three of them, who have teamed with me many times, are Douglas Smith, Stephen Grand, and Libby Stern. Rosemary Barker is the most astute copy editor I have ever met. Thanks again, Steve, Doug, and Libby, for your encouragement and for all else that you have done to make the course a success, and to you, Rosemary, for your vital contribution.

Over the years this book has had other incarnations, other editions, configurations, and publishers. Laura Warner, then (in later editions) Marci Taylor, and then Cydney Capell and Sara Holzinger assisted with hundreds of editorial decisions. I thank Shannon O'Dunn who was chief author of a lab manual whose content is partly included here. Felix Cooper and his associates drafted elegant graphics in the earlier days. By this point, I have transformed most of those paper and plastic images into computer graphics, including more than 100 new ones for this, the 10th edition.

Finally, I would have been "nowhere" without the expert guidance of scientific colleagues, or suggestions from students about how to say something better. I've turned for help to John Wilson, L. Jan Turk, James Sprinkle, William Sill, Alan Scott, Peter Schultz, David Schramm, Suzanne Schoenner, William Rust, Timothy Rowe, George Ridge, Ross Nicholson, William Muehlberger, Fred McDowell, Earle McBride, John Maxwell, Ernest Lundelius, Mary Long, Donald Larson, Wann Langston, Lynton Land, Martin Lagoe, J. Richard Kyle, Edward Jonas, F. Earl Ingerson, Paul Hudson, Christopher Henry, Charles Helsley, Robert Heller, Wulf Gose, William Galloway, Robert Folk, William Donn, Stephen DeLong, Lou Deans, Dwight Deal, Ian Dalziel, Andrew Czebieniak, Arthur Cleaves, Stephen Clabaugh, William Carlson, Fred Bullard, L. Frank Brown, Alan Blaxland, Philip Bennett, Christopher Bell, Daniel Barker, and Victor Baker. My wife, Mary, has given her support during my seemingly unending hours composing in front of a computer, striving to meet some deadline.

Leon E. Long
May 2001

This book is dedicated to Mary, love of my life.

PREFACE TO THE 11TH AND 12TH EDITIONS

Almost all of this revision is of chapters devoted to lab material. I am indebted to Vanessa Svihla, one of my teaching assistants, for numerous excellent suggestions for improvement, innovation, or correction. Vanessa, you are already a master teacher.

1

Cosmic Beginnings

Heavy chemical elements were created when a star violently exploded, becoming visible on earth in A. D. 1054. The Crab Nebula is an expanding cloud of explosion debris. [*Hale Observatories photograph*]

For more than 3000 years of recorded history, thoughtful people have speculated about the universe. Their ancient questions, so easy to pose and so difficult to solve, are largely unanswered today. How did all this matter and energy begin? Indeed, did the universe have a beginning, and will it come to an end? Is the universe finite, or unlimited? What is it like? Are the scientific laws familiar to us in the laboratory just as valid on the universal scale of size?

Among the multitude of objects in the universe is located that infinitesimal speck of matter upon which we live. Clearly, the origin and history of the earth must somehow be connected to that of everything else. Great progress has been made in answering such profound, occasionally disturbing, questions about cosmic beginnings. The scientist who is struggling to understand such a grand subject is keenly aware of human limitations. He knows that we shall never see to the edge of the universe (if there is an edge), and that a human lifetime is only a moment compared with the age of the universe (if indeed it has a finite age). Our comprehension is so narrow, so limited. It is like seeing only the tip of an iceberg whose vast bulk is hidden beneath the waves. In view of these limitations, how can we proceed?

ORIGIN OF THE UNIVERSE

One useful way to attack scientific problems is to construct a *model*. For example, everyone knows that a model railroad is a miniature object that looks and acts like the real thing. Other models may be sets of symbols, strictly mathematical. Whatever the case, a model is a simple notion in which a part of nature is considered as though it were isolated from the rest. Because models are artificial and oversimplified, all of them are "wrong" in one way or other. But they generally are based upon familiar objects, and they can be very useful to represent a thing or idea that we are trying to understand.

Models are created to enable us to make predictions about the real world. Further observations either confirm the prediction, or require the model to be modified or perhaps discarded altogether. For example, before the time of Copernicus a widely accepted model placed the earth at the center of the solar system. This model predicted the motions of the other planets and of the sun as seen from the earth. Copernicus found that a simpler model, in which the sun lies at the center, explained the observations even better, and over the centuries this basic idea has been abundantly confirmed.

Figure 1-1. Messier 101, a spiral galaxy turned face-on toward our own galaxy, is located in the northern night sky in the constellation Ursa Major (Big Bear). [*Hale Observatories photograph.*]

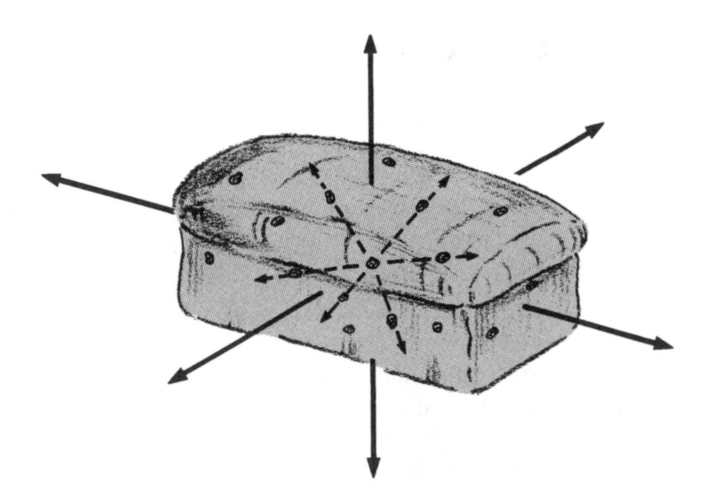

Figure 1-2. As the loaf of raisin bread rises (expands), every raisin, both on the surface and in the interior, moves farther from every other raisin.

Structure of the Universe

Any model of the origin of the universe must begin with observations of its structure. Early in the 20th Century it was discovered that the universe is populated, as far as can be seen in all directions, with local concentrations of matter called *galaxies.* At least a thousand million galaxies are located within the seeing range of large telescopes. Our own galaxy, the Milky Way, is a disk-shaped collection of about 100 thousand million stars, plus dust and gas not condensed into stars, and probably some extremely massive objects such as "Black Holes" from which light is unable to escape. In the thickened central bulge of the Milky Way, stars are most densely crowded. Toward the edge, our galaxy is thinner, and possibly flung out into broad spiral "arms" like those of a distant but similar galaxy (Figure 1-1). Between the arms are dark, relatively empty lanes.

Astronomers have devised clever ways to estimate sizes of galaxies and distances between them. The measurements show the star-populated disk of the Milky Way to be about 100 thousand light-years across, some 60 times greater than the thickness of the disk. (One light-year, about 10 trillion kilometers, is the distance that light travels through empty space in one year.) Our galaxy is one of a local cluster of 26 galaxies typically spaced 1 to 2 million light-years apart. The local cluster in turn is part of a supercluster numbering thousands of galaxies, and such clusters of clusters extend to the limits of the visible universe.

Models of the Universe

Among the many important contributions of the physicist Albert Einstein is his theoretical model of a closed four-dimensional universe. (A fourth dimension, which is time multiplied by the speed of light, is introduced because an observer in one part of the heavens cannot recognize an event in a distant part until the message borne by light reaches him. The signal may have been traveling for a very long time. We see things not as they *are*, but as they *were*.) Einstein's model had some peculiar properties not possible for us to imagine except by reference to a more homespun analogy, a lump of raisin bread dough (Figure 1-2). In a sense, we are like an insect that is crawling around over the lump of dough and which, upon returning to its starting point, would conclude that its universe is "closed." Similarly, light energy in principle could circumnavigate the real universe back to its beginning point because space is curved.

Einstein's early model of the universe was also static, analogous to a lump of dough of fixed size. This feature was worrisome because Einstein was aware that the force of gravity should draw the galaxies (the "raisins") toward one another, causing the universe to collapse. Inasmuch as no such catastrophe seemed to be in the making, he had to postulate that a mysterious force must exist to counteract the recognized force of gravity.

In the 1920s a series of astounding discoveries made the static model obsolete and set the stage for all modern thinking about cosmic origins. Studies undertaken at Mount Wilson Observatory, California, definitely established the existence of numberless galaxies outside of the Milky Way. Other breakthroughs quickly followed when astronomers trained their newly refined spectrographs upon these distant aggregates of stars. A spectrograph can sort out the complex mixture of wavelengths of light (the light *spectrum*) reaching the earth from such sources. A typical spectrum appears as a set of bright lines, each corresponding to a particular wavelength (Figure 1-3).

The Red Shift

Similar lines had been previously observed in the laboratory, and it was known that they correspond to the chemical elements when heated to the point that they give off light. Comparisons of spectrums promptly informed the astronomers that stars in the farthest reaches of the heavens are made of the same elements that are familiar to us on earth, except for certain peculiarities.

For example, the lines registered from galaxies in our local cluster appear similar to lines produced by a source of light in the laboratory, but for more distant clusters the spectral lines are distinctly offset on the photographic plate (Figure 1-3). The offset is in the direction of longer wavelengths, which would be perceived by the eye as a reddening of color. Thus this observation came to be known as a "red shift" of the light. The farther the distant galaxy is from us, the greater is the red shift of its light spectrum.

Some astronomers proposed that the light is reddened as it passes through dust, just as we see a red sky at dawn or at dusk. This is reasonable, but soon the red shift was noted in all directions in the sky, not just in regions where dust is present. A more plausible explanation makes use of the *Doppler effect*, which describes how one would receive light waves coming from a moving source. Suppose that a source at point *A* is sending out waves in all directions (Figure 1-4). If it is stationary with respect to observers at *B* and *C* then the expanding circles of waves are uniformly spaced. On the other hand, if source *D* is moving to the left, it partly catches up to its own waves as it continues to give off more waves; consequently the waves received by observer *E* are crowded together (wavelength shortened). Conversely, from the viewpoint of observer *F*, the wavelengths are lengthened—they are red-shifted. Thus the red shift signifies that the distant galaxies are traveling away from us. The substance of the universe is receding in all directions! This expansion is the single most important fact that can be stated about the universe as a whole, and naturally the idea plays a prominent role in every modern model of its origin.

But why are the galaxies rushing away from *us*? Are we by chance at the center of the universe? The raisin-bread analogy helps at this point. When the loaf rises, every raisin grows more distant from every other raisin (Figure 1-5). Light from the Milky Way would appear red-shifted to a very distant observer, just as light from his galaxy appears red-shifted to us. There is nothing unique about either his or our position in the universe.

The Big Bang

In the light of this evidence, Einstein abandoned his static model with its postulate of an antigravity force. Many other features of his original version, such as the curvature of space, have been retained in

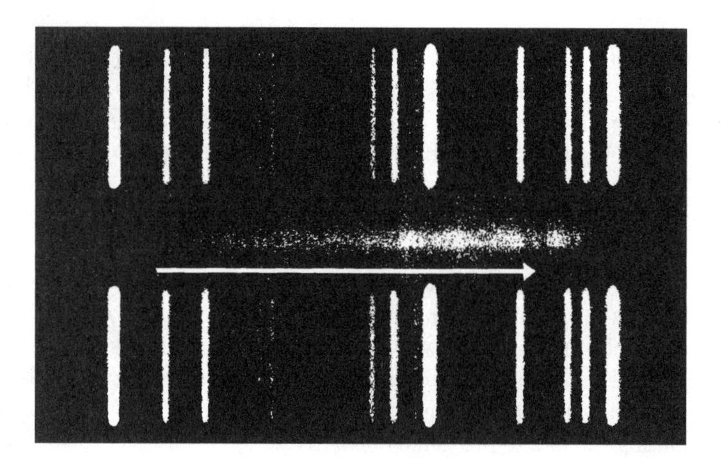

Figure 1-3. Upper and lower strips with vertical lines are reference spectrums created by an incandescent lamp. They help to identify the spectral lines due to a distant cluster of galaxies (center strip). An arrow indicates the extent to which a faint line from the distant galaxies has been shifted toward the right, in the direction of lengthened wavelengths (reddened light). The red shift in this case is equivalent to a recession of the distant galaxies at 60 thousand kilometers per second. [*Hale Observatories photograph.*]

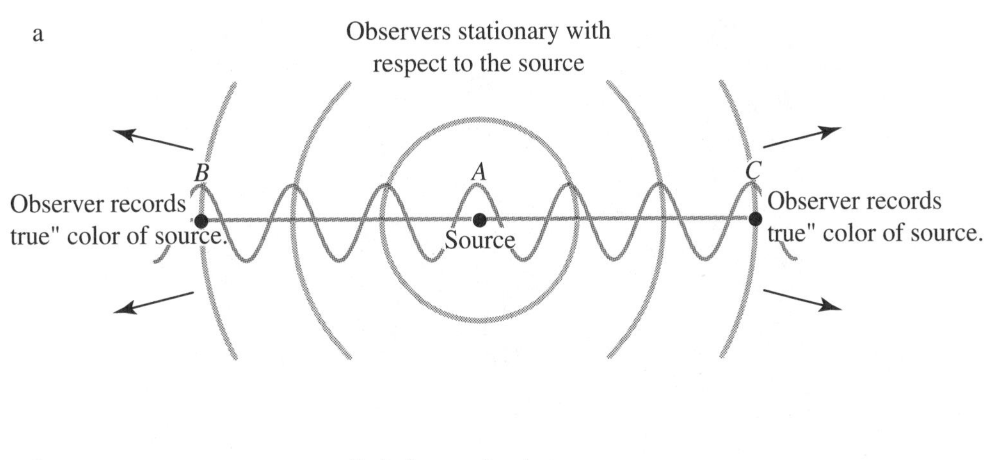

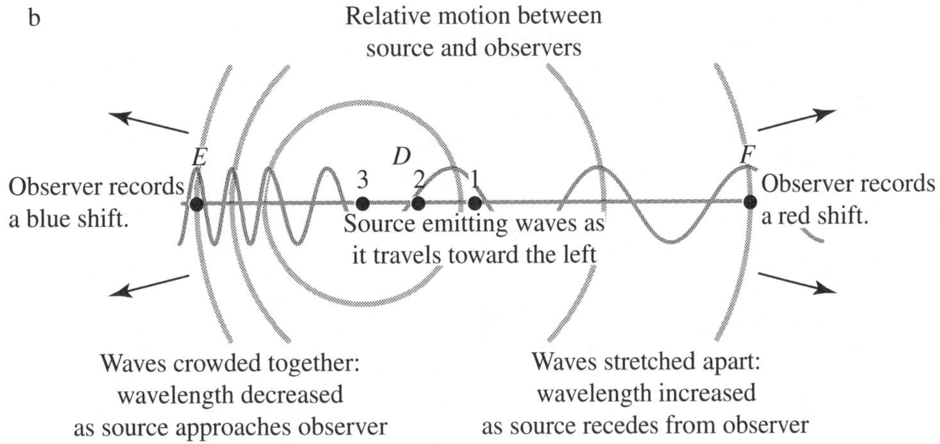

Figure 1-4. *(a)* Radiation may be pictured as a wiggly line in which the wavelength is the distance between crests of adjacent wiggles. Waves travel away from the source in all directions, as symbolized by expanding circles. In the stationary situation, the circles are centered upon the source (they are concentric) and the same wavelength is recorded by observers on the left and on the right. *(b)* If the source itself is traveling while emitting waves, each expanding circle is centered upon the point where the source happened to be at the moment that circle was launched. An observer being approached by the source would receive crowded-together circles (wavelength shortened, equivalent to more bluish light). An observer from whom the source is receding would receive stretched-apart circles (wavelength lengthened, equivalent to more reddish light).

more recent models. It is tempting to take the notion of an expanding universe to a logical conclusion. If we imagine the clock being turned back, we must conclude that in past times the galaxies were closer together. According to modern estimates the Big Bang (the beginning of expansion) took place about 13.7 billion years ago (the time is known quite accurately), when the contents of the universe were compressed into a dense nucleus.

Will the expansion continue forever? If so, the universe is "open", or infinite (Figure 1-6(*a*). On the other hand, if the universe is actually "closed", or finite, then the expansion will eventually slow to a stop. The force of gravity will pull the universe back together to a compressed point from which it rebounds, and these gigantic oscillations, each about 100 billion years in duration, will repeat indefinitely (Figure 1-6(*b*).

Whether the universe is open or closed depends upon the average density of matter in space; if the density is greater than approximately 5 atoms per cubic meter, then the force of gravity, which attracts every particle toward every other particle, will be sufficient to reverse the outward flight of the galaxies, and the universe is closed. If the density is less than this critical value, the universe is open. Our current understanding is that the universe is "flat," which is yet a third possibility (Figure 1-6(*c*)). In a flat universe, expansion continues but ever more slowly as gravity continues to drag back on the fleeing galaxies.

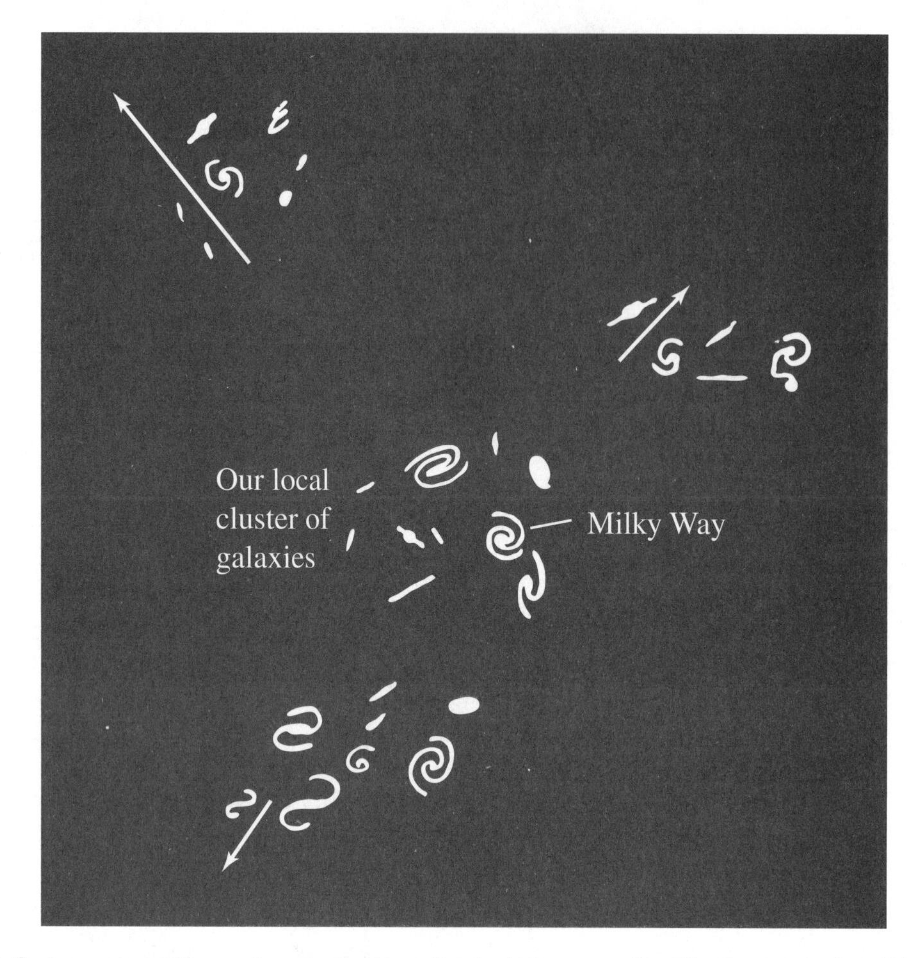

Figure 1-5. In an expanding universe, clusters of galaxies are receding from one another. The rate of recession itself increases with increasing distance between clusters.

Einstein showed that matter and energy are equivalent. Matter can be transformed into energy, and energy can be transformed into matter. Thus it is useful to consider the physical contents of the universe together, as made up of "matter-energy." About 95% of the universe consists of "dark matter" and "dark energy." Calling them dark is to admit that we do not know what these things are. Astronomers see the effect of gravity exerted by dark matter, but they cannot detect it directly; dark matter is invisible. An explanation of dark energy may require that Einstein's anti-gravity force be revived. Einstein regretted that he had postulated anti-gravity, calling the idea the greatest blunder of his career, but it may be correct after all. The more we learn, the more mysterious this universe appears to be!

ABOUT ATOMS

So far, we have considered the universe on the grandest scale of time and distance. We may gain another valuable insight by viewing nature on the ultramicroscopic scale of size. The "raw stuff" of the world is composed of 92 naturally occurring chemical elements, plus 22 additional elements (at latest count) that have been made artificially. (This is ordinary matter, not dark matter.) The abundances and origin of ordinary matter are now believed to be rather well understood. This information in turn provides important clues to the origin of the sun and the solar system. But first, let's briefly review some details of the structure of matter.

Structure of Matter

The early Greeks debated whether matter is *continuous* or *discrete*. If it is continuous, then in principle it could be divided indefinitely into the tiniest pieces that are like larger pieces in every respect except size. On

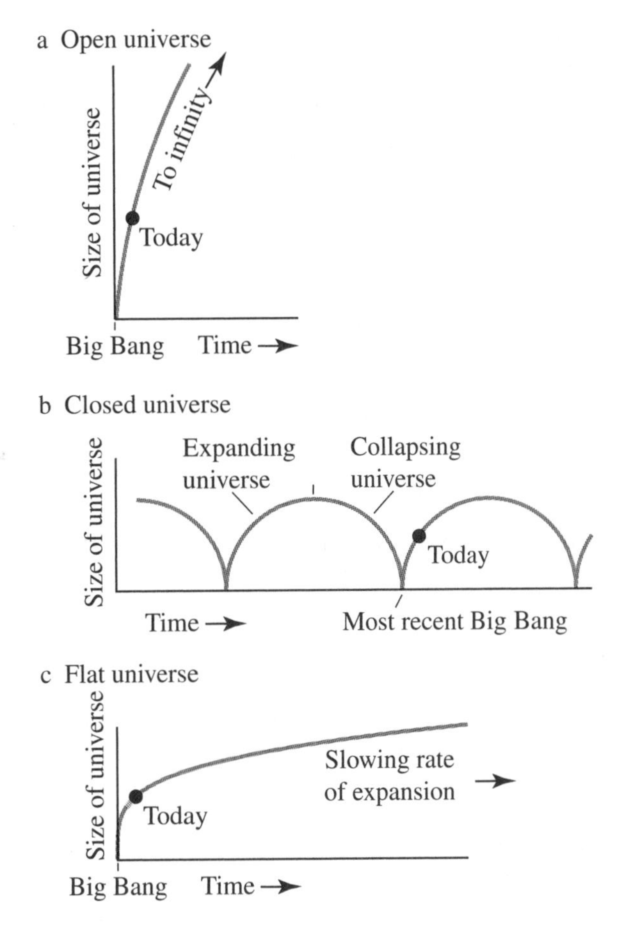

Figure 1-6. *(a)* An open Big-Bang universe continues to expand without limit in space and time. *(b)* A closed Big-Bang universe expands, then collapses, repeating the cycle indefinitely. Today happens to be an expanding phase of development. Each collapse destroys all evidence of the previous existence of the universe. *(c)* A flat universe continues to expand but ever more slowly, approaching but never quite reaching a static condition.

the other hand, if matter is discrete, then it is composed of *fundamental particles*. When combined together, these particles are responsible for the properties of matter, but the properties of these particles when in isolation are completely different. We now know that the model of discrete particles is the correct one.

Physicists are excited about their most recent findings concerning the nature of matter. It seems that the particles once thought to be fundamental are composed of particles that are yet more fundamental! For our purposes, ordinary matter is composed of *protons, neutrons,* and *electrons* (Table 1-1) that are associated together forming *atoms*. In the center of the atom is a *nucleus*, a composite of protons and neutrons bound together by immensely powerful (but short-range) nuclear forces. A diffuse cloud of electrons outside the nucleus is responsible for the external size and shape of the atom. Although the nucleus occupies only about one-trillionth of the volume of an atom, it contains more than 99.95 percent of the total weight.

The number of protons in the nucleus defines the particular chemical element. For example, all atoms with only 1 proton form the simplest possible element, hydrogen, which is identified by the symbol H. By definition a helium (He) nucleus has 2 protons, carbon (C) has 6, oxygen (O) has 8, uranium (U) has 92, and so on. Table 1-1 reminds us that protons and electrons have equal electrical charges but with opposite sign. Thus if the numbers of protons and electrons are the same, these charges cancel one another and a *neutral atom* results. If electrons were to be removed from or added to a neutral atom, then the electrical charge would not be balanced and a positive or a negative *ion* would be the result.

What of the role of the neutron, the other type of nuclear particle? Associated with the protons in a nucleus may be various numbers of neutrons. For example, in the element oxygen whose nucleus

Table 1-1. *Nuclear Particles*

Particle	Mass	Electrical charge	Location
Proton	Heavy*	Positive	In nucleus
Neutron	Heavy	Zero	In nucleus
Electron	Light	Negative	Outside of nucleus

**The mass of an electron is roughly 1/2000 of the mass of a proton or neutron. One millionth of a gram of matter (one microgram) contains approximately a million billion atoms!*

contains 8 protons (by definition, else it would not be oxygen), there may be 8, or 9, or 10 neutrons (Table 1-2). Each combination of neutrons with 8 protons is known as an *isotope* of oxygen. To refer to an isotope, we write the total number of nuclear particles as a left-hand superscript. For example, the isotope with 8 protons and 8 neutrons is written as ^{16}O, pronounced "oxygen 16." Of the more than 2300 known isotopes, 287 are found in nature, the remainder having been created artificially. If we refer simply to oxygen, then we mean the mixture of the isotopes ^{16}O, ^{17}O, and ^{18}O that occur in nature.

ORIGIN OF THE ELEMENTS

Our attempts to understand the origin of the universe seem to have grown very complex. Far from having to account just for the elements as such, we must describe how several hundred isotopes of these elements came to be, each with unique properties that also must be understood. For example, what is the significance of the mass of the isotope? Will it remain stable (unchanged) forever, or will it spontaneously transform into some other isotope in the process known as radioactive decay? Here also, a model can help us to organize a wide variety of observations.

Cosmic Abundances

Let's begin with the composition of the universe. What isotopes, and how many atoms of each were created? The earth is not an easy place to seek answers because this dense, solid body is definitely not an average fragment of the universe. Almost all of the matter resides in stars or in star-like material not yet condensed into stars. We estimate the abundances of the light gases by analyzing the spectral lines from stars (like those in Figure 1-3), and for the heavier chemical elements the best data are provided by meteorites which are the most primitive solid objects available to us. Promptly it was discovered that every one of the stable isotopes is found in nature! It is as though a grand experiment were conducted such that everything that *can* be created, *was* created.

A graph (Figure 1-7) summarizes the results of the analyses. Let us take 1 million silicon atoms as a point of reference. Hydrogen is about 100 thousand times *more* abundant than silicon. Heavy elements are approximately a million times *less* abundant than silicon. The graph shows that 98 percent of the universe consists of hydrogen and helium, the two lightest gases. Our own solar system, dominated by the sun, is almost exactly of this composition. Beyond these two elements we see a very sharp decrease in the abundances of other light elements (region I, dark shading in Figure 1-7), and a peculiar high-abundance "peak" for the medium-weight element, iron (region II). Elements heavier than iron are present in tiny but fairly uniform amounts (region III).

Table 1-2. *Stable Isotopes of Oxygen*

Isotope	Number of protons	Number of neutrons	Total
^{16}O	8	8	16
^{17}O	8	9	17
^{18}O	8	10	18

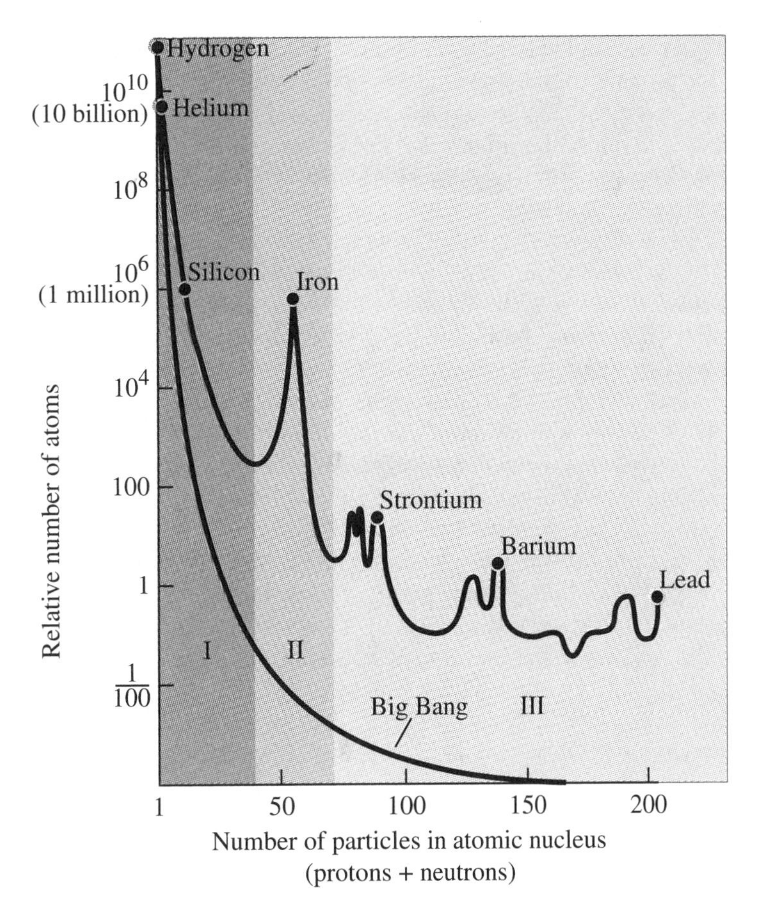

Figure 1-7. There is such an enormous variation in the cosmic abundances of the chemical elements that the data can be shown only by a compressed scale (vertical axis) in which each labeled unit is 100 times smaller than the unit above, and 100 times larger than the unit below. A few elements are identified as points of reference. As shown by the lower smooth curve, the Big Bang created hydrogen and much of the helium, the two lightest elements, but only negligible amounts of elements heavier than helium. The latter elements have been subsequently created by various processes operating in stars.

Synthesis of the elements

Once stars had formed, internal processes continued to provide energy and they caused further changes of composition. The simple and abundant elements, hydrogen and helium, were probably the starting points from which all the others arose. Only a little of the starting material has been "used up," yet generous quantities of even the heaviest elements have been formed, a rather odd situation perhaps.

Suppose that we begin with nothing but the very lightest elements which were created by the Big Bang. Protons, which are nuclei of hydrogen atoms, have identical positive electrical charges which cause them to repel one another. Nevertheless, in the intensely hot interior of a star many of the particles are traveling at such high speed that in spite of the repulsion, they collide and fuse together, releasing energy and building up heavier and heavier nuclei.

First-generation stars that condensed out of the primordial material could initiate the following set of reactions:

$$4\,{}^{1}H \xrightarrow{\text{(fusion taking place via several intermediate steps)}} {}^{4}He + \text{energy}$$
$$3\,{}^{4}He \xrightarrow{\text{(fusion)}} {}^{12}C + \text{energy}$$
$${}^{12}C + {}^{4}He \xrightarrow{\text{(fusion)}} {}^{16}O + \text{energy}$$

Fusion of hydrogen into helium, the first reaction mentioned above, is the chief source of the sun's energy and it will maintain the sun for billions of years to come. Only the stars that are much more massive than our sun can sustain the third reaction on the list. Note that each succeeding reaction uses the nuclear "ashes," the products of the previous reaction, as "fuel" for the reaction that follows. Only a little of the fuel for any given reaction has already been consumed (there are not many ashes), which is why the abundance curve in region I of Figure 1-7 drops so steeply.

Iron, cobalt, and nickel (region II) are the most stable of all elements. Thus these elements, once formed, simply tend to stockpile leading to high abundances. To put it another way, the reactions are trending toward a condition of greatest stability in which everything would consist of iron. Fortunately, only about 1 percent of the universe has already progressed that far!

How can elements that are even heavier and less stable than iron have been created? Suppose that in a very massive star an iron-rich central core has formed. Since no more energy can be released by fusion of iron nuclei with something else, the nuclear fuel supply has been exhausted. No longer is there a supply of internal energy to support the outer layers of the star from below by the pressure of radiation. Now the star must draw upon the force of gravity, the only remaining source of energy. Instantly the star collapses, then explodes in a titanic *supernova* that for a few weeks may outshine all the rest of the galaxy! Accompanying the explosion are reactions that release a flood of neutrons which are instrumental in building up the heaviest elements (region III, Figure 1-7).

The solar system contains the heavy elements, yet the sun has never exploded as a supernova. (Such an catastrophe likely would have destroyed the planets.) If the heavy elements were not manufactured in the sun, they must have been made somewhere else, then incorporated into the sun which therefore cannot be a first-generation star. And as we shall see, the planets condensed from more of the same material that formed the sun. Early in the history of the Milky Way there probably were quite frequent supernova outbursts, possibly one or two per year. Material containing heavy elements was ejected from the early explosions, then mixed into dust clouds that were later to condense forming other stars and planets.

ORIGIN OF THE SOLAR SYSTEM

Models for the origin of the sun, the planets, their moons, and miscellaneous debris in the solar system are rapidly improving, thanks to new data from moon rocks and from probes that have landed upon or flown near the more distant planets. Basic to our model must be the recognition that the solar system is indeed *systematic*. Take the motions of the planets, for example. All 9 planets and their more than 50 satellites orbit in nearly the same plane, which is also close to the plane of the sun's equator. All the planets revolve about the sun in the same direction in nearly circular orbits. The sun itself rotates in this direction. The period of rotation is similar for seven of these planets. Distances between planetary orbits have a simple relationship, each orbit being about 75% larger than that of the next inner planet. So accurate is this formula that it was used to guide successful searches for three major bodies including the planet Uranus.

Chemical regularities are just as pronounced. The inner planets—Mercury, Venus, Earth, Mars—are small, dense, rocky bodies clothed in relatively tenuous atmospheres (Figure 1-8). According to the formula

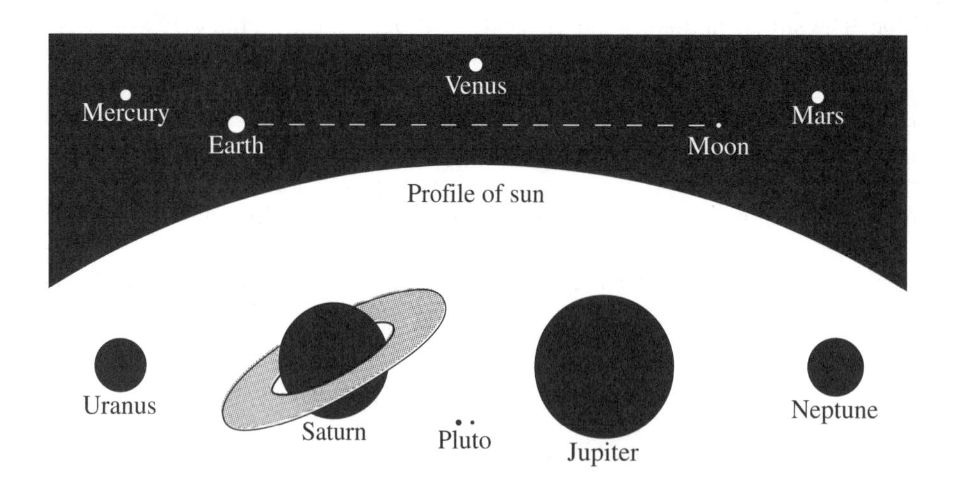

Figure 1-8. Inner planets are much smaller (and more dense) than outer planets. Both the size and distance of the moon are shown in scale relative to the earth.

just mentioned, another planet should occupy the large gap beyond the orbit of Mars. This space is populated, not by a single planet, but by tens of thousands of small objects, the asteroids. Beyond the asteroid belt are the outer planets—Jupiter, Saturn, Uranus, Neptune, Pluto. Except for Pluto, they are large but of low density. In fact, the outer planets are almost nothing but the gases hydrogen and helium, with some methane (CH_4) and ammonia (NH_3). Only a little rocky material may reside deep in their interiors.

Another significant observation to be explained is the *angular momentum* of the sun and planets (Figure 1-9). In this instance, angular momentum is equal to the mass of a planet (m) times its velocity (v) times its distance from the sun (r). Similarly, we could speak of the angular momentum of a single particle revolving about the spin axis of the sun or a planet. The total angular momentum would be the sum of the angular momentums of all the particles making up the spinning body. Surprisingly, about 98 percent of the angular momentum of the solar system resides in the motion of the planets. To put it another way, the sun's 27-day period of rotation is remarkably long. If the sun had "slung off" the planets, we would expect the sun to be rotating rapidly. It is likely that the planets were not extracted out of the sun, but instead they accumulated independently and at the same time.

Yet another consideration is the growing body of evidence that other stars are accompanied by planets. A number have already been identified, and astronomers may be able to use orbiting telescopes to observe these bodies directly. Studies of planetary systems that are still forming will help us to understand the origin of our own system. It would also be comforting to the scientist who is seeking a *general* explanation of reality to know that our status in the universe is not unique.

Toward a Reasonable Model

Let us draw the available information together into a plausible explanation of the solar system. Scattered here and there in the spiral arms of the galaxy are large clouds of uncondensed gas and dust—regions such as the Lagoon nebula (Figure 1-10) where the density of matter may be up to 10 thousand times greater than elsewhere. A spiral arm is believed to signify where a high-density wave, or shock wave, is passing through the galaxy. Temporarily, as the front of the shock wave reaches a given region, the diffuse material is highly compressed, perhaps enough to condense into more substantial clouds. Embedded within the Lagoon nebula are distinct dark "clots" in which matter is locally accumulated. The concentrations are actively shrinking so that within 2 or 3 million years, by the time that a clot has shrunk to the size of the solar system, a new star will be born almost literally overnight.

Our own system probably originated as one of these clouds. During shrinkage, parcels of cosmic material traveling in random directions began to interfere with one another, forcing adjustments of the motion. Slowly the infalling cloud was transformed into a more organized, rotating, flattened disk. At the center, a protosun (earliest sun) began to assemble somewhat tentatively (Figure 1-11). Already it was becoming hot as the force of gravity continued to drive the cosmic material together. The remainder of the disk, like the protosun, consisted mostly of gases with a small amount of metal and rocky material

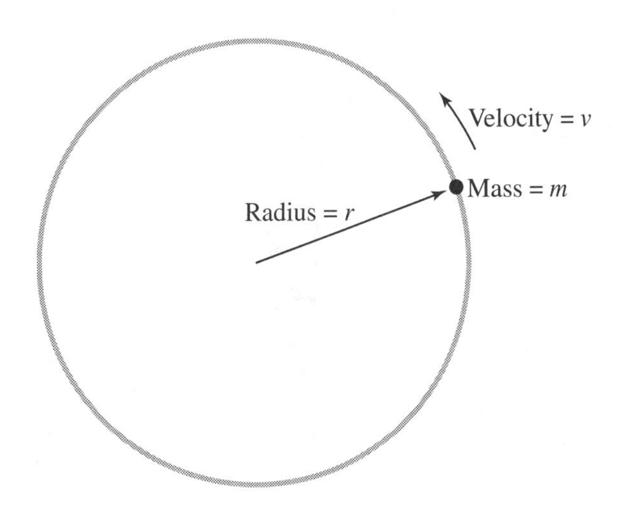

Figure 1-9. If a mass m is revolving about a center of motion with a velocity v at a distance r from the center, then angular momentum is defined equal to mvr.

Figure 1-10. The Lagoon Nebula is a diffuse cloud of dust and gas about 36 light-years across, located in the night sky in the constellation Sagittarius. Small dark spots are local high concentrations of matter. [*Hale Observatories photograph.*]

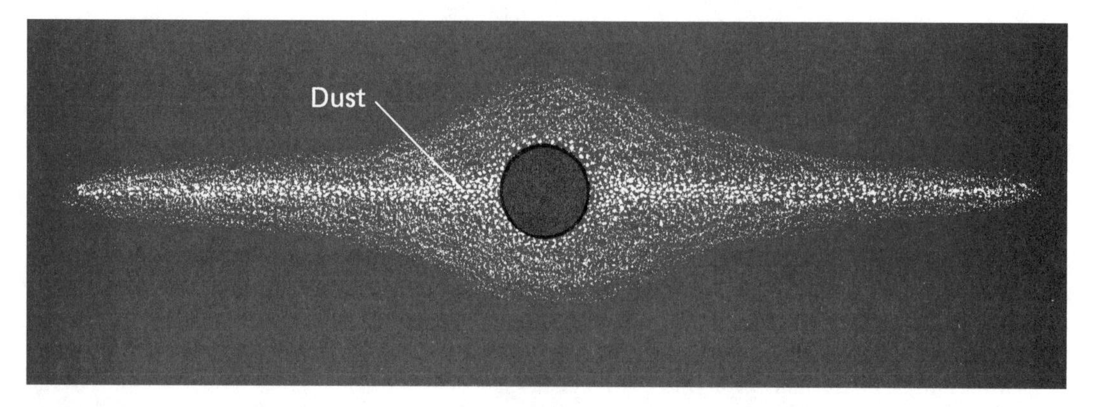

Figure 1-11. Presumably the evolving solar system once appeared as a flattened, rotating disk encircling a massive accumulation at the center. The disk became the system of planets; the central bulge became the sun. Similar disks are observed today surrounding newborn stars.

mixed in. At this point the disk contained something between 2 and 10 times the combined mass of the modern planets.

Near the protosun, high temperatures prevented solid material from condensing. At greater distances a frozen "snow" of methane and ammonia glued the dust particles into globs that eventually grew to about the size of basketballs. About this time, the sun no doubt acted as newborn stars today are observed to do. They flare up, emitting intense radiation and shedding off much of their mass back into space. Repeated blasts of solar "wind" caused the region nearest the sun to be scoured clean of gaseous substances, leaving only chunks of metal and rock with just a trace of water and gases dissolved inside. The region of the outer planets was stripped too, though less severely. This complicated sequence of events was responsible for the striking chemical and size differences that were to develop between the inner and outer planets. Matter that was blasted far beyond the orbit of Pluto may occasionally revisit us in the form of comets.

Meanwhile, larger objects known as *parent bodies* had accumulated, which continued to experience collisions causing them either to shatter or stick together. Some meteorites are made of fragments that were broken, recemented, rebroken, etc. The largest accumulations developed enough gravitational attraction to draw in more fragments, and thus the planets were born. Intense bombardment of the accreting planets continued for about 700 million years, and then for some unknown reason it suddenly ceased. Today we continue to receive only the occasional meteorite that is big enough to dig an impact crater, but the ancient cosmic catastrophe is still registered in the faces of the moon and the other inner planets which are peppered with craters large and small.

The earth emerged from this period of chaos looking more like the moon than our familiar home. Already, though, processes of geological change were beginning to modify our planet from the surface to its very center. The special qualities of the earth—the presence of continents, oceans, an oxygen-rich atmosphere, and of life—all of these were to come later. It is remarkable that the moon did not experience a similar radical set of changes. We shall explore these themes of contrast and development in the following chapters.

SUMMARY

Models are used as a means to focus attention upon essential ideas of a scientific problem, and to make verifiable predictions of conclusions that were not obvious at the outset. The universe is populated by galaxies: aggregates of stars and other matter exemplified by our own galaxy, the Milky Way. The universe originated approximately 14 billion years ago in the so-called Big Bang. The Doppler effect is responsible for the red shift of light wavelengths from very distant galaxies; the red shift indicates that the universe is expanding. Recent studies suggest that the universe is neither open (expanding without limit) nor closed (periodically expanding and collapsing), but rather, at a balance point between these two possibilities. Most of the universe consists of dark matter and energy that can be detected only indirectly, and whose properties are unknown.

Ordinary matter is made up of atoms which in turn are composed of nuclei which contain positively charged protons bonded with neutrons which have no electrical charge. Negatively charged electrons occupy a diffuse cloud outside the nucleus. The number of protons in a nucleus defines a particular chemical element; this number, in combination with a specified number of neutrons, defines a particular isotope of that element.

Most of the universe consists of hydrogen and helium which are starting materials for synthesis of successively heavier elements by fusion in interiors of stars. Iron is anomalously abundant because it is the most stable element. Very heavy elements were manufactured in supernova outbursts. The condensing solar system inherited all of these chemical elements from the debris of earlier supernova explosions.

The organization of the solar system implies that all of its components had a common origin. Inner planets are dense, relatively small, and composed of rock and metal. Outer planets are of low density, relatively large, and composed mostly of gases. A diffuse cloud of dust and gas condensed to a protosun surrounded by a rotating disk. Material violently ejected from the protosun swept away much of the disk material, of which the remainder later coalesced into the planets. Following a long episode of sweeping up of cosmic debris, the inner planets including the early earth were left covered with impact craters.

2

The Double Planet

Full moon. [*Yerkes Observatory photograph*]

Each of the planets is unique in some interesting way. Saturn is encircled by beautiful rings; colossal cyclones and mega-thunderbolts agitate the atmosphere of giant Jupiter; the hot surface of Venus lies permanently hidden beneath dense clouds; Mars is the other planet most likely to harbor life. One well-known planet is accompanied by a single, exceptionally large satellite. This "double planet" is, of course, the earth and the moon. Even from a distance of 380 thousand kilometers, the moon raises strong tides in parts of the ocean, and exerts other influences that are still being investigated.

Never before have expeditions so kindled our imaginations as the Apollo voyages to the moon have done. Scientific discoveries from these space missions have resolved old disputes about the earth-moon system and they have raised new, unanticipated questions. The moon still preserves the opening "chapter" of planetary development, a record that long ago was obliterated on earth. A closer look at the moon will help us to understand better how the earth took form.

METEORITES

A useful place to begin our study of the double planet is with *meteorites*: solid objects that, while orbiting the sun, have accidentally collided with the earth. Although most meteorites underwent early chemical and physical changes, they are the nearest thing to original cosmic material that we have. Meteorites provide a good "first guess" upon which to build models of the compositions of the earth and moon.

In ancient times, meteorites were revered as evidence of the workings of great forces in nature. The Bible records (in *Acts* 19:35) that the people of Ephesus, some 2 thousand years ago, were official keepers of a sacred stone that had fallen from the sky. During the following centuries, though, most people regarded the idea of stones from heaven as superstition in spite of occasional eyewitness reports to the contrary. Then, on April 26, 1803, a shower of 2 to 3 thousand meteorites fell in France near Paris. At last, this well-documented fall in a populated area convinced the graybeards of the French Academy, the most prestigious scientific society in Europe, of the reality of these visitors from outer space. Today many questions remain unanswered in spite of the vast amount of meteorite research accomplished since the early 1800s. John Wood, a meteorite expert, has commented, "Probably in no other branch of natural science is there such a wealth of observational data coupled with such a lack of unanimity in interpretation." One difficulty is that meteorites have originated in an environment totally unfamiliar to our everyday experience.

Stony and Iron Meteorites

With few exceptions, meteorites can be simply classified as "stony" or "iron." Since these types are so different, we must first estimate their frequency of occurrence before making up an inventory of cosmic chemistry. Most of the specimens on display in museums were not actually seen to fall. As might be expected, nearly all of them are distinctive, easily recognized iron meteorites. Moreover, iron meteorites are extremely resistant to attack by weathering. Some of them have not rusted away, even after lying on the earth's surface for hundreds of thousands of years! Stony meteorites look more like ordinary rocks and they decompose more quickly, becoming part of the soil.

Clearly, only the objects that were actually observed to fall are significant for a correct census of meteorite types. By this standard, stony meteorites are by far the most abundant:

Meteorite type	Percent abundance
Stony	93
Iron	6
Miscellaneous	1
	100

A meteorite is named after the post office nearest the point where it was found. Exotic names such as Abee, Cold Bokkeveld, and Sikhote-Alin are common vocabulary to the meteorite specialist. About 3000 meteorites are preserved in collections. Roughly one-third of them were seen to fall, the remainder having been discovered afterward.

A Closer Look

Strictly speaking, the *iron* meteorites are not pure iron, but an intergrowth of two kinds of iron-nickel alloy. One alloy consists of iron with less than 8 percent nickel, whereas the other contains more than 20 percent nickel. A smoothly polished slab that has been lightly etched with acid reveals a complicated network of the two alloys (Figure 2-1). This pattern may extend throughout a meteorite as large as a meter across, proving that the entire meteorite mass consists of a single crystal.

As we shall see in Chapter 3, a crystal is distinguished by the regular ordering of the atoms composing it. Such perfection of the atomic pattern implies that the meteorite material cooled slowly, providing ample time for the atoms to settle into equilibrium positions. Slow cooling would have taken place deep in the interior of a large body from which heat energy could escape only very slowly. In an early stage of formation of the solar system, there were many of these so-called "parent bodies" which later were to collide together, building the planets. A few parent bodies are still preserved in the asteroid belt, between the orbits of Mars and Jupiter. Even today the asteroids occasionally suffer collisions, and meteorites are the fragments which have resulted from such shattering encounters. A collision could knock the meteorite closer to the disturbing gravitational pull of Mars or Jupiter, and eventually the wayward meteorite could be deflected to intersect the earth's orbit.

How large were the parent bodies? A clever application of metallurgy comes to our aid here. As temperature declines, nickel atoms will slowly diffuse out of the alloy with the higher nickel content, to

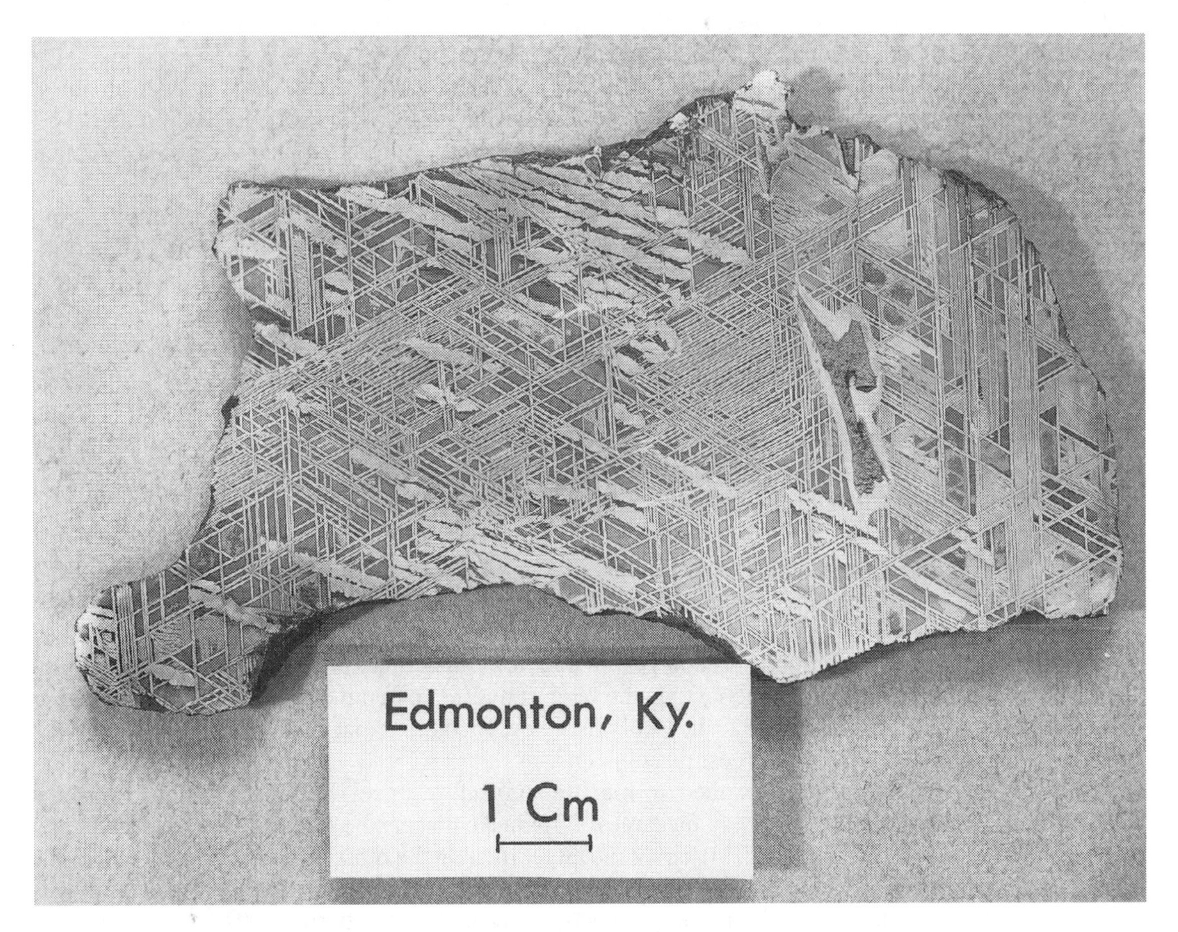

Figure 2-1. A cut, polished slice of the Edmonton iron-nickel meteorite. An inclusion of an iron-nickel-phosphorus mineral appears at the right center of the photograph. Only rarely is the external shape and size of a fallen meteorite the same as when the body was orbiting around the sun. Like the nose cone of a space reentry vehicle, the forward surface of a meteorite is intensely heated and partly stripped away during its fiery plunge through the atmosphere. [*Smithsonian Astrophysical Observatory photograph.*]

enter the low-nickel alloy. But as temperature continues to drop, diffusion becomes more and more sluggish, and then ceases. Experiments and model calculations based upon such factors as diffusion rates and nickel contents show that cooling may have been as incredibly slow as 1°C per *thousand* years! From this information we calculate that the parent bodies were several kilometers in diameter.

Although *stony* meteorites look superficially like common rocks, on closer examination we see that they are quite distinct. It is true that oxygen and silicon are the most abundant elements both in stony meteorites and most rocks. But stony meteorites also have nickel and iron metal, whereas in ordinary rocks the nickel and iron are chemically combined with other elements. Myriads of pinhead- to small pea-sized spherical grains found in many stony meteorites are a source of puzzlement. One of the earliest proposals about their origin may turn out to be the most accurate. H. C. Sorby, a British geologist who pioneered the study of rocks under the microscope, thought that the spherical grains are fused droplets of the original "fiery rain." Some of them are squashed along flattened contacts, as though flung together while still molten. Eventually, stony meteorite material accumulated into parent bodies which may have had cores of iron-nickel alloy.

Cosmic Cannonballs

Just as the very existence of meteorites was long disputed, not all geologists today agree upon the evidence for impact of one of these cosmic cannonballs. Like the circumstances of meteorite origin, the enormous velocity and shock of a major impact are quite outside our daily experience. For example, if a large meteorite were to strike the earth at a low, glancing angle, why would it not dig an elongated gash? Why does a meteorite dig a *crater* that is typically circular? To understand what happens, let us consider the results of model calculations as shown in the sequence in Figure 2-2. Upon impact, the energy of meteorite motion is abruptly transformed into heat energy sufficient to vaporize even an object made of iron. In fact, the largest fragment likely to survive the collision in one piece would be only 3 meters or so in diameter. Thus it is the explosion, not simply a plowing action, that excavates a circular crater regardless of the angle of approach.

About a dozen meteorite impact craters are known certainly, but more than a hundred others are suspected but not yet proven to be of impact origin. The most famous, though not the largest, is in northern Arizona (Figure 2-3). Iron meteorites especially seem to make craters. Perhaps this indicates only that surviving pieces of iron are easily spotted, but it could also be that stony meteorites break up into smaller, less damaging fragments while plunging through the atmosphere. Meteorite craters are eventually eroded away or filled with sediment. The most ancient recognized crater is a little more than 2 million years old.

On a larger scale are about 75 enormous circular structures, from several kilometers to as much as 90 kilometers (55 miles) in diameter. (Note, however, that not all circular areas were created by impact. They may register broad updoming or downwarping of the earth, or they may be a byproduct of volcanic eruptions.) Suppose that the head of a very large comet were to strike the earth. Space probes that encountered Halley's Comet in 1986 confirmed that comet heads are "dirty snowballs" consisting of frozen water, methane, and other volatile substances with embedded dust and organic compounds. Fortunately, humankind has never witnessed the impact of a comet, for the explosion would far outrival any other known type of catastrophe. The largest impact for which there is geologic evidence released an estimated 5 *million* times more energy than the biggest hydrogen bomb ever exploded. No imaginable nuclear war could ever compare to it. Geologists now recognize that many extinctions of living species may have resulted from such cosmic collisions.

How would the earth have absorbed so much energy all at once? Because rock has a limited strength, there is also a limit to the size of the largest earthquake that can be set in motion. Impact energy that exceeds this limit is used, instead, to disrupt the target rock on the most intimate scale. Consider the common mineral *quartz* in which atoms of silicon and oxygen are arranged in a symmetrical pattern, as shown in Figure 2-4(a). Intense shock instantly converts the neat atomic pattern in a *crystal* of quartz into the disorganized array of atoms characteristic of a *glassy* substance [Figure 2-4(b)]. In extreme cases, large volumes of rock may melt, or even vaporize.

Because the damage extends so deeply into the earth, giant impact structures persist for very long periods in spite of continued erosion. The largest of them, the Vredefort Ring in the Republic of South Africa, is judged to be about 2 billion years old, which is nearly half of the age of the earth.

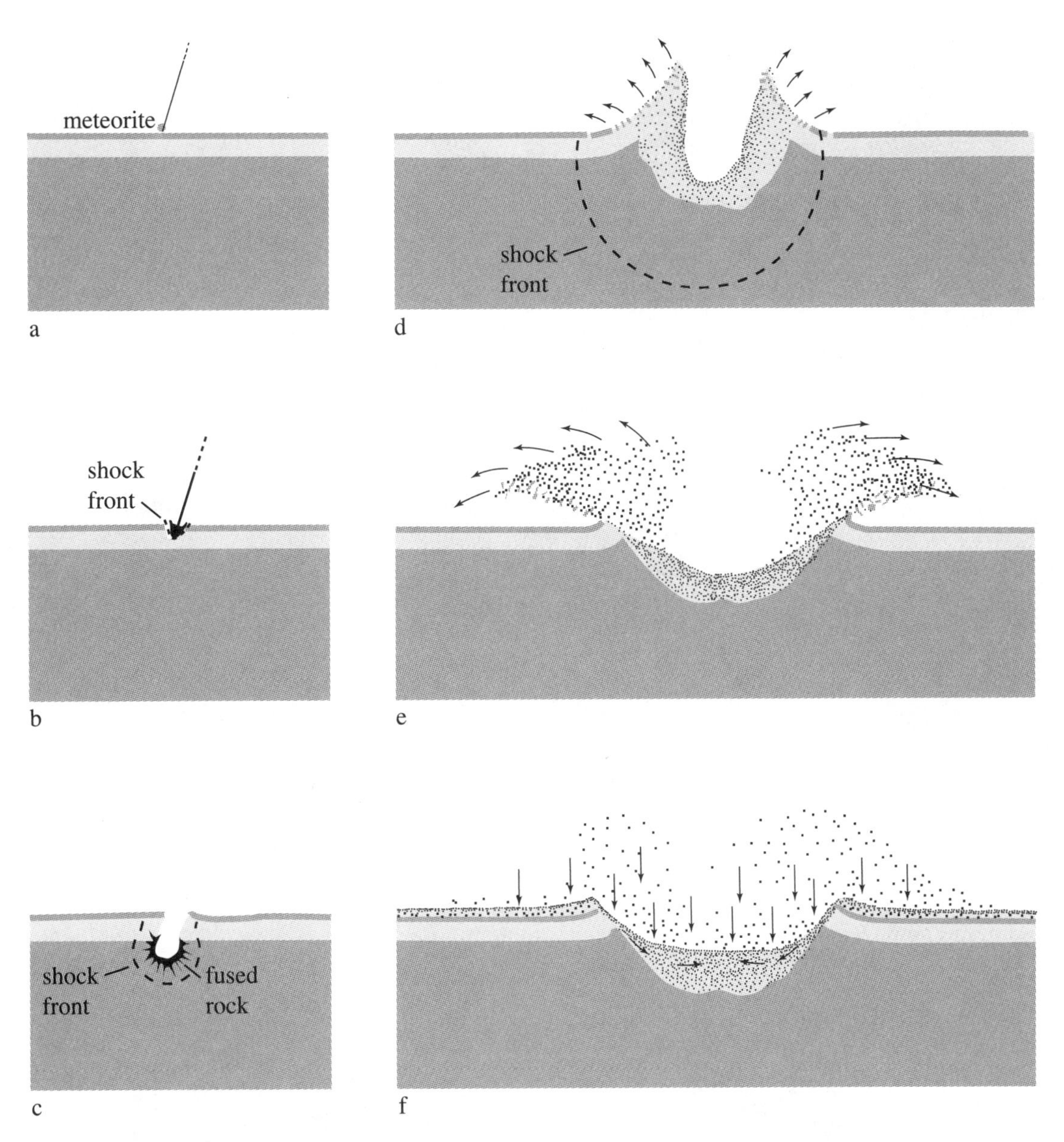

Figure 2-2. Sequence of events during the impact of a meteorite. A relatively small meteorite can excavate a very large hole! The most deeply buried material disrupted by an impact explosion falls back into the crater or onto its rim. Target material that initially lay just below the ground surface is ejected greater distances from the crater. This relationship was useful in identifying the depth of origin of material cast out of craters on the moon. [*After E. M. Shoemaker, "Penetration Mechanics of High Velocity Meteorites, Illustrated by Meteor Crater, Arizona,"* Report of the International Geological Congress, XXI session, part XVII, *Berlingske Forlag, Copenhagen, 1960.*]

THE MOON

Populated as it is by thousands of craters, the face of the moon presents quite a contrast to the earth where craters are few. We recognize, of course, that lunar craters are exposed only to the vacuum of outer space; there is no wind or water on the moon to attack them. What is the origin of these craters? Were they volcanic, created by an *internal* source of energy, or were they fashioned by the *external* energy of bombarding meteorites? Data from the Apollo flights have settled that long-standing debate while brilliantly confirming the importance of both kinds of process. That is, much of the lunar surface material

Figure 2-3. Aerial photograph of the Barringer Crater, northern Arizona. An iron-nickel meteorite weighing approximately 2 million metric tons blasted out the crater, which is about 1.2 kilometers across and 0.2 kilometer deep, in an explosion equivalent to the detonation of 30 million tons of TNT. Energy of motion of the meteorite was abruptly transformed into heat energy which vaporized the projectile, leaving only scattered fragments on the crater rim and nearby plains. [*U. S. Geological Survey photograph by W. B. Hamilton.*]

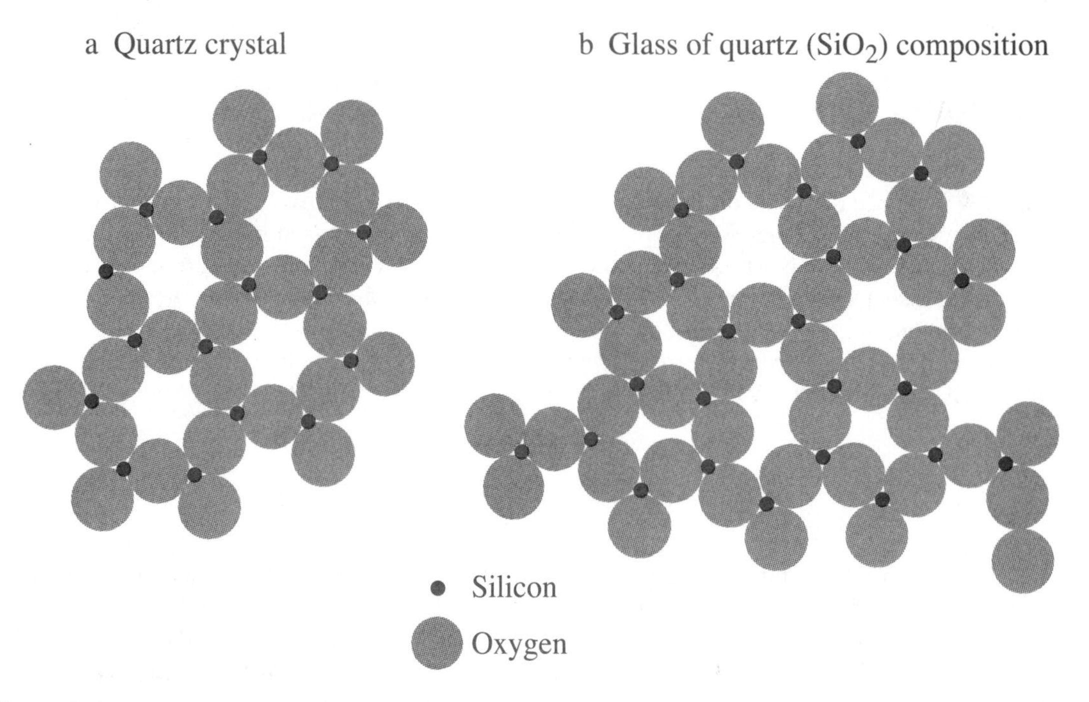

Figure 2-4. (*a*) Oxygen and silicon atoms in quartz are precisely arranged in a regular network. (*b*) If a quartz crystal is severely shocked, the atoms are thrown into the confused disarray characteristic of a glassy substance.

is of volcanic origin, but all of the important craters so far investigated were found *not* to be volcanic; they have been blasted out of the surface by impact.

The Face of the Moon

Let us note some of the fascinating details that are visible on the side of the moon that is always turned facing toward the earth (Figure 2-5). The light and dark areas apparent to the unaided eye were first studied telescopically by Galileo in the early 1600s. He discovered the dark patches to be relatively smooth regions of low elevation; he named them *maria* (singular: mare) which is Latin for "seas," though it is not certain that Galileo understood the areas to be literally covered by water. The more brightly reflecting regions are uplands which he named "terrae" (lands). Today we disregard the Latin, referring to the latter simply as lunar *highlands.* Later and better telescopes revealed a variety of landforms that are important to our interpretation of lunar history. Among these are craters, some of which are centers of far-flung, radiating *crater rays.* Sharp valleys, the lunar *rilles,* are common in some areas. Everywhere, the moon is cut through by a network of intersecting fractures.

Lunar maria may be classed as circular or irregular. Mare Imbrium ("Sea of Showers," an odd name seeing that there is no water on the moon), is the grandest of the circular maria visible from earth (Figure 2-6). Its area is equal to that of Colorado, plus New Mexico and Arizona. The Imbrium surface, some 3 to 6 kilometers lower than the surrounding highlands, is remarkably flat, or more accurately, it conforms closely to the overall spherical shape of the moon. Here and there, hills rise above the plain, in part joining to form indistinct, mostly buried concentric rings.

The near edge of Mare Orientale is barely visible from earth, the remainder being on the moon's far side (Figure 2-7). When orbiting cameras took photographs from a more advantageous position it became evident that Mare Orientale is the most spectacular lunar feature of all. This gigantic circular

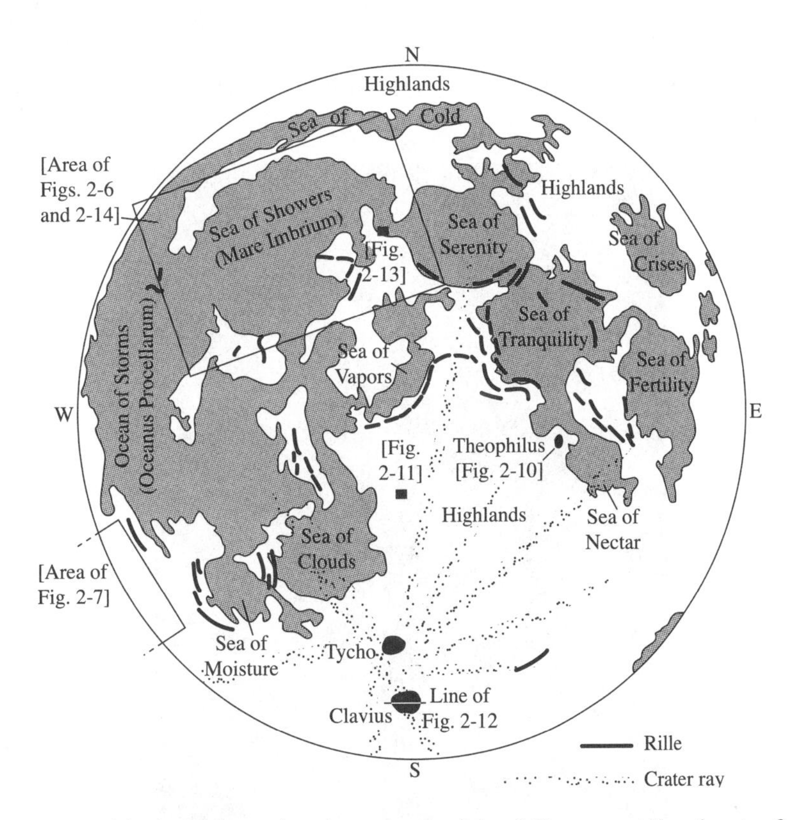

Figure 2-5. Compare this drawing to the photograph of the full moon at the chapter front. Names given to the lunar maria are totally whimsical! Oceanus Procellarum, an irregular mare, is the largest of the flat lava-covered plains. Its indistinct boundaries merge with Mare Imbrium and other low areas. Crater rays extend out from Tycho over most of the moon's visible face. Because the Sea of Crises is so near to the edge, a foreshortened perspective makes this mare, which is actually circular, appear to be oval.

Figure 2-6. Mare Imbrium, the "eye" of the Man in the Moon, is seen here in a closer view. [*Mt. Wilson Observatory photograph.*]

Figure 2-7. Orientale, another circular mare, is much like Mare Imbrium except that its rugged, fractured face has not been flooded by lava. Surrounding Mare Orientale is a vast apron of loose material blasted outward from the central region. [*National Aeronautics and Space Administration (NASA) photograph.*]

structure is 900 kilometers across (about the size of Mare Imbrium), but the fractured rings of Mare Orientale stand bold as mountain ranges which must have been raised up almost instantaneously by the impact event.

Mare Imbrium and Mare Orientale illustrate a fundamental difference between the moon's near and far sides. For some unknown reason, mare basins on the near side have been flooded with lava, whereas those on the backside have not (Figure 2-8). Another mystery is the reason for the long delay before the lava was emplaced. Fractures, conduits for the lava to come up, were created by the impact that excavated the Imbrium basin, but we know from age determinations (explained in Chapter 11) that lava did not fill the basin until hundreds of millions of years later.

The highlands that cover two-thirds of the moon's visible face are complex and little understood. Rock comprising the highlands is both lighter in color and less dense than rock in the maria, suggesting that the highlands material had been molten, and had separated and floated upward to the moon's surface like scum rising to the surface of a pond. The highlands terrain appears to be a fantastic jumble of craters that were partially destroyed by later, overlapping craters, then modified locally by volcanic outpourings. The entire moon was likely surfaced by highlands at the end of an initial intense bombardment which has been called the "lunar cataclysm." Then the circular mare basins were dug, and much later some of them were filled by quiet upwellings of dense, dark lava, following which bombardment by occasional meteorites has continued until the present day.

Collision of a sizable meteorite will set the entire moon in vibration. Sensitive instruments implanted on the lunar surface by Apollo astronauts constantly monitor this ordinarily dead body for

Figure 2-8. The moon's far side is a rough highlands saturated with craters. Smooth, lava-filled mare basins similar to Mare Imbrium (Figure 2-6) are conspicuously absent on the far side. Even the dark plains visible near the edge belong to the front face. [*National Aeronautics and Space Administration (NASA) photograph.*]

tremors of impact origin. Records of moonquakes were a considerable surprise. Earthquake motions quickly abate whereas on the moon the ringing, or reverberation, continues for an hour or more. The difference between earthquakes and moonquakes is best explained by the presence on earth of water which quite literally dampens the vibration. The moon is devoid of H_2O, whether in liquid form or chemically combined in the rocks. (We speculate that ice may permeate the surface rubble in secluded parts of the polar region.) Dry lunar rock is extremely strong and rigid, a good transmitter of vibrational energy.

Actually, the moon is not quite completely dead. With the passage of time the fresh, sharp-textured rims of young craters become rounded and subdued (Figure 2-9). Contours of the lunar surface are smoothed as loose rubble slides downhill. Continual pelting by meteorites causes the uppermost few meters of material to be overturned, or "gardened." This churning action is so effective that every part of the lunar surface must have received and contributed particles to every other part! Subtle features such as crater rays (Figure 2-5) are gradually destroyed. Samples of ray material from the giant crater named Copernicus proved to be fine particles of glass (created by shock?) splashed out of the crater in a radiating pattern. Crater rays are too thin to cast shadows, and some of them are visible only to orbiting astronauts who can view them from peculiar angles.

a

Figure 2-9. A photograph of part of the moon *(a)* is interpreted in a drawing *(b)*. An older meteorite crater with rounded, subdued features has been nearly obliterated. Younger, sharply sculptured craters are indented into the older material, and even more recently, material blasted out of a distant mare basin was superimposed upon all of these older features. [*National Aeronautics and Space Administration (NASA) photograph.*]

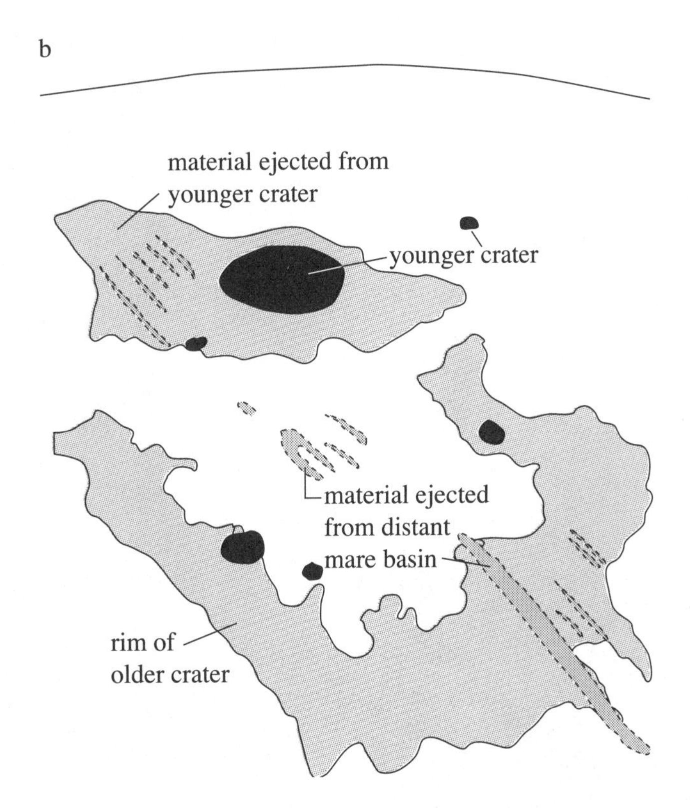

Figure 2-9. *Continued.*

Figure 2-10. The elevated rim of the crater Theophilus, photographed here by a lunar orbiter, suggests meteorite impact, but various origins could be postulated for the central hills. They could be an accumulation of volcanic rock, but more likely they are a mass of material that rebounded after a meteorite impact. Surrounding Theophilus and other lunar craters are thick blankets of ejected material whose volume nicely matches the size of the local crater cavity. [*National Aeronautics and Space Administration (NASA) photograph.*]

The rilles are channels in the lunar surface. Straight rilles probably formed from displacements of the rock along fractures, but the origin of meandering rilles that look like river channels, as in Figure 2-13, is not well understood. Photographs taken on the rim of Hadley Rille show that layers of volcanic rock in the canyon walls had been cut by some agent of erosion which almost certainly was not running water. A better possibility is that the meandering rille was an underground tube that carried lava. After draining, the roof collapsed leaving an open valley.

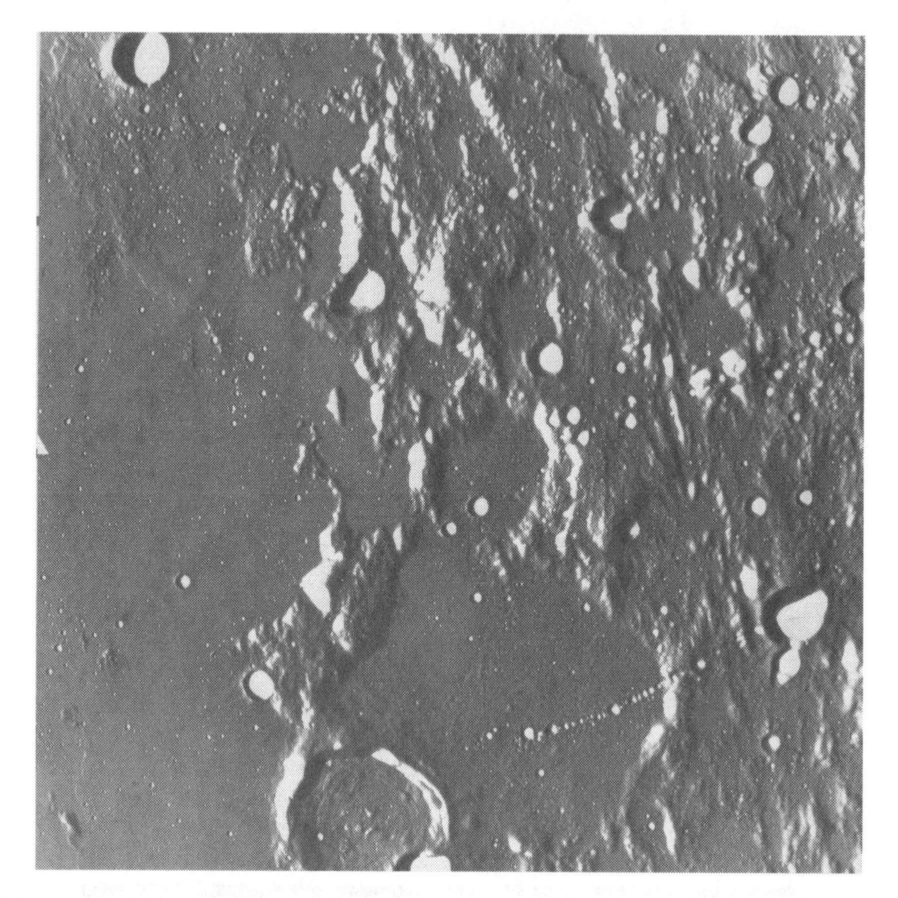

Figure 2-11. Are the lined-up lunar craters of impact origin, or volcanic origin? Would a swarm of meteorites have dug the precise chain of craterlets seen here? [*National Aeronautics and Space Administration (NASA) photograph.*]

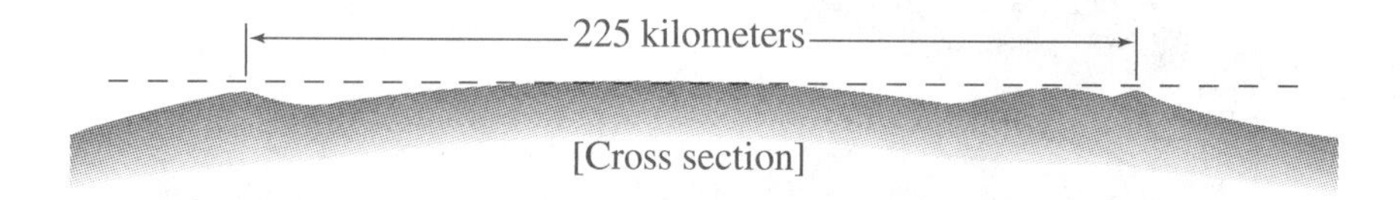

Figure 2-12. The horizon of a lunar plain appears only 2 kilometers distant from a standing astronaut. So pronounced is the curvature of the moon's surface that a person in the center of the crater Clavius cannot see the rim!

Lunar fractures, like the rays, are seen only under proper lighting conditions. Some fractures are subtle breaks oriented in a crisscross grid pattern on a wide scale. Other profound systems of fractures radiate from the large circular maria out over the entire face of the moon. Impacts that created these mare basins were moon-shattering!

Lunar Stratigraphy

As historians of natural events, geologists wish to assemble a connected story of the moon's origin and development. Working only from photographs, they were able to prepare detailed maps of much of the moon long before the first astronauts landed. These maps indicate the appearance of the surface (smooth or rough, light or dark, etc.) and its topography. From this information we may deduce the sequence of events that took place. For example, sharply sculptured craters would be more recently formed, whereas

Figure 2-13. Lunar rilles are not well understood. Many of them originate in a crater, meander across the moon for great distances (up to 700 kilometers), and mysteriously disappear. [*National Aeronautics and Space Administration (NASA) photograph.*]

older craters are rounded and subdued, well on their way to obliteration (Figure 2-9). All craters, younger and older, might be submerged beneath a series of lava flows. If this lava plain were itself an ancient feature, it would be densely peppered with yet more craters, some recent and some of them appearing to be quite old. A more recent lava plain would have fewer craters and all of them would appear to be more youthful. The logic is really quite simple.

These ideas are part of the science of *stratigraphy,* the interpretation of strata, or layered deposits. One of the basic principles of stratigraphy is the *law of superposition,* which states that *in a series of undisturbed strata, younger material lies above older material.* Let us see how this common-sense rule applies to the region of the moon around Mare Imbrium (Figures 2-6 and 2-14). Which came first, Mare Imbrium or the rugged terrain surrounding it? The faint traces of interior rings in Mare Imbrium are similar in size to the distinct fractured rings of its sister mare, Orientale (compare with Figure 2-7). In both cases they were probably cast up by stupendous impacts responsible for digging the mare basins. The crater Archimedes obviously formed after the excavation of the Mare Imbrium basin in which it rests (see Figures 2-6 and 2-14), but note that the smooth floor of Archimedes is at approximately the same elevation as the surrounding material. In contrast, the rough crater floors of Copernicus and Eratosthenes are depressed below the level of the mare surface. Crater rays cast out of Copernicus overlie everything else, including the floor of Eratosthenes (Figure 2-14).

Thus from a single photograph we may conclude the following sequence of events: (1) creation of the Mare Imbrium basin and surrounding rim, (2) formation of the crater Archimedes, (3) flooding of the Imbrium basin and floor of Archimedes with lava, (4) formation of the crater Eratosthenes, followed by (5) excavation of Copernicus. Material that was deposited upon other material, or a structure (such as a crater) that cuts across something that was already there, had to have formed later. Obviously these rules are just as useful in figuring out sequences of events on earth.

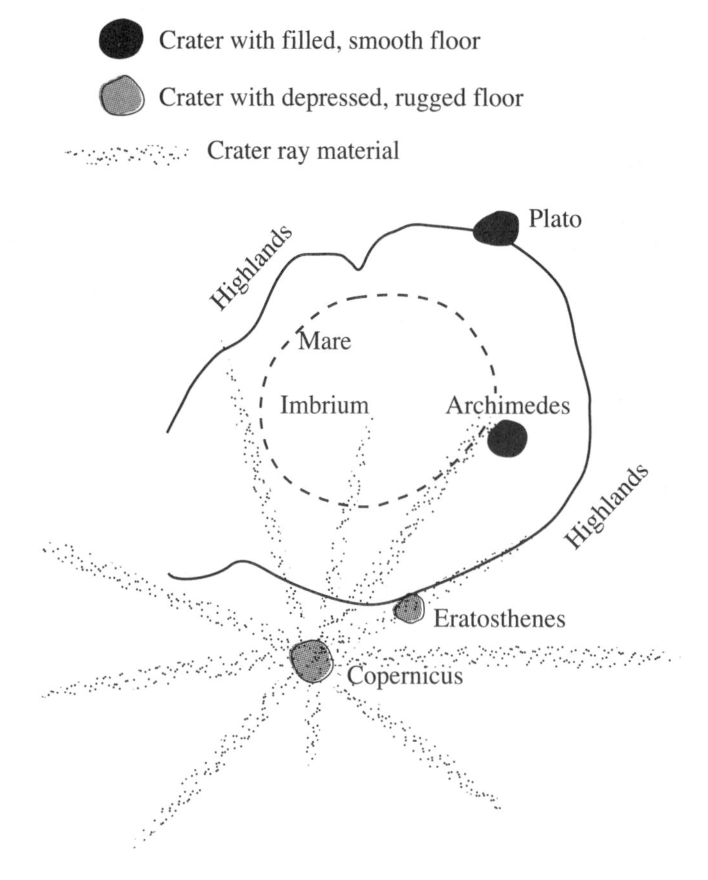

Figure 2-14. Compare this drawing with Figure 2-6. Geologists have interpreted a detailed history, not only of the Mare Imbrium region, but of much of the rest of the moon.

EARTH AND MOON COMPARED

By this point, certain major differences between natural events that were important on the moon and on the earth are becoming apparent. In part these distinctions arise because the moon is so much smaller than the earth. The diameter of the moon is about 3500 kilometers (Figure 2-15), and its volume is only 2 percent of the earth's volume. The mass of the moon can be calculated from observations of its orbit. Once we know the mass and volume, we can calculate its overall density (mass per unit of volume). This value, 3.3 grams per cubic centimeter, is significantly less than the 5.5 grams per cubic centimeter which is the average density of the earth. Of course, the material buried in the center of the much larger earth is under higher pressure than at the center of the moon. The greater compression of the earth material cannot account for all the density difference, however. In addition to factors related to difference in size, the moon and earth must be made up of different mixtures of light and heavy substances. This immediately establishes that the two celestial bodies did not have the same origin.

Earth's Internal Structure

In Chapter 16 we shall see how earthquake waves can be used as a "probe" of the inaccessible deep interior of our planet. They show that the earth contains a central *core* which is overlain by two other major layers (Figure 2-16). Occupying the innermost 16 percent of the earth's volume, the core is made of very dense material. Above it lies the *mantle* which constitutes the great bulk of the earth, 83 percent. Resting upon the mantle like a thin scum is the outermost layer, the *crust*, containing the remaining 1 percent of volume. No one has ever drilled through the crust into the mantle, although there are a few places where we can have a look at mantle material which has been thrust up and over the crust. Seeing that we have only a sparse number of direct observations, the compositions of the mantle and core must remain somewhat mysterious. Most geologists find an analogy with stony and iron-nickel meteorites to be

Figure 2-15. The moon superimposed on a map of the "lower 48" United States. The surface area of the moon slightly exceeds that of Africa.

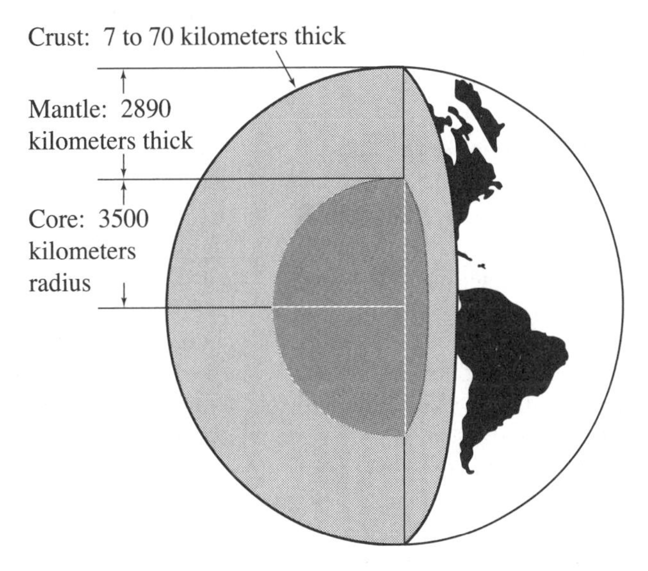

Figure 2-16. A cut-away view of planet Earth shows its three major divisions. On the scale of this drawing, the crust is so thin that it is contained entirely within the thickness of the outer line.

rather persuasive. It could be that the earth's core is a segregated mass of iron-nickel metal, whereas the mantle and crust are composed of silicate and oxide minerals like those in stony meteorites.

When the effect of the enormous pressure deep in the earth is taken into account, the known densities of the core and mantle rather nicely satisfy the meteorite model. The core is deepest and most dense; the mantle is less dense, and the crust even less so. For that matter, ocean water overlies the crust, and atmospheric gases lightly rest upon everything else. Our picture is of concentric shells—spheres within spheres—a very stable arrangement. More accurately, the earth is *almost* stable. Heat energy could cause parts of the interior to expand, thereby becoming less dense than overlying material. Stability would be restored only if the less dense material were to rise, and more dense material were to sink. It is this reserve of energy which creates internal movement, thereby distinguishing the "live" earth from the "dead" moon.

How did this layered condition come about? Most likely when the earth originally accumulated, the rock and metal were intimately mixed together. Actually this was an *un*stable condition because much of the dense metal was distributed throughout the outer part of the earth. Initially the earth must have been quite hot, though probably not hot enough to melt completely. This *original heat* was generated by collisions of infalling particles as the mass of the earth accumulated. To this was added *heat from radioactivity* (a subject of Chapter 11) which in the early days was produced roughly 4 1/2 times more rapidly than it is now. Moreover, long ago the moon was nearer to the earth. Tides were raised not only in the ocean; they also vigorously flexed the body of the solid earth. The *heat from tidal stressing* is similar to what one gets by rapidly bending a stiff wire back and forth, and it was yet another important source of energy.

Now, suppose that a pocket of liquid iron-nickel alloy, the material that would melt at the lowest temperature, had formed. Dense liquid metal would seep downward through the mixture of solid metal and rock. The less dense silicate rock that initially happened to be lying below would be displaced upward. Thus the metal began to be segregated deep in the earth as the silicate collected together above the metal, in a process known as *differentiation*. This exchange of positions within the earth released *heat of differentiation* which we may think of as energy due to friction as the materials moved past one another.

When added to heat from the other sources, the heat of differentiation melted yet more material which caused the differentiation to go faster and faster. The core material sank catastrophically to the center of the earth, releasing so much heat so suddenly that the entire earth probably melted at that time. It must have been a spectacular fiery ball!

We have noted the relatively small size and low density of the moon. A core, if present at all, can be no more than 2% of the lunar volume. Even though there is no great amount of iron in the moon, the lunar substance also differentiated, releasing so much heat that at one stage the moon was covered with a universal "ocean" of molten rock.

Atmosphere, Hydrosphere

Just as the earth's core, mantle, and crust were not original features, the atmosphere and hydrosphere (water in the ocean, glacier ice, rivers and lakes, and underground) were likewise absent at the beginning. Evidence for this conclusion is seen in the *inert gases*: helium, neon, argon, krypton, xenon, and radon. Atoms of these chemical elements are so unreactive that they do not combine with one another or with any other element under natural conditions. As seen in Figure 2-17, these elements are enormously depleted on earth compared to their abundances in the original solar cloud. It is for good reason that these have been called the "rare" gases. Generous amounts of water, nitrogen, carbon dioxide, and other chemically active gases are present at the earth's surface, but the figure shows that rare gases are present in only a millionth to a ten-billionth part of their cosmic abundances. Meteorites experienced a similarly severe loss of gases. The largest class of stony meteorites rather closely resembles the "condensable" part of the sun—just the material that would exist as a solid at room temperature.

This situation provides an important clue to how the earth must have formed. It is quite a complicated story. First the solar cloud condensed, then accumulated into parent bodies as already mentioned. At this time most of the H_2O retained in these bodies was chemically combined with the solid material. This is possible in *hydrous minerals* whose chemical formulas include hydrogen and oxygen. When hydrous minerals are decomposed by heating, water can be given off. Yet another way to incorporate volatile substances into rock is by trapping them in countless microscopic *fluid inclusions*. In the meantime the chemically inert gases were not trapped and were mostly lost into space.

As the parent bodies crashed into the growing planet, and even later when much of the primordial earth melted, the contents of the world ocean remained locked up inside the earth. Although this idea may seem unreasonable, we must keep in mind that the ocean is barely a thin film of liquid when viewed on the scale of the whole earth. A mixture of stony and iron meteorite-type material would have contained about 0.5 percent H_2O present in hydrous minerals. Release of this much water to the surface would have filled the ocean many times over. Either a large amount of water is still residing below, or it too was lost into space.

The water ascended to the earth's surface just as it does today, through volcanic eruptions and hot springs. Water was released quickly at the beginning while the earth was still very hot, and even today the delivery rate is embarrassingly rapid. We calculate that over the course of earth history, the ocean

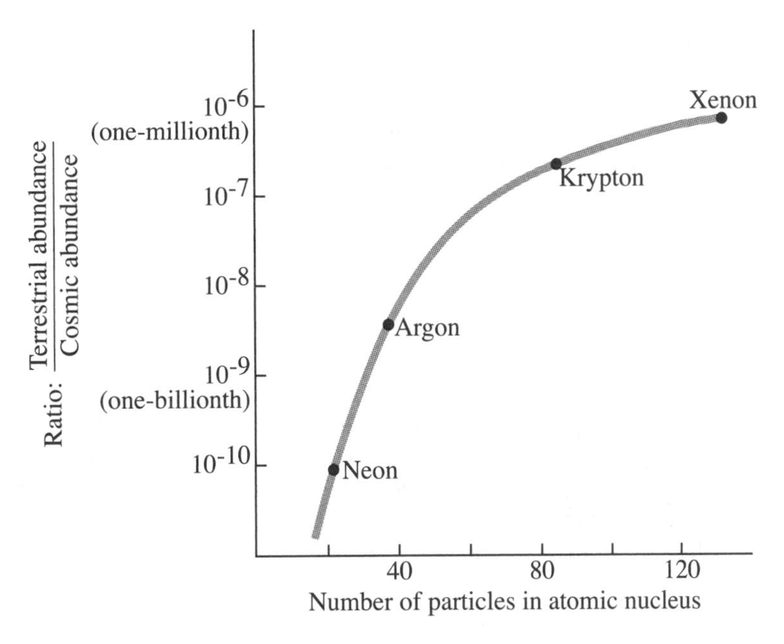

Figure 2-17. A substantial fraction of average cosmic material consists of the rare, or inert gases. If the solar disk, from which the planets formed (Chapter 1) had inherited an average cosmic composition, a later event must have severely depleted these gases from the developing earth. All of the inert gases were lost to an extent, but light gases to a much greater degree than heavy gases. For example, the extent of depletion of neon (light) was nearly 10 thousand times greater than depletion of xenon (heavy).

should have been filled more than 100 times! Then why is the ocean not many times larger than it actually is? Here we see evidence for a familiar geologic process, *recycling.* Less than 1 percent of the water is coming up for the first time; the remainder is water that first ascended, then descended into the earth, was heated, then re-ascended, again and again.

As for water and atmosphere on the moon, it is obvious that things turned out far differently. In view of the small size of the moon, we might expect less of these volatile substances to be released, but that does not fully explain why the moon is a completely waterless, airless place. Most of the lunar atmosphere is artificial, consisting of exhaust from visiting rockets. Consider the constant motion of atoms in a gas (Figure 2-18). Most of them are traveling near a "most probable" speed, but the gray area under the tail of the curve represents a small number of atoms that are moving at higher speeds. An atom speeding away from the moon faster than 2.3 kilometers per second, or away from the earth faster than 11.1 kilometers per second, will never return. By this means, the moon eventually lost all of its gases while the earth experienced significant loss only of hydrogen and helium, the two lightest gases.

Not only did the moon lose its liquid water, but it lost water stored in hydrous minerals and it even lost zinc, cadmium, lead, and other metals that form gaseous compounds at temperatures of hundreds of degrees. Lunar rocks are rich in aluminum, calcium, and titanium whose compounds are extremely resistant to melting or vaporization. Probably at one time the moon material passed through a hot formative stage, much hotter than the earth ever experienced. Clearly, the lunar environment has always been hostile to life.

In Hindsight

An unexpected benefit of lunar studies has been the light they shed on the earliest history of the earth. Because of its superior size and stronger gravitational attraction, the earth must have been cratered by giant meteorite strikes about 50 times as frequently as the moon. But the face of the lively planet upon which we live has been recycled again and again. Such was not the case for the moon. For reasons not

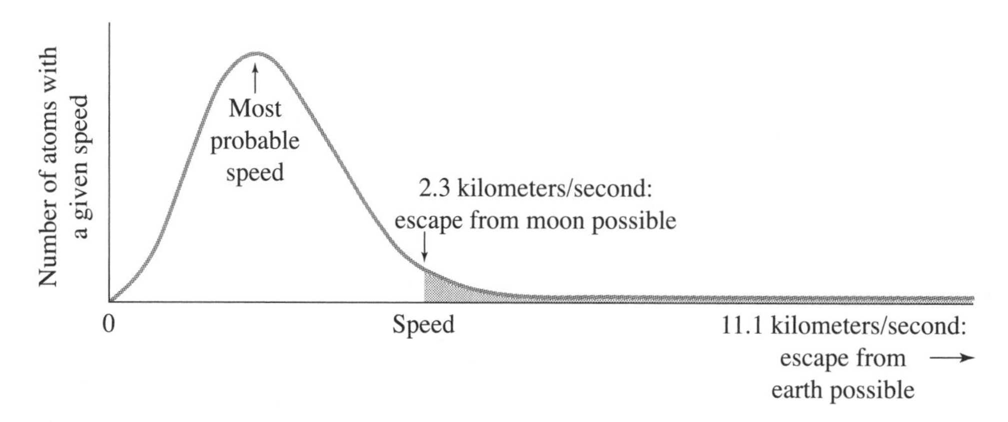

Figure 2-18. Collisions with other atoms continually change the speed and direction of motion of an atom in a gas. If a series of chance collisions should knock an atom of the lunar atmosphere into an upward flight direction at a speed that exceeds 2.3 kilometers per second, that atom escapes the moon. A speed exceeding 11.1 kilometers per second is required to escape the stronger gravity of the earth. At any one instant, a considerable number of atoms may be escaping the moon, but only a trivial number of atoms in the earth's atmosphere are moving fast enough to leave the earth.

fully understood, the moon long ago rather abruptly became a dead planet. Signs of internal activity (volcanism, etc.) ceased about the same time that the *oldest* rocks preserved on earth were being formed. The moon records the otherwise missing first chapter in the story of the solar system.

ORIGIN OF THE EARTH-MOON SYSTEM

Before speculating on the origin of the earth-moon system, let us take note of one more source of data, the orbits of these two complementary bodies. Figure 2-19 (upper diagram) shows, in exaggerated form, the effect of lunar tides which are raised mostly in the ocean but partly in the solid earth as well. As the earth rotates, the tidal bulges on the earth's near and far side tend to remain directly in line with the moon, thus creating the twice-daily ebb and flow so familiar to people who live on a coast.

That is, the bulges *almost* line up with the centers of the earth and moon. Actually, friction prevents the crest of the tide from subsiding immediately as the earth's rotation carries it past the point directly below the moon (lower diagram). Thus the crests on the near and far side are slightly out of line, by about 2°. The masses of these bulges of water and deformed solid earth are attracted by gravity to the mass of the moon. As a result, the gravitational force tends to hold back the earth's rotation while propelling the moon forward in a sort of "slingshot" effect. This causes the earth's daily period of rotation to grow longer while the moon recedes from the earth.

These changes take place much too slowly to attract casual notice. Each year, the length of day is increased by about 0.000015 seconds as the moon pulls farther away from the earth about 3.2 centimeters—the length of this line segment (——————————). However, the earth and moon have probably been interacting like this for 4.5 billion years, plenty of time for these gradual changes to have accumulated into a very large total effect.

Supporting evidence on this subject has been provided by a certain species of fossil coral that lived about 400 million years ago. These animals built their skeletons of faint, almost microscopic growth layers which are plausibly interpreted as daily additions (Figure 2-20). Numerous growth layers are grouped into obvious larger ridges, called annulations, which indicate yearly variations in weather, food supply, etc. Modern corals exhibit about 360 daily growth lines per annulation, corresponding roughly to the number of days in a year. The ancient fossils contain an average of about 400 growth layers per annulation, suggesting that it took only 21 or 22 hours for the earth to complete a rotation.

Hypothetical: no tidal friction

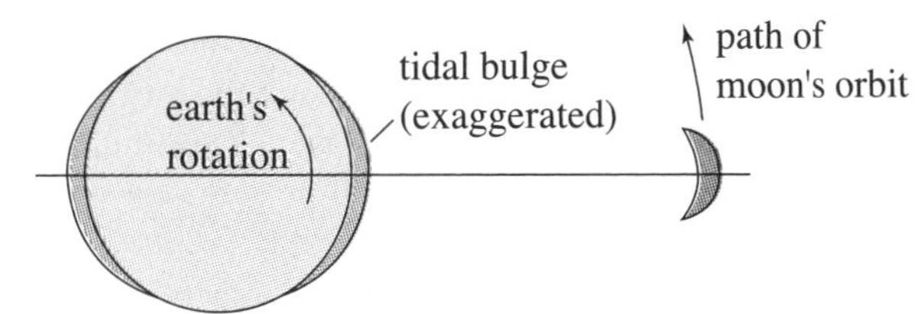

Actual: earth's nearside tidal bulge "leads" the moon.

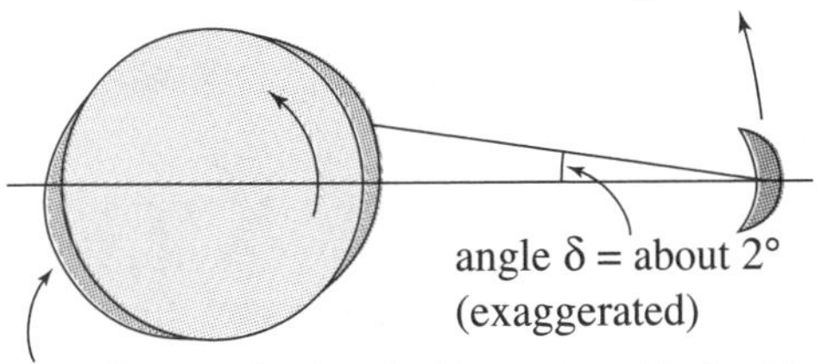

smaller gravitational effect of earth's farside tidal bulge, which is farther from the moon

Figure 2-19. Friction prevents the tidal bulge from subsiding the moment that the earth's rotation has carried the bulge past a point directly in line with the moon. For this reason, on the earth's near side (bottom figure) the tidal bulge slightly "leads" the moon by about 2°. Gravitational attraction between the moon and the tidal bulge pulls the moon forward in its orbit while retarding the rotation of the earth.

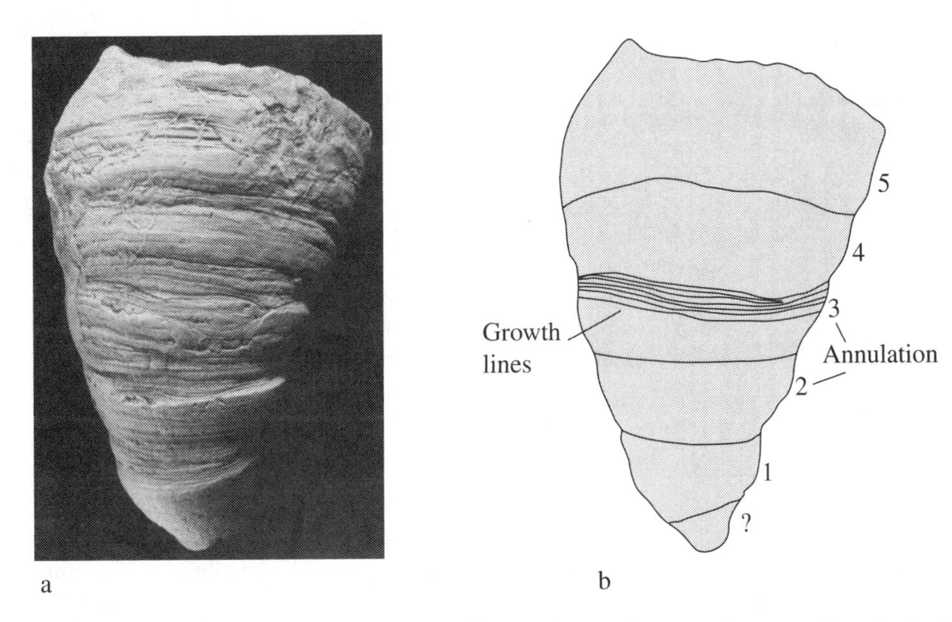

Figure 2-20. (*a*) Growth annulations on this specimen of an extinct coral suggest that the individual lived about 5 or 6 years. [*Judy Camps.*] (*b*) Superimposed upon the annulations are numerous much finer (and fainter) growth layers, believed to represent daily variations in the character of calcium carbonate deposition.

How Did the Moon Originate?

Tidal interactions are a key factor that must be acknowledged in every theory of the origin of the moon. What would happen if, in our imagination, we were to "run the clock backward"? Certainly the moon was closer to the earth, but where would it have come from? At present we must admit much uncertainty. Calculations of the effect of all known forces, past and present, are unconvincing to the skeptic. Data from the Apollo landings on the moon have filled more than 50 thousand pages of scientific literature, but they have not fully settled the controversy. The American geophysicist S. F. Singer aptly remarked: "Of the many proposed modes of the origin of the moon, some violate physical laws; many are in conflict with observations; all are improbable."

Fission In 1898, Sir George Darwin, son of the Charles Darwin of biological evolution fame, proposed that the moon was spun off the earth. If this were the case, the moon would have been the "daughter" of the earth, derived from its body. Darwin argued that as dense material sank to the core, the earth rotated more and more rapidly, just as a spinning ice skater would speed up by pulling the arms in close to the body. A bulge appeared which became more accentuated, eventually to split into a separate body, the moon. An appealing feature of the fission theory is the close agreement between the density of the moon and the density of the outermost portion of the earth which presumably gave birth to the moon. A serious objection is that the moon literally would never have gotten off the ground. Calculations indicate that the newly separated moon would have been torn apart and would have fallen back into the earth.

Capture Other scientists have postulated that the moon formed in some other part of the solar system, possibly nearer to the sun where the intense heat could have boiled away all liquids and gases. A moon with this origin would have been a "captive mistress" of the earth. If the moon's orbit about the sun had been highly elongated, the moon might have spent part of the time in the near vicinity of the earth which allowed the possibility of capture by the earth. The attractive feature of this idea is that, with independent origins, it is easier to explain why the compositions of the moon and earth are so different. On the other hand, calculations of the lunar orbit in the distant past suggest that capture was an exceedingly unlikely event, bordering on impossible.

Origin in earth-circling orbit A third possibility, the one heavily favored by researchers today, is that the moon assembled from a ring of material that had been emplaced around the earth. Rings are common in the solar system, being known to encircle the outer planets: Jupiter, Saturn, Uranus, and Neptune. Ring material was supposedly blasted off the earth by an early collision with a body estimated to be about the size of the planet Mars (Figure 2-21). The idea that peculiarities in motions of planets were the result of collisions with massive infalling bodies is receiving serious consideration. It could explain, for example, why the spin axis of Uranus is tipped at such a crazy angle, or possibly why the front and back faces of the moon are unalike. This third manner of origin would have the moon to be the earth's "twin sister," formed in association with the earth at about the same time.

SUMMARY

Most meteorites are stony, consisting chiefly of silicate minerals in which the elements silicon and oxygen predominate. A minor class, iron-nickel meteorites, consist of intergrowths of two types of iron-nickel alloy. Meteorites are broken remnants of slowly cooled parent bodies that once measured tens to hundreds of kilometers across. Intense bombardment by meteorites during the accumulation of inner planets and their moons had left the surfaces saturated with craters. The earth has relatively few craters only because they are quickly destroyed by processes of erosion and deposition.

The front face of the moon consists of light-colored, low-density, rugged highlands and depressed mare basins filled with smooth, dark-colored, high-density lava. Mare basins on the back side are not filled with lava. The moon is "dead"—devoid of liquids, gases, life, and nearly all signs of internal activity. Because of this deadness, evidence for the earliest events in planetary history is preserved on the moon. Moonquakes continue to reverberate for long periods due to absence of water in strong, rigid lunar rocks. The only process of erosion is disturbance of the surface by infalling meteorites. Craters of all sizes were created by this means. Lunar stratigraphy, interpreted from photographs, can be used to decipher complex sequences of events.

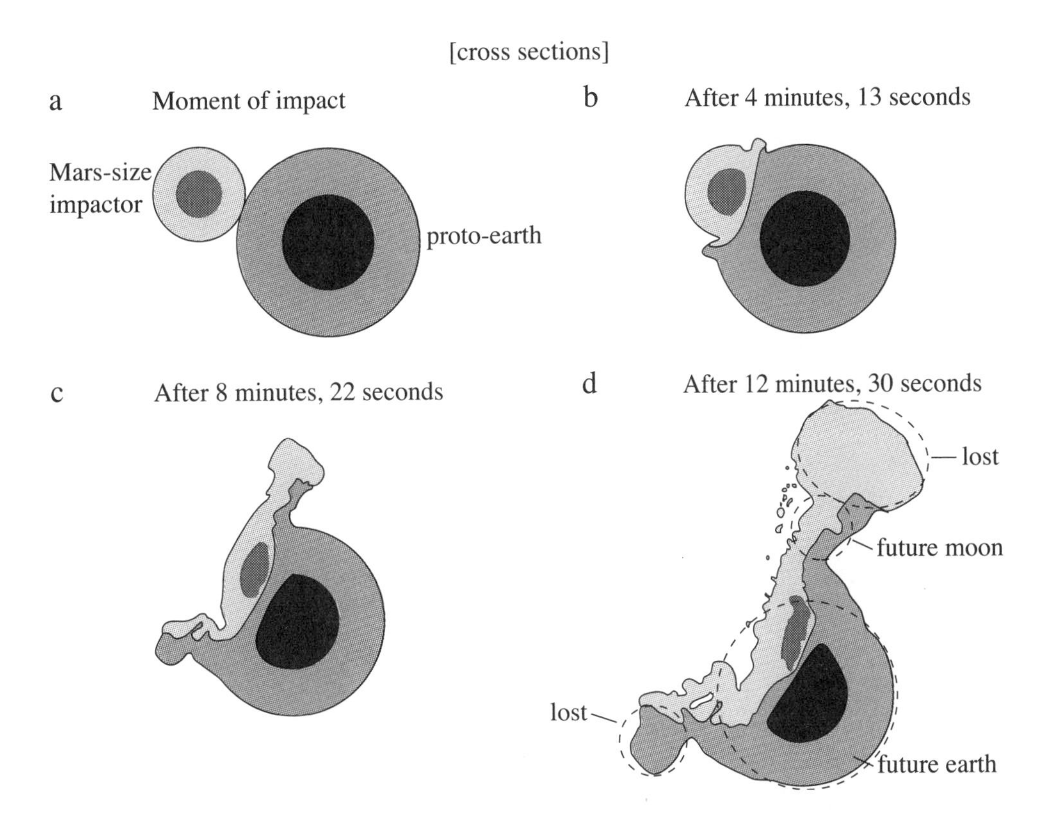

Figure 2-21. According to the prevailing hypothesis, the moon originated by a horrendous collision between the proto-earth, and another planet whose diameter was about half as large. Computer calculations suggest these events: (*a*) By the time of impact, each planet had already differentiated into an iron-nickel core surrounded by a mantle composed chiefly of silicate minerals. (*b*) Both planets deformed as the two merged together. (*c*) Much of the enormous energy of the impact was transferred to an outward-traveling jet composed of mantle material derived from both planets. (*d*) Material within the upper ellipse and lowermost circle was traveling so fast that it was lost entirely from the earth-moon system. More slowly traveling material, enclosed by the upper circle, escaped from the earth, collected into a orbiting ring, then condensed into the moon. Dense core material did not become incorporated into the moon, thus explaining the moon's relatively low density. Core material from the impacting planet later joined the core of the proto-earth. [*After M. W. Kipp and H. J. Melosh, Short note: a preliminary numerical study of colliding planets,* Origin of the Moon, *Lunar and Planetary Institute, Houston, 1986.*]

The earth, 50 times larger than the moon, consists of a core (1/6 of its volume), mantle, and crust (1 percent). When the earth differentiated into these component parts, enough heat was released probably to melt the entire planet. As a result the earth is density-stratified from the core outward to its atmosphere. Much of the original liquid and gas were lost, but enough H_2O remained dissolved in the interior to account for the world ocean as the water emerged to the surface by volcanism and hot spring activity. Almost all water released from the interior today is recycled.

Tidal drag causes the earth's rotation rate to slow down while the moon's orbit gradually recedes from the earth. Ideas about the origin of the moon have been very controversial. It could have split off from the earth very early during differentiation, or it could have been captured by the earth from some other orbit, or, by far most plausibly, the moon material could have been assembled from a ring blasted off the early earth by a huge impact.

3

Plane Faces

Cluster of quartz crystals. [*Judy Camps*]

The earth is made mostly of rocks. In turn, rocks are aggregates of minerals. And what is a mineral? The word was coined in the Middle Ages to refer to something that could be mined, a buried material of economic value. But long before that, perhaps as early as 6 to 7 thousand years ago, mankind was already putting some 40 minerals to practical use.

The science of mineralogy developed only very gradually. At first, minerals were incorrectly classified with fossils, rocks, alloys, even with porcelain, glass, and pigments! Today the word "mineral" is defined in ways that differ from the scientific meaning of the term. A corporation lawyer might refer to "mineral rights" in regard to coal or petroleum, neither of which is a mineral in a geologist's sense. In some situations even water is, legally speaking, a mineral.

This chapter, which considers the makeup of the solid earth, uses the word in a more restricted sense. A mineral is a *naturally occurring*, *inorganic* substance in which the atoms are *systematically arranged*; it is a *crystalline* form of matter. This concept took shape in two major scientific advances. The first came when analyses showed that a mineral species has a restricted range of chemical composition. The second achievement was truly revolutionary. It took into account not only *what* atoms are present, but *how* they are positioned in a crystal. Let us explore some of these amazing developments.

CRYSTALS

Perfectly formed crystals have been prized as gemstones since ancient times. Someone has remarked that their beauty lies in the planeness of their faces. Why are crystals bounded by flat surfaces? Straight lines and flat planes simply do not occur in nature purely by chance. (Not all crystals exhibit flat faces. For example, during its transport down a river system, a once beautifully faceted crystal could have been abraded into a rounded grain of sand.) Another regularity of crystals was discovered in the 1600s by Nicolaus Steno, a professor of anatomy who also was keenly interested in rocks and minerals. He noted that *corresponding faces of different crystals of a mineral all intersect at the same angle.*

For example, consider two crystals of quartz, the mineral studied originally by Steno (Figure 3-1). Quartz crystals may vary in shape from long, slender needles to short, stubby forms. In spite of these differences, the angles between faces *a* and *b* are identical in both crystals, and so are the angles between faces *a* and *c*, or between *b* and *c*. Suppose that crystal 1 were cut through the middle along the shaded

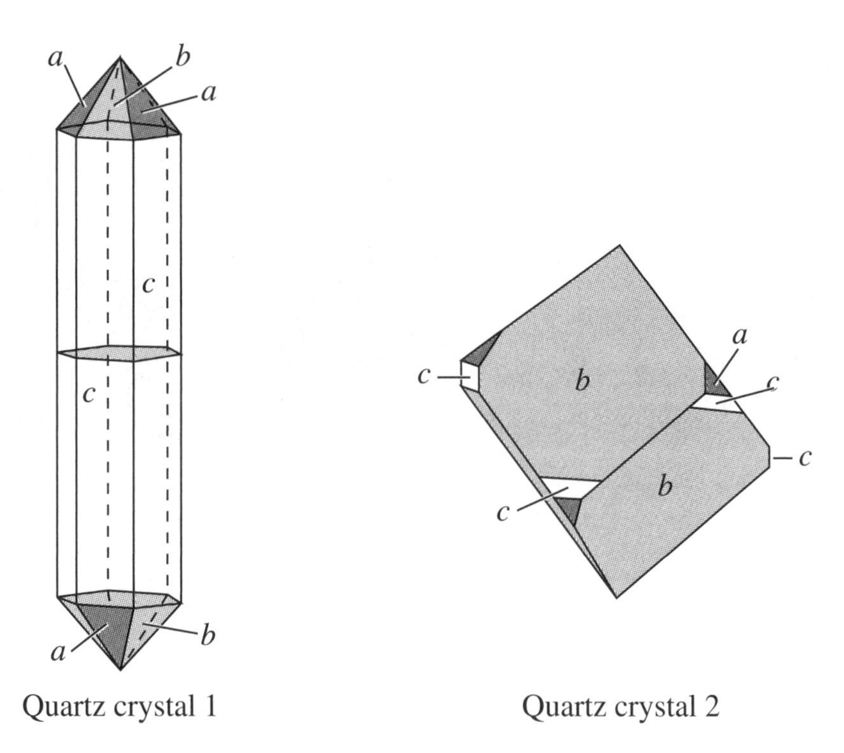

Figure 3-1. Quartz crystals may assume many forms, some elongated, others short and squat. Here are two of them.

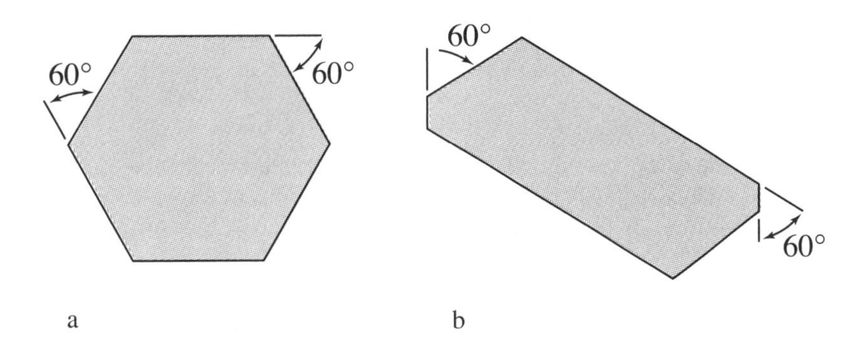

Figure 3-2. These quartz crystals have been sliced along a plane perpendicular to the faces labeled *c* in Figure 3-1, then turned cut-face upward.

plane. Viewed end-on in Figure 3-2*a*, this plane is seen to form a perfect hexagon. The corresponding plane through quartz crystal 2 might be a distorted hexagon [(Figure 3-2(*b*)]. Even so, any two sides in both crystals join at an angle of 60°. Angles between crystal faces of other minerals differ from the angles of quartz. These characteristic angles are a help in identifying minerals.

In 1784 a French crystallographer, R. Haüy (HAY-you-wee), proposed a model to explain the external regularity of crystals. He suggested that in a crystal, numbers of identical "building blocks" are stacked together as illustrated by one of his drawings (Figure 3-3). Ordinary table salt (sodium chloride) can illustrate this simple notion. If we were to crush a cube of table salt, examination with a magnifying glass would show that the powder consists of many tiny cubes. Note that it is not necessary that each

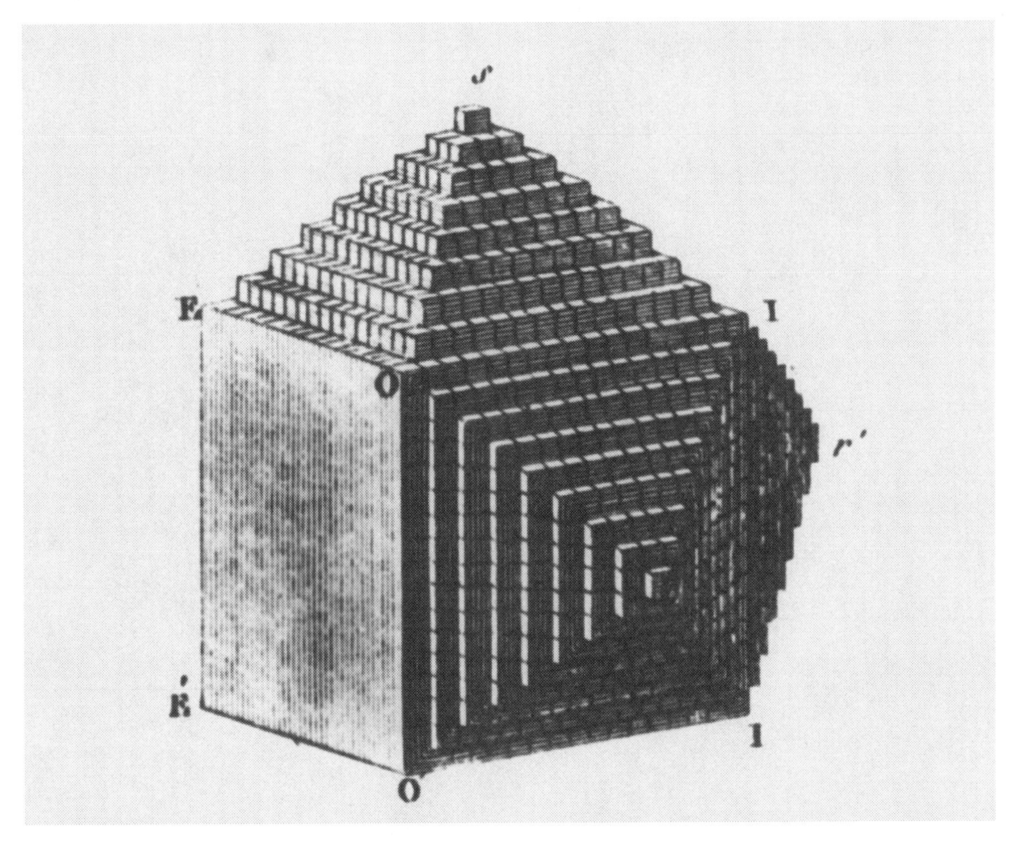

Figure 3-3. Building blocks in the Haüy model are not necessarily miniature replicas of the entire crystal. In this sketch by Haüy, a rather complex crystal form is constructed of numerous simple rectangular units. [*René Haüy, as appearing in Walter J. Moore,* Physical Chemistry, *Prentice-Hall, Inc., Englewood Cliffs, NJ, 1972.*]

repeated small unit should have the same shape as the entire crystal. In Figure 3-3 for example, small cubes are used to build a more complicated shape.

Probing Crystals with X-rays

Are the tiny salt cubes made of even smaller cubelets? How far can this reasoning go? What are Haüy's *ultimate* building blocks? More than a century was to pass before discovery of x-rays would make possible the answer to that question. In those days, the nature of x-rays was just as obscure as the nature of crystals. Do x-rays consist of waves, or a stream of particles, or what? Thus they were called *x*-rays, to denote an unknown quantity. Then in 1912 the German physicist Max von Laue thought of training x-rays on crystals, and in doing so he solved both mysteries together. His hunch was that x-rays are similar to visible light, but more penetrating. Moreover, he reasoned, it could be that crystals have flat faces and fixed interfacial angles because their atoms are arranged in an orderly pattern. The results of his experiments brilliantly confirmed both postulates. X-rays are waves, and crystals are internally ordered.

An obvious candidate for some of the earliest x-ray experiments were crystals of our familiar example, sodium chloride. As Laue predicted, x-rays create a symmetrical pattern of spots on a photographic film after passing through this substance (Figure 3-4). Spots on either side of a central vertical line are seen to correspond. They are also arranged symmetrically about the central point of the pattern. Unlike the image of a person's ribs in a chest x-ray, these spots are not a picture of the atoms themselves. Unfortunately the information is far less obvious than that. Let us see, at least in principle, how x-rays reveal the atomic structure of crystals.

A convenient way to represent wave motion is by a wavy line—a series of crests and troughs (Figure 3-5). The distance between adjacent crests, or between neighboring troughs, represents the *wavelength* of the x-rays. Suppose that we shine an x-ray beam, for which there is but a single wavelength, upon a crystal (Figure 3-6). These x-rays are reflected, some from the topmost layer of atoms, and

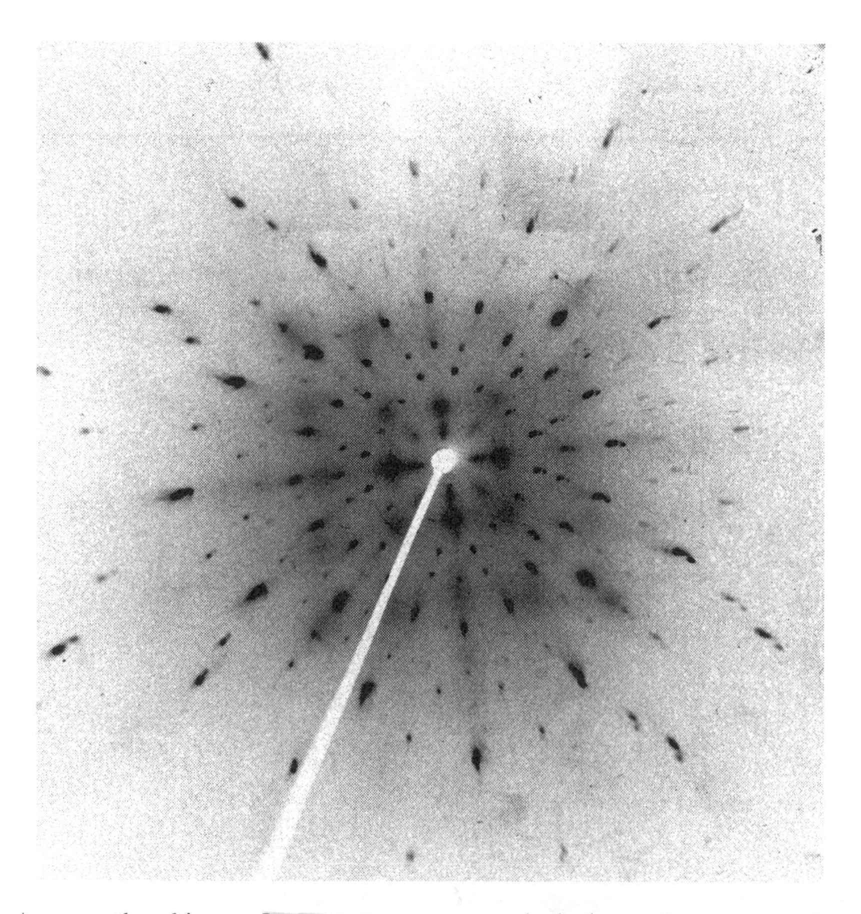

Figure 3-4. Among other things, a Laue x-ray pattern reveals the internal symmetry of atomic positions in sodium chloride (shown here) or in other crystals. Symmetry must be considered in determining the locations of atoms in crystals. [*Luis Rendon.*]

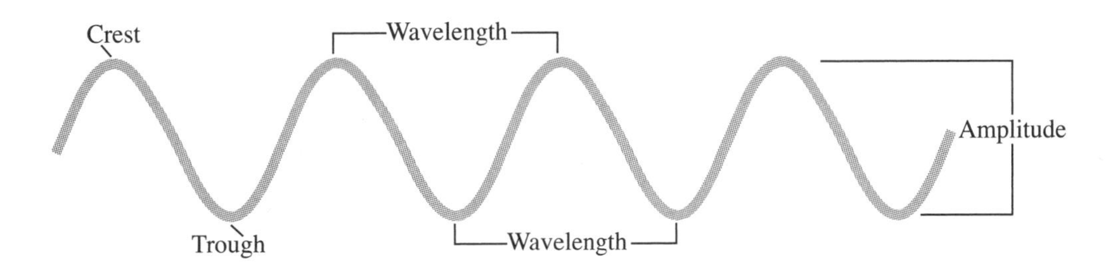

Figure 3-5. In this representation of a wave form, uniform spacing of crests or troughs indicates a single value of the wavelength.

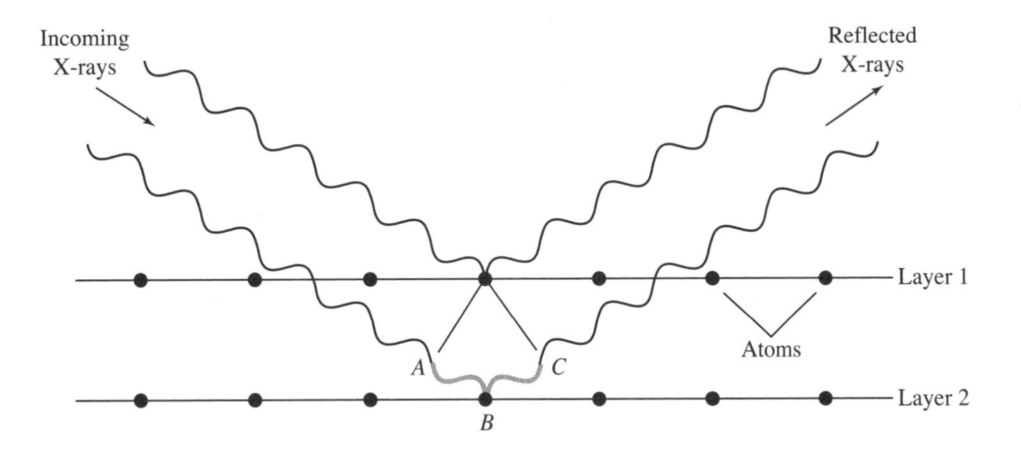

Figure 3-6. Distance $\overline{AB}$ is one wavelength, and so is distance $\overline{BC}$. X-rays reflected off Layer 2 have traveled distance $\overline{ABC}$, or exactly two wavelengths farther than x-rays reflected off Layer 1. Upon emerging from the crystal, the two reflected waves are synchronized; they are "in phase" with one another.

some from deeper layers that lie parallel to it. If reflected x-rays emerging from deeper layers are exactly "in step" with those reflected off the upper layers, the x-rays will reinforce one another.

As seen in Figure 3-6, the x-rays reflected from Layer 2 must travel distance $\overline{ABC}$ farther than x-rays reflected off Layer 1. If distance $\overline{ABC}$ is equal to some exact whole number of wavelengths, the entire crystal will reflect the x-rays. Otherwise, the waves cancel one another, and there is no reflection. Since the x-ray wavelength and the distance between layers of atoms are fixed, distance $\overline{ABC}$ will be an integer number of wavelengths only if the incoming rays strike the crystal at certain angles. Or, to put it another way, we can learn the spacing between planes of atoms by observing the angles through which the crystal "flashes out" reflections.

But why are x-rays not reflected in *every* direction? Atoms should lie on any plane that passes through the crystal in any orientation whatsoever. The situation here is somewhat like a marching band on a football field (Figure 3-7). If the musicians can keep in step (and not all can!), we should be able to sight along columns, along rows, or along various diagonals of marchers. Along diagonals they are more widely spaced than along rows or columns. Similarly, out of many possible layers of atoms in a crystal, only a few layers contain enough atoms to give a significant reflection.

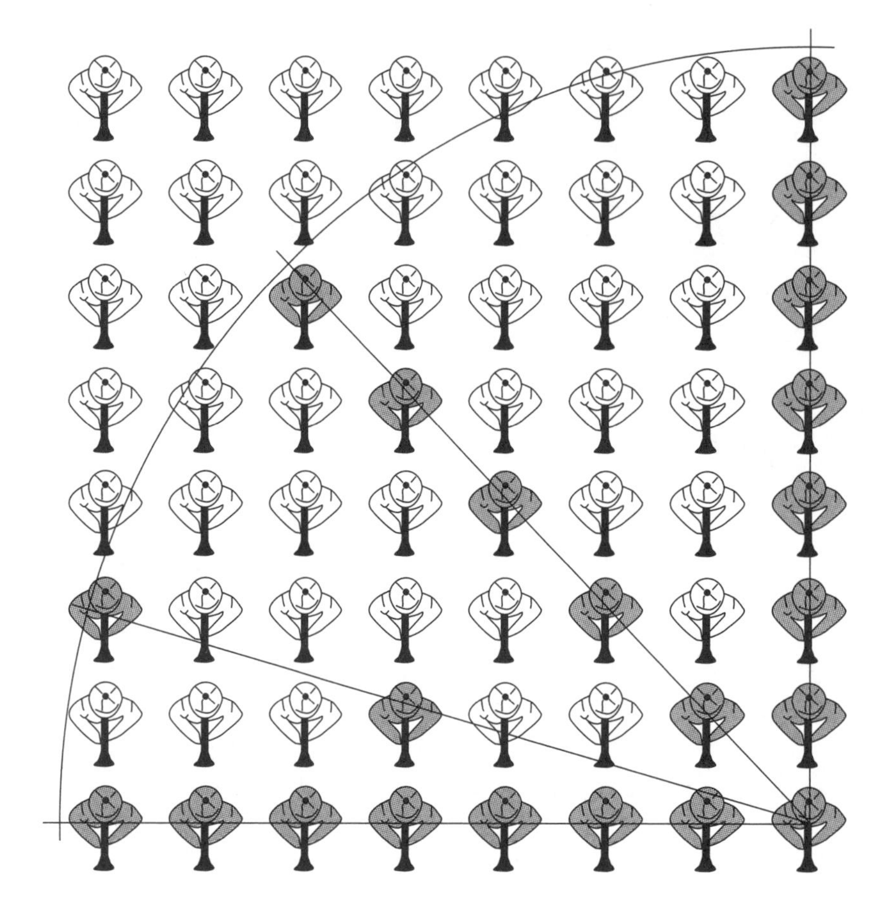

Figure 3-7. Evenly positioned marchers are analogous to layers of atoms in a crystal. Distances between marchers (or between atoms) vary according to direction. A row or column in this band contains eight marchers, but the same distance along the major diagonal includes only six musicians. Another diagonal contains only three. [*Bill R. Deans.*]

Figuring out the atomic arrangement in a crystal calls for much skill and artistry. An x-ray crystallographer must know the chemical formula, and (in due respect to Haüy) she carefully studies the external shape of the crystal. She obtains various sorts of x-ray patterns. Then she proposes a geometrical pattern of the atoms, and calculates the x-ray pattern that such a crystal ought to give. If the calculation based on the proposed model does not correspond closely to the photographic images, she must refine the model again and again until it does agree acceptably. All the simple atomic structures were described long ago. The millions of calculations necessary to describe complex crystal structures are done nowadays by computers.

X-rays can also be used to identify minerals. For example, some materials are so fine-grained that individual crystals are too small to see, even with a microscope. A chemical analysis would be difficult to interpret if several different minerals were mixed together. On the other hand, an x-ray analysis is simple and accurate. We may easily match the x-ray data, from the sample of unknown identity, with data already obtained from positively identified minerals.

Unit Cells

Let's return to the question posed above: What *are* Haüy's tiny building blocks? With the benefit of x-ray analyses, we may identify each block as a *unit cell.* Picture a simple crystal in which the pattern of the atoms extends indefinitely in all directions (Figure 3-8). A unit cell is the smallest and simplest fragment of this three-dimensional pattern that is needed to convey the information of the atomic positions. An entire crystal is made up of countless numbers of unit cells joined together.

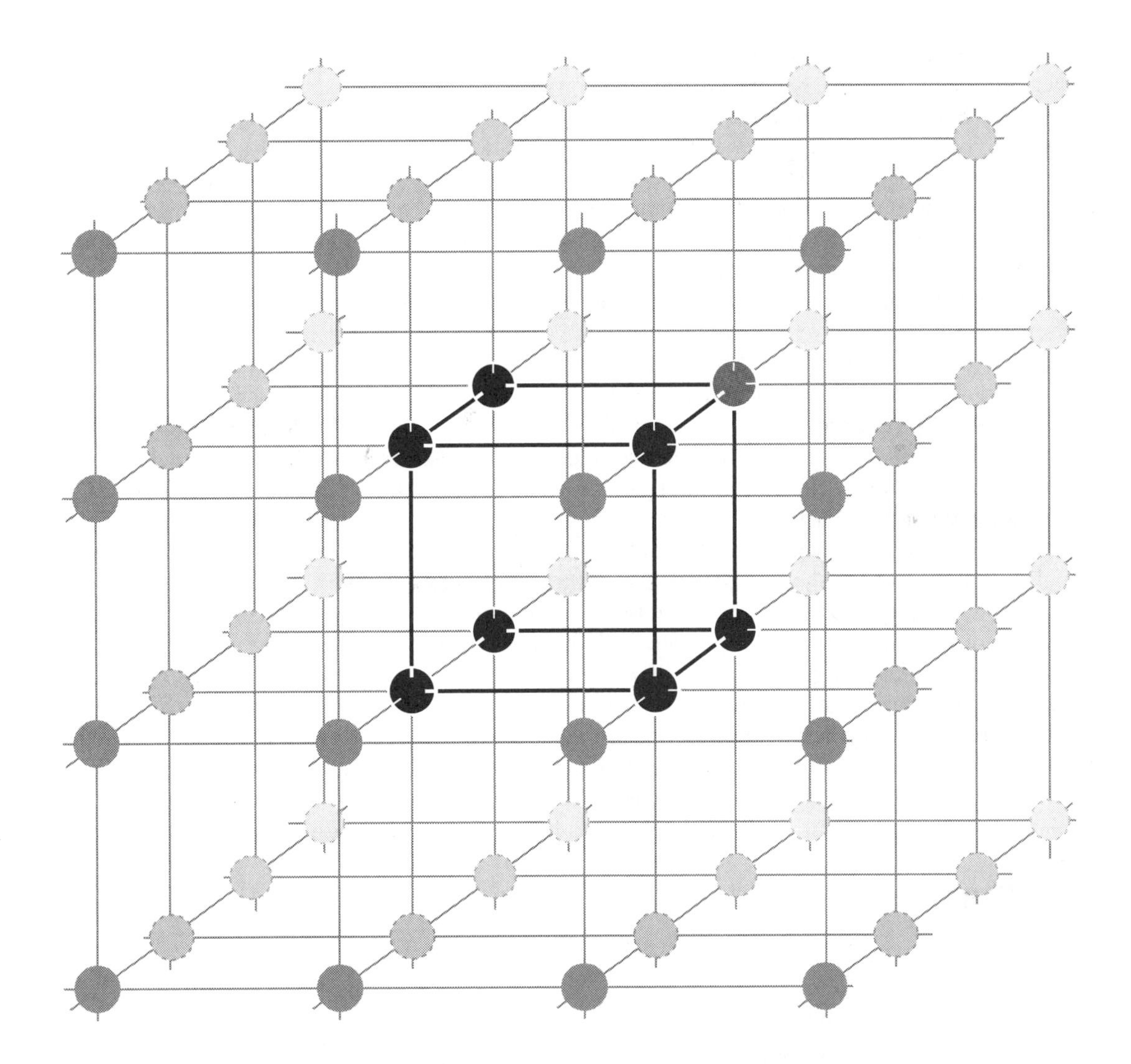

Figure 3-8. In this example, a crystal is assembled of cubic unit cells joined together in a continuous pattern repeated in all directions. Focus on the colored atom. Not only does it occupy the corner of the boldly emphasized unit cell, but it participates equally in cells to the side, to the rear, and above it. A unit cell contains an atom at all 8 corners, but each of the atoms also participates in 8 surrounding unit cells. Therefore, 8 atoms x 1/8 "credit" for each atom gives one atom per unit cell.

MINERALS

Now we are ready to consider the most common minerals that make up the earth (quartz, mica, gypsum, calcite, etc.). Most of the 5 thousand known mineral species are exceedingly rare; only a few crystals are known of some of them. Most of the earth's crust is made of about 50 minerals or mineral families. Of these, only about one-half to one-quarter are likely to be encountered day in and day out by a professional geologist. Obviously, the minerals must be composed of whatever atoms are at hand. Therefore, the *abundances* of chemical elements play a key role in determining which minerals are most common. Also important are the *size* and *charge* of the atoms. These factors set limits upon what could be, in principle, an almost infinite number of possible mineral compositions and structures.

A Delicate Balance

What forces bind atoms together in a crystal? In Chapter 1 we saw that an atom consists of a positively charged nucleus surrounded by a cloud of negatively charged electrons. It is common knowledge that oppositely charged particles are mutually attracted, whereas particles with the same charge repel one another. Since atoms contain *both* positive and negative charges, the result is a situation of delicately balanced forces. Suppose that two atoms are brought closer and closer together. As the electron clouds touch, then begin to overlap, they will experience a strong force of mutual repulsion. Because of this interplay of forces, the atoms in a crystal will settle into equilibrium positions that depend on the charges and sizes of the electron clouds, and on the nature of all the other atoms in the vicinity. These positions are repeated over and over throughout the crystal, like the marchers who must stay in fixed positions in the band formation (Figure 3-7), but with an added consideration. Marchers who play bass tubas must stay a respectful distance apart, whereas players of piccolos (the tiniest instrument) can crowd closer together without interfering. We would have very unevenly spaced rows and columns unless the tuba players and piccolo players were mixed together. In a crystal, positive and negative ions similarly must be intermixed.

Another factor important in chemical bonding is the arrangement of electrons in "shells" about the nucleus. The innermost shell, or zone, is occupied by 2 electrons; the next shell is fully occupied if it contains 8 electrons, etc. An atom with a filled outermost shell is "saturated," and highly reluctant to form chemical bonds with other atoms. The inert gases such as neon and argon illustrate this condition.

Ionic bonding In each of the chemical elements except for the inert gases, the outer electron shell is only partially occupied. One way that atoms of these elements can achieve greater stability is through completion of the shell by receiving or donating electrons. Gain or loss of electrons does not change the number of protons in the nucleus. Thus the atom assumes a net electrical charge; it has become an ion that can form chemical bonds with other ions of the opposite charge.

Sodium chloride is a good example of an ionic crystal. A neutral sodium atom has two "closed" shells containing 2 and 8 electrons respectively, plus the beginning of a third shell populated by a single electron. In the sodium nucleus there are 11 positive charges (protons) corresponding to the 11 electrons. The third electron shell of a neutral chlorine atom lacks one electron for completion. In a sodium chloride crystal the outermost, rather loosely attached electron of sodium is transferred to the vacant position in chlorine (Figure 3-9). This leaves the sodium with an unbalanced *positive* charge; it has become a *cation*. In the process, the chlorine atom with an additional electron has become a *negatively* charged chloride *anion*. Mutual attraction between Na^+ and Cl^- holds the crystal together.

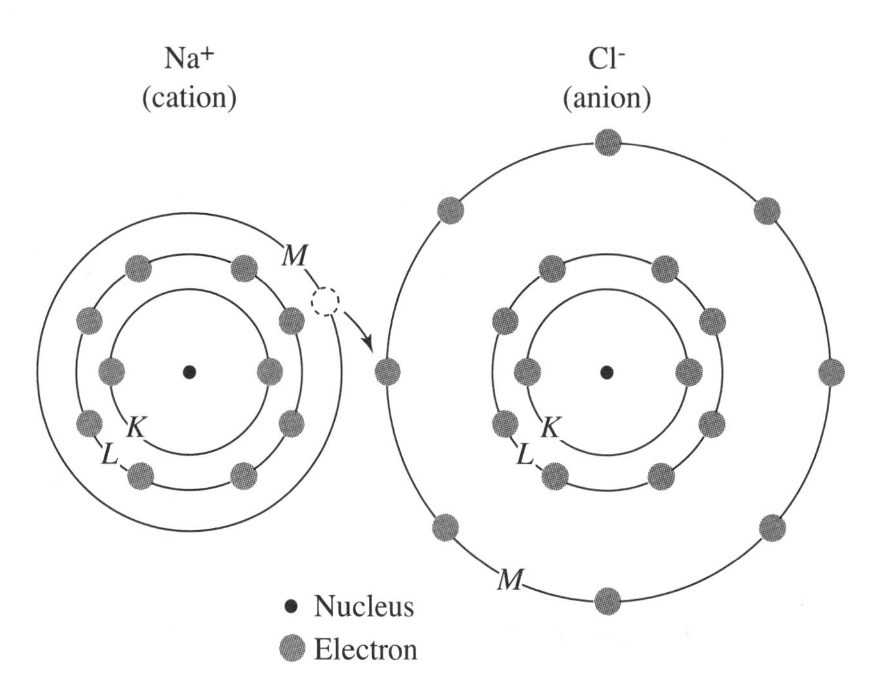

Figure 3-9. *K*, *L*, and *M* designate the electron shells, symbolized here in schematic form. When Na^+ and Cl^- are bonded together, the sodium ion donates its eleventh electron, that otherwise would be the sole occupant of the *M* shell, to fill a vacancy in the *M* shell of chlorine.

The structure of sodium chloride, the first to be determined by x-rays, is also one of the simplest (Figure 3-10). It is a three-dimensional checkerboard of alternating sodium and chloride ions. Each sodium cation is surrounded by 6 "nearest neighbor" chloride anions, and vice versa. Forces of attraction and repulsion are nicely balanced. Oppositely charged ions touch one another, whereas ions with the same charge are held apart at somewhat greater distances. Taken as a whole, a crystal of sodium chloride is electrically neutral.

Covalent bonding Another way in which the outer electron shell can be saturated is through *covalent* bonding. Oxygen molecules (O_2) provide a splendid example of this type of bond. An isolated oxygen atom lacks two electrons to complete a filled shell. By combining, each of the two oxygen atoms united together in a molecule can achieve a filled outer shell by *sharing* electrons with its partner (Figure 3-11). Covalent, or shared-electron bonding is the dominant type in organic chemistry, the chemistry of carbon compounds.

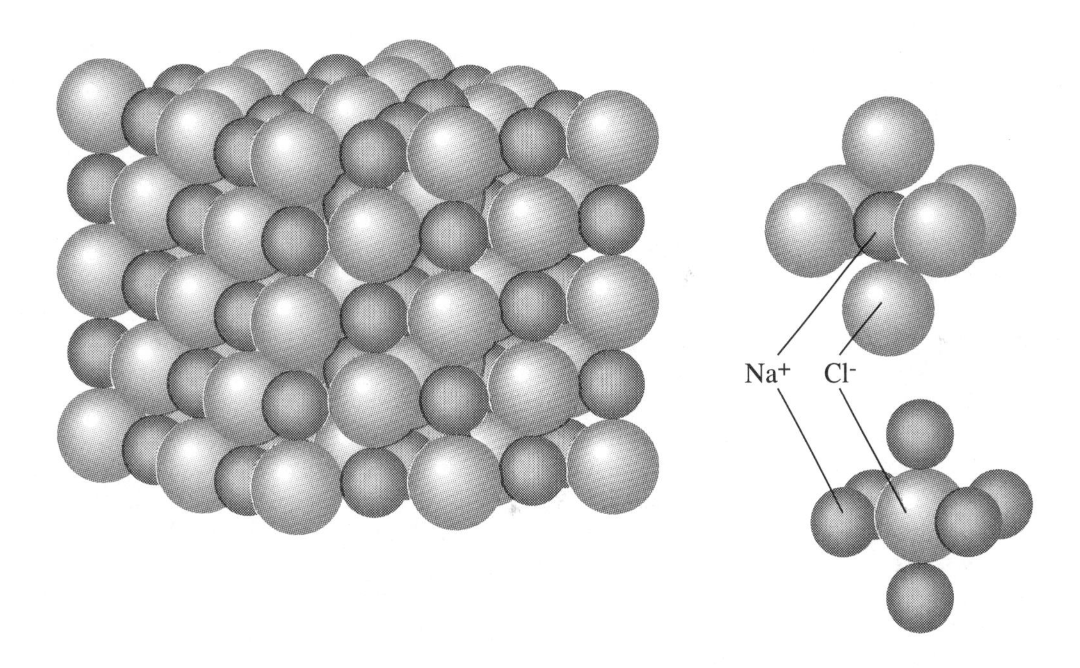

Figure 3-10. Crystal structure of sodium chloride. The right-hand drawings show that 6 chloride ions surround each sodium ion, and that 6 sodium ions surround each chloride ion.

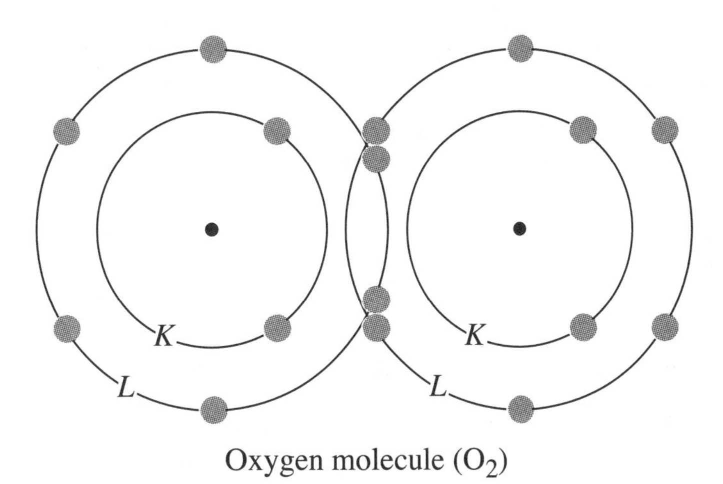

Figure 3-11. In the O_2 molecule, covalently bonded oxygen atoms mutually share certain of the *L*-shell electrons.

Covalent and ionic bonds are similar and different in several respects. Both may be strong or weak. A mineral with strong chemical bonds is a hard substance, difficult to break or scratch because strong bonds are not easily ruptured. It so happens that carbon atoms are covalently bonded in diamond, the hardest mineral, but some minerals held together by ionic bonds are also extremely hard. Actually, every bond in a crystal is partly ionic and partly covalent. Nothing in nature is absolutely pure.

The Silicate Structure

By now, the number of chemically analyzed samples of rock must be in the millions. They include all known rock types from all over the earth. Table 3-1, a grand average summary for rocks in the earth's crust, shows that only eight chemical elements account for nearly 99 percent of the total. Whether considered according to weight or numbers of atoms, oxygen and silicon are by far the most abundant elements. Moreover, oxygen atoms are comparatively large, so that oxygen occupies almost 94 percent of the *volume* of the crust. We have essentially a packing of large but light oxygen atoms, amongst which the generally small but dense silicon and metal atoms are stuffed.

Thus, oxygen and silicon are the chemical backbone of the earth's crust. What governs how these two species of atom are to combine? Oxygen is a strongly nonmetallic element with an ionic charge of -2. Chemical properties of silicon are suggestive of both metals and nonmetals. In the presence of oxygen, silicon behaves more as a metal, assuming an ionic charge of +4. Silicon cations and oxygen anions must be intermixed, just as Na^+ and Cl^- are in sodium chloride. Fewer silicon ions with +4 charge are able to neutralize more numerous oxygen ions with -2 charge.

Clearly, because there are more silicon and oxygen ions than anything else, there will be an important class of minerals, known as *silicate* minerals, that incorporate these two chemical elements. How shall we combine the large oxygen with the small silicon? Consider the three-dimensional object known as a *tetrahedron* (Figure 3-12). As the term "tetra" implies, a tetrahedron has four faces (and four corners). Superficially it resembles an Egyptian pyramid except that the base of a tetrahedron is a triangle, not a square. X-ray analyses show that four large, spherical oxygen ions are positioned on the corners of a tetrahedron. Because of the curvature of the oxygen spheres, there is a small, curiously shaped hole in the center of the tetrahedron that can be occupied by a silicon ion. Since we have one silicon ion to four oxygen ions, we may symbolize the association as SiO_4. Note that the tetrahedral association of ions is *not* electrically neutral! Its charge is 1 x (+4) for silicon, plus 4 x (-2) for oxygen, which gives a net charge of negative 4 (-4).

Electrical neutrality can be restored to the overall crystal in two ways. In most silicate minerals, other cations such as K^+, Na^+, Ca^{2+}, and Al^{3+} are located in spaces among the silicon-oxygen tetrahedrons. (In certain minerals, Al^{3+} substitutes for Si^{4+} in the center of a tetrahedron.) The remainder of the excess negative charge is neutralized by the silicon-oxygen tetrahedrons themselves. It is accomplished by a linking together at their corners to form chains, or sheets, or more complex structures. A negatively

Table 3-1. *Abundances of Chemical Elements in the Earth's Crust*

Element	*% by weight*	*% by number of atoms*	*% by volume*	*Relative size of ions*
Oxygen (O)	46.6	62.6	93.8	(O^{2-})
Silicon (Si)	27.7	21.2	0.9	(Si^{4+})
Aluminum (Al)	8.1	6.5	0.5	(Al^{3+})
Iron (Fe)	5.0	1.9	0.4	(Fe^{2+})
Calcium (Ca)	3.6	1.9	1.0	(Ca^{2+})
Sodium (Na)	2.8	2.6	1.3	(Na^+)
Potassium (K)	2.6	1.4	1.8	(K^+)
Magnesium (Mg)	2.1	1.9	0.3	(Mg^{2+})
All other elements	1.5	100.0*	100.0*	
	100.0			

**Includes only the first eight elements.*

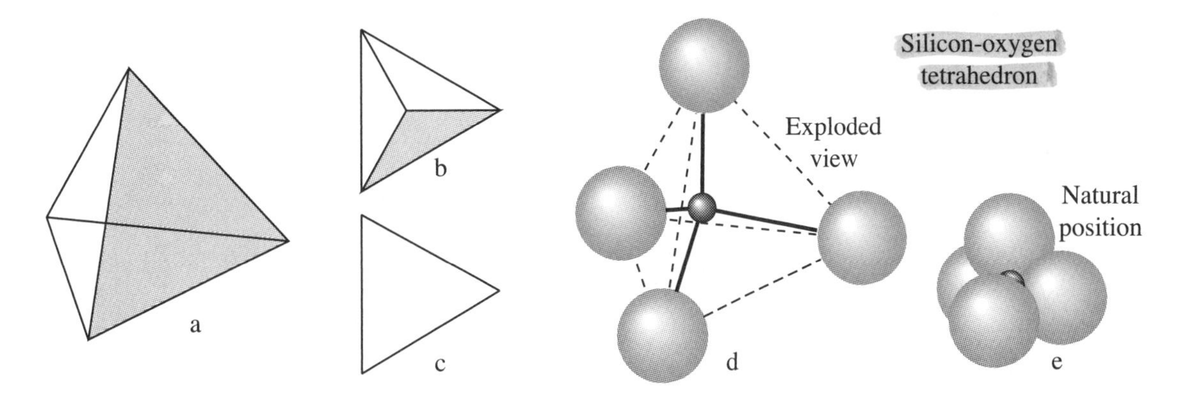

Figure 3-12. The tetrahedron, a solid figure, as viewed (*a*) in perspective, (*b*) from above, and (*c*) from below. Oxygen and silicon atoms fit together in a tetrahedral arrangement (*d* and *e*). In the natural position, the silicon is actually concealed from view, like a grape hidden in a pile of oranges.

charged oxygen that is shared between two tetrahedrons does "double duty" (Figure 3-13). By linking, the adjacent tetrahedrons partly merge together. They require fewer oxygens for a given number of silicons, and consequently the negative charge of the entire assemblage of ions is reduced.

Chemical bonds between these oxygen and silicon atoms are about equally covalent and ionic in character. We know that the bonds are very strong because the tetrahedrons maintain a rigid, undistorted shape and size no matter what the remainder of the silicate structure may be like.

Some Silicate Minerals

Long before the discovery of x-rays, mineralogists had worked out a classification of minerals based upon properties such as color, density, crystal shape, hardness, etc. X-ray analyses have enriched this classification by showing how the atomic structure of minerals can explain these other, more self-evident features. Here is a survey of the important families of silicate minerals, distinguished by the manner in which the silicon-oxygen tetrahedrons are joined together.

Isolated tetrahedrons *Olivine* (OLi-veen) exemplifies a family of silicate minerals in which the tetrahedrons are not linked at all; no oxygens are shared between adjacent tetrahedrons (Figure 3-14). Metal ions in olivine are either Mg^{2+} or Fe^{2+}, which may be present in any proportion. The atomic structure is the same whether the mineral is pure magnesium olivine (Mg_2SiO_4), or a mixture such as $MgFeSiO_4$, or pure iron olivine (Fe_2SiO_4). These two metal ions readily substitute for one another

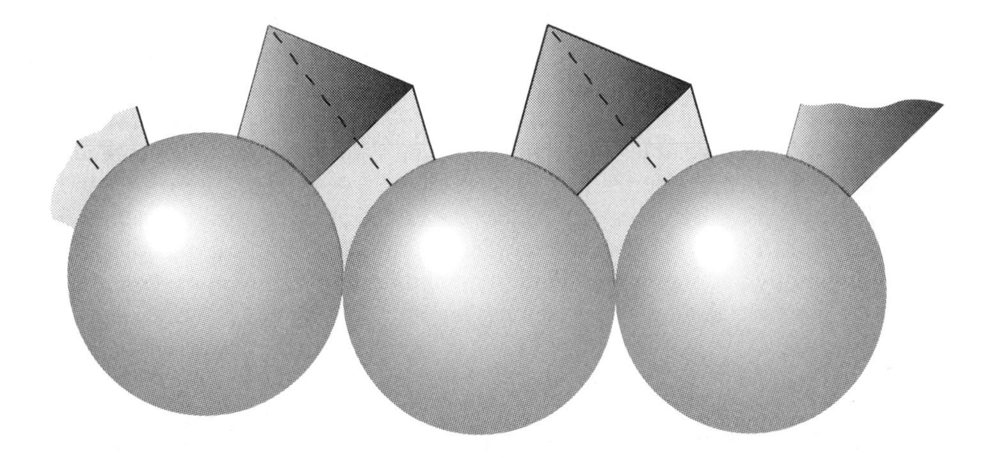

Figure 3-13. Skeleton outlines of linked tetrahedrons are pictured from a perspective view. A shared oxygen atom serves each of the adjacent tetrahedrons equally well.

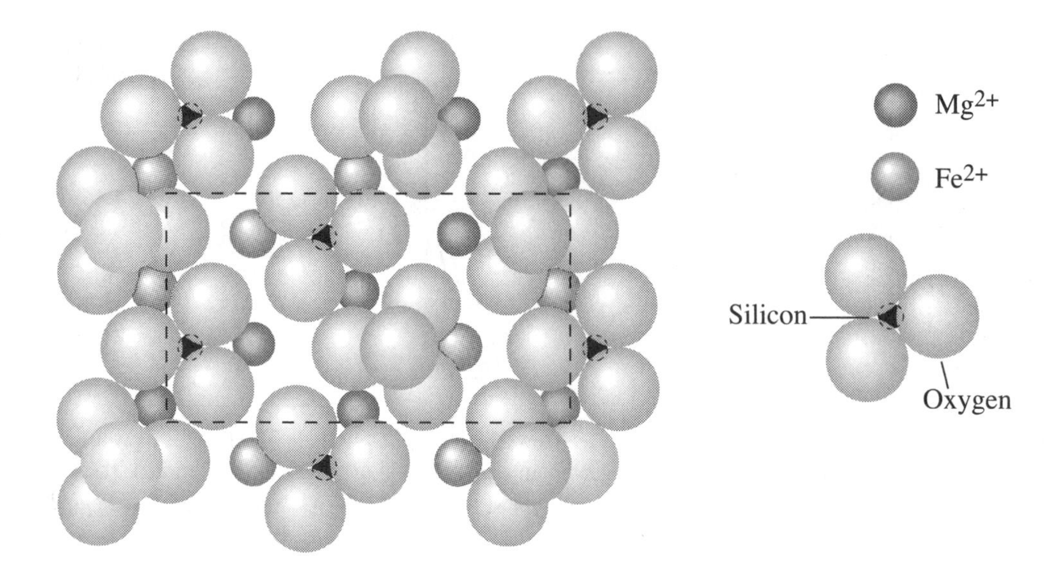

Figure 3-14. Silicon-oxygen tetrahedrons in olivine form rows and columns in all three dimensions. Cations of magnesium (Mg^{2+}) and ferrous iron (Fe^{2+}) occupy regular prescribed positions amongst the tetrahedrons, and either ion many occupy any cation site: a situation of mutual substitution. The box encloses the atoms in one unit cell—the simplest fragment of the repeating pattern.

because of their similar sizes and identical +2 charge. Mutual substitution occurs not only in olivine, but in many other minerals that contain abundant iron and magnesium. As a group, these *ferromagnesian* minerals are quite dense, and in color they range from very dark green or brown to almost opaque black.

There is a striking relationship between the atomic structure and the physical properties of olivine. Closely packed oxygen ions are connected to silicon and to magnesium or iron by strong chemical bonds. Therefore, olivine is one of the hardest, most dense minerals. Because the bonds are oriented in various directions in the crystal, there is no especially preferred plane of atoms along which an olivine crystal might break. Instead, the crystal tends to *fracture*—to break along irregular surfaces. Fire bricks made of olivine are used to line furnaces. What does this imply about the strength of the chemical bonds?

Single chains Another family of silicates is the *pyroxene* (PEERoc-seen) group. Pyroxenes, the most abundant ferromagnesian minerals in the earth's crust, are prominent in a great variety of rocks of different origins. In these minerals, silicon-oxygen tetrahedrons are linked corner-to-corner into long chains [Figure 3-15(*a*)]. Some of the net negative electrical charge is neutralized by linkage; the remainder is neutralized by layers of Mg^{2+} and Fe^{2+} ions that substitute freely for one another, just as in olivine [Figure 3-15(*b*)]. The pyroxene group is much more complex than olivine, however. Cation sites in pyroxene can also accommodate calcium, sodium, aluminum, titanium, and other metal ions.

Double chains Linkage of tetrahedrons into chains is the hallmark of yet another family of silicates, the *amphiboles*. In these minerals, two rows of silicon-oxygen tetrahedrons are joined side by side, forming double chains (Figure 3-16). Amphiboles outrival the pyroxenes in complexity. Both are ferromagnesians, but the cation sites in amphibole minerals can take up metal ions of almost any size or charge. This is especially true of *hornblende*, the most abundant species of amphibole. Hornblende is the "garbage can" of the mineral world, incorporating ions that are rejected by other, more discriminating mineral structures.

We would expect pyroxenes and amphiboles to be similar in many ways. Most of these minerals are rather hard and dense. Chemical bonds within the silicon-oxygen chains are stronger than bonds connecting the chains to the remainder of the structure. Crystals of pyroxene or amphibole strongly tend to split parallel to the chains, not across them: these minerals display good *cleavage*, or tendency to break

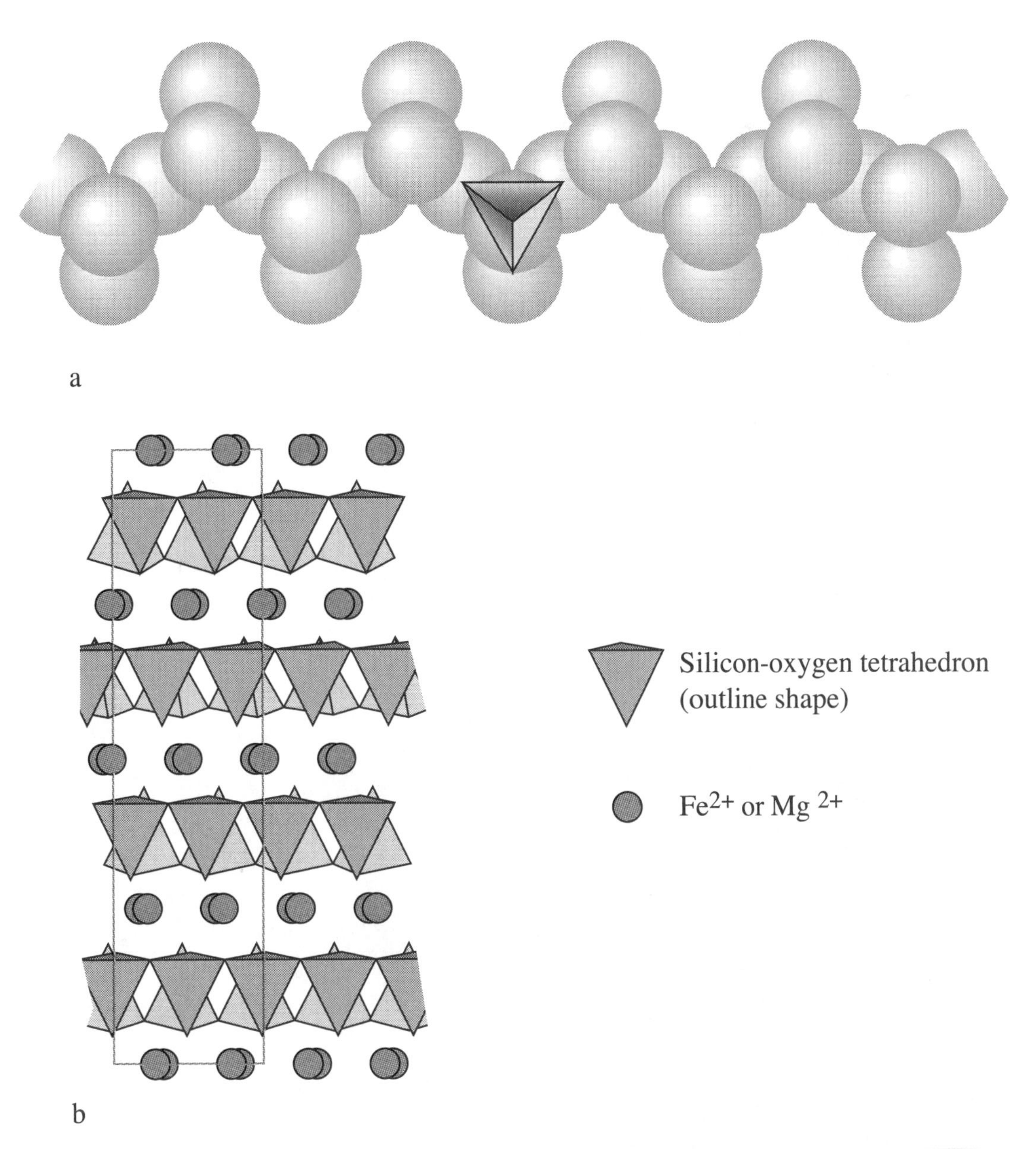

Figure 3-15. (*a*) A short segment of the Si-O tetrahedron chain characteristic of the pyroxene group of silicate minerals. (Silicon atoms are concealed from view.) (*b*) In enstatite, one of the pyroxene minerals, layers of these single chains alternate between layers of Mg^{2+} and Fe^{2+} ions. The box encloses the atoms in one unit cell.

along flat surfaces. Individual crystals may be bladelike or needlelike, even fibrous like strands of hair. (Asbestos is a trade name for certain fibrous varieties of amphibole.) Angles between planes of cleavage in pyroxene and amphibole are different. This detail, which shows particularly well under the microscope, provides a handy way to identify and distinguish the two groups.

Sheets A natural extension of the linkage theme brings us to minerals built around sheets of silicon-oxygen tetrahedrons [Figure 3-17(*a*)]. These sheets, which are basic to the *mica* family of minerals, display the most obvious relation between atomic structure and physical properties to be seen in any of the silicates. Mica splits into very thin, uniform flakes that may be either isolated, or stacked together into mica "books" (Figure 3-18).

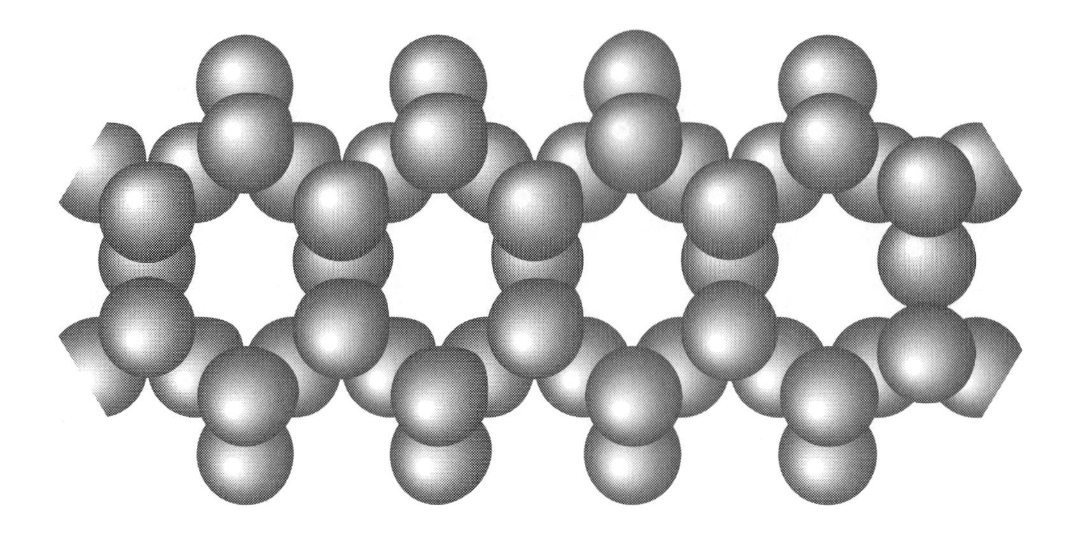

Figure 3-16. The backbone of the amphibole family of minerals is the double chain of connected tetrahedrons. Not shown are Mg^{2+}, Fe^{2+}, and other metal ions positioned amongst the chains.

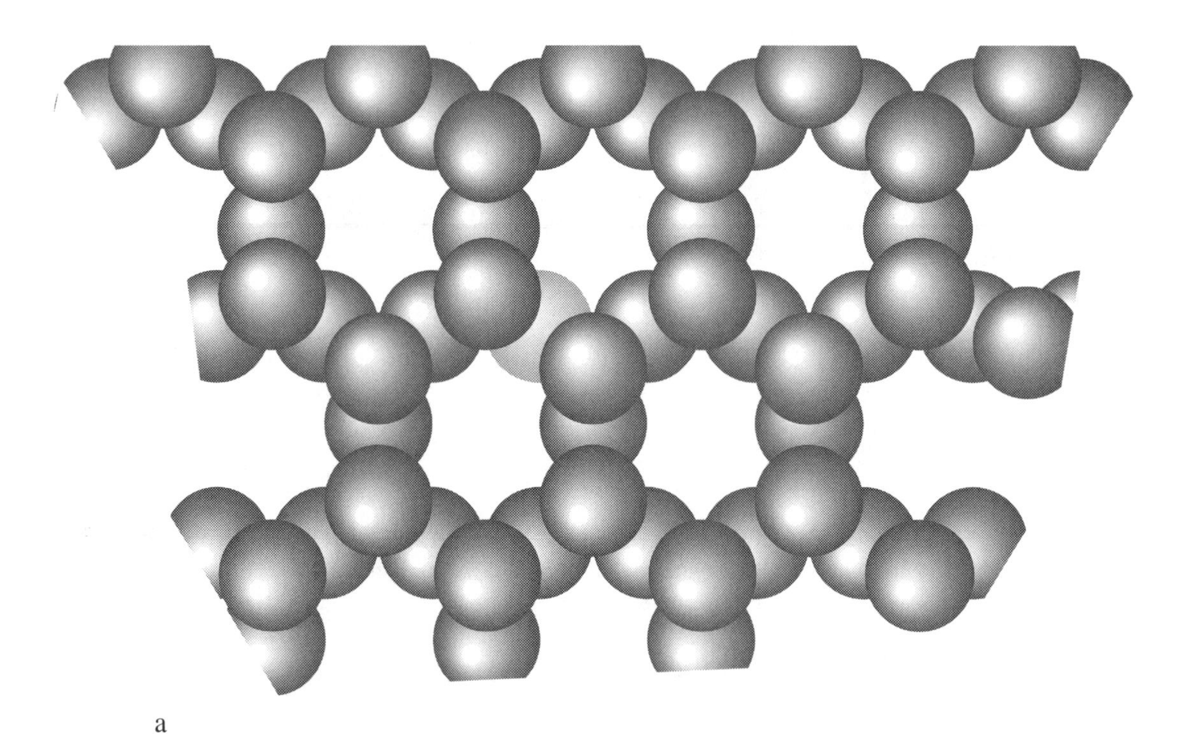

Figure 3-17. (*a*) Tetrahedrons are linked together in a continuous sheet in the mica family of silicate minerals. (*b*) Viewed edgewise, the skeleton outlines of layers of tetrahedrons, layers of potassium, and magnesium or iron ions are seen in biotite, a prominent variety of mica. Biotite cleaves into flakes along the potassium layers. The box encloses the atoms in one unit cell.

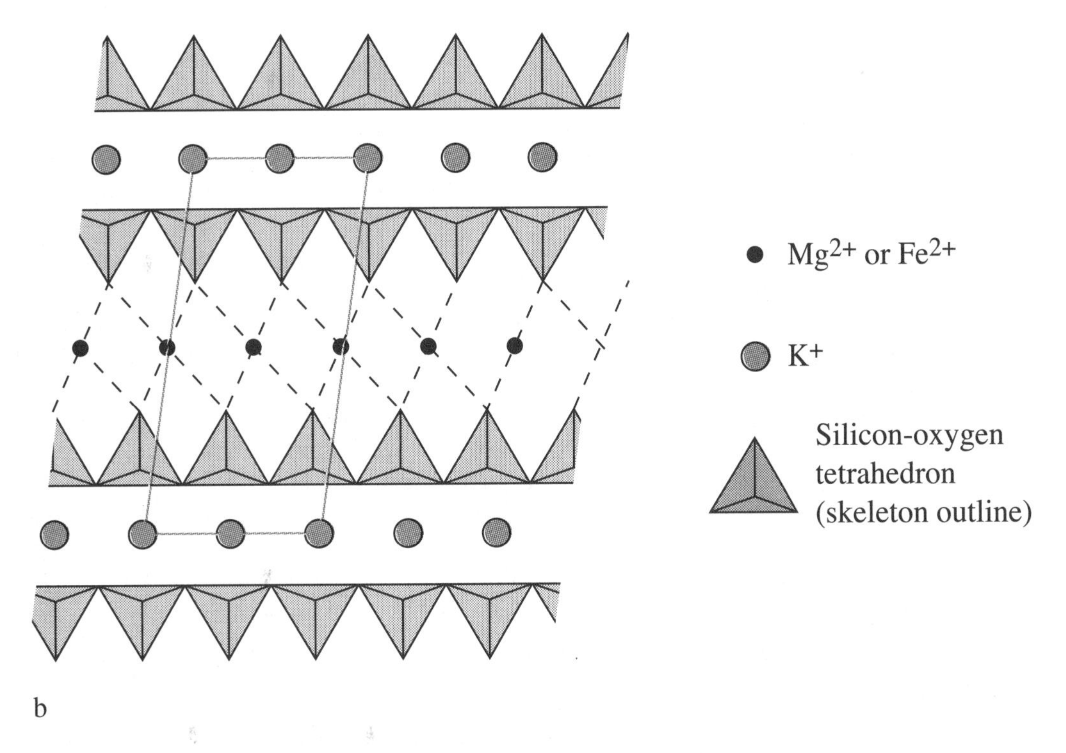

Figure 3-17. *Continued.*

Figure 3-18. Uniform, thin flakes are the pages in "books" of mica. This mineral is an ingredient in wallboard cement, roofing material and in earlier days, in electronic devices where it served as an electrical insulator. [*Judy Camps.*]

In *biotite,* a very common, dark-colored mica, Mg^{2+} and Fe^{2+} ions are sandwiched between opposed sheets of silicon-oxygen tetrahedrons [Figure 3-17(*b*)]. *Muscovite,* somewhat less common than biotite, is a transparent mica that contains Al^{3+} ions in the place of biotite's magnesium and iron. Muscovite is the first silicate mentioned thus far that is not a ferromagnesian mineral. Rather weakly bonded layers of K^+ ions separate the double sheets of tetrahedrons in biotite and muscovite. The excellent cleavage of mica into flexible, springy flakes is due to breakage of bonds between the potassium layer and adjacent tetrahedrons.

Another interesting family of silicates with sheet structure are the *clay minerals.* Because individual flakes of clay minerals are typically less than one- or two-millionths of a meter across, extremely high magnification under an electron microscope is needed for us to observe their shapes. In fact, a single crystal may consist of only a few thousand unit cells. Microscopic and x-ray studies show that some varieties of clay minerals are tiny, flat plates; others are curled up into hollow tubes.

The layers that are analogous to potassium layers in biotite [see Figure 3-17(*b*)] may contain not only K^+, but also Na^+, Ca^{2+}, Mg^{2+}, etc., feebly held by weak chemical bonds. Water molecules and dissolved metal ions may enter and leave these "exchangeable" sites so readily that the chemical composition and unit-cell dimensions vary from day to day, depending upon humidity. Small wonder that such clay is a slick, plastic substance that, with its ability to shrink and swell, is not a very desirable foundation material beneath a building. A variety of clay mineral called *kaolinite* is the chief ingredient in pottery and chinaware, and is used to give body to paint, paper, and canned soup.

Framework silicates We have seen how the silicon-oxygen tetrahedrons of silicate minerals may be isolated, or joined together as single or double chains, or as continuous sheets. Finally, we note the *framework* silicates in which the linked tetrahedrons are folded into complex three-dimensional patterns. Of the ten or so groups of framework silicates, the *feldspars* and *silica minerals* are by far the most important. Neither of these two families includes a single representative of the true ferromagnesians.

Feldspars are chemically simple, but structurally they are frightfully complex. Metal ions in the common varieties of feldspar are potassium, sodium, and calcium. These three cations may substitute for one another, but not so freely as iron and magnesium do in the ferromagnesian minerals. Sodium and potassium both have a +1 charge, but quite different sizes (see Table 3-1). This moderate incompatibility is one reason why the atomic structure of feldspar is so complicated.

The sizes of calcium and sodium ions are similar, but the charges are not equal. If a Ca^{2+} ion were to substitute for Na^+ in feldspar, then an adjustment of ionic charge somewhere else would be required to preserve electrical neutrality. Actually we have a double substitution: calcium for sodium in atomic positions between tetrahedrons and simultaneously, aluminum (Al^{3+}) for silicon (Si^{4+}) in centers of tetrahedrons. In this rather complicated manner, a complete mutual substitution between Na^+ and Ca^{2+} is possible. Feldspar with these metal ions is called *plagioclase*. Potassium-bearing feldspar does not participate in a wide range of ion substitutions. It is called simply "potassium feldspar" or "K-feldspar."

We reach the ultimate in the cross-linkage of silicon-oxygen tetrahedrons with the silica minerals. In the most common representative, *quartz,* every oxygen atom is shared between tetrahedrons. All the negative charge of oxygen is satisfied by positively charged silicon. This being the case, the charge balance is 1 x (+4) for silicon, against 2 x (-2) for oxygen, and the chemical formula of quartz is SiO_2. As already noted, the tetrahedrons are joined only at corners, leading to a rather open structure in which the tetrahedrons are oriented in a number of directions. Because all of the chemical bonds are strong and with various orientations, quartz breaks along fractures (irregular surfaces), not along cleavage planes (flat surfaces). Quartz is one of the least dense but one of the hardest of minerals.

Quartz has a very pure, simple composition (SiO_2) and it is ordinarily transparent, but the barest traces of impurities can impart beautiful tints of rose, yellow, smoky gray, etc. In many instances, color is an excellent guide to identifying a mineral, but we must beware that for some minerals the color could be misleading, owing its existence to an impurity.

Summary of silicates Table 3-2 summarizes some of the relationships among the silicate minerals. For each mineral family, the number of oxygens is given relative to 4 silicon atoms (the lowest common denominator). The proportions of silicon to oxygen systematically increase down the list. Isolated tetrahedrons in olivine can be packed tightly together, but the silicates with corner-linked tetrahedrons are more extravagant of space. And so, density decreases and the volume of the unit cell increases.

Figure 3-19. Cleavage is well developed in large feldspar crystals; indeed, two varieties of the mineral are named according to the angle between cleavage planes. Feldspar is an ingredient in porcelain and glass. [*Judy Camps.*]

Table 3-2. *Summary of Silicate Structures*

Structure	*Mineral group*	*Includes ferromagnesian minerals?*	*Si/O*	*Density, g/cm²*	*Volume of unit cell, cubic angstroms**
Isolated tetrahedrons	Olivine	Yes	SiO_4, or Si_4O_{16}	3.4	300
Single chains	Pyroxene	Yes	SiO_3, or Si_4O_{12}	3.1 to 3.3	430
Double chains	Amphibole	Yes	Si_4O_{11}	3.1 to 3.3	925
Sheets	Mica Clay minerals	Either yes or no	Si_2O_5, or Si_4O_{10}	2.8 to 3.3	980
Framework	K feldspar Plagioclase feldspar,	No	(Si, Al)$_4O_8$	2.5 to 2.8	800 to 1500
	Silica minerals	No	SiO_2, or Si_4O_8	2.6	

**One angstrom is one ten-billionth of a meter.*

What then is the composition of the earth's crust? Chemically it is mostly silicon and oxygen. From the viewpoint of crystal structure, it is a network of silicon-oxygen tetrahedrons. As minerals go, feldspar is more abundant than all the other hundreds of mineral species combined.

SOME NONSILICATE MINERAL GROUPS

Silicates account for all but a few of the common rock-forming minerals. Most of the remaining mineral families have relatively simple crystal structures and chemical formulas. Here are some of these minerals, classified according to their anion compositions.

Carbonates These minerals are based upon the chemical bonding of various metal ions to the *carbonate* ion (CO_3^{2-}). Calcium ions and carbonate ions are arranged in alternating layers in *calcite* ($CaCO_3$), the most common carbonate mineral (Figure 3-20). This mineral shows excellent cleavage along layers of atoms oriented in several directions in space. Calcite crystals can assume more varied shapes and sizes than do the crystals of any other mineral (Figure 3-21). Calcite may be deposited by animals as protective shell material, or it can precipitate from hot water solutions, or as dripstone in a cave, or from evaporating sea water, or in numerous other ways. A knife blade can scratch the surface of calcite; hydrochloric acid (HCl) makes the mineral fizz violently as it decomposes, giving off carbon dioxide gas. These simple tests are handy for quick identification. Vast quantities of calcite are decomposed by heating to form quicklime (CaO), an ingredient of Portland cement. More calcite goes into blast furnaces where it serves as a flux in the manufacture of steel.

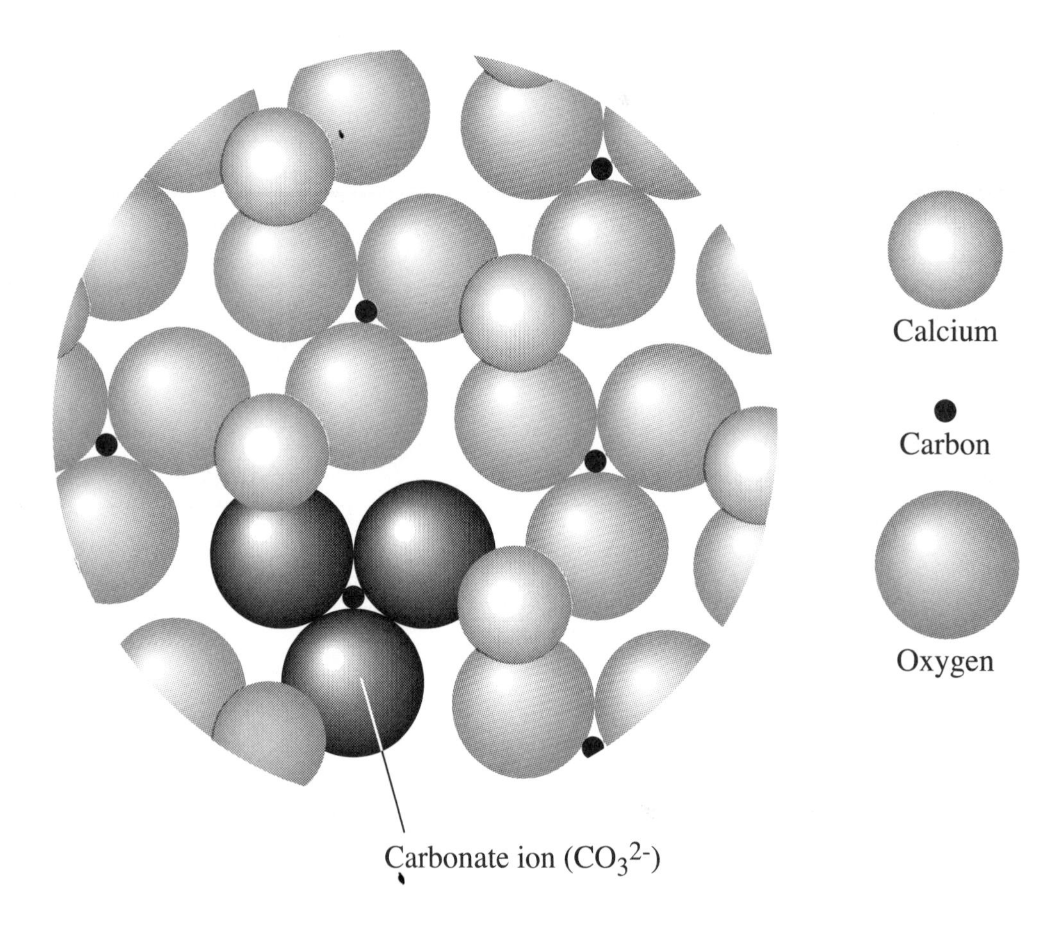

Figure 3-20. A view looking through superimposed layers of ions in calcite. A layer containing calcium ions (Ca^{2+}) rests upon a layer of carbonate ions (CO_3^{2-}), beneath which is another Ca^{2+} layer, then a CO_3^{2-} layer, etc.

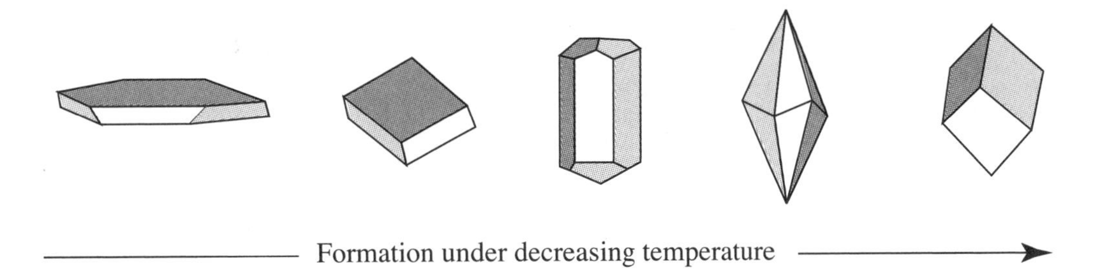

Figure 3-21. During the growth of a crystal, a plane oriented in one direction may accumulate atoms more rapidly than planes with other orientations. Different sets of planes are favored depending upon conditions of temperature, pressure, absorption of minor impurity ions, etc. Thus, crystals of the same mineral, with the same atomic structure and chemical composition, may assume different shapes. More than 600 crystal forms are known for the mineral calcite!

Oxides In view of the abundance of oxygen, the importance of the oxide minerals comes as no surprise. *Hematite* (Fe_2O_3) and *magnetite* (Fe_3O_4) are prominent sources of iron. In the simple structures of these two minerals, the iron atoms are concealed in small openings amongst very closely packed oxygen atoms. The close packing and the high density of iron make hematite and magnetite to be the most dense of the common minerals. Hematite illustrates another property, called *streak,* useful in identifying a mineral. If a piece of hematite is dragged across a plate of unglazed porcelain, a dark red trail of dust (its streak) is left behind. Magnetite, as its name implies, can be attracted by a magnet, and may even act as a magnet.

Sulfides Copper, silver, zinc, lead, nickel, and other economically important metals are commonly found in nature bonded to the sulfide ion (S^{2-}). By far the most abundant sulfide mineral is *pyrite*: FeS_2. This opaque, dense, brassy yellow mineral known as "fool's gold" is a source of both iron and

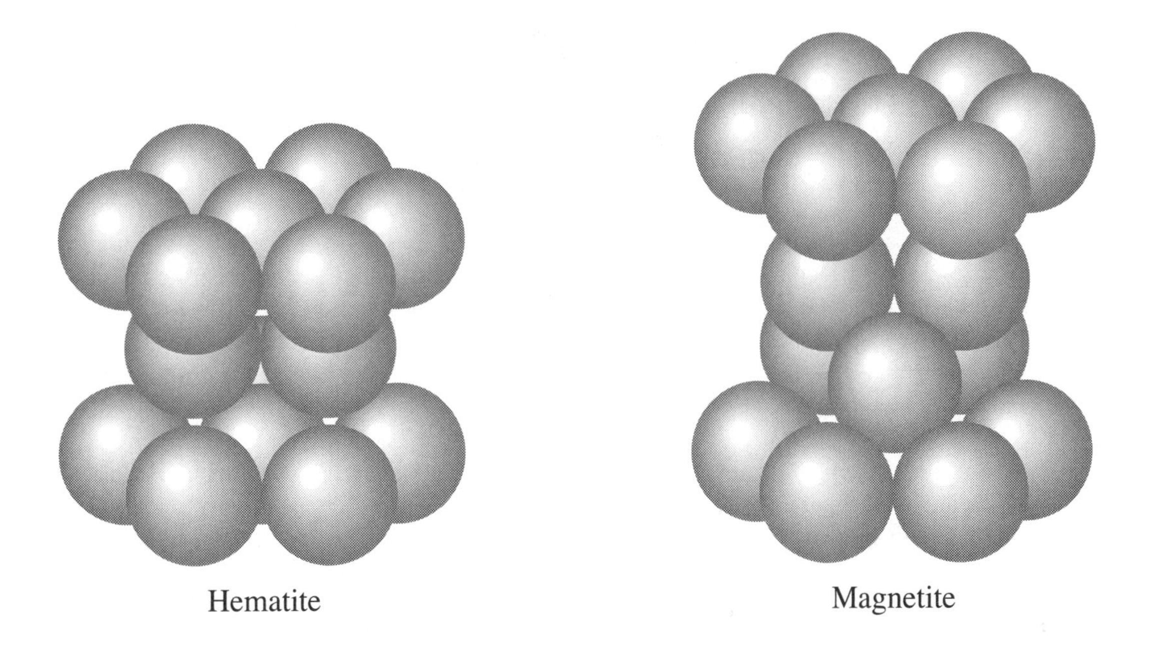

Figure 3-22. Two ways to pack equal-sized spheres as close together as possible are illustrated by the way that oxygen atoms are positioned in hematite (Fe_2O_3) and magnetite (Fe_3O_4). Small but dense iron atoms are tucked out of sight amongst the oxygen spheres.

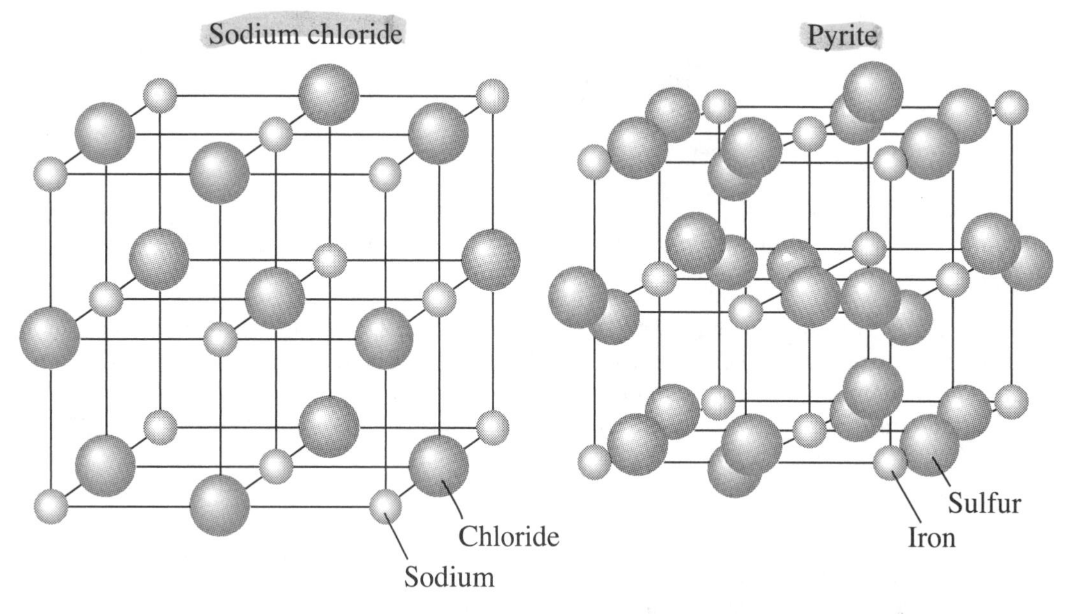

Figure 3-23. (*a*) Crystal structures of sodium chloride and pyrite are similar. In pyrite, we find iron in place of sodium, and dumbbell-shaped clusters of two sulfur atoms in place of chloride ions. (*b*) A common shape of pyrite crystals is the cube—the same as the shape of the unit cell.

sulfur where it occurs in large masses. The atomic structures of pyrite and of sodium chloride are similar in an interesting way (Figure 3-23).

Sulfates In this family of minerals the characteristic anion is sulfate, SO_4^{2-}. Sulfur in this situation is about the same size as the silicon ion (Si^{4+}). Thus by analogy to a silicate mineral, sulfur in a sulfate mineral is surrounded by four oxygens located on the corners of a sulfur-oxygen tetrahedron. *Gypsum* ($CaSO_4 \cdot 2H_2O$), our chosen example of a sulfate mineral, is generally deposited by the intense evaporation of sea water containing dissolved calcium and sulfate ions. Water molecules occupy regular prescribed positions in the crystal structure. They "really belong" and are not present simply as an impurity, and thus gypsum is a hydrous mineral. Gypsum has excellent cleavage because the bonds between layers of water molecules and other layers in the structure are easily broken. The mineral is so soft that a fingernail can scratch it. Commercial uses of gypsum include the manufacture of cement, fertilizer, and wall sheetrock.

Halides Another mineral group contains ions of the halogen elements: fluorine, chlorine, bromine, and iodine. Like gypsum, many of these halide minerals are quite soluble; they too form as a residue after sea water has evaporated. Easily the most common representative is rock salt, *halite* (Figures 3-10 and 3-23). Salt is used to season food, to melt ice from roads, and as a raw material in making chlorine gas and many other products.

Other mineral groups Anions in other minerals may contain vanadium, arsenic, phosphorus, uranium, boron, or bismuth as examples from a host of possibilities. Many of these minerals are vital sources of rare metals necessary to modern technology, but their abundance in the earth's crust is insignificant. Finally, some minerals are simply chemical elements in the free, or native, state. Prominent examples are gold, sulfur, and two forms of carbon, graphite and diamond.

SUMMARY

A mineral is a naturally occurring, inorganic substance in the crystalline state whose chemical composition is fixed or may vary over a restricted range. Corresponding faces of crystals of the same mineral all intersect at the same angle. Atoms in a crystal are positioned in a regular, repeating, three-dimensional pattern. Analyses of patterns of x-rays that have passed through a crystal are used to determine its atomic structure (the geometric pattern of its atoms). A unit cell is the minimum fragment of the pattern that contains all the information necessary to build the entire structure.

Abundances of chemical elements, and sizes and charges of ions dictate which minerals can form and what their atomic structures may be. Ionic bonds are formed by attraction of positively charged ions (cations) to negatively charged ions (anions). In covalent bonds, electrons are shared by the bonded atoms.

Oxygen and silicon are by far the most common chemical elements in the earth's crust. In silicate minerals, four oxygen ions occupying corners of a tetrahedron are grouped about a relatively small central silicon ion, forming the SiO_4 association whose net charge is -4. Electrical neutrality is achieved by the presence of associated positively charged metal ions, and by corner-to-corner linkage of tetrahedrons, which reduces the need for negatively charged oxygens which are shared by adjacent tetrahedrons.

Atomic structures of minerals determine properties such as color, density, and whether the mineral breaks by fracturing irregularly or cleaving along flat planes. Silicate minerals are classified according to increasing complexity of these structures. Important examples are olivine (tetrahedrons not linked), the pyroxene family (tetrahedrons linked into single chains), the amphibole family (double chains), the mica and clay mineral families (sheets), and feldspars and silica minerals (framework, highly complex). The first three groups, and biotite mica are comprised of dark, dense ferromagnesian minerals in which Fe^{2+} and Mg^{2+} ions freely substitute for one another in the crystal structure. Ca^{2+} and Na^{+} can substitute mutually in plagioclase feldspar. Muscovite mica, most clay minerals, and feldspars and silica minerals are non-ferromagnesians.

Other common mineral families are classified according to their characteristic anions such as carbonate (CO_3^{2-}), oxide (O^{2-}), sulfide (S^{2-}), sulfate (SO_4^{2-}), halide (F^-,Cl^-, etc.), or others. Many of these minerals, although relatively rare, are important economic resources. Properties of minerals that are useful for identification are hardness, density, color (though not infallibly), streak, fracture *vs.* cleavage, and decomposition by acid.

4

Minerals

INTRODUCTION, OVERVIEW

Rocks are familiar to all of us as the natural material of the earth, commonly exposed in areas of little or no vegetation cover such as in cliffs, roadcuts, quarries, or outcrops. Rocks in turn are composed of one or more species of **minerals**. Before examining the most common minerals and learning how to identify them, let us first look at the "big picture," the three classes of rock. These classes are **igneous** rock (material cooled and solidified from a melted condition), **sedimentary** rock (material transported and deposited by wind, moving water, or glacier ice), and **metamorphic** rock (igneous or sedimentary rock whose character has been changed, typically under conditions of deep burial).

One of the must fundamental concepts in the subject of geology, known as the **rock cycle**, states that any of these rock types may be converted by recycling into any other type. Figure 4-1 shows that any rock may be melted, to become igneous. Any rock may be weathered, eroded, and deposited as a sediment, and any may be transformed into a metamorphic rock in an environment of elevated temperature and pressure.

Implications of the rock cycle are profound.

1. Except for meteorites, which are a very minor quantity of infallen cosmic material, the entire substance of the earth has been present ever since the time of its accumulation about 4.55 billion years ago.
2. Because of recycling, it is highly unlikely that we shall ever find a surviving primordial rock, preserved intact from the formation of the earth.
3. There is no fixed schedule of recycling. Some rocks have survived since very ancient times; others are of intermediate age, and yet others have formed only "yesterday." A pattern in which rocks of many ages are found together is especially the case for the continents. In contrast, recycling of ocean-floor rocks is wholesale (all-encompassing) and because this recycling is relatively rapid, ocean-floor rocks everywhere are young compared to the age of the earth.
4. Recycling requires the expenditure of energy, mostly the earth's internal heat energy. Sunlight, and energy associated with the force of gravity are also important to the rock cycle.
5. Earth's heat energy drives the motions of tectonic plates (discussed at length later in this course), causing continents to drift, mountain belts to be uplifted, etc. Particular rock types are

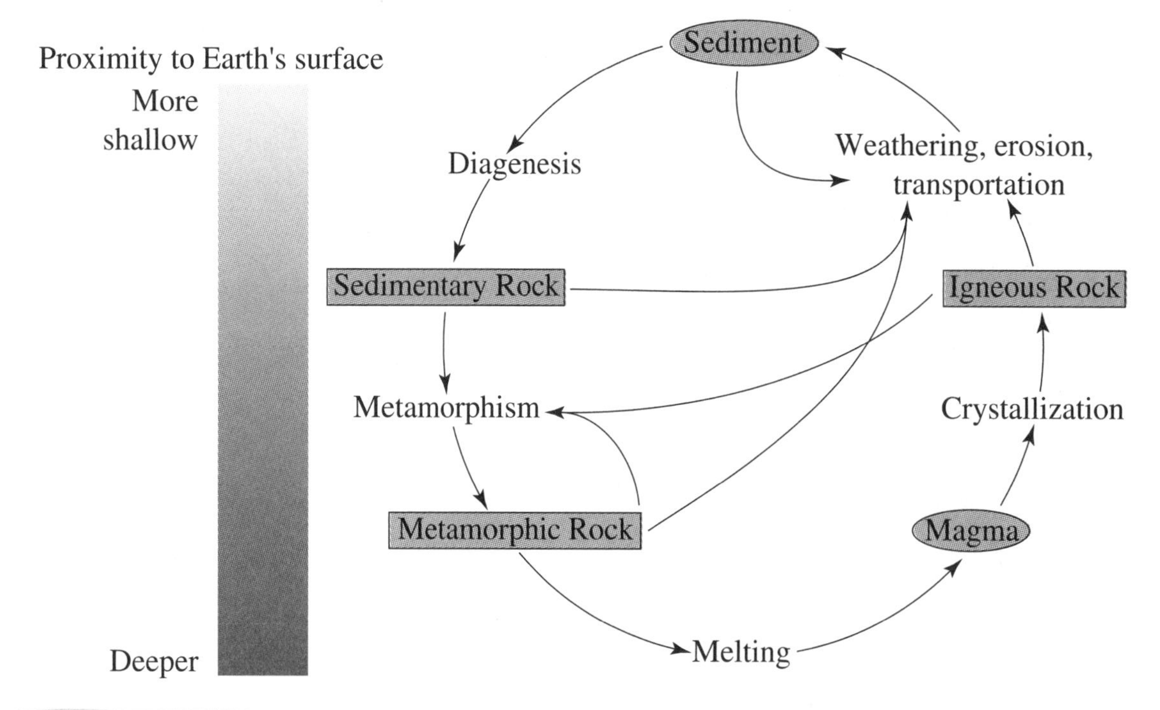

Figure 4-1. Rock Cycle

associated with particular plate-tectonic settings. For instance, where plates are pulling apart, molten material ascends from the deep earth where it freezes, forming oceanic crust of igneous origin. Where tectonic plates are in collision forming mountains, the rocks are deformed, heated, metamorphosed, and partly melted to make varieties of igneous rock unlike those of the ocean floor. Ocean-floor rocks and metamorphosed rocks in a mountain belt are typically recycled quite promptly. (On the time scale of the earth, "promptly" means taking place within tens to scores of millions of years, not hundreds of millions, to billions of years.)

Weathered material transported by rivers is deposited at the margins of continents as thick accumulations of sediment. If an area of the interior of a continent has been stretched and thinned, that region of downwarp also receives poured-in sediment eroded from the surrounding land surface.

DEFINITION OF ROCK

Rock is any coherent, naturally occurring substance, generally composed of minerals. This broad definition includes many different kinds of earth materials. Some, such as rock salt, are composed of only one kind of mineral. A few rocks are not composed of minerals at all. Coal is a rock consisting of compressed plant material which is not a mineral, as we shall see. For some rocks, the minerals that comprise them are primary to the definition. For example, granite is a rock that *must* be composed chiefly of the minerals feldspar and quartz; if the rock had some other mineral composition it would be called by another name. On the other hand, the sedimentary rock called conglomerate contains fragments of other rocks that may be of any origin or composition whatever. Concrete is not a rock because it does not originate naturally. Some substances (for example, glacier ice) are rock because they *do* occur naturally, even though we normally do not think of ice as being rock.

Coherency is also important to our definition. Lava is not a rock while it is yet a hot liquid. Loose beach sand would have to be cemented together in order to become a sedimentary rock, sandstone. Geologists may refer to very lightly cemented sediment as rock even though we might be more inclined to call it "dirt." For all their usefulness, definitions have their limitations!

DEFINITIONS OF MINERAL

The study of minerals is the area of geology most commonly translated into a satisfying hobby for the layperson. Indeed, one need not be a full-fledged geologist to appreciate the aesthetic and intrinsic value of minerals, and enjoy identifying and collecting them. The primary objective of this chapter is to introduce the most common minerals selected from a kingdom of several thousand species, and to define the various physical criteria used to distinguish one mineral species from another.

In order to be considered a mineral, a substance must satisfy four criteria: *it must be naturally occurring, inorganic, have a definite chemical make-up, and be crystalline in nature*. The implications of these criteria are discussed below:

Naturally Occurring: Rules out man-made substances. While it is possible to "grow" materials in the laboratory which might be indistinguishable from a natural specimen, these are not considered minerals. The only important application of this rule would be in relation to synthetically produced rubies, sapphires, emeralds, or other gems. These may be superior in appearance to nature's often-flawed examples of the same material, but the synthetic gems have no investment value.

Inorganic: This means that minerals are not, and never were, living. Minerals which contain carbon are the only "gray area" here. Diamond (C) *may* have an organic background; graphite (C) almost certainly does; and calcite ($CaCO_3$), the material of clam shells and coral reefs, is definitely a *product* of organic processes. However, these are accepted as minerals by convention.

Definite Chemical Make-up: The basic identity of a mineral is in its chemistry. Each species contains specific elements in definite proportions. SiO_2 is the chemical formula for one of the most common continental crust mineral species, quartz. This formula states that any crystal or fragment of quartz has one silicon atom for every two oxygen atoms. Both FeS and FeS_2 are valid minerals, but they are not the *same* mineral. A few minerals do have defined and acceptable limited substitution of one element for another; this will be indicated by ( ) in the chemical formula.

Crystalline: In crystalline materials, the component atoms are arranged in an orderly network at specific distances and angles to one another. This property may be demonstrated by x-ray analysis. Megascopically, crystallinity is shown in the external symmetry of crystals, and the consistent breakage patterns of many species. Although quartz and volcanic glass both may satisfy the first three mineral criteria, only quartz is crystalline, and therefore a mineral. No *glass* is a mineral because these types of materials, like liquids, lack a definite atomic arrangement.

PHYSICAL PROPERTIES

Each mineral species has a discrete chemistry, and therefore can be identified by chemical tests. Since this approach is not very practical for field work, mineralogists have established a series of physical properties which will suffice to distinguish the more common minerals from one another. These properties are listed and described below in order of frequency of application.

In mineral identification not all of these properties apply to, or are important for, each species. Some minerals have one specific property which serves to identify them quickly (hardness of diamond, grooves on plagioclase), while others can be recognized by a combination of features (fracture and hardness of quartz, luster and color of sulfur). You should understand all the physical properties as defined, and recognize the minimum number of specific properties needed for identification of each mineral to be learned.

I. **HARDNESS**: This is a measure of the resistance of a mineral to scratching, and is evaluated on a relative scale of 1 to 10. Lower numbers indicate less resistance to scratching.

Each mineral on this scale can scratch a mineral with an equal or lower number, but none with a higher number. For example, calcite can scratch calcite, your fingernail, gypsum, or talc, but nothing with a hardness greater than 3. All minerals have a hardness either equal to or between the minerals listed on this scale. Pyrite ("fool's gold"), for example, has a hardness of 6, the same as orthoclase; sphalerite can scratch calcite but not fluorite, and so has a hardness of $3\frac{1}{2}$. Minerals with a hardness of less than 6 will not withstand prolonged wear as gemstones.

Use considerable pressure in testing for hardness. Make a small scratch about $\frac{1}{4}$-inch long to minimize defacing the samples. Wipe any apparent scratches with your finger to be sure the mark is genuine, and not just a powder streak from the softer mineral. When using the glass test plate, place it flat on the laboratory table to avoid injury.

Mohs Hardness Scale

1: Talc
2: Gypsum
($2\frac{1}{4}$: fingernail)
3: Calcite
($3\frac{1}{2}$: copper coin)
4: Fluorite
5: Apatite
($5–5\frac{1}{2}$: Steel nail, knife)
($5\frac{1}{2}–6$: glass)
6: Orthoclase
7: Quartz
8: Topaz
9: Corundum
10: Diamond

II. **LUSTER**: The appearance of a mineral's surface in reflected light.

Metallic Luster: these minerals have a "metallic glint" and reflect light effectively; they are opaque and relatively heavy.

Non-Metallic Luster: The most common are:

- Adamantine = brilliant, like that of a polished diamond.
- Vitreous = glassy, like glazed porcelain or quartz.
- Resinous = like resin; sphalerite is an example.
- Pearly = similar to that created by transparent microscopic scales in natural pearls; talc, some gypsum.
- Silky = resulting from parallel fibers; asbestos, "satin spar" gypsum.
- Earthy = dull, little reflection; kaolinite, goethite.

III. **COLOR**: This would seem to be a simple attribute to deal with, and yet it really does not work very well for mineral identification. Colors are subjective to the observer, and unreliable for many specimens. Quartz, fluorite, calcite, and other fundamentally colorless minerals may take on the full spectrum of hues depending on trace element contamination. Also, small crystals usually look lighter in aggregate. In some specimens a thin surface coating of exotic material may be misleading. Color is most dependable for the metallic minerals.

IV. **STREAK**: This is the color of a mineral when powdered. Streak is generally uniform even if the color of uncrushed material varies. Most non-metallic minerals have a non-diagnostic white streak, but metallic samples have a dependable streak. Specimens may be crushed in a mortar, but the usual practice is to drag them across the abrasive surface of an unglazed tile. The latter approach is useless with substances which are harder than the streak plate ($5\frac{1}{2}$ to 6).

V. **CLEAVAGE**: This is the tendency of a mineral to split along certain planes determined by internal atomic arrangement and bonding strength. Cleavage planes, produced by rupture in some minerals, should be distinguished from crystal faces. Crystal faces are the surfaces bounding a crystal, the natural shape a mineral takes on when room for growth is present. Calcite, for example, may *grow* in elongated six-sided pyramids or a variety of other shapes, but always *cleaves* into a rhombohedron. Rhombohedrons have faces shaped like parallelograms ▱. Quartz has no cleavage. Halite (table salt) and galena characteristically break into cubes, or portions thereof, and thus have cubic cleavage.

VI. **FRACTURE**: This is the non-planar breakage of minerals; i.e., no well-defined cleavage. Fracture may be described as uneven (rough), splintery, or conchoidal (curved breaks typical of glass). Quartz has conchoidal fracture.

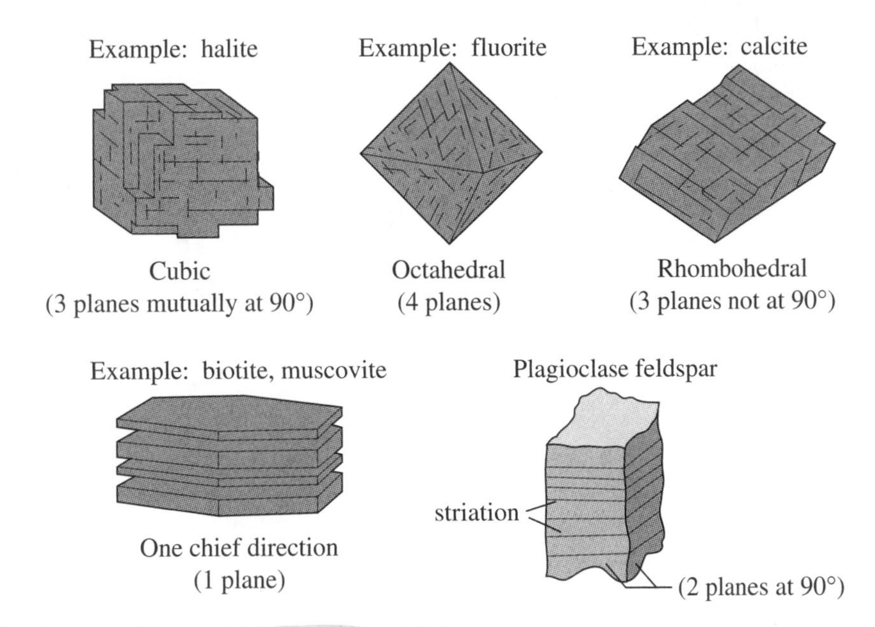

Figure 4-2. Common Types of Mineral Cleavage

VII. **CRYSTAL FORM**: Most minerals will take on a definite external geometric form when unobstructed growth is allowed. This form is an expression of the orderly internal atomic arrangement, or crystallinity. Whole crystals and crystal faces are therefore an aid to identification. A complete study of crystallography is beyond our scope here.

VIII. **MISCELLANEOUS**: Other properties that are less common or even unique to certain minerals include:

- Natural magnetism (magnetite)
- Feel—talc feels slippery; halite feels greasy.
- Specific gravity—galena is dense; halite is not.
- Effervescence in acid—calcite reacts with cold weak hydrochloric acid (HCl).
- Tenacity—reaction under stress; brittle (galena), flexible (talc), elastic (muscovite), malleable (native copper)
- Crystal habit—characteristic external form; crystalline (garnet), granular (olivine), fibrous (asbestos)
- Double refraction—transparent calcite transmits a split image.
- Fluorescence—emission of color under ultraviolet radiation (fluorite, some calcite, some diamonds, beryl). Ultraviolet wavelengths are too short to be perceived by the human eye, and thus do not qualify as "light."
- Odor—moist kaolinite gives off earthy odor.
- Crystal arrangement—closely spaced, fine parallel striations (twinning planes) on plagioclase feldspar. On either side of a twinning plane the atomic structure "flips": right-facing, then left-facing, then right-facing, etc.

ATOMIC STRUCTURE OF MINERALS

You have noted minerals that have flat crystal faces, or flat surfaces of cleavage. Corresponding surfaces join at angles that are the same in all crystals of a given mineral. Flat surfaces signify planes of atoms. The diagnostic angles, the flat surfaces, and other aspects of crystal symmetry reflect the way that atoms in a mineral are organized into a regular, three-dimensional repeating pattern. A unit cell contains the minimum group of atoms needed to provide complete information about the pattern. Once a unit cell is established, building a crystal is just a repetition of many such cells fitted together, much as identical bricks fit snugly together in a wall.

We may picture atoms as balls, joined together by chemical bonds represented as rods. Here we see a unit cell for the mineral quartz consisting of oxygen atoms (large balls) and silicon atoms (small balls). Note that a single unit cell is only that portion of the pattern contained within the faint outline.

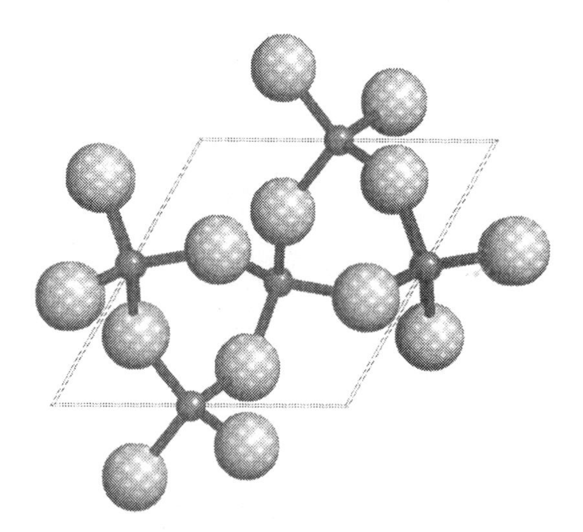

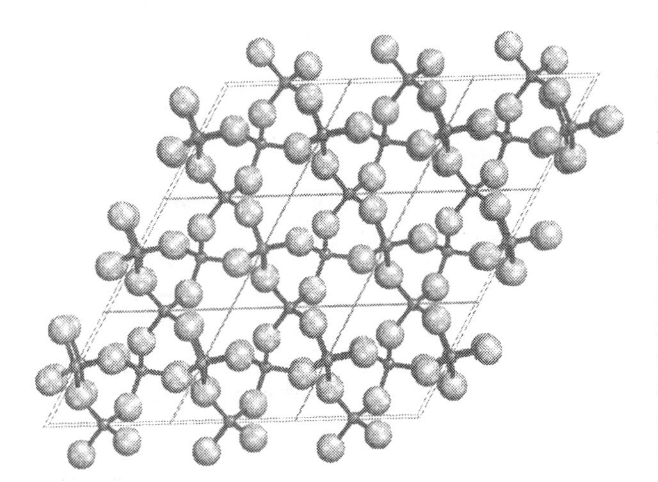

On the left, the unit cell pattern is shown repeated a few times in two dimensions. In an actual crystal the pattern is repeated countless times in three dimensions.

In silicate minerals, four oxygen atoms surround a silicon atom, each oxygen positioned at a corner of a three-dimensional geometric figure called a tetrahedron (right). Quartz (SiO_2) contains only these two chemical elements, but other silicate minerals (below) additionally contain atoms of iron, magnesium, potassium, etc. that have assigned positions in the unit cell.

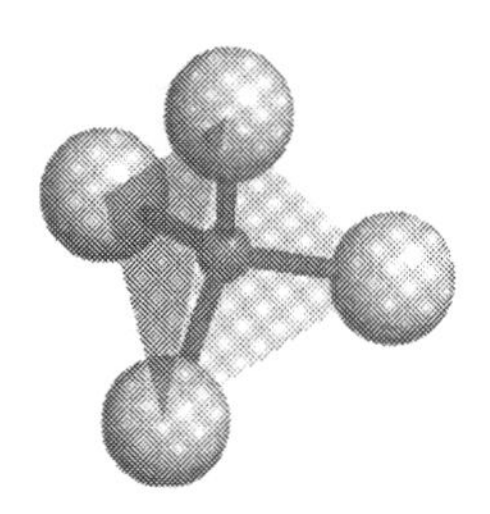

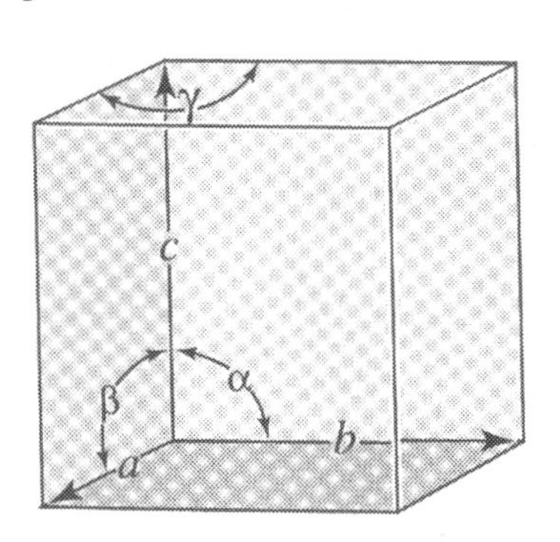

A unit cell can be characterized by the lengths of three axes (*a*, *b*, *c*) that intersect one another at specified angles (α, β, γ). This figure is a transparent diagram of a cube, the simplest possible form of a unit cell. Its axes, all of the same length, intersect at mutual right angles. In more complex unit cells, the axes are of unequal lengths or meet at oblique angles. Whatever the case, each atom in a crystal structure participates in the pattern by occupying a specified position inside its unit cell.

CRYSTAL SYSTEMS

Although there are more than 5 thousand minerals, each unit cell design falls into one of only six categories whose shapes form the basis of *crystal systems*. Refer to the description above of a cube in which axes *a*, *b*, and c meet one another at angles α, β, and γ. A concise description of a cube is $a = b = c$ (i.e., axes of equal length), and $\alpha = \beta = \gamma = 90°$. Each of the six crystal systems is named below, described by this terminology, and illustrated by the unit cell outline and atomic structure of a common mineral.

Fluorite: CaF_2

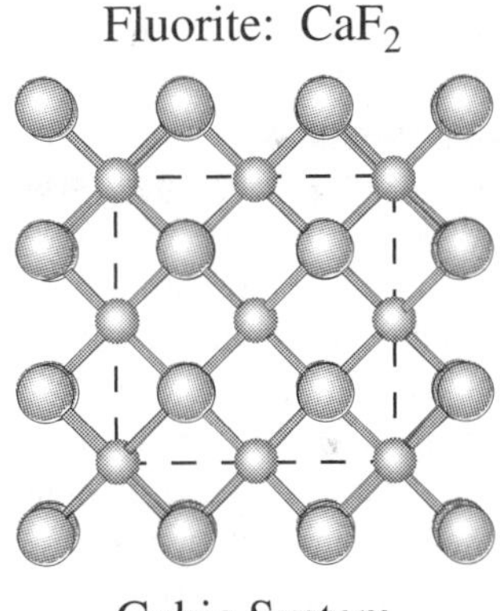

Cubic System
$a = b = c; \alpha = \beta = \gamma = 90°$

Zircon: $ZrSiO_4$

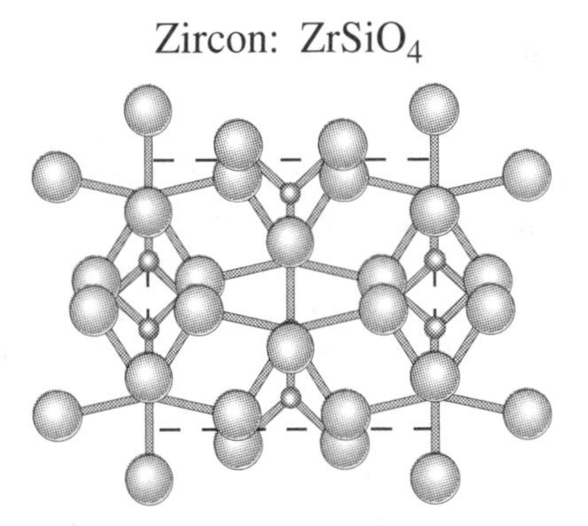

Tetragonal System
$a = b \neq c; \alpha = \beta = \gamma = 90°$

Quartz: SiO_2

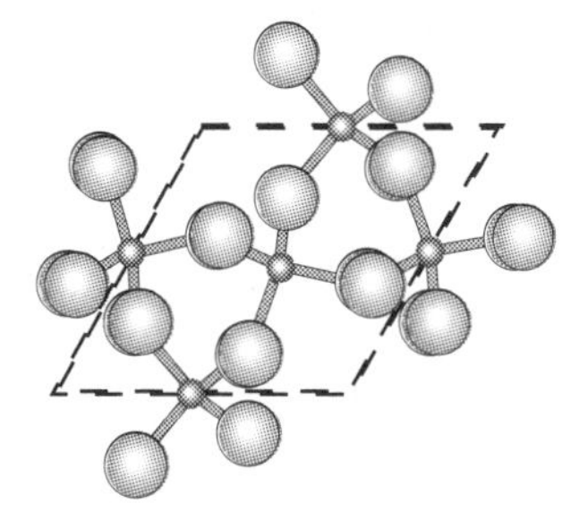

Hexagonal System
$a = b \neq c$; $\alpha = \beta = 90°$, $\gamma = 120°$

Olivine: $(Ca,Mg)_2SiO_4$

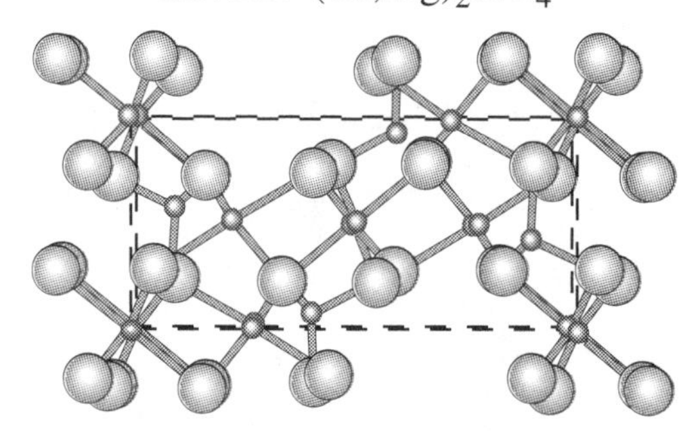

Orthorhombic System
$a \neq b \neq c$; $\alpha = \beta = \gamma = 90°$

Hornblende: complex silicate

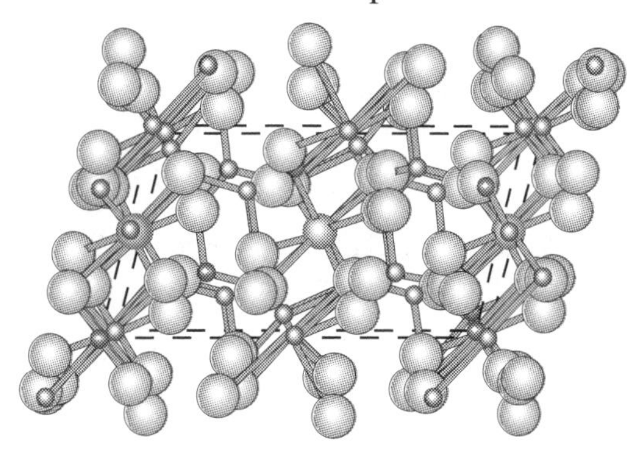

Monoclinic System
$a \neq b \neq c$; $\alpha = \beta = 90° \neq \gamma$

Na plagioclase feldspar: $NaAlSi_3O_8$

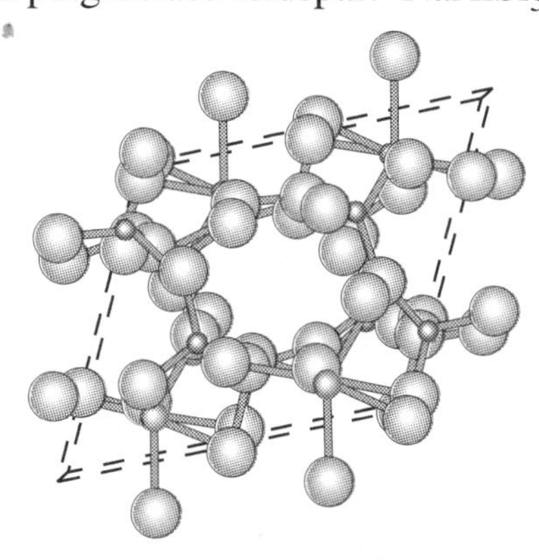

Triclinic System
$a \neq b \neq c$; $\alpha \neq \beta \neq \gamma$

MINERAL CLASSIFICATION

An **ore** has a practical definition; it is an earth material in which a metal resource is sufficiently concentrated to be of economic value. In ore minerals, the metals are iron, lead, zinc, copper, silver, or others of a long list belonging in the medium to heavy end of the periodic table of chemical elements. These metal atoms may be bonded with oxygen atoms forming an **oxide** mineral, or with sulfur atoms forming a **sulfide** mineral, or the valuable metal may be the free, uncombined **native element** such as native copper or gold.

Everything else in our rather simplistic classification are the non-ore minerals that comprise "ordinary rock." In these, the abundant metals are aluminum (Al), magnesium (Mg), iron (Fe), sodium (Na), potassium (K), and calcium (Ca). Except for medium-weight iron, all of them are relatively light chemical elements. Most minerals are **silicates** based upon a structure in which a silicon atom is surrounded by four oxygen atoms that occupy the corners of a tetrahedron. Iron, magnesium, and other metal atoms are situated externally amongst these closely knit silicon-oxygen (Si-O) tetrahedrons. (In some minerals, aluminum can substitute for silicon.) As the name implies, **ferromagnesian** silicate minerals are rich in iron and magnesium. Ferromagnesian minerals are characteristically dark-colored and dense.

Rounding out the picture are four other mineral families important in ordinary rocks. They are **oxide** minerals mentioned above, **carbonate** minerals in which metal atoms are combined with the carbonate ion (CO_3^{-2}), **sulfate** minerals in which metal atoms are associated with the sulfate ion (SO_4^{-2}), and **halide** minerals in which metal atoms are combined typically with the chloride (Cl^-) or fluoride (F^-) ion. Whether colored or clear transparent, most non-ore minerals will transmit light. Even if the color is such a deep brown or green as to appear black, light will pass through the mineral crystal if it is ground to a thin slice.

A typical ore mineral is opaque with a metallic luster, quite dense, with a characteristic colored streak. Ore minerals are more dense than ferromagnesian silicate minerals, which are more dense than non-ferromagnesian silicates. Relatively low density, various types of non-metallic luster, and a colorless, rather uninformative streak characterize the silicate, carbonate, sulfate, and halide minerals. Even the ordinary rocks commonly contain tiny amounts (less than one percent) of ore minerals.

Each mineral has a unique chemical composition (or limited range of composition) and unique atomic three-dimensional pattern. Silicate minerals comprise by far the bulk of the earth's crust. Let's look at this, the most important class, in more detail.

Major group	**Example of a mineral species**	**Important metal ions (in addition to Si in Si-O tetrahedrons)**	**Ferro-magnesian?**
Olivine family*	Olivine	Fe, Mg	yes
Pyroxene family	Augite	Fe, Mg	yes
Amphibole family	Hornblende	Highly diverse compositions	yes
Mica family	Biotite	Fe, Mg, K	yes
	Muscovite	K, Al	no
Clay mineral family	Kaolinite	Highly diverse compositions	no
Feldspar family	Potassium feldspar	K, Al	no
	Plagioclase feldspar	Variable: 100% Na to 100% Ca	no
Silica family	Quartz	None; only Si-O tetrahedrons	no

**Families of silicate minerals are distinguished according to whether the Si-O tetrahedrons are isolated from one another (as in olivine), or linked together in single chains (as in pyroxene), double chains (as in amphibole), sheets (as in mica or clay minerals), or yet more complex organization (as in feldspar and quartz). In some instances the form of the whole crystal closely mimics the arrangement of Si-O tetrahedrons on the atomic scale. Each mineral family is composed of numerous species in which chemical compositions or other characteristics differ from mineral to mineral.*

DESCRIPTIVE MINERAL TABLE

The Descriptive Mineral Table (pp. 68–72) presents characteristic features of 27 ore- and rock-forming minerals. The table separates the mineral species into two categories: those with metallic luster (Group I) and non-metallic luster (Groups II and III). Within each group, the species are arranged in order of increasing hardness. Streak is emphasized as an especially useful property by which to distinguish minerals with a metallic luster, whereas types of luster are emphasized for non-metallic minerals. A column titled Conspicuous Features includes other unique or notable mineral characteristics. Items that are underscored describe the most diagnostic properties.

The twenty minerals that comprise Groups I and II are very common; they form the basis for study of igneous, sedimentary, and metamorphic rocks in following chapters. A miscellaneous assortment of seven mineral species in Group III includes well-known but very rare and precious minerals (native gold, fluorite, topaz, diamond) or minerals that play a specialized role in sedimentary rocks (dolomite) or metamorphic rocks (chlorite, staurolite).

Descriptive Mineral Table

I. Minerals with Metallic Luster

Name and Composition	*Hardness*	*Color*	*Streak (not luster)*	*Conspicuous Features (most diagnostic are underlined)*
Graphite C Elemental carbon	1	Silver-gray	Black	Marks paper like a pencil; feels greasy, Low density. One chief direction of cleavage.
Galena PbS Lead sulfide	2½	Silver-gray	Black	Cubic or octahedral crystals, bright metallic luster, dense. Cubic cleavage. Commonly so fragile that a hardness test is difficult.
Pyrite FeS_2 Iron disulfide	6	Light brass-yellow	Black	Occurs in cubes with grooved faces, and pyritohedrons with five-sided faces. Called "fool's gold"; much less dense than true gold. Poor cleavage; fragile. Note how streak differs from color.
Magnetite Fe_3O_4 Iron oxide	6	Black	Black	Magnetic, granular or octahedral crystals common. No cleavage. Dense, but not a dense as galena.

II. Minerals with Non-Metallic Luster

Name and Composition	*Hardness*	*Color*	*Luster (not streak)*	*Conspicuous Features (most diagnostic are underlined)*
Talc $Mg_3Si_4O_{10}(OH)_2$ Hydrous magnesium silicate	1	White to pale green	Pearly	Extremely soft; feels soapy. Impurities may increase apparent hardness. Commonly in scaly masses. One chief direction of cleavage.

Name and Composition	Hardness	Color	Luster (not streak)	Conspicuous Features (most diagnostic are underlined)
Native Sulfur S	1½–2½	Yellow	Resinous	Yellow color, low hardness, low density. Detectable sulfur odor. Commonly in well-developed block crystals, or as a fine coating on volcanic rocks; flammable.
Gypsum $CaSO_4 \cdot 2H_2O$ Hydrous calcium sulfate	2	Colorless, white, occasional pale orange	Vitreous, pearly	Selenite is clear; satin spar is fibrous; alabaster is massive. Selenite may occur as large (to 3m) sword-like crystals, or as bladed groups incorporating sand and known as "desert roses." Cleavage in one directions best developed.
Kaolinite $Al_2Si_2O_5(OH)_4$ Hydrous aluminosilicate	2–2½	White, cream	Earthy, dull	Soft, powdery texture. Smells earthy when damp. Generally in clay-like masses with dull appearance. Commonly so soft and powdery that it crumbles when its hardness is being tested.
Biotite Mica $K(Mg,Fe)_3AlSi_3O_{10}(OH)_2$ Hydrous potassium aluminum ferro-magnesian silicate	2½	Dark brown, black	Vitreous	Dark mica. Occurs as six-sided mica "books" and as scattered flakes. Peels into thin, elastic, greenish-brown sheets along one direction of cleavage.
Muscovite Mica $KAl_2(AlSi_3O_{10})(OH)_2$ Hydrous potassium aluminum silicate	2½	Colorless, pale green	Vitreous to pearly	Transparent mica. Occurs as "books" and as scattered flakes. Peels into thin, elastic, transparent sheets along one direction of cleavage.
Halite NaCl Sodium chloride	2½	Colorless, salmon, pastels	Vitreous to greasy	Dissolves easily in water. Commonly has stepped-down "hopper" faces. Occurs as crystal masses or coatings on other material. Cubic cleavage. Tastes salty.

Name and Composition	*Hardness*	*Color*	*Luster (not streak)*	*Conspicuous Features (most diagnostic are underlined)*
Calcite $CaCO_3$ Calcium carbonate	3	Colorless white; rarely pastels	Vitreous	Effervesces freely in cold dilute hydrochloric acid. Doubly refracting. Commonly in rhombohedral crystals; hundreds of other forms known. May be fluorescent. Rhombohedral cleavage.
Earthy Hematite Fe_2O_3 Iron oxide	5	Dull brownish red to bright red	Submetallic to earthy	Characteristic red-brown streak. Commonly earthy and too powdery for accurate hardness test. May be granular or oolitic. Crystals rare; no cleavage.
Hornblende Complex hydrous ferromagnesian silicate with Ca, Al, Na	$5\frac{1}{2}$–6	Greenish-black to black	Vitreous	Barely scratches glass. Shiny on cleavage faces; opaque; commonly splintery at edges. Generally massive; occasionally in chunky crystals. Two cleavage angles: 124 and 56 degrees.
Augite Similar to hornblende, but anhydrous	6	Dark green to greenish black	Vitreous	Opaque prismatic crystals. Generally duller and greener than closely related hornblende. Two cleavages (87 and 93 degrees) and uneven fracture.
Orthoclase Feldspar (Potassium Feldspar) $KAlSi_3O_8$ Potassium aluminosilicate	6	White, pink, salmon	Vitreous	Will scratch glass. Wavy internal pattern distinguishes it from plagioclase when present. Color is commonly but not invariably pink. May be massive, or in large, well-developed coffin-shaped crystals. Two good cleavages (90 degrees).
Plagioclase Feldspar $NaAlSi_3O_8$ to $CaAl_2Si_2O_8$ Sodium and/or calcium aluminosilicate	6	White, gray	Vitreous	Will scratch glass. Two good cleavages (90 degrees). "Record groove" striations on cleavage faces. Rectangular cleavage faces common in igneous rocks.
Olivine $(Mg,Fe)_2SiO_4$	$6\frac{1}{2}$–7	Olive green	Vitreous	Crystals commonly appear as glassy green beads, isolated or in masses. Crystals may be finer, appearing as a sugary mass that is a somewhat lighter color. Color distinctive. Conchoidal fracture.

Name and Composition	*Hardness*	*Color*	*Luster (not streak)*	*Conspicuous Features (most diagnostic are underlined)*
Quartz Family SiO_2	7		Vitreous	Crystals are 6-sided prisms, commonly with terminations and steps perpendicular to long dimension. Crystals may be in clusters, or line cavities in rock; some weigh several hundred kilograms. Conchoidal fracture; no cleavage.
Rock crystal		Colorless		
Milky quartz		White		
Smoky quartz		Gray, brown		
Rose quartz		Pink		
Amethyst		Purple		
Citrine		Yellow		
Chert		Various		
Garnet $Fe_3Al_2(SiO_4)_3$ Iron-calcium-magnesium aluminum silicate	7–7½	Brown, red; also purple, green, pink, black, yellow	Vitreous to resinous	Commonly in shades of red-brown, Dodecahedral crystals have diamond-shaped faces. Color and hardness aid identification. Transparent to opaque. No cleavage.
III. Other Minerals				
Chlorite Hydrous aluminous ferromagnesian silicate	2	Light to dark green	Vitreous to earthy	Green color and mica-like appearance, except that (unlike mica) the flakes are not elastic.
Native Gold Au	2½–3	Gold, rose, or white	Same as color	Most dense natural substance (sp. gravity = 19). Malleable. Gold streak. Small rare crystals, or dendrites (branching growths), or nuggets in sedimentary deposits.
Dolomite $CaMg(CO_3)_2$ Calcium magnesium carbonate	3½–4	White, yellow, pink	Vitreous to pearly	In cold dilute HCl, effervesces slowly when powdered. Commonly associated with calcite. Generally in rhombohedral crystals.

Name and Composition	*Hardness*	*Color*	*Luster (not streak)*	*Conspicuous Features (most diagnostic are underlined)*
Fluorite CaF_2 Calcium fluoride	4	Colorless, pastels, purple	Vitreous	Cubic or octahedral crystals. Octahedral cleavage. Generally fluoresces in ultraviolet radiation.
Staurolite $FeAl_4Si_2O_{10}(OH)_2$ Hydrous iron aluminosilicate	7–7½	Brown	Vitreous to dull	Generally prismatic crystals, commonly twinned to form diagnostic cruciform crosses. Pitted, rough crystal faces.
Topaz $Al_2SiO_4(OH,F)_2$ Hydrous fluoro-aluminosilicate	8	Colorless, white, golden yellow, light blue	Vitreous	Striations on crystal faces. Glassy, prismatic crystals with one direction of basal cleavage exhibiting diamond-shape cross section.
Diamond C Elemental carbon	10	Colorless, pastels	Adamantine to greasy	Octahedral crystals with greasy luster. Hardest natural substance. Four well-developed directions of cleavage.

Crystals of Minerals

The abundant mineral *calcite* ($CaCO_3$) can assume more different crystal forms than any other mineral can. These calcite crystals have a dagger-like appearance.

Light reflects from shiny cubes of *galena* (PbS), a dense mineral that is a prominent source of lead metal. In this photograph, calcite (the light-colored mineral) assumes a more rod-like crystal form.

Crystals of *garnet*, a complex silicate mineral, have the form of a dodecahedron (a solid figure with 12 flat faces). This characteristic crystal form makes garnet easy to identify.

But beware! The flat faces on this specimen of beryl (another complex silicate mineral) are cut and polished; they are not the natural crystal faces. Both natural minerals and their artificially made counterparts may be starting points for creating gemstones.

Photo 4-a. Minerals

Tourmaline, a complex silicate mineral, is also a favorite material for cutting gemstones.

Crystal form is the shape of a crystal permitted to grow freely in an open space with no interference. *Cleavage* is the tendency for a crystal to break along flat planes. The transparent mica, *muscovite*, exhibits excellent cleavage. You can pry flexible muscovite flakes into thinner sheets with your fingernails.

Quartz (SiO_2) may exhibit beautiful crystal faces, but quartz has no cleavage. Quartz breaks along irregular surfaces, not along smooth flat surfaces.

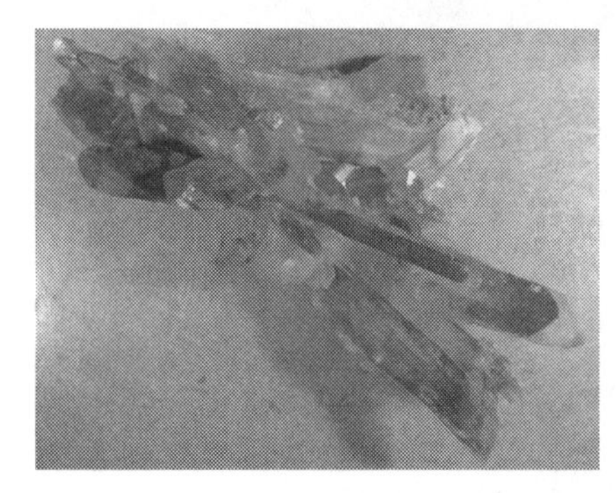

Another common mineral is the very soft *gypsum* ($CaSO_4 \cdot 2\ H_2O$). Here, the variety called selenite exhibits both well developed crystal faces and cleavage.

Photo 4-b. Minerals

Definition of a Rock

- A rock is any coherent, naturally occurring substance generally composed of minerals.
  - Examples: granite, sandstone, obsidian (no minerals), glacier ice.
  - Common non-rocks: beach sand, molten lava, concrete.

Rock Cycle

- **ROCK CYCLE:** any rock type can become any other rock type.
- There are 3 rock types: igneous rocks, sedimentary rocks, and metamorphic rocks.

Definition of a Mineral

A mineral is a substance with these characteristics:

- Naturally occurring
- Inorganic (never lived, although graphite, diamond, and calcite may be bioproducts of organisms)
- Definite chemical composition - for example, quartz (SiO_2) or pyrite (FeS_2) - or limited range of compositions (for example, Fe and Mg in a complex mineral named olivine)
- Crystalline - has an ordered arrangement of atoms
- *These four criteria cause each type of mineral to have its own unique properties.*

Properties of Minerals: Tools for Identification

- Hardness
- Luster
- Color
- Streak
- Cleavage
- Fracture
- Cleavage *vs.* crystal form
- Miscellaneous properties

Hardness

- Measure of the resistance of a mineral to scratching (not breakage)
- **Mohs Hardness Scale** (Softest = 1, Hardest = 10)

1 - Talc	*KNIFE, NAIL: 5-5.5*
2 - Gypsum	6 - Orthoclase
FINGERNAIL: 2.25	*GLASS PLATE: 6*
3 – Calcite	7 - Quartz
PENNY: 3.5	8 - Topaz
4 – Fluorite	9 - Corundum
5 – Apatite	10 - Diamond

Luster

- The way a mineral reflects light
- METALLIC: opaque, looks like a metal such as gold, silver, iron, etc.
- NON-METALLIC: (needs to be more descriptive)
  - *VITREOUS* or *GLASSY* (Samples 3, 12) - strong glint (shiny like glass)
  - *PEARLY* (talc, some gypsum) - looks like mother-of-pearl
  - *RESINOUS* - reflects light in a manner similar to syrup or tree sap ("glazed")
  - *EARTHY* - dull, little or no reflection

Color

- The intrinsic color of the mineral
- NOTE: color is rarely diagnostic - generally a very poor identifier. Some examples...
- Sulfur is normally yellow.
- Pyrite is normally brassy.
- Quartz can have almost any color!

Streak

- The color of the powdery residue of a mineral left behind when it is dragged across an unglazed porcelain plate (hardness of plate = 6).

Cleavage

- Breakage of a mineral along a flat plane of weakness.
- **How To Describe Cleavage:**
- If you see only 1 set of parallel planes...
  - Denoted '1 direction of cleavage' (mica was used as an example in class).
- If you see only 2 sets of parallel planes, you must give the intersection angle of the two sets.
  - Denoted '2 directions of cleavage at 90°' (if they intersect at a right angle).
- If you see 3 sets of parallel planes, denoted
  - '3 directions of cleavage at 90°' (termed CUBIC - salt has cubic cleavage) or
  - '3 directions of cleavage not at 90°' (termed RHOMBOHEDRAL).

Fracture

- Uneven breakage (non-planar breakage)
  - conchoidal: see obsidian or quartz; breaks along a surface marked by concentric circles
  - splintery: like splinters in wood (sample 16)
  - uneven: a "catch-all" term for non-diagnostic, non-planar breakage

Crystal Form

- How a mineral grows
  - May be difficult to distinguish from cleavage.
  - If crystal grows out of an apparent flat cleavage face, the face isn't cleavage – it is crystal form.

Miscellaneous

- *Some minerals have very helpful (unique) diagnostic properties.*
  - Magnetite exhibits magnetism.
  - Sulfur smells like rotten eggs (after scratching the surface).
  - Calcite fizzes when HCl (hydrochloric acid) is applied to it.
  - Halite (rock salt) tastes salty.
  - Some minerals are exceptionally dense because they are composed of heavy elements, or contain closely-packed atoms.

Mineral Classification

- Metals
  - Combined with oxygen = oxide minerals
  - Combined with sulfur = sulfide minerals
  - Not combined with other elements = native (native gold, native copper, etc.)
- Silicates (Si is an important ingredient)
- Ferromagnesian (Fe, Mg) - dark and dense

GEOLOGY TOUR OF TEXAS MEMORIAL MUSEUM

A portion of an early lab period will feature a walking tour of the geology display in the basement of the Texas Memorial Museum. Here are some things to note in the museum, or on the way to it.

On the Way to the Museum

Faults in Limestone
Some of a hillside was excavated to provide space for the parking garage on San Jacinto Blvd. Small faults are visible in the limestone outcrop along the south side of the garage (nearest the Texas Memorial Museum). A fault is a fracture along which the rock on the two sides has experienced significant movement. Several small faults are present here. Pick a distinctive stratum and trace it to a fault, thence continuing on the far side. Approximately how much was the relative displacement?

At the Museum Entrance

Calcite, Limestone, Marble
Calcium carbonate, which comprises the mineral calcite, may have many appearances. It is the chief ingredient of the sedimentary rock limestone, and also of marble which is metamorphosed limestone. Deeply colored marble makes up the facing stone on the walls of the museum entrance, but light-colored limestone on the museum exterior is also made of calcite. When the marble was subjected to stress, it tore open along small fractures that were later filled by white calcite precipitated from solution. Even though the marble has been deformed, fossils are still recognizable.

In the Museum Basement

Note: the basement displays are being renovated and they may be relocated or not available.

Forms of Quartz
Quartz (SiO_2) breaks by fracturing irregularly, not by splitting along flat cleavage planes. Flat faces are the crystal form that can develop if the mineral was precipitated in an open volume such as a fluid-filled pocket in the host rock.

Meteorites
A meteorite "find" is a specimen that someone happened to discover by chance. A "fall" is a meteorite observed to plunge to earth, then picked up. More than 90% of meteorites are made of silicate minerals; they are called stony meteorites because they look much like ordinary rocks. The remaining few percent are made of dense iron-nickel alloy. Most of the meteorites on display in museums are "finds," and they are the highly noticeable iron-nickel type. Only by taking a census of actual meteorite "falls" can we correctly estimate the abundances of stony and iron-nickel meteorites.

Occasionally a huge meteorite strikes the earth, its energy of motion instantly transformed into heat. The resulting fireball blasts a crater and ejects melted target rock into the sky. Tektites are composed of glass; they were molten blobs launched into outer space, that had traveled thousands of kilometers like an intercontinental ballistic missile before falling back to the earth.

Fish Fossil from the Austin Chalk
A giant fish fossil was preserved in Austin Chalk. Chalk is a fine-grained variety of limestone, and Austin Chalk is a geologic formation—a distinctive body of rock large enough to be symbolized on a geologic map. Geologic formations are typically named according to what they are made of (chalk) and where they are well exposed to view (Austin). There is a narrow foot bridge across Waller Creek, next to the Drama Department between the Texas Memorial Museum and the Department of Geological Sciences. From the bridge you can see Austin Chalk comprising the banks of the creek.

Petrified Wood
The tree stump is a fossil created when dissolved silica (SiO_2) was brought to the site of deposition and precipitated, replacing the original woody material.

Flying Reptiles
Pterosaurs (TARE-o-sours) were flying reptiles, now extinct. Other vertebrate animals that can fly include birds, and bats which are mammals. In each group of animals, the wing is based upon a different plan of bone structure. The skin of a bat wing is stretched among the elongated but separated fingers. In contrast, the fingers in a bird wing are fused together. In their day, the pterosaurs "solved" the problem of flight by means of a wing whose membrane was stretched across an enormous extension of the fourth finger only.

Cretaceous Marine Reptiles
Spectacular fossils in this display are of now-extinct reptiles that lived during the Cretaceous Period, an interval of geologic time from 135 to 65 million years ago.

Much can be learned about diet and general life style of an animal by analysis of its teeth. The skeleton of a mosasaur was discovered on Onion Creek near Austin. Its teeth indicate that it was a carnivore. Some of the bones in the paddle of the mosasaur, a swimming reptile, correspond to the bones in the wing of a pterosaur, a flying reptile, but they differ in size and shape.

(Far side of display.) A nearly complete skeleton of a plesiosaur, a long-necked swimming reptile, was discovered in the bank of Shoal Creek in northwest Austin by an amateur paleontologist, and restored for display by students of Austin Community College. The animal's skull was recovered but it is too badly shattered and deformed to make a good display. Dark material between the ribs is a remnant of the shale matrix that encased the fossil.

Fossil Teeth of Mammoths and Mastodons
A large display is devoted to extinct members of the elephant family, the mammoth and mastodon, whose teeth also provide important clues to diet. Although any animal that chanced to get caught between the massive grinding teeth of one of these huge animals would not have fared well, we know that the mammoth and mastodon were strict vegetarians both from the teeth and from stomach contents in individuals that have remained frozen for thousands of years since the height of the Ice Age.

Texas Building Stones
Texas contains many varieties of granite of different colors, and sizes and arrangements of the large crystals. In spite of the striking color differences, the mineral and chemical compositions are almost identical.

Rock Cycle
The processes by which rocks are changed into other rocks is called the rock cycle. Refer to the circular diagram (Figure 4-1, p. 60), for a discussion of the rock cycle.

Sedimentary Rocks
Sedimentary rocks may be classified as chemical or mechanical. A chemical sediment originated by the precipitation of dissolved ions. A mechanical, or clastic sediment originated by deposition of solid particles that were eroded from some pre-existing rock and transported to the site of deposition.

5

Born of Fire

Lightning display at night accompanying an eruption of the new volcano Surtsey, on the coast of Iceland. [*Sigurgeir Jónasson*]

The study of rocks is the major part of geology, although by no means the whole subject. Our earth is so immense and so complexly interrelated within, that in a sense we need to know about all of it in order to understand any of it. We might ask how any particular rock body got to be that way. Why is it positioned "here" rather than "over there?" What role did heat energy, or the force of gravity, or the presence of life play in its origin? This and the next several chapters take up the theme of the origin of rocks with a look at some of their general features. Following this we shall consider the subjects of geologic time, the fossil record, and other important parts of the fabric of geology.

We have seen that rocks are composed of minerals, chiefly members of the several families described in Chapters 3 and 4. Rocks can be assigned to four categories according to their manner of origin. Like all classifications, this one is artificial with its share of exceptions to general rules. Nevertheless, it is useful enough to have been accepted universally by geologists.

Originating as a clump of cosmic matter, the earth was probably converted entirely (or nearly so) into igneous rock when it melted, differentiated, and then solidified. At the same time, the beginnings of an ocean and atmosphere appeared at its surface. Water and air proceeded to attack the igneous rock, causing it to be weathered both mechanically and chemically. Products of weathering were transported by wind, moving water, or ice, to be deposited as sedimentary rocks. But sedimentary rocks were not the end of the line, geologically speaking. Any rock can be transformed under conditions of high temperature and pressure into metamorphic rock, the final class. Intense metamorphism can cause a rock to melt partially, thus returning it to the igneous stage again. Weathering, deposition, metamorphism, melting, solidification—these processes have been repeated continually since the earth's beginning. Let's look at the first two classes of rock in more detail.

COSMIC MATTER

Cosmic matter, the original condensate of the solar system, is found on earth today only in the form of meteorites that, as we saw in Chapter 2, come in stony and iron-nickel varieties. Stony meteorites are composed of feldspar, olivine, and other familiar minerals, plus minor amounts of minerals that occur rarely or not at all in ordinary rocks. It is estimated that a rather trivial 85 thousand tons of cosmic material fall to the earth each year. Once this material has been weathered, it cannot be restored to the original state of cosmic matter. But igneous, sedimentary, and metamorphic rocks *can* be converted, one type into another, and back again through processes of recycling.

IGNEOUS ROCKS

Igneous rock has crystallized from melted material, or *magma*. The term "igneous" comes from a Latin word meaning "fire-formed" or "born of fire." A few magmas may be entirely liquid, but most of them consist of a hot mush of crystals suspended in melted silicate material that includes dissolved H_2O and other fluids. Liquid magma that erupts through the earth's surface is called *lava*. Ironically, although igneous rocks comprise at least 80 percent of the volume of the crust, we have never made direct observations of the environment in which magma is forming. That is because the melting takes place at depths of at least several kilometers in the earth, to 150 or 200 kilometers (100 miles) in extreme instances. Therefore it has been necessary for studies of the origin of igneous rocks to proceed along indirect lines.

Observations in the Field and in the Laboratory

An obvious place to begin with rocks of all kinds is out where they are, in what is familiarly called the "field." Systematic field work, begun in the 1700s, is the occupation today of thousands of geologists. A field geologist describes the various rocks and makes a map of their distribution (Figure 5-1). Additional studies, generally accomplished at the home base, may include a microscopic examination of samples, chemical analyses, and identification of fossils. These data are used to interpret the geologic relationships, and to reconstruct a history of past events.

Field investigations have provided staggering amounts of information. For one thing, they have shown us what is actually "out there" needing to be explained. They have also pointed to generalities that are significant far beyond the confines of a local area. For example, suppose that we observe that certain types of igneous rock are associated with one another in many places around the world. This would suggest that the same processes had created the distinctive assemblages of these rocks wherever they are found.

a

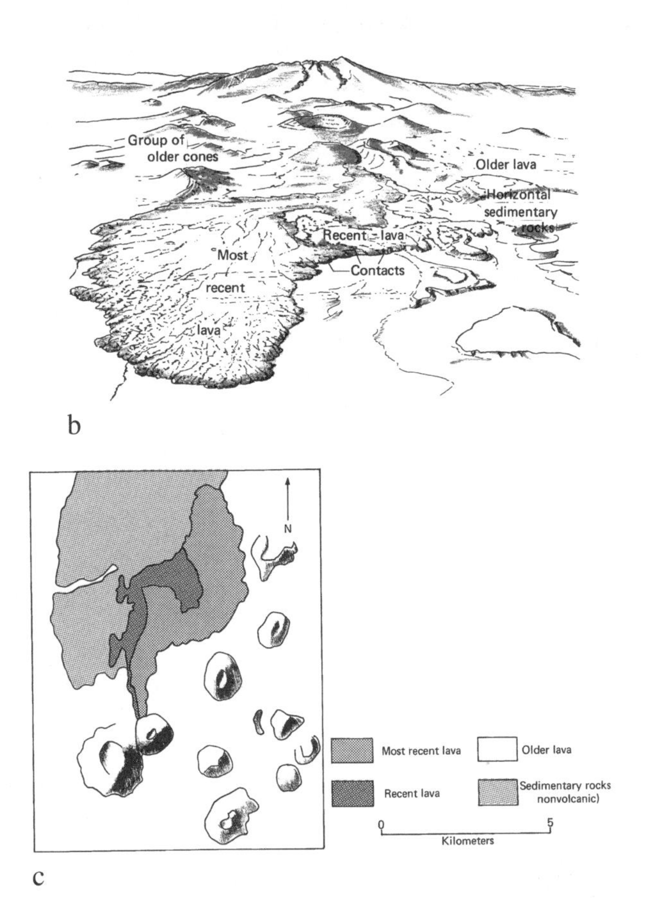

Figure 5-1. An oblique aerial photograph (*a*) southward across the San Franciscan volcanic field, near Flagstaff, Arizona, is interpreted in a drawing (*b*). Lava flows of different ages are easily distinguished from one another by superposition and by relative freshness of appearance. [*Photograph © John S. Shelton from* Geology Illustrated *by John S. Shelton and line drawing based upon* Geology Illustrated, *W. H. Freeman and Company. Copyright © 1966.*] A geologic map of the foreground area (*c*) indicates four rock types and several of the volcanic cones. The map eliminates the foreshortened perspective of the aerial photograph. Moreover, the map is based on a careful examination of the rocks. In most areas, the resemblance between a photograph and a geologic map is much less obvious than in this example. [*Adapted from Harold S. Colton,* Cinder Cones and Lava Flows, *Northland Press, Flagstaff, Ariz., 1967.*]

Sometimes the careful field descriptions must be supplemented by geologic research that takes another line of approach. Consider, for instance, that when a magma is crystallizing, not all of the different species of mineral would appear at the same time. We ask, which minerals were first to form, while the cooling magma was yet at a high temperature, and which other minerals formed later? Clues to the answer might be seen in the rock *texture*: the sizes and shapes of its mineral grains, and the relationships among them. For example, if grains of mineral species A are enclosed within the crystals of mineral species B, this would be evidence that mineral A crystallized first and that mineral B grew around it later.

In doing science, then, our goal is to understand not only what the rocks *are*, but how they *became* that way. How can this be done? What we see in the field was established long before there were human observers, and unfortunately we cannot transport ourselves back in geologic time to see how it happened. However, we might get a plausible notion by re-creating natural processes in the laboratory, by artificially melting and solidifying samples of igneous rock. Laboratory simulations would give insight especially into rocks that originated at the surface, or not far beneath. It is much more difficult to reproduce the extremely high temperatures and pressures that exist at great depth in the earth.

Most early experiments were carried out at normal atmospheric pressure, as appropriate for a cooling lava flow. It was necessary to develop special apparatus that could exert conditions of both high pressure and high temperature upon the sample. Early versions of such apparatus consisted of a massive hydraulic press equipped with an electrical resistance furnace. Indeed many of these machines are still being used, especially for experiments in which H_2O is one of the ingredients in the experimental sample. In more recent instruments, the sample is placed between two diamonds carefully shaped into a pair of tiny anvils (Figure 5-2). Heating is done by shining an intense laser beam through the transparent diamond onto the sample. The diamonds, because of their great strength, can transmit an enormous pressure greater than the pressure at the center of the earth (although we cannot yet reproduce the simultaneous high temperature and high pressure at the earth's center).

In a typical experiment, a sample consists of precisely measured amounts of simple, pure substances which are made to react together at a controlled high temperature and pressure. After the chemical reaction is complete, the sample is "quenched" by being suddenly restored back to ordinary room temperature and pressure. The final reaction products might consist of the same minerals that occur in a natural igneous rock. For example, a mixture of CaO, Na_2O, MgO, FeO, Al_2O_3, and SiO_2 might react together to form the minerals olivine, pyroxene, and plagioclase feldspar.

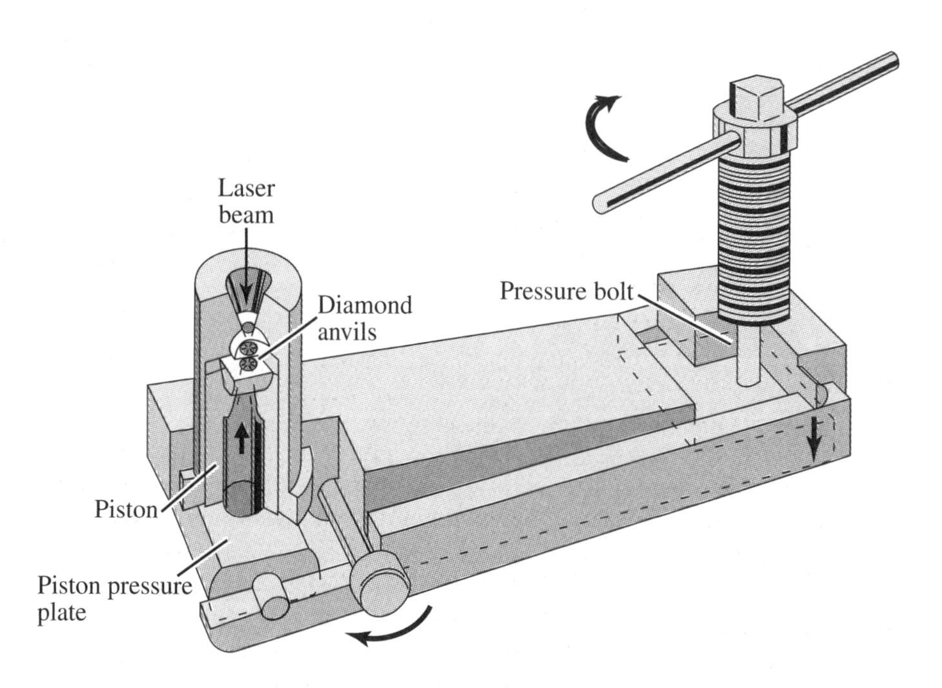

Figure 5-2. A diamond-anvil high-pressure cell operates like a nutcracker. Twisting of the handle transmits force through a lever arm to the sample which is contained between the diamond anvils. The enormous pressure is achieved by a device that a person can hold in the palm of a hand!

Laboratory simulations have clarified many knotty problems that have long puzzled the field geologists. For instance, why is it that quartz and olivine rarely occur in the same rock? Experiments showed that these two minerals are incompatible at high temperature; they react together forming pyroxene and in so doing, one or both of the original minerals disappear. Experiments are also developed to infer the earth's composition at the great depths which we shall never see directly. What we do see coming to the surface is lava, and so a new question might be posed as follows: What set of minerals, when melted just slightly at high pressure (i.e., deep in the earth), will form lava of that particular composition? Laboratory simulations have given such decisive information that geologists feel quite confident in identifying what type of rock composes the upper portion of the earth's mantle.

The very simplicity of such controlled experiments is both a strength and a weakness of the method of re-creating natural processes. A simple association of minerals may be easy to understand, but not be very realistic. Of course, the experiments are becoming ever more sophisticated, but probably another generation or two will go by before we can claim to have a thorough experimental understanding of igneous rocks.

Extrusive Igneous Rocks

Few natural events have ever terrified people more than do major volcanic eruptions. They are so powerful and unpredictable! Legends of great eruptions can be traced back thousands of years to times when traditions were passed down only by word of mouth. Some of the early Greek and Roman writers described volcanic phenomena quite accurately. Yet others were convinced that volcanoes are sustained by the fiery breath of giants, or that they are gateways to the forge of Vulcan, god of the underground. These people were carried away by enthusiasm for ridiculous ideas that a few observations would easily have dispelled.

Systematic study of volcanoes began early in the 18th Century. Like other sciences, volcanology developed in spurts as new interpretations and techniques made their appearance. For many decades, volcanologists have performed the necessary but preliminary task of describing and classifying volcanic phenomena—a worthy pursuit that continues today. With the recent exploration of hitherto unknown regions such as the ocean floor and the surface of the moon, and with more advanced laboratory studies, our understanding of volcanism has entered a new phase of rapid development.

The earth today seems to be experiencing intense volcanic activity (Figure 5-3). In Iceland, 200 young volcanoes have erupted within recorded history of the past thousand years. On a world basis, more than 6000 separate eruptions have been recorded, many of which have damaged valuable agricultural or other land. As the world population grows, human life and property become crowded ever closer around these hazardous volcanoes. Thus to make accurate predictions of volcanic eruptions is an important objective of research in volcanism. About 530 volcanoes are considered to be active—to have erupted within historic times and poised to erupt again. Only a few volcanoes erupt continually.

The list of active volcanoes would probably be several times longer if submarine eruptions could be detected. In the deep ocean, cold sea water quenches the lava so that no billowing clouds are able to rise above the site of eruption. Exploration of the ocean floor provides abundant evidence for frequent and copious injection of magma up into the oceanic crust, to the extent of some 30 to 40 cubic kilometers (8 cubic miles) each year.

Active lifetimes of volcanoes vary greatly, some being astonishingly long by human standards. Most volcanoes are undoubtedly like the famous Parícutin, in west central Mexico, which suddenly burst forth in a corn field in 1943. Parícutin quickly built a cone to an impressive height of 400 meters (1300 feet), but within just 9 years of its birth, the volcano abruptly went dead. In contrast, the active lives of giant volcanoes such as those that make up the island of Hawaii extend over several million years. The vigorous activity of the Hawaiian volcanoes, and their long lifetimes, have caused them to become the largest single mountain peaks on earth.

Variations in composition and eruptive style among volcanoes are equally impressive. An eruption may bring forth a quietly flowing liquid or an explosive outpouring of already solidified particles. Lava may issue from a central crater atop a volcanic cone, or from an elongated fissure in the ocean floor. The congealed lava may be rich in dark ferromagnesian minerals, or consist of light-colored feldspar and transparent quartz. In any case, the igneous material emerges through the earth's crust to the land surface or into a body of water; it is therefore said to be *extrusive* igneous rock.

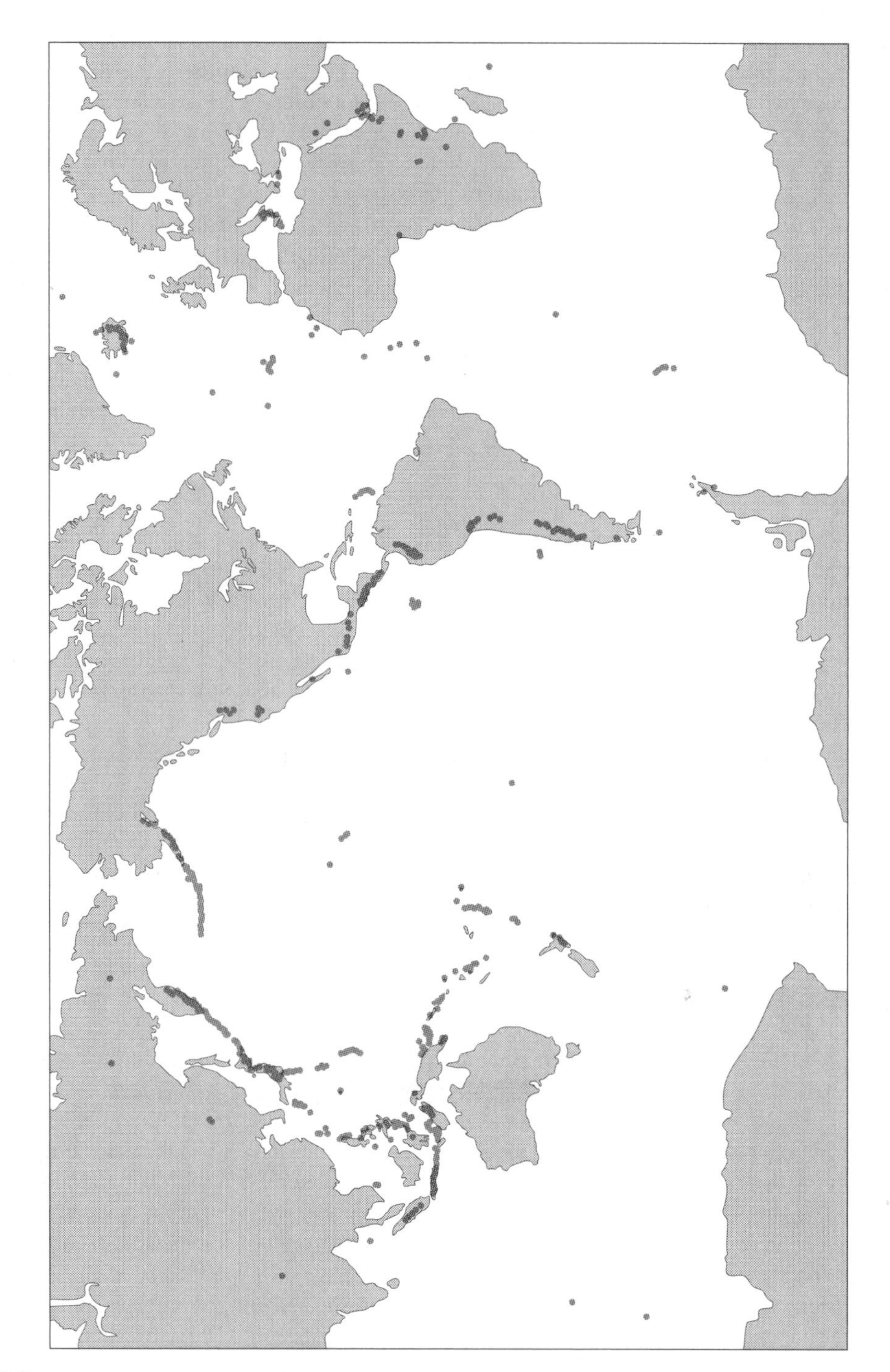

Figure 5-3. Many, perhaps most of the world's active volcanoes are unknown, concealed from view beneath the ocean waters. The "Ring of Fire" bordering the Pacific Ocean is especially prominent. Volcanoes are abundant in the Mediterranean region and in Africa, but are rare in the interiors of the other continents. [*After Gordon A. Macdonald,* Volcanoes, *Prentice-Hall, Inc., Englewood Cliffs, New Jersey, 1972.*]

Types of eruption Why this great variety of eruptive styles? Important factors here are the environment and rock composition, and another factor—the presence of water—that may not be obvious in the final product. Measurements show that a magma may contain 3 or 4 percent, to as much as 17 percent, of its weight in dissolved H_2O. Water can dissolve other substances, but in this case it is dissolved *in* other substances. As melted silicate material begins to cool, the silicon and oxygen atoms link together forming silicon-oxygen tetrahedrons, and these in turn join with metal ions to form crystals of olivine, mica, feldspar, etc. During the growth of these crystals, some of the H_2O can be incorporated into hydrous minerals such as mica, but most of it remains in the melt which becomes more and more water-rich as the volume of remaining melt continues to decrease.

An important property of the magma is *viscosity*, which describes how rapidly the magma will change shape under the influence of applied forces. A high-viscosity magma is "stiff," and a low-viscosity magma is "runny." In Chapter 3 we noted that Si-O tetrahedrons are isolated in olivine, whereas in mica they are linked together in sheets; in feldspar or quartz the structure of linked tetrahedrons is even more complex. During cooling of the magma, the tetrahedrons are already beginning to assemble before the first crystals actually appear. A magma rich in iron and magnesium, which is about to crystallize into olivine or other ferromagnesian minerals, would contain only fragments of tetrahedrons or perhaps short disorganized segments of chains. This magma would have a low viscosity and it would not be able to trap much dissolved H_2O. In contrast, a magma rich in silica would crystallize mostly into feldspar and quartz; during crystallization, long twisted strands of Si-O tetrahedrons would form and become ensnarled, making it difficult for the magma to flow (Figure 5-4). This magma would be highly viscous (resembling toothpaste), and it would be able to contain a large amount of water.

In the latter case, the final result may be quite dramatic as the rising body of magma approaches the earth's surface. Release of the confining pressure permits the dissolved water to flash into steam whose equivalent volume suddenly increases by a thousand times. The result is a tremendous explosion, such as the one that blew off the top of Mount St. Helens. This once beautifully symmetrical volcano became swollen in 1980 with hot, water-laden magma that had intruded into the base of the cone. On the morning of May 18, some very jeopardized, excited observers on the ground and in a plane flying over-head suddenly realized that the top of the mountain was "coming to pieces." There was no time to analyze the ensuing events (the pilot gained sufficient speed for a rapid exit only by putting the plane into a power dive), but photographs taken at the time revealed later what happened. A landslide broke loose at the crest and roared down the slope (Figure 5-5). With this confining mass of rock removed, the magma

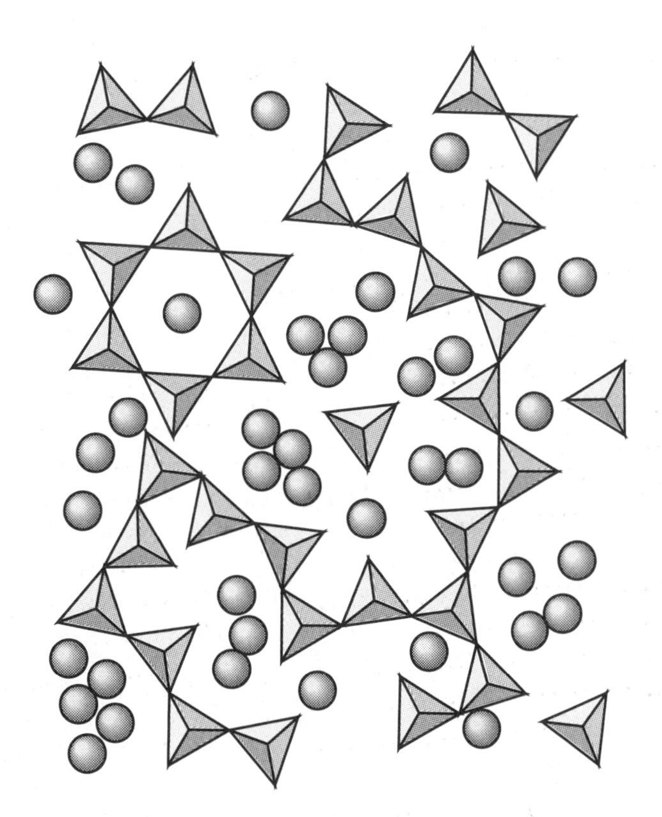

Figure 5-4. In this schematic drawing of silicate magma beginning to crystallize, triangles represent silicon-oxygen tetrahedrons and circles represent ions of magnesium, iron, potassium, etc. The crystal structure is only "halfway" organized; Si-O tetrahedrons have formed and are joined corner-to-corner but, beyond that, no regular pattern of atoms has become established.

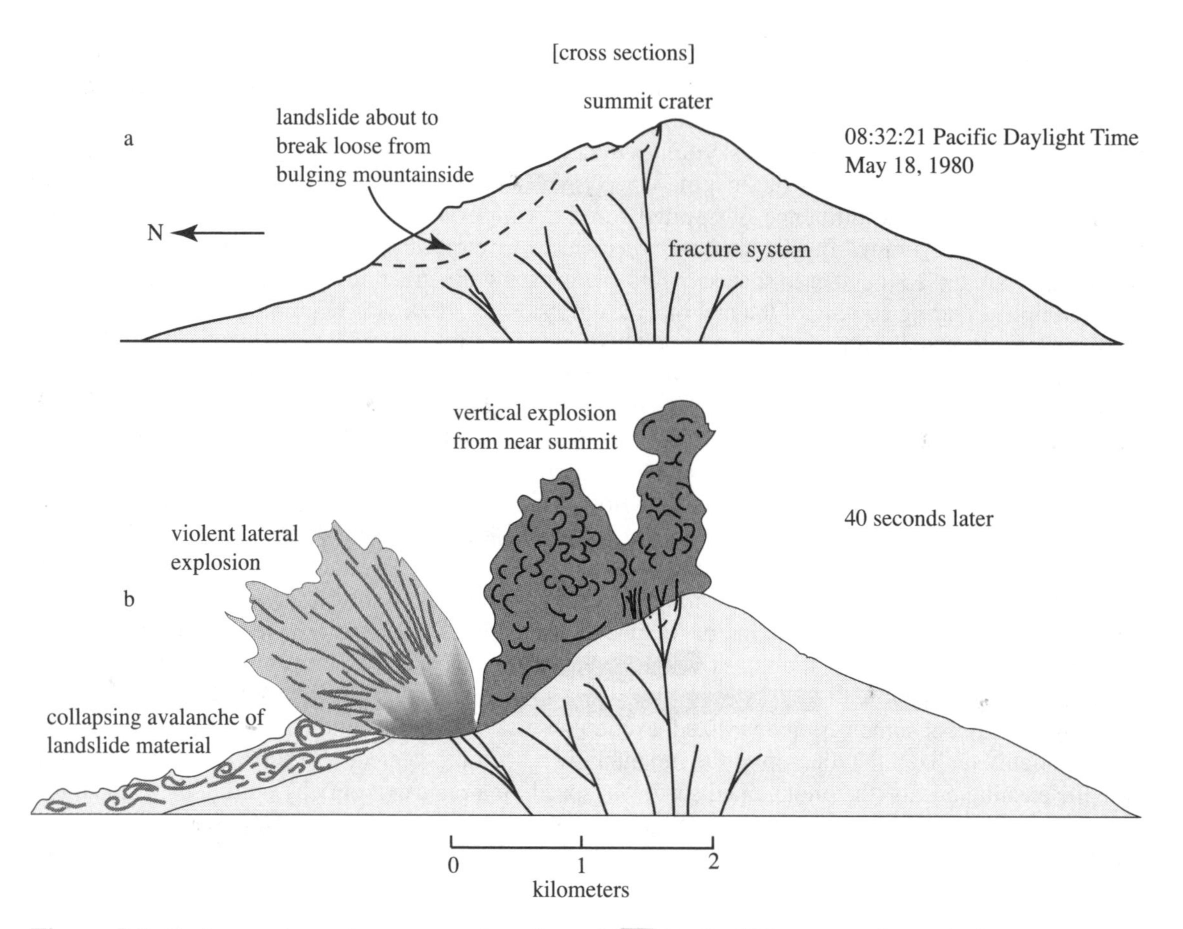

Figure 5-5. In these schematic cross sections through Mount St. Helens, gas-charged viscous magma was stored within the base of the volcano. A landslide broke loose (upper drawing), releasing the confining pressure and permitting explosive eruption (lower drawing). Figure 5-9 shows the location of Mount St. Helens. [*From drawings by Anthony J. Irving based on eyewitness photographs.*]

frothed up just as a shaken bottle of champagne does when the cork is popped. The explosion sent approximately one cubic kilometer of mountain top in various directions. Very fine volcanic dust shot skyward, then drifted downwind to be deposited in a broad swath to the east. Some of the finest dust was distributed by wind currents all around the Northern Hemisphere. Coarser particles, saturated with steam, were blasted laterally down the slope, destroying all life forms along the way.

The eruption of Mount St. Helens was insignificant compared to that of Krakatau, a volcano in Indonesia that was nearly totally demolished in 1883 in a series of violent explosions that have been called "the loudest noise on earth" (Figure 5-6). This catastrophe pulverized 20 times as much rock as at Mount St. Helens, during which an amount of energy was expended equivalent to the explosion of 200 million tons of TNT. Fearsome as it was, the destruction of Krakatau was trivial compared to some events whose results are preserved in the geologic record. The world's greatest volcanic plateau extends 800 kilometers (500 miles) down the mountainous backbone of western Mexico. In this region are deposits that are hundreds or even thousands of times larger still. Fortunately humankind has never witnessed these super-catastrophic events which took place 30 to 40 million years ago.

The solid rock remaining as the only visible evidence of a volcanic explosion clearly bears the imprint of the departed gases. Particles, that come in all sizes from fine dust to huge blocks, are collectively referred to as *pyroclastic,* from a Greek word meaning "fire-broken." Two common types of pyroclastic material are light frothy glass, or *pumice*, and deposits of pulverized fine particles known as *tuff* (pronounced "tough"). Under the microscope, tuff exhibits tiny, delicate, curved platelets of glass (Figure 5-7) which are the shattered remnants of gas bubbles.

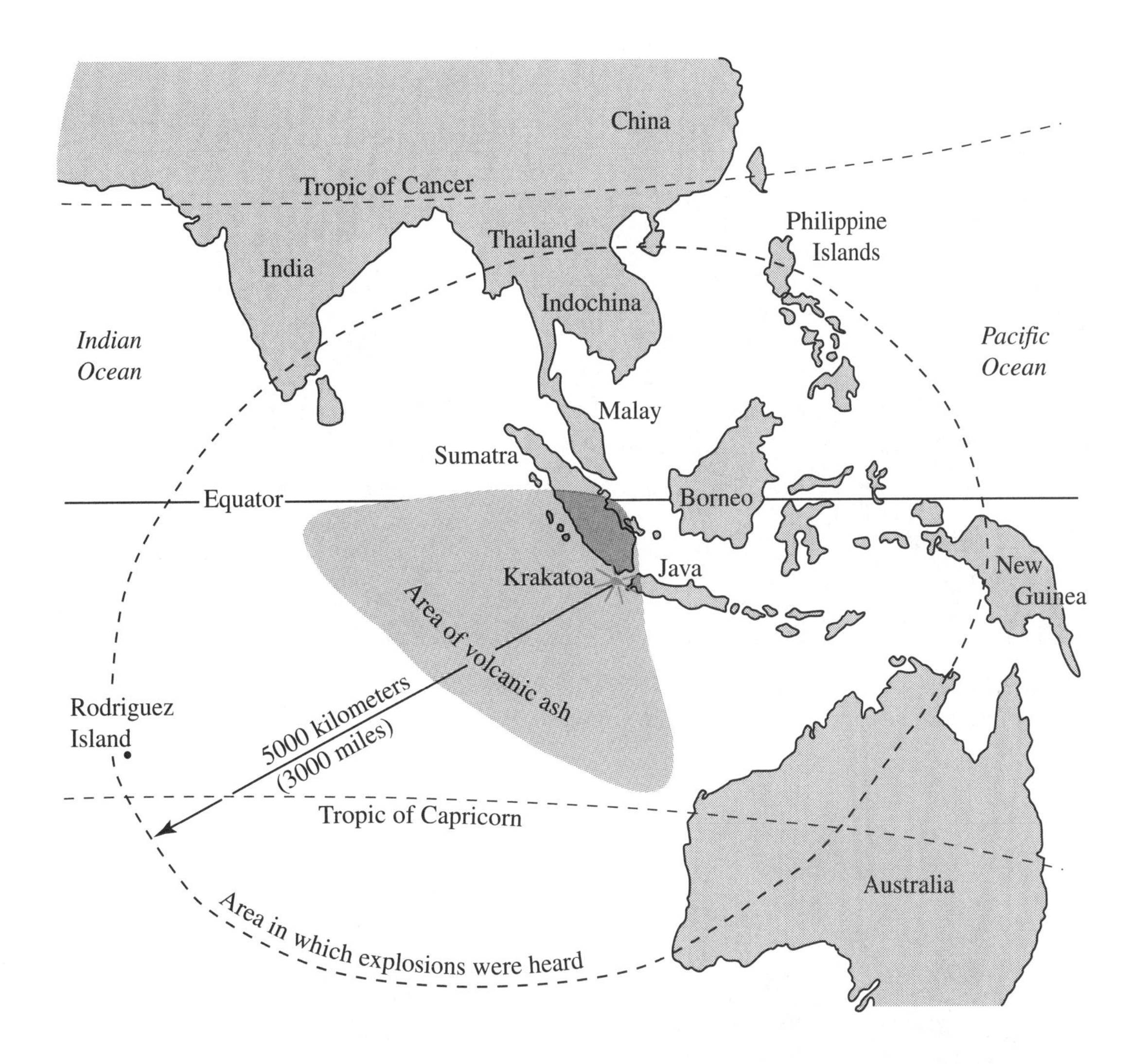

Figure 5-6. When superheated water flashes into steam, its volume increases at least by a thousand times. Effects of the catastrophic disruption of Krakatau, both the noise and the spewed-out volcanic ash, spread outward great distances. Sounds of the explosion traveled about 4 hours before reaching the outer fringe of the area of detection! [*Source: Fred M. Bullard,* Volcanoes of the Earth, *2nd revised edition, copyright © 1984. Reprinted by permission of the author and The University of Texas Press.*]

Basalt Most eruptions are not of this spectacular, dangerous variety. By far the most abundant volcanic rock is *basalt* (baSALT), a product of a generally quiet, nonexplosive outpouring (Figure 5-8). Basalt underlies the floor of the ocean basins and in certain areas it builds volcanic edifices that rise above the floor. Examples are the Hawaiian Islands in the mid-Pacific Ocean, and Iceland in the north Atlantic. Basalt dominates in the ocean basins which occupy 70% of the earth's surface. On the continents, basalt is less abundant, yet it comprises millions of square kilometers in the Columbia River field of Oregon and Washington (Figure 5-9), the Deccan Plateau of India, and the Paraná Basin of southern Brazil, largest of the continental volcanic fields.

Basalt is made of pyroxene which is a ferromagnesian mineral, plagioclase feldspar rich in calcium (rather than sodium), and minor amounts of magnetite or other members of the iron-titanium oxide family. Some basalts also contain olivine and feldspathoids, which are framework silicate minerals that resemble feldspar. (Refer to Chapter 3 for a review of the structures and compositions of these minerals.) Consequently, basalt is a dark, dense rock containing less silica than most other lavas. Rich in ferromagnesian minerals, basalt is said to be *mafic,* a word coined from "ma" for magnesium and "fic" for iron.

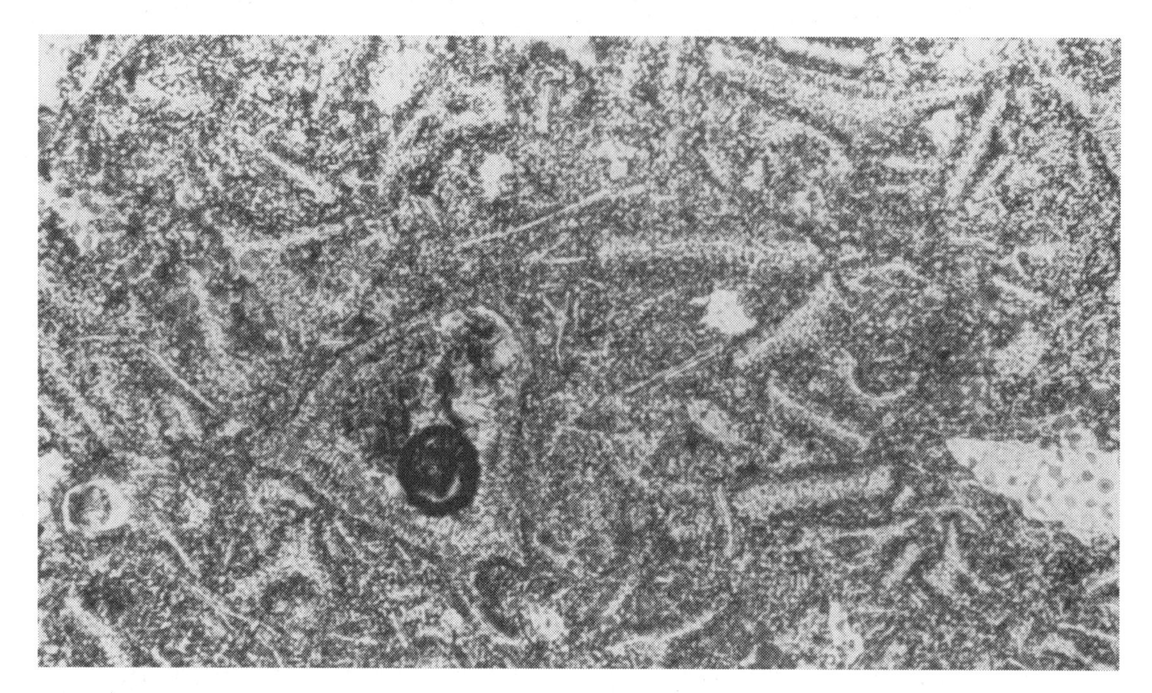

Figure 5-7. Sharp, curved fragments in this volcanic ash are shards of glass, set in a matrix of extremely fine particles of glass and crystalline material. [*Courtesy Eric Swanson.*]

Figure 5-8. Streams of molten basalt rolled down from a fissure eruption high on the flank of Kilauea Volcano, Hawaii. Upon reaching inhabited land near the coast, the basalt displaced a community that once lay in the middle distance in this photograph. Liquid basalt does not "flow like water" (its viscosity being at least 100 thousand times greater than that of water), but the front of a flow can advance as rapidly as 400 meters per hour, and single flows extending 300 kilometers (nearly 200 miles) are known.

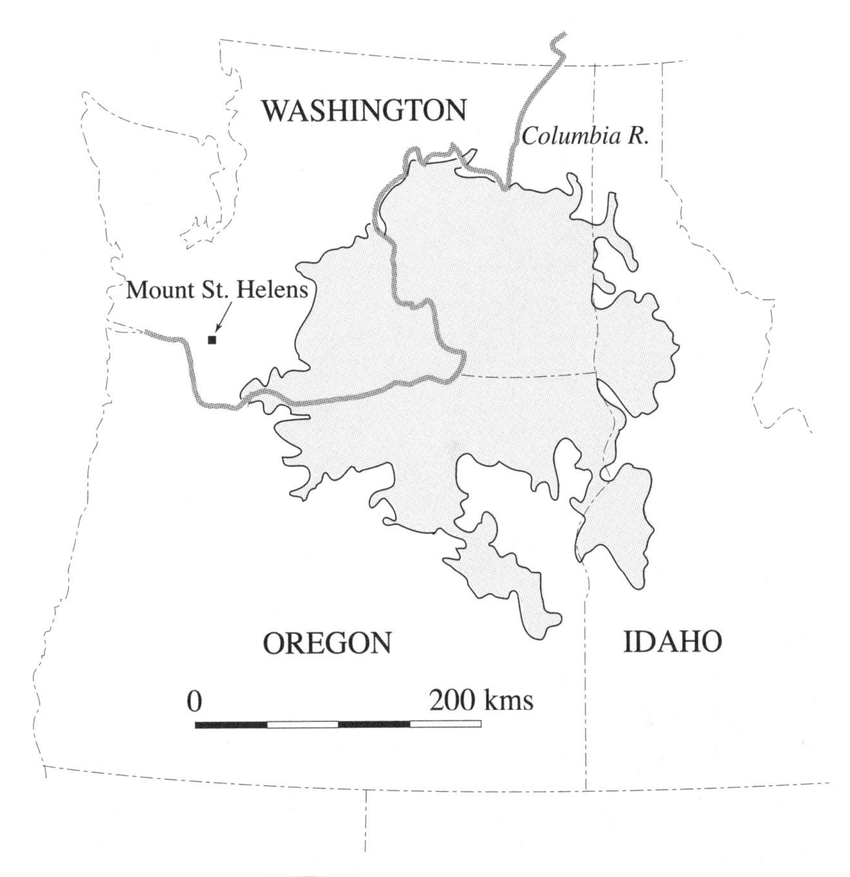

Figure 5-9. Basalt in the Columbia River volcanic field (shaded) was erupted between 13 and 17 million years ago.

Basaltic lava is vented to the surface at about 1200°C; by the time it cools to 900°C, within a matter of minutes to a few weeks at most, the basalt is completely solid. (It may remain too hot to touch for many years.) When the rock begins to solidify, innumerable tiny seed crystals appear throughout its mass. As each crystal grows larger, it competes for more material with about the same degree of success as its neighbors. The end result is a rock so uniformly fine-grained that individual crystals can be distinguished only under a microscope. Indeed, a fine-grained texture is the chief characteristic of volcanic, or extrusive igneous rocks in general. In some basalts, a more complicated texture consists of large crystals, commonly of olivine, embedded in a matrix of fine crystals. A possibility is that this rock crystallized in two stages, the first stage being slow cooling at depth in the earth which provided ample time for the olivine crystals to grow large.

Basaltic lava chills quickly once it reaches the surface. A pliable glassy skin congeals, while the lava inside is still liquid. As the liquid part continues to move along, the smooth skin wrinkles into a corrugated surface forming *pahoehoe* (pah-hoy-hoy) lava. In an underwater extrusion, it is common for the interior liquid to squeeze through a breach in the skin and form a new pahoehoe "toe." Toe after toe may break loose, and these soft bags of lava may tumble downslope, forming lava *pillows* (Figure 5-10).

If liquid pahoehoe lava is severely stretched, for example by flowing over a cascade, it may lose its dissolved gases and abruptly convert into a jagged, clinkery form known as *aa* (ah-ah). Pahoehoe and aa are words inherited from the language of the native Hawaiians. What does a barefoot Hawaiian say as he clambers across aa lava? "Ah, ah, AH, *AH*!"

Volcanic landforms We have seen that the mineral composition of an extrusive igneous rock determines the viscosity of the magma, and consequently how much water may be trapped inside. This can lead to such extremes of behavior that viscosity becomes a natural basis for describing volcanic eruptions.

Basalt that forms extensive lava sheets may pour forth quietly across the countryside, flooding stream valleys and plains, and devastating the works of mankind. Although the encroaching lava flow

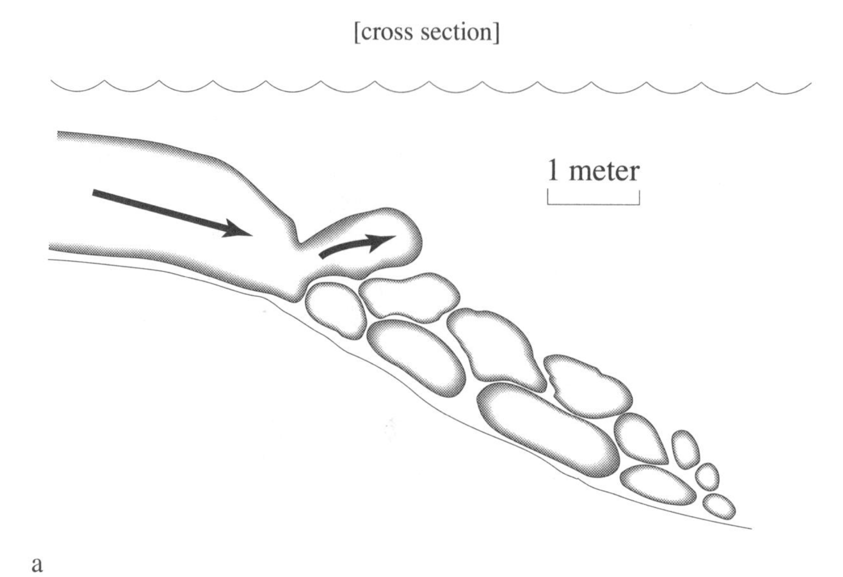

a

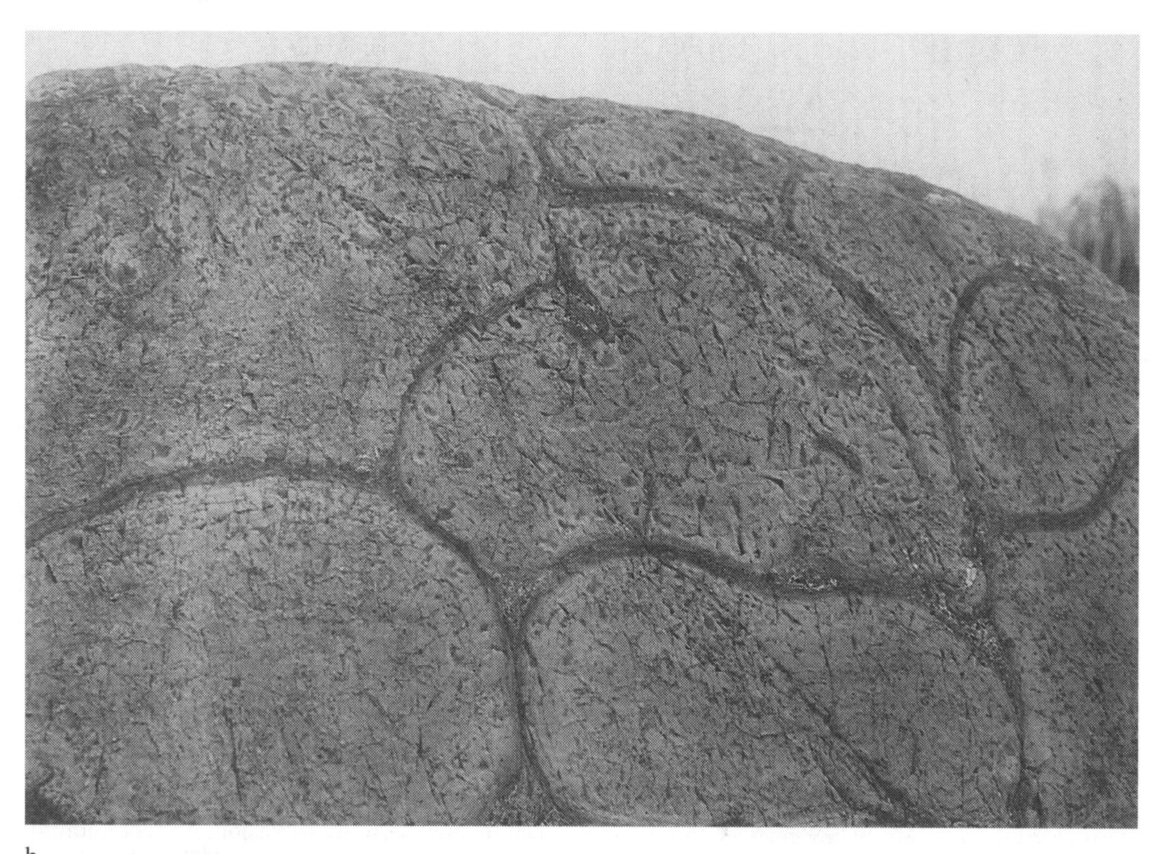

b

Figure 5-10. Lava pillows, typically about the size of a very large bed pillow, indicate underwater eruption. (*a*) Sketch of pillows forming; (*b*) photograph of pillows, showing rinds that formed when the hot lava was chilled against cold water. [*Photograph from Geological Survey of Canada, Ottawa.*]

cannot be easily stopped or diverted, at least people have ample opportunity to get out of its way. From time to time, the basalt from a given source may come up through different sets of fissures. Solidified lava in a more recently active fissure would cut across the previously deposited lava flows (Figure 5-11), forming a transecting sheetlike body, or *dike*. Here we have another useful way to tell the sequence of

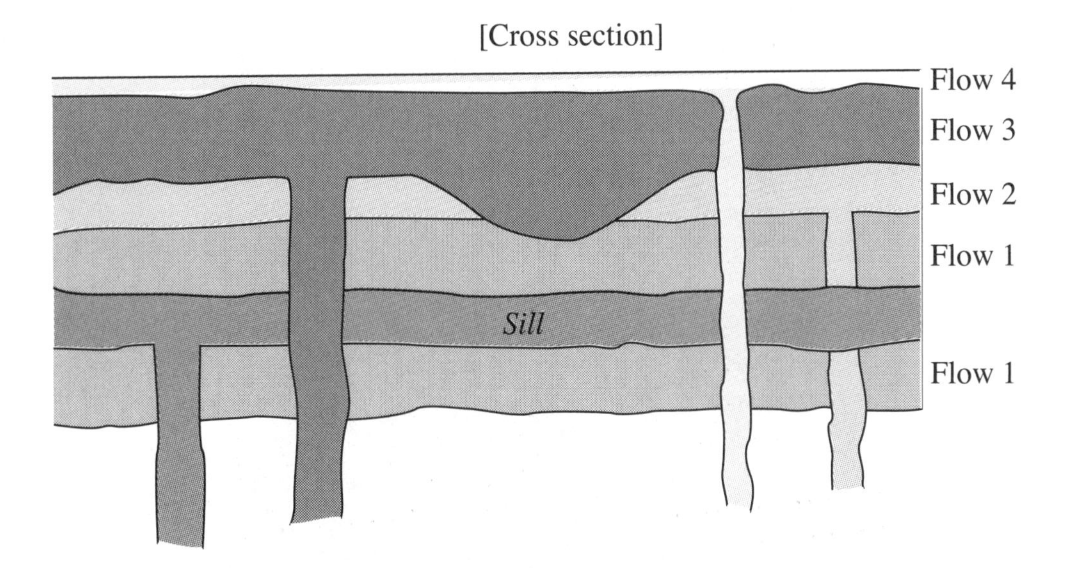

Figure 5-11. Many volcanic fields are complicated mazes of lava flows laced by dikes that were once conduits that fed lava upward to flows higher in the sequence. This cross section suggests that a long time interval elapsed after flow 2 was deposited. During this period, erosion carved a stream drainage on the land surface. Later the stream was disrupted by being filled with lava. *S* denotes a sill.

geologic events, thanks to the *law of crosscutting relationships* which states that *a rock body is older than another body that cuts through it.*

During its ascent, the magma might encounter a buried surface such as the contact between two strata. If the magma is injected along such a contact, it forms another type of sheetlike igneous body, a *sill.* Dikes and sills are similar except that a dike crosscuts the local structure, whereas a sill runs parallel to it. (A dike does not have to be vertical, nor is a sill necessarily horizontal.) A sill may look deceptively like just another lava flow when in fact it is younger than the flows both above and below it.

In some places basalt may erupt from fissures that continue to pour forth lava for a very long time. Thick, lens-shaped piles of lava whose gentle slopes are no steeper than a few degrees accumulate as *shield volcanoes* (Figure 5-12). Eruptions of the active Hawaiian shield volcanoes, Kilauea and Mauna Loa, come from long continuous rifts, sometimes from near the summit and at other times farther down on the flanks. These volcanoes are built of thousands of individual flows, each only a few meters thick.

Kilauea has become a classic locality for volcanic studies, thanks to the activities of the Hawaiian Volcano Observatory operated by the U. S. Geological Survey. At the summit of the volcano is an oval-shaped depression about 3 by 4 kilometers across and up to 400 meters deep (Figure 5-13). This large *caldera* is evidently a collapse feature formed by the withdrawal of magma from below. At times the caldera of Kilauea holds a seething, rising and falling lake of lava. Occasionally the lava spurts high as fountains or "curtains of fire." In spite of their spectacular appearance, the lava fountains do not pose an explosion hazard.

Careful measurements show that Kilauea inflates gradually before an eruption, then deflates rapidly when the lava erupts or drains back out of the caldera. The top of Kilauea is a surveyor's nightmare; reference marks may shift horizontally and vertically by as much as 0.1 meter (3 or 4 inches) from year

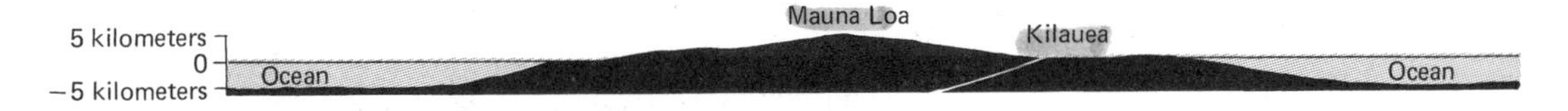

Figure 5-12. A profile through Hawaii, without vertical exaggeration, shows the gentle slopes of shield volcanoes that have merged together to form the island. Most of the volcanic mass is below sea level. [*Source: Fred M. Bullard,* Volcanoes of the Earth, *2nd revised edition, copyright © 1984. Reprinted by permission of the author and The University of Texas Press.*]

Figure 5-13. Incandescent lava spurts upward through a lava lake in Halemaumau, a deep pit within the caldera of Kilauea. The wall in the background is constructed of numerous thin, solidified lava flows. [*From Willie T. Kinoshita, Robert Y. Koyanagi, Thomas L. Wright, and Richard S. Fiske, "Kilauea Volcano: The 1967-68 Summit Eruption,"* Science, *vol. 166, no. 3904, 1969. Copyright 1969 by the American Association for the Advancement of Science*.]

to year. These observations can be described by a mathematical model that postulates the filling and emptying of a reservoir that lies a few kilometers below the summit. Movement of magma is accompanied by small earthquakes whose positions can be located accurately. Numerous observations of the quakes enabled geologists to plot the "plumbing system" of lava conduits leading up to the surface (Figure 5-14). Indirect evidence shows that the lava does not originate inside the volcano, but rather that the magma was "sweated out" of rocks located a much deeper 30 to 50 kilometers (30 miles) below the surface.

Lava that is richer in silica does not flow like basalt. A contrasting action of lava is illustrated at Stromboli, located between Sicily and mainland Italy (Figure 5-15), which is one of the few volcanoes that sustains a constant, mild eruption. Strombolian lava is puffed out as showers of thick, pasty clots accompanied by a dense cloud of white steam. At the summit of Stromboli is a *crater*, a volcanic depression that differs in size and origin from a caldera. A crater is simply a bowl surrounding the vent through which the material is erupted, and as such it is rarely more than 1 kilometer across, in contrast to a caldera which may be up to 30 kilometers or more in diameter. A crater forms as rock is blown out of the bottom and piles up on the rim. A caldera forms as the floor sinks.

Vulcano, though located only 50 kilometers from Stromboli (Figure 5-15), exhibits another long step in the direction of explosive violence. Vulcano does not clear its throat constantly; instead, the pressure builds up in the blocked throat until a series of major explosions hurls aloft ominous black clouds of hot, already solidified particles—dust, volcanic ash, and chunks of pumice. Torrential thunderstorms often accompany these eruptions of pyroclastic material, probably because the fine dust particles are able to "seed" the condensing raindrops. Once cleared, the vent may send forth a great volume of lava.

One of the most famous of all eruptions was the A.D. 79 outburst of another Italian volcano, Mount Vesuvius (Figure 5-15). The coastal town of Pompeii at the foot of Vesuvius was plunged into complete darkness for three days. An avalanche of mud, locally exceeding 20 meters in thickness, caused more destruction in the nearby community of Herculaneum than did the fall of ash directly from the sky at Pompeii. The mud flows consisted of tuff that, although of volcanic origin, had been reworked into mud by an intense storm.

Fortunately an even more destructive type of eruption is a rare event. For years, geologists had puzzled over the origin of certain widespread layers of volcanic rock that differ considerably from basalt flows. The rocks in question, *rhyolite*, consist mostly of light-colored minerals, especially feldspar and

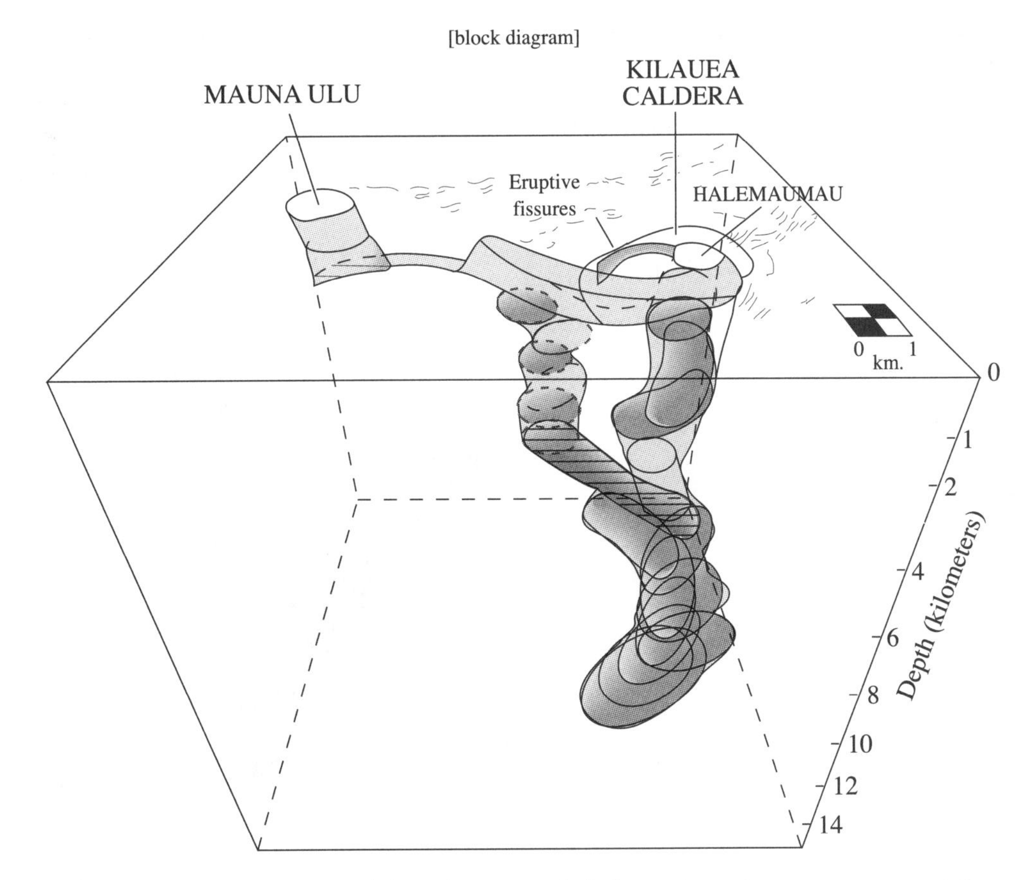

Figure 5-14. Beneath Hawaii a conduit snakes upward, forks, and continues on to vents at the surface. In this block perspective view toward the south, the passageway is pictured by stacked horizontal slices. Figure 5-13 is a photograph of the pit of Halemaumau. [*After Michael P. Ryan, Robert Y. Koyanagi, and Richard S. Fiske, "Modeling the Three-Dimensional Structure of Macroscopic Magma Transport Systems: Application to Kilauea Volcano, Hawaii,"* Journal of Geophysical Research, *vol. B8, p. 7120, 1981. Copyright by American Geophysical Union.*]

quartz. Many deposits contain flattened pumice fragments and tiny fragments of glass that have been compacted and welded into a solid mass. Up to this point, the only known extrusive rocks in which feldspar and quartz predominate were viscous domes or spine-like plugs. How, then, could a single sheet, like one in Mexico and west Texas, come to extend across 10,000 square kilometers?

The first clue to this intriguing problem came with astonishing ferocity in Martinique, a Caribbean island. At the northern end of the island stands Mount Pelée, whose slumber for hundreds of years had been punctuated by only two minor eruptions. On May 8, 1902, renewed eruption culminated in a series of four deafening explosions that hurled out a cloud of glowing fragments entrained in superheated steam. Traveling downslope at 150 kilometers per hour, the cloud instantly wiped out 30,000 lives in a city at the base. These widespread sheets thus did not travel as liquid flows, but rather as a surge of "fluidized" material which clings to the earth (Figure 5-16). The hot fragments release dissolved steam and thus remain suspended as they rush on and on for many kilometers unless they encounter a high topographic barrier. The great plateau in western Mexico, mentioned above, is the world's largest continuous exposure of *ignimbrite* ("shower of fire"), the result of this kind of eruption.

Intrusive Igneous Rocks

Not all magma reaches the earth's surface. A second category, *intrusive* igneous rock, crystallized at depths of from several hundred meters to as much as 20 or 30 kilometers (20 miles). The magma was intruded, or injected, into its surroundings which are called the *host* rock. Intrusive rocks that crystallized at even greater depths never show up at the surface except for rare "foreign" pieces sent up in volcanic

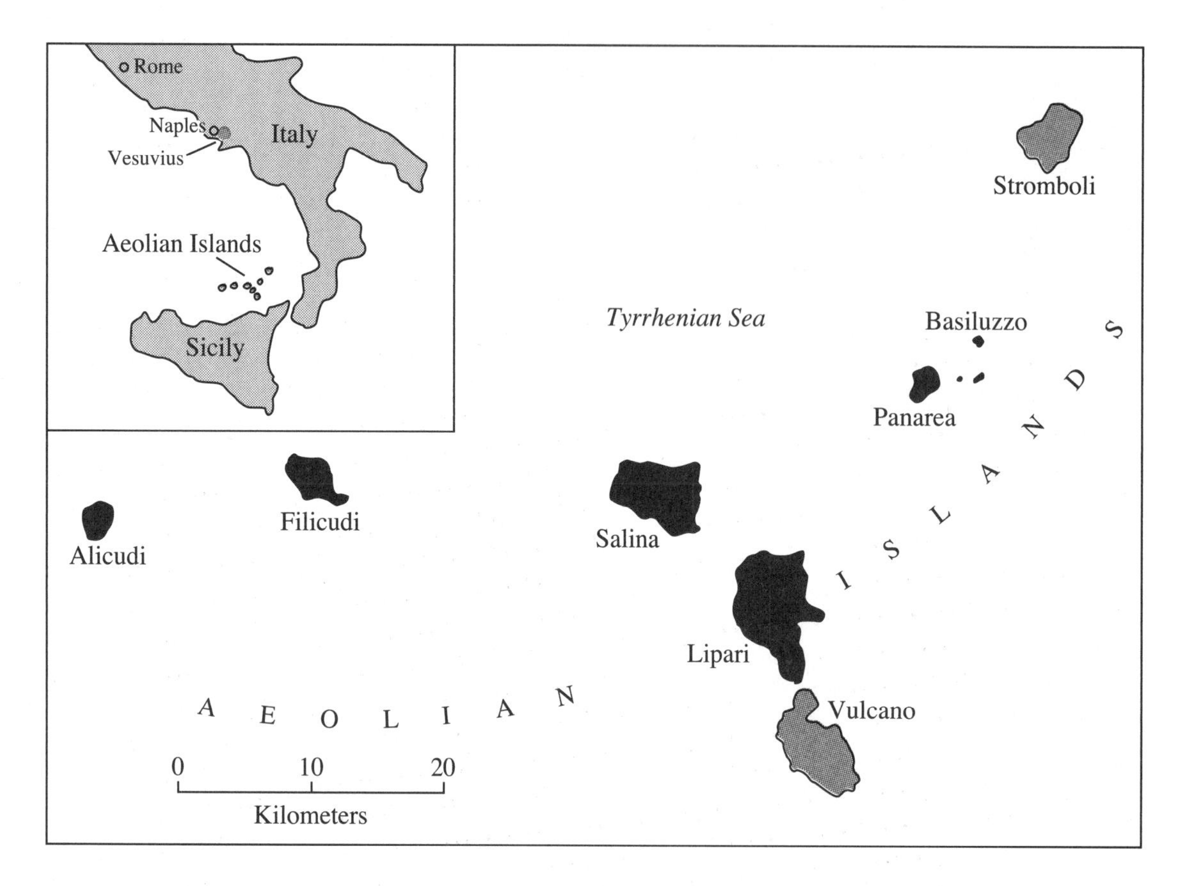

Figure 5-15. Locations of Stromboli, Vulcano, and Vesuvius. Stromboli has erupted continuously for at least the past 25 centuries. [*Source: Fred M. Bullard,* Volcanoes of the Earth, *2nd revised edition, copyright © 1984. Reprinted by permission of the author and The University of Texas Press.*]

conduits. Intrusive rocks originate in a part of the earth never observed by man, a region from which heat escapes only very slowly. Calculations suggest that it takes millions of years for a large mass of intrusive magma to cool. This exceedingly prolonged period of crystallization in such an inaccessible environment makes intrusive rocks difficult to study.

Textures of intrusive igneous rocks are an outcome of their very slow cooling. You recall that during the quick chilling of liquid basalt, numerous tiny crystals form together, all at once. During the leisurely cooling of intrusive rocks there is opportunity for the first few seed crystals to grow large and to anneal together forming even fewer but larger crystals. Thus the presence of large crystals is characteristic of intrusive rocks.

Granite and granodiorite For years the origin of the two most common intrusive rocks, *granite* and *granodiorite,* has been vigorously debated. Granite consists of quartz, potassium (K) feldspar, and a smaller abundance of plagioclase feldspar rich in sodium (Na). Scattered crystals of biotite, muscovite, or hornblende may also be common. (Refer to Chapter 3 for a review of the structures and compositions of these minerals.) Granodiorite differs only slightly; it contains more plagioclase than K feldspar and is somewhat richer in the dark, ferromagnesian minerals. In general, though, both of these rock types are light-colored and of moderate density (about 2.7 grams/cm^3). Granite and granodiorite are *felsic* igneous rocks, rich in feldspar ("fel") and quartz ("sic," for silica).

These two types of rock make up major portions of the continents, especially where deep-seated forces have crumpled the rocks into mountain ranges. Enormous masses of granite and granodiorite, *batholiths,* are scattered around the margins of the Pacific Ocean (Figure 5-17). They are the largest nearly homogeneous bodies of rock accessible to humans. The Canadian Coast Range batholith, for example, is the area of Kansas or Minnesota. Batholiths are located not only in mountainous regions, but also in vast low-lying areas that were once mountains but which, after millions of years, have been eroded down almost to sea level. Ocean basins are nearly devoid of granite and related intrusive rocks.

Figure 5-16. In 1968, Mayon Volcano, Philippines, one of the world's most symmetrical cones, sustained a series of explosive Peléan-type eruptions. The vertically rising cloud is condensed steam; the angry dark cloud beneath is a tempestuous avalanche of hot fragments surging downslope at speeds up to 50 meters per second. As usual, these eruptions were accompanied by spectacular lightning strikes and violent thunderstorms. [*Bernardo Tolentino, Photography SIX-SIS Studio, Legaspi City, Albay, Philippines.*]

Origin of Granite After two centuries of investigation and debate, geologists are still considering new possibilities for the origin of granite magma, and its style of emplacement into the crust. Field observations indicate that granite batholiths must have formed at considerable depth. It can be established that thousands of meters of overlying rock have been eroded off the tops of some batholiths, while the yet uneroded part of the batholith must extend downward at least several additional kilometers.

In many batholiths the granite cuts abruptly across the surrounding host rock (Figure 5-18) suggesting that it had remained rigid even while being strongly heated by the invading magma. Relationships

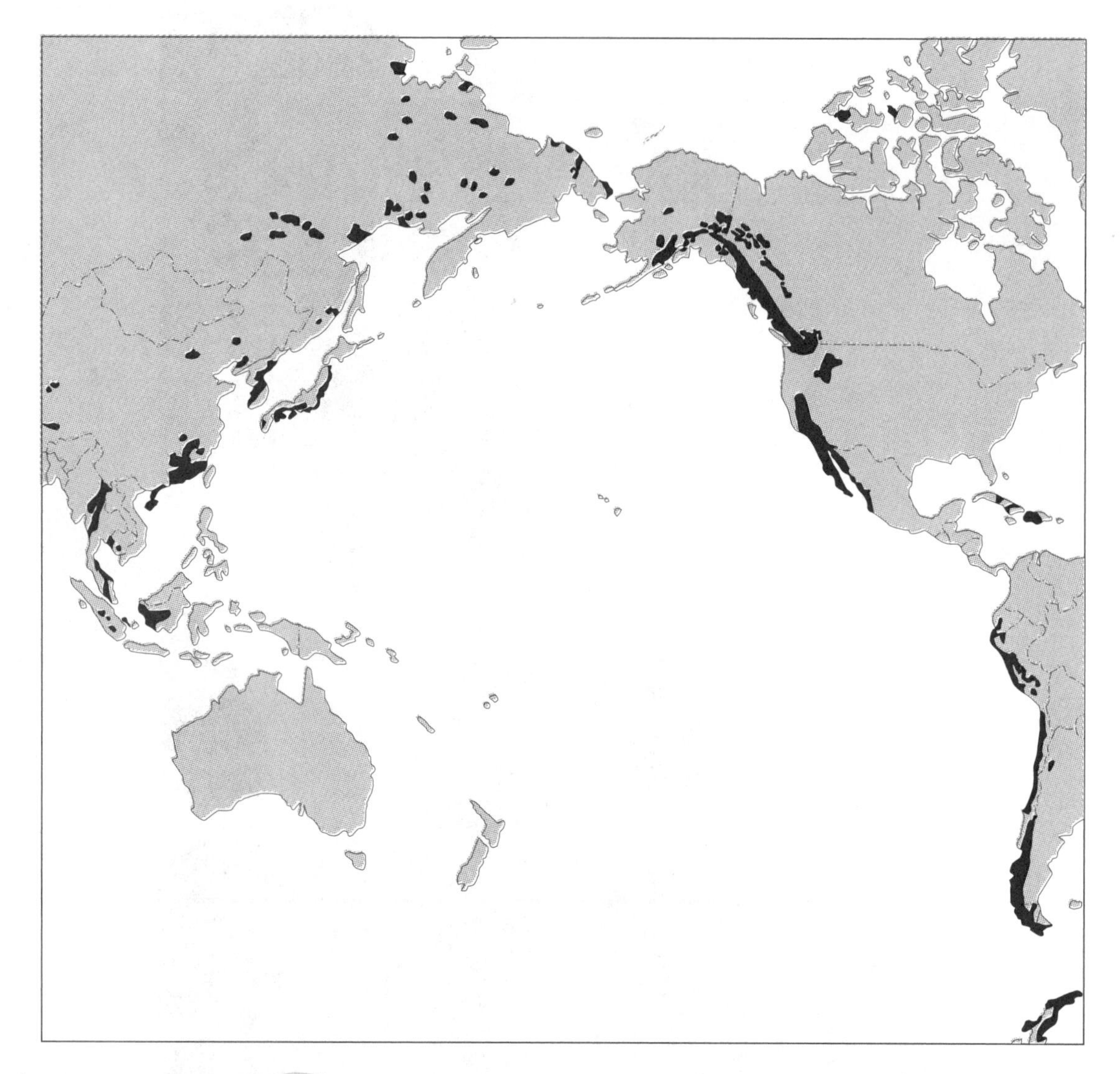

Figure 5-17. The batholiths (in black) that are marginal to the Pacific Ocean originated within the past 200 million years. Compare the distribution of batholiths to the distribution of active volcanoes (Figure 5-3). Could the batholiths, the volcanoes, and the Pacific Ocean itself be united in a common origin? [*After Paul C. Bateman and Jerry P. Eaton, "Sierra Nevada Batholith,"* Science, *vol. 158, no. 3807, 1967. Copyright 1967 by the American Association for the Advancement of Science.*]

at the borders of other batholiths are not as simple. Indistinct margins of these bodies gradually progress from host rock, into rock that appears increasingly granite-like, and finally into unmistakable granite. In some places the rock has become a curious "half-and-half" mixture of contorted host rock saturated with layers and stringers of granite (Figure 5-19). This granite must have remained more or less in the same spot where it formed, as though the local host rock had partially melted to form granitic liquid.

How then is granite magma generated in nature? An obvious way is simply to melt older granite, making new magma. Another possibility is by melting some other rock, such as certain types of sandstone or shale, that have the same chemical composition as granite. Thousands of experiments with artificially-made granite magma have shown yet other, more subtle ways to create this familiar igneous rock. As noted above, granite is a felsic rock, rich in quartz and feldspar, in contrast to basalt which is a mafic rock, rich in ferromagnesian minerals. Suppose that we progressively heat a rock consisting of an assortment of felsic and mafic minerals. Experiments show that different mineral species in this mixture do not all melt at the same time or temperature. The composition of the first-formed liquid is not average rock, but instead it is richer in felsic (granitic) constituents. Only if the rock were totally melted would the liquid have the same composition as the original solid material.

Figure 5-18. This intrusive, light-colored granite in Manitoba exhibits a sharp contact where it has invaded the dark-colored basalt host rock.

Figure 5-19. Pods or thin layers of granite (light-colored) are intimately mixed with the host rock in this outcrop in Manitoba. Both rock types are contorted, as though squeezed like toothpaste while in a plastic condition. The helmet indicates the scale of the photograph.

In view of this, we see that granite magma could result from partial melting of many of the earth's common rocks. Suppose that just a small fraction of a mass of some other rock, even a mafic rock such as basalt, were melted and the liquid drained away. The early-formed liquid would be more like granite, and if this liquid were to crystallize into mafic and felsic minerals, then be partially melted again, the next-generation liquid would become even more felsic. Another possibility is to start with a large body of totally liquid magma. During cooling, the first-formed crystals will consist of mafic minerals, and as these dense crystals sink to the floor of the magma chamber, the remaining liquid would become enriched in silica, aluminum, potassium, and sodium, which are felsic constituents of granite. Whether by partial melting and separation of early-formed liquid, or by partial crystallization and separation of early-formed crystals, the result is the same—to separate the mafic constituents from the felsic constituents of a rock. It is a process of *igneous differentiation* that when repeated many times can produce a great variety of igneous rock types.

In Chapter 2 we saw how differentiation caused partitioning of the whole earth into crust, mantle, and core. When regions of the mantle have partially melted, low-density magma rose toward the surface where it crystallized, forming the crust. In this sense the granitic crust is the "daughter" of the mafic mantle. Differentiation of a pocket of magma within the crust acts in a similar manner. Melting and differentiation can occur on many scales, whether by local partial melting that permeates a rock with streaks and lenses of granitic magma, or whether blobs of magma have coalesced into a huge mass of batholithic scale. Where granite magma invades high into the crust, there is a sharp contrast between liquid magma that breaks cleanly across strong, brittle host rock as seen in Figure 5-18. Granitic magma that is emplaced into a deeper, hotter zone would tend to permeate and become deformed along with the somewhat softened host rock. The observed style of granite behavior would vary according to the depth in the crust exposed by erosion at a particular place.

MAKING MAGMA

If igneous rocks have crystallized from melted material, then what process would have caused melting to occur in the first place? In Chapter 16 we shall note seismic evidence that the earth's mantle and crust are almost entirely solid; there is no large reservoir of ready-made liquid waiting to be tapped, and so magma originates only by melting something originally a solid. One obvious way to do this is to raise its temperature, but additional considerations are important. High *temperature* plays a role in melting but so does *pressure*. As temperature rises, the atoms in a crystal vibrate with more energy, eventually to the point of breaking chemical bonds, and the solid has melted. The same atoms, now at higher energy in the liquid state, occupy a larger volume. Conversely, if atoms in the liquid were forced closer together under high pressure, the liquid would freeze into a mass of crystals occupying a smaller volume. Thus, raising the temperature has an effect opposite to raising the pressure. Deeper in the earth the temperature is higher, promoting melting, but the pressure is also higher, inhibiting melting.

Consider a plot of temperature (horizontal axis) *vs.* pressure (vertical axis) or corresponding depth in the earth (Figure 5-20). Suppose that a material melts at temperature T_1 under low-pressure conditions (P_1) at the earth's surface. At depth (P_2), the same material melts at a higher temperature T_2, more thermal energy being required to expand the liquid against the confining effect of pressure. A deeply buried solid melts either with rising temperature at constant pressure (horizontal arrow), with diminishing pressure at constant temperature (vertical arrow), or by a combination of these P-T changes. Melting would occur, even at constant temperature, if internal movements were to bring mantle material up to more shallow depth, in the process of *decompression melting*.

Finally, a third way to induce melting is by *adding water* to a material. H_2O, the great promoter of chemical reactions, has a unique power to break chemical bonds. It acts as a flux, lowering the temperature of melting. In another chapter we shall note a means by which to drag water down into the mantle.

SUMMARY

Geologists conduct studies in the field where they make systematic observations of the natural situation, supplemented by laboratory simulations of geologic processes. Rocks are classified according to their manner of origin, and one type of rock may be transformed into another by processes of recycling. Cosmic matter consists of meteorites. Igneous rocks originated from magma, which typically consists of

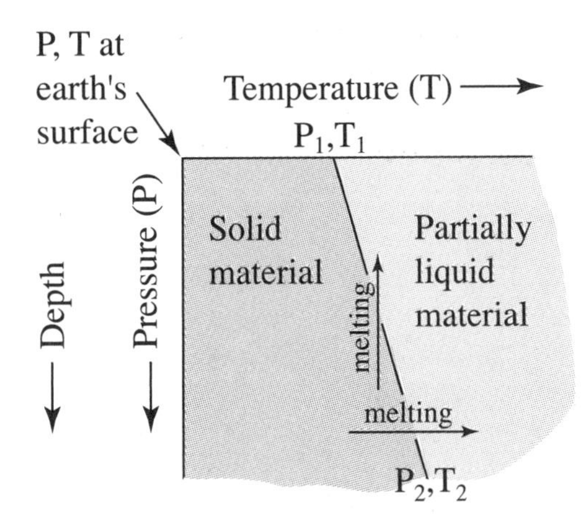

Figure 5-20. When heated through the melting temperature, all of a simple, solid chemical compound (or mineral) would transform into liquid. During heating of a rock that consists of several mineral species, the melting temperature refers only to the *beginning* of melting, and the temperature must rise considerably higher to achieve complete melting. Effects of pressure and temperature upon melting are made even more complicated by addition of H_2O to the rock which is not considered in this diagram.

crystals suspended in melted silicate material, also containing dissolved fluids. Magma that breaks through the land surface, or into a body of water, solidifies rapidly as fine-grained extrusive igneous rock. Magma that crystallizes slowly, at depth beneath the earth's surface forms coarse-grained intrusive igneous rock. Texture refers to the sizes, shapes, and arrangements of mineral grains in an igneous rock.

Variations in the style of volcanic eruption depend upon the geologic environment and composition of the magma. Silica-rich magma tends to be highly viscous, hence able to trap dissolved H_2O whose sudden release is responsible for explosive eruption. Less viscous silica-poor magma, containing a smaller abundance of volatile constituents, erupts more quietly.

The most abundant extrusive igneous rock is fine-grained, dark, dense basalt, a product generally of quiet eruption, which comprises the floor of the world ocean and occupies substantial areas of the continental surface. Basalt consists chiefly of pyroxene and Ca plagioclase feldspar. Basaltic liquid forms widespread sheets and builds shield volcanoes having gentle slopes. Rhyolitic eruptions may also form sheets, not by flow of liquid as basalt does, but by expulsion of hot particles buoyed in fluid suspension by release of dissolved H_2O.

Igneous land forms and structures include dikes (crosscutting tabular bodies) and sills (tabular bodies parallel to local structure), craters (bowls surrounding a volcanic vent) and calderas (large areas that have subsided due to withdrawal of magma from below).

The most abundant intrusive igneous rock is light-colored, coarse-grained granite, a rock of moderate density. Granite consists chiefly of K feldspar, Na plagioclase feldspar, and quartz, accompanied by minor abundances of muscovite, biotite, or other ferromagnesian minerals. Batholiths are bodies of hundreds to thousands of cubic kilometers of granitic rock which commonly form in regions experiencing mountain uplift.

Granitic magma may result from melting of rocks whose composition is similar to that of granite, or by igneous differentiation. Differentiation may occur by separation of a partial melt, in which the first melt to form is more granite-like than the original rock, or it may occur by removal of crystals from magma, in which the crystals are less granite-like than the original magma. In either case, many such steps of differentiation are required to create granitic continental crust from its ultimate source, mantle rocks.

Magma forms only by melting of some pre-existing solid material. Melting is induced by raising the temperature, but a deeply buried rock can melt by reduction of confining pressure, a process of decompression melting, the latter accomplished by moving material from greater depth to more shallow depth. Addition of H_2O lowers the temperature of melting by acting as a flux (breaker of chemical bonds).

6

Igneous Rocks

INTRODUCTION

Igneous rocks are produced when melted rock material, called **magma**, solidifies. The term "igneous" comes from the Latin word *ignis*, meaning fire, and implies that heat is needed to create magma. Typically some suspended crystals and dissolved gases are also present in the molten rock material. **Lava** is magma that flows out onto the earth's surface.

Igneous rocks are the most abundant type in the earth's crust. They comprise about 80 percent of the volume of continents, and over 95 percent of the oceanic crust. In North America an old, largely igneous terrain called the Canadian Shield crops out over 5 million square kilometers (2 million square miles). About 0.5 million square kilometers of the U.S. Pacific Northwest have been covered by lava flows of the Columbia Plateau. Most large continental mountain ranges contain considerable igneous material and some, such as the Sierra Nevada and the Cascade Range, are almost entirely igneous. So are nearly all of the world's oceanic islands.

Whether the formation of igneous rocks is gentle and slow, or violent and swift, it always involves the solidification of magma. The considerable amounts of heat needed to produce magma may originate from several diverse sources. Chief among them is the decay of radioactive isotopes, always an energy-releasing process. Part of the earth's internal heat is original, retained since the time of its accumulation 4.55 billion years ago. More heat was produced soon after accumulation when dense material sank to the center of the earth, forming its core. Some heat is generated by tidal force, by which gravitational interaction with the Moon causes the solid earth to flex back and forth.

Whatever the source of heat, the resulting magma eventually cools and crystallizes into a solid igneous rock that is composed typically of several different mineral species. In fact, the magma has *frozen*, at a very high temperature. Unlike the freezing of a single, simple substance such as H_2O ice, a complex igneous melt does not crystallize suddenly, nor at a single temperature. One of the constituent minerals will crystallize earliest, then the others sequentially as the temperature drops. Factors that influence the temperature and the sequence of crystallization include pressure, the amount of H_2O dissolved in the melt, and the overall chemical composition of the magma. Crystallization of magma is a complicated subject still under intense investigation by petrologists, who are specialists in igneous rocks.

Notwithstanding all this, we may employ a simple guideline known as Bowen's Reaction Series (Figure 6-1) in honor of the pioneering experimental work of the igneous petrologist, N. L. Bowen. If a magma contains sufficient iron and magnesium for ferromagnesian minerals to crystallize, we note that olivine crystallizes earlier, at a higher temperature. Augite, a member of the pyroxene family, tends to crystallize later at a lower temperature, but preceding the crystallization of hornblende (an amphibole), and so on down the line. We can determine this sequence by sampling lava at various stages while it is congealing, by observing the behavior of artificial magma under controlled conditions in the laboratory, and by examining the rock *texture* (the sizes, shapes, and arrangements of mineral grains). For example, early-formed pyroxene crystals may have been "eaten into" by reaction with the remaining magma, and the dissolved pyroxene re-precipitated as amphibole.

Magma composition is similar to the composition of the source rock being melted. Magma ascends into the ocean basins from melted portions of the mantle whose rock is dense, dark-colored, rich in ferromagnesian minerals. This magma, and the solid rock that crystallizes from it, are **mafic** ("ma" = magnesium and "f" = ferrous or ferric iron), or **ultramafic** (exceptionally mafic). The upper part of the continents consists of **felsic** rock rich in feldspar ("fel") and silica minerals ("si") such as quartz. Magma of intermediate composition is most commonly generated at the margins of continents where zones of melting may be both felsic and mafic.

According to Bowen's Reaction Series, calcium-rich plagioclase feldspar crystallizes at a higher temperature, and sodium plagioclase at a cooler temperature. Experiments show that for a magma of felsic composition, the minerals Na-plagioclase, K-feldspar, muscovite, and quartz, constituents of granite, tend to crystallize together over a narrow range of temperature. Keep in mind that Bowen's Reaction Series is *only a generalization* about magma behavior, to which there are exceptions. In a following chapter, we will use Bowen's Reaction Series to gain insight into the process of weathering.

In Figure 6-1, the upper box encompasses olivine, augite, and Ca-rich plagioclase feldspar, which are major minerals in basalt or gabbro. The lower box includes biotite mica, Na-rich plagioclase, K-feldspar, and quartz, the important minerals in rhyolite or granite (muscovite occurs in some of these rocks).

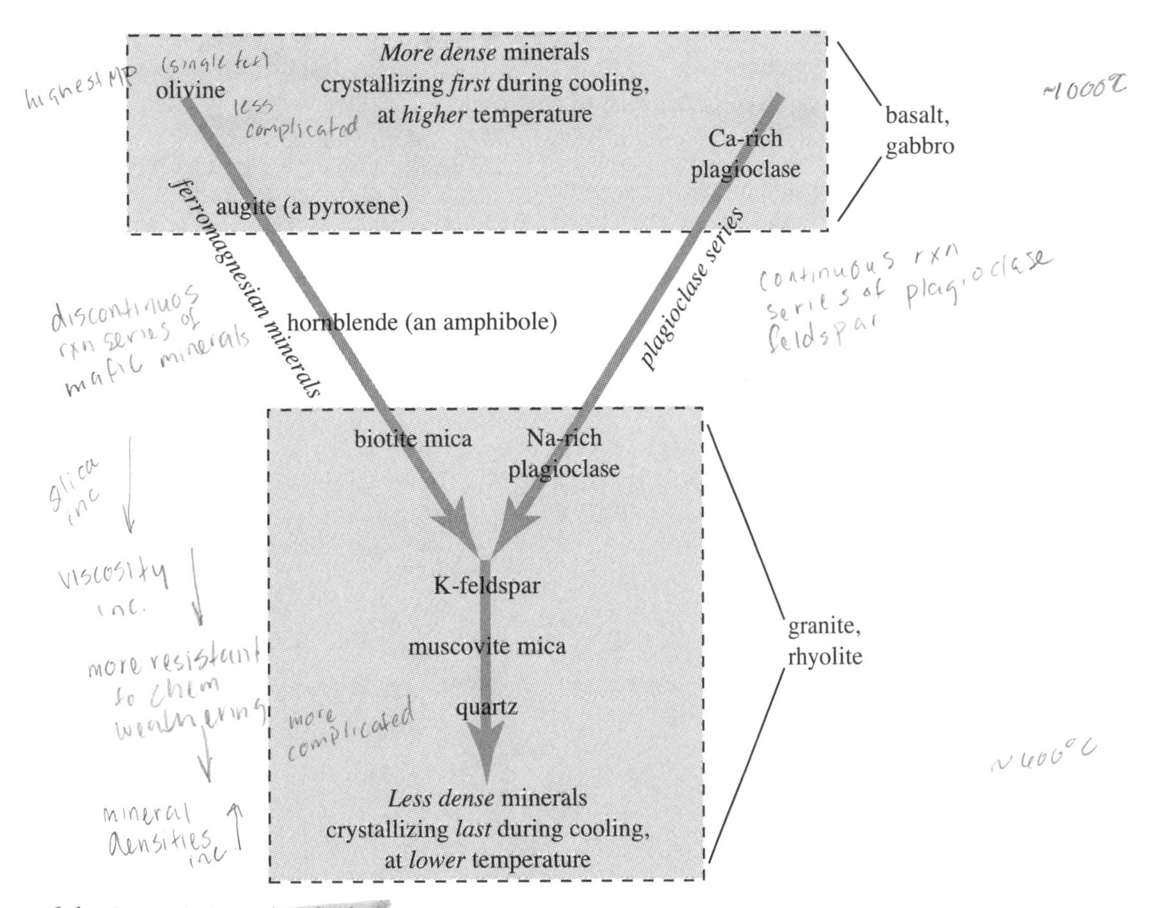

Figure 6-1. Bowen's Reaction Series

IGNEOUS ROCK TYPES

Igneous rocks are classified according to two aspects of their origin—the magma composition and where it solidifies. Table 6-1 on page 109 incorporates these two fundamental factors in designating common types of igneous rocks. Felsic rocks, originating in the continental crust, are at the extreme left, and rock types become progressively darker and more dense (more mafic) toward the right, to peridotite which is characteristic of the earth's mantle.

The vertical dimension of the chart organizes the information upon the basis of texture, especially the sizes of mineral crystals. The bottom two rows correspond to **plutonic** (intrusive) rocks, formed when magma solidifies below the earth's surface to produce mineral crystals large enough to see with the unaided eye. A relatively coarse texture indicates that these rocks had cooled deep in the earth, very slowly because heat is trapped by the insulating effect of rock overhead. Slow cooling permits large crystals to form, but there are other potential factors. In a **pegmatite**, in which huge crystals may be centimeters to meters across, growth is not only at depth but from a silicate magma charged with dissolved H_2O. Such magma is highly fluid (having low viscosity) permitting the ions to move easily through it. In effect, the growing crystals can "reach out" long distances to add material to themselves.

In the top three rows of the chart are named the **volcanic** (extrusive) rocks that solidify quickly on the earth's surface, and whose crystals are accordingly small. Indeed, **obsidian** and its frothy equivalent, **pumice**, have no crystals at all. **Tuff** is a fine-grained product of volcanism so explosive that the rock material has completely shattered. Tuff may be felsic to mafic, but it is chiefly felsic. A **porphyry** is an igneous texture in which a few larger crystals are set in a matrix of much smaller crystals. A plausible way to create porphyry is in two stages: first at depth during which the large crystals form slowly, then a quick ascent to the earth's surface where the remaining magma quenches quickly into a mass of finer crystals. Large crystals in a porphyry are called **phenocrysts**, which may be any of a variety of mineral species noted below.

- Rhyolite porphyry: quartz, or feldspar, or muscovite
- Dacite porphyry: biotite
- Andesite porphyry: amphibole or pyroxene
- Basalt porphyry: olivine, or pyroxene, or Ca plagioclase feldspar

Note that with a more mafic rock type, the phenocrysts themselves are more mafic.

Table 6-1. *Igneous Rock Classification*

	Felsic Rocks: light minerals predominate		Intermediate Rocks	Mafic Rocks: dark minerals predominate	Ultramafic Rock:

100%
75%
50%
25%
0%

K feldspar (pink or white)
quartz (colorless)
sodium-rich plagioclase (white)
plagioclase feldspar
calcium-rich plagioclase (gray)
hornblende (black)
augite (black to dark green)
olivine (olive green)
muscovite (transparent) or biotite (black)

IGNEOUS ROCK TEXTURE							
Volcanic	glassy		**obsidian**, **pumice** (vesicular)				
Volcanic	small crystals		**rhyolite**, **rhyolite tuff**	dacite	andesite, andesite tuff	**basalt**, **scoria** (vesicul.)	
Volcanic	both large and small crystals		rhyolite porphyry	dacite porphyry	**andesite porphyry**	basalt porphyry	
Plutonic	large crystals	syenite	**granite**	granodiorite	diorite	**gabbro**	**peridotite**
Plutonic	very large crystals		**granite pegmatite**				

Volcanic Rocks **Plutonic Rocks**

Rhyolite tuff breccia. (Photo by Gary Jacobson.)

◄ Chemical Equivalents ►

Granite.(Photo by Gary Jacobson.)

Andesite porphyry. (Photo by Gary Jacobson.)

◄ Chemical Equivalents ►

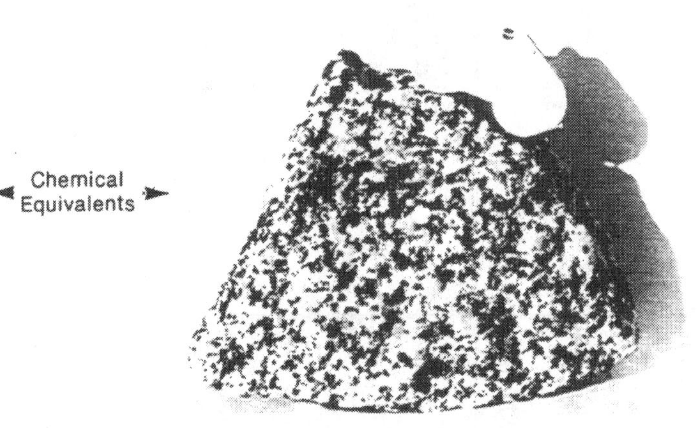

Diorite. (Photo by Gary Jacobson.)

Olivine basalt porphry. (Photo by Gary Jacobson.)

◄ Chemical Equivalents ►

Augite plagioclase gabbro. (Photo by Gary Jacobson.)

Photo 6-1. Igneous Rock Types

Plutonic Rock Bodies

Plutonic rocks occur as several types of intrusive bodies, categorized on the basis of their size, shape, and geometric relationship to rock present in the area prior to igneous invasion (country rock). The most common igneous bodies are:

- **Batholith**: large (> 100 km^2 exposed surface area) irregular shaped plutons with no known bottom.
- **Stock**: small batholith (< 100 km^2 exposed area).
- **Dike**: tabular (sheet-like) pluton that cuts across the structure of country rock.
- **Sill**: tabular pluton that is mostly parallel to the structure of country rock.
- **Laccolith**: sill with a domed upper surface that has deformed the overlying rock.

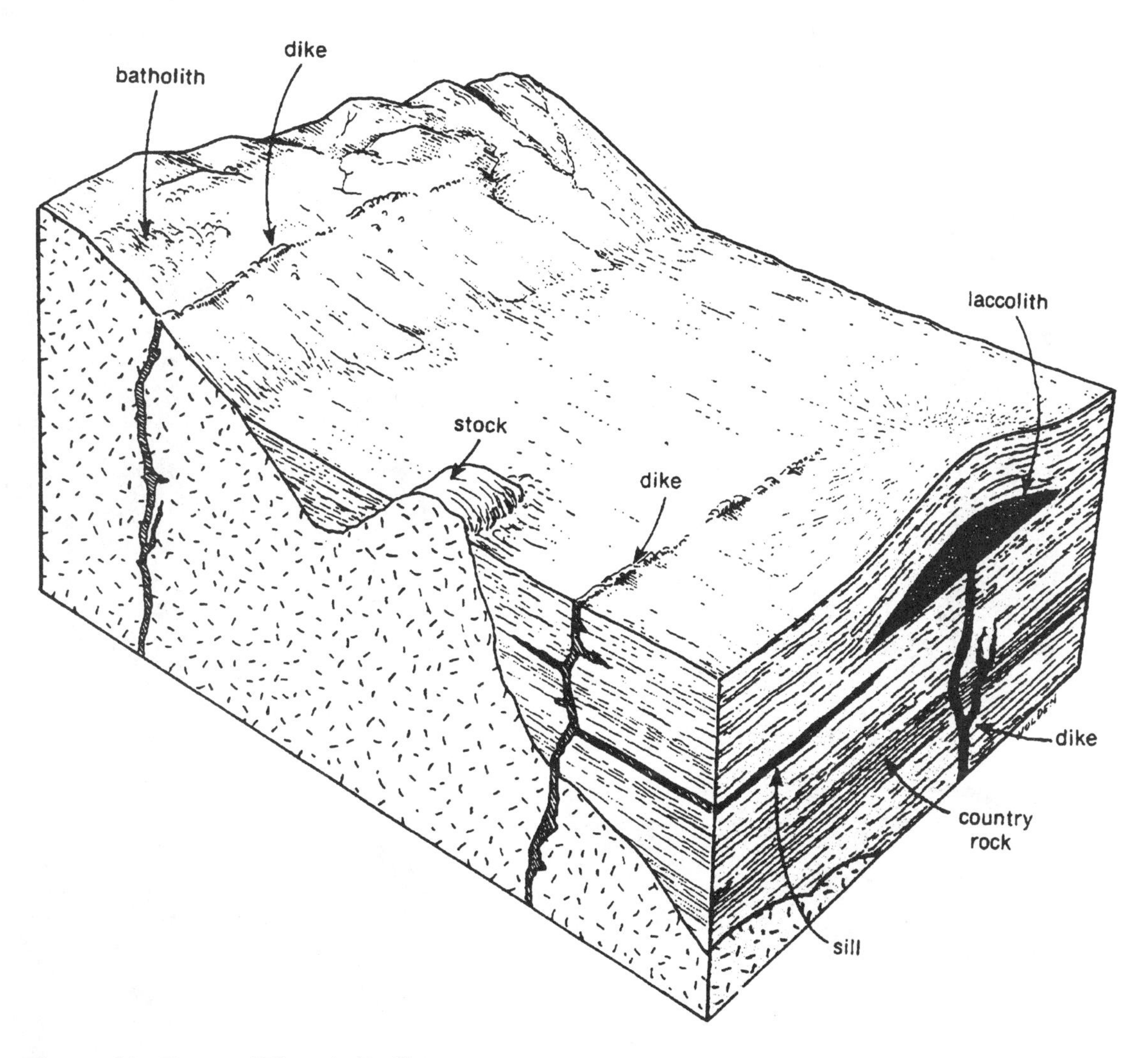

Figure 6-2. Types of Plutonic Bodies

A diabase sill has intruded between older sedimentary layers in the northern Rocky Mountains. (Photo by Shannon O'Dunn.)

The boulder of Colorado pegmatite shows large (.5m) crystals of muscovite and orthoclase. (Photo by Shannon O'Dunn.)

Massive columnar joints (columns to + 2m diameter) in exposed laccolith, Devil's Tower, WY. (Photo by Evans Winner.)

Resistant dike etched out of country rock, Colorado Rockies. (Photo by Shannon O'Dunn.)

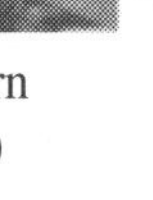

Expansion fractures (joints) in granodiorite, Southern California Batholith. (Photo by Shannon O'Dunn.)

Undigested country rock remnants (xenoliths) in granite, Southern California Batholith. (Photo by Shannon O'Dunn.)

Photo 6-2. Plutonic Rock Types and Bodies

Volcanic Landforms

Volcanic activity has created many famous mountains and dramatic terrains (Table 6-2). Most of these have developed where slabs of the earth's rigid outer shell (lithosphere) are pulling apart, colliding, or are moving slowly over localized hot spots in the mantle. Thus, we find extrusive igneous processes located in well-defined zones, such as the Pacific Ring of Fire and the Hawaiian Island chain.

Characteristics of various volcanic landforms are often determined by the type of magma extruded. Felsic magmas with considerable water content, generated where continental lithosphere melts, are associated with explosive volcanic events and the production of huge volumes of **pyroclastic** debris. Pyroclastic (fire-broken) is the term for magmatic materials that have been explosively ejected from a vent, and are partly or totally solidified before hitting the ground. Because larger amounts of ejected material statistically collect nearer the vent, tall cone-shaped *composite* volcanoes are formed as the pyroclastics alternate with lava flows.

Dry, low-viscosity mafic magmas originating in the upper mantle usually emerge quietly, and flow a long distance before solidifying. Flows are relatively thin, but areally extensive, and pyroclastic deposits are rare. Resulting landforms have a subdued profile. The cooling effect of sea water retards the spread of oceanic lava flows. Basalt lavas on land will first fill in topographic irregularities, and then continue to build great thicknesses of nearly horizontal flows called plateau basalts or *fissure flows*.

The classic shield shape of Mauna Loa rises above more frequently active Kilauea on Hawaii. (Photo by Shannon O'Dunn.)

Amboy Crater, a very young (2,000 to 6,000 yrs.) basalt cinder cone, Mojave Desert, California. (Photo by Chuck Monds.)

Columnar jointing in basalt lava flow, the Devil's Postpile, California. (Photo by Roland Brady.)

A wisp of smoke may be seen emerging from the summit of this active New Zealand composite cone. (Photo by Shannon O'Dunn.)

Photo 6-3. Volcanic Landforms

Table 6-2. *Volcanic Landforms*

	10 Km. Composite Volcano (*Stratovolcano*)	100 Km. Shield Volcano	> 100 Km. Fissure Flows
Angle of slope	Steep: 5° base, 30° summit	Shallow: 10° base, 2° summit	Shallow: ± 0°
Construction	Interlayered pyroclastic and flow material; surrounding landscape may have layers of tuff	Layers of flows, with minor pyroclastic material	Layers of flows
Rock type	Most commonly andesite	Basalt	Basalt
Viscosity	High	Low	Low
Volatile abundance	High	Low	Low
Explosive tendency	High	Low	Low
Examples	Large volcanoes in the Pacific Ring of Fire (Andes, Cascades, Japan, Philippines, etc.), and in the Mediterranean Sea area	Deep-ocean basin volcanoes (Hawaiian Islands, Iceland, Canary Islands, Galápagos Islands)	Columbia Plateau (northwestern US); localities in South America, India, Iceland, and Siberia

The symbols below are the conventional representations for rock types described in Chapters 6, 8, and 10. They will be used on maps, cross sections, and other diagrams throughout the remainder of the book.

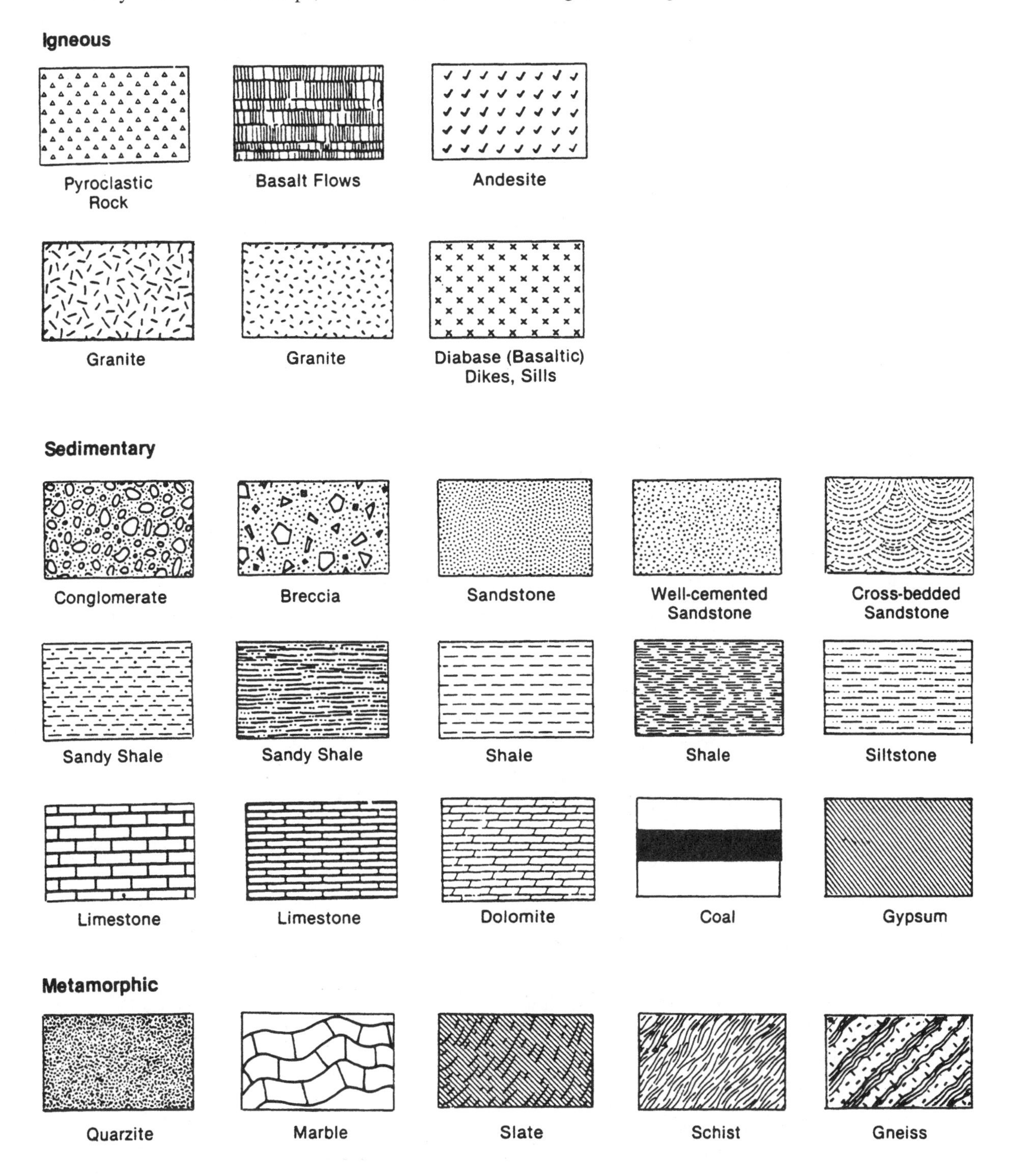

Figure 6-3. Rock Symbols

Igneous Rocks

- Formed by crystallization (or solidification) of melted material
- Molten material within the earth, MAGMA, cools to form PLUTONIC, or INTRUSIVE igneous rock.
- Molten material that emerges at the earth's surface, LAVA, cools to form VOLCANIC, or EXTRUSIVE igneous rock.

Some Definitions

- MAGMA: a combination of melted silicate material, volatiles, and possibly already solidified crystals
- VOLATILES: substances that are gases at low temperature, chiefly H_2O

Viscosity

- VISCOSITY: resistance of a substance to flow. Examples: pine sap (higher viscosity) *vs.* water (lower viscosity)
- Viscosity increases as the lava starts to cool.
- The more complex the silicates melted in the magma, the higher the viscosity (examples of complex mineral structures: quartz, orthoclase).

Classification of Igneous Rocks

- Classified by MINERAL COMPOSITION and TEXTURE
- BOWEN'S REACTION SERIES: (N. L. Bowen, 1911)

Bowen's Reaction Series

- Generalization about magma behavior and sequence of crystallization
- Silica tetrahedron: one silicon bound to 4 oxygens
- Continuous and Discontinuous Series
- Minerals crystallizing along the discontinuous series have distinctly different mineral structures (isolated, chain, double chain, sheet, framework).
- Olivine contains isolated SiO_4 tetrahedrons.
- Quartz is a framework silicate in which every tetrahedron is linked at its corners to four other tetrahedrons (every oxygen atom is shared).

Significance of Bowen's Series

- Minerals that crystallize first have higher melting points than minerals down the series.
- Complexity of silicate structures increases down the series.
- Viscosity of the magma increases down the series.
- Minerals lower down the series are more resistant to chemical weathering.
- Mineral densities decrease down the series.

Terms Related to Mineral Composition

Silicic?

- Felsic: igneous rocks rich in light-colored minerals such as orthoclase and quartz
- Intermediate: igneous rocks rich in minerals such as Na-Ca plagioclase and hornblende
- Mafic: igneous rocks rich in dark-colored ferromagnesian minerals (augite, hornblende) but with abundant plagioclase feldspar
- Ultramafic: igneous rocks composed chiefly of dark-colored ferromagnesian minerals, especially olivine and augite, with no plagioclase

Terms Related to Texture

- Crystal Size:
  - Fine-grained: less than 1mm
  - Medium-grained: 1-2 mm
  - Coarse-grained: larger than 2 mm
  - Pegmatitic: very coarse-grained, approx. 5cm to as large as a house
- Porphyry: igneous rock with large crystals (PHENOCRYSTS) set in a matrix of fine-grained crystals (GROUNDMASS)

Cooling History

- Absence of crystals (glassy) indicates extremely rapid cooling (quenching).
- Absence of crystals (frothy) indicates extremely rapid cooling with high dissolved gas content.
- Small crystals indicate rapid cooling.
- Large crystals indicate slow cooling.
- Pegmatitic texture indicates slow cooling in the presence of H_2O.
- Porphyritic texture indicates two distinct cooling histories: slowly at depth, then rapidly at the surface.

Igneous Landforms

- Plutonic rock body: sill, dike, batholith
- Volcanic landform: fissure flow, shield volcano, composite volcano
- Crater (constructional feature) (example: Mt. Rainier, Washington State)
- Caldera (destructional feature) (example: Crater Lake, Oregon)

Mafic Magma

- Mafic magma typically has a higher temperature than felsic magma.
- Higher-temperature magmas commonly have:
  - lower viscosity
  - lower volatile content
  - less explosive tendency (lava rather than pyroclastic material)

Volcanic Terms

- Pyroclastic rock: explosively erupted as hot but nevertheless solid particles
- Tuff: explosively erupted, fine-grained volcanic rock whose grains are commonly welded together
- Vesicles: cavities in a volcanic rock, once occupied by gas bubbles

7

Recycled Rocks

Sedimentary strata, deposited horizontally, have been tilted and eroded in a mountainous region in Southeastern Europe. Deformation of rocks here and elsewhere has permitted study of great thicknesses that otherwise could be reached (if at all) only by drilling. [*Courtesy Robert Folk*]

Among the inner planets and their satellites, Mercury and the Moon are naked solids; Venus is shrouded in a dense, hot atmosphere consisting of carbon dioxide with only a little water. Likewise, the thin air of Mars contains just a trace of H_2O. Only our planet Earth has a well-developed ocean and oxygen-rich atmosphere in which living things may flourish. Water and atmospheric gases continually attack rocks at the surface, forming weathering products to be carried away and deposited as sediment. This chapter introduces the sedimentary rocks, which illustrate yet other ways by which the earth's crust is recycled. The theme is amplified in a subsequent chapter, Depositional Systems.

WEATHERING: A TRANSITIONAL STAGE

Weathered material is special; it does not qualify as sediment because it has not been transported, yet it differs drastically from fresh bedrock. A weathered layer is absent in much of the Sahara Desert of Africa where it almost never rains. In parts of Brazil where intense tropical weathering has prevailed for millions of years, the layer may be hundreds of meters thick. Where erosion is active, the top of a mature weathered zone is being removed while the bedrock underneath continues to decompose. Fresh rock material enters at the bottom, experiences a complex set of weathering changes in between, and passes out at the top, during which the zone maintains a constant size and appearance. In this regard it is like a waterfall which maintains a constant size and shape as water passes through it.

Weathering of Granite

In Chapter 5 we considered the composition and origin of granite. Now let's follow the weathering decomposition of this rock. Quartz, feldspar, mica, and the other minerals in granite have crystallized in a hot and deep environment, where the pressure is high. What happens when the rock is exposed to the cool wetness of the earth's surface? Will it last forever as implied by the tombstone manufacturers' favorite term for granite, "Rock of Ages"? Definitely not! This is surprising, perhaps, because granite does not even begin to melt until the temperature exceeds 700°C. Surely it would be stable at a surface temperature of a mere 25°C. But the idea of stability is more subtle than that. Not only temperature, but also pressure, the chemical composition of the rock, and the presence of H_2O or other fluids must be considered. Chemical reactions may proceed in opposite directions in the depths of the earth and at the surface.

For example, consider the relationship of the stability of a mineral to its density and grain size. Moderate- to high-density minerals with closely packed crystal structures are stable under high pressure; low-density minerals with open crystal structures are favored at the earth's surface. Water tends to be driven out at high temperature and pressure. Thus H_2O in fresh, unweathered granite is not present as water molecules, but rather is locked up in the crystal structures of minor hydrous minerals such as biotite, muscovite, or hornblende. During weathering, the large crystals of granite are reduced to ever smaller size. At first the rock simply falls apart into a mass of loose-fitting coarse grains called *grus*. But with continued attack many of these grains decompose chemically, then re-form as very tiny crystals of minerals which incorporate H_2O supplied from the atmosphere.

Clay minerals are a product of the weathering of feldspar, the most abundant mineral in granite. Crystal sizes of clay particles vary, but can be less than a millionth of a meter, too small to be individually visible except with an electron microscope. Accompanying these changes is a spectacular increase in the surface area of the material. If a feldspar crystal one centimeter on a side were transformed into typical clay, the surface area of these microscopic but numerous particles would be about a million times greater, exceeding the area of a basketball court. Thus water, carbon dioxide, and oxygen are able to gain intimate access into every part of the decomposing mass.

Mechanical weathering Mechanical weathering simply breaks down larger pieces of rock into smaller pieces, whereas chemical weathering causes the original minerals in a rock to be transformed into a new and different set of minerals. The weathering of granite nicely illustrates these contrasting types. Granite magma solidifies underground, beneath a thickness of as much as several kilometers of rock. Millions of years later, after erosion has removed the overlying material, the granite is exposed at the earth's surface where it is no longer confined under pressure. Its response is to expand and to develop fractures, or *joints*. As weathering continues, the joints pop apart along sweeping curved sheets which separate, crumble, and slide downhill to join a pile of rubble at the base. By this continual process of *exfoliation* (from the Latin "to strip off leaves"), the granite may be exposed as bald *exfoliation domes* (Figure 7-1).

Figure 7-1. One of the most spectacular of all exfoliation domes is Half Dome, in Yosemite National Park, California. Its summit towers about 150 meters (500 feet) above camera level. Curved exfoliation slabs of this homogeneous igneous rock are 3 or 4 meters thick down to just a few centimeters thick. In the foreground, a boulder has partially decomposed into grus. [*U.S. Geological Survey photograph by F. C. Calkins.*]

Ice wedges and growing tree roots may also help to pry rock apart, or the intense heat of a forest fire may cause the surface to flake off. What about the less extreme but never ending temperature changes between day and night? The sun would make the rock expand during the day, and since the different minerals in granite expand at different rates, the heating would create internal stress, eventually causing the rock to shatter. Accelerated simulations were done in which a sample was subjected over and over to a large temperature change of more than 100°C. Almost no cracking or crumbling was visible after the rock had been "tortured" for an equivalent of 244 years of daily heating and cooling. Perhaps this form of weathering has been overrated, but when the cool-down cycle was performed by dousing the rock with water instead of a blast of dry air, rock decomposition set in after the equivalent of only 2 1/2 years' worth of days and nights.

Note that with the introduction of water, we also have the possibility of a chemical attack. A mechanical release of pressure can allow a rock to expand, but chemical weathering also causes expansion if the volume of the weathering products is larger than the volume of the original minerals. Chemical weathering can have a mechanical consequence.

Chemical weathering A handy rule of thumb is that for every 10°C rise in temperature, the speed of chemical reactions doubles. We would expect mechanical weathering to prevail in polar regions simply because chemical weathering there is very slow. In passing through temperate into tropical settings, we see chemical weathering play an increasing role. This is true for chemical breakdown of all the major minerals of granite, except quartz which is highly stable in the weathering environment. Quartz grains may be washed or blown about, but only moist tropical weathering applied for millions of years is able to dissolve them.

Water is so effective in promoting chemical attack because it is more than simply the H_2O molecule. For one thing, a small proportion of water molecules dissociate forming ions:

$$\underset{\text{Water}}{H_2O} \rightleftharpoons \underset{\text{Hydrogen ion}}{H^+} + \underset{\text{Hydroxyl ion}}{OH^-} \qquad (7\text{-}1)$$

For another, hydrogen ions appear when carbon dioxide, a minor gas in the atmosphere, dissolves in water:

$$\underset{\text{Water}}{H_2O} + \underset{\substack{\text{Carbon}\\\text{dioxide}}}{CO_2} \rightleftharpoons \underset{\substack{\text{Hydrogen}\\\text{ion}}}{H^+} + \underset{\substack{\text{Bicarbonate}\\\text{ion}}}{HCO_3^-} \tag{7-2}$$

Yet another source of hydrogen ions is from burning of fossil fuels, creating "acid rain."

The uniquely small size and highly concentrated electrical charge of these hydrogen ions enable them to break and re-form chemical bonds effectively. This activity wrecks a silicate structure. Feldspar succumbs to the attack along these lines:

$$\underset{\substack{\text{Potassium}\\\text{feldspar}\\\text{(framework structure)}}}{2KAlSi_3O_8} + \underset{\substack{\text{Hydrogen}\\\text{ion}}}{2H^+} + \underset{\text{Water}}{9H_2O} \rightleftharpoons \underset{\substack{\text{Kaolinite, a}\\\text{hydrous clay mineral}\\\text{(sheet structure)}}}{Al_2Si_2O_5(OH)_4} + \underset{\substack{\text{Silicic acid}\\\text{(in solution)}}}{4H_4SiO_4} + \underset{\substack{\text{Potassium}\\\text{ion (in solution)}}}{2K^+} \tag{7-3}$$

Inasmuch as feldspar is the most abundant mineral, the most common product of granite weathering is kaolinite or one of the other clay minerals. A profound reorganization must take place as the complex framework structure of feldspar is dissolved, then precipitated as the sheet structure of a clay mineral. According to reaction (7-3), ions that are released into solution include potassium (but also Na^+ and Ca^{2+} if the decomposing feldspar is plagioclase), and silicon in the form of silicic acid. Rivers carry these ions down to the sea where they may remain in solution, or the ions may be precipitated as other minerals. For example, sodium ions (Na^+) released by the weathering of plagioclase feldspar are the chief source of salt in the ocean.

What happens to the released ions of ferrous iron (Fe) that are abundant in biotite and other ferromagnesian minerals? Iron promptly oxidizes upon contact with oxygen in the air, to precipitate as hematite ("rust": Fe_2O_3) or other iron oxide minerals. At the earth's surface these iron-containing minerals are some of the most insoluble of natural substances. Typically displaying warm hues of red, yellow, orange, or brown, they provide brilliant scenery in deserts even where present only in trace amounts.

More about Stability

The American geologist S. Goldich assembled the information in Table 7-1 in his pioneering studies of chemical weathering of silicate minerals. To appreciate its significance, we first need to consider the formation of crystals during cooling of a magma. The earliest crystals to appear are composed of the mineral that is stable at the highest temperature. All of the other minerals remain melted; they can crystallize only after the temperature drops. In a magma that contains sufficient magnesium and iron, the most stable mineral is olivine, which is followed at lower temperatures by the appearance of pyroxene, amphibole, biotite, etc. Similarly, the table shows that calcium plagioclase feldspar is more stable than sodium plagioclase at high temperature.

Prof. Goldich noted that at *low* temperature the situation is just the reverse. Quartz, muscovite, and K feldspar, which are among the latest to crystallize from a magma, are by far the most resistant to chemical weathering at surface temperatures. Weathering causes olivine and calcium plagioclase promptly to go to pieces. Stability of a mineral depends upon the environment.

Table 7-1. *Weathering Series of Silicate Minerals*

(Most stable at magmatic temperatures)	Olivine	Ca plagioclase feldspar
	Augite (a variety of pyroxene)	
	Hornblende	
	Biotite mica	(Ca, Na) plagioclase feldspar
(Most stable in the weathering environment)	Potassium feldspar	
	Muscovite mica	
	Quartz	Na plagioclase feldspar

Note the progression down the list from olivine, with the least complex crystal structure, to quartz, with the most complex structure. It is the same progression described in Chapter 6. *(After S. S. Goldich, "A Study in Rock-weathering,"* Journal of Geology, *vol. 46, pp. 17–58, 1938.)*

Soils

Geologists, farmers, and engineers think of soil differently, and this has led to much confusion. Farmers and most of the rest of us view soil as the layer of ground, typically about two meters thick, that supports plant growth. To a construction engineer, soil is the material that can be scooped out, in contrast to hard bedrock which must be drilled and blasted. A geologist considers soil to be the end product of weathering. Here the focus is upon the conversion of primary minerals into other minerals, and the movement of dissolved ions or tiny clay particles in the weathered zone.

Soils are so complex that they are difficult to classify. Which property should we use as a basis of classification: grain size, original bedrock, degree of maturity, color, chemical composition, fertility, thickness, slope of the land surface? This is not a trivial question because the aim of a good classification is not just to invent technical terms, but to convey practical understanding about origins or processes. All of these variables are perhaps influential, but which of them are the most important?

Studies suggest that initially the composition of the bedrock governs the development of soil. It is no surprise that immature soils differ from one another chiefly because of differences in the bedrock. A soil just beginning to form by weathering of basalt, which consists of pyroxene and calcium plagioclase, would obviously differ from new soil accumulating on the adjacent hill where the granite bedrock consists of quartz and potassium feldspar.

But as soil organisms (chiefly microscopic) produce waste products such as carbon dioxide (CO_2), ammonia (NH_3), and methane (CH_4), and later deposit their accumulated dead remains, these chemically active substances cause dramatic changes that tend to obscure the initial differences. The soil has acquired an organic content, and indeed it is this feature, plus the fact that the material has not been transported, that distinguishes most soil from sedimentary rock.

Local climate governs the composition of a fully mature soil. Once the soil zone has become thick and rich in organic matter, and once weathering has broken down even the more resistant minerals, it is less significant whether the original bedrock was basalt or granite. If climate is the controlling factor, then we would expect to see similar associations of soils according to climatic zone, without regard to bedrock. There would be soil types typical of semiarid grasslands, other soils associated with wet tropics, evergreen forests, etc. This is what is generally observed.

Here we are using some scientifically based common sense to infer the working of a natural process that cannot be manipulated in the laboratory, or which is too slow for much to occur during a human lifetime, or which took place in the ancient past. Although we may be unable to cause the process to happen or observe a significant change, we reason from circumstances (correlation of soil types with climate rather than type of bedrock) what in fact did happen.

Now, suppose that the climate changed after a certain soil had formed. We would observe something unexpected, an *anomaly*, in this case an old soil out of equilibrium with modern climatic conditions. This might cause us to postulate that in the past the climate was different, or it could create a more fundamental doubt whether our theory about climatic control is correct after all. Although both possibilities must be kept open, it is well to note that a good theory is based upon thousands or even millions of consistent observations, and thus we should be cautious not to scrap the theory unless there is no other alternative.

With maturity comes the development of "horizons," or distinctive layers within the soil. These horizons differ both in number and composition according to climatic region. Where there is sufficient rainfall there is typically an uppermost, *O* (for "organic") horizon that is dark-colored, saturated with decayed plant debris. Beneath it lies the *A* horizon from which the soluble material has been leached away by water. Downward-percolating water has enriched the underlying *B* horizon by depositing some of this soluble or extremely finely divided material such as clay particles. In most places the *B* horizon marks the deepest penetration of plant roots. Lower still is the *C* horizon in which new soil is just beginning to form. This horizon, which contains fragments of partly decomposed bedrock, merges down into the *R* horizon which, strictly speaking, is bedrock, not soil.

Variations on the theme of soil horizons seem to be almost endless. About 40 soil groups, each with related subgroups, are recognized in the United States alone. A useful distinction is made between soils in the generally higher rainfall area east of the Mississippi River and those in the more arid region to the west. In humid regions the soluble Ca^{2+} ions are leached entirely from the soil. They enter the groundwater, later to be discharged into the local stream. The *B* horizon of these soils is enriched in particles of insoluble iron oxide and clay, which contains much aluminum. Hence these soils are nicknamed *pedalfers*, for ped ("under foot"), al (aluminum), and fer (iron).

Figure 7-2. The leached *A* horizon in this soil profile in Minnesota consists of an uppermost zone darkened by decayed grass roots, above a bleached zone rich in grains of quartz. Below it lies the dark *B* horizon that has been infiltrated by clay particles. Unweathered cobbles of glacial debris, the bedrock, are visible in the *C* horizon at the bottom of the photograph. [*Courtesy Dwight Deal.*]

Farther west in the Great Plains and beyond, where much of the water evaporates after seeping a short distance into the ground, the calcium ions migrate to deeper levels but are not removed altogether. Deposits of calcium carbonate that cement the *B* horizon of these soils are known as *caliche* (ca-LEECH-e), or hardpan. Caliche may be abundant even where there is no source of this material in the bedrock. The wind can deposit a fine dust of calcium carbonate which dissolves and is carried down into the soil, there to reprecipitate. These soil types are called *pedocals*: ped + cal (calcium).

Another important group of soil types called *laterite*, after the Latin word for "brick," is the product of intense or very prolonged chemical weathering. Like brick, laterite is yellow to rusty red because of iron oxide minerals. Commonly the *B* and *C* horizons are missing, and the severely leached *A* horizon is composed entirely of insoluble oxides. In cases of extreme weathering even the iron oxide minerals dissolve, leaving only the aluminum oxide minerals. Such soils are important sources of aluminum for industry.

Lush tropical jungles conceal the unhappy fact that lateritic soils are among the least suited on earth for agriculture. Sustained heat and wetting-drying cycles enable bacteria to decompose the organic matter efficiently, and thus dense vegetation may grow because of warmth and high rainfall and *in spite of* the infertility of the laterite. Lateritic soil underlies a vast area inhabited by a third of the world's population (Figure 7-3). Nature has dealt harshly with man's effort to carve farmland out of the tropical rain forests, as for example in the Amazon region of Brazil. Here the vegetation takes part in local recycling, as dissolved ions that are withdrawn by a plant are promptly returned to the soil when the plant dies. When crops are grown the cycle is broken; the precious ions are removed with the harvest. Not only is the soil further impoverished, but after a few years of cultivation, fields lying exposed to the sun turn quite literally into pavements of solid brick.

Chemical weathering is responsible for creating valuable mineral deposits. Long-sustained wet tropical weathering can dissolve everything except the aluminum or iron oxide minerals which remain behind, concentrated. These ore deposits are an extension on the theme of lateritic soil. Copper sulfide

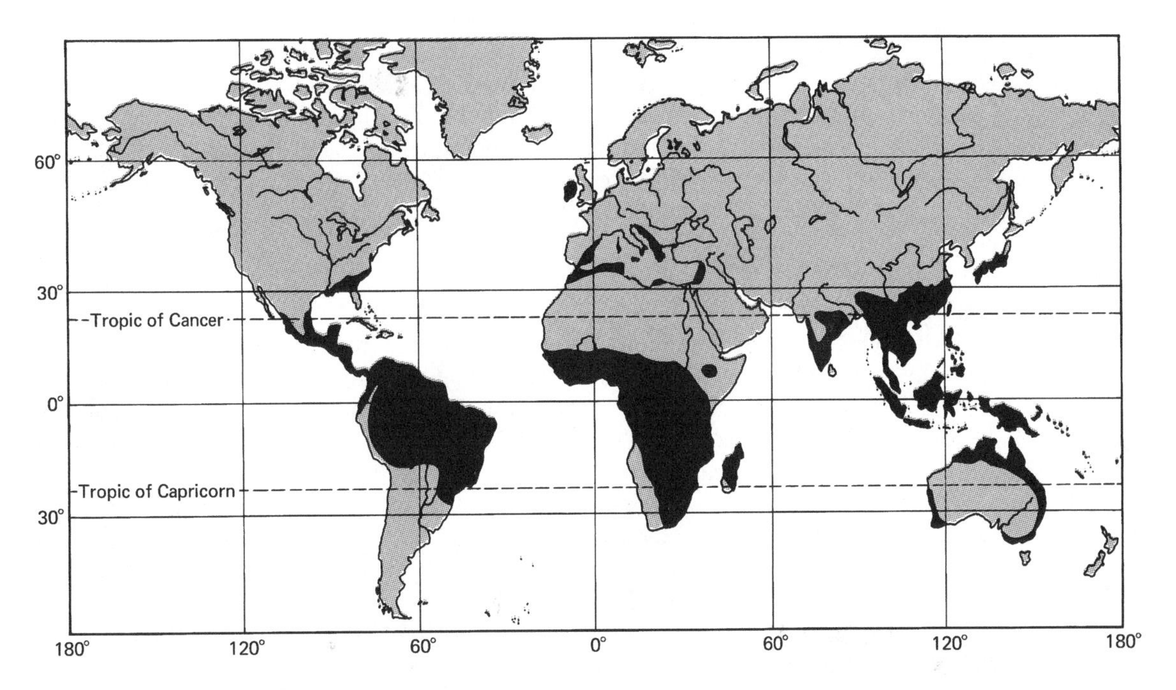

Figure 7-3. Lateritic soils (black) are confined mainly to the tropics. [*After R. Ganssen and F. Hädrich,* Atlas zur Bodenkunde, *Bibliographisches Institut AG, Mannheim, 1965.*]

minerals, present in minor abundance in an igneous rock, may be dissolved by groundwater. The copper ions seep to a deeper level where they are re-precipitated as a zone of concentrated ore. This process is analogous to creation of the *B* horizon of a soil. Such ore deposits are like ordinary soil, except that they have resulted from weathering of vastly greater duration or intensity. World climate is constantly changing such that an ore deposit produced in ancient times may be located far from the tropics today. Some large copper deposits formed in this manner in Canada, which is definitely not tropical.

How rapid is weathering? Generally the process is so slow that rates are difficult to estimate. It is necessary to find a rock whose age of exposure to weathering is known. Temperature and availability of water have much to do with weathering rates. According to one study, the Great Pyramid in the desert of Egypt should stand for another 1000 centuries. Yet in the humid tropical climate of the West Indies, a soil two meters thick formed on volcanic ash in only 40 centuries. Weathering slows way down once a mature soil profile has developed. In Australia and Africa, some landscapes and their associated soil cover have just "sat there" for tens of millions of years!

SEDIMENTARY ROCKS

Sedimentary comes from the Latin word for "settling," which is what gravity causes dense particles to do when they are suspended in a fluid medium. Fine windblown sand skips along, staying close to the earth, or pebbles may roll along a stream bed during times of flood. Mud stirred up into the water of a shallow bay will slowly settle out of suspension. In these and most other situations, the sediment gravitates into roughly horizontal *strata* (layers). Almost all sedimentary rocks are stratified, but so are some igneous rocks such as basalt flows or sheets of ignimbrite, as we learned from a preceding chapter. Unlike the igneous rocks, sediments are deposited under "cool" temperatures on the surface or under a body of water or ice. About 75 percent of the continents and nearly all of the ocean floor are veneered by sedimentary rock, but because sediments are deposited superficially, this rock type accounts for only about 5 percent of the crust, and a trivial part of the earth's total bulk. Even so, much of the earth's igneous and metamorphic rock originated as sediment that has been *recycled* by melting or recrystallization.

If all the world's sedimentary rock were distributed uniformly, the layer would be somewhat less than a kilometer thick (about 3000 feet). Actually, there are great variations in thickness from place to place. Over much of the ocean floor the thickness is several hundred meters or less. Where sediments have been dumped off the edge of a continent for millions of years, the pileup may exceed 15 kilometers (10 miles), far deeper than the bottom of the deepest drill hole. *Rates* of deposition also may vary enormously. A sediment thickness of 100 meters has accumulated within the past 2000 years at the mouth of the Mississippi River. Yet at Galveston, Texas, a coastal city some distance to the west, only 0.3 meter was deposited in the same length of time, and in the mid-ocean, far from any source of sediment, the equivalent thickness is about 1 centimeter (0.01 meter).

From Weathered Granite to Sediment

We noted that when granite is weathered, some of the rock remains as solid fragments and some of it dissolves. What kinds of sedimentary rock might these products of weathering become?

Terrigenous clastics Let's consider first the solid fragments. Table 7-1 reminds us that quartz, muscovite, and potassium feldspar are best able to resist chemical weathering. These minerals, especially the very durable quartz, are concentrated in *terrigenous clastic* sediments. "Terrigenous" means derived from the land surface, and "clastic" means broken (that is, obtained by breakdown of a pre-existing rock). Terrigenous clastic sediments may be composed either of original minerals (for example, feldspar) or their weathering products (for example, clay) eroded from the source of sediment.

The particle size is a basis for further classification. If the fragments vary from large boulders or cobbles down to pea-sized pieces, the rock is a *conglomerate*. Smaller particles are characteristic of the sedimentary rock called *sandstone*, still smaller particles characterize *siltstone*, and the smallest make up mudstone or *shale*. A summary of particle sizes in terrigenous clastic sediments shows three rather clearly defined groups (Figure 7-4). There is roughly twice as much shale as all other sediment types combined. This fact is not obvious because easily eroded shale commonly occupies valleys where it lies

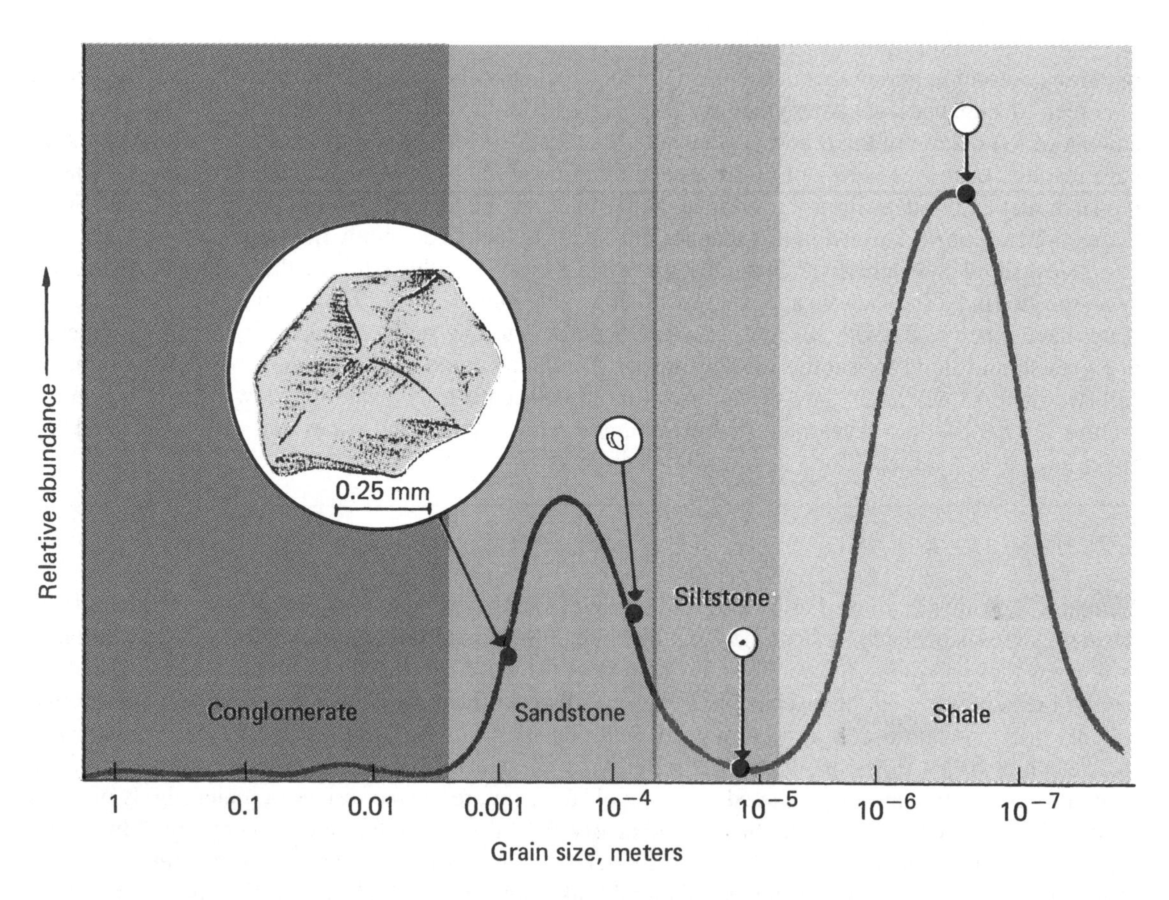

Figure 7-4. An abundance diagram for terrigenous clastic sediments also shows the relative sizes of typical grains of coarse sand, fine sand, and silt. An individual clay particle is invisible at this magnification.

unnoticed beneath vegetation, whereas sandstone may stand out as bold cliffs. Erosion of a sedimentary rock is another example of recycling. Its particles may be weathered, eroded, and redeposited, and so on for cycle after cycle.

There is also a relationship between particle size and composition. Do the three groups have different origins? Boulders and cobbles are large fragments still recognizable as "whole rock" (aggregates of crystals), which must have been deposited in an environment where the energy was high enough to transport such massive pieces. Conglomerate could have been transported by flood waters, for example, or down steep slopes as landslide material.

Particles in sandstone are mostly single crystals, broken apart from one another then knocked together by wind, wave action, or stream flow, with two important results. The abrasion will make the grains smaller, and it will round off the sharp edges and corners. Thus we may distinguish an "immature" sandstone, which has angular grains and a variety of minerals, not all of which are resistant to chemical or physical breakdown. Apparently these were transported quickly or only a short distance to the site of deposition. Immature sandstone would accumulate, for example, along the mountainous West Coast of North America. Grains in a "mature" sandstone have been transported with a lot of energy, or for a long distance. They are well rounded and consist mostly of quartz, the mineral best able to withstand abrasion and weathering. Fine sand carried from Pennsylvania to the mouth of the Mississippi River would be deposited as a mature sandstone.

Nature's mill can grind particles down only so much, however. The fluid medium that transports sediment also surrounds and cushions the impact of the jostling particles, limiting their ability to damage one another. Experiments in which quartz sand was propelled by water around a tank showed that a 0.5-millimeter cube would have to be rolled a distance equal to 50 times around the equator to become rounded into a sphere. This is an absurd impossibility in nature, and thus the rounding of small grains likely did not take place in a water medium. Mechanical abrasion of windblown sand is about 10 thousand times more effective because the wind blows much faster and the air cannot as effectively cushion the impacts.

As sandstone strata are deposited, they may develop internal structures that reveal how the material was transported. Consider sand grains being driven by wind up the flank of a dune. After they have gone over the summit, they reach the lee side of the dune which is protected from the blowing wind. Cascades of sand occasionally slide down the lee slope forming steeply dipping beds, and because these layers are contained within the larger sheet of sand which is horizontal, they are called *crossbeds*. A gently inclined side of the dune faces toward the wind, and a steeply inclined side faces away from the wind. Now, suppose that we encounter an ancient stratum of sandstone tens of meters thick (Figure 7-5), in which fine quartz grains are well rounded and about the same size. This sandstone would be a good candidate for earlier dune deposition. Our hypothesis would be strengthened if the sandstone contains huge crossbeds, and we would know the direction of prevailing wind even though it blew 160 million years ago. This interpretation could lead to larger speculations about such things as climate and ancient arrangement of continents.

Crossbeds and other sedimentary structures such as ripples (Figure 7-6) can be created by wind or especially during flood by flowing water. Water-laid crossbeds are smaller and of different shape than those laid by wind, but they are just as useful. An asymmetrical crossbed would not appear the same facing upward as it would facing downward. We could use crossbedding to tell if a stratum has been turned upside down, which is not such a preposterous idea in a region where the rocks have been strongly deformed. In the Alps, for example, any particular bed is about as likely to be upside down as right-side up, and so we could employ crossbedding to trace the contortions of the rock made by faulting and folding.

If a mineral grain cannot be abraded to extremely small size, then why does shale consist of submicroscopic particles? In shale, the clay is not an original mineral that has been mechanically reduced to fine size, but rather it is a product of chemical weathering of feldspar.

Chemical sediment: carbonates The odd-sounding term "chemical sediment" is not meant to imply that terrigenous clastics lack a chemical composition. Rather, it means that chemical sediment was precipitated directly from ions dissolved in water. You recall that plagioclase feldspar in granite contains sodium, and also a minor amount of calcium which is released by weathering. This calcium can be

Figure 7-5. The tiny image of a man standing at the base of this sandstone cliff gives a sense of the scale of the crossbeds. Thicknesses of individual cross beds permit calculation of the size of the dune in which they originated. The ancient dune was hundreds of meters high, rivaling the largest sand dunes known anywhere today. [*U.S. Geological Survey photograph by David M. Rubin.*]

incorporated into the chemical sedimentary rock *limestone*, most of which is composed of *calcite*: calcium carbonate ($CaCO_3$).

Probably 90 percent of the world's carbonate sedimentary rocks have been deposited by living organisms. Animals such as corals, snails, and clams build skeletons or shells of calcium carbonate. Single-cell floating organisms, *Foraminifera*, construct fragile shells of $CaCO_3$ (Figure 7-7). Certain algae strengthen their cell walls with a calcareous coating which ends up as a fine carbonate mud.

The chemical reactions that control the deposition of limestone may be quite complicated. Dissolved carbonate ions come ultimately from carbon dioxide in the air which reacts with water:

Figure 7-6. Wind or flowing water can cast loose sand grains into ripples. A sand grain migrates up the gentle slope on the up-current side of a ripple, then cascades steeply down its leeward slope. Asymmetrical ripples tell which direction the current was flowing, in this example from right to left. [*Courtesy Robert L. Folk.*]

$$\underset{\text{Water}}{H_2O} + \underset{\substack{\text{Carbon}\\\text{dioxide}}}{CO_2} \rightleftharpoons \underset{\substack{\text{Carbonic}\\\text{acid}}}{H_2CO_3} \tag{7-4}$$

The carbonic acid further decomposes to form bicarbonate ions (HCO_3^-) and carbonate ions (CO_3^{2-}). All of these various carbon-containing substances and dissolved calcium ions are present together in a state of balance. If some environmental factor were to change, the balance could be upset causing solution or deposition of solid $CaCO_3$.

For example, absorption of atmospheric carbon dioxide causes rainwater to become acidic, therefore corrosive. Upon entering the earth, the groundwater would dissolve limestone, forming caverns and opening fissures. Warming of tropical waters drives away the dissolved CO_2, causing the opposite reaction: precipitation of calcium carbonate onto the sea floor. Ocean water is a complex chemical system. The upper part of the ocean water mass is oversaturated with dissolved calcium carbonate, but at a depth greater than about 3 kilometers (2 miles) it is slightly undersaturated. In *over*saturated water, calcium carbonate would tend to precipitate, whereas in *under*saturated water the $CaCO_3$ would dissolve. Dead foraminiferans, which lived in the upper waters, "rain" down into deeper water where their shells dissolve, and we do not find carbonate sediments at the bottom of the deepest ocean.

Limestone is being deposited today in both shallow and fairly deep water (Figure 7-8). More than a third of the ocean floor is covered with fine ooze, a soft carpet made from the skeletons of foraminiferans and other micro-organisms. Toward land the ooze, although present, is overwhelmed by an abundance of clastic sediment which is shed off the continent.

Organic reefs, made up of coral, oysters, calcareous algae, and similar organisms, are built in shallow tropical waters. Some reefs are just small patches perched here and there on a submerged shelf. In productive waters and with sufficient time, reef deposits can accumulate to spectacular thicknesses—at

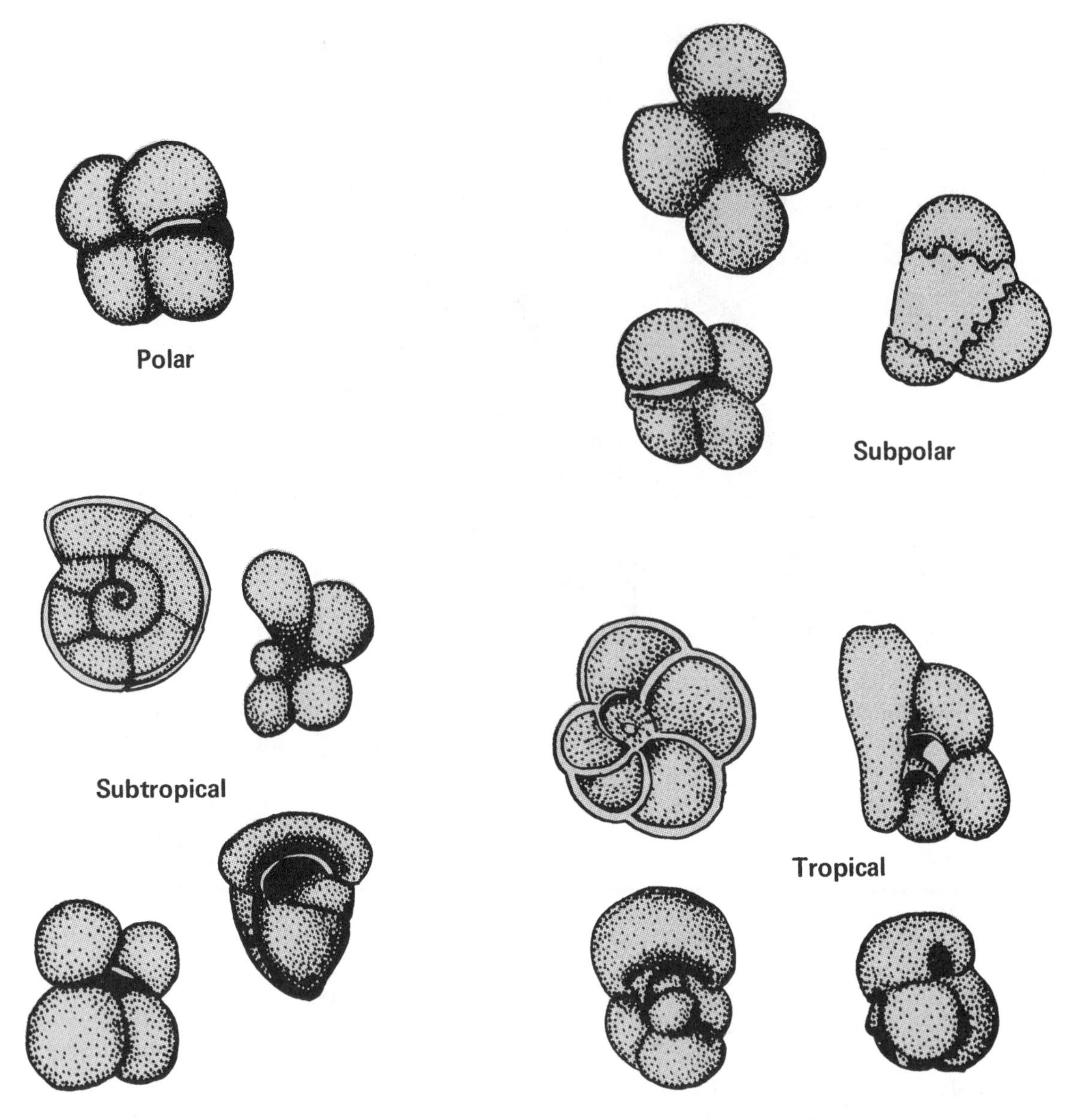

Figure 7-7. The more common species of Foraminifera exhibit a variety of forms of calcium carbonate shells. Some of these organisms are cold-water species; others thrive only in warmer waters. Abundances of temperature-sensitive species in buried oceanic sediment reflect the warm and cold intervals of past climates. Magnification: 60 times.

least 4.5 kilometers (3 miles) in the Bahamas near Florida. Carbonate reefs are well developed in only a few places, but that was not always so. There have been times when the land surface was eroded down almost to sea level. It is easy to imagine how a slight down-warping of the continent or up-warping of the sea floor would cause the ocean water to "slop over" onto the continents. In fact, vast, shallow "epicontinental" seas have flooded some areas on at least 20 separate occasions. These environments were ideal for limestone to accumulate on a grand scale.

Profound changes may accompany the transformation of original soft sediment into sedimentary rock. One example is introduction of cement into the pores of loose sand, making it more dense and hard and changing it into a rock, sandstone. (A petroleum geologist tries to find sandstone that is poorly cemented, for a well-cemented sandstone is too "tight," lacking the open voids that can store oil or gas.) Another process is the replacement of original carbonate sediment by *chert*, which is microcrystalline quartz (Figure 7-9). Yet another example is the conversion of limestone into *dolomite*. We have seen (Chapter 3) that calcite has alternate layers of Ca^{2+} ions and CO_3^{2-} ions [Figure 7-10(*a*)]. In well-formed

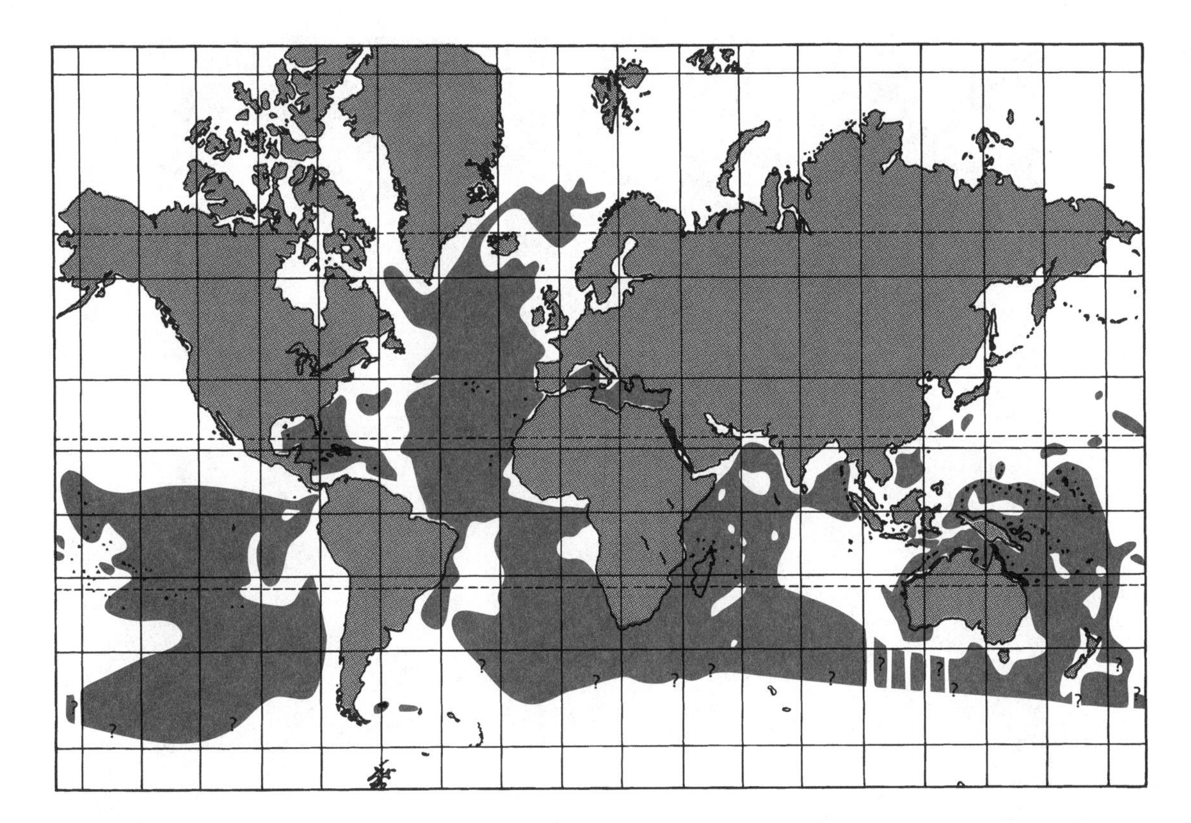

Figure 7-8. Deep ocean basins are carpeted with an ooze consisting of skeletons of foraminiferans and other floating organisms. Reef complexes border the continents. The Great Barrier Reef (largest in the world), off northeastern Australia, is more than 1600 kilometers long. [*After John Rodgers, "The Distribution of Marine Carbonate Sediments: A Review," in* Regional Aspects of Carbonate Deposition, *Society of Economic Paleontologists and Mineralologists, Special Publication 5, 1957.*]

dolomite, the Ca^{2+} in every second cation layer has been replaced by Mg^{2+} [Figure 7-10(*b*)], and thus the formula of dolomite is $(Ca,Mg)CO_3$. Both the mineral and the rock made of this mineral are called dolomite.

The origin of dolomite is a major unsolved scientific problem. Although plenty of magnesium is available dissolved in seawater, living organisms do not secrete dolomite. Originally a calcium carbonate mineral was deposited, then transformed into dolomite through replacement of some of the calcium by magnesium. But when and how does this take place? Laboratory simulations have not succeeded in making dolomite under normal sedimentary conditions. Dolomite is being produced in arid environments such as the Bahamas and the Persian Gulf, where mudflats along the shore experience intense evaporation. The loss of water permits capillary action to draw a strong magnesium-containing brine up through the mud. Some dolomite in ancient sedimentary rocks may have originated in this manner, but not enormous sheets such as the one exposed in the gorge below Niagara Falls. This layer of dolomite extends from upstate New York to as far away as Wisconsin. Geologists are at a loss for a modern analog, as nothing of that large a magnitude is forming today.

Carbonate sedimentary rocks are typically rather pure, chemically simple rocks, but their textures show much fascinating detail. As mentioned in Chapter 5, texture refers to the sizes and shapes of the mineral grains, and how they are positioned in relation to one another. Many textures can give clues to the environment of deposition. Solidified carbonate mud, made of cemented microscopic particles, was deposited in quiet water, as are the microscopic clay particles in the more familiar "dirt" mud. Reef organisms flourish in open water where the limestone may be broken up by pounding waves, then recemented as a jumble of fragments. And since "clastic" means broken, this limestone is a chemical sediment that becomes a clastic sediment by recycling. It is analogous to a terrigenous clastic conglomerate, or an immature sandstone. Still other limestone is a mass of tiny spheres, like fish roe, glued together by carbonate cement. Appropriately, this rock is called *oolite* after the Latin word for "egg" (Figure 7-12). Oolite is commonly deposited in underwater dunes.

Figure 7-9. When matrix rock in this specimen had been partially dissolved away by acid, delicate fossil shells that long ago had been replaced by insoluble chert were exposed. [*Smithsonian Institution photograph.*]

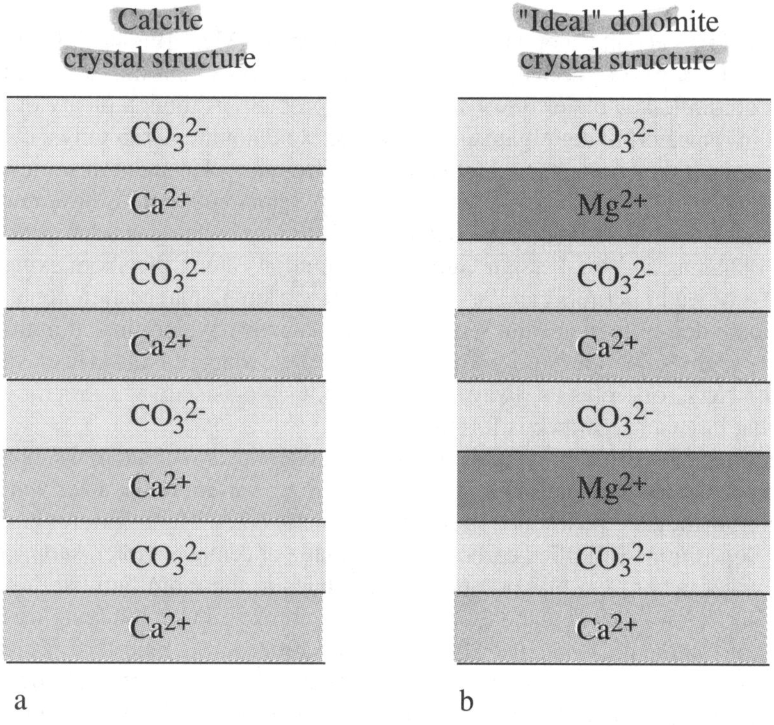

Calcite crystal structure	"Ideal" dolomite crystal structure
CO_3^{2-}	CO_3^{2-}
Ca^{2+}	Mg^{2+}
CO_3^{2-}	CO_3^{2-}
Ca^{2+}	Ca^{2+}
CO_3^{2-}	CO_3^{2-}
Ca^{2+}	Mg^{2+}
CO_3^{2-}	CO_3^{2-}
Ca^{2+}	Ca^{2+}
a	b

Figure 7-10. Cation layers in calcite (seen edge-on) consist only of Ca^{2+}, whereas in dolomite they are alternately Ca^{2+}, Mg^{2+}, Ca^{2+}, Mg^{2+}, etc.

Figure 7-11. This area in the Bahamas is flooded at high tide but exposed during low tide. A broken crust of dolomite forming at the surface is somehow related to a drawing up of very saline water from below, but the means by which dolomite is made is not known. [*From E. A. Shinn and others, "Recent Supratidal Dolomite from Andros Island, Bahamas," in* Dolomitization and Limestone Diagenesis, *Society of Economic Paleontologists and Mineralogists, Special Publication 13, 1965.*]

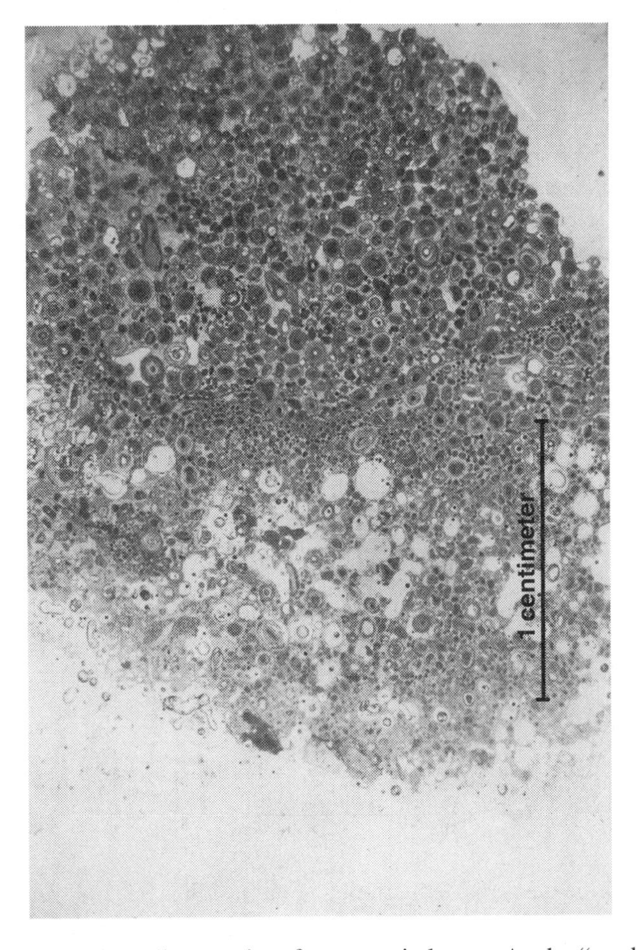

Figure 7-12. Spherical grains in oolite consist of concentric layers. As the "seed" nuclei were tossed about by vigorous currents, they accumulated coat upon coat of calcium carbonate. [*From N. D. Newell and J. K. Rigby, "Geological Studies on the Great Bahama Bank," in* Regional Aspects of Carbonate Deposition, *Society of Economic Paleontologists and Mineralogists, Special Publication 5, 1957.*]

Chemical sediment: evaporites Weathering of feldspar releases sodium and potassium ions into solution; these ions eventually enter the ocean. After dissolved substances have been poured in for countless ages, why hasn't seawater become a super-concentrated brine like the Dead Sea? There must be ways to remove these ions by precipitating them onto the sea floor. We noted that the chemistry of seawater is complex. So are the reactions through which a sort of submarine "weathering" can fix ions that were released during weathering of the land. Table 7-2 shows the rates of recycling of various ocean constituents, including its H_2O.

Evaporation can make seawater become supersaturated even with ions that are normally soluble. About 3 percent of sedimentary rocks consist of *evaporite* deposits which are mostly gypsum ($CaSO_4{\cdot}2H_2O$: see Chapter 3), but there is also much halite (NaCl), anhydrite ($CaSO_4$), and potassium salts (KCl, etc.). Evaporite deposits have been lifted above sea level in Israel, New Mexico, Germany, Russia, and elsewhere. Even in the desert, salt is prone to be washed right back into the sea where it started. Measurements of the dissolved load of rivers suggest that evaporites are eroded about 10 times

Table 7-2. *Mass Balance between Rivers and the Ocean*

Substance brought by rivers	Number of times the ocean would have been replenished during the last 1% of earth history*
Water	1250
Na^+	0.6
Cl^-	0.4
Ca^{2+}	41
SiO_2	2250

*"All the streams run into the sea, yet the sea is never full. To the place where the streams come from, there they return again." (the Bible, Ecclesiastes 1:7). Today, we realize that water and *all other substances* are recycled. *[After J. I. Drever,* The Geochemistry of Natural Waters, *Prentice-Hall, Inc., Englewood Cliffs, NJ, 1988.]*

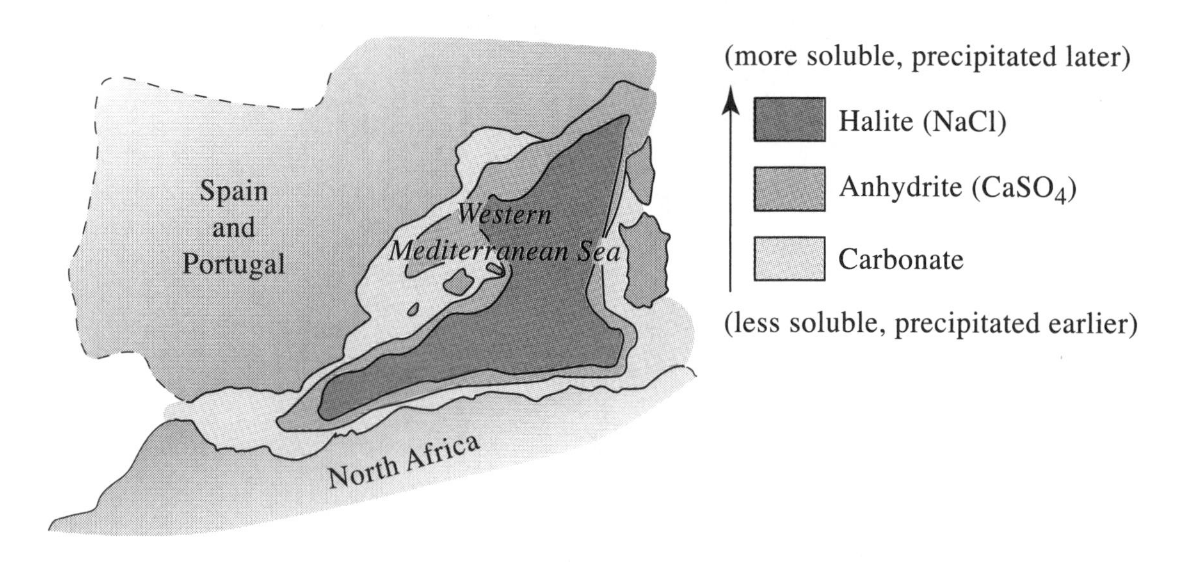

Figure 7-13. Drilling of the western Mediterranean Sea floor has revealed an astonishing series of concentric deposits of evaporite sediments. This pattern of least-soluble minerals on the rim, to most-soluble in the center, is obtained if an isolated body of salt water grows smaller as it deposits salt from an ever more concentrated residual brine. About 6 million years ago, the Mediterranean Sea, blocked off from the Atlantic Ocean, very nearly dried up. Brine pools lay exposed to the hot sun thousands of meters below sea level at the bottom of the parched Mediterranean basin. [*After K. J. Hsü and others, "Late Miocene Desiccation of the Mediterranean,"* Nature, *vol. 242, no. 5395, 1973.*]

more readily than other kinds of rock. Evaporites are recycled rocks indeed! Even though salt is vulnerable to solution, the amount preserved as evaporite sediment is nonetheless twice the amount of salt in the ocean.

SUMMARY

Weathering causes rocks that formed in a hot or deep environment to reach equilibrium with the cool, wet, low-pressure conditions of the earth's surface. Weathering may be simply a mechanical disintegration, for example causing a homogeneous rock such as granite to pop apart (exfoliate) along joints. More advanced weathering is accomplished by chemical attack, during which new minerals form, typically with very small particle size. Many of these minerals are hydrous (hydrogen-containing), the result of reactions with atmospheric H_2O. Chemical weathering may also cause mechanical disintegration because the products of weathering occupy more volume than the original set of minerals. The rate of chemical reactions increases sharply with increasing temperature and with availability of moisture. Consequently mechanical weathering prevails in polar regions, chemical weathering in the humid tropics. Quartz is highly resistant to weathering; feldspar weathers into clay minerals while Ca^{2+}, Na^+, and K^+ ions are released into solution. These ions are eventually precipitated as chemical sediment. Weathering of ferromagnesian minerals releases iron which is incorporated into insoluble oxide or hydroxide minerals. Minerals that are *most* stable at high (magmatic) temperature are the *least* stable (most susceptible to weathering) at the earth's surface.

Soil is a layer of weathering products mantling the bedrock. The composition of immature soil is governed chiefly by the composition of the bedrock, whereas the composition of a mature soil is determined by climate. In a typical mature soil the uppermost, *A* horizon is enriched in organic matter. Material leached from the *A* horizon is deposited in the *B* horizon underneath. The still lower *C* horizon consists of bedrock just beginning to decompose into soil. In pedocals, calcium carbonate is enriched in the *B* horizon; in pedalfers, oxides of iron and aluminum are deposited. Laterite is intensely leached soil in which little else besides these oxide minerals remains. Intense or sustained soil-forming processes can create valuable deposits of ore minerals.

Sediment transported by wind, water, or glacier ice is deposited under low-pressure, low-temperature conditions at the earth's surface. Sedimentary strata (layers) cover most of the earth's surface, both above and below sea level, having been deposited at greatly varying rates and thicknesses.

Terrigenous clastic sediment was eroded from a source area, transported, and deposited as solid particles. This sediment type is classified according to particle size, from conglomerate (coarsest and least abundant) through sandstone, siltstone, to shale (finest and most abundant). Abrasion and chemical attack during transportation cause some minerals to disappear, and cause rounding-off of grains of minerals (notably quartz) that are resistant to weathering. Crossbeds, sedimentary layers inclined to a stratum, provide information about the environment of deposition and the direction that the wind or water was flowing.

Chemical sediment is deposited from ions dissolved in water. Limestone is a carbonate sediment composed of calcite ($CaCO_3$) which was deposited chiefly through the activity of living organisms. It may originate as a fine ooze in quiet water, as shell or skeletal material, or as oolite shoals. Any of these may be recycled as clastic particles. Dolomite, $(Ca,Mg)CO_3$, forms by partial replacement of calcium in $CaCO_3$ by magnesium ions. Dolomite is not deposited directly. Chert may originate by replacement of a pre-existing carbonate sediment with microcrystalline quartz. Evaporite sediments are deposited when seawater is so strongly evaporated that normally soluble ions (Na^+, Ca^{2+}, K^+) become supersaturated. Principal evaporite minerals are gypsum ($CaSO_4 \cdot 2H_2O$), halite (NaCl), and anhydrite ($CaSO_4$).

8

Sedimentary Rocks

INTRODUCTION

Sediment consists of ions (single atoms or small groups of atoms having an electrical charge), or else visible particles that have been transported and deposited. Agents of transportation may be blowing wind, moving water, or flowing glacier ice, all of which operate at the surface of the earth. Sediments form a thin, discontinuous cover over much of the earth's surface that lies above sea level, and they blanket virtually all of the ocean floor. Although most sedimentary rocks exhibit prominent layering, or **stratification**, it is not a unique characteristic—lava flows and ash-flow tuffs, products of volcanic eruption, also may be stratified. However, sedimentary rocks have formed in a cool environment, in contrast to the hot origin of igneous rocks. During transport, the sediment tends to move from higher to lower elevation under the influence of gravity. The result is that, with few exceptions, sedimentary stratification is approximately horizontal. Geologists refer to this condition as the Principle of Original Horizontality. If the strata are not horizontal today, generally it is because they were displaced some time after deposition [Photo 8-1(*a*)].

CLASSIFICATION

Sediments are classified according to two types of origin and composition. **Terrigenous clastic** sediment originates when a source rock is weathered, eroded, and the products of erosion are transported as solid particles to the point of deposition. **Mechanical** weathering simply breaks down larger pieces into smaller pieces, whereas **chemical** weathering partially dissolves the original minerals, or transforms them into new minerals that are stable in the weathering zone. "Terrigenous" means "derived from the land," which is where most erosion takes place. "Clastic" means "broken," in reference to the disintegration of the source rock into particles. Sediment is thus made of recycled material that formerly was part of an igneous, metamorphic, or possibly a pre-existing sedimentary rock [note the Rock Cycle, (Figure 4-1)]. Terrigenous clastic sedimentary rock is further classified according to particle size, which may vary from microscopic flakes of clay, to silt, to sand, to pebbles or cobbles [Photo 8-1(*b*, *c*)], to boulders, or even to fragments on the scale of kilometers.

Chemical weathering releases not only solid particles, but also dissolved ions that travel down rivers, and contribute to the saltiness of the ocean. Eventually the ions present in the water column over a given spot of the sea floor may be precipitated as non-clastic material, which in turn is classified as **chemical** sediment or **biochemical** sediment. (Of course, terrigenous clastic sediment is also composed of chemical elements.) Chemical sediment originates if dissolved ions are too concentrated to remain in solution. For example, sea water may become supersaturated by intense evaporation, by which the water escapes into the atmosphere while the ions remain behind as a deposit of halite (rock salt). Under certain conditions, limestone or rock gypsum also may precipitate by this means. Biochemical sediment originates through the activity of living organisms—for example, when a clam or oyster utilizes dissolved ions to secrete its calcium carbonate shell material.

According to the crystallization scheme described by Bowen (Figure 6-1), olivine is the most stable ferromagnesian mineral, and calcium-rich plagioclase is the most stable feldspar in a high-temperature magma. During cooling, olivine and Ca plagioclase would crystallize first, while potential crystals of other minerals remain melted. Quartz is least stable, the final mineral to crystallize at the lowest temperature.

The American geologist S. Goldich studied metamorphic and igneous rocks containing a variety of common minerals, and noted dramatically different relative stabilities of minerals in the cool, moist, low-pressure weathering environment at the earth's surface. Goldich's Weathering Series (Figure 8-1) is the opposite of Bowen's sequence of crystallization from a cooling magma (Figure 6-1). Quartz, typically the last mineral to crystallize from a magma because it is least stable at high temperature, is the most stable mineral at the earth's surface (most resistant to chemical weathering). Conversely, olivine or Ca plagioclase quickly decompose under weathering attack. Indeed, the sequence of relative stability shown in Figure 6-1 is more accurately followed *up* the chain during weathering, than *down* the chain during igneous crystallization.

Freshly deposited sediment consists of loose, commonly water-soaked material; it is "dirt" or "fresh mud." Upon burial, unconsolidated sediment transforms into sedimentary rock by the process of **diagenesis**, in which some of the sediment dissolves and re-precipitates, or circulating groundwater

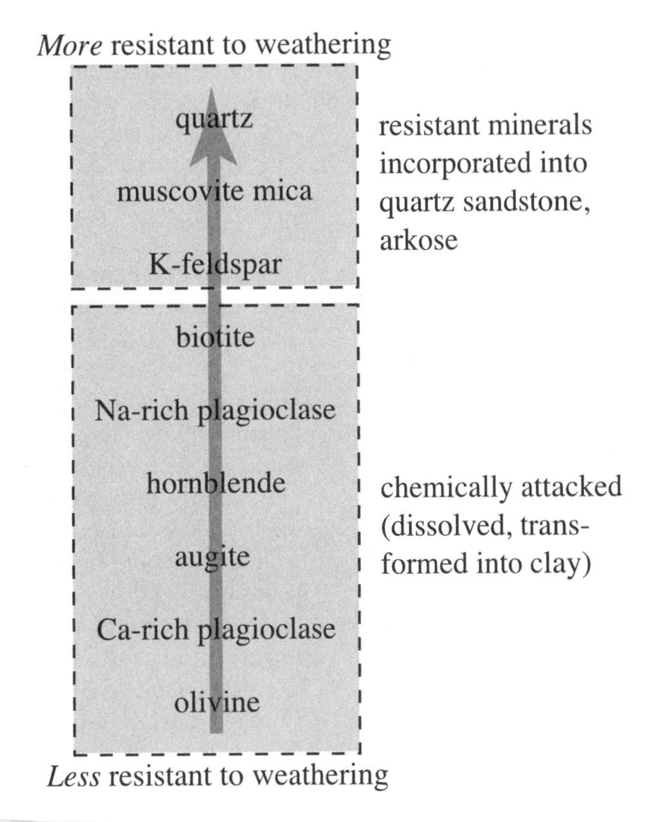

Figure 8-1. Goldich's Weathering Series

introduces cement, or original minerals react together forming new mineral species. Profound as these changes may be, they fall short of metamorphism which is a process that operates at substantially elevated temperature and pressure.

SEDIMENTARY MATURITY

With the passing of years, both persons and sedimentary clastic particles become more mature. Metaphorically speaking, the hard knocks of life conspire to smooth off the sharp corners and edges of one's youthful personality. Literally speaking, impacts knock off the sharp corners and edges of a particle during sedimentary transport. Maturity does not depend upon how long ago a person lived, or how ancient the sediment may be. Rather, maturity corresponds more to how many years that person lived, or the duration and vigor of reworking during sedimentary transport.

As the particles abrade one another, *reduced particle size* becomes a sign of increasing sedimentary maturity. There is an upper limit to how heavy a particle the transporting medium can move along. Blowing wind can move nothing larger than sand-size grains. Within a gently flowing stream, turbulence (chaotic internal motions) can suspend nothing larger than microscopic clay particles. Sand and gravel sink to the bottom, hopping or rolling along the channel bed. This winnowing process *sorts* the particles, segregating them from one another according to size. In well sorted, mature sediment, such as on many beaches, the particles are of similar size. In poorly sorted, immature sediment, particles of greatly different sizes are deposited together by nature's "bulldozer," which shoves boulders and mud indiscriminately.

Sedimentary transport is sporadic; the particles are in motion at times and simply resting most of the time. All the while, they are subject to weathering attack, or to being dissolved by groundwater. Quartz greatly resists attack, whereas other common silicate minerals and carbonate minerals are prone to attack. As the latter minerals disappear during weathering and transport, the sediment becomes more nearly uniform mineralogically. Highly mature sandstone consists only of quartz whereas in immature sandstone, feldspar or mica may have persisted in addition to the quartz. Arkose is sandstone rich in feldspar, but even here, quartz dominates. Rock debris deposited by a melting glacier is extremely immature. A glacier transports fragments embedded within the ice, not able to interact with one another.

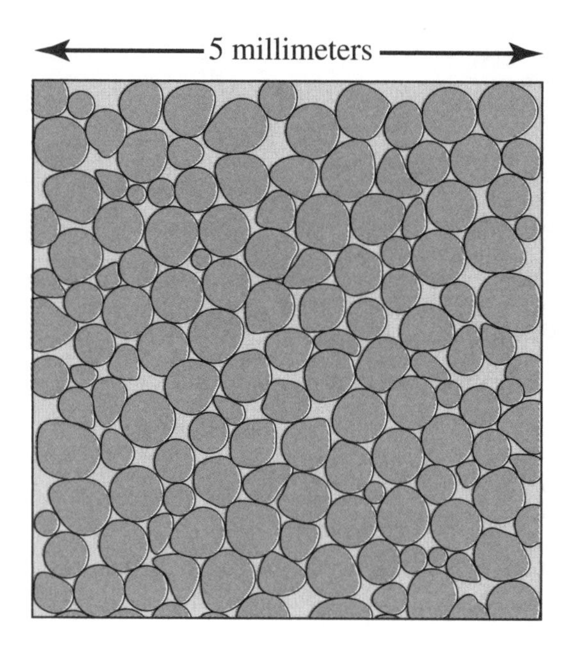

Pictured here are well sorted, well rounded sand grains (note the length scale). This mature sediment could have been deposited as wind-blown dune sand. The texture is *grain-supported*—the grains touch and mutually support one another. Spaces among the grains could be open, or they could be filled with water, oil, or gas that can move easily through the open, porous structure. Such rock would be a good target for drilling a well for water or oil. During diagenesis, migrating fluids bearing dissolved material could precipitate cement in the pores, transforming loose sand (sediment) into sandstone (sedimentary rock). Well-cemented sandstone would be "tight," unable to store or transmit water, oil, or gas.

In this poorly sorted, immature conglomerate, the gray matrix consists of clay particles (mud) enclosing larger, moderately well rounded fragments up to the size of small boulders. Its texture is *mud-supported*, and because mud is highly impermeable, the rock is not a suitable target into which to drill a well.

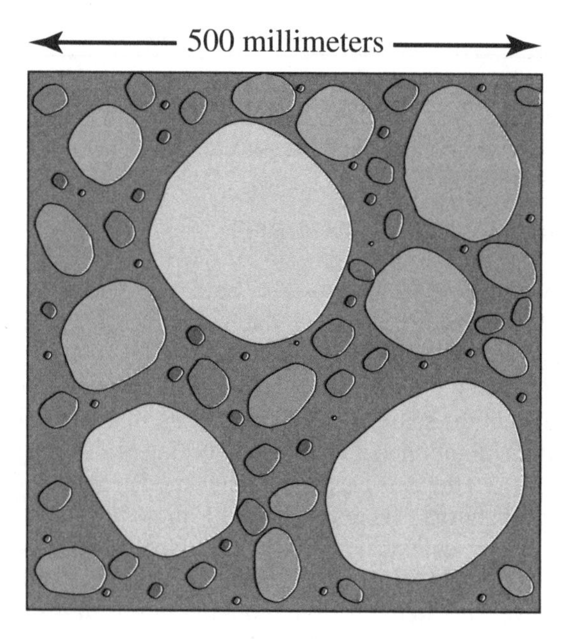

Roundness is another index of maturity. Water, a more viscous fluid, cushions the impacts much more effectively than does air, a less viscous fluid. The ultimate rounded shape, approaching a sphere, develops through innumerable high-speed impacts sustained by wind-blown sand grains. Because of their high mass (and momentum), stream-transported boulders are also damaged by impact even in a water medium, and tend to be somewhat rounded. Cobbles washed by the waves back and forth on a beach are mostly flat discs.

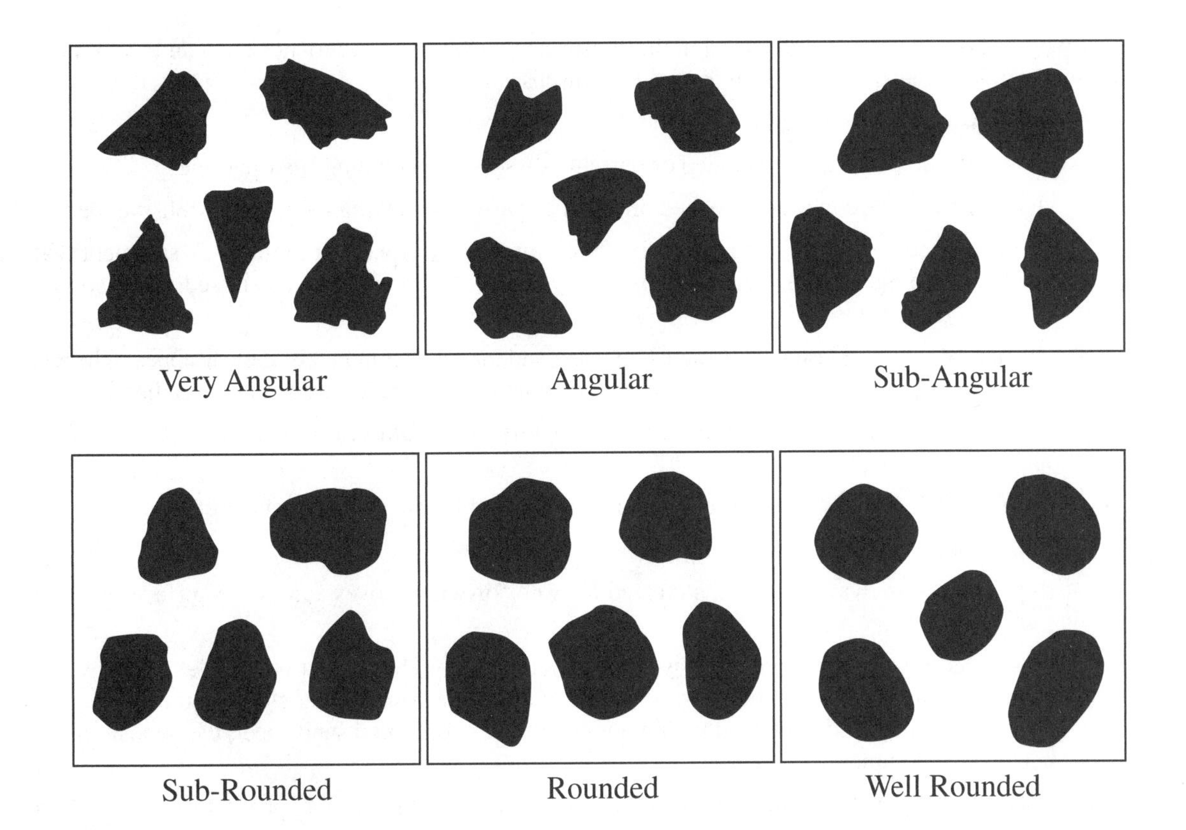

These particles, which are very well sorted according to size, illustrate different degrees of rounding.

DEPOSITIONAL ENVIRONMENTS

Sediment is deposited in an immense variety of environments, from mountain streams to the deepest ocean abyss, under low energy (quiet) to high energy (typically catastrophic) conditions (Figure 8-2). These environments are dynamic, continually changing as a result of sediment pouring in, or through participation in earth movements. For example, sediment known to have originated beneath the sea (because it contains marine fossils) may be uplifted to become dry land. Sediment can be deposited only where there is space to accommodate it. In a relatively stable environment, millions of years may transpire with deposition of sediment only a few meters thick. Where sediment is in abundant supply and the earth's crust is sinking, a deposit thousands of meters thick can accumulate rapidly.

Whether thick or thin, coarse or fine, distinctly or poorly stratified, containing abundant fossils or no fossils at all, the sedimentary rock itself contains clues about the nature of the environment of deposition. Fossils [Photo 8-1(*d*)] are important to the interpretation because most organisms can live only in specific environments. High energy is required to transport large particles, whereas sediment consisting only of fine particles probably was deposited in a low-energy environment. Mountain uplifts are rapidly eroded, becoming a source of abundant sediment that enters rivers. Eventually this sediment ends up in thick delta deposits, or possibly in the deep ocean immediately offshore of the delta. Ocean basins distant from a continental runoff are "starved" of sediment, remote from a source of clastic input.

DISTINCTIVE FEATURES

Geologists study sedimentary rocks on every scale of size. Some features are submicroscopic, or large enough to be observed with a 10-power hand lens, or by the unaided eye. Other diagnostic characteristics can be noted only in the field, in exposed rock outcrop. Yet other observations pertain to the entire sedimentary body, both in outcrop and buried in the subsurface. Several characteristics that can be observed in a hand sample in the laboratory or in the field are discussed below.

- **Particle size:** In general, during transportation:
  - coarse clastic particles are abraded or partially dissolved, becoming finer particles.
  - sharp corners and edges are knocked off angular particles, making them more well-rounded.
  - particles become better sorted (their sizes are more nearly equal). In Figure 8-3, sediment that is adjacent to the granite source rock is poorly sorted, whereas more distant sediment (stipple and dash patterns) is well sorted.
  - chemical weathering continues to attack feldspar and many other minerals; they disappear whereas quartz gains persist because they are highly resistant to chemical or mechanical weathering.

  These changes during transportation cause "immature" sediment to become more "mature" (not "younger" becoming "older").

- **Sedimentary structures** refer to forms that were created by the agent of transportation.

  For example:
  - ripple marks are wave-like forms created as water or wind moves across the surface of loose sediment.
  - cross-bedding consists of internal layers that are inclined with respect to the bed as a whole. For example, sand wafted over the crest of a dune will tumble down the far slope, coming to rest as a locally inclined bed contained within a much thicker horizontal sand sheet, the deposit of the entire dune complex.
  - mud cracks form by shrinkage when wet fine-grained sediment is exposed to drying for an extended period of time.

- **Fossils** indicate whether sediment was deposited on dry land, or in fresh water, normal marine water, hypersaline water, etc. because organisms are restricted to specific habitats.

- **Cement** is deposited in pore spaces among particles during diagenesis. Common cements include silica, calcium carbonate, and iron oxide. Where the rock is oxidized the cement may impart rich colors of red, brown, orange, or yellow hue. Iron in the chemically reduced state gives the rock a blue, green, or purple color.

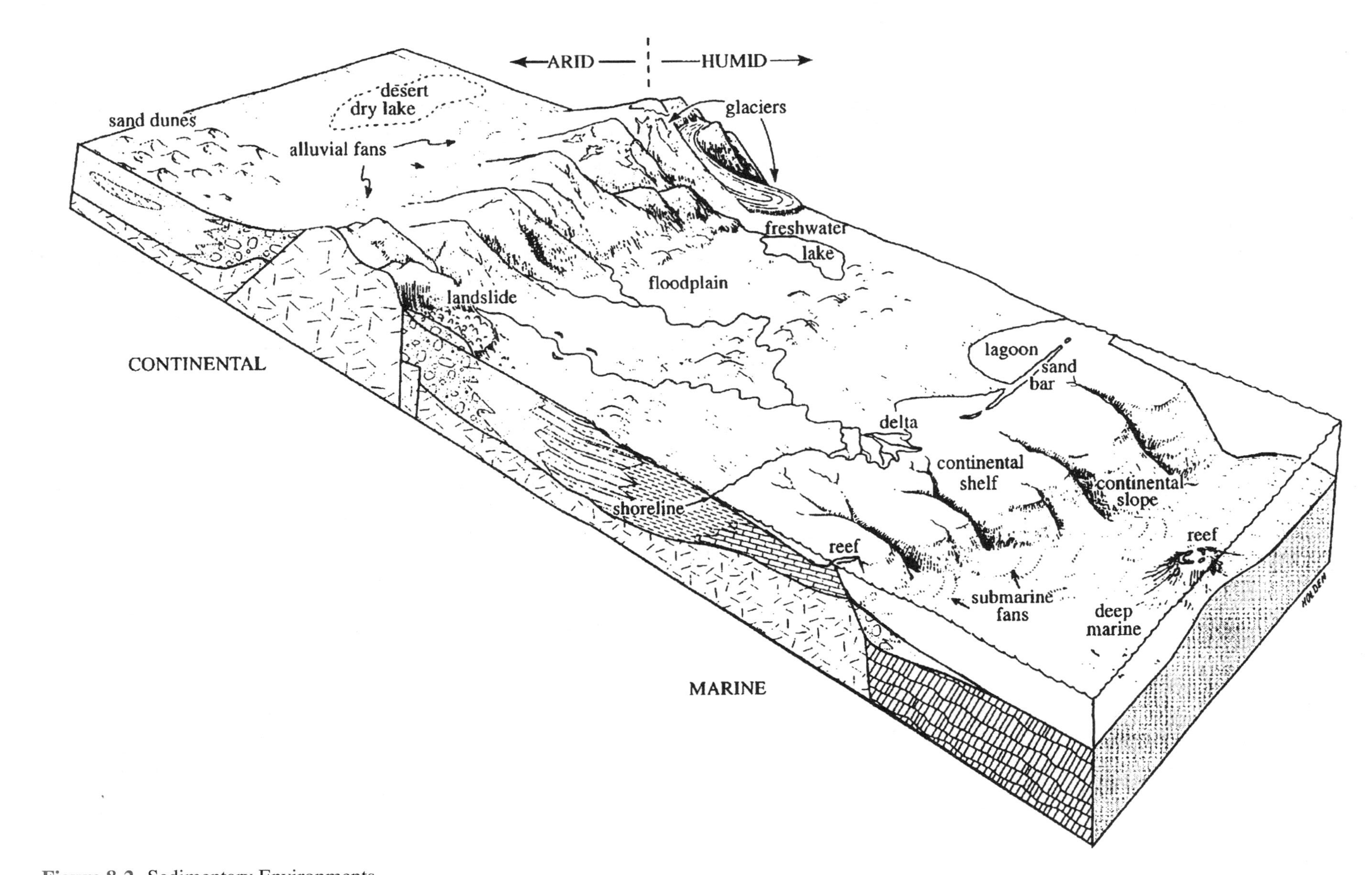

Figure 8-2. Sedimentary Environments

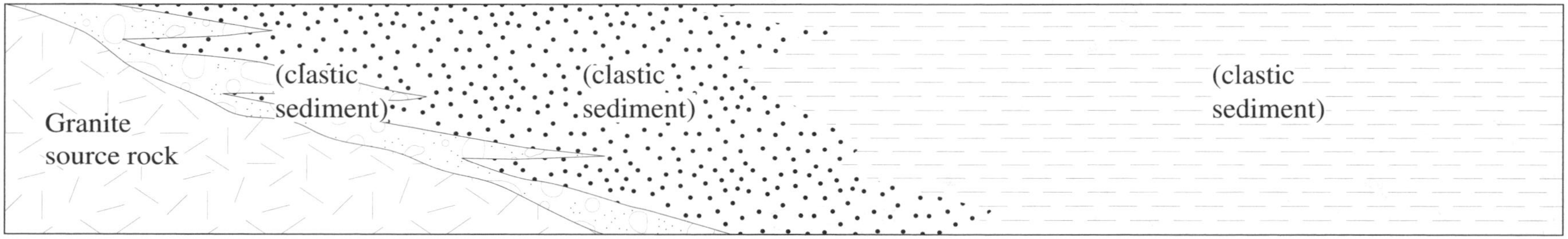

[Schematic cross section]

Near to source (coarser, more angular, more poorly sorted particles)

Transport of clastic particles ⟶

Distant from source (finer, more rounded, better sorted particles)

Granite source rock

(clastic sediment)

(clastic sediment)

(clastic sediment)

Distance from source	Near ⟶		Far
Energy of environment of deposition	High ⟶		Low
Size of the largest transported particle (related to energy)	Large ⟶		Small
Angularity *vs*. roundness	Angular (sharp corners and edges) ⟶	Rounded	
Degree of sorting	Poor (wide range of particle sizes) ⟶		Good (narrow range of particle sizes)
Minerals present	Both stable (e.g., quartz) and unstable (e.g., feldspar)	Chiefly stable (e.g., quartz)	Stable (e.g., clay derived from weathered feldspar)
Maturity	Immature ⟶		Mature
Examples	Breccia, arkose, conglomerate	Quartz sandstone, siltstone	Mudstone, shale

Figure 8-3. General Trends for Clastic Sedimentary Rocks

Table 8-1. *Terrigenous Clastic Sedimentary Rocks*

Range of Particle Size	Rock Name	Distinctive Features	Energy of Environment of Deposition
2 mm or larger	Conglomerate	Rounded grains up to boulder size (or larger), set in a matrix of finer material.	High-energy: stream bed subject to violent flooding, steep slope whether above or below sea level.
	Breccia	Similar to conglomerate, except that fragments are angular.	Limited transport of fragments; may be indicative of cavern collapse or landslide.
Sand-size: 1/16 to 2 mm	Quartz sandstone	Highly variable: rounded or angular quartz grains, with or without distinct stratification or sedimentary structures, lithified by cement with numerous possible colors. May contain minor feldspar.	Beach or nearshore deposit, point bar in river meander, certain alluvial plains. Sand dune or other wind-blown deposit.
	Arkose	Similar to quartz sandstone, except that 25% or more of the particles are feldspar, typically angular and coarse. May contain mica or other granitic constituents.	Near to granitic source rock, typically in alluvial fan or floodplain.
	Graywacke	Gray or greenish-gray, dense, fine-grained sandstone. Quartz rare; feldspar and rock fragments common, generally as angular particles in a dark silt or clay matrix.	Rapid deposition in offshore marine environment by submarine slumping or underwater mudflow in region experiencing mountain deformation.
Silt-size: 1/256 to 1/16 mm	Siltstone	Fine-grained rock with slightly gritty feel. Separates along bedding planes with difficulty.	Low- to moderate-energy aqueous environment: river, nearshore marine. May be wind-blown material.
Clay-size: less than 1/256 mm	Shale	Smooth feel because particles are very small (clay-size). Splits easily along closely-spaced bedding planes.	Low-energy aqueous environment: lake, continental shelf, lagoon, deep marine.

Chemical and Biochemical Sedimentary Rocks

Composition	Rock Name	Distinctive Features	Environment of Deposition
$CaCO_3$	Limestone	Reacts vigorously with cold dilute HCl. Typically light-colored. May have body fossils and trace fossils (e.g., burrows).	Evaporite; organic or inorganic precipitation in marine water (deep ocean floor, reef, lagoon, intertidal zone) or fresh water (cavern, hot spring).
$CaMg(CO_3)_2$	Dolomite	Reacts sluggishly with HCl when powdered to increase surface area. Typically light-colored. Fossils rare.	Shallow to deep marine. Inorganic partial replacement by Mg for some of the Ca in pre-existing calcium carbonate.
$CaCO_3$	Chalk	Reacts vigorously with cold dilute HCl. Generally porous and easily broken. A compacted mass of microscopic calcareous shells.	Mostly shallow marine. Organic.
$CaCO_3$	Coquina	Shell fragments cemented with calcite. "Shell breccia."	Shallow high-energy marine setting with abundant shell-building organisms.
NaCl	Rock salt	Rock form of halite. Normally a coarse crystalline aggregate. Colorless, or pale orange or rarely other colors.	Low-energy site of evaporation of natural waters: coastal marine or desert intermittent lakes.
$CaSO_4 \cdot 2H_2O$	Rock gypsum	Can be scratched by fingernail. Chiefly in compact granular masses. May exist as transparent slabs ("satin spar") or exhibit fibrous texture.	Same as halite.
SiO_2	Chert	Massive. Conchoidal fracture. Broken surfaces resemble unglazed porcelain.	Deep ocean ooze of microscopic siliceous shells of single-celled organisms. Inorganic precipitation from sea water. Replacement of pre-existing carbonate.
Complex organic molecules	Lignite, bituminous coal	Dark brown to black, low density. Commonly banded. May contain recognizable plant remains. Tendency to crumble.	Decomposed and altered remains of plants deposited in marshes, swamps, or estuaries.

Characteristics of Sedimentary Rocks

- Deposited at the earth's surface by wind, water, glacier ice, or biochemical processes
- Typically deposited in strata (layers) under cool surface conditions. This is in contrast to stratified volcanic rock (tuff), which has a hot origin.

Types of Sedimentary Rock

- **Clastic**: made up of **CLASTS** (broken-off particles) and **CEMENT** (typically calcite, quartz, or hematite)
  - Examples: sandstone, siltstone, conglomerate
- **Chemical/Biochemical**: deposited by inorganic means such as precipitation or evaporation (commonly consisting of one mineral), or originated through the activity of living organisms
  - Examples: limestone, chert

Weathering

- **Weathering**: changes that take place in a rock exposed at the earth's surface
- **Mechanical Weathering:** breaking larger pieces into smaller pieces (clasts), with no change of chemical composition
- **Chemical Weathering:** original minerals partially dissolve, and new minerals form that are more stable at the lower temperature and pressure, and more moist environment at the earth's surface.

Transportation and Deposition

- **Clastic sediment**: clasts are transported by wind, moving water, glaciers, and/or gravity.
  - Clasts are deposited when the transport energy is not sufficient to move the particles. As transport energy diminishes, the larger particles are deposited first.
- **Chemical sediment**: dissolved ions are precipitated from solution by biological activity, chemical change, or evaporation.

Energy of Environment

- **High-energy** environments can carry both large and small particles. Typically the conditions are catastrophic (landslide, flood).
- **Low-energy** environments (lake, deep ocean) can carry only small particles.

Texture (clastic rocks only)

- Particle size
  - Clay (very fine-grained): <1/256 mm
  - Silt (fine-grained): 1/256 to 1/16 mm
  - Sand (medium-grained): 1/16 to 2 mm
  - Pebbles (coarse-grained): >2 mm
- Particle size indicates the energy of the transporting medium. Larger grain size: more energy needed.
- Cement: calcite, quartz, or hematite cement is common.

Maturity of Clastic Sediment

Note: maturity does not refer to "older" or "younger" rock.

- **Textural maturity:**
  - Angularity: well rounded, subrounded, angular
  - Sorting: well sorted (all particles the same size), poorly sorted (different sizes together)
- The longer the time and distance of transportation, the better the rounding and the degree of sorting.
- **Mineralogical maturity:** (Goldich's Weathering Series)
  - Removal of clay
  - Presence of feldspar indicates immaturity.
  - Quartz is most resistant to chemical weathering.

Sedimentary Structures, Misc.

- Bedforms created by the agent of transportation
  - Stratification: horizontal layering at time of deposition
  - Symmetrical ripples: wave action
  - Asymmetrical ripples: wind or flowing water, indicating direction of current flow
  - Crossbeds: internal layering at an angle inside a stratum (lee side of a ripple, or lee side of a sand dune)
  - Mud cracks: develop in fine-grained sediment exposed to drying for an extended period.
- Coquina
- Evaporation of sea water: first calcite, then gypsum, then halite precipitating in a sequence

Chemical/Biochemical Rocks

- **Limestone** ($CaCO_3$) – formed by precipitation of calcite. Mostly in marine environments, comprised of the shells of dead organisms
- **Dolomite** [Ca,Mg (CO_3)] – formed as Mg partially replaces Ca in limestone
- **Gypsum** ($CaSO_4 \cdot 2H_2O$) and **Halite** (NaCl) – precipitated as sea water evaporates
- **Chert** (SiO_2) – altered microscopic shells of silica-secreting organisms
- **Coal** (mostly C) – altered plant remains

Sedimentary Rocks

- **DIAGENESIS**: physical and chemical changes occurring in sediment after deposition
- Diagenesis includes compaction, and cementation of loose sediment into coherent rock.
- Diagenesis takes place at much lower temperatures than metamorphism.

9

Transformed Rocks

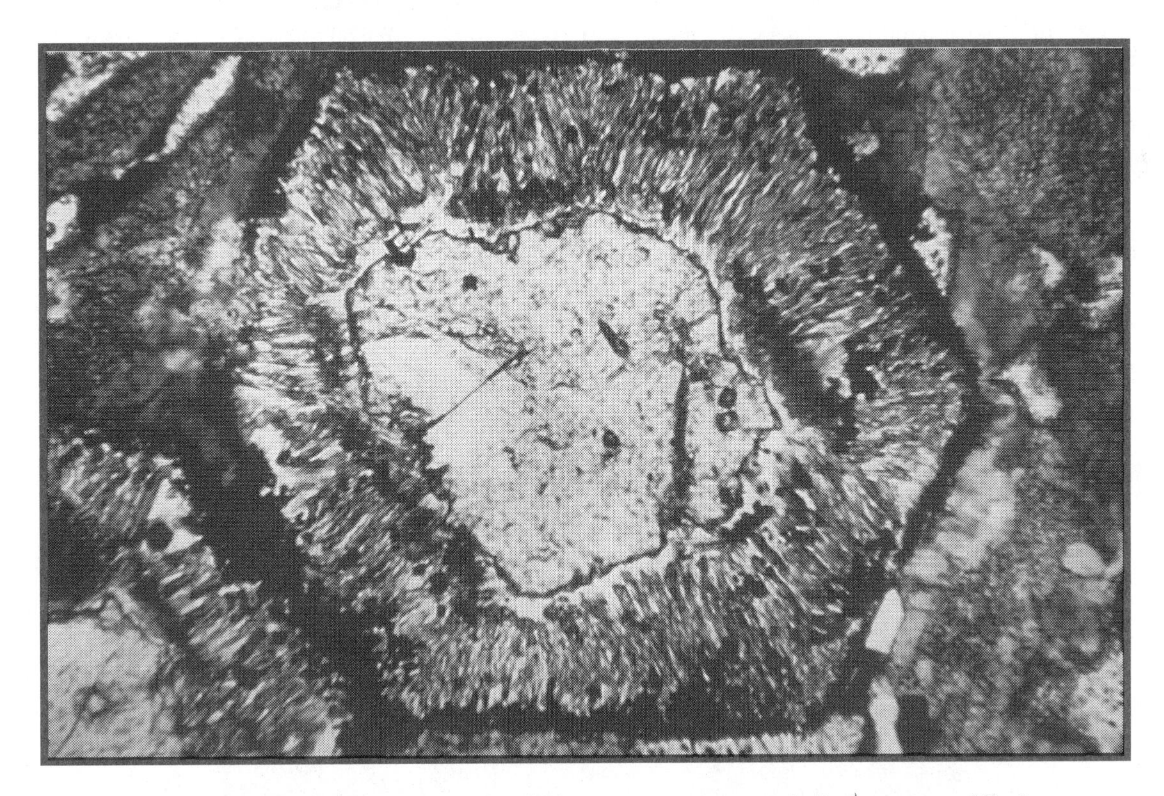

A six-sided crystal, about 2 millimeters across and shown magnified, once consisted of the mineral garnet. Ancient metamorphism in central Texas caused the mineral grain to be modified. Some of the original garnet remains in the interior, but the outer part has been replaced by small crystals of feldspar and hornblende that in turn are surrounded by a rim of black magnetite. [*Courtesy William D. Carlson*]

We have followed the cycling of granite, from its origin in the cooling of an underground mass of magma, to its eventual exposure to weathering at the earth's surface. At this point the granite decomposed into the hydrous clay mineral, kaolinite (see equation 7-3) and residual grains of quartz which were later deposited as a terrigenous clastic sediment. What if the sediment, for example a quartz sandstone with a little kaolinite, were to be progressively buried beneath a deforming mountain range. When this material is returned to great depth, would it become granite again? Yes, possibly, but not in any simple manner. For one thing, equation 7-3 also shows that dissolved K^+ ions are lost during weathering. A mixture of quartz and kaolinite does not contain potassium, and so melting and solidifying it cannot make granite whose chief mineral is potassium feldspar.

But there is another reason why the cycle from an igneous rock, through all those stages and back to an igneous rock again, can be so complicated. While it was heating up but before melting had taken place, the buried sediment would experience *metamorphism.* "Metamorphism" comes from a Greek word meaning "to transform." A metamorphic rock was originally igneous or sedimentary, but it has been transformed sufficiently that we are justified calling it a new rock. And since all rocks have been transformed at least slightly, how shall we define metamorphism? The weathering of granitic feldspar into clay, or the conversion of limestone into dolomite are changes that are as profound as any known to geologists. Why don't these processes qualify as metamorphism?

The factors essential to metamorphism are *high pressure* and *high temperature*. Pressure can affect a rock uniformly in all directions, but during metamorphism it is often accompanied by application of *shear stress*—force that is applied to the rock along certain directions only. We may picture shearing as the breaking of a rock along countless thin planes that accommodate motion, one plane slipping past other planes. Most metamorphism occurs very deep in the earth. Like granite and other intrusive igneous rocks, the metamorphic rocks are exposed to view only after prolonged erosion has taken place.

Metamorphic transformation may be anything from a mere baking or hardening of the rock to a reconstitution so far-reaching that every mineral grain has either recrystallized or reacted with other minerals. At very high temperature some of the rock may even melt. Igneous bodies are commonly emplaced into metamorphic terrains, but the metamorphic rocks themselves were recrystallized *in the solid state.* Evidence for the original identity of the rock may be quite dramatic. For instance, the elongated quartz rods seen in Figure 9-1 were once pebbles in a conglomerate, a sedimentary rock. During metamorphism the quartz pebbles were squeezed in one direction and stretched in another direction by shear stress, while remaining solid. If they had actually melted, they would not be recognizable as transformed quartz pebbles.

Figure 9-1. Metamorphism of this conglomerate in California has flattened the pebbles, but they still can be clearly identified. [*From L. E. Weiss,* The Minor Structures of Deformed Rocks, *Springer-Verlag New York, Inc., New York, 1972.*]

ROLE OF WATER IN METAMORPHISM

Familiar chemical reactions with solid materials also involve liquids or gases (for instance, dissolving salt in water). Experiments indicate that if mineral grains were placed in contact with one another for millions of years, at high temperature and pressure, they would not react. Most minerals are extremely inert. If that is so, how can metamorphism be a solid-state process? In fact, metamorphism *does* involve a trace of water which occupies pore spaces or which coats the grains as a thin film. During metamorphism, water is dissolved in the rock, rather than the other way around. Much of this H_2O is supplied by metamorphic breakdown of the hydrogen-containing clay minerals and muscovite.

Let's return to our sediment consisting of quartz and a little kaolinite. As temperature and pressure increase, the kaolinite reacts with the quartz to form pyrophyllite, a metamorphic mineral whose formula contains H_2O (Table 9-1). Most of the very abundant quartz still remains after all of the kaolinite has disappeared. At even higher temperature and pressure the pyrophyllite becomes unstable; it is replaced by andalusite or kyanite (Table 9-1) whose formulas do not contain H_2O. At even higher temperature or pressure, andalusite or kyanite may transform into sillimanite.

Notice that these three minerals have the *same* chemical composition; only the arrangements of aluminum atoms and silicon-oxygen tetrahedrons in their crystal structures are different. Each mineral is stable under particular combinations of pressure and temperature (Figure 9-2). For example, the rock would contain kyanite if metamorphism had taken place at relatively low temperature but high pressure. If both pressure and temperature had been very high, the mineral would be sillimanite rather than kyanite. Andalusite would signify relatively low-pressure metamorphism. All three minerals could co-exist only at the unique combination of pressure and temperature represented where the heavy lines join near the center of the diagram. (The temperature happens to be 500°C, at a pressure that the rock would experience if buried about 12 kilometers [7 miles] beneath the surface.) By observing which of these minerals is present, we may reach some important conclusions about the conditions of metamorphism. It is just one more example of how geologists act as historians of the earth.

This reasoning raises a problem because, unlike human history, geologic history in a sense can be "undone." If metamorphic rocks are stable at high temperature and pressure, why do they even exist at the earth's surface where temperature and pressure are low? We have seen how readily one assemblage of minerals may be transformed into a different assemblage. As the metamorphic rock in our example is unburied by erosion of the rocks overhead, why doesn't it go back to being quartz and kaolinite again? Most metamorphic rocks show only a faint hint of this reversal, or none at all. The chief explanation is that H_2O, the great promoter of chemical reactions, had been driven away in the meantime. It is the *loss* of water that prevents the chemical reactions from reversing direction.

During metamorphism, how far do the various substances travel within the rock? Ions may have traveled only a few millimeters when the outer part of the garnet crystal, shown at the front of this chapter, was

Table 9-1. *A Simple Metamorphic Series*

	Equilibrium assemblage	Chemical formula of silicate* (quartz: SiO_2, always present)	Atomic structure	Remarks
Increasing metamorphic intensity ↓	Kaolinite + quartz	Kaolinite: $4SiO_2 \cdot 2Al_2O_3 \cdot 4H_2O$	Sheet	Starting material (surface temperature and pressure)
	Pyrophyllite + quartz	Pyrophyllite: $4SiO_2 \cdot Al_2O_3 \cdot H_2O$	Sheet	Decreasing H_2O content
	Andalusite + quartz	Andalusite: $4SiO_2 \cdot 4Al_2O_3$	Complex	Anhydrous (no H_2O)
	Sillimanite + quartz	Sillimanite: $4SiO_2 \cdot 4Al_2O_3$	Complex	Anhydrous
	Kyanite + quartz	Kyanite: $4SiO_2 \cdot 4Al_2O_3$	Complex	Anhydrous

*Expressed in an unconventional manner to emphasize the changing proportions of silica, aluminum oxide, and water in the mineral that is in equilibrium with quartz.

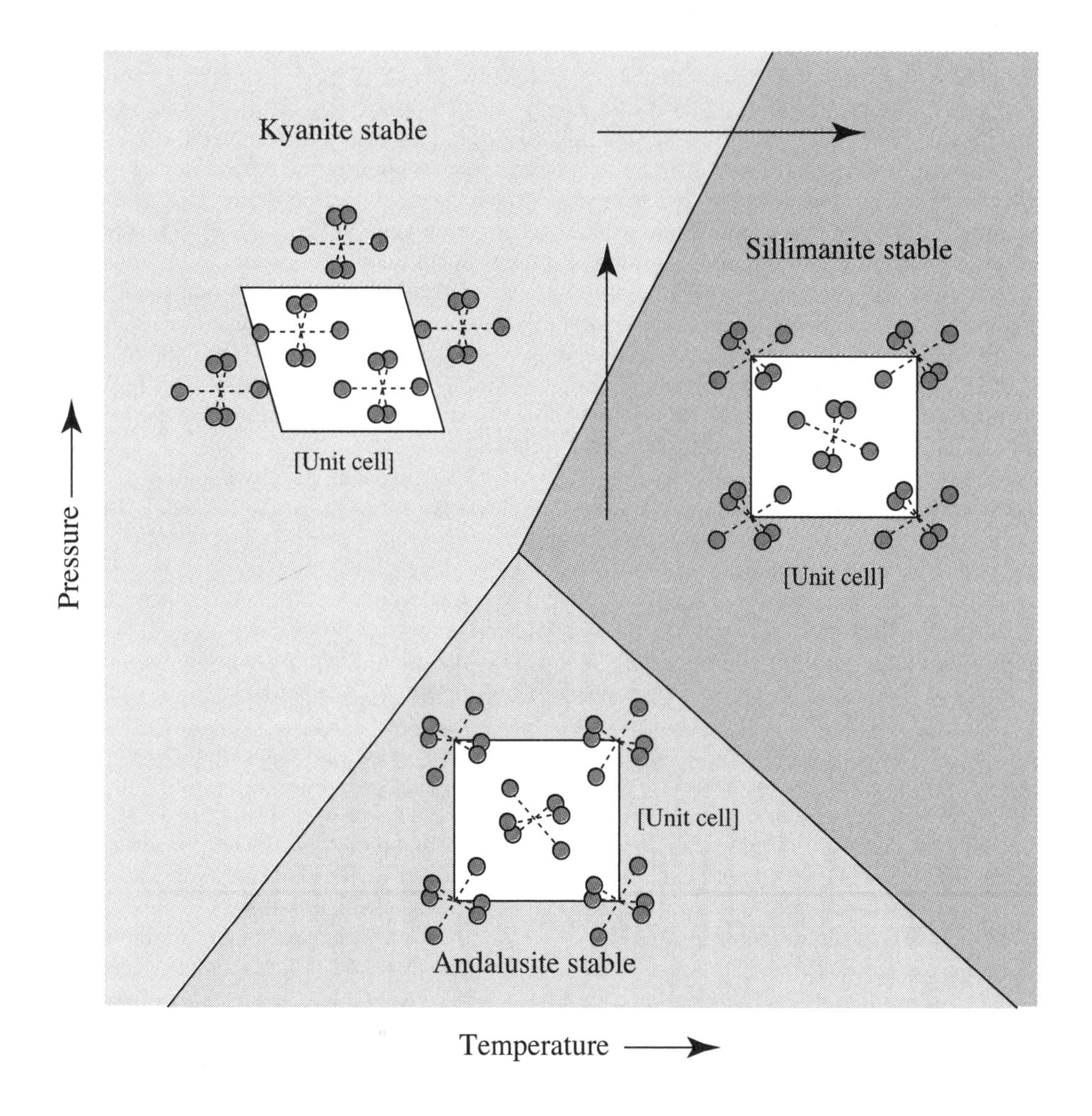

Figure 9-2. A stability diagram of andalusite, sillimanite, and kyanite also shows the differing arrangements of oxygen atoms around aluminum atoms in the crystal structures of these minerals. An increase in temperature at constant pressure (horizontal arrow) could cause kyanite to transform into sillimanite. An increase in pressure (vertical arrow) could have the opposite effect—the transformation of sillimanite into kyanite.

replaced by other minerals. Here the chemical "budget" was balanced locally, and it is a common situation. On the other hand, recent research has discovered that water and carbon dioxide have an amazing power to transport material long distances. The upward-moving fluids can "stew" dissolved sodium and potassium out of the lower crust and emplace these elements into the upper crust, creating a wholesale change of the rock compositions on a scale of kilometers.

TYPES OF METAMORPHISM

Elevation of temperature and pressure and application of shear stress can operate in various combinations with different results. The earth has always been in a state of unrest as the crust is warped upward into plateaus, depressed below sea level, mashed and crumpled into folds (Figure 9-3), torn asunder by faults, invaded by bodies of magma. Metamorphism is commonly an important part of this scenario.

Major faults are not simple ruptures; they are zones of shear that may be hundreds to thousands of kilometers long and as much as several kilometers wide. As the rocks on either side are forced past one another for great distances, they get crushed and smeared out by *dynamic* metamorphism. Although the original minerals may still be present, they have become involved in a mechanical style of metamorphism that radically changes the texture. At first, zones of finely crushed grains appear throughout the rock. With extreme shearing, the entire rock is "cold-welded" into a hard, flinty mass of tiny crystals (Figure 9-5). Disruption of the rock by *shear stress* is the chief agent of change in dynamic metamorphism.

Another style of metamorphism is seen along the margins of some igneous intrusions. Heat and fluids (mostly H_2O) escaping from the hot magma can penetrate the surrounding, or host rock, causing it to become *contact*-metamorphosed (Figure 9-6). Metal ions carried in the fluid can be precipitated as valuable ore deposits in the enclosing rock. The original form of sedimentary layering or fossils may be faithfully preserved, even though the contact-metamorphosed rock has been transformed into a mass of tiny new crystals. This result is the opposite from that of dynamic metamorphism, in which the original structures of the rock are obliterated even though the original set of minerals may not have been changed. *High temperature* is the chief ingredient in contact metamorphism. More accurately, it is the large difference in temperature between hot magma and cooler host rock that seems to be important. Most large granite batholiths are not surrounded by contact-metamorphic zones because at the time of igneous intrusion, the host rock was nearly as hot as the magma.

A third type, by far the most common, is *regional* metamorphism. Shear stress, high pressure, and high temperature are all likely to be important ingredients here. As the name implies, regional metamorphism affects very large areas in which rocks that formed near the surface have been brought down to great depth where they recrystallize, attaining equilibrium with the conditions of the new environment. Regional metamorphism is in progress deep in the immense pile of sediment beneath the coastal plain along the Gulf of Mexico. This region provides an example of a quiet burial metamorphism, not accom-

Figure 9-3. An outcrop of folded metamorphic rock in central Texas. [*Courtesy William Workman.*]

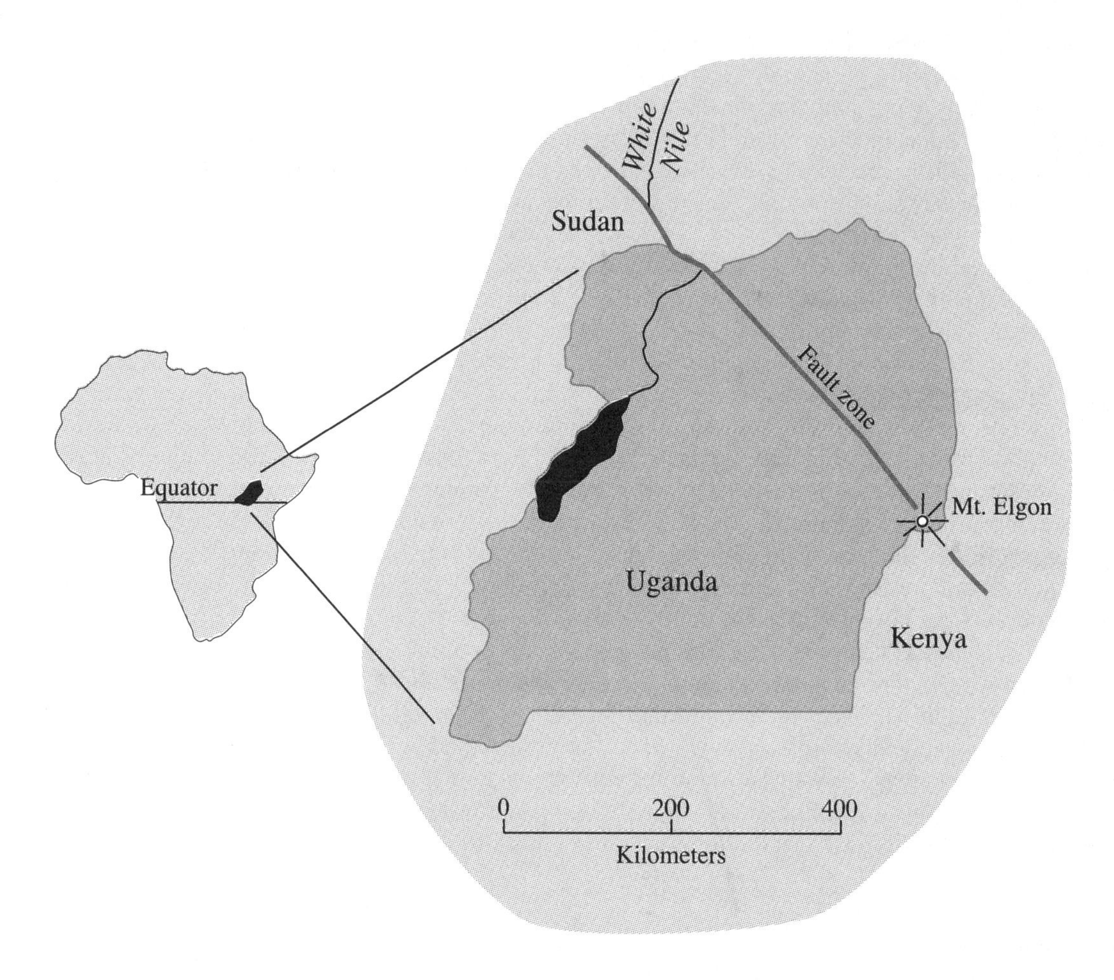

Figure 9-4. An ancient fault system can be traced for hundreds of kilometers from Sudan across Uganda into Kenya. Mount Elgon, a colossal volcano on Uganda's eastern border, has erupted through this belt of intensely crushed rock. The White Nile abruptly turns to follow this somewhat more easily eroded zone for some distance before resuming its northward course.

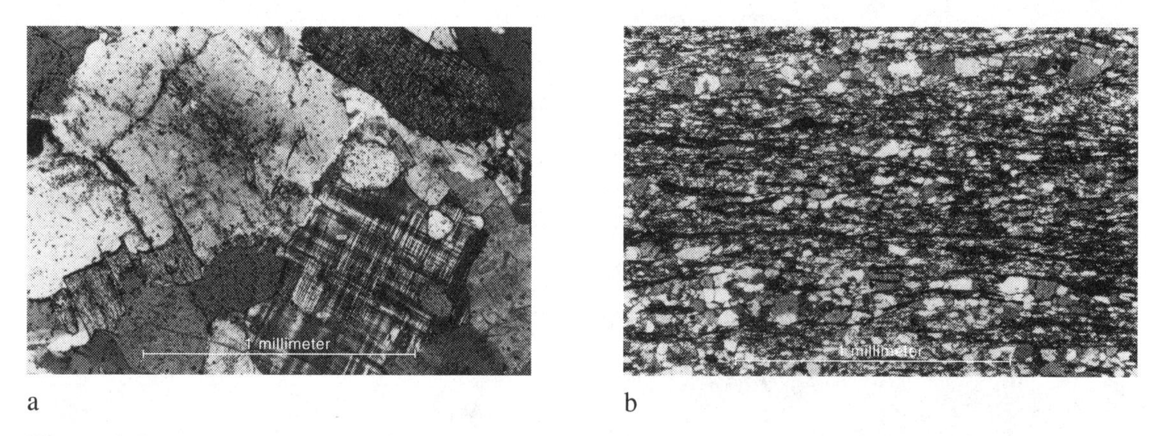

Figure 9-5. These photomicrographs show a progressive shear metamorphism of granitic rock. Unaffected igneous rock (*a*) has been sheared out into zones of fine-grained material (*b*) in which the crystals are ground too small for visual identification.

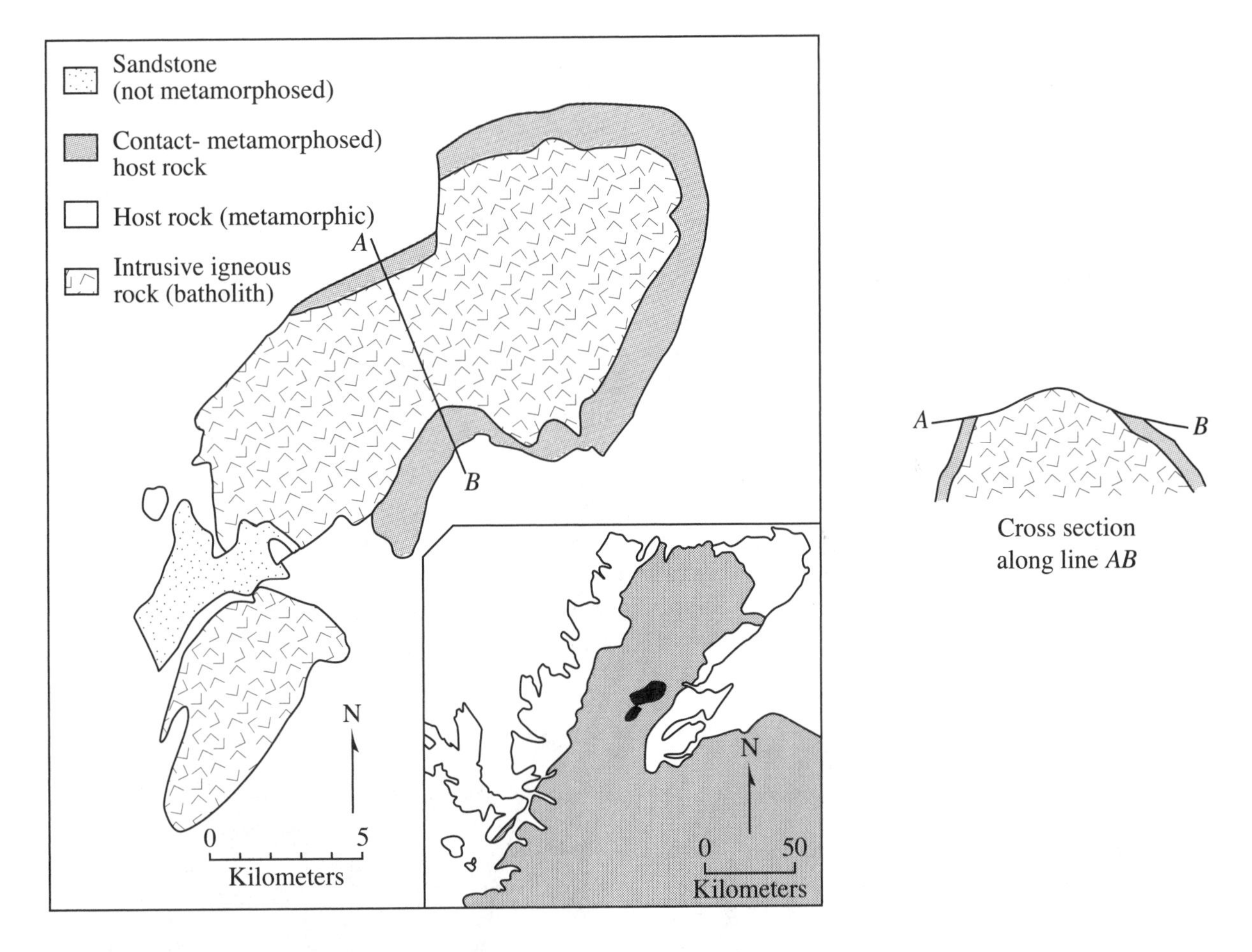

Figure 9-6. A granite batholith in Scotland (see inset map) reveals a complex history. When emplaced, the magma contact-metamorphosed the sedimentary host rock along its margins. More than 100 million years later, the entire shaded area (inset map), including the granite and its metamorphic fringe, was metamorphosed on a regional scale. A rock can be metamorphosed more than once. [*After L. E. Long, "Rb-Sr Chronology of the Carn Chuinneag Intrusion, Ross-shire, Scotland,"* Journal of Geophysical Research, *vol. 69, p. 1590, 1964. Copyright by American Geophysical Union.*]

panied by melting or strong deformation of the rock. Much more vigorous regional metamorphism is probably active beneath southern California, or the Alps of New Zealand, or the Himalayas of Tibet and northern India—earthquake country where mountain-making is currently in progress.

COMMON METAMORPHIC ROCKS

Let's review some steps in the rock cycle, beginning with weathering and erosion of granite or basalt. A great sorting takes place as solid particles are segregated into various types of clastic sediment, and dissolved ions reach the sea where they are precipitated as chemical sediment. Shale and immature sandstone are complex mixtures of different minerals. On the other hand, mature sandstone contains little besides quartz, and limestone is mostly calcite. After metamorphism, these two rocks are still composed of quartz or calcite, but the textures have been changed. Rounded grains in a quartz sandstone are recrystallized into a mosaic of interlocking crystals, something like pieces of a jigsaw puzzle, in the metamorphic rock *quartzite* (Figure 9-7). Limestone recrystallizes into a more coarse-grained mass of calcite crystals in its metamorphic equivalent, *marble*.

Quartz grains in sandstone are stronger than the cement that binds them together. The rock feels gritty because it fractures *around* the grains which project above the broken surface. A surface of quartzite feels sugary because it fractures *through* grains and cement alike. Quartzite is the strongest and most resistant to erosion of any of the common rocks (Figure 9-8), but marble offers no more resistance than limestone does to being dissolved by acidic groundwater.

Metamorphism of shale or mudstone includes both a change of texture, and reactions of the original minerals to form new metamorphic minerals. At the outset, shear stress causes the sheet-like clay particles to rotate into a parallel arrangement within the rock. Tiny parallel wisps of muscovite mica appear; this mineral, which also has a sheet structure, enables the entire rock to split into thin, flat-sided plates characteristic of *slate*. Deformed fossils can be identified in slate (Figure 9-9), but in more severely metamorphosed rocks the fossils are generally destroyed.

The theme of parallel layering of crystal faces (especially the flat mica flakes) is carried out in most metamorphic rocks which are thus said to exhibit *metamorphic foliation*. (Earlier we noted the term "exfoliation" in reference to sheets popping apart during weathering.) Beyond the slate stage, especially if water is still present, the reorganization into new minerals becomes very evident. Two other rock types deserve mention. *Schist* is a coarse-grained rock, strongly foliated because mica is abundantly present. Other metamorphic minerals such as garnet or staurolite (complex silicate minerals) may be present in schist (see Figure 9-11). *Gneiss* (pronounced "nice") is a strongly metamorphosed rock in which layers rich in dark ferromagnesian minerals alternate with lighter-colored quartz-feldspar layers (Figure 9-10). Schist and gneiss are convenient terms to describe appearance without regard to origin. With increasing intensity of metamorphism, the rock becomes so transformed that it is not possible to tell its original

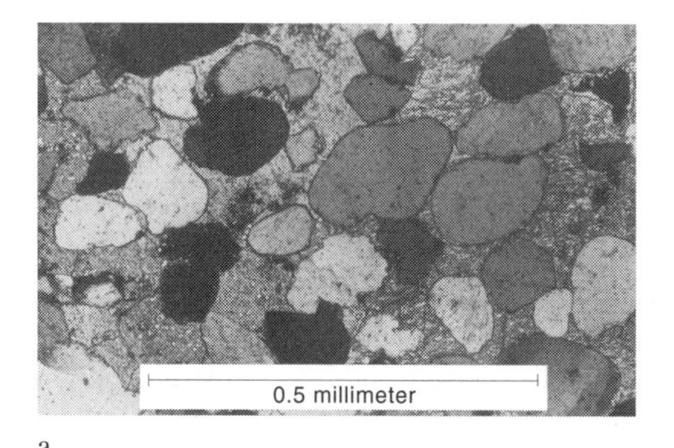

a

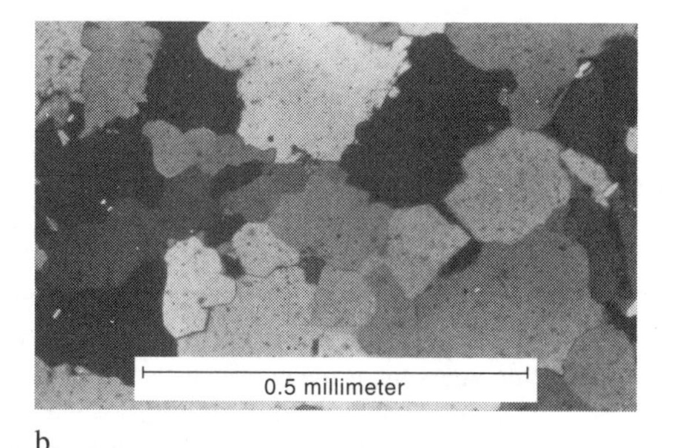

b

Figure 9-7. Rounded quartz grains, bonded together by a precipitated cement in sandstone (*a*), become recrystallized into an interlocking mass of crystals in quartzite (*b*). Quartz grains appear white, or various shades of gray, depending on their orientation which determines whether they will transmit or partially block the passage of polarized light. [*(a) Courtesy Earle McBride.*]

Figure 9-8. Quartzite ridges in the Republic of South Africa stand sharply above a plain that is underlain by less resistant rock. [*Courtesy Daniel Barker.*]

Figure 9-9. This fossil trilobite (an extinct marine animal) in North Wales became weirdly deformed as it and the enclosing rock were compressed. [*From L. E. Weiss,* The Minor Structures of Deformed Rocks, *Springer-Verlag New York, Inc., New York, 1972.*]

identity. Under the most extreme metamorphic conditions, all the hydrous minerals disappear. In some terrains, rocks that were once buried 20 or 30 kilometers are now exposed as monotonous expanses of a simple feldspar-pyroxene rock.

Figure 9-10. Layers in gneiss from New York have been deformed into numerous small folds. Although the gneiss was probably once a sediment or a volcanic rock, these layers are not necessarily original depositional bedding. Gneissic layering is a feature developed in the rock by metamorphism. [*Judy Camps.*]

ANCIENT REGIONAL METAMORPHISM: A CLASSIC STUDY

One of the first systematic studies of metamorphism was reported in 1893 by the British geologist George Barrow. The small area in Scotland that he examined provides an ideal case example of regional metamorphism (Figure 9-11). Barrow found that metamorphism is barely noticeable in a narrow strip of land next to a major fault (southeast corner of map). A short distance to the northwest, tiny crystals of biotite appear in the rock, in addition to the familiar major constituents, quartz and feldspar. At still greater distances, metamorphic garnet, then staurolite, then kyanite, and finally sillimanite appear. It was clear to Barrow that the degree of metamorphism increases in a northwesterly direction. He drew lines on a map (Figure 9-11) to show the first appearance of each of these minerals, and called the lines *isograds* because they mark zones of equal "grade" or intensity of metamorphism.

One could argue that the isograds simply indicate variations in composition of the original rock. Barrow nicely responded to this criticism by pointing to an impure quartzite layer that surely must have been a uniform sandstone when deposited. Today, the metamorphic isograds cut *across* the quartzite (Figure 9-11).

What determines the intensity of metamorphism? Is it temperature, pressure, shear stress, chemical composition, availability of H_2O? After a century of field and laboratory study, we know of course that it is a combination of all these factors. Perhaps we can reason about conditions of metamorphism by use of information in Barrow's map and in Figure 9-2. Note that a kyanite-containing zone lies south of the region that contains sillimanite. Kyanite is stable at high pressure, and so is sillimanite but at a higher temperature (Figure 9-2). Thus we infer that the pressure was quite high, and that the temperature of metamorphism increased in going from south to north (horizontal arrow in Figure 9-2).

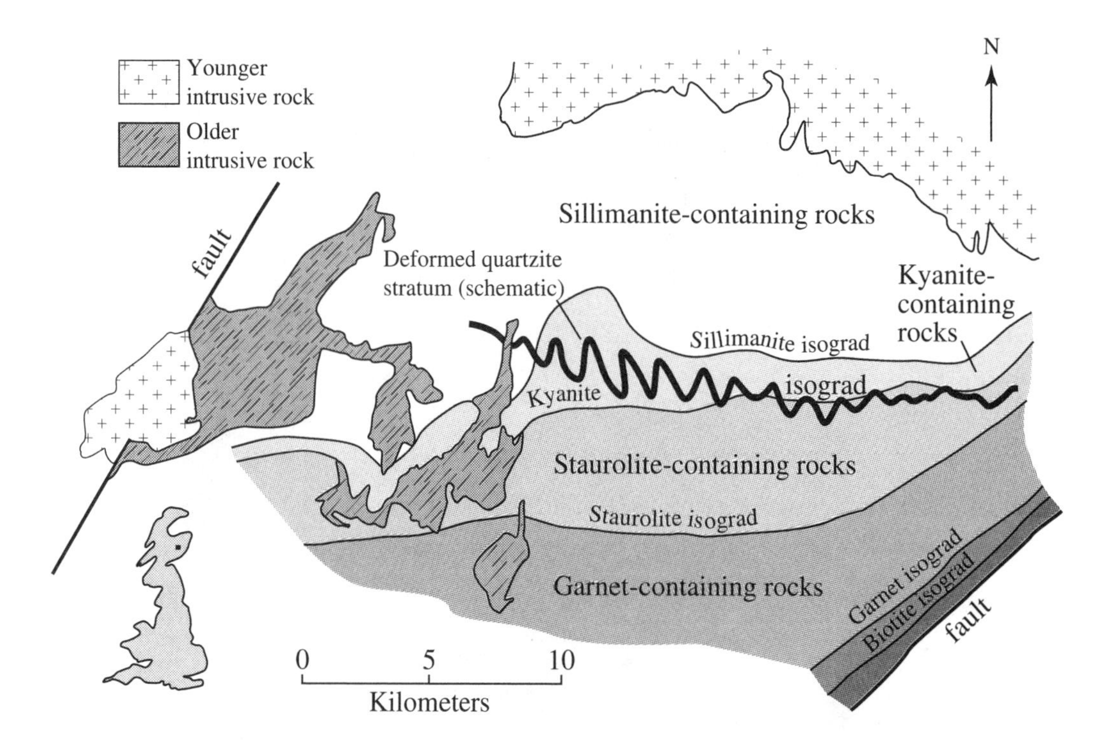

Figure 9-11. Barrow's map of an area in Scotland (see inset map) shows several igneous bodies, and isograds crossing a region of metamorphosed sedimentary rock. [*After G. Barrow, "On an Intrusion of Muscovite-Biotite Gneiss in the Southeastern Highlands of Scotland, and Its Accompanying Metamorphism,"* Quarterly Journal of the Geological Society of London, *vol. 49, 1893.*]

SUMMARY

Metamorphic rocks originate when igneous, sedimentary, or even pre-existent metamorphic rocks are recrystallized in the solid state, transformed into a new set of minerals which are stable under conditions of elevated temperature and pressure. Presence of shear stress and traces of H_2O greatly increase the rate and degree of metamorphism. After the water has escaped from the rock during the heating-up stage of metamorphism, further reactions are greatly inhibited. Metamorphism may be a result of mechanical shearing of rock (dynamic metamorphism), or heating and permeation of fluids through rock that is adjacent to an igneous intrusion (contact metamorphism). Regional metamorphism, the most important style, affects vast areas wherever rocks that formed near the surface are brought to great depth in the earth. High temperature, high pressure, deformation by shearing, and activity of H_2O are all important ingredients in regional metamorphism. Each of the common metamorphic minerals kyanite, andalusite, and sillimanite is stable only under specific combinations of pressure and temperature. Presence of a particular mineral broadly indicates the conditions of metamorphism.

Tough, erosion-resistant quartzite is metamorphosed sandstone; marble is metamorphosed limestone or dolomite. Foliation in metamorphic rock is created by a parallel alignment of grains of minerals, such as mica, that have platy or sheet-like form. Metamorphism of shale produces slate—fine-grained rock having extremely well developed foliation. Other common metamorphic rocks are schist which is a coarser-grained, well-foliated rock with abundant mica, and gneiss which is a more generalized layered metamorphic rock in which mica is not abundant. Metamorphism of a wide variety of rock types can produce schist or gneiss. Intensity of metamorphism may be seen to have varied across a region on a scale of kilometers. Metamorphic isograds are drawn on a map to indicate appearances of diagnostic minerals which indicate variations of temperature, pressure, or activity of H_2O.

10

Metamorphic Rocks

INTRODUCTION

Metamorphism comes from a Greek word meaning "to transform." During metamorphic recycling, the character of an igneous, sedimentary, or even a pre-existing metamorphic rock is changed, generally under conditions of **elevated temperature and pressure**. This change may be anything from just a subtle touch, to a transformation so profound that it is not possible to tell what the original, or **parent rock**, may have been like. High temperature and pressure are associated with the interior of the earth, where magmas originate. Although metamorphism may be a very hot process, it stops short of actual melting which would have created an igneous rock. It is common, however, for metamorphic rocks to be intimately associated with intrusive igneous rocks.

METAMORPHIC PROCESSES

High temperature causes chemical reactions to speed up dramatically. Effects of metamorphic reactions are most obvious in a parent rock that had formed in a distinctly different environment. Consider the sedimentary rock, shale, for example. Clay minerals in shale, being products of chemical weathering under the cool, low-pressure conditions of the earth's surface, are not stable at high temperature and pressure. Suppose that shale were to be deeply buried and subjected to mechanical stress, perhaps within a mass of rock being deformed into mountains. The atomic structures of its clay minerals would break down while reorganizing to form a new set of minerals that are stable at high temperature and pressure. If deep erosion were to expose this rock at the earth's surface, the metamorphic minerals at the surface would be just as out of equilibrium as the original clay minerals were when they were buried and heated. The metamorphic minerals would be recycled to become clay, or some other mineral species that is stable in the weathering zone.

Low-grade metamorphism does not completely obliterate all of the original features of the parent rock, for example cross-bedding or fossils in a sedimentary rock, or gas vesicles in a basalt flow. Already with very low-grade metamorphism, some of the original minerals in the parent rock are beginning to be destroyed as new mineral species appear. The texture of the rock also changes; platy minerals such as mica flakes become aligned parallel to one another, imparting a structure to the rock that runs in some particular direction. This texture, called **metamorphic foliation**, is not bedding, and indeed its orientation may be quite different from that of original layering. In most rocks that have experienced **high-grade** metamorphism, the foliation is well developed and the transformation has erased much of the evidence for the rock's original identity. Reorganization of the rock chemistry and the appearance of distinctive textures are summarized as **metamorphic recrystallization**.

STYLES OF METAMORPHISM

High temperature, high pressure, and deformation of the rock by shearing may act together in different combinations. If a hot magma were to invade the earth's crust near to the surface, it would strongly heat the rocks in contact with it, but not necessarily under a condition of high pressure. Heat and fluids escaping from a cooling batholith would subject a zone of host rock adjacent to the magma to **contact metamorphism**, whose effects die out within a short distance from the igneous body. If the chemical compositions of the igneous rock and host rock are very different, as for example for a granite magma emplaced into limestone, the contact metamorphic effects developed in the limestone may be spectacular.

Major mountain ranges form where tectonic plates (a subject to be discussed) are in collision. Areas that are hundreds to thousands of kilometers in dimension may be experiencing metamorphism in which high temperature, high pressure, shear stress, and a permeating fluid medium are acting together. These rocks are subject to high-grade **regional metamorphism** in the midst of the collision zone. Toward the edge of the region so affected, the intensity would diminish to low-grade regional metamorphism, and yet farther away, the rock would be unmetamorphosed (Figure 10-1).

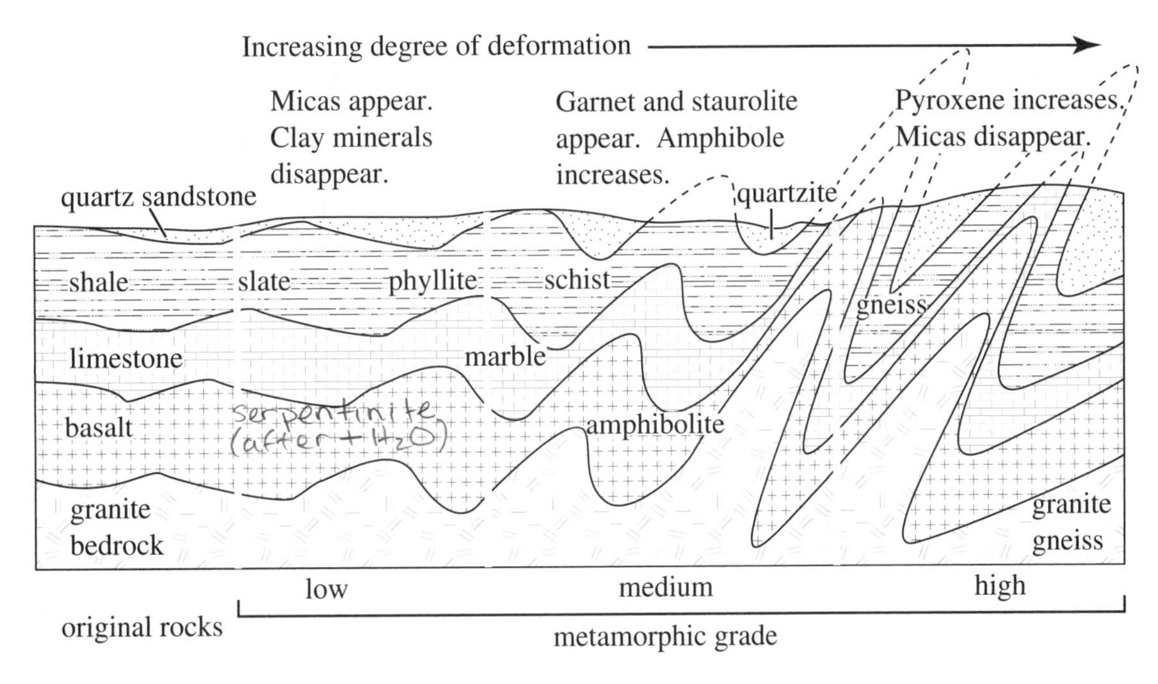

Figure 10-1. Progressive Metamorphism of Different Parent Rocks

Metamorphic Rock Classification

	Color	Rock name	Distinctive features	Typical parent rock
Non-foliated	light color	Marble	Reacts with hydrochloric acid (HCl). Color streaks or blotches may be present. Look for calcite rhombohedrons if coarse. Rare "ghost fossils."	Limestone, Dolomite
		Quartzite	Interlocking quartz grains fracture across original grain boundaries. May have a sugary texture; smoother and harder than sandstone.	Quartz sandstone
	green	Serpentinite	Lime green to dark green or black; dense. Slickensided surfaces (striated by internal movement) are common.	Mafic or ultramafic rock
	dark gray to black	Hornfels	Dense, fine-grained rock with conchoidal fracture.	Any fine-grained rock
		Anthracite coal	Shiny, low-density black rock; may have semi-conchoidal fracture and display partings or banding.	Lignite, bituminous coal
	Crystal size	**Rock name**	**Distinctive features**	**Typical parent rock**
Foliated	microscopic crystals	Slate	Dull to shiny; splits into thin slabs. Harder than shale. Commonly dark gray, brown, red, or green.	Shale, siltstone, silicic volcanic rock
		Phyllite	Nearly invisible mica crystals impart satiny sheen on foliation surfaces. Commonly gray or gray-green.	Shale, siltstone
		Schist	Visible aligned platy or elongate minerals impart a foliation. Mica abundant; garnet or staurolite crystals common.	Shale, phyllite, volcanic rock
		Amphibolite	Dark, dense, mafic rock with aligned hornblende crystals.	Mafic igneous rock, graywacke
	large crystals	Gneiss	Coarse-grained rock with alternating light (felsic) and dark (mafic) layers due to segregation of mineral species.	Any silicate rock

Quartzite. (Photo by Gary Jacobson.)

Serpentinite with prominent slickensides (grooves on a fault plane). (Photo by Gary Jacobson.)

Anthracite coal. (Photo by Gary Jacobson.)

Slate. (Photo by Gary Jacobson.)

Biotite schist. (Photo by Gary Jacobson.)

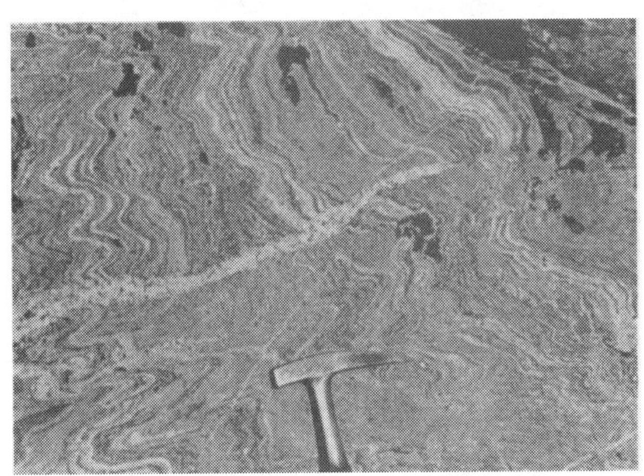

Gneiss showing distorted foliation and small cross-cutting dike, Southern California Batholith. (Photo by Allen Bassett.)

Photo 10-1. Metamorphic Rock Types

Metamorphic Rocks

- **METAMORPHISM:** a process that occurs typically at elevated temperature and pressure to produce changes in texture and assemblage of minerals present in the original, or parent rock
- Includes recrystallization: making new minerals from original minerals, or changing the texture of the rock
- Metamorphism is a solid state transformation.

Factors of Metamorphism

- **High temperature**: lower limit ~150°C (diagenesis) and upper limit ~ 700°C to 900°C (melting of granite or basalt)
- **High pressure**: commonly due to overlying rock or force applied during mountain building
- **Shear stress**: deformation of rock, typically in association with mountain building
- **Presence of fluids** (especially H_20): active in making and breaking chemical bonds

Styles of Metamorphism

- **Contact metamorphism**
  - Achieved as heat energy passes from a cooling body of magma into the enclosing (or host) rock
  - Occurs at **high temperature** and (typically) low pressure
  - Normally affects a small area.
- **Regional metamorphism**
  - Associated with mountain building
  - **High temperature, high pressure, and shear stress**
  - Affects a large area.

Metamorphic Grade

- Low-grade (mild) metamorphism: small changes in texture and/or mineralogy of parent rock (150-200°C)
- High-grade (extreme) metamorphism: radical changes in texture and/or mineral composition of the rock

Metamorphic Texture

- **Foliation**: Parallel alignment of platy mineral grains (such as mica) in a rock caused by directed stress.
- Foliated textures:
  - **slaty cleavage**: parallel alignment of microscopic platy minerals (mainly mica). LOW-GRADE METAMORPHISM
  - **phyllitic texture:** parallel, but wavy, foliation of fine-grained platy minerals (mainly mica and chlorite) exhibiting a shiny or glossy luster. LOW-GRADE METAMORPHISM
  - **schistosity:** parallel to sub-parallel foliation of medium to coarse-grained platy minerals. INTERMEDIATE TO HIGH-GRADE METAMORPHISM
  - **gneissic layering:** discontinuous light and dark layering due to mineral segregation. INTERMEDIATE TO HIGH-GRADE METAMORPHISM

Metamorphic Texture (continued)

- **Nonfoliated** texture:
  - absence of parallel layers of platy minerals
  - may exhibit stretched grains (ductile deformation)
  - normally composed of stubby, interlocking grains approximately the same size

Textural Changes

- Other changes that can occur during metamorphism:
  - Crystals grow in size.
  - Minerals can become segregated from one another to form compositional layering (as in gneiss).
  - Crystal shapes can become distorted (ductile deformation).
  - New minerals can form (polymorphic transformation)

Mineral Assemblages

Depend upon:

- chemical composition of parent rock
- intensity of metamorphism (involving temperature, pressure, shear stress)

Mineral assemblage can change with no change in bulk chemical composition.

Shear Stress (directed stress)

- Distortion or deformation (change in shape or size, or both)
- Development of lineation: single, preferred orientation of elongated crystals (such as hornblende)
- Development of foliation: crystals with platy habit (such as mica) lining up parallel

Index Minerals

- Diagnostic minerals indicate a restricted range of pressure-temperature conditions of metamorphism.
- General appearance with increasing metamorphism:
  - Low grade → high grade
  - Mica appears (clay disappears) → garnet and staurolite appear; amphibole increases → pyroxene increases (mica disappears)
  - H_2O-rich----------------------------------- → H_2O-absent

Increasing Metamorphic Grade

Mudstone/shale (parent rock)

→ slate → phyllite → schist → gneiss

(fine-grained) → (medium-coarse grained)

Bulk Composition

- Although a mineral assemblage may change with an increasing grade of metamorphism, the bulk chemical composition of the original parent rock commonly does not change (except for loss of water).
- Examples:
  - **Quartz sandstone-----------------quartzite**
  - **Limestone/dolomite---------------marble**
  - **Basalt--------------------------------amphibolite**
  - **Granite------------------------------granite gneiss**

"... Milestones on the Eternal Path of Time"

The Acasta Gneiss, approximately 4 billion years old, is exposed in this lakeside cliff in the uninhabited reaches of far northern Canada. Although ancient rocks in western Australia contain individual crystals that have been recycled through erosion of an unknown source that is older (4.1 to 4.4 billion years), the Acasta Gneiss is the world's oldest preserved entire coherent rock. [*Courtesy Todd Housh*]

In previous chapters we have considered the earth's materials and how these substances are cycled from one form into another. The sedimentary strata visible in yonder hill might consist of clastic particles, weathered from a gneiss, which itself was the result of metamorphism of a granite. This chapter addresses the subject of geologic *time*, the well-known "fourth dimension." Our understanding of the earth must include not only what it is made of, but also when the events took place leading, for example, from granite to gneiss to sandstone. Geologists are historians of the earth.

The earth is generally considered to be exceedingly ancient, and indeed the phrase "geologic time" or "deep time" is commonly used to refer to periods of seemingly limitless duration. But we may pose more specific questions: How old is our planet? Did the earth maintain the same appearance while recycling, or did it experience a non-repeating progression of stages? How old is the most ancient crust that has been preserved without being recycled? When did life begin? We already have answers to some of these weighty questions. Originating about 4.55 billion years ago, the earth has evolved through a series of distinctive stages leading to its present state. The oldest surviving piece of crust is 4 billion years old, and life has been present for most of that unimaginable length of time.

Not everyone accepts this view of the earth's antiquity. The notion of an ancient earth is contrary to the personal theology of many, calling themselves "creationists," who believe that God created the earth suddenly as we see it today, only a few thousand years ago. Part of the creationist-scientist controversy has to do with Biblical interpretations, and partly it is a problem of the nature of earth science. We cannot witness an event that happened in the remoteness of a time past, just as we cannot directly examine something that is remotely distant in space, for example in the earth's deep interior. Thus, geologists must employ indirect means to study these past events and inaccessible places. Some of their interpretations are based more upon the weight of circumstantial evidence than upon experiments that can be repeated in the laboratory.

To the creationists, this is not good enough. They believe that the only valid science is based upon experiments that are under human control, experiments that any skeptic could verify at any time by repeating them. Geologists vigorously object to this restrictive viewpoint. They affirm that natural phenomena that are too large, or distant, or ancient for us to control or to observe fully are nevertheless valid subjects of study by any available means. Circumstantial evidence becomes compelling when many thousands of diverse sorts of observations point to the same conclusion. A case in point is the overwhelming amount of evidence for an ancient earth that has been accumulated by geologists. Geology, astronomy, and evolutionary biology are "historical" sciences in the sense that much of the research is interpretation of what has already happened in nature. Experiments are also performed, but not as extensively as in physics, chemistry, and experimental biology, subjects in which most of the research consists of laboratory manipulations in "real time."

THE DISCOVERY OF TIME

And so, not everyone looks at the world from the scientific viewpoint, not even in this so-called "scientific age." In fact, until relatively recently there was no such thing as science and only a sketchy concept of human history, much less a history of the earth. Ideas of antiquity grew slowly along with other early discoveries in geology. Let us consider some of the major turning points along the intellectual pathway that has led us to recognize our place in the stream of time.

Early Speculations

People in ancient civilizations had no compelling reason to ponder the events of the past, which was thought to be irrelevant. Consider the situation of the classical empires of the Middle East: there was communal life and the beginnings of technology, including use of fire and domestication of plants and animals. The predictable flow of day and night, the seasons, and more occasional events such as the succession of rulers, battles fought, the rise and decline of empires—all of these shared a sort of timelessness. Life went on, generation after generation, without much obvious change in culture or quality. The pressing issue of the day was survival of the social order rooted in the Natural Order. Records of family descent were important to enable each person to find a rightful place in the social order. But events that had occurred decades or a few centuries earlier were already fading into the realm of mystery and mythology.

The Greek philosophers also considered the universe to be static, hence time was of no great consequence. Plato thought that the world's beginning was more than 9,000 years previously; Aristotle argued that time is unbounded and the universe eternal. To the Greeks, the important thing was to discern the eternal realities behind and beyond the flux of events. It was a viewpoint that even encouraged a contempt for the past. For example, in the opening of a historical account, Thucydides wrote:

> Judging from the evidence which I am able to trust after most careful inquiry, I should imagine that the former ages were not great, either in their wars or anything else.

If nature and human affairs are endlessly recycled, what point is there to delve into the essential sameness of some previous era?

The Rule of Authority

A second phase of thought in Western civilization was the shift from philosophical speculations to appeals to authority, specifically to *Genesis*, the first book of the Bible. It is a compelling authority to multitudes of people, more than 2 billion if the adherents of Judaism, Christianity, and Islam are included. Strictly speaking, the majestic opening of the Bible ("In the beginning God created the heavens and the earth") makes no commitment about the date of creation. The following verses describe a continued reorganization of creation taking place in six "days," culminating in the appearance of mankind. The creative days have been variously interpreted as time spans ranging from 24-hour periods to indefinitely long periods of geologic time. Another event of geologic importance in *Genesis* is the Great Flood that nearly destroyed mankind. Its extent has also been variously interpreted from a worldwide event to one of local importance only.

A famous estimate of the date of creation, 4004 B.C., was made by Archbishop Ussher, a contemporary of Shakespeare. This figure, which was placed in the margins of many Bibles, soon came to be venerated almost as much as the sacred text itself. Many other Bible scholars have tried to sum up the genealogies (family lineages) described in the Old Testament, but have found troublesome gaps in the record. Some 600 attempts to estimate the number of years from the time of Jesus back to the beginning have resulted in as many different answers. Even with all these uncertainties, a literal interpretation of Biblical chronology could allow no more than a few thousand years for the age of the earth.

For centuries most intellectuals were creationists who understood the creation story in *Genesis* in a strictly literal sense. They knew of no evidence that would cause one to believe otherwise. And since a creation that was concluded in six 24-hour days and a later worldwide flood were brief, spectacular events, most of these same people were *catastrophists*. That is, they considered the Biblical flood to have deposited the sedimentary rocks with their contained fossils. Mountains had been uplifted suddenly, catastrophically, accompanied by giant earthquakes. This was the assumption even though the only catastrophes ever observed were much more minor and local.

Advent of the Scientific Method

Meanwhile, a new intellectual climate was beginning to take shape, one that would encourage the study of nature for its own sake, not just as a pale reflection of the Mind of God. Surprisingly, a church controversy over authority became an important step toward the new world view. In the frequent disputes between Protestants and Catholics, each side, in order to be convincing, had to base its case on historical arguments acceptable to the other side. In the midst of this dissent was born a technique known as textual criticism, through which the ancient texts were carefully examined for internal consistency and compared with other writings from the same period. Once the texts were assigned to a chronological order, the influence of earlier writers upon later writers became more apparent. Scholars slowly began to realize that history was *not* an endless repetition after all, but rather an evolutionary development in which the achievements of each new era were based upon those inherited from the previous era. It was only logical to extend this approach to reading the strata, the "pages" of the book of geology.

At first, the new interpretations were cautious attempts to maintain the Biblical account as a sort of scaffolding upon which further geologic evidence would be placed. An influential naturalist was G. L. L. de Buffon, who wrote prolifically in the late 1700s. He suggested that the six Biblical creative "days" had each lasted from 3000 to 35,000 years, a time scale that we now recognize as being far too short. More importantly, he argued for an approach that may seem obvious to us but which was an astonishing suggestion at the time: a *systematic examination of the geologic record itself.* Buffon opened his book *Epochs of Nature* with these words:

> Just as in civil history we consult warrants, study medallions, and decipher ancient inscriptions, in order to determine the epochs of the human revolutions and fix the dates of moral events, so in natural history one must dig through the archives of the world, extract ancient relics from the bowels of the earth, gather together their fragments, and assemble again in a single body of proofs all those indications of the physical changes which can carry us back to the different Ages of Nature. This is the only way of fixing certain points in the immensity of space, and of placing a number of milestones on the eternal path of time.

Another eminent (and controversial) personality was a Scot, James Hutton—gentleman farmer, physician, traveler, and above all, keen observer (Figure 11-1). Hutton loved to visit the rocky coast of his homeland, where he was impressed with the degradation caused by the ceaseless buffeting of the waves. And yet, he recognized that water-laid sedimentary rock may be found on some mountain summit. Hutton correctly interpreted a locality in Berwickshire (Figure 11-2) that seemed to summarize perfectly his growing conception of a dynamic planet.

To him, the relationships shown in Figure 11-2 could have come about only in the manner shown in Figure 11-3:

1. The nearly vertical beds of sedimentary rock (slightly metamorphosed) must have been deposited as horizontal strata. Hutton accepted the now long-recognized principle of "original horizontality" of stratified rocks.

Figure 11-1. ". . . the eminent old geologist, Dr. James Hutton, rather astonished at the shapes which his favorite rocks have suddenly taken." Hutton, a controversial figure, was beset by many who were critical of his radical ideas. [*From John Kay's* Edinburgh Portraits, *1842.*]

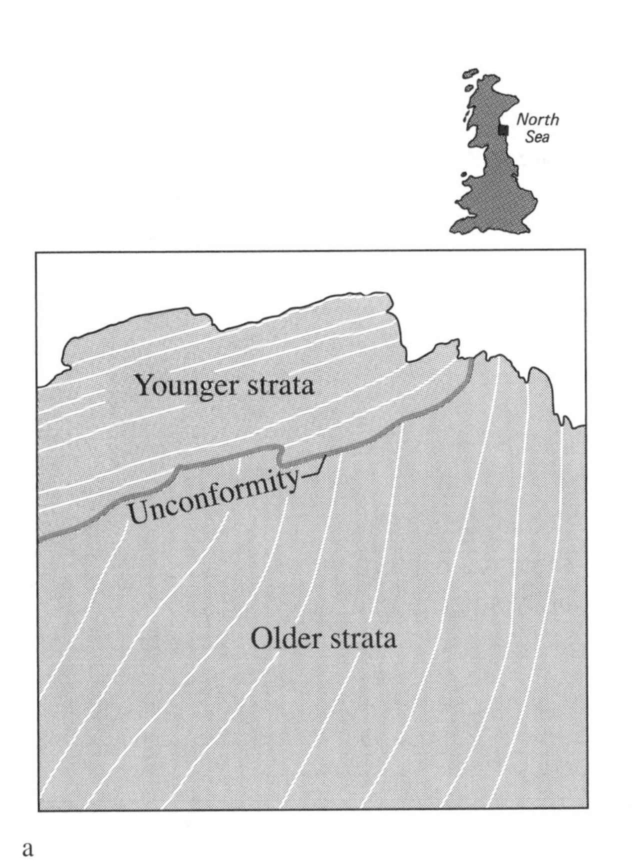

a

b

Figure 11-2. "Hutton's unconformity" on the coast of the North Sea (inset map) is seen in a photograph (*b*) and as a drawing (*a*) in which the unconformity (a buried surface of erosion) and the relationships of the older and younger strata are emphasized. [*(b) Crown Copyright Geological Survey photograph. Reproduced by permission of the Controller, Her Britannic Majesty's Stationery Office.*]

2. The beds were buckled by deforming forces.
3. A lengthy interval of stability followed, during which some of the deformed strata were eroded away.
4. Again the area was depressed below sea level, and more sedimentary beds deposited (horizontally) across the beveled, upturned edges of older rock.
5. Once again the region was uplifted, and tilted gently. Both the older and younger series of beds have continued to be eroded until the present day.

The buried erosion surface, or ***unconformity***, that separates the older and younger series of beds, represents the period of time during which a part of the previously deposited geologic record was destroyed. As Hutton put it:

> This earth, like the body of an animal, is wasted at the same time as it is repaired... It is thus destroyed in one part, but it is renewed in another.

Which of the events mentioned above was catastrophic? Deposition by a flood or landslide is catastrophic, but where in Figure 11-2 are the cobbles and boulders that one would expect to see, transported by the intense energy of a catastrophe? The older beds must have already been transformed into coherent, hard rock before they were deformed, else they would have slumped into wild contortions. (Slumping of soft sediment is well known in other places.) Hardening of the rock is not catastrophic nor is its erosion, even on a storm-battered coast. Nor were the rocks deformed catastrophically, for they would have broken instead of bending into the folds shown in Figure 11-3.

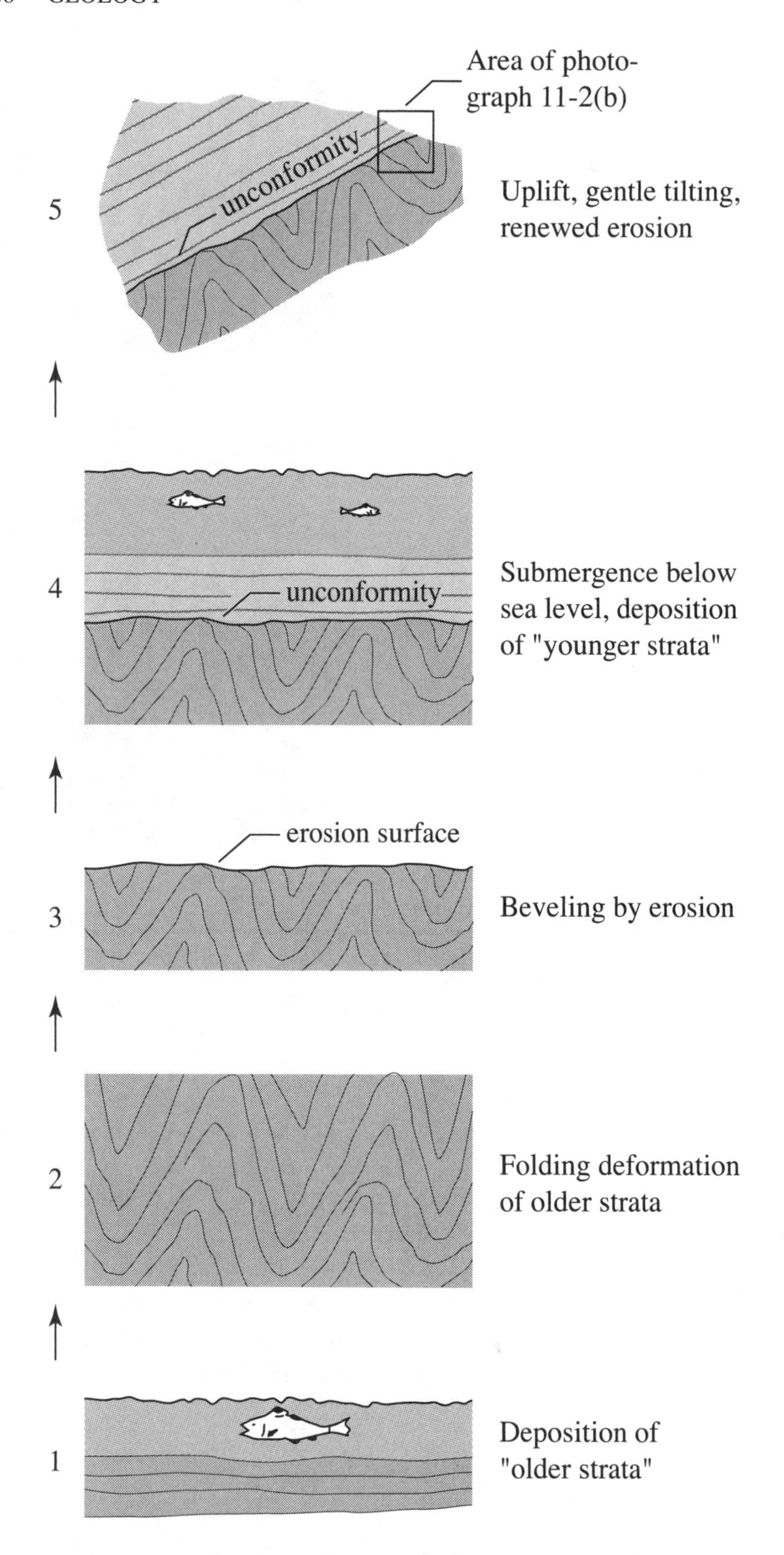

Figure 11-3. According to the law of superposition, older rocks (unless disturbed) lie beneath younger rocks. Therefore, cross sections of this sort that display a series of events are normally sequenced from bottom to top.

None of the relationships seen in Figures 11-2 and 11-3 requires a catastrophic origin. However impressive the results, they were more likely a product of commonplace, gradual events operating over a long time period. Hutton found cause to wonder whether earth cataclysms are the rule or the exception. While acknowledging catastrophes, he proposed that "the past history of our globe must be explained by what can be seen to be happening now." Later this idea came to be known as *uniformitarianism*, to emphasize the continued application of uniform processes. It is the plodding tortoise (long-sustained everyday processes), not the flashy hare (sudden catastrophes) that has "won" the geologic race. The uniformitarian viewpoint soon prevailed, and rightly so. Nevertheless, geologists today are finding it necessary to question this philosophy. New evidence (Chapter 15) argues that worldwide catastrophes have indeed occurred with possible consequences including the extinctions of dinosaurs and other creatures.

Wisely, Hutton did not attempt, from the scanty evidence available, to place exact dates on geologic events. Instead, he adopted a noncommittal viewpoint "... that we find no vestige of a beginning,—no prospect of an end." Hutton's critics attacked this radical philosophy, accusing him of encouraging atheism, infidelity, and immorality. He replied that he really had not "deposed the Almighty Creator of the Universe from His Office," but only that "in nature, we find no deficiency in respect of time."

Toward a Geologic Clock

Even before Hutton's day there had been attempts to quantify our knowledge of geologic time. All of these methods, both early and modern, are based upon the principle of an hourglass (Figure 11-4). Information about the *size* of a reservoir is combined with the *rate* at which it is being emptied or filled, to calculate *how long* the emptying or filling process has gone on. For instance, if two-thirds of the sand has already fallen to the lower chamber of the hourglass pictured in Figure 11-4, and it takes one hour to empty, then sand has already been falling for 40 minutes.

In 1715 the British astronomer Edmond Halley (for whom the famous comet is named) published a paper about ocean salt functioning as a geologic hourglass. He reasoned that, since salt is delivered to

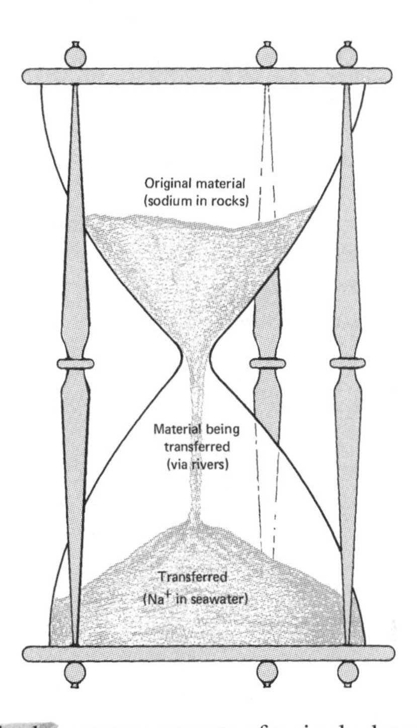

Figure 11-4. Joly's hourglass singles out two aspects of a single dynamic situation. The total salt content of the ocean (specifically, the dissolved Na^+) corresponds to the pile of sand at the base of the hourglass. The rate of salt addition is symbolized by the density of sand grains still in mid-air. Sand in the top compartment (continents waiting to be eroded) is immaterial to Joly's formulation.

the sea by rivers, the sea should become steadily more salty. If sea salt were observed to increase by 1% during a period of one century, for example, then the total sea salt must have required 100 centuries to accumulate. Halley complained that the Greek and Latin authors had not recorded their measurements of ocean salinity, for he thought that surely a noticeable enrichment could be detected over the past 2,000 years. In retrospect we see that the increase would be trivial in this short interval. Halley's time scale was approximately a million times shorter than the currently accepted age of the earth.

Years later the Irish geologist J. Joly published a paper that takes a different view of the sea-salt hourglass. Rather than waiting for the salt content to increase over a period of time, Joly considered how much salt is already present in the ocean reservoir, and how rapidly salt is being delivered to it. His equation is very simple:

$$\frac{\text{Total salt content of ocean}}{\text{Rate of salt addition}} = \frac{\text{grams}}{\text{grams/year}} = \text{years (time of accumulation)} \qquad (11\text{-}1)$$

Joly recognized that salt present initially in the ocean, or extra salt leached out of evaporite deposits, or any of a dozen other possible complications could invalidate his calculations. After applying corrections according to the best available information, he obtained:

$$\frac{1.24 \times 10^{17} \text{ grams}}{1.39 \times 10^{9} \text{ grams/year}} = \text{about 90 million years} \qquad (11\text{-}2)$$

This age was shockingly older than any age previously estimated, but it was still 50 times too short. The source of error was Joly's ignorance of the recycling of salt. The ocean approximates a "steady state" condition, by which salt is added and removed at the same rate. And since there is no record of salt formerly added but since removed, there is no way to estimate how long it had been accumulating.

Another hourglass reservoir is the total thickness of the world's sedimentary rocks. This thickness, divided by the thickness deposited each year, equals the duration of accumulation. The sedimentary hourglass is also subject to serious deficiencies. No place, not even the floor of the ocean, has received sediment since the time of the earth's beginning. Rates of deposition may range from nil to very high at different times or in different environments. Unconformities signify that previously deposited sediment has been eroded away.

Clearly a better timepiece, not subject to so many irregular influences, was needed. Shortly before the turn of the 20th Century the search for this new, hoped-for clock was fulfilled in the discovery of radioactivity by the French physicist, Henri Becquerel. The radioactivity clock was to revolutionize and solidly quantify our vision of time in earth history.

USING RADIOACTIVITY TO TELL TIME

Within a few years after the discovery of radioactivity, physicists had learned many important characteristics of this natural phenomenon. In Chapter 1 we saw that the nucleus of an atom is composed of protons and neutrons. Each chemical element is defined by its unique number of protons, but various numbers of neutrons may be associated with the given number of protons. A proton-neutron combination specifies an isotope of that element. (Please review Tables 1-1 and 1-2.) Some isotopes are stable; others are unstable, or *radioactive.* For example, consider the chemical element rubidium (Rb), in which all the nuclei contain 37 protons. If 48 neutrons are also present, that nucleus has 85 particles and the isotope is ^{85}Rb. If 50 neutrons are present, the nucleus is ^{87}Rb. Both are isotopes of rubidium, but ^{85}Rb is stable whereas ^{87}Rb is radioactive.

Nuclear stability is determined by competition between opposing factors. An immensely powerful nuclear force binds the protons and neutrons together, but energy contained in the nucleus tends to disrupt it. Some of this internal energy is released through the process of *radioactive decay.* In most types of decay, a particle with mass is also expelled from the nucleus, causing it to transform into an isotope of another element. We say that a radioactive or *parent* atom has decayed into a radiogenic or *daughter* atom.

If the daughter nucleus is stable it simply persists, but if the daughter is radioactive, it will decay into yet another daughter isotope. The decay of an isotope of uranium, for example, begins a long progression through radioactive daughters until finally a stable isotope of the element lead (Pb) is reached.

Thus radioactive atoms in the earth are steadily disappearing, being replaced by stable daughter atoms. It is rather like grains of sand that depart from an upper "parent" reservoir to accumulate in a lower "daughter" reservoir of an hourglass (Figure 11-4). Unlike the sea-salt and sedimentary-rock hourglasses, the radioactivity clock is not subject to reversals or variations of rate. Daughter cannot turn back into parent, nor is any environmental extreme of temperature or pressure in the earth able to change the probability that a radioactive atom will decay within a given period of time. This is assured because all other forces are trivial in comparison to the nuclear force that is involved in radioactive decay.

Nevertheless, with all the certainty of a predictable rate, we can never know exactly when the decay event will happen to any particular atom. Because radioactive decay is a *statistical* process, we can accurately predict only the average behavior of a large population of atoms. A convenient way to describe the rate of decay is through the notion of a *half-life*: the length of time required for one-half of an initial number of radioactive atoms to decay. Surely the very term "half-life" is a strange one. Sand falls through an hourglass at a steady rate until, after a length of time, the last particle has fallen. Why not speak of a "whole-life," or simply "lifetime"? An hourglass does not resemble the radioactivity clock in every respect. How then can we use the concept of half-life to tell geologic time?

Isotopic Ages

Suppose we start with a large number of radioactive atoms at an arbitrary time "zero" (Figure 11-5). Obviously, decay will have reduced the size of the remaining population at any later time. After one half-life (abbreviated $t\frac{1}{2}$) has gone by, half the original atoms are still left. We can apply the same reasoning when we halve the remaining atoms during the *next* half-life, and so on. With each succeeding half-life, the fraction of radioactive atoms becomes smaller as follows: ½ after one $t\frac{1}{2}$, then ¼ after 2 $t\frac{1}{2}$, then ⅛ after 3 $t\frac{1}{2}$, then $\frac{1}{16}$, $\frac{1}{32}$, etc. Eventually the remaining fraction becomes very small, approaching but never quite reaching zero, as shown by the black curve in Figure 11-5. Two half-lives for radioactive decay do *not* equal a whole-life (total disappearance). We cannot express a whole-life, an infinite length of time.

What happens when the population has been reduced to only a single remaining radioactive atom? (It eventually decays.) A half-life accurately describes the behavior of a statistically *very large number* of atoms, not the last few atoms to which a more complicated mathematical formula pertains. Any rock or mineral sample contains a great many atoms. Approximately a million billion (10^{15}) atoms are present in one-millionth (10^{-6}) of a gram, a speck of matter almost too small to see with the unaided eye.

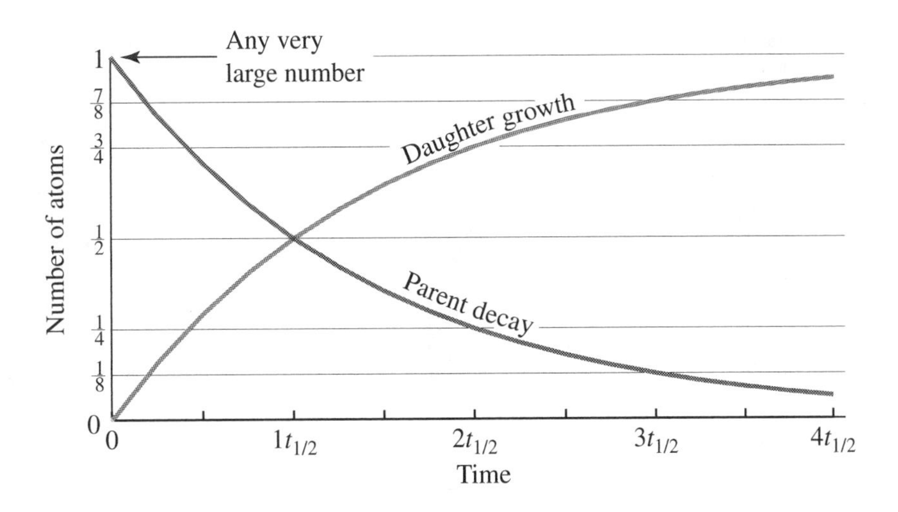

Figure 11-5. A parent decay curve and a daughter growth curve describe the smoothly varying, time-dependent abundances of parent and daughter isotopes.

Each parent isotope has a unique half-life. Some radioactive species are so unstable that half of the atoms will have decayed within a billionth of a second. Other isotopes are so nearly stable that millions to billions of years are required for half of the radioactivity to disappear. The half-life of a truly stable isotope is of infinite duration. Some species of radioactive atoms were present when the earth formed. Ancient though the earth is, the longest-lived parent isotopes are still present. Most of the radioactivity is at a very low level, not hazardous to our health.

Radioactivity does not cause atoms to be annihilated, but simply to change identity from parent to stable daughter. The number of daughter atoms increases at the same rate that parent atoms disappear (Figure 11-5). While the *sum* of parent and daughter atoms does not change, the *proportion* of daughter to parent is initially zero, and becomes larger with the passage of time (Figure 11-6). The daughter/parent ratio, which can be measured in the laboratory, is the moving "hand" of the radioactivity clock, the basis for calculation of an *isotopic age.* It is amazing, perhaps, that almost every ordinary rock contains within itself such specific information about its unique age and origin.

Just as geologic events are very ancient, the radioactivity clock must be based upon isotopes with very long half-lives. If a half-life were too short, almost all of the parent would have decayed away by today. Conversely, if the half-life were too long, almost no daughter will have appeared. Either way, it would not be possible to make accurate analyses. The earth is endowed with several radioactive isotopes with suitable half-lives (Table 11-1). They are isotopes of chemical elements that are distributed in a wide variety of rocks. Potassium is a major part of feldspar and mica, and a minor constituent in hornblende. Rubidium, being similar chemically, is concentrated in the same minerals as potassium. Uranium may be quite abundant in crystals of zircon, a very hard silicate mineral that is present in many rocks. Except for potassium, all of the elements mentioned in Table 11-1 are generally very rare (parts-per-million or parts-per-billion) but have abundances that can nevertheless be measured accurately. An isotopic age is designated according to the parent and daughter. For example, a rubidium-strontium age (or Rb-Sr age) is based upon the measured ratio of daughter ^{87}Sr to parent ^{87}Rb.

How can the extremely long half-lives mentioned in Table 11-1 be measured? Obviously we cannot watch and wait for billions of years until one-half of the radioactivity has disappeared! One method is to prepare a chemical compound containing a known number of radioactive atoms. This material is

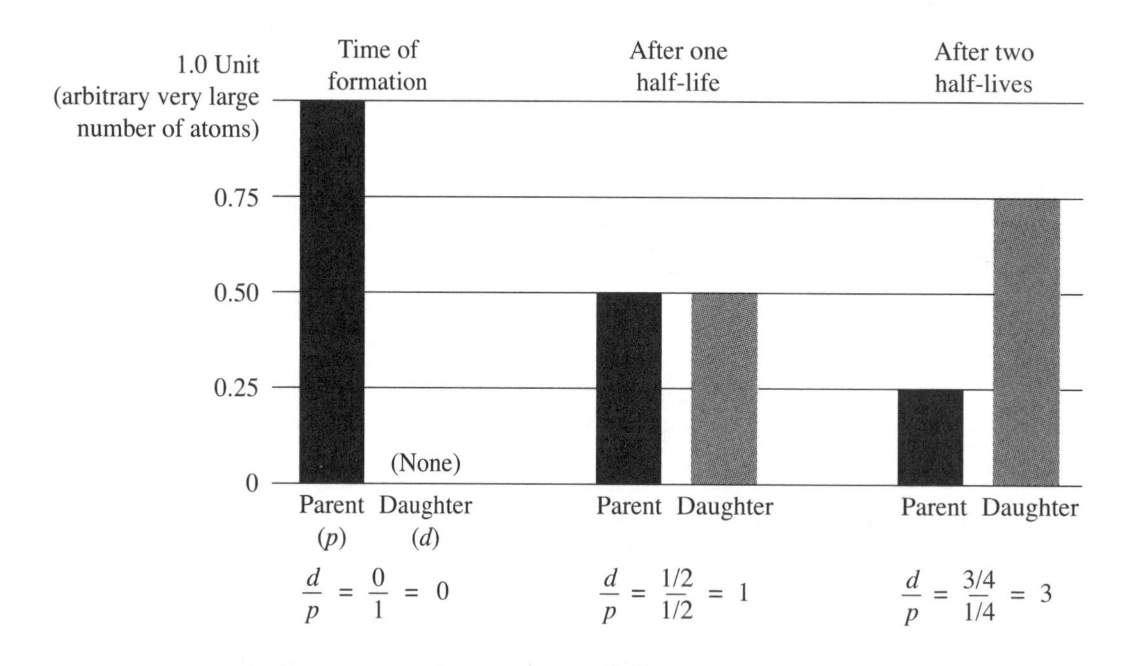

Figure 11-6. The height of each bar is proportional to the number of atoms of parent or daughter. The ratios pictured here apply only to the situation after a whole number of half-lives has elapsed. A simple formula has been derived to express the daughter/parent (*d/p*) ratio at any arbitrary time.

Table 11-1. *Parent and Daughter Isotopes Used for Isotopic Age Determinations*

Parent	Daughter	Half-life (billion years)
^{40}K	$^{40}Ar + ^{40}Ca$*	1.3
^{87}Rb	^{87}Sr	50
^{147}Sm	^{143}Nd	106
^{235}U	^{207}Pb	0.70
^{238}U	^{206}Pb	4.5

*A ^{40}K nucleus may decay to either ^{40}Ar or ^{40}Ca. It is necessary to measure only the accumulated ^{40}Ar daughter.

placed in a *radioactivity counter*, a device that registers the decay events, atom-by-atom. There are so many atoms in the sample that, even though the half-life is exceedingly long, a large number of atoms decay in just a few days. Knowing the number of radioactive atoms and rate of decay, we may calculate how long it would take for half of them to decay.

Mass Spectrometers

Geologists have devised elegant methods to analyze parent and daughter. Most elements consist of a mixture, or *spectrum*, of isotopes. Suppose we wish to learn how much Sr has been produced by decay of ^{87}Rb in a rock sample. It is necessary to separate the isotopes of Sr because, of its four stable isotopes, only one of them (^{87}Sr) is the daughter. A complex, expensive instrument called a mass spectrometer (Figure 11-7) can accomplish this separation on the basis that each isotope has a different mass. A tiny amount of purified Sr, extracted from the rock sample, is painted onto a metal ribbon and introduced into

Figure 11-7. This mass spectrometer is designed to analyze solid materials. Ions of different masses (different isotopes) start out together at the ion source (*S*). As they travel through a magnetic field at position *M*, lighter ions are deflected more than heavier ions (forked black line). The ion collector (*C*) can receive only one isotopic mass at a time; ions of other masses simply hit the walls of the tube and are not recorded.

the machine at location *S*. After pumpdown to a high vacuum, the ribbon is heated in order to drive off some of the sample in the form of positive ions (Sr^+). A high voltage "gun" propels these ions along a tube where they pass between the poles of a powerful magnet, *M*. The magnetic field bends the path of flight of the ions upward, lighter ions being deflected more than heavier ions. By the time the ions of different masses reach a collector (*C*), they are separated from one another, ready for individual analysis.

Meaning of Isotopic Ages

In order for long-lived parent isotopes to be incorporated in the earth, they must have existed before the earth did. A use of the radioactivity clock is to tell the age of that ultimate ancient event, the creation of the chemical elements. Once the earth had formed, its crust continued to recycle such that, on the average, each atom in it has been a part of five different rocks. What then is meant by the age of a rock? For that matter, what is meant by your age and mine? We understand it to be the number of years since birth, but a person's age could also be defined as the time since fertilization, or perhaps some event that followed birth. The concept of "age" may be subtle, requiring a careful definition. Let us examine what sort of rock-forming events are signified by daughter/parent ratios in the three great classes of rock.

Igneous rocks Suppose that a body of rock deep in the earth were to melt, and send magma to the surface as a volcanic eruption. The magma would contain some potassium-40 and also some daughter argon-40 generated previously by radioactive decay in the deep source (Table 11-1). However, the argon, being an inert gas, would promptly escape into the atmosphere at such high temperature. In this manner the isotopic clock is "reset"—the previously accumulated daughter isotope is separated from parent isotope. Upon cooling, the magma might crystallize into feldspar, mica, and hornblende, all of which contain potassium but no argon. Once the temperature has dropped below about 500°C in the case of hornblende, or about 300°C in the case of mica, the daughter argon (even though it is a gas) is trapped in the crystals where it continues to accumulate. A potassium-argon age of the volcanic rock refers to a time of cooling and crystallization, when argon began to be retained. Cooling of an intrusive igneous body, such as granite, is much slower because thousands of meters of overlying rock retard the loss of heat. A K-Ar age of mica in granite would also refer to the time since it cooled below 300°C, but that point in time might be millions of years after the granite had completely solidified.

None of the daughter isotopes in the other isotopic age methods (Table 11-1) is a gas that is able to escape. Inheritance of previously created daughter ^{87}Sr, ^{143}Nd, etc., which are brought in with the magma, would falsely indicate an age that is too old. Some very clever procedures have been invented to evaluate and make a correction for the "built in" quantities of these daughter isotopes. Properly applied, the Rb-Sr, Sm-Nd, and U-Pb methods are also indicators of the time of crystallization.

Sedimentary rocks The age of a sediment is understood to be the length of time since it was deposited. Suppose that pieces of a granite were eroded, transported, and deposited as a conglomerate. Parent and previously accumulated daughter isotopes would simply be transported together. It would be like carrying a clock from room to room, while not resetting it. An isotopic age would refer to the time of granite formation, not to the time when chunks of granite were incorporated into a sediment.

Thus the deposition of terrigenous clastic sediment, which is composed of particles derived from an older source terrain, cannot be dated by isotopic age methods. What *can* be dated is the source terrain, or chemical changes, such as the growth of new clay particles, that occurred in the sediment after deposition. In some circumstances it is possible to date the time when a chemical sediment was precipitated from material dissolved in sea water. For example, the evaporite mineral sylvite (KCl) could be analyzed by the K-Ar or Rb-Sr method.

Metamorphic rocks Contained within a metamorphic rock is a record of *two* kinds of age: the time since the rock first formed, and the time since it was recrystallized by metamorphism (Figure 11-8). For that matter, some rocks have been metamorphosed more than once. So complex is the sequence of events that a complete history for metamorphic rocks has been worked out in only a few localities. Table 11-2 describes a more than 3.7-billion-year geologic history in southwestern Greenland.

GREAT EVENTS IN EARTH HISTORY

Although something is going on all the time in our restless planet, isotopic ages show that geologic history has been punctuated by occasional profound happenings. Here are some of these momentous events.

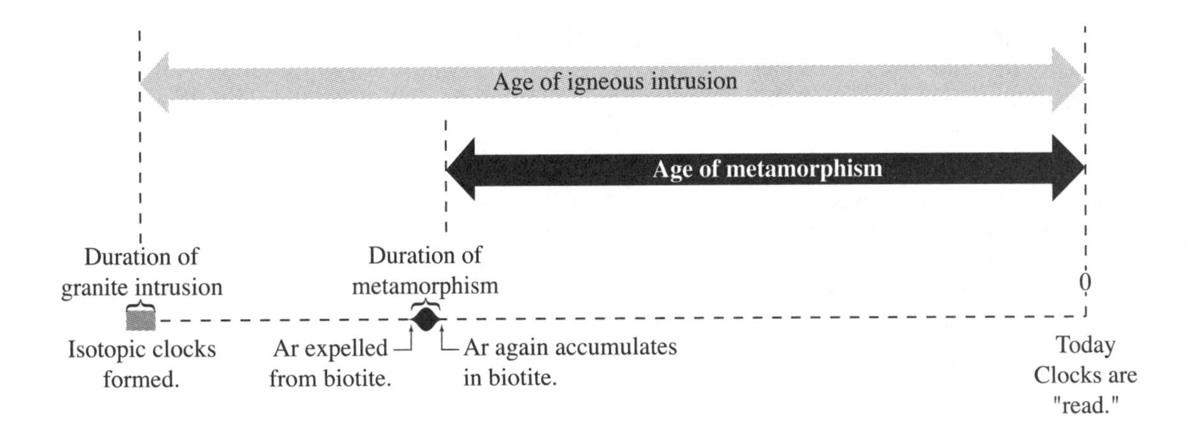

Figure 11-8. A time line shows the history of a metamorphosed granite. The isotopic ages refer to the time interval from a past event (such as metamorphism) to the present day, *not* to the duration of that event. In this example, the K-Ar clock in biotite was reset by metamorphic heating, whereas the U-Pb clock in zircon crystals was unaffected by metamorphism. Therefore, the U-Pb clock gives the age of intrusion of the granite, and the K-Ar clock gives the age of metamorphism.

Table 11-2. *Greatly Simplified Geologic History of Ancient Crust in Southwestern Greenland*

Geologic Event	Age (billion years ago)
1. Deposition of volcanic and sedimentary rocks	Before 3.7
2. Burial, high-grade metamorphism, intrusion of large igneous bodies	3.7
3. Extrusion of basalt, deposition of more sediment	3.0
4. Faulting, more metamorphism, intrusion of sills	Not dated
5. Intrusion of large bodies of granite and granodiorite, more metamorphism	2.8
6. Intense deformation, folding of the rock in several directions	Not dated
7. Emplacement of granite, termination of regional metamorphism	2.5
8. Intrusion of dikes, regional heating, faulting	1.5 (?)
9. Intrusion of dikes	0.05

[*Compiled from: R. F. Dymek, "Supracrustal rocks, polymetamorphism, and evolution of the SW Greenland Archean Gneiss Complex," in* Patterns of Change in Earth Evolution *(H. Holland and A. Trendall, ed.), 1984, and other references cited therein.*]

Age of the Elements

Chapter 1 discusses how the heavy chemical elements originate in prodigious explosions of supernovas. Explosion debris was mixed into the dust cloud that was to become the earth and solar system. Astonishingly, we can estimate the time of this creation event even though the solar system did not even exist at the time. One of the created isotopes was iodine-129 (^{129}I) which decays to an isotope of the inert gas, xenon (^{129}Xe). The half-life for decay, 16.4 million years, is so short that no ^{129}I remains today. But when the solar system was organized long ago, some ^{129}I was still present. Radioactive iodine was incorporated into meteorites, there to decay into "excess" daughter ^{129}Xe. The isotopic information from meteorites tells us that the heavy elements were created only a few tens of millions of years before the solar system, and that the solar system was condensed within a few million years, in a geological "instant."

Age of the Earth

One of the objects forming at that time was the earth. The age of the earth cannot be determined by direct analysis, for there are no rocks that have escaped recycling. The same is true of the moon, which is about 2% of the size of the earth and in which important volcanic activity ceased about three billion years ago. Even the meteorites show the effects of melting and metamorphism that occurred presumably in their parent bodies (Chapter 2). The parent bodies were tens of kilometers in diameter before being disrupted by collisions. We see that the smaller the body, the sooner the loss of internal heat caused it to "go dead." Meteorites thus represent the original cosmic stuff most closely. Isotopic ages of meteorites are a maximum of about 4.55 billion years, which we take to be the age of all the objects in the solar system. (More recent ages of certain meteorites are attributed to later events, for example collisions in space.) Analyzed materials of the earth, moon, Mars, and meteorites share similar chemical and isotopic patterns—strong circumstantial evidence that these bodies originated together, at the same time.

The Oldest Rocks

Geologists have long searched for the oldest remnant of the earth's crust. Such rocks would permit a test of the principle of uniformitarianism—whether processes in the very early earth were similar to those operating today. The most ancient rock yet discovered is the Acasta Gneiss in the Canadian Arctic, at 4.0 billion years. Zircon crystals in metamorphosed sedimentary rocks of western Australia are 4.1 to 4.4 billion years old, but these are recycled clastic particles eroded from a source that has not been found, and may no longer exist. Rocks substantially older than 3 billion years are present in southern and eastern Africa, in India, several parts of Russia, Antarctica, Greenland, and northern U.S. Very ancient rocks are patchily distributed over each of the continents.

Where are rocks that have survived from the first half-billion years? Having not a single example, we can only surmise what the earth was like then. A more complete record of early events is preserved in the moon which experienced an intense meteorite bombardment, the "lunar cataclysm" that terminated about 4.1 billion years ago. Very likely the earth experienced a "terrestrial cataclysm" at the same time, in which all traces of the earlier crust were destroyed.

Age of the Ocean and the Appearance of Life

Living organisms cannot survive indefinitely unless liquid water is present in their environment. Thus a primordial ocean, very warm perhaps but at a temperature below the boiling point of water, had to accumulate before life could appear. Fossil remains have been discovered in some of the world's most ancient known sedimentary rocks, about 3.5 billion years old, in localities in the Republic of South Africa and in the desert of western Australia at a place whimsically named the North Pole. These fossils are of microscopic, single-celled organisms that resemble modern algae and bacteria. It will be difficult to establish the true time of the origin of life, for processes of metamorphism have destroyed whatever fossils may have been present in most of these ancient sediments. Some researchers have postulated that there are fossils in the 3.8-billion-year-old rocks of southwestern Greenland, but it is now generally agreed that the "fossils" are of inorganic origin.

Ages of the Crust

What sort of local geology would be revealed during a casual stroll outdoors? We would discover igneous, sedimentary, or metamorphic bedrock, but with characteristics that vary greatly from place to place. Most of us live in low-lying, well-watered areas that are situated close to agriculture and the other amenities of civilization. Would it be a surprise to learn that this rather flat terrain is actually the eroded remnant of a once great mountain chain? Not if a time scale of billions of years is allowed; it would be more surprising to find a region that had remained *stable* for such a long time.

Two styles of earth movement may be distinguished. Mountain-making processes include faulting and folding of rocks, commonly accompanied by igneous activity and metamorphism at depth beneath the deforming mountain range. A later chapter explains these intense crumplings as a result of collision between horizontally moving "plates" that contain oceanic or continental crust. In another style of upheaval, the earth's crust may warp up or down with only minor igneous or metamorphic activity, folding or faulting. Plateaus and broad basins are examples of land forms that are produced by these more gentle, chiefly vertical movements.

North America: a case study The appearance of every landscape has been shaped by the events of a long preceding history. First the rocks were created (by volcanism, sedimentary deposition, etc.), then deformed (folded, faulted, warped up or down, perhaps metamorphosed, etc.), and today the land surface is being eroded. Formation, deformation, and erosion could have taken place repeatedly. Let us see how these processes worked together to create the structure of a familiar continent, North America (Figure 11-9). Complex mountain chains occupy the eastern and western margins of the continent. These mountain belts, for example the Sierra Nevadas or Appalachians, were formed at different times and are currently in various stages of wasting away by erosion. Through the center of the continent stretches a vast lowland, some 5000 kilometers (3000 miles) from the Arctic Ocean south to the Gulf of Mexico.

The interior lowland in turn consists of three subunits. An immense plain called the *Canadian Shield* occupies the eastern two-thirds of Canada and a small part of the northernmost United States (Figure 11-9). Although the Canadian Shield is quite flat, nearly at sea level, and with no high peaks, its rocks clearly attest to involvement in intense mountain-making activity. For example, in a typical part of the shield in Ontario, deforming forces have crumpled high-grade metamorphic rocks into an accordion-like mass of tight folds (Figure 11-10). Erosion has removed the upper part of the folds (reconstructed by dashed lines in the cross section), but the keel of a downfold is still preserved. Rocks in the shield

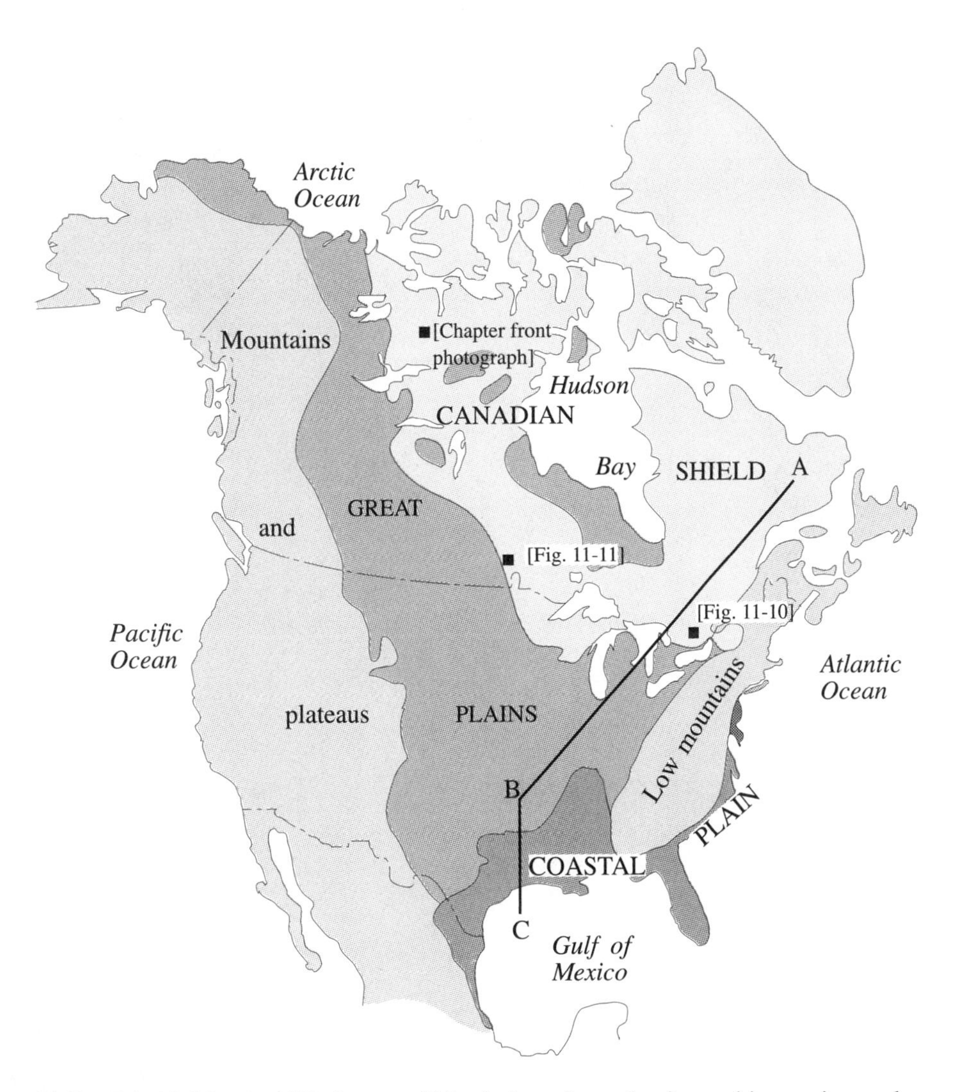

Figure 11-9. This highly simplified map of North American physiographic provinces shows the Canadian Shield, Great Plains, and Coastal Plain. Ancient basement is exposed at the surface in the Shield, whereas in the Great Plains, flat-lying sedimentary rocks lie unconformably upon basement. A cross section along line *ABC* appears in Figure 11-12.

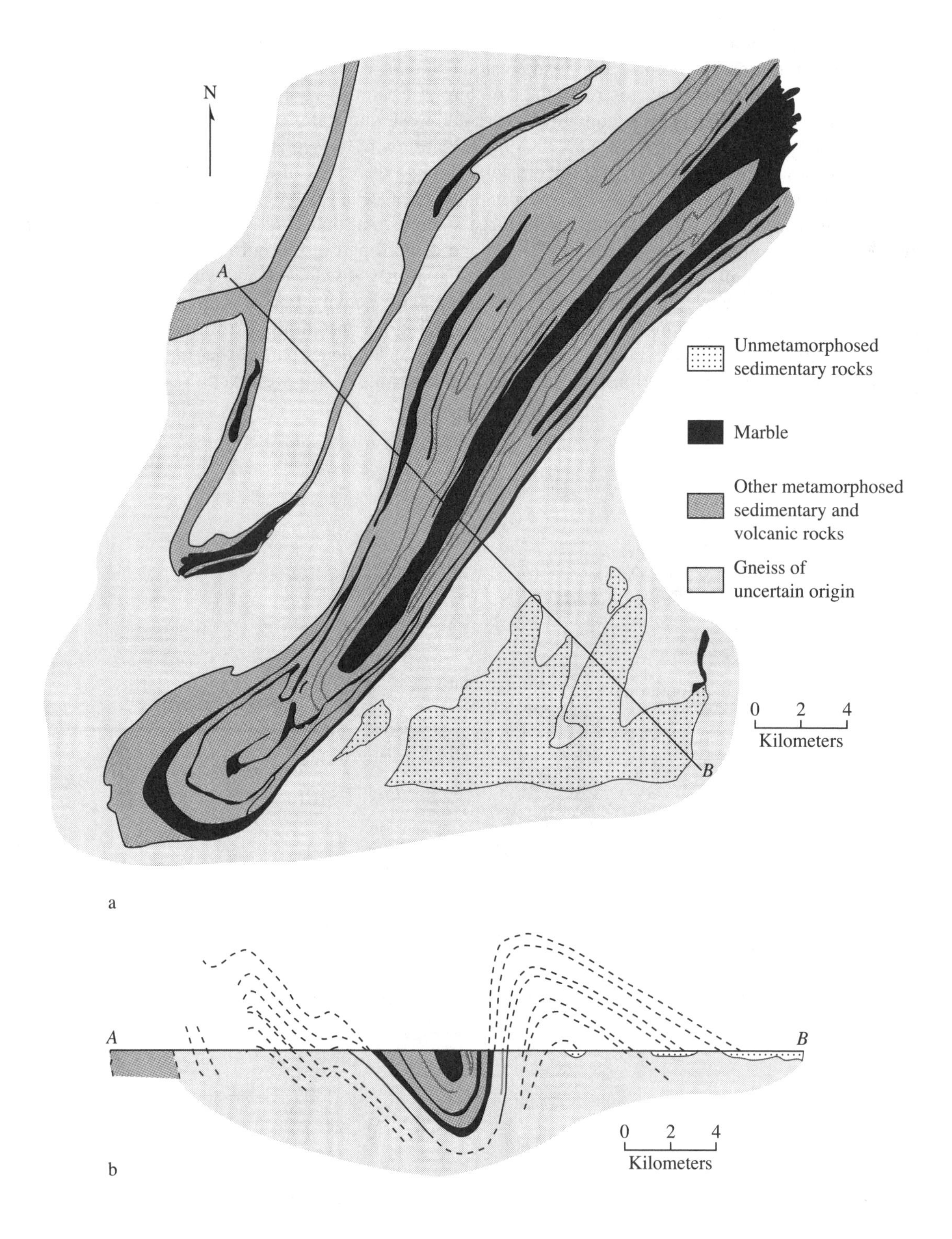

Figure 11-10. (*a*) A geologic map of a small portion of the shield in Ontario shows a mass of layered metamorphic rocks that have been tightly pinched into a canoe-shaped downfold. The keel of the fold runs northeast through the middle of the rock outcrop pattern. (*b*) In cross section along line *AB*, the surface of the shield is seen to be essentially flat. Once-horizontal layers now stand nearly vertical, and in the core of the downfold they are even slightly overturned. [*After J. W. Ambrose and C. A. Burns, "Structures in the Clare River Syncline: A Demonstration of Granitization," in* The Grenville Problem, *Royal Society of Canada, Special Publication 1, 1956.*]

have been torn by faults and invaded by dikes and other intrusive igneous bodies ranging up to batholithic size. Mineralized zones contain gold, copper, nickel, and other valuable economic metals.

What is a level plain today (Figure 11-11) must have once resembled the rugged Alps or Himalayas. After the ancient mountain-making activity had ceased, the terrain stabilized, becoming subject to prolonged erosion that has exposed rocks that were formerly very deeply buried. Geologists refer to these igneous and metamorphic "underpinnings" of the continent as the *basement.* A shield is a very large, stable, low-lying region in which ancient basement rocks are exposed at the surface.

Another lowlands region, the Great Plains, occupies the central United States and runs along the west side of the Canadian Shield (Figure 11-9). This area, known as a *platform,* is like the shield except that in a platform the basement is covered unconformably by a veneer (typically about a kilometer thick) of younger sedimentary strata. Thus the earth's crust is not *perfectly* stable—after being eroded to a low plain, it may be depressed below sea level, or sea level may rise. Sediment would be deposited, then eroded off after broad regional upwarping, and the cycle of transgression and retreat of the sea may repeat. In any event, these are not the strong deformations that were active in forming the basement.

Of course, there are exceptions to this theme of stability. Downfaulting movements of the platform in North Dakota, Illinois, Michigan, and the Oklahoma-Texas Panhandle have created local deep basins that became filled with thick sediment. Erosion has planed off the sedimentary cover in upbulged spots in the Black Hills of South Dakota, St. Francois Mtns. of Missouri, and Llano Uplift of central Texas, revealing the basement. These regions are too small to qualify as shield, just as minor patches of sedimentary rocks lying upon the shield in the vicinity of Hudson Bay in Canada (Figure 11-9) are too small to qualify as platform.

Thirdly, the Coastal Plain, especially along the Gulf of Mexico, is underlain by great thicknesses of even younger sediment borne by rivers to the margin of the continent (Figure 11-9). Ancient basement rocks are not likely to be present here, and in any case the sedimentary pile is much too thick to have been drilled through to its bottom.

Figure 11-11. Much of the Canadian Shield is bare rock, scoured clean by an ice sheet and now, after the melting of the ice, dotted with countless thousands of lakes. This scene in Manitoba illustrates the typical low relief of some tens of meters.

Cross section line *ABC* (Figure 11-9), from northeastern Canada to the Gulf of Mexico, is shown in vertical profile in Figure 11-12. The structure of the basement in North America is like a ramp sloping southward. At its highest point—the Canadian Shield—erosion has already stripped off the surficial rocks. Erosion is slowly nibbling at the sedimentary cover bordering the shield, and lowering the landscape generally. Debris products, carried down the Mississippi River system, are dumped into the Gulf of Mexico whose shore is advancing into the Gulf due to accumulation of sediment. North America is a cannibal; it grows in one place while its own substance is being consumed somewhere else.

Isotopic Ages Shields and platforms are present on each of the continents (Figure 11-13). They are the regions where stable basement is present, in contrast to unstable mountains such as the Andes which are being uplifted, or basins such as the Gulf of Mexico which are subsiding beneath a heavy load of sediment. For many years the geology of the basement was considered too difficult to understand. Early geologic maps depicted the sequence and structure of the superficial sedimentary rocks in great detail, while the far more complex basement was simply colored a monotonous brown on the maps. Eventually field geologists summoned the courage, as it were, to tackle harder problems. They found it possible to unravel a complicated geologic history, even where the rocks are recrystallized and structurally disturbed. This work would not have been possible without isotopic age information, for one cannot tell the age of a rock simply from its appearance.

Thousands of isotopic ages from the basement of North America have revealed a systematic pattern (Figure 11-14). Small remnants of the most ancient rocks, more than 80% of the age of the earth

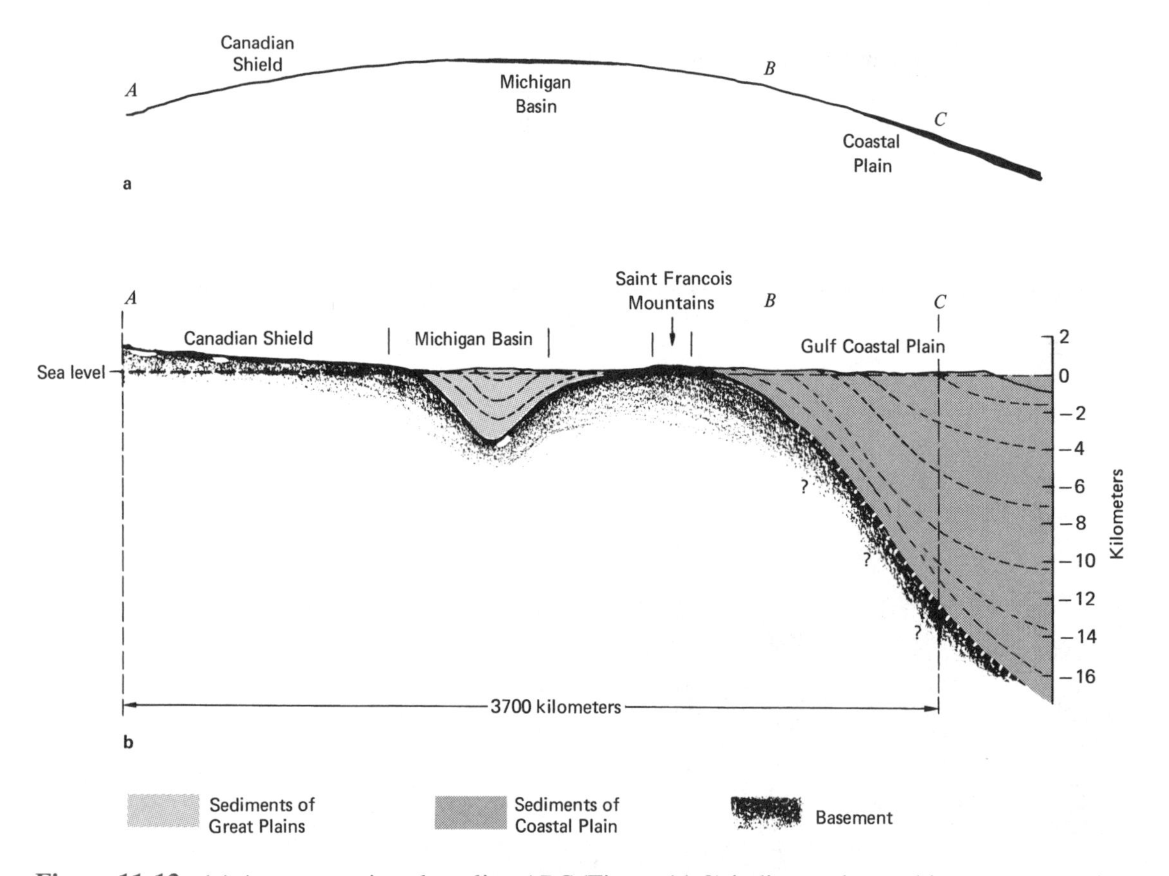

Figure 11-12. (*a*) A cross section along line *ABC* (Figure 11-9) indicates the earth's curvature and sediments of the Michigan Basin (a deep sag in the basement, filled in with sediment) and the Coastal Plain in true scale. Surface irregularities and the thickness of the sedimentary "skin" are insignificant on the scale of the whole earth, hence difficult to picture. (*b*) Most cross sections are drawn with the earth's curvature removed and, to convey more information, with a large vertical exaggeration (a factor of 80 times in this drawing). Here, the cross section has been deliberately drawn through the Michigan Basin and the St. Francois Mountains, Missouri (a "high" where basement is exposed). A cross section oriented through almost any other part of interior North America would show the top of the basement to be a rather monotonous flat surface.

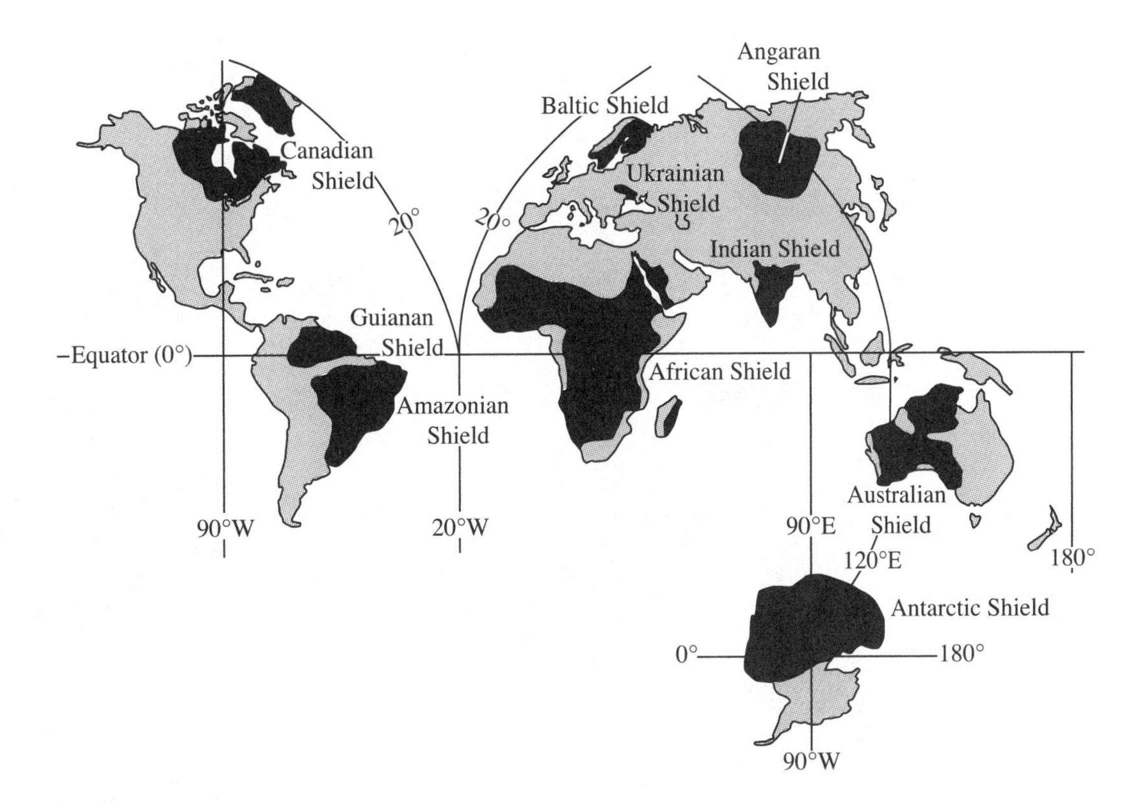

Figure 11-13. At least one shield or large platform is present in every continent. Stable basement underlies most of Africa and Antarctica.

itself, are preserved in local spots, for example in Labrador. This ancestral terrain may have been more extensive, but overprinted by metamorphism that obliterated the isotopic record of its origin. Much of the vast province in Canada that is older than 2.5 billion years (Figure 11-14) in fact may be much older, perhaps by a billion years. Some of this ancient "nucleus" was overprinted yet again by metamorphism and igneous activity around 1.8 to 1.9 billion years ago, in a zone that cuts across the older basement. A 1.0 to 1.2 billion year old belt runs down the eastern seaboard, beneath the southern States and into Mexico. Much younger crust makes up the Atlantic and Pacific margins of the continent in which mountain ranges are not yet completely eroded away. In general, the isotopic ages become progressively younger toward the edge of North America, as though the continent had grown larger with time. (However, other continents do not display a consistent concentric pattern of ages.)

Every half billion years or so, episodes of metamorphism, igneous activity, and mountain deformation affected both North America and many other parts of the world. Very little happened during the long quiet interludes, except for erosion of the continents and deposition of sediment. Mountain-building activity in the earth seems to pulsate in a grand rhythm. These events, which centered at roughly 2.6 billion years, 2.1 billion years, 1.7 billion years, 1.1 billion years, and (in the Southern Hemisphere) 0.6 billion years ago, join our list of profound happenings, "magic number dates" in the history of the planet.

SUMMARY

Up until about two centuries ago, intellectuals in Western civilization had generally assumed that the age of the earth is no more than a few thousand years. They were catastrophists who believed that the earth had taken shape rapidly, in great upheavals. But isotopic age determinations and systematic studies of geologic relationships in the field have revealed that the earth originated billions of years ago. James Hutton proposed that "the past history of our globe must be explained by what can be seen to be happening now." This uniformitarian viewpoint leads to the conclusion that the earth is ancient. Uniformitarianism states

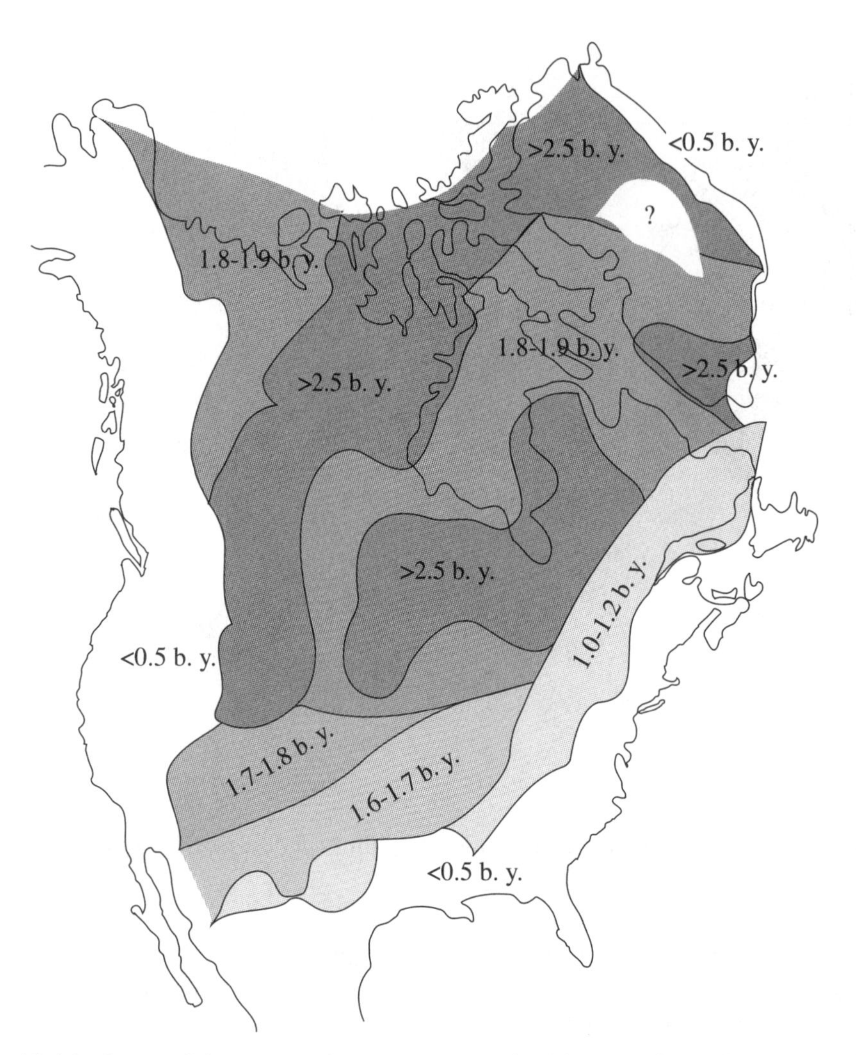

Figure 11-14. Some of the apparently younger areas in this map of North American isotopic age provinces are actually more ancient rock that has been caught up in renewed deformation and metamorphism for a second, or even a third time. Trends of older, once mountainous belts are abruptly cut off and transected by trend directions of younger belts. "b.y." stands for "billion years." [*After P. F. Hoffman, "United Plates of America, the Birth of a Craton,"* Annual Review of Earth and Planetary Science, *vol. 16, 1988.*]

that commonplace geologic processes (such as erosion and deposition of sediment), if sustained over very long periods of time, may produce extensive accumulated results. Geologic "clocks" based upon accumulation of sedimentary strata, or of salt in the ocean, give age estimates that are too young because the geologic record is partially destroyed by recycling.

During radioactive decay, the nucleus of an unstable (or parent) isotope emits energy (and in most types of decay, also a particle with mass), thus transforming into a radiogenic (or daughter) isotope. The rate of radioactive decay, a statistical process, does not vary with environmental changes in temperature, pressure, or chemical bonding between the radioactive atom and other atoms. Half-life is the length of time required for one-half of an initial number of radioactive atoms to decay; each radioactive isotope has a unique, fixed half-life.

The half-lives of isotopes used to date geologic events (^{40}K, ^{87}Rb, ^{147}Sm, ^{235}U, ^{238}U) are billions of years. These isotopes were present when the earth originated. With the passage of geologic time, daughter atoms (respectively ^{40}Ar, ^{87}Sr, ^{143}Nd, ^{207}Pb, ^{206}Pb) were created as the parent atoms disappeared. Calculation of an isotopic age (for example, by the K-Ar method) is based upon the measured ratio of accumulated daughter (^{40}Ar) to remaining parent (^{40}K) in a rock or mineral. In all analyses, corrections must be made for the amount of daughter present when the rock formed. A mass spectrometer is an instrument used to separate the isotopes and measure their abundances.

An isotopic age of an igneous rock refers to the time when it crystallized and cooled to the point that daughter isotope could accumulate. Transportation of clastic particles does not reset the isotopic clock, hence the age of deposition of clastic sediment cannot be determined by isotopic methods. Two kinds of age pertain to a metamorphic rock: the time of the primary rock-forming event, and the more recent time of metamorphic recrystallization.

Heavy chemical elements were created in supernova explosions not long before the earth, meteorites, and other objects in the solar system condensed, 4.55 billion years ago. The most ancient known rocks are approximately 4 billion years old. The age of the oldest known fossils, about 3.5 billion years, is only a minimum for the existence of life on earth.

Basement refers to the metamorphic and igneous rocks of the continental crust. A shield is a very large, stable area of low elevation and relief in which ancient basement rocks are exposed at the earth's surface by erosion. In a platform, the stable basement lies beneath a relatively thin cover of younger sedimentary rocks. This sedimentary cover rests upon an unconformity, a buried surface of erosion. Basement rocks in North America are organized in large provinces of characteristic age of formation—2.6, 1.7, and 1.1 billion years being the most prominent values.

12 All Life Is One

Life on earth originated in an atmosphere devoid of free oxygen. Could the chemistry of life on some distant planet require a nonoxidizing atmosphere, like that of the early earth? [*From* The Scientific Endeavor, *Rockefeller Institute Press, National Academy of Sciences, Washington, D.C., 1965*]

All life is one. Implications of this simple statement have been explored by scientists, philosophers, and theologians who may have come to very different conclusions. In what sense can all life be one? Are species of organisms related to one another only because one divine Creator has given them life? Or was there no Creator, but only impersonal forces causing atoms to react with one another? Or could the Creator have made these forces and used them to fashion the world? Is each group of organisms a special creation, or is each related to the others by evolution from a common ancestor?

For ages, these difficult cosmic questions have been addressed quite appropriately by myth and poetry. A myth is a story about events that are too profound to capture in normal language. The deep meaning of a myth grabs our emotions while also appealing to our intellects. Some have claimed that science, which deals with observable phenomena and whose language is so precise, has supplanted our need for mythology. This may be true for scientific questions that are well understood, but for the origin of life about which almost nothing is known, even scientific speculation carries a "flavor" of mythology. But no matter; both science and the wonderful myths have come to stay, and henceforth our cosmic considerations must be held accountable to scientific evidence.

One scientist with revolutionary insight was an Englishman, Charles Darwin, whose book *On the Origin of Species* appeared in 1859. He was the first to present carefully documented arguments for a theory of *organic evolution*—the hypothesis that all living species have shared a common history. Individuals of the same *species* are members of an interbreeding population whose offspring are also fertile, capable of continuing the line of descent. An interbreeding population is known as a "gene pool" because, just as a drop of water in a pool potentially could communicate with any other drop, in a gene pool the units of heredity (genes) are continually distributed throughout the population by mating encounters.

By "evolution" Darwin meant "descent with modification." All living things have ancestors, and since every generation inherits a new combination of characteristics, an evolution of sorts is guaranteed. No event as complex as biological reproduction ever repeats itself exactly. Even so, this self-evident reasoning might explain only minor variations within a species. For a new species to originate, a population must split into two populations that eventually become so different that they can no longer interbreed. Repetition of this process through geologic time would give rise to the 20 million species that are estimated to exist.

But how does one explain the enormous diversity of these millions of species? How did this profusion of ants and apple trees, of bacteria, birds, and human babies come into being? What role did dinosaurs, dodos, and other extinct creatures play in the succession of life? And what has the subject of geology to do with all this? Before Darwin's day, explanations of the origin of species were not based upon a lengthy time scale. Most people believed in a young earth, for geologists had just begun to gather the evidence for its great antiquity. Darwin was deeply impressed by this evidence, reasoning that although intervals of millions of years may not prove the case for evolution, at least plenty of time was available for the process to work even if it were very slow. Appreciation of the enormous extent of geologic time is an important contribution to the theory. Another geologic contribution is provided by *fossils*: ancient remains of organisms entombed in the rocks. Fossils leave a record of what actually happened during the development of life. *Paleontologists*, experts in the study of fossils, must be acquainted not only with the fossil record but also with modern organisms that in their turn will become part of the fossil record.

ORIGIN OF LIFE

Until the mid-1800s, the origin of life was considered not to be a problem. Reproduction by sexual and asexual means was well known, of course, but it was thought that life could occasionally arise by *spontaneous generation*. In wet weather, for example, a marsh would seem to bring forth countless insects, mice, and frogs that were not born or hatched from eggs. Animals simply appeared as though directly from the mud. But results of later experiments, culminating with the elegant work of Louis Pasteur, contradicted the idea of spontaneous generation. Pasteur showed that decay occurs only if living microbes have invaded the decaying object. The dictum that "Only life can beget life" seemed to hold no exceptions, even down to the level of microscopic organisms. Earlier naturalists were incorrect; marshlands were indeed filled with mice and the eggs of insects and frogs that had escaped their notice. Pasteur's definitive work caused researchers to conclude that the origin of life is beyond the scope of science. Pessimism prevailed, and investigations were discontinued for several decades. Modern researchers have revived the studies, while being aware of the many knotty scientific and philosophical problems.

A Modern Scientific Myth

Let us postulate that, just as the functioning of life is a natural phenomenon, so also was its origin by natural means. Because the origin is a fact of history, we cannot reproduce it in a laboratory in the same manner that we can study the force of gravity by dropping a ball again and again. We can only perform experiments that simulate conditions of the primitive earth, and interpret whether a natural origin of life is probable. Scientific mythology!

The pathway of origin will proceed from simple to more complicated, from "mere matter" to something living. It is a *chemical* evolution that took place very early in earth history, to be followed, once organisms were established, by *biological* evolution that is the theme of Darwin's book. Although living material is by far the most complex known form of matter, perhaps a classification (Table 12-1) will make it appear less formidable. We have already studied a classification based upon increasing complexity. Silicate minerals (Chapter 3) contain atoms of silicon and oxygen, that are further organized into Si-O tetrahedrons, that are yet further organized into chains, sheets, or more complex structures.

Similarly, 99 percent of living substance is composed of just four light chemical elements: hydrogen (H), carbon (C), nitrogen (N), and oxygen (O). These atoms, and much smaller amounts of other elements, are organized into small organic molecules which join together as large organic molecules. For example, an important group of small organic molecules are 20 *amino acids*, the simplest amino acid consisting of 10 atoms, to 27 for the most complex amino acid. A long, infolded chain of hundreds of amino acid units is linked together to form *protein.* Protein molecules perform a great variety of functions in living cells. Some are employed in metabolism, others in the structural framework, others to recognize and combat germs, and so on. Other simple groups of atoms comprise adenine (abbreviated *A*), guanine (*G*), thymine (*T*) and cytosine (*C*). These are linked together with sugar and phosphate (also small molecules) to make a very large molecule, deoxyribonucleic acid (DNA) which may contain as many as billions of atoms. DNA is a storehouse of information that is used both to direct the activities of a cell and to transmit its inheritance to the next generation.

Given the environmental conditions of the early earth, how could these small organic molecules have formed naturally, and then by stages become organized into large molecules, and finally into cells that reproduce, utilize food, respond to stimuli—in short, are "alive"? To get started, we need H, C, N, and O and suitable sources of energy. As discussed in Chapter 2, a primitive ocean emerged from the earth's

Table 12-1. *A Hierarchy of the Organization of Life*

Increasing complexity of organization ↑

Level	Example		Scientific discipline
Species	Grizzly bear, *Ursus arctos horribilis*		Ecology, Genetics, Paleontology
Population	Grizzly bears in Yellowstone National Park		Ecology, Genetics, Paleontology
Organism	One grizzly bear		Ecology, Genetics, Paleontology
Organ system	Circulatory		Genetics, Paleontology
Organ	Heart		Biochemistry, Genetics, Paleontology
Tissue	Muscle		Biochemistry, Genetics, Paleontology
Cell	Muscle cell	Living	Biochemistry, Genetics, Paleontology
Organelle	Nucleus	Nonliving	Biochemistry, Genetics
Giant molecule	Deoxyribonucleic acid (DNA)		Organic Chemistry, Biochemistry, Genetics
Small molecule	Guanine (G)		Organic Chemistry, Biochemistry, Genetics
Atom	H, C, N, O, etc.	Particle physics	Organic Chemistry, Biochemistry
Subatomic particle	proton, neutron, electron	Particle physics	Organic Chemistry, Biochemistry

interior through volcanoes, accompanied by the atmospheric gases N_2 and CO_2. Volcanoes may also spew out methane (CH_4), ammonia (NH_3), hydrogen sulfide (H_2S), and hydrogen (H_2), gases that are known as chemically reducing substances. These compounds are abundant in the atmospheres of Jupiter and Saturn which are more like original cosmic material. In contrast, the earth's atmosphere has become oxidizing and, indeed, 21 per cent of it consists of free oxygen (O_2). But initially there was no source of this substance; oxygen in volcanic gases is not O_2, but rather in chemical combination with other elements.

Early sources of energy included radioactivity, volcanism, and giant meteorite strikes, all of which were far more intense than today. A great variety of chemical reactions were likely to occur. In 1953, the American biochemist Stanley Miller and his Ph.D. supervisor, Harold Urey, performed a pioneering experiment in which a Jupiter-like mixture of water, methane, ammonia, and hydrogen was cycled through a sparking chamber (Figure 12-1). After several days of this simulated lightning discharge, the mixture turned yellow by accumulation of organic molecules, including amino acids. In subsequent experiments the gases were chosen to be more like those of the earth's early atmosphere, and other

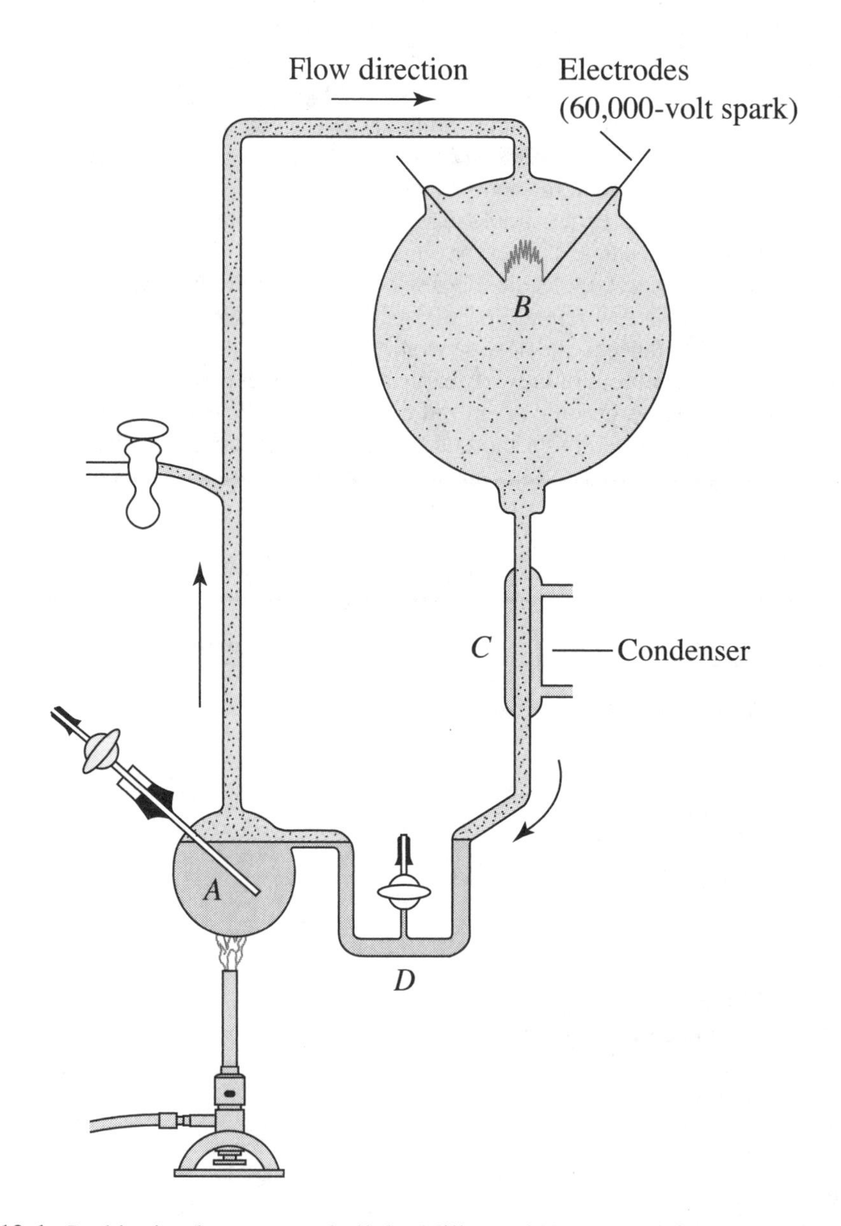

Figure 12-1. In this simple apparatus built by Miller and Urey, vapor from the boiling of a primordial brew (*A*) ascended into a sparking chamber (*B*). Products of chemical reactions in the sparking chamber were cooled and condensed (*C*), then returned through a U-tube (*D*) which prevented the backflow of vapor.

energy sources were tried including radioactivity, light, and ultraviolet radiation. These experiments too were successful, such that by now all of the common small molecules essential to life have been created in this simple, yet realistic manner. To this list of earth-formed organic molecules we may add a rich variety of molecules that occur in comets and carbon-containing meteorites, that were deposited on earth by their impacts.

Thus the simple organic molecules were either supplied ready-made or they were synthesized under natural conditions. This does not explain a peculiar fact about the amino acids present in living organisms. Consider how atoms are arranged in a molecule of alanine, one of the amino acids (Figure 12-2). Although atoms could be positioned in a left-handed configuration (*a*) or a right-handed configuration (*b*), almost all living things use only left-handed amino acids. In one sense, it has to be this way because a mixture of types could not fit together well in a protein chain, nor could organisms with a left-handed chemistry digest food consisting of right-handed molecules. Simulations of nature by Miller and Urey and others produced both left- and right-handed molecules. Some unknown process must have permitted only left-handed amino acids to be incorporated into protein, perhaps from the very beginning. It is an example of *natural selection*, which as we shall see is active at all levels of the organization of life (Table 12-1) from the lowest to the highest.

The next step, natural synthesis of large complex organic molecules such as protein and DNA, is even less well understood. Only in protected environments could these molecules avoid being oxidized by traces of O_2, decomposed by ultraviolet radiation, or simply dissolved by water. Already at this early stage we encounter an important property of life, which is to *assemble itself*. An objection often raised by critics of our postulated origin of life is that the universe seems only to "run down." Heat is dissipated, iron rusts, and dead things decay. A condition of order progresses naturally to disorder, not the other way around. Only life is capable of repair and self-renewal, and so it is argued once again that it takes life to beget life. But things are not quite that simple because much of life does not function in a state of equilibrium. Even if the universe as a whole were slipping into chaos, the tiny part of it that is alive is headed in the opposite direction. Internal structures of a living cell may become incredibly well ordered, always at the cost of producing more disorder in its environment. None of this violates any of the laws of physics.

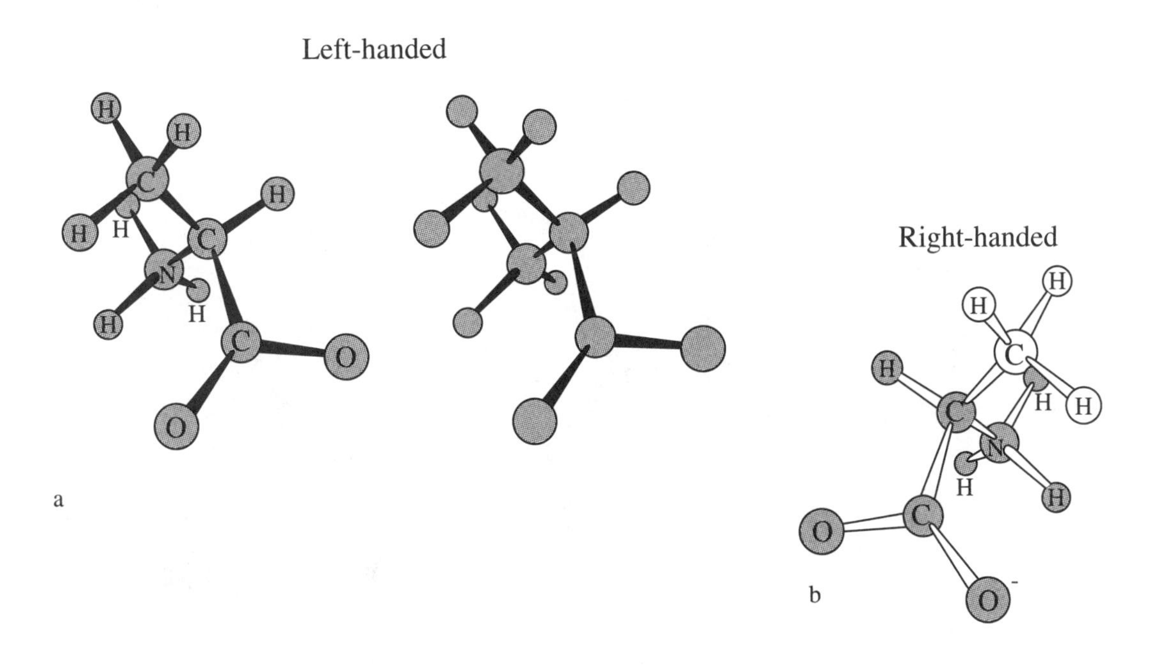

Figure 12-2. Amino acids can exist in both left-handed and right-handed forms, but only the left-handed type is synthesized by living cells. (*a*) In this perspective view of alanine, the second simplest amino acid, the connecting rods represent chemical bonds. Relax your eyes as you stare straight ahead at the paired figures of alanine. The visual images will fuse together, enabling you to see the molecule stereoscopically, in three dimensions. (*b*) The shaded atoms are common to all 20 amino acids. Unshaded atoms (CH_3 in the case of alanine) are different in each amino acid.

Intriguing experiments provide a glimpse of how the precursors to life might have become self-organized. If a preparation of linked amino acids is boiled in seawater, as by an underwater volcano, tiny spheres of bacterial size assemble themselves in the brew (Figure 12-3). They mimic bacteria by forming chains and producing buds that swell and break off from the original sphere. And like bacteria, they are composed of double-walled membranes. Possibly the organization of complex molecules took place in the protected micro-environments offered by such membranes.

In the functioning of life today, the task of self-organization is performed by DNA. This remarkable molecule is shaped like a spiral staircase (Figure 12-4) whose sides are composed of double strands of sugar and phosphate, tied together by "treads" that are pairs of the units A, C, T, and G mentioned above. A always pairs with T, and C with G (see the figure). It is the sequence of A-T and C-G pairs that codes the information in DNA. "Messenger" RNA molecules, which are similar to DNA, run along the DNA strand to read this sequence, then carry the instructions into other parts of the cell for execution. Our knowledge of DNA has explained many things about genetics, the science of heredity. A gene is a sequence of about 1500 A-T and C-G pairs that codes for the production of a chain of amino acids in protein. By controlling which proteins are manufactured, and when, the genes control the structure, chemistry, involuntary functions, and many of the behavior patterns of the organism.

Analogies between the functioning of a complex computer code and the DNA code are striking. For example, both codes contain IF...THEN...ELSE statements: if a particular condition is true, then proceed with the following steps, otherwise jump to another part of the code and do something else. The genetic code of DNA and its associated messenger RNA is universal. For example, the sequence *G-C-A* in messenger RNA codes for the manufacture of alanine (Figure 12-2) throughout all of the living kingdoms from bacteria to humankind. This unity of biochemical pathways is powerful circumstantial evidence that life is connected by a common origin and history.

When a cell divides, the genetic information must be duplicated before it is distributed to the two daughter cells. Double-stranded DNA unwinds and separates, so that new complementary strands can form alongside the original strands (Figure 12-5). During the duplication, the resulting DNA is checked for errors which are corrected on the spot. New copies of DNA are thus astonishingly accurate—a miscopy of the *A-T-C-G* sequence occurs only about one time in 100 million. Nevertheless, inaccurate copies do get made, and if they occur in reproductive cells they are passed on to future generations.

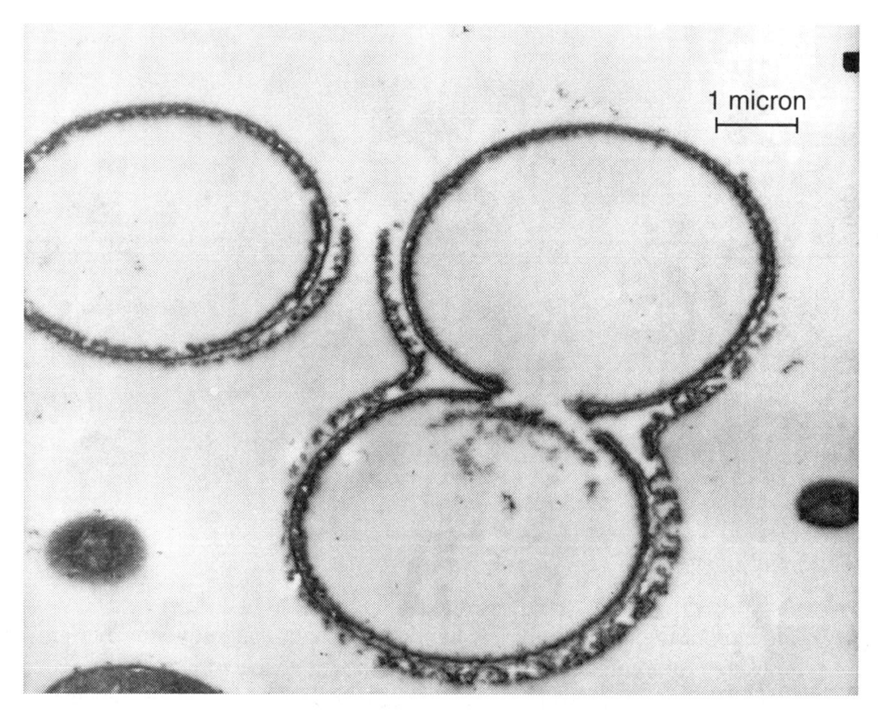

Figure 12-3. An electron microscope picture of stained microspheres shows one unit in the act of dividing. The double wall shown here is considerably thicker than the outer double membrane of a bacterium. A micron is one-millionth of a meter. [*Courtesy S. W. Fox.*]

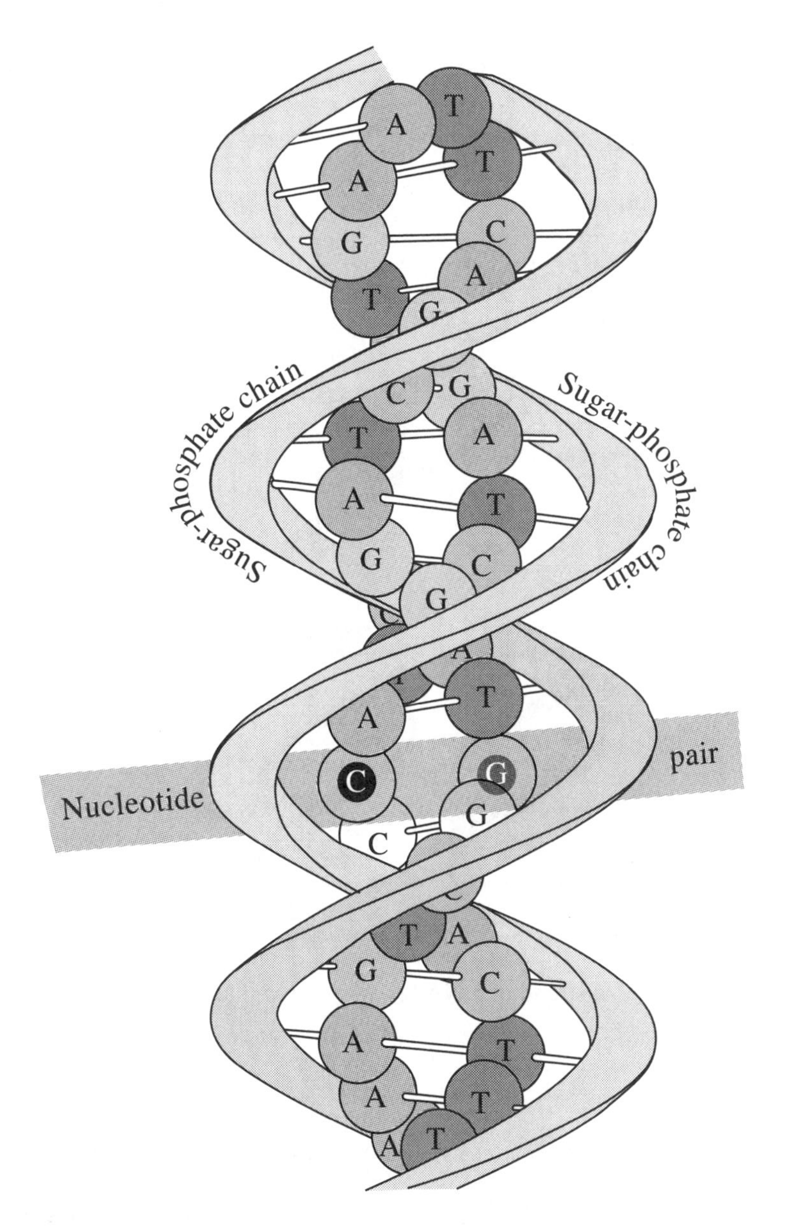

Figure 12-4. Double twisted chains of sugar and phosphate form the "backbone" of DNA. Four nitrogenous bases—thymine (T), cytosine (C), adenine (A), and guanine (G)—are attached to the backbone by chemical bonds. Adenine always pairs with thymine, and guanine with cytosine. Two bases, together with their accompanying sugar and phosphate, form a segment of the DNA molecule known as a nucleotide pair (shaded bar).

The First Organisms

To return to Table 12-1, we see a plausible pathway by which nature could have organized itself from subatomic particles to atoms to small molecules. Origins of giant molecules, the next stage, are poorly understood, and we do not know how the first cells came into existence. Higher on the list, Table 12-1 refers to tissues, organs, and organ systems. Here we have not only chemistry, but real live creatures that feed, fight, and breed with one another. We must turn to fossils in order to learn more about upper levels in the hierarchy of life. If life evolved into ever greater and greater complexity, then the earliest life forms should have been the most simple. The fossil record splendidly confirms this prediction; the most ancient organisms are of lowly bacteria and blue-green algae (more accurately known as Cyanobacteria), each microscopic individual a single cell of ultimate simplicity. (Or was the earliest life that simple? A

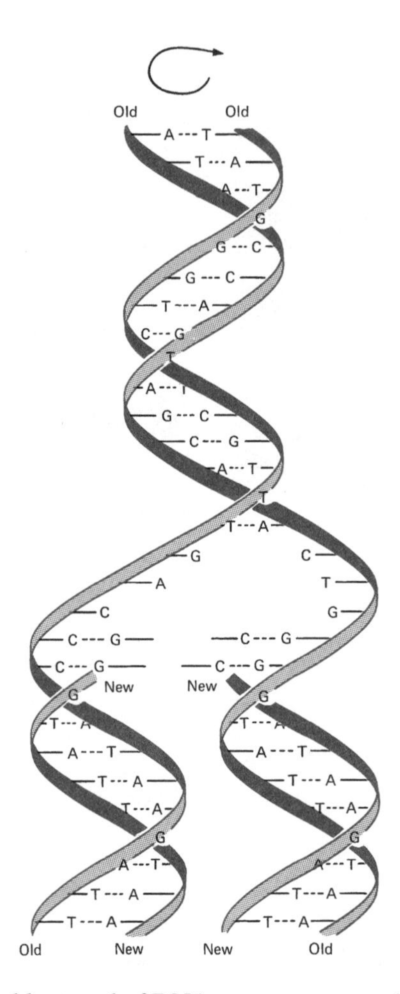

Figure 12-5. An unwinding double strand of DNA serves as a template, or gauge, for the formation of two DNA molecules.

modern bacterial cell can synthesize an impressive 3 to 6 thousand chemical compounds at a rate of a million reactions per second.)

The record of the most ancient fossils is very meager. Almost all fossils are harbored in sedimentary rock, and not much early sediment has survived the recycling processes of weathering, erosion, or metamorphism. Primitive organisms did not secrete *hard parts* such as bone or shell material. Their single cells are visible only under a microscope, although structures built by colonies of countless individuals are obvious enough. While lying in sediment for billions of years, large organic molecules that were synthesized by the proto-organisms have partly decomposed into smaller molecules, with loss of information about their original character. All that we know about the dawn of life is tantalizing at best.

However, if our premise is correct that life developed throughout a long history, then we would expect modern organisms to bear the imprint of their ancient origin. A body form, a life style, a way to obtain needed energy, all are inherited from the past. It would be legitimate to compare and contrast different groups of organisms because they are in fact related. Let us pause to consider a reasonable scientific classification.

Realms of the Living

In the opening chapter of *Genesis*, the first book of the Bible, we find what may be the earliest and most primitive classification of living organisms. We read about seed plants, birds that fly, sea monsters and fish that swarm the waters, cattle and creeping things and other beasts of the earth, and humans. The Bible makes useful distinctions according to habitat (*where* an organism lives) and niche (*how* it lives), just as a modern ecologist does. Habitat and niche can be observed in "real time," the here and now. An evolutionary classification takes into account not only these but also information from biochemistry and microbiology, and the historical record of fossils. This procedure is more subtle than one based upon obvious characteristics, and its startling conclusions may appear anything but self-evident.

For example, biologists recognize that differences on the microscopic level of cells and organic molecules are far more fundamental than the traditional distinction between plants and animals. In plants, animals, fungi, and protozoans, which are known as *eukaryotes* ("truly nuclear"), the cell contains organelles. An organelle is a structure, such as the nucleus, that is separated from the rest of the cell by a membrane [Figure 12-6(*b*)]. All of the DNA in eukaryotic cells resides in these internal "packages." The cells are relatively large, typically 0.01 to 0.1 millimeter across. Eukaryotes may reproduce sexually or asexually.

By contrast, in bacteria and Cyanobacteria, which are called *prokaryotes* ("pre-nucleated"), the cell lacks a nucleus and other organelles [Figure 12-6(*a*)]. The strand of DNA is a single closed loop in the midst of the cell. Almost without exception, prokaryotes are tiny single-celled organisms, 0.001 to 0.01 millimeter across, that ingest small molecules directly from the environment. Prokaryotes may reproduce in varied ways, but never by a conventional sexual mode in which the female and male make equal genetic contributions to the offspring.

Any attempt to classify organisms according to niche, habitat, or mode of reproduction would be deeply frustrated by numerous inconsistencies. Living and fossil prokaryotes and eukaryotes, on the other hand, are distinguished absolutely from one another. A classification of all living things into five *kingdoms* (Figure 12-7) recognizes these differences and also helps to make sense of the fossil record. As the name implies, kingdom *Prokaryotae* includes the prokaryotes. The other four kingdoms are

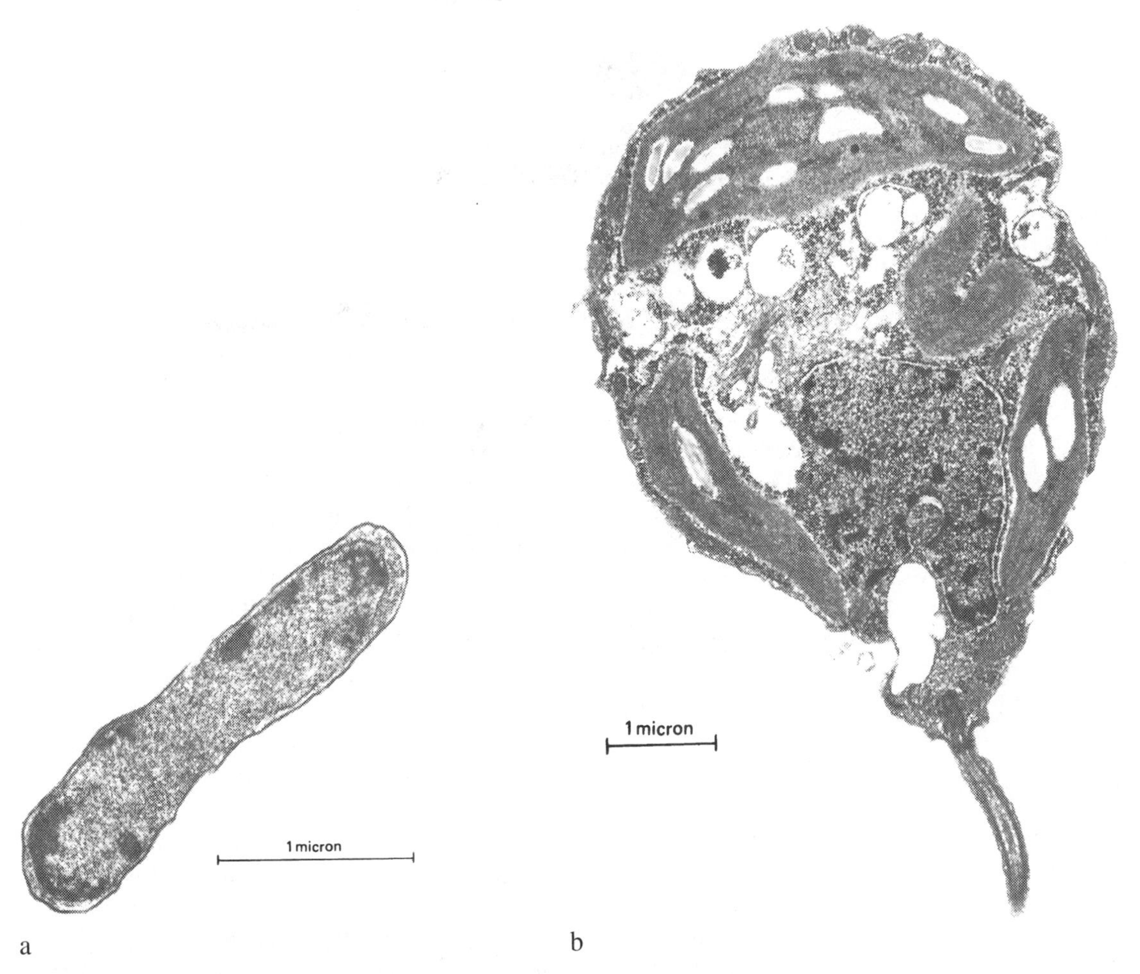

Figure 12-6. (*a*) Components of this cell of a common intestinal bacterium (prokaryotic) are ill-defined. [*Courtesy Robert W. Riess.*] (*b*) In contrast, this cell of a green alga (eukaryotic) contains a nucleus, plastids, mitochondria, and other organelles. [*Courtesy Marjorie Maguire and Robert W. Riess.*]

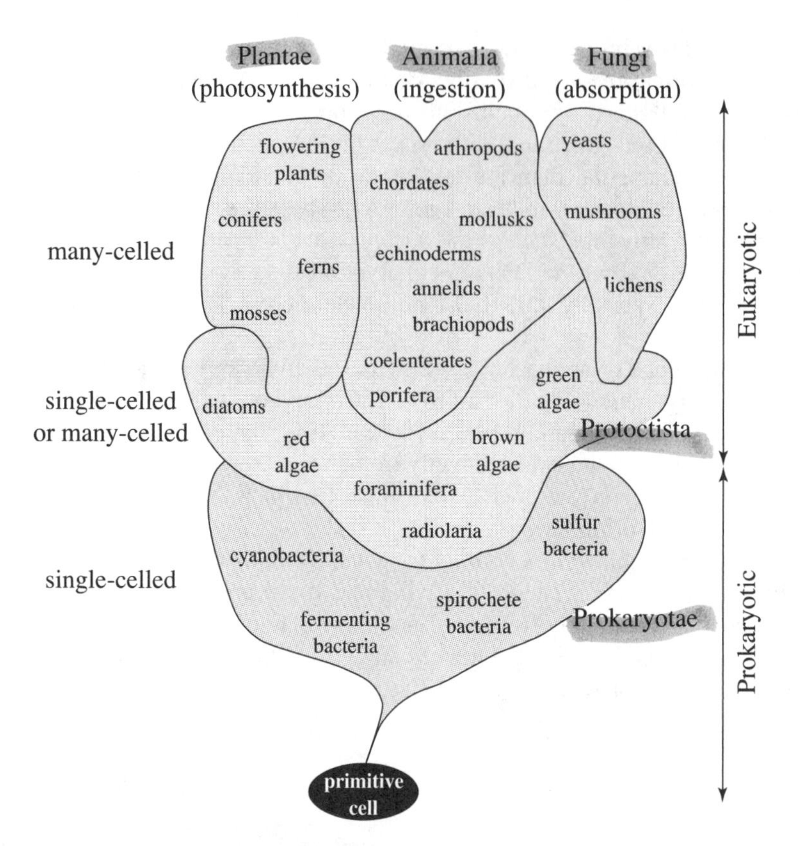

Figure 12-7. Formerly only the plant and animal kingdoms were recognized, but the great diversity of life seems to require an expanded classification to five kingdoms. Some researchers believe that 5 kingdoms may eventually go to 25 or 30! That miscellaneous group, the Protoctista, would be the chief subject of a reclassification.

eukaryotic, in which members of the *Fungi* and the familiar *Animalia* and *Plantae* are many-celled. Finally, a host of both single-celled and many-celled organisms that do not fit into any other classification are lumped together as *Protoctista*.

Kingdoms are further subdivided into 90 or so *phyla* (singular, phylum). It is disappointing that only about one-third of these have hard parts, or would leave tracks or trails, and thus the different phyla are not uniformly represented in the fossil record. An example of a prokaryotic phylum is Cyanobacteria which comprises the most ancient known fossils. Cyanobacteria thrive in virtually every environment today. Foraminifera (mentioned in Chapter 7) are an example of a protoctist phylum whose tiny shells have contributed to vast deposits of limestone. Mushrooms, molds, and yeasts, being soft-bodied fungi, have left scarcely a trace in the rock record. Prominent among plant phyla are Angiospermophyta (flowering plants) and Coniferophyta (conifers such as pine or redwood). Abundant fossil shells have been deposited by clams, oysters, snails, and others of the animal phylum Mollusca. Vertebrate animals such as you and I are members of the phylum Chordata. Appendices A and B contain thumbnail descriptions of prominent animal and plant phyla.

Chemical Consequences of Life

Organisms can employ an astonishing variety of means to satisfy their most basic requirements. They must obtain food and water, and protection from hostile surroundings that might include predators, toxic chemicals, or harmful ultraviolet rays from the sun. Animals and fungi ultimately must depend for food upon other organisms that can make their own through the process of *photosynthesis*. With sunlight as a source of energy, photosynthesis takes the simple environmental molecules H_2O and CO_2 as a starting point to manufacture glucose which is further used in metabolism. Plants and green algae release O_2 as a waste product of photosynthesis, but photosynthesizing bacteria do it differently. For example, the sulfur bacteria utilize hydrogen sulfide (H_2S) instead of H_2O, and excrete sulfur (S) instead of oxygen.

Animals and other organisms that require oxygen gas, whether in the air or dissolved in water, are said to be *aerobic*. Organisms that are indifferent to the presence or absence of O_2, or to which this gas is actually a deadly poison, are *anaerobic*. Earth's primitive atmosphere, being volcanic and nearly devoid of O_2, could have sustained only the anaerobic organisms. With no free oxygen, no high-altitude layer of ozone (O_3) would have been established to absorb incoming ultraviolet radiation. On the other hand, the modern oxygen-rich atmosphere is so reactive that elaborate chemical protections are needed to prevent aerobic organisms from "burning up." When anaerobic life originated, the sun's ultraviolet rays were even more intense and lethal than today. A beneficial ozone protection from the sun resulted when photosynthesizers introduced oxygen into the atmosphere, but this gas was toxic to anaerobes and aerobes alike. With such hostilities about, it is difficult to explain how life got established. Organisms must have been adapted only to specific environments, just as today.

The proto-organisms likely did not manufacture the complex organic molecule, chlorophyll. Plants and green algae must have chlorophyll in order to perform photosynthesis. Perhaps the first organisms "ate" the organic soup produced in the manner of the Miller-Urey experiments (see Figure 12-1), obtaining energy by fermentation. The advent of photosynthesis, that great milestone in the history of life, brought about three important consequences. (i) Organisms could make food directly from abundant water and carbon dioxide. (ii) Atmospheric oxygen began to increase, from barest traces to the present-day 21 percent. (iii) Respiration, the utilization of food with release of energy, became possible through reactions that employ oxygen. Aerobic respiration is as much as 18 times more efficient than fermentation which is the anaerobic mode of respiration.

The appearance of life had very profound consequences at the earth's surface. Organisms may release oxygen to the atmosphere, or precipitate iron oxide, or calcite that forms limestone, or silica that eventually becomes chert, or bone that is the basis of phosphate deposits. Of course, not all these products appeared immediately or in large quantities. Atmospheric oxygen was introduced very early, but it would be another 3 billion years before animals appeared having bone.

Initially the oxygen reacted with much iron that was dissolved in streams and in the ocean, causing deposition of *iron formations* rich in the insoluble iron oxide minerals hematite and magnetite. Apparently oxygen could not begin to accumulate in the atmosphere until it had first "used up" the iron by combining with it, forming a precipitate. Nearly all of the great iron formations, which are mankind's chief source of this important metal, are older than 1.9 billion years. Thus some types of rock were formed at unique times, not to be repeated in earth history. Recall that the principle of uniformitarianism (Chapter 11) does not insist that the earth has always looked the same, but only that the same natural processes (such as precipitation of insoluble minerals) operate uniformly.

Primordial Fossils

Billions of years ago, parts of the earth's surface were green, but no familiar plants or animals graced the landscape. Rocks and wet spots were coated monotonously with bacteria and algae. And yet, within these lowly microbes, or perhaps in precursor organisms that no longer exist, was slowly evolving the most fundamental chemistry of life: photosynthesis, respiration, manufacture of protein, inheritance by means of the DNA code. So perfected were these chemical pathways that today the same are in use throughout the entire realm of earthly nature. All life is one!

Even the most ancient fossils are of photosynthesizing organisms, therefore relatively "advanced." It happens that Australia contains a spectacular record of several of the critical stages in life's development. As mentioned in the preceding chapter, one fossil locality consists of 3.5-billion-year-old sedimentary rock at North Pole, remote in the Outback of Western Australia. Figure 12-8*a* shows sedimentary rock containing structures that resemble cones nestled within cones. These fossils, called *stromatolites*, were deposited during the upward growth of Cyanobacteria whose tiny sheaths trapped layer upon fine layer of sediment. By coincidence, one of the few places where stromatolites are forming today is not far away in Shark Bay, on Australia's west coast [Figure 12-8(*b*)]. High rates of evaporation have made the water very salty in secluded parts of Shark Bay that are rather isolated from the open ocean. Cyanobacteria can survive in this harsh environment, but it is too saline for the snails that normally graze upon them. In ancient times, when there were no snails, stromatolites formed in abundance in many parts of the world.

By now, nearly 350 groups of ancient microfossils have been identified in several thousand localities around the world. Indirect chemical evidence places the origin of eukaryotes at about 1.7 billion

a

b

Figure 12-8. (*a*) Stromatolites in Western Australia are the world's most ancient known fossils. For scale, the pen is about 6 inches long. [*Geological Survey of Canada Photo No. 205428 by Ralph Thorpe.*] (*b*) Highly saline Shark Bay, Australia, is one of the few places where modern algal colonies can escape being grazed upon by snails. The biscuit-shaped structures, consisting of fine sediment bound together by algal filaments, are soft enough to be cut through by a knife. [*Courtesy P. F. Hoffman.*]

years ago; the oldest confirmed eukaryotic fossils are about 1.4 billion years old. According to a fascinating and widely regarded theory, eukaryotes originated by a fusion, or symbiotic partnership, of cells inside cells. Organelles called mitochondria are the energy powerhouse of the eukaryotic cell. Chlorophyll is contained within plastids, the organelle that performs photosynthesis. And yet, mitochondria resemble purple bacteria and plastids resemble Cyanobacteria, both of which are prokaryotes. Both organelles carry their own DNA which is more like that of prokaryotes than the DNA in the nucleus. Possibly the microscopic beating cilia that can propel eukaryotic cells originated by the fusion of a spirochete bacterium.

ORGANIC EVOLUTION

Thus far we have deferred the question of *how* organic evolution could take place. There are some who would wish to defer that question forever, as it may arouse feelings of great uneasiness. Charles Darwin himself had felt uneasy, delaying publication of his theory for almost two decades while accumulating more evidence. Finally another eminent but more impatient biologist, A. R. Wallace, was about to publish his own similar conclusions and the two men resolved the issue of scientific priority by announcing jointly. History has given Darwin most of the credit, as he deserved. Another influential figure was Charles Lyell, the greatest geologist of the day, who continually urged his friend Darwin to commit his book *On the Origin of Species* to print.

If, as the biologists and paleontologists say, "Nothing about the living kingdoms makes sense except in the light of evolution," then why is the theory such a threat to some persons? Is it because evolution seems to them to deny the unique qualities of humanity by regarding us as "merely" a part of nature? The same question distressed Darwin, who once confided in a letter that the assertion that species are not forever fixed is "like confessing a murder."

His ideas highly offended both philosophers and theologians (Figure 12-9). Philosophers objected, not because Darwin had invented a rival philosophy, but because he ignored them. He was the father of "population thinking" in which random events, rather than the will of a person, determine what happens. If statistical fluctuations describe a phenomenon, it may be impossible to link an observed effect to a particular cause. To the philosophies of the day this was unacceptable.

Notions about the place of humankind in the universe held by the nineteenth century theologians were also challenged. Perhaps unconsciously the Church had borrowed an image of creation from the ancient Greeks who had often watched a sculptor fashion some complex form, such as of a human figure, from a chunk of marble. Just so, it appeared reasonable that in six days the Divine Sculptor had perfected a world over which humans, the glory of creation, were to rule. From an evolutionary perspective, we do not enjoy such an exalted position. Our race is one with the rest of nature, having inhabited this speck of dust orbiting an obscure star for but a few fleeting seconds. It was threatening to be made to feel so infinitesimal. Let us examine Darwin's pioneering theory, as updated in the light of modern research.

Processes of Evolution

At least in his earlier years Darwin was obsessed, as nearly all geologists are, with a desire to visit remote parts of the earth. He was appointed as naturalist aboard the small British research ship, *Beagle*, during a leisurely five-year discovery mission around the world (1831–1836). He visited the Galápagos Islands,

Figure 12-9. To this day, the theory of evolution has been a controversial subject, especially with those who feel, as this cartoonist did, that it threatens the uniqueness of human beings.

an archipelago some 1000 kilometers (600 miles) west of mainland Ecuador (Figure 12-10). These and other volcanic islands nestled in the Pacific vastness are ideal natural settings for the study of evolution. They originated as a fiery sterile mass, so distant from the mainland that not even birds would likely encounter them. Colonization events are almost freakishly rare and geologically recent: in the Galápagos, less than 3 million years ago according to isotopic ages of the volcanic rocks.

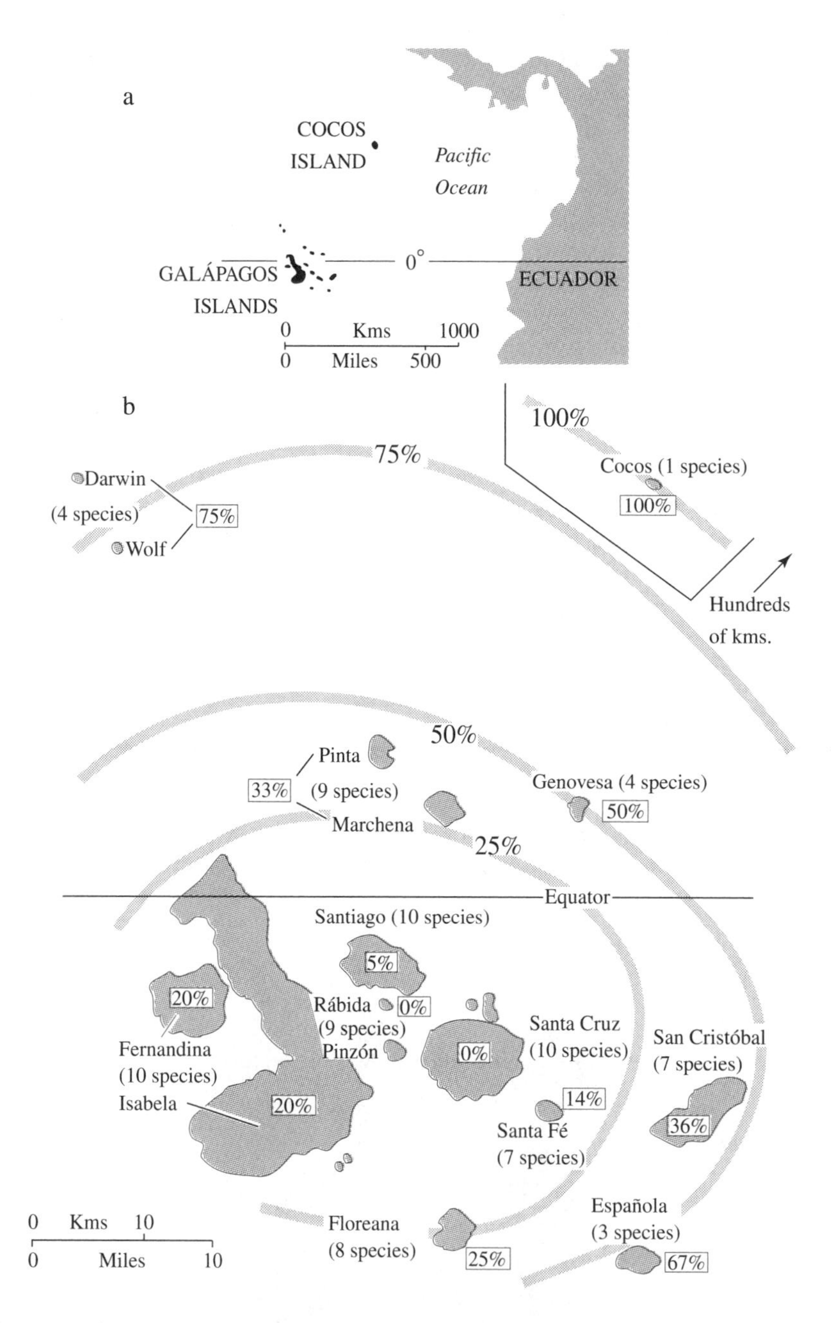

Figure 12-10. (*a*) An index map locates the Galápagos Islands and Cocos Island, 800 kilometers to the northeast. (*b*) Contour lines and numbers in boxes refer to the percentage of species of Darwin's finches resident on a particular island that live there *only*. The more isolated the island, the fewer species and the greater proportion of them that live nowhere else. In the extreme case, distant Cocos Island has only one species that is unique to it. More species (as many as 10) live together on islands in the center of the archipelago because intercommunication is relatively easy. The distribution is explained if members of one ancestral species had made a rare, chance crossing from the originally inhabited island to a neighboring island, and so on from island to island. The gene pool on each newly colonized island then remained quite isolated and evolved to the point that a new species arose.

Darwin observed a remarkable distribution of species of finch unique to these islands. These drab little birds are not distinguished by their plumage, as is generally the case among bird species, but instead upon the form of the beak. Indeed, an individual may often mistake another for one of its own species until catching sight of the other's beak. Stout crushing beaks of three ground-dwelling species are large, medium, or small according to the sizes of seeds they eat. The longer and more pointed beak of another species probes the flowers of prickly pear cactus. Beaks of tree finches are suited to catch insects, and there is even a specialized "warbler" species and a "woodpecker" species, both finches. Species on remote islands typically occur nowhere else, while resembling most closely the species on islands nearest to them. Moreover, Galápagos finches are more like finch species in mainland Ecuador than those in more distant parts. Similar distributions of unique species of birds and insects pertain to the Hawaiian Islands and other isolated spots.

Darwin wondered why, if these species arose by separate divine creations, the creative power was so prodigally expended just in these islands, and why the finches so closely resemble one another. He wrote: "One might really fancy that from an original paucity of birds in this archipelago, one species had been taken and modified for different ends" (i.e., different niches). In the Galápagos it appears that *speciation,* or splitting into different species, took place as populations were isolated geographically. Finches of one island do not visit adjacent islands except as blown across by storms or other rare accidents. Interbreeding would continually mix the gene pool within a population, while the gene pools isolated in different islands would slowly diverge. Of course, there is more to the process of speciation than geographic isolation, for we also see that as many as 10 species occupy the *same* island (Figure 12-10).

More about Classification In the 1700s the great Swedish naturalist, Carl Linné, established a useful classification of organisms that has come to be universally accepted. It is based upon comparisons of the numbers of characteristics that are shared or not shared amongst species of organisms (Figure 12-11). Linné's observations were of obvious physical structures, whereas today we are able to compare molecular sequences in the DNA code, amino acids in protein, etc., or sequences in the fossil record. No matter what the type of observation, the patterns that emerge are much the same because all life is one. Linnéan classification is a nesting of smaller groups within larger. Similar species are included in the same genus, similar genera in the same family, similar families within orders, and so on up to classes, phyla, and kingdoms.

Suppose that we represent species as holes put in a target by shotgun pellets (Figure 12-12). The smaller the distance between holes, the more similar the corresponding two species. The target is a single time plane representing today, and the space between the target and shotgun represents geologic time back to life's origin. According to the left-hand pattern (*a*), we might conclude that today's species had the same source (as though there were just one shotgun blast) but are otherwise not related. To the contrary, the pattern actually observed is diagram (*b*) which is the Linnéan hierarchy of clusters within larger clusters. This pattern would result if one pellet had left the gun, broke apart while in flight, and breakup of fragments (speciation) had continued until the moment of impact. Evolutionary theory describes the three-dimensional world of living things throughout the fourth dimension, time. Stable or changing environments will strongly influence whether a population remains stable, splits into new species, or goes extinct.

Natural Selection Biologists have discovered an astonishing amount of genetic variation in populations. In eukaryotes, the DNA is packed densely with protein into *chromosomes,* thread-like bodies in the cell nucleus. An individual inherits a characteristic number of chromosomes, half of them from each parent. There are 8 chromosomes in the cells of fruit flies, 46 in humans, 48 in potatoes, for example. When reproductive cells are made, the chromosomes may break in several places and exchange pieces, then they are assorted randomly into different reproductive cells, and further randomly combined when the female's egg unites with the male's sperm.

Although Darwin lacked a modern understanding of genetics, he knew that sexual reproduction continually recombines the hereditary information, and thus each individual is unique. And yet, something more is needed to produce a long-term evolutionary change, some process whose effect is *not* random. While pondering the problem, he happened to read a somber little book, *First Essay on Population* by Thomas Malthus, an English clergyman. Malthus noted how rapidly organisms can reproduce themselves. In an ideal environment the number of individuals continues to double with the passage of time according to a *geometrical* progression such as 1, 2, 4, 8, 16, 32, etc. But Malthus was also aware that a finite earth cannot accommodate the unlimited growth of a population. He pointed out that human food supply at best can be improved only according to an *arithmetic* progression such as 1, 2, 3, 4, 5, etc.

Step 1
Populations described

Population	A	B	C	D	E	F	G	H
Distribution of comparable structures numbered 1 to 6							1	1
					2	2		
				3	3	3		
	4	4	4					
				5	5	5	5	5
	6	6	6	6	6	6	6	6

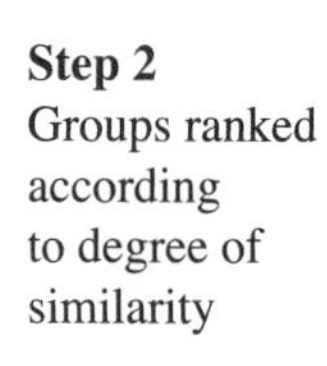

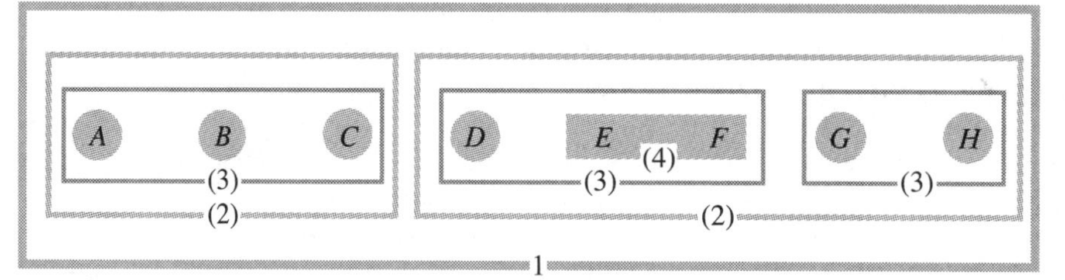

Step 3
Classification

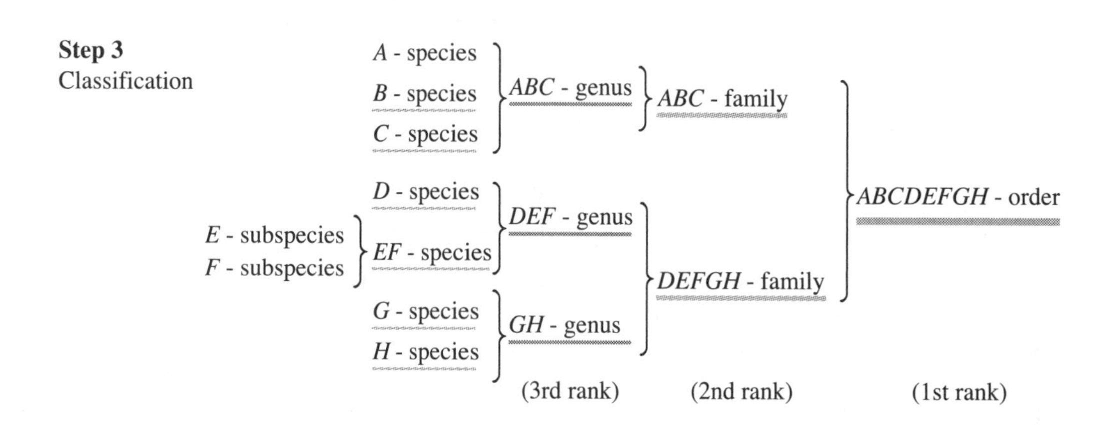

Figure 12-11. Multivariate analysis is used to relate groups of species into larger assemblages. Natural populations are first carefully described (step 1), then assigned to larger groups of populations depending on degrees of similarity (step 2). The groups are designated as genus, family, etc., and baptized with formal names (step 3).

Other organisms are even less able to manipulate their food supplies, and so the result is the same for all: a tendency to overpopulation that is held in check by limitations of the environment including starvation, disease, and predation. No wonder this scenario has been called the "dismal theorem" of Malthus!

Darwin immediately saw the potential of the dismal theorem as a mechanism of evolution. He wrote:

> As many more individuals of each species are born than can possibly survive; and as, consequently, there is a frequently recurring struggle for existence, it follows that any being, if it vary however slightly in any manner profitable to itself, under the complex and sometimes varying conditions of life, will have a better chance of surviving, and thus be *naturally selected* . . . Any selected variety will tend to propagate its [own kind in] new and modified form.

Natural selection favors the survival of the more fit individuals until they can transmit their genes to the next generation, whereas the less fit individuals die before they reproduce. If an antelope survives by out-

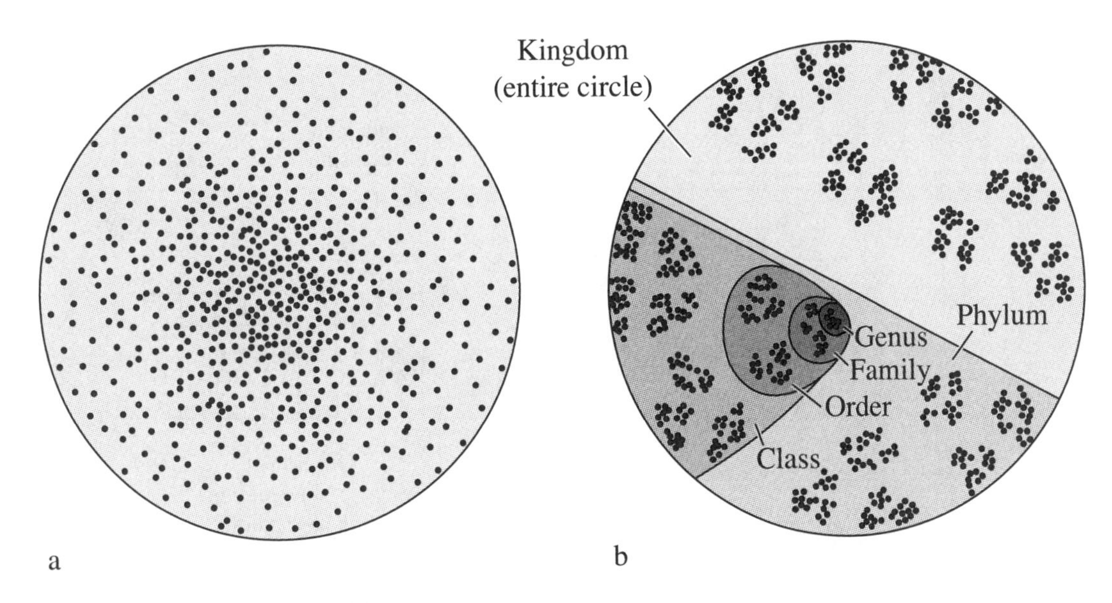

Figure 12-12. In each of these shotgun patterns, a dot represents a species.

running a pack of wild dogs, it is fit in the sense of Tennyson's poetic phrase "Nature red in tooth and claw," but fitness assumes many other forms. Most of the competition for survival is among members of the *same* species because they are striving for the same means of support; they occupy the same niche. Fitness may include superior resistance to disease, or ability to gather food, attract a mate or pollinating insect, elude or destroy enemies, adapt to changing environment.

Relationships among fitness, natural selection, and an individual's genetic makeup are extraordinarily complex. Some genes are "good" in the sense of promoting the survival of the individual, others are "bad," and most genes are probably neutral. They commonly function, not as independent units, but together as larger systems that contain both good and bad genes. Finally, it is an entire individual organism with its assorted good and bad genes that survives or fails to survive by natural selection.

Mutation Thus far, we have seen that natural selection is able only to remove something that was already present. Natural selection may explain the death of an individual before it has reproduced, or even the extinction of an entire species, but how can something genuinely *new* be created? The answer to this question is found at the molecular level of inheritance. When the DNA molecule replicates during cell division, an imperfect self-copy, or *mutation* may result. Radioactivity, cosmic rays, foreign chemical substances, or simply the normal vibration of atoms can cause chemical bonds to break and reorganize in some new configuration, a modified genetic code (Figure 12-13). Mutations are random, their effects unpredictable, just as a random change in a computer code would produce an unpredictable result. Possibly the new code will be expressed as a change of structure, body chemistry, or behavior that is neutral in its effects on the recipient, or the mutation may be harmful, even lethal. At other times when the circumstances of survival are changing, a mutation may actually be advantageous. For example, if a temperate zone were becoming more arid, a rodent would benefit if its body chemistry could convert solid food directly into H_2O so that the animal would not have to seek drinking water. Because the mutated individual is better adapted to the new environment, its survival would be selected *for*, not against. Mutations inject new potentialities that diffuse throughout a population as the genetic information is reshuffled during mating. This information continually changes complexion as the individuals who bear it are selected for or selected against according to environmental circumstances. In all, the species is able to survive within a limited geographic range.

The Course of Evolution

Much of evolutionary theory has been developed by experiments in the laboratory, but its conclusions must be tempered by comparison with the fossil record. Review Figure 12-12, in which the analogy of a shotgun target represents the diversity of species at a single moment of time. Another commonly used

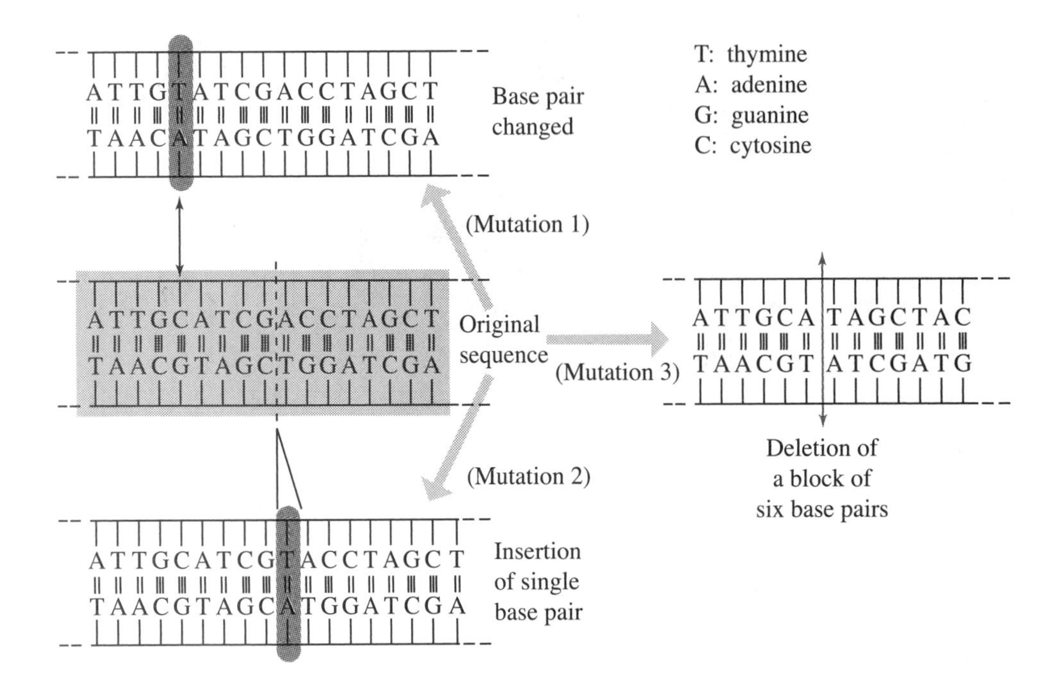

Figure 12-13. The original sequence of nucleotide pairs in part of a DNA molecule is shown in the center (with strands untwisted). Mutations can occur by at least three different means, as shown in the accompanying figures. [*After J. D. Watson,* Molecular Biology of the Gene, *W. A. Benjamin, Inc., New York, 1970.*]

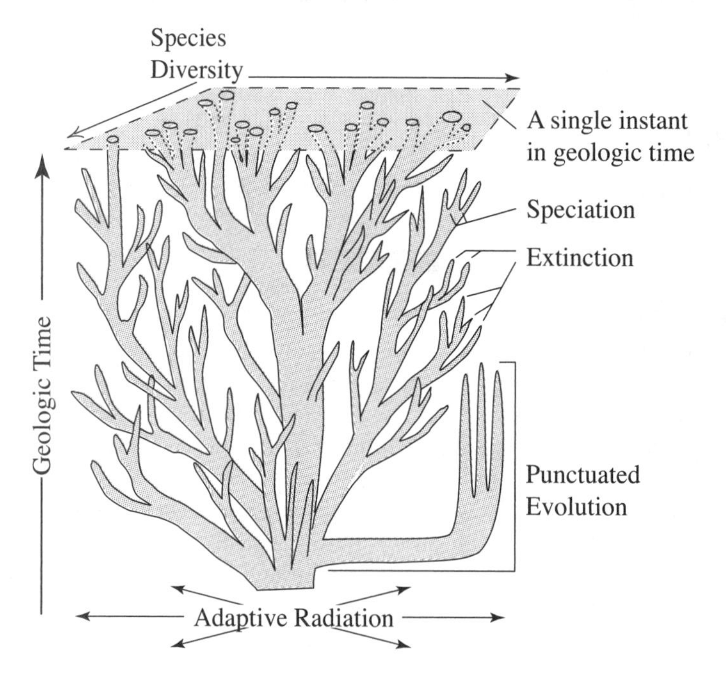

Figure 12-14. In the tree of life, the same information shown in Figure 12-12 appears in a single time "slice" (dashed horizontal plane). Speciation is represented by the forking of two branches, and extinction by the upper termination of a branch.

analogy, a "tree of life" (Figure 12-14), adds a dimension by picturing the growth of diversity through geologic history. From time to time there has been a great explosion of evolution, or *adaptive radiation*, a branching-out of the tree of life into numerous new species. Traditional evolutionary theory has emphasized how gradual changes, sustained over millions of generations with occasional events of speciation, can create such diversity. In this case, the tree of life would be represented as a cone expanding upward into a thicket of branches, as seen in the central and left-hand part of the diagram. Gradual, stately change is possible and even plausible, but is it correct?

Paleontologists have long been troubled by the notion because it implies that numerous intermediate forms should fill the evolutionary gaps between major groups of organisms. Convincing transitional fossils do exist, for example midway between reptiles and birds, as we shall see in Chapter 15. But it is also common to observe a great thickness of strata (deposited over a long period of geologic time) in which there is no significant variation of a fossil species, overlain by strata containing an abrupt new set of species. Creationists take this pattern to be evidence against evolutionary theory, while ignoring the well-established existence of intermediate fossil forms. Paleontologists correctly point out that the fossil record is far from complete. Perhaps no sediment had been deposited while the evolutionary transition was in progress, or perhaps the sediment had been eroded. Nevertheless, the general rarity of transitional fossils is embarrassing, and suggests a need to modify the theory. Perhaps evolution could be punctuated and episodic.

Indeed, there would be no evolution at all if the environment remained absolutely stable (Figure 12-15). In this setting, natural selection would maintain a community of perfectly adapted organisms exactly as they are, forever. At the other extreme, environmental stress could be so catastrophic that no organism survives, however well adapted. If a huge meteorite were to smash into the earth, the organisms living in the target zone would be more unlucky than ill-adapted. A giant meteorite strike could trigger a

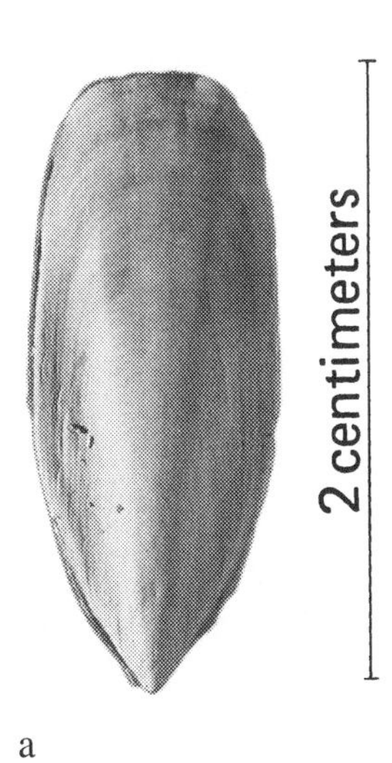

a

b

Figure 12-15. Shell *a* is a modern specimen of genus *Lingula*, a brachiopod that burrows in mud flats. Shell *b* is a fossil *Lingula* more than 300 million years old that appears almost identical to *a*. Organisms that have evolved very little over long periods of time are referred to as living fossils. [*Judy Camps.*]

chain of events causing a global, or mass extinction of species. Survival is questionable for the individuals of any species around the fringe of its geographic range. Suppose that a small population living at the margin were to be split off, becoming both genetically and geographically isolated (Figure 12-16). Theory and experiment show that the gene pool in a small interbreeding population is much more easily modified than in a large population. A combination of stress and small population is a high-risk proposition, resulting either in extinction or survival through very rapid evolution. Its rapidity and the small number of individuals that are affected make it unlikely for transitional forms to be fossilized. If the barrier between the original and the evolved splinter population were to disappear, a competition for survival would take place which the new species just might win. This would explain the abrupt replacements of fossil species, following which things are likely to settle down into another period of prolonged stability. These episodes of rapid change, followed by long periods of stability, are called *punctuated evolution*, represented in the tree of life by the horizontal branch that turns sharply upward.

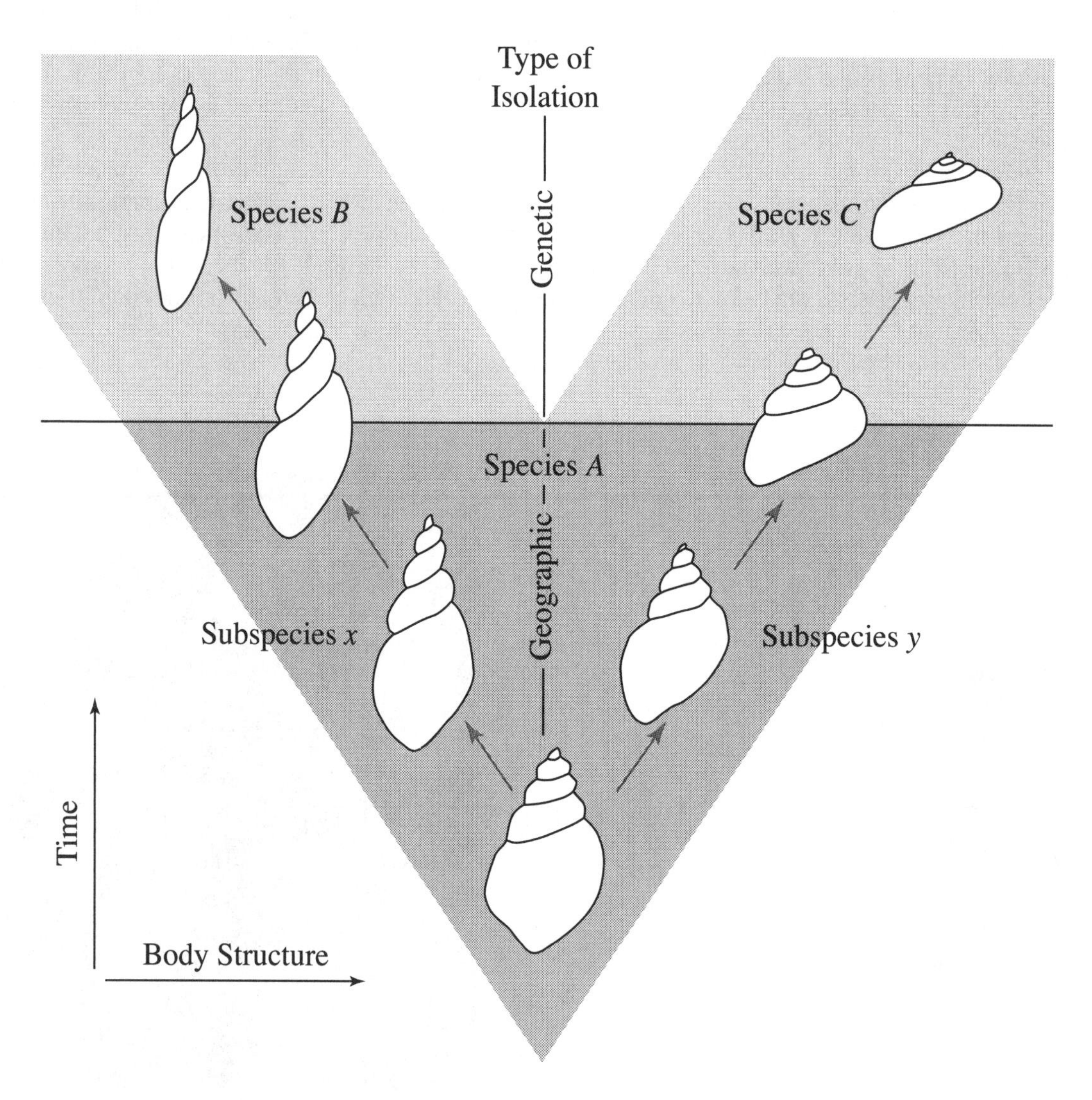

Figure 12-16. Geography is also an important factor in evolution. Here a snail population (species *A*) is distributed in different areas in which the niches vary slightly. Evolution leads to the establishment of subspecies *x* and *y* that are geographically isolated but with *can* interbreed if brought together. With time, the genetic divergence creates new species *B* and *C* that *cannot* interbreed even if the geographic barrier were to be removed. [*After R. C. Moore, C. G. Lalicker, and A. G. Fischer,* Invertebrate Fossils, *McGraw Hill Book Company, New York, 1952.*]

SUMMARY

A species of organism consists of members of a gene pool, or interbreeding population(s) whose fertile offspring are able to continue the hereditary line of descent. As postulated by Charles Darwin, organic evolution means descent with modification. Organic evolution normally proceeds at the extremely slow pace of geologic time. Until the previous century it was widely believed that living creatures could originate directly from mud by a process of spontaneous generation, but extensive experiments show that only a living organism is able to beget another individual.

Before life existed, the light chemical elements H, C, O, N, S, etc., were already abundantly present at the earth's surface. They could have been emplaced by impacts of comets, and certainly there was a primitive ocean and atmosphere of volcanic origin. Volcanoes emit H_2O, CO_2, N_2, H_2, SO_2, CH_4, and other simple environmental molecules, but not free oxygen (O_2). Simulation experiments prove that lightning, volcanism, or other natural sources of energy can organize these substances into small organic molecules, including amino acids. These in turn are linked together as complexly infolded chains to form proteins, which are large organic molecules that are major constituents of living cells. Deoxyribonucleic acid (DNA) is a long chain molecule, consisting of a double twisted strand, that contains coded information. DNA directs the cell functioning, and when the cell divides, the DNA is also replicated and emplaced in the daughter cells. Self-assembly, self-repair, and self-replication are key characteristics of all life. To date, laboratory simulations of primitive earth conditions have not been able to synthesize life, nor even DNA and most of the other complex organic molecules. Nevertheless, the fact that all life is based upon common pathways of biochemical reaction is strong circumstantial evidence for a common origin and evolution.

The very ancient fossil record is meager because most of the older rocks have not survived geologic recycling, and because the earliest organisms did not construct hard parts (shell or skeleton). There is no fossil record of the earliest living cells. From about 3.5 billion years ago (age of the oldest known fossils) until about 1.4 billion years ago, all organisms were prokaryotes, which reproduce asexually and whose tiny cells lack nuclei. These fossils resemble modern bacteria and Cyanobacteria (blue-green algae). Colonies of these organisms trapped layers of fine sediment, forming stromatolites.

Later to appear were eukaryotic organisms whose generally larger cells contain nuclei and other organelles (internal structures enclosed by membranes). All many-celled organisms—animals, plants, fungi, many protoctists—are eukaryotes. The earliest organisms must have been anaerobic, able to live in the absence of O_2. This gas was gradually introduced into the atmosphere as a by-product of photosynthesis, by which organisms utilize CO_2 and H_2O to make their own food. Much of the early-produced O_2 combined with dissolved iron, causing sedimentary iron formations to precipitate.

Kingdoms of living organisms are classified upon the basis of comparisons of body structure, biochemistry, and behavior into a hierarchy of smaller units of classification, each one containing sub-categories, and so on down to the level of a single species. Organic evolution is a theory to explain a unified origin of all living species by natural processes. Darwin's concept was inspired by Thomas Malthus, who emphasized the tension for survival of a population that tends to grow by a geometric progression (1, 2, 4, 8, etc.) while limited by a food supply that increases only arithmetically (1, 2, 3, 4, etc.). Through natural selection, better adapted individuals live long enough to pass their genetic information to the next generation, whereas more poorly adapted individuals die before reproducing. Fitness for survival includes not only the ability to obtain food, but other complex activities such as attracting a mate, eluding enemies, or resisting disease. Survival competition may be among individuals in a local population of the same species, or between species.

Modified genetic information is introduced into a gene pool through mutation, or imperfect replication, of the DNA code in reproductive cells. The effects of mutation are randomly unpredictable; typically they are harmful, but during a period of changing environmental circumstances, the mutation may confer a survival advantage. When a small sub-population becomes geographically isolated from the main population, the former may evolve rapidly, especially in a stressful environment. With sufficient evolutionary change the sub-population may have speciated, become a new species unable to interbreed with the parental stock. During adaptive radiation, many new species originate to occupy new habitats (places) and niches (modes of living). According to fossil evidence, the process of speciation may be gradual, or there may be long intervals of stability punctuated by rapid speciation.

13

Reading the Strata

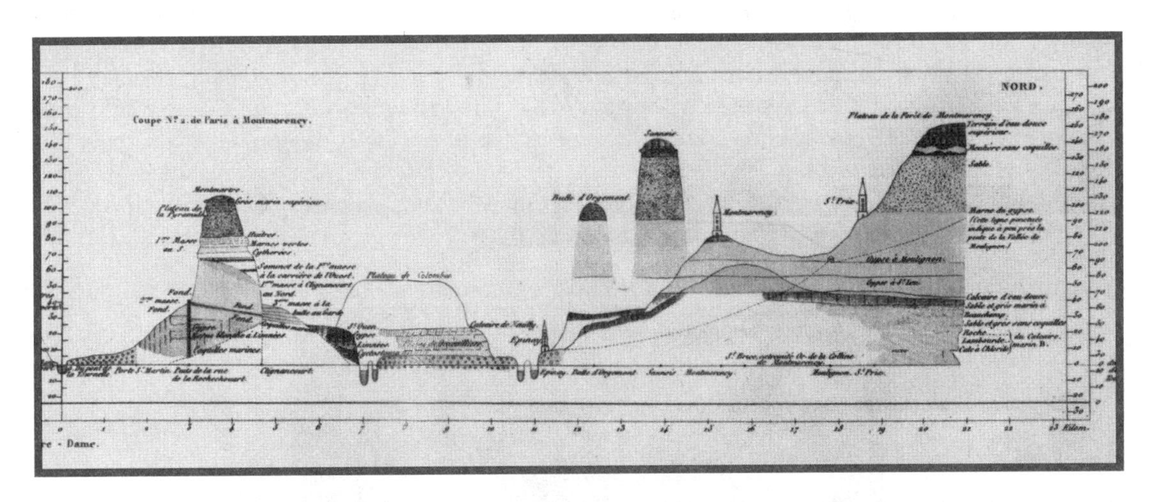

The French naturalist Georges Cuvier made some of the earliest correlations of sedimentary strata that have been partially eroded away. This drawing shows a correlation in the vicinity of Paris. [*From Georges Cuvier,* Description Géologique des Environs de Paris: *Edmond D'Ocagne, Éditeur-Libraire, Paris, 1835*]

As we have seen, the earth's surface is highly active. Rocks may be weathered, eroded, and deposited as sediment, only for this cycle to repeat again and again. Fossils are a record of the conditions of ancient life. Suppose that in going from the bottom to top of a sequence of strata we see a variation of fossil types. Is this pattern a result of earlier species becoming extinct or new species evolving as the sediments were deposited? Or were the species simply adapted to a particular environment of deposition, unable to continue living there because the environment was changing? Interpretations of sedimentary relationships and data from fossils are the stuff of *stratigraphy*—the science of the strata. Each sediment was deposited under unique circumstances, at a unique point in earth history, producing an endless variety in the rock record. How are we to read it?

MAKING FOSSILS

By far the most abundant fossils are the "hard parts" that provide body support for an organism. For example, they could be silica spicules of a sponge, or plates of calcite embedded in the body of a starfish. Generally these tiny disconnected pieces simply scatter when the dead soft tissue decomposes. Other animals construct massive hard parts such as an external shell. Only rarely is the shiny, pearly-luster *original material* preserved; more often partial dissolution has made the shell porous with a dull, chalky appearance. If the enclosing sediment hardened and then the shell dissolved completely, a *mold,* or hollow impression is left preserving the form of the external surface of the shell. Or a mold may form, later to be filled by fine sediment that hardened into a solid *cast* that also preserves the organism's external shape and size (Figure 13-1). Another type of cast is a common theme with snails, whose shells consist of aragonite, a calcium carbonate mineral whose crystal structure is similar to that of calcite. In this instance, after the soft tissue rots away the body cavity is filled by fine mud that hardens. Later the shell dissolves because aragonite is a relatively unstable substance, leaving a *steinkern* (German: "stone kernel"), or cast that preserves the internal form of the shell.

Figure 13-1. The coiled shell of a snail (left) is fully preserved; an external cast, though made of hardened mud, would look much the same. A steinkern, or internal mold (right), preserves the form of the interior of the shell. [*Judy Camps.*]

A revealing, but much rarer, mode of fossilization is simply the preservation of the entire animal including its soft parts. Best known are whales and mammoths that have stayed frozen ever since the most recent wide-scale glaciation, some 15 thousand or more years ago (Figure 13-2). These remains are considered to be fossils because of their great age, even though they do not fulfill a handy rule of thumb that says, "If it still stinks, it's not yet a fossil." The stench is reported to be unbearable when one of these relics of the Ice Age becomes exposed and starts to thaw. Extreme desiccation may also preserve soft tissue, as in mummified extinct sloths found in caves in the western U. S. Delicate entire bodies of insects are trapped in amber, which is hardened tree resin.

Living bone is a rather porous structure consisting of hard calcium phosphate filled with a maze of cavities that contain blood vessels, marrow, connective tissue, etc. (Figure 13-3). Upon burial, the bone may be *permineralized* by groundwater that slowly deposits insoluble material in the pore spaces. Most fossil bone is therefore very dense and solid. Permineralization often preserves delicate features of tissue, even down to the microscopic level of individual cells. Addition of material has caused the bone to become *petrified*—"turned into stone."

Figure 13-2. Cave paintings in France, dating from a period when humans and mammoths lived together, consistently picture a large fleshy hump atop the head—a feature that is not preserved in the skeleton. Although the paleontologists were quite puzzled, later findings of entire frozen mammoths have vindicated the authentic realism of these remarkable paintings. [*American Museum of Natural History.*]

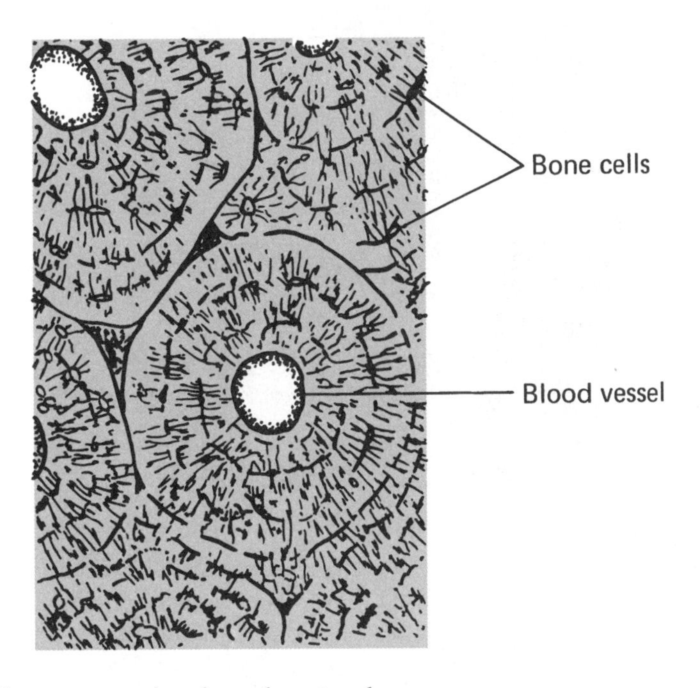

Figure 13-3. This is a cross section through mature bone.

Petrifaction may also occur through *total replacement* of the original substance, atom by atom, by silica, calcite, or pyrite. Silicified plant material is very common in which growth rings, or even individual cells, may be studied in great detail by cutting the fossil into numerous closely spaced slices. Through this technique of serial sectioning, certain extinct plants that flourished millions of years ago are better known than many species of living plants. Figure 7-9 shows a spectacular example of replacement of entire animal shells by silica.

Yet other fossil types are impressions and compressions. An *impression* is simply a shallow depression in the rock surface, an outline of a shape such as of a leaf [Figure 13-4(*a*)]. A *compression* of a leaf is a flattened film, a carbonized residue of the original substance [Figure 13-4(*b*)]. In some compressions the

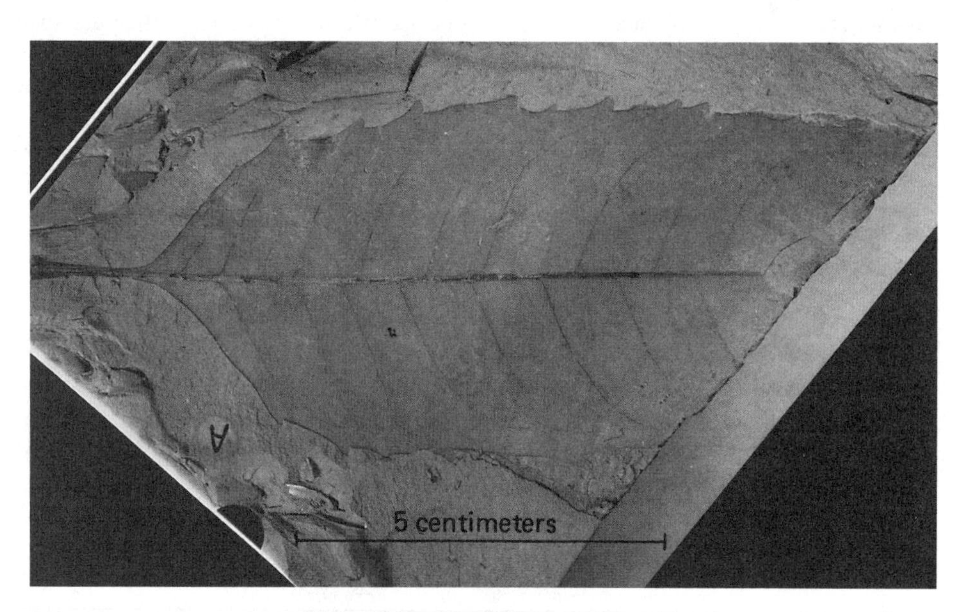

a

b

Figure 13-4. (*a*) Only the outline of the vein system and of the leaf margins remains in a leaf impression. [*Courtesy David Dilcher.*] (*b*) A carbonized film remains in this compression of fern leaves. Often the fossil-bearing sedimentary rock can be split along a bedding plane to reveal a compression on one slab and a counterpart impression on the other slab. [*American Museum of Natural History photograph.*]

original carbon has been replaced by silicate minerals. When the fossil is split open, one rock slab contains the compression which, being actual material, is called the "part." The impression that fits around the compression is the "counterpart." Paleontologists study both the parts and the counterparts, which contain complementary information. Certain compressions of leaves, seeds, or fruit can be separated from the rock matrix and inflated, by soaking, to three-dimensional objects that resemble the original.

Famous compressions in British Columbia, Canada, are of trilobites and other many-jointed animals that were smothered by undersea mud slumps. After mud had infiltrated between the animal's thin back coverplate and rows of delicate gills beneath, and between these and rows of legs, the resulting intermingled compressions and impressions were squashed and distorted. In reconstructing a three-dimensional image, a paleontologist must carefully tease the microlayers apart with a vibro-drill. Some scientists have to be patient, and accomplished artists too.

Trace fossils are a record, not of what the organism *was*, but of what it *did*. *Coprolite*, which is fossil excrement, informs us about diet. For example, the diet of ancient hyenas was high in calcium, undoubtedly through eating bones just as hyenas do today. Burrows, tracks, and trails are evidence for the creature's habitat and lifestyle. Unknown wormlike animals bored through the mud in a corkscrew pattern, searching for food particles. The same pattern can be created by a computer program, suggesting that the groveling of these animals was genetically "programmed." Footprints at a dinosaur waterhole in Queensland, Australia, indicate that hundreds of animals of at least two species, adults and juveniles together, stampeded in terror at the approach of a carnivorous dinosaur. Tens of millions of years later the same scenario is played around African waterholes—hundreds of zebra and antelope fleeing in panic at the sudden appearance of a lion.

PRINCIPLES OF STRATIGRAPHY

Another aspect of stratigraphy is concerned with the arrangement of the layers themselves. Seeing that we may observe erosion and sedimentary deposition directly, it is no surprise that the basic principles of stratigraphy were formulated long ago. Nevertheless, there were some early misconceptions based upon limited data. Noting that strata may extend for great distances, naturalists assumed that global catastrophes such as the biblical Flood of Noah had wrapped the earth in a sedimentary blanket like the concentric layers of an onion. A simple terminology was devised to describe the onionskin field relationships.

Almost any very large area covered by sedimentary rocks, for example, Texas (Figure 13-5), will serve as an illustration. Deep in the heart of Texas is an oval area called the Llano Uplift, an upbulge of the earth's crust where erosion has stripped away the covering rocks, revealing an underlying metamorphic and igneous basement. Ancient deformed rocks, deeply eroded remnants of a former mountain range, would have been termed Primitive according to this scheme. Undeformed but very hard sedimentary rocks, full of fossils, that lie atop the basement would be labeled Secondary. Persons two centuries ago considered the Secondary rocks to be deposited by the Noachian deluge. Even younger fossiliferous strata of the Gulf Coastal Plain rest upon the Secondary rocks and were partly derived from them. These soft Tertiary (third to form) sediments are more like "dirt" than rock. Finally, sediments along the coast and in the modern river valleys were deposited in a fourth, or Quaternary, episode.

This classification turned out to be too simple. Ages of supposed Primitive rocks were shown to differ greatly from place to place. Nor are the physical characteristics an infallible guide. Very hard, high-grade metamorphic rocks may be relatively young, and there are instances of ancient sediment so soft that it can be scooped up by hand. Moreover, the earth was never enveloped by concentric onionskin layers. As noted in Chapter 11, the earth behaves more like a cannibal, one area being eroded or dissolved to supply sediment for deposition somewhere else. Even so, the old terms Tertiary and Quaternary, though originating in a concept now abandoned, have persisted in our technical vocabulary. We still say that the Texas Coastal Plain sediments are of Tertiary age, and the modern floodplain sediments are Quaternary.

Some stratigraphic rules are rigid "laws" whereas others are only general principles, or guidelines. Some are self-evident; the application of others may be quite subtle. Let's examine the important principles, keeping in mind that most of them pertain equally well to volcanic rocks which are also stratified.

1. *Law of superposition: in an undisturbed sequence, younger strata lie above older.* Superposition establishes the relative ages of deposition in a succession of strata, but only if they are undisturbed. What manner of "disturbance" would complicate the application of this law? It would

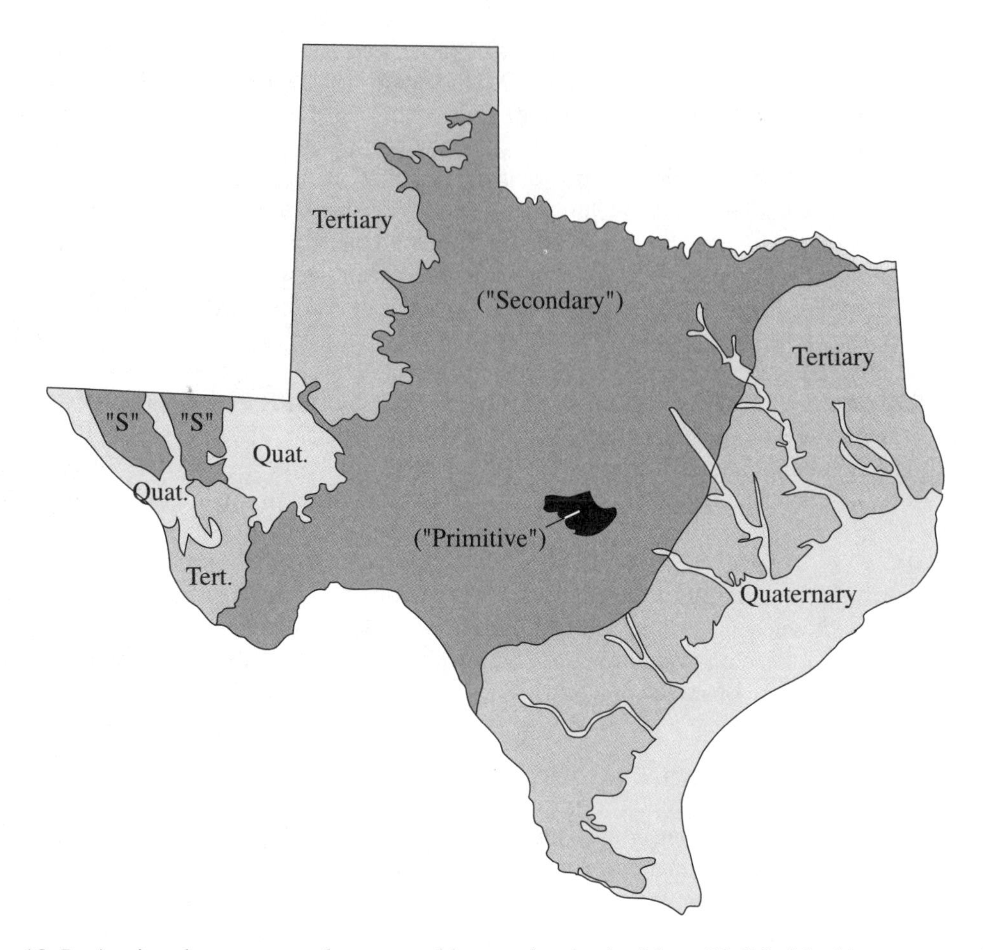

Figure 13-5. Ancient basement rocks exposed by erosion in the Llano Uplift (black) are concealed elsewhere beneath a cover of sedimentary rocks. "Primitive" and "Secondary" are terms no longer used, but "Tertiary" and "Quaternary" are part of our modern vocabulary. Tertiary refers to younger sediments in the Coastal Plain and Panhandle (northwest corner), and a volcanic terrain in the far west. Quaternary sediments, the latest to be deposited, occupy river floodplains and a belt bordering the Gulf of Mexico.

not simply be uplifting of submarine sediments to form dry land, nor even bending into gentle folds nor offsetting by faults. Strata would have to be deformed to the point of being turned upside down, or faulting action would have to shove older rocks up and over younger strata. Such intense contortions are common in the world's great mountain belts where the beds in any local cliff are as likely to be upside down as right side up. In the Alps or Himalayas the law of superposition may not guarantee which is the "right way up," but fortunately in most places the use of this powerful stratigraphic principle is straightforward.

2. *Principle of original horizontality: strata are deposited in horizontal layers.* Gravity causes particles in motion to sink to the lowest elevation, thus to distribute on an approximately level surface. It is true that large boulders hurled out of a volcano could be plastered steeply on its slope, or the profile of a sand layer on a dune could be as much as 35° from horizontal. But these exceptions to the principle of original horizontality are quite rare. In the case of sandstone that is a record of ancient sand dunes, the dipping layers would become shingled crossbeds within a much thicker horizontal layer (see Figure 7-5). We may generally assume that dipping strata were not deposited that way, but subsequently have been tilted. In our reconstruction of the sequence of geologic events it will be necessary to indicate that a disturbance had caused them to become inclined.

3. *Principle of lateral continuity: strata initially extended uninterrupted to the margin of the basin of deposition.* At first, this guideline appears to suggest only that strata once extended where they extended, but it is much more subtle than that. It addresses the effects of another type of disturbance, erosion. Suppose that distinctive sandstone strata (black, Figure 13-6) are exposed on the side of a mesa, and also across the valley on another mesa. Were these strata laterally continuous before the valley was eroded? Do they *correlate:* are they equivalent to one another?

Stratigraphic correlation

On closer examination we see two possible kinds of correlation. The sandstone layers, which are *bodies of rock*, evidently once connected across as shown by dashed lines. Moreover, the law of superposition states that the upper stratum is the younger, providing for another kind of correlation based upon *relative age of deposition.* Correlation of bodies of rock and ages of deposition may be obvious enough locally, but when applied over a larger region the correlation becomes more problematical. We could follow the lower stratum all the way around the flanks of mesa *A*, but in mesa *B* the correlation is less certain. Note that the lower sandstone pinches out and disappears toward the right-hand side of mesa *B*. Perhaps it is a lens-shaped body that was deposited in a stream channel. Or perhaps the field geologist could not trace its continuation because bedrock on the hill slope is concealed beneath rubble. In doing field geology, one must make many judgments based on hints of evidence.

Other layers are astonishingly continuous. A stratum of limestone deposited upon the floor of a shallow tropical sea may extend broadly over a distance that is a million times as great as its thickness. But even where each layer is uniform throughout, a situation known as "layer cake" stratigraphy, the strata were deposited in a limited area. Universal onionskin strata do not exist.

In the early 1700s John Strachey worked out a more complex example of correlation while tracing the occurrence of coal in southwestern England. His cross section (Figure 13-7) pictures a set of dipping beds with layer-cake uniformity of thicknesses. Faulting has broken them and displaced the left-hand block upward a short distance. Later the dipping beds were beveled off by erosion, and horizontal beds were deposited unconformably on top, themselves eventually to become somewhat eroded. A geologic cross section is of practical use because in crossing the fault, the mining operation would "lose" a coal seam. Should the miners be instructed to drill upwards or downwards to re-encounter it?

Layer-for-layer correlation may not be feasible because the coal seams look alike, or they may be concealed or eroded away in places. So Strachey did what modern geologists continue to do. He recorded the succession, thicknesses, and compositions of the beds in a variety of places, and mentally grouped some of them into convenient "packages." He used the information from an entire sequence of strata in order to discern a more general pattern. Today we define a geologic *formation* as a persistent stratum or group of strata that are distinctive and are thick enough to be shown on a geologic map. Formations are given local geographic names, typically in recognition of a place where they are well exposed. A formation may consist of just one rock type (for example, Rochester Shale), or if there is a mixture of rock types it is simply called a formation (for example, Chinle Formation). Scale of size is important, as most maps cover rather large areas. Normally a stratum less than a meter thick would be included amongst many others in a formation, whereas a succession that is kilometers thick would be subdivided into several formations. Ultimately, though, the definition and naming of a formation is the stratigrapher's arbitrary choice. Labels are in people's minds, not attached to rocks.

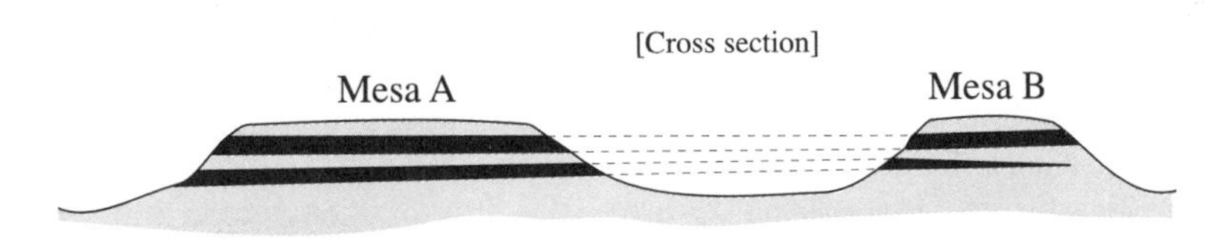

Figure 13-6. In arid regions, as in parts of the western United States, the strata commonly erode back as bold cliffs. This cross section shows that an upper, persistent sandstone bed correlates across the entire area. The lower sandstone unit does not.

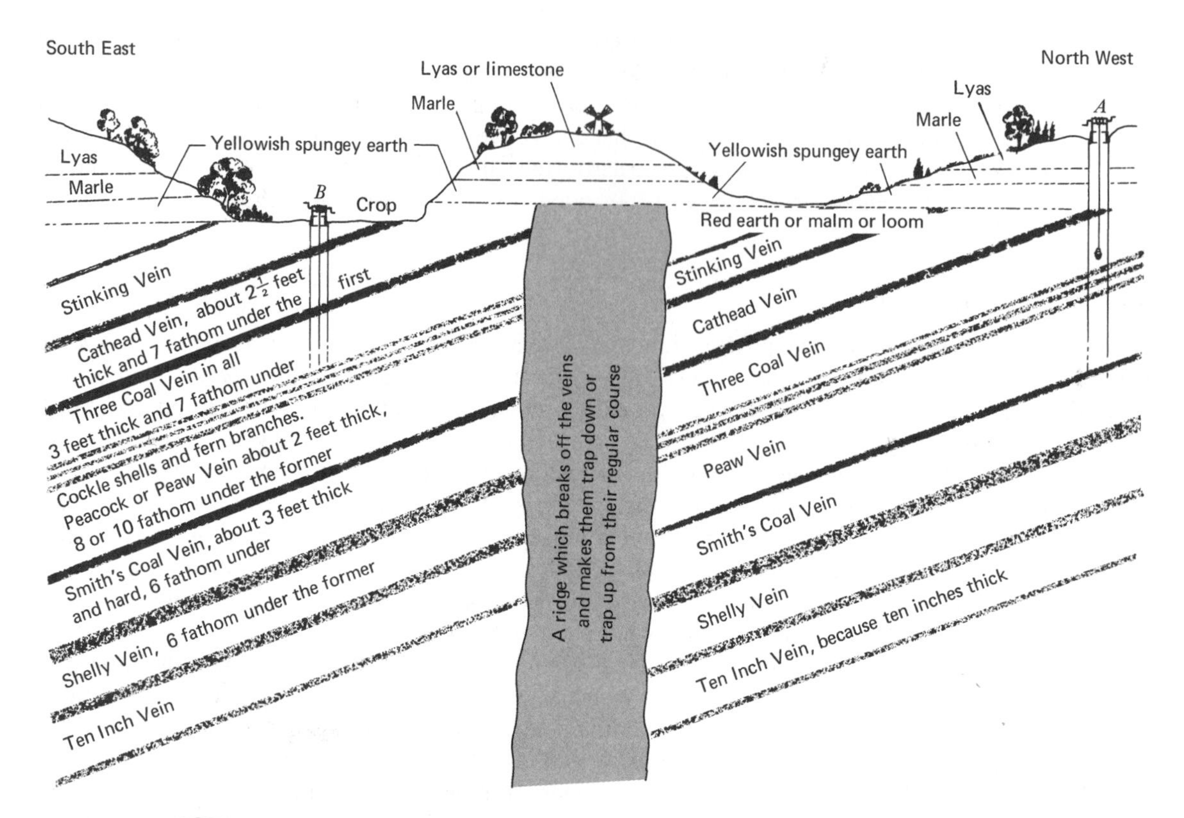

Figure 13-7. Strachey's early stratigraphic correlations made use of some rather quaint descriptive terms, listed here as he formulated them. It seems a shame that modern technical vocabulary, in the interest of precision, has had to give up colorful language. [*After John Strachey,* Philosophical Transactions of the Royal Society of London, *vol. 30, 1719.*]

We must not confuse the correlation of bodies of rock with correlation of ages of deposition. A delta and a beach (discussed in Chapter 23) will serve to illustrate the problem. Any large delta consists of several distinct environments of sedimentary deposition. Where a stream enters the sea, its burden of transported sand and mud becomes separated. Heavy sand particles are distributed by wave action along the coast, while light particles of mud are wafted farther from land before sinking to the sea floor. Possibly limestone is precipitating in clear tropical waters even farther offshore, beyond the delta. Millions of years later a geologist would likely define the delta shore deposit as sandstone Formation A, the offshore delta mud as shale Formation B, and the marine deposit as limestone Formation C [Figure 13-8(*a*)]. In this example, different formations (rock bodies) were deposited at the same time.

The opposite situation is illustrated by a beach that exists during a time of changing relationship between land and sea [Figure 13-8(*b*)]. Suppose that the land surface were sinking very slowly, or sea level were rising. As the shoreline transgresses across the land, the associated beach deposit would transgress with it, accumulating as a sheet of sand resting upon the former land surface and overlain by younger sediment. In this example, parts of the same formation differ significantly in age of deposition. The ancient beach was millions of years in the making, its age correlating with the ages of many formations elsewhere.

Thus our stratigraphic interpretations must take into account both *geologic time* and *environments of deposition*. Geologic time is the elusive factor, for we cannot experience past events. We can only observe their results. As discussed in Chapter 11, an isotopic age of a clastic sediment provides, not the sought-for time of deposition, but rather information about the age of the source terrain whose erosion supplied the clastic particles. That terrain could be older by any arbitrary length of time. Occasionally an explosive eruption spreads fine volcanic ash over an area of active deposition. Here is a datable igneous stratum, formed "instantly," that makes an excellent time-marker horizon. Ages of two such dated horizons sandwiched in the midst of the beach formation [Figure 13-8(*b*)] verify that deposition had continued over a very long time interval. Volcanic outbursts are highly infrequent, however. We need to have more commonly available evidence for the passage of geologic time.

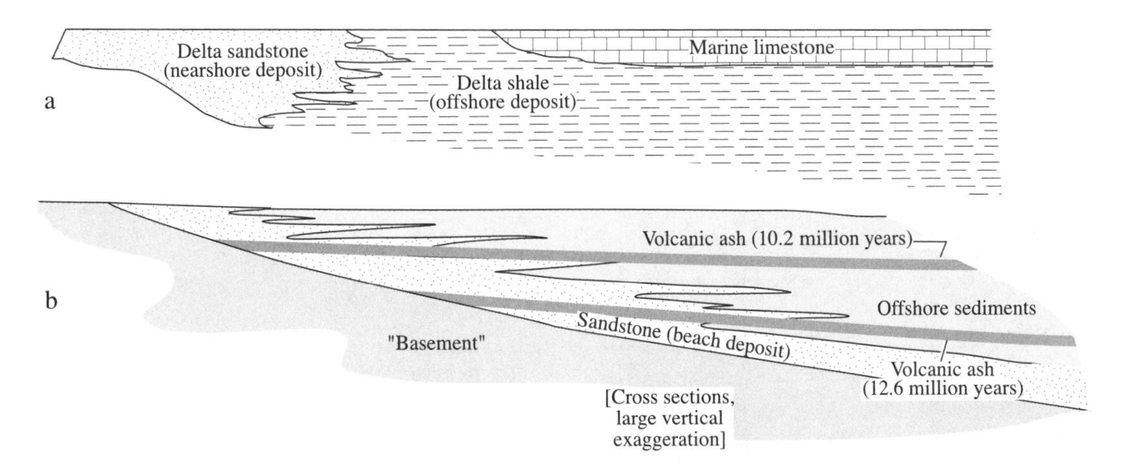

Figure 13-8. (*a*) In a delta environment, nearshore sand and offshore shale were deposited simultaneously, while limestone was precipitating even farther offshore in clear tropical water. (*b*) Crystals of zircon or feldspar in a stratum deposited by explosive volcanism can be dated by isotopic age methods. Volcanic strata shown here indicate the surface of deposition at two selected "instants" in geologic time. Their ages reveal that deposition of the beach was in progress for more than two million years.

Dating with fossils

Even though certain of the ancient Greeks and Romans had shrewdly conjectured that fossils are remains of organisms, people in the late eighteenth century generally disregarded them as freaks of nature or tricks of the Devil. An Englishman, William "Strata" Smith, took fossil evidence seriously and recognized therein an important relationship. Smith was a surveyor for construction of the canals used in those days to transport heavy cargo. "Fossil," meaning "dug up," described both his occupation of digging up the earth and his lifelong obsession. While collecting fossils throughout southern England both on and off the job, he noticed that assemblages of fossil types are ordered in a sequence from lower to higher, just as the strata are. Having gained experience with the pattern, he would amaze his friends by quickly sorting random piles of fossils correctly according to their host stratum or relative age. His generalization becomes our fourth, and final principle of stratigraphy.

4. *Principle of faunal succession: there is a systematic progression of fossil forms in going from lower (older) to higher (younger) strata.* We may wonder why William Smith showed no special curiosity about the reasons for this marvelous index of geologic age. He just knew that, as an empirical observation, it works. Partly it may have been his limited education; he felt inferior to the learned members of the Geological Society of London who ignored his efforts for years but later, to their credit, deeply honored his contributions by bestowing upon Smith an important medal and citation. In fact, no one had an adequate explanation for the principle of faunal succession. The great French naturalist, Georges Cuvier, proposed that God had populated the sea with animals, then wiped them out with a mass extinction, then repopulated the area with a new, somewhat different assemblage, over and over. Cuvier was wrong in part, not realizing that fossils of the same age in distant regions of the world show no evidence for catastrophic extinctions. It would be almost another half century before Charles Darwin published a theory of organic evolution to explain faunal succession.

Faunal succession (or equally, floral succession) is an immensely powerful principle because it can establish worldwide correlations (Figure 13-9). That is, it can do so provided that the fossil organisms being compared were once distributed worldwide. Some species are *cosmopolitan,* dispersed over vast areas of the globe. Others are *endemic,* confined to geographically restricted environments. Polar bears, lions, and most penguins are endemic to the far north, tropical, and far south regions. *Homo sapiens* (humans, you and I) are cosmopolitan on land, and certain species of floating foraminifera (Chapter 7) are cosmopolitan over vast areas of ocean (Figure 13-10). No organism is abundantly distributed everywhere.

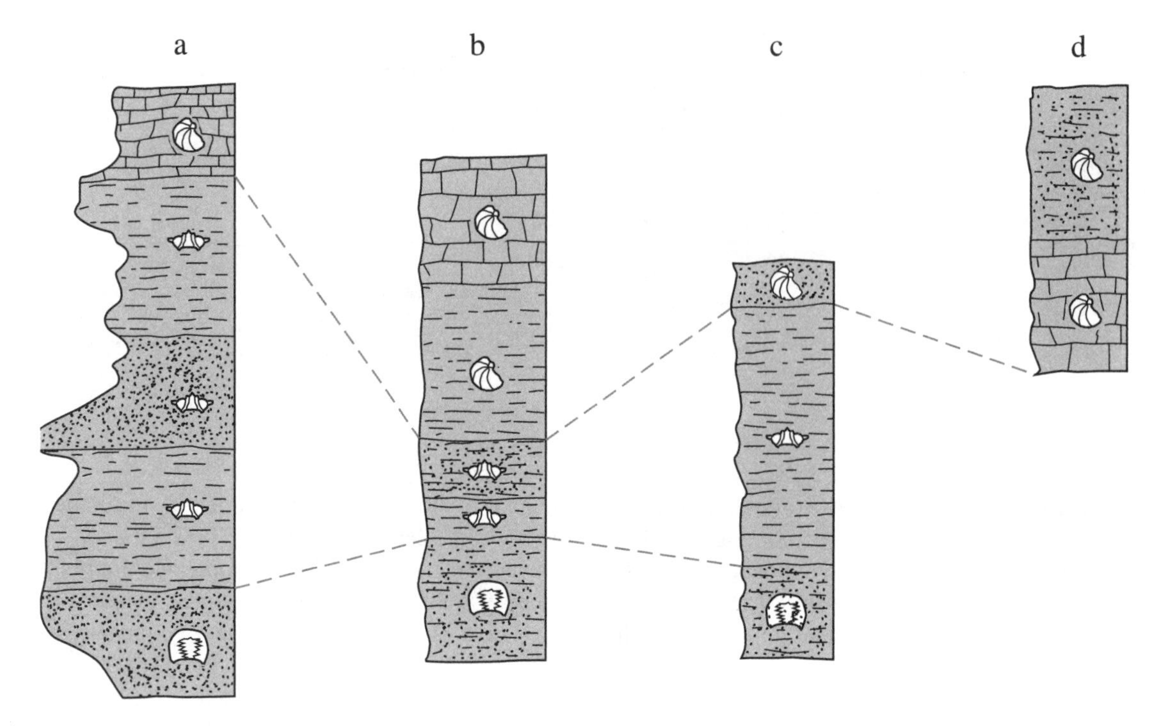

Figure 13-9. Sequences of strata (*a, b, c, d*) can be correlated over long distances, even on a worldwide scale, by matching the successions of fossils. Assemblages are correlated, not just one species. (Recall the saying, "There is safety in numbers.") Thicknesses and rock types of the correlated strata may vary from place to place. These characteristics closely depend upon the environment of deposition. On the other hand, appearances and extinctions of cosmopolitan species are indications of the passage of time.

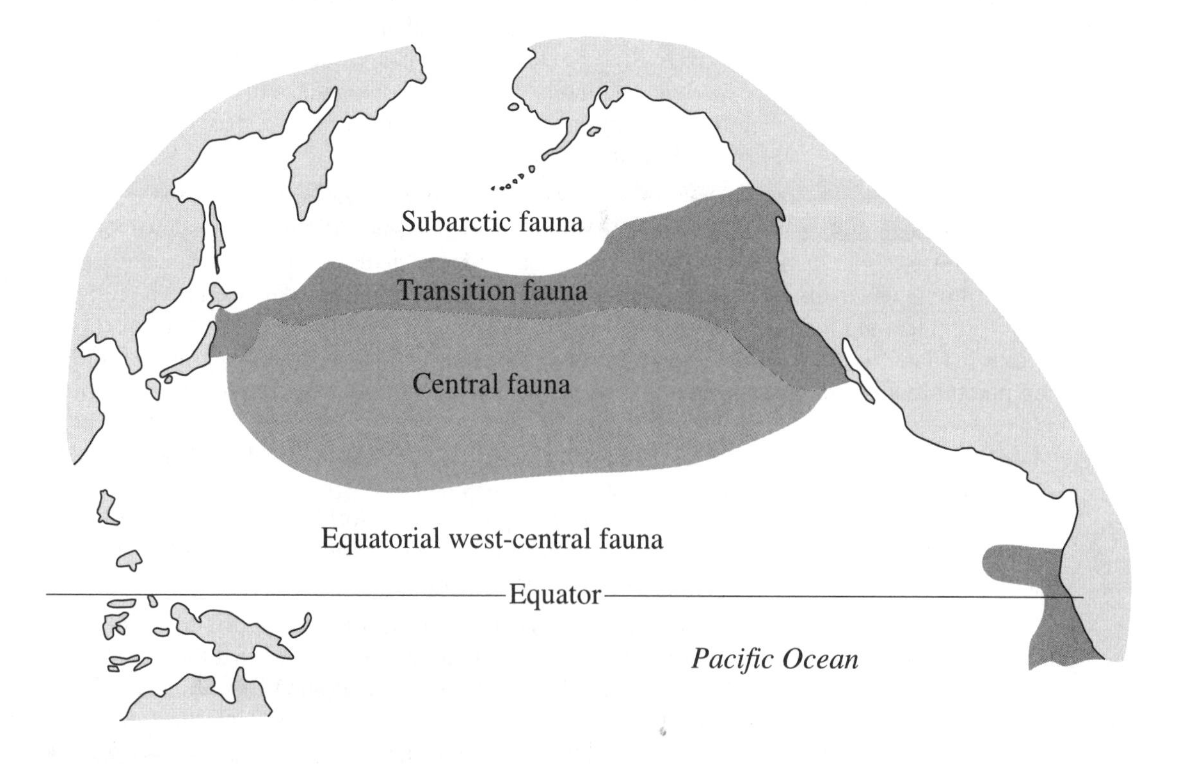

Figure 13-10. Assemblages of floating foraminiferans occur over large areas of the Pacific, most of them restricted to water masses of characteristic temperature and salinity. Only five species are found throughout Pacific waters, and none is truly cosmopolitan in all of the world's oceans.

Here also we see the influences of the environment of deposition *vs.* passage of geologic time. Endemic species are better indicators of the nature of a local environment (Figure 13-11); cosmopolitan species are better indicators of geologic age. Recognizing the potential of the principle of faunal succession, William Smith sought funding to publish a grand summary of his life work showing the correlations in map form (Figure 13-12). His masterpiece appeared in 1815, the first geologic map ever to be assembled on a large regional scale. It looks strikingly like a sophisticated modern geologic map of England and Wales. Soon thereafter, George B. Greenough published a map based upon rock types (lithologies). Geologic units in Smith's map correspond to different ages; units in Greenough's map correspond somewhat crudely to different environments of deposition. A given period of geologic history is unique, whereas there are numerous environments that coexist at all times. Today, Greenough's type of map is compiled only for specialized purposes.

GEOLOGIC TIME SCALE

Already it was becoming clear how to construct a global geologic time scale. Armed with their new tools, geologists jumped on the stratigraphic bandwagon. As they traveled widely throughout Europe, Russia, and elsewhere, they defined formations, described fossils, and recorded assemblages. Soon they began to perceive the big pattern. Sequences of strata, some very thick and probably long in time of deposition, contain the same characteristic faunas and floras whether in England, Germany, or the end of the earth. Excitement ran high as every bit of countryside was viewed from a new perspective. Would the strata

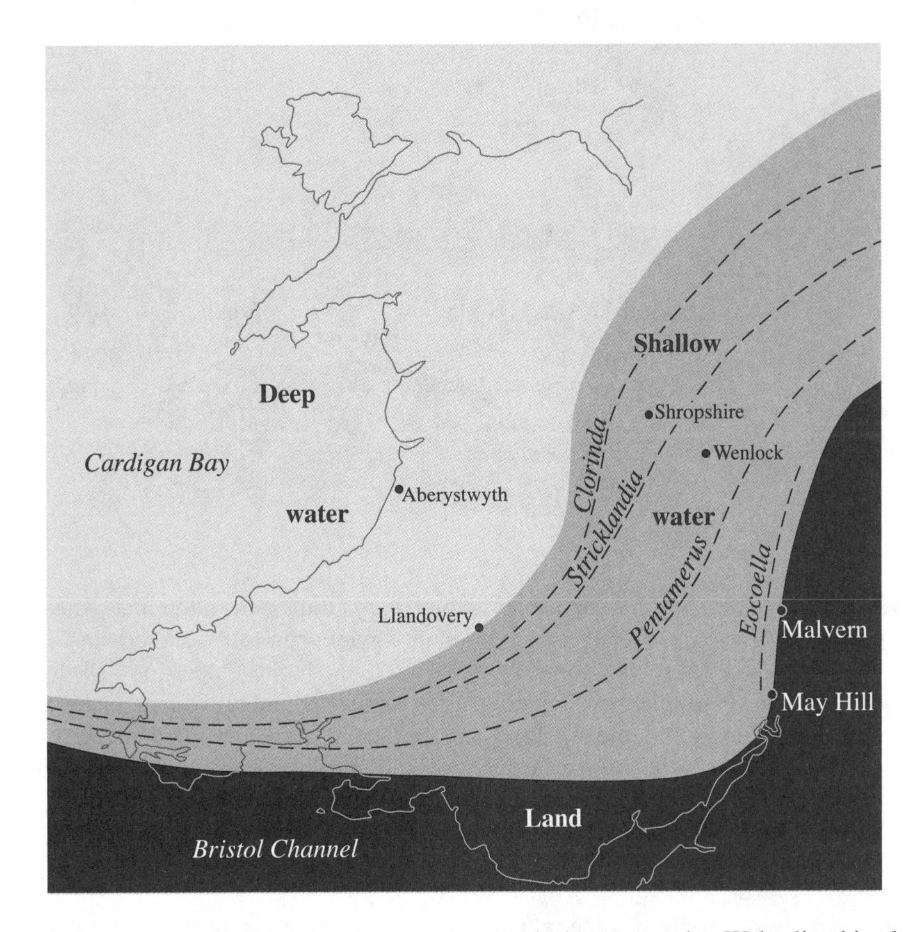

Figure 13-11. Brachiopod species from sedimentary rocks in present-day Wales lived in sharply zoned communities. These attached organisms apparently were highly endemic and water-depth sensitive. [*After A. M. Ziegler, "Silurian Marine Communities and Their Environmental Significance,"* Nature, *vol. 207, no. 4994, pp. 270-272, 1965.*]

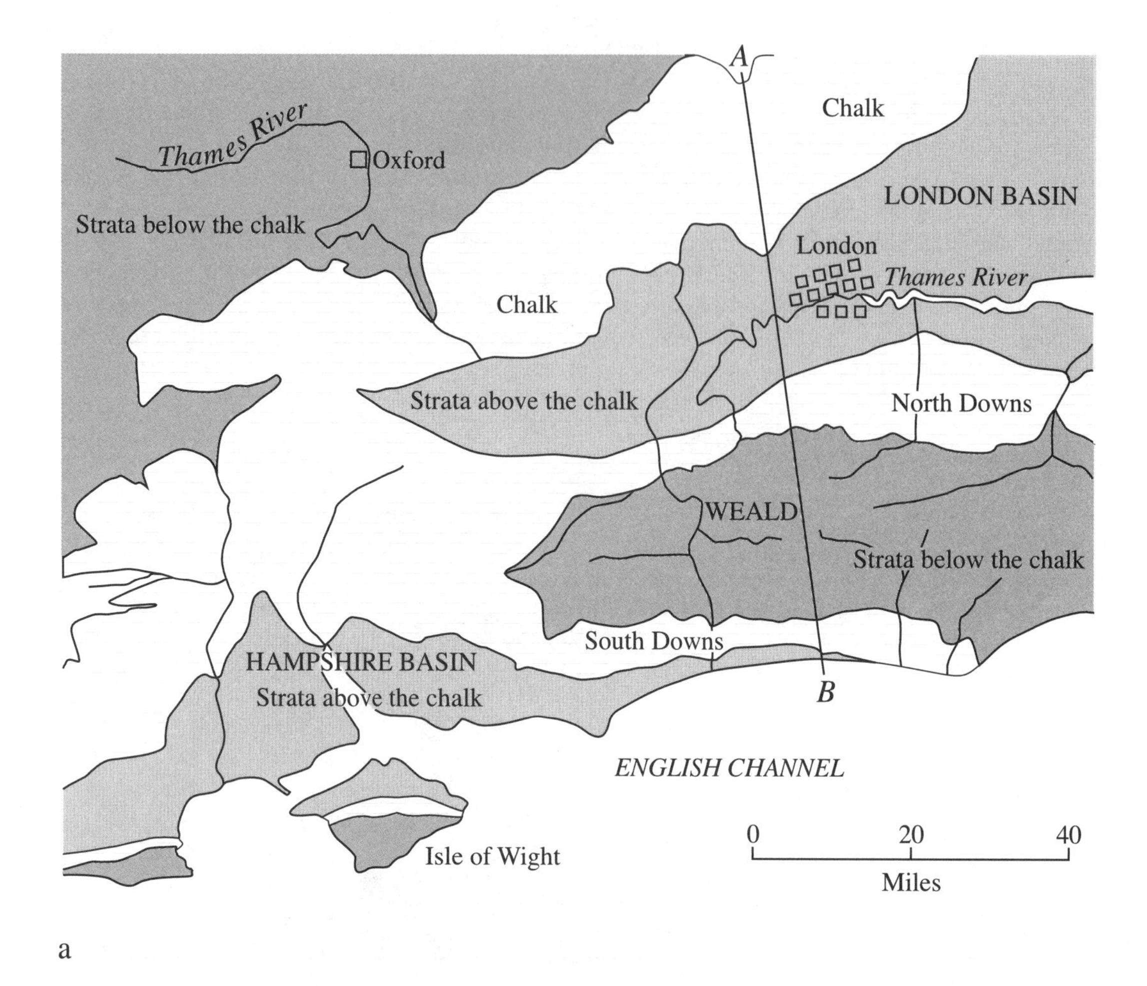

a

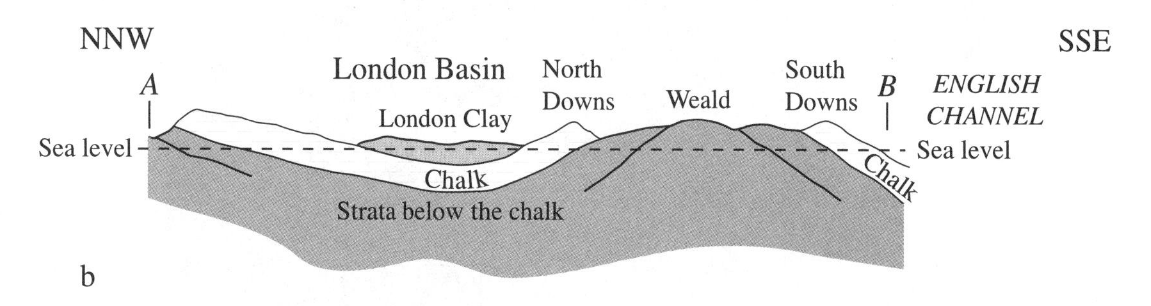

b

Figure 13-12. (*a*) In William Smith's early map, sedimentary strata show a looping pattern because they are not horizontal. The rocks were gently warped into giant open folds, and erosion has beveled the surface, removing strata where they formerly projected to the highest elevations. (*b*) In the cross section along line *AB* (see map), the beveling effect of erosion is apparent. Older strata are exposed at the surface in the core of an upfold (the Weald). The London Clay, youngest in the local sequence, is preserved in the keel of a downfold but has been removed everywhere else. A resistant formation, the Chalk, trends across the countryside as a prominent ridge where its upturned edge is being eroded back. [*After William Smith, 1815.*]

contain familiar fossils, or fossils of some previously undocumented age waiting to be assigned a position in the sequence? Even to this day, not all countrysides have been analyzed in such a manner.

Of course, a terminology had to be invented for different geologic ages so that the geologists could communicate with one another. The names Cambrian (after the Roman name for Wales), Silurian (after an ancient tribe), Jurassic (after the Jura Mountains) and many others were defined in a haphazard, almost whimsical manner. It is important to keep the idea of physical objects (the strata) strictly separated from the concept of time. A division of time is called a geologic *period*, and rocks deposited during that period comprise a geologic *system*. We say that strata of the Cambrian System were laid down during the Cambrian Period. Terminology was expanded into a hierarchical system. A geologic *eon* encompasses more than one *era*, an era consists of several periods, and a period contains several *epochs*, as seen in Figure 13-13.

Aren't all these definitions rather arbitrary? Strata and their fossils are real enough, but there is no label on the rocks to announce the boundary between one system and the next. In an effort to base the terminology on clearly evident features, some stratigraphers proposed that a geologic system should include all of the strata between a lower unconformity and an upper unconformity. But this definition proved inadequate because an unconformity indicates that some of the rock record has been removed. It means that for a portion of bygone geologic time, the evidence has been lost.

Finally it was agreed that assemblages or "congregations" of fossils would be used to distinguish eras, periods, and epochs. Any given fossil species exists only in a particular interval in the sequence of strata. The limited *stratigraphic range* of a species corresponds to its limited range of existence in geologic time. Untold numbers of species have come and gone. Thousands of stratigraphic ranges, all of them different and many overlapping, have been pieced together. Ranges of cosmopolitan species are especially helpful in carrying the correlations across between regions populated by different localized (endemic) species.

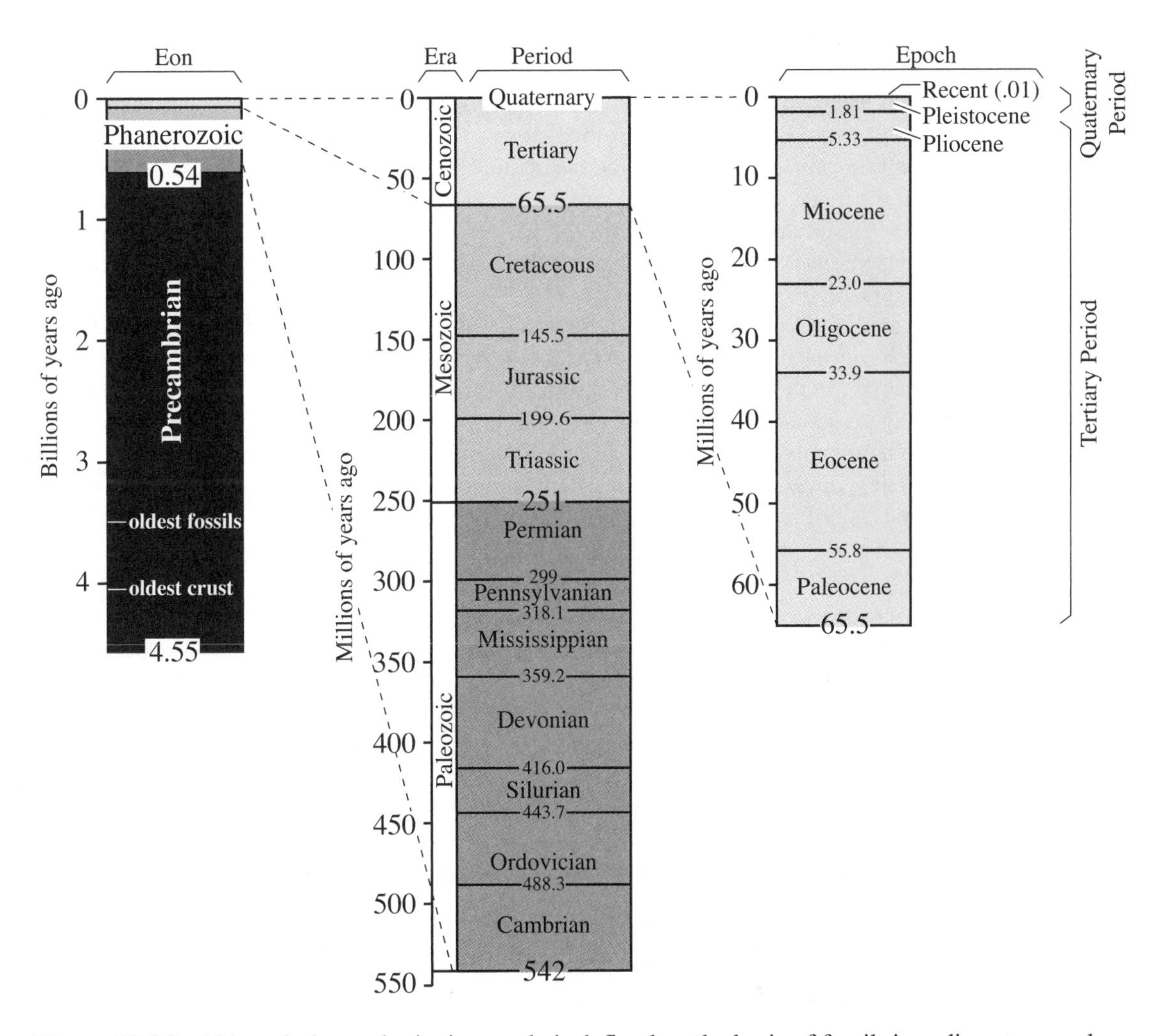

Figure 13-13. Although the geologic time scale is defined on the basis of fossils in sedimentary rocks, isotopic ages of associated volcanic rocks date the sediments indirectly in terms of millions of years.

Powerful new tools are being developed to correlate strata according to magnetic and isotopic properties. In a later chapter we will note that the earth's north and south magnetic poles have exchanged positions from time to time. A magnetic direction is imprinted upon minerals being precipitated in pore spaces in the sediment, consistent with the direction of the earth's overall magnetic field at that point in time. If the ancient magnetic record has been locked into these minerals, it registers as intervals of strata that are "normally" magnetized (magnetic direction like it is today), and "reversely" magnetized strata, back and forth rather like a dot-dash telegraph code. Another correlation technique makes use of the abundances of stable isotopes of carbon, ^{12}C and ^{13}C. The ratio of abundance of ^{13}C to ^{12}C in sea water has fluctuated during geologic time, and so has the $^{13}C/^{12}C$ ratio in carbonate sediments deposited from sea water. Patterns of magnetic directions and isotope ratios can be correlated in marine sediments across the globe, even in sediments that contain no fossils.

Dating the Time Scale

Stratigraphic relationships and the principle of faunal succession establish only a *relative sequence* of events. Isotopic ages have added to the grand perspective by assigning numbers of years to ages of earth events (Figure 13-13). Among the "milestones" noted in Chapter 11 are condensation of the solar system 4.55 billion years ago, formation of the oldest known mineral grains of 4.2-billion-year age (recycled into younger rocks), and the most ancient evidence for life at 3.5 billion years. Up until 0.55 billion years ago, all organisms were soft-bodied and rarely fossilized. A multitude of organisms that appeared since that time have deposited a record rich in hard parts—fossil skeleton or shell material—and so it is natural to define two great, unequal episodes in the history of life. The earliest 7/8 of geologic time, from the earth's origin until about 550 million years ago, pertains to the *Precambrian* (before the beginning of the Cambrian Period). Other technical terms acknowledge the primacy of the fossil record. The final 1/8 of geologic time comprises the *Phanerozoic* ("evident life") Eon, which is further divided into the *Paleozoic* ("early life"), *Mesozoic* ("middle life"), and *Cenozoic* ("recent life") Eras. Profound worldwide extinctions terminated the Paleozoic and Mesozoic Eras. An estimated 95% of marine species were wiped out 245 million years ago at the close of the Paleozoic Era. Another spectacular extinction ended the Mesozoic Era and the reign of dinosaurs, 65 million years ago. Definitions of the geologic periods and their epochs are also based upon first appearances and final extinctions. Epochs of the final two periods, the Tertiary and Quaternary, are considered especially important because the stratigraphic record is so well preserved (Figure 13-13).

Volcanic strata are interbedded here and there among the sedimentary rocks. Volcanic minerals include feldspar which can be dated by the K-Ar and Rb-Sr methods, and zircon to which the U-Pb method is applied. Dating the volcanic strata enables us to assign ages to the closely associated fossil-bearing sediments (Figure 13-14). The isotopic ages are so accurate that the various subdivisions of Phanerozoic time are now known within plus-or-minus 2%. In view of how haphazardly the geologic systems were defined, it is amazing that we have a convenient small number of them, and that the corresponding time periods are of roughly equal length.

Life in Transition

By this point, some of the inadequacies of the fossil record are quite evident. Organisms get chewed up, even their hard parts becoming digested, decayed, or scattered, or the entire stratum is eroded away. Abundant "death assemblages" consisting of transported fossils attest to the ability of waves or currents to heap together similar-sized particles (Figure 13-15) but otherwise they contain little information about the once-intact living community in its sedimentary setting. Preservation is so incomplete that it is difficult to estimate how many species ever existed, even within a factor of ten or so. It may have been as many as 3 *billion* (Figure 13-16), of which only one species in 10 thousand ever became preserved in the record! On the other hand, a paleontologist can also be deceived into identifying too many species. Juveniles and adult individuals must not be listed as separate species, nor females and males which in some species have strikingly different body sizes or forms (Figure 13-17).

Occasionally a fossil assemblage is discovered in which even the soft-bodied organisms, preserved by very rapid burial, have escaped destruction by scavenging or contact with oxygen. By good fortune one of these wonderful "mother lodes" of paleontology was deposited just before the Precambrian-to-Phanerozoic transition, and another deposit dates from the Middle Cambrian, about 40 million years later. The Precambrian animals, all of them soft-bodied and relatively simple, had occupied only a few

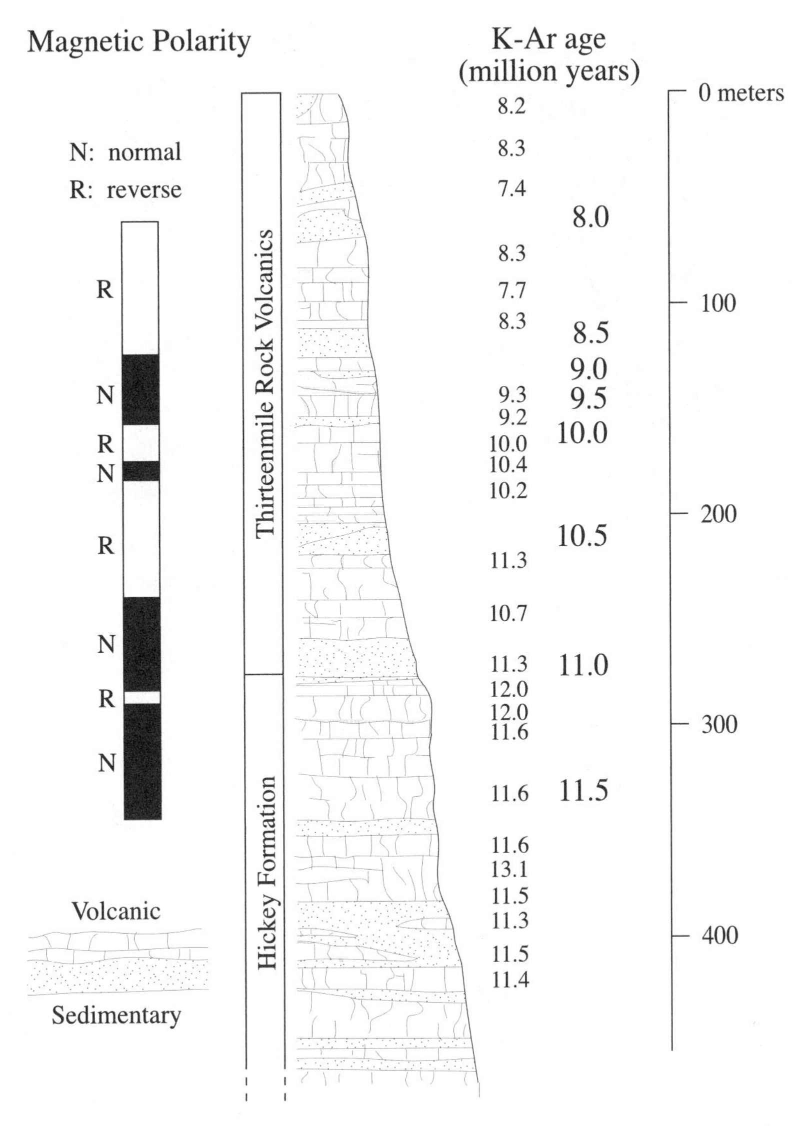

Figure 13-14. Volcanic and sedimentary strata comprise two geologic formations in central Arizona, pictured here in cross section as if exposed by erosion in a steep cliff. Numerous samples were analyzed for normal or reverse direction of magnetic polarity, and more than 20 samples were also dated by the potassium-argon method. Individual analyses (left-hand column of age data) are generalized in the right-hand column. The entire sequence was deposited in less than 1/1000 of geologic time during the Miocene Epoch (compare with Figure 13-13). [*After E. H. McKee and D. P. Elston, "Reversal Chronology from a 7.13- to 11.5-M.Y.-Old Volcanic Sequence in Central Arizona: Comparison with Ocean Floor Polarity Record,"* Journal of Geophysical Research, *vol. 85, p. 327-337, 1980. Copyright by American Geophysical Union.*]

niches and habitats. The later fauna postdates the Cambrian explosion of animal species having complex anatomy and ecological relationships.

Counts of species and of individuals in living communities and in these rare deposits reveal how very biased most of the fossil record is. Perhaps 20 percent of the major groups of organisms are known exclusively from three fossil localities! Animals that attach to the sea floor are far more likely to be fossilized than those that move about. Mud-dwellers are well preserved, inhabitants of a sandy sea floor moderately so, and, out of a thousand species that live in an uplands, only one is likely to be preserved in river alluvium. Bias of preservation works in a perversely opposite sense too. An astronomical quarter of a million foraminifera may be jammed together in one ounce of marine sediment.

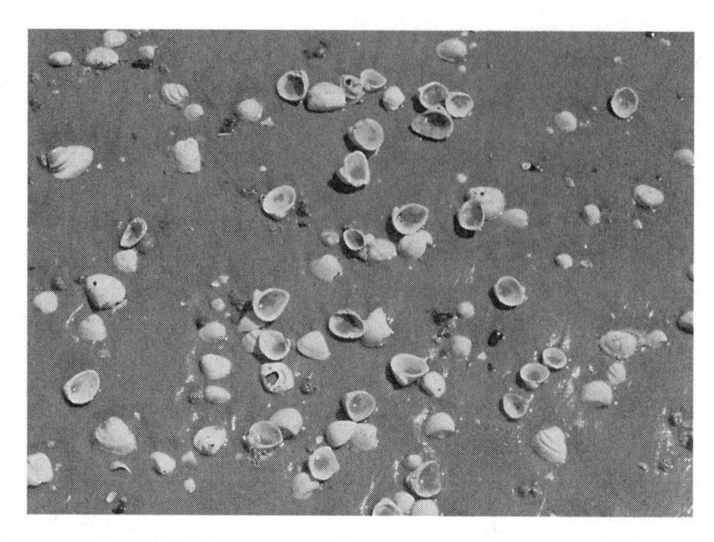

Figure 13-15. This modern beach is littered with clam shells cast up by storms. Some ancient sedimentary strata are similarly paved with shells. Apparently hurricanes were common long ago, just as they are today. [*Courtesy Daniel Houston.*]

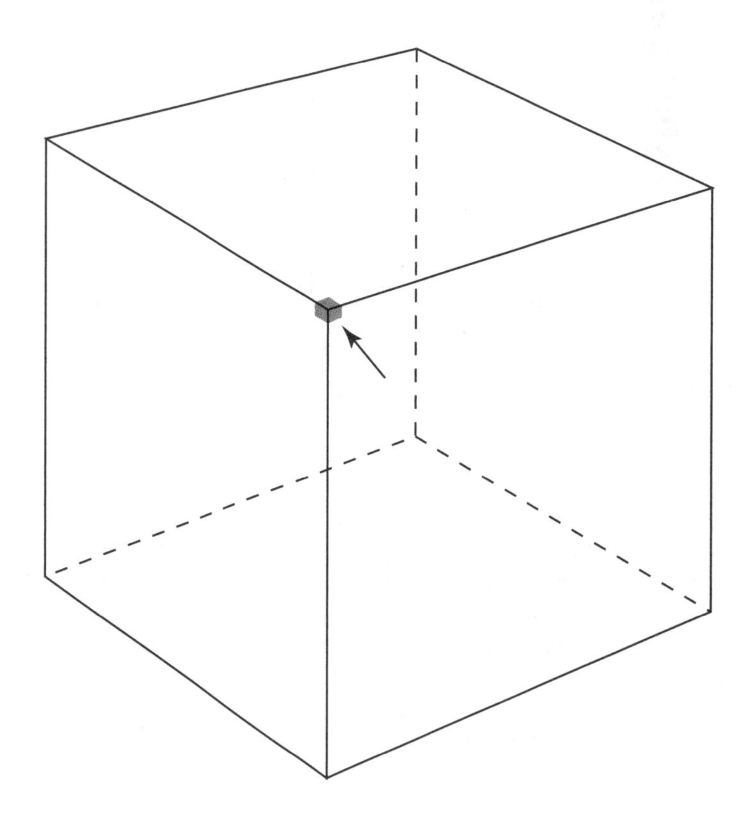

Figure 13-16. Only about one species has been discovered as fossils for every 10,000 species that ever existed. The volume of the shaded cube (arrow) relative to the larger cube indicates this minute fraction.

But the greatest legacy of these mother-lode deposits has been the insight they provide into the character and early evolution of *metazoans* (many-celled animals). No science fiction writer has ever imagined creatures more bizarre than these. It is as though nature were experimenting with life forms that today are not only unknown, but unthinkable. After attempting for years to classify these critters into the familiar phyla, the paleontologists finally concluded that new phyla had to be defined. Let's look at some of the earliest metazoans and their life styles.

Figure 13-17. Numerous specimens of this fossil ammonite, a marine mollusk similar to the modern chambered nautilus, were studied in Germany. Adult animals are present as two distinct populations of larger or smaller individuals, as though comprising two species. Oddly, the numbers of individuals in each population commonly are about equal. For this and other reasons it is more likely that the smaller animals are males (slanted arrow) and the larger are females (looking-glass mirror) of the *same* species. In most modern invertebrate animals, females are larger than males. [*Courtesy U. Lehmann.*]

Our first example is at a famous site near a lonely train stop in South Australia named Ediacara (ee-dee-ACK-ara), whose fauna of latest Precambrian age has since been discovered in other localities worldwide. A shallow marine community included "worms," jellyfish-like disks, "feathers" as in an old-fashioned quill pen (Figure 13-18), and even a "lawn sprinkler." Some animals were stabilized on the sea floor with a ballast weight rather like a sand bag. Most of these creatures were gutless ribbons, sheets, or pancakes, some more than a meter across but only a millimeter thick. Their body structures were of a sort totally unknown today—a hydraulic quilt whose overlapping sections are interconnected, like the compartments in an air mattress. You recall (Chapter 12) that oxygen was emplaced into the atmosphere

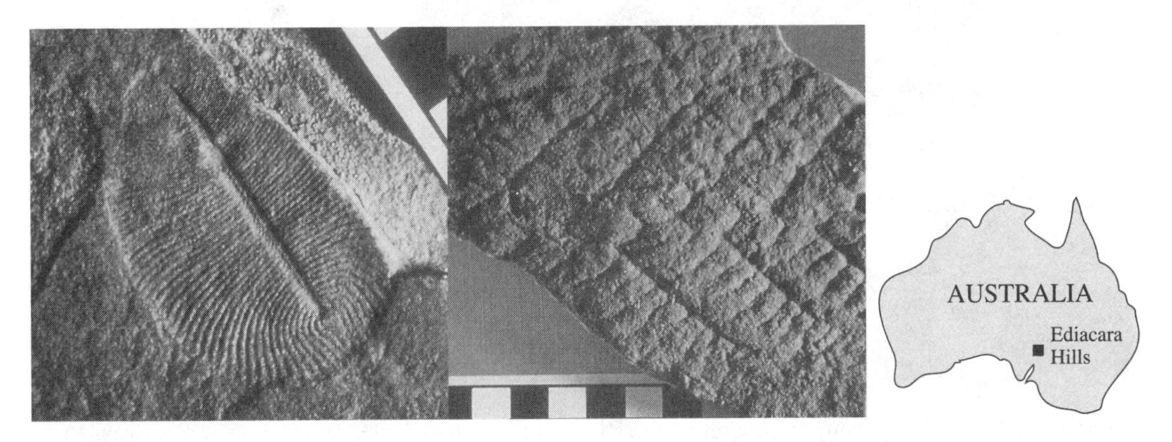

Figure 13-18. Neither of these ancient metazoans closely resembles any known living organism. Ruler scale in centimeters. [*Courtesy J. W. Schopf.*]

as a by-product of photosynthesizing organisms. If oxygen was not yet at a high concentration by late Precambrian times, a flattened body plan with a large surface area would have been advantageous to promote gas exchange.

Innovations of the Cambrian evolutionary explosion included animals with hard parts (only tiny mineralized patches at first) and segmentation. Arthropods appeared, which account for nearly 80% of modern animal species (Appendix A). Most prominent among them were trilobites whose bodies contained as many as 30 nearly identical segments. The highly successful trilobites did not go extinct until the end of the Paleozoic Era, but when our second example of a fossil bonanza was being deposited, they were just one group among other "experimental prototype" animals. An incredible revelation of early metazoan life is afforded by the Burgess Shale, uplifted high in the Rockies of British Columbia (Figure 13-19), from a stratum only a meter or two thick, exposed over less than the length a football field. Conditions there during the Middle Cambrian were ideal for preservation in mud banks at the foot of a towering underwater reef escarpment. Every so often, when a mass of mud slumped into deeper water, the hapless entrained animals were instantly suffocated. Even the contents of the latest meal were preserved in their alimentary tracts.

Ediacaran animals were passive feeders only. Burgess Shale fauna occupied a balanced ecology of familiar underwater habitats and niches. There were carnivores, herbivores, scavengers, parasites, burrowers, swimmers in shallow water and in deep water, feeders of particles whether suspended or buried in sediment. There were known phyla including sponges, various worms, mollusks, echinoderms, and arthropods, and a menagerie of unlikely types that look as though assembled from odd parts. Who would have dreamed up *Opabinia* with its nozzle and five eyes, or *Nectocaris* which looks like an arthropod in the front and a fish in the rear, or aptly-named *Hallucigenia* standing on its struts, or *Anomalocaris* whose circular mouth armed with teeth probably could constrict like a nutcracker (Figure 13-20)? These and representatives of other previously unknown phyla outnumber the familiar animal phyla in the Burgess Shale. Now that similar faunas have been discovered in faraway China and elsewhere around the world, we may confidently expect the discovery of many more examples of fossilized "weird wonders."

Figure 13-19. C. D. Walcott, discoverer of the Burgess Shale fossil site, returned year after year to this quarry in a spectacular setting in the Canadian Rockies, where he collected some 35 thousand specimens. This and later extensive collections are under current study. [*Courtesy James Sprinkle.*]

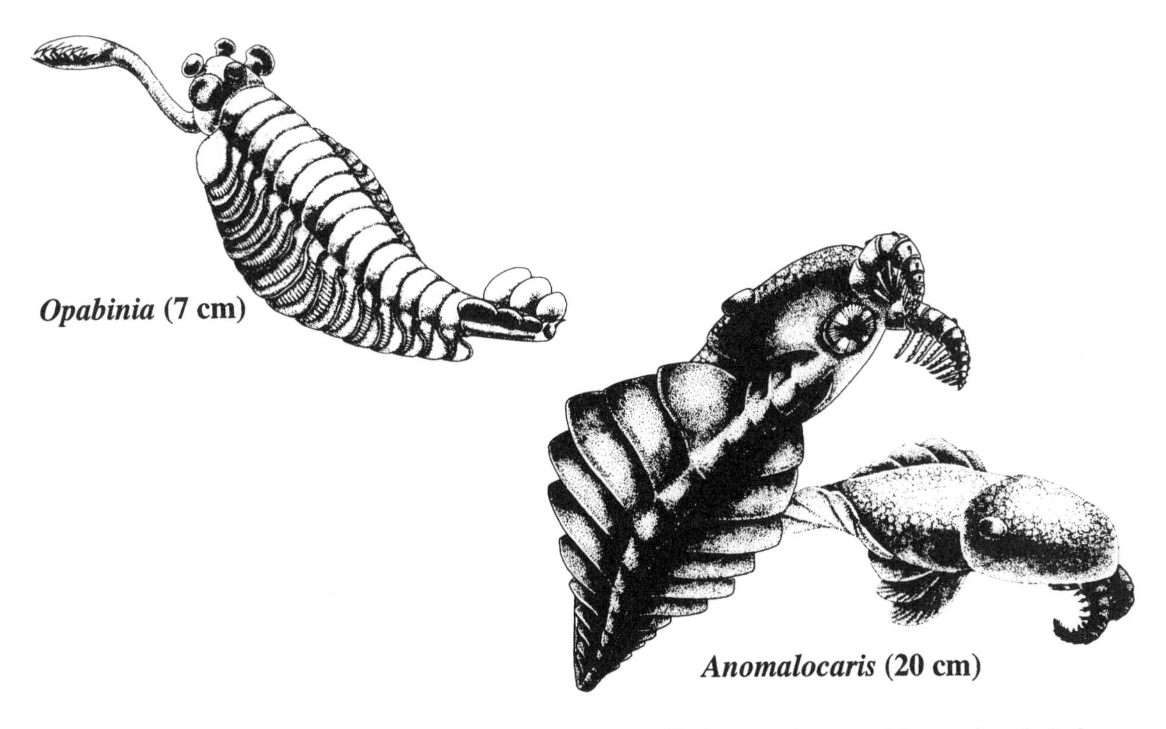

Figure 13-20. By today's standards, some of the Burgess Shale animals are so bizarre that their form and function are unrecognizable. It has not been fully confirmed, for example, that *Hallucigenia* is an entire animal. This fossil could be a piece broken off some larger, as yet unknown animal. [*From S. J. Gould,* Wonderful Life. *Copyright © 1989. By permission of W. W. Norton & Company. Drawn by Marianne Collins.*]

Who could have predicted that arthropods and mollusks would survive to this day, whereas the animals mentioned above would soon disappear? It is commonly assumed that the modern lineages of organisms, simply because they are the survivors, were always "meant to be" in the sense that natural selection favors the superior individuals or groups of organisms. But paleontologists are gathering evidence that the evolutionary tree did not expand smoothly with a just a bit of cosmetic pruning of ill-adapted outer branches. Review Figure 12-14, the tree of life that shows the increase of species diversity through geologic time. During the Cambrian and Ordovician, the evolutionary pathway may have been more like Figure 13-21 in which numerous early branches were abruptly clipped off. Weird wonder animals, the first metazoans, appeared with all manner of body structures and for a time they flourished in the face of very little competition. How and why they became extinct while others survived is not immediately apparent. After the crisis of early experimentation, the surviving phyla settled down to a future evolution that, for all of its spectacular developments, was to be modest by comparison. In a following chapter we shall review the amazing story of the geologic history of the vertebrates.

SUMMARY

Fossils, ancient remains of once-living organisms that occur chiefly in sedimentary rocks, are rarely preserved as an intact original shell or an entire frozen or mummified body. Much more commonly the fossil consists of a mold (a cavity that preserves the former size and shape), an external or internal cast (hardened filling of a mold), or as petrified material. Petrifaction may occur by permineralization (precipitation of minerals in pore spaces) or by total replacement of the organism by mineral material. A fossil compression is a flattened thin film of generally carbonaceous residue whose counterpart is a fossil impression, a shallow indentation where the rock matrix had surrounded the compression. Tracks, burrows, and coprolites (excrement) are examples of trace fossils, records of the organism's activity rather than of the organism itself.

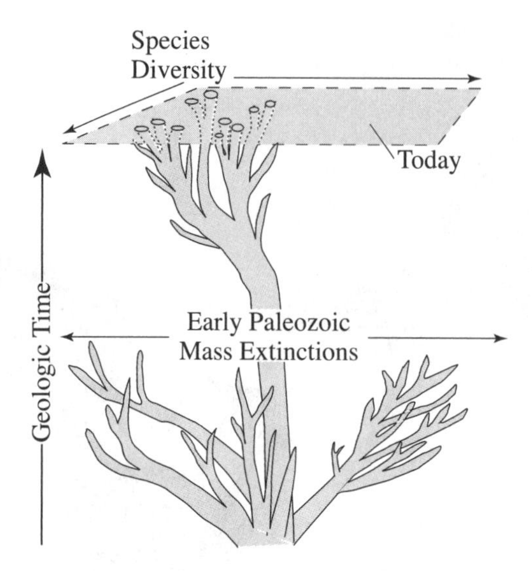

Figure 13-21. Compare this drawing with Figure 12-14, which shows an expanding cone of ever-increasing species diversity throughout geologic time. In reality, the evolutionary tree of life with an initial high diversity may have been severely pruned early in the Paleozoic Era.

The early stratigraphic notion of global concentric onionskin layering of sedimentary strata is incorrect; areas are being eroded to supply sediment for deposition elsewhere. Stratigraphic laws or principles include (a) the law of superposition: in an undisturbed sequence, younger strata lie above older; (b) the principle of original horizontality: most strata are deposited in horizontal layers; (c) the principle of lateral continuity: strata initially extended uninterrupted to the margin of the basin of deposition; and (d) the principle of faunal succession: there is a systematic progression of fossil forms in going from lower (older) to higher (younger) strata.

These principles make it possible to correlate, or demonstrate the equivalency, of strata from place to place even though the sediments may have been faulted, folded, buried, or partially eroded. Geologic formations, which are bodies of rock, may be correlated. A formation is a persistent stratum or group of strata that are distinctive and thick enough to depict on a geologic map. In general, the characteristics of a formation are determined by the type of sediment that is available and by processes of deposition in a given environment (for example, sand distributed by waves on a beach). Alternatively, the basis of correlation may be the age of deposition, accomplished through dating associated volcanic strata by isotopic methods, or through use of the principle of faunal succession. Each fossil species (or assemblage of species) exists only in a limited stratigraphic range, corresponding to a unique period of geologic time. Cosmopolitan (widely distributed) fossil species are useful for broad, even worldwide time-correlation of strata. Endemic (geographically restricted) fossil species are more useful indicators of environments of sedimentary deposition. Other techniques include the correlation of patterns of carbon isotope ratios, or of normal or reverse magnetism in marine sedimentary sequences.

A geologic time scale based upon faunal (and floral) succession has been calibrated by isotopic ages. Phanerozoic sedimentary rocks, deposited during the final 1/8 of earth history (from 550 million years ago until today), commonly contain abundant fossils of complex organisms with hard parts. Fossils in Precambrian sediments, formed during the earliest 7/8 of geologic time, comprise a very sparse record of relatively simple organisms without hard parts. In a hierarchy of terminology, geologic epochs are subdivisions within periods, periods within eras, and eras within eons. Major extinctions terminated the Paleozoic and Mesozoic Eras.

The fossil record is very meager compared to the number of organisms that ever existed, and it is heavily biased toward preservation only of hard parts. Fossil deposits that include the soft parts of organisms are exceedingly rare and instructive. Famous among these are the latest Precambrian Ediacara fauna deposited just before the Cambrian outburst of evolutionary innovation, and the Middle Cambrian fauna from the Burgess Shale, British Columbia. Numerous members of these faunas cannot be classified in any phylum living today.

14

Fossils and Geologic Time

INTRODUCTION

The interpretation of geologic history has developed greatly since the 17th century, when the relative antiquity of a bone fragment was established by the fact that it would adhere to the tongue, and rocks were often classified as antediluvian (before the Flood of Noah described in the Bible) or postdiluvian. Development of the earth and the evolution of living organisms during the most recent half-billion years, at least, has become quite well understood. Considering that the estimated age of the earth is 4.55 billion years, this may not seem too impressive to a beginning student in geology. However, as we have seen in Chapter 4, rock materials are constantly being recycled into younger forms, typically with destruction of the earlier rock and its contained fossils. Most of the record of the earliest earth and of the origin and early evolution of life simply may no longer exist in readable form. Moreover, life on earth prior to 550 million (0.55 billion) years ago was predominantly microscopic and lacking hard parts (shell material, skeleton), thus leaving a very meager record. Therefore, in this chapter we will concentrate on the rich fossil record deposited in the last 1/8 of the earth's history, a time interval known as the *Phanerozoic* ("evident life").

FOSSILS AND THEIR CLASSIFICATION

A fossil is defined as *any evidence of past life,* implying evidence of life which has not existed for some time. Evidence may be in many forms and need not involve actual remains; a frozen woolly mammoth, a prehistoric bone, petrified wood, and footprints are all considered valid fossils. Even worm burrows and the isolated gizzard-stones of dinosaurs qualify. The study of fossils is called **paleontology**.

The internationally used system of naming plants and animals, contemporary or fossil, was first presented by the Swedish botanist Carl von Linné in the 1758 edition of his book *Systems Naturae*. In the Linnaean classification, plants and animals are grouped according to their inferred origin—i.e., their degree of similarity. The relationship is established by comparative anatomy and embryonic development. A paleontologist dealing with fossils rarely, if ever, has the opportunity to examine soft part anatomy or embryos, and so must rely heavily on hard part anatomy such as shell fragments or bones. For this reason, the correct grouping of fossil organisms is necessarily somewhat speculative. Several known fossils defy attempts to place them in the most fundamental level of subdivision, the plant or animal kingdom. The complete Linnaean classification for three organisms is shown below. Note that humans and dogs, being more closely related to one another than to a clam, share more categories:

Linnaean

Classification	Modern Human	Domestic Dog	A Fossil Clam
Kingdom	Animalia	Animalia	Animalia
Phylum	Chordata	Chordata	Mollusca
Class	Mammalia	Mammalia	Pelecypoda
Order	Primates	Carnivora	Prionodesmacea
Family	Hominidae	Canidae	Pectinidae
Genus	*Homo*	*Canis*	*Pecten*
Species	*sapiens*	*familiaris*	*healeyi*
Individual	Carl von Linné	Spot	——

The scientific name of a living or fossil organism consists of the generic and specific names (always italicized) along with the name of the person who first described it, and the year that description was published. The full scientific name for the fossil clam above is *Pecten healeyi* Arnold, 1906.

For more than two centuries the Linnean classification scheme has prevailed because the naming procedure is simple and its concise hierarchy of smaller groups contained within larger groups is easy to understand. Recent advances in the science of *taxonomy* (classification of organisms) have called into question the usefulness of some aspects of the Linnean system. Linné's choice of seven levels of organization (species, genus, etc.) is arbitrary and these categories are now viewed as inadequate to describe relationships in detail. Spectacular new fossil discoveries have enriched our knowledge of the history of life, and computers may be programmed to examine complex comparisons amongst fossils and living organisms. Linné assumed that species are related according to the degree of similarity of body structures. The fossil record is in general agreement with this notion, but not in all cases.

Researchers are vigorously exploring a new method of analysis called *cladistics*. Consider a named group of organisms—for example, birds. A *clade* comprises all the members of that group including those living today, and back through geologic time to the earliest common ancestor. Cladistics is an interpretation of *lineages*, of continuous lines of descent from parents to their offspring who in turn became the next generation of parents. The fossil record is vital to cladistic analysis by providing data about past life. In their modern forms, both Linnean and cladistic analyses assume that all life is connected historically through organic evolution, described by Charles Darwin as "descent with modification."

Characteristics of a lineage may persist stably through an interval of geologic time, then a split, or *speciation*, occurs into two or more lineages. For example the Jurassic fossil *Archaeopteryx* displays impressions of feathers, but it also has characteristics such as teeth, separated fingers, long skinny tail, etc. that are shared by "conventional" dinosaurs but not by modern birds. Fossil evidence is consistent with a branching off of the bird lineage, while the other dinosaurs were to continue for another 100 million years. Countless branchings gave rise to the diversity of species living today. Hence cladistics, from the Greek word "klados" meaning branch or twig.

Let's return to our definition of a clade as including all members of a lineage including the earliest common ancestor. According to the Linnean viewpoint, birds came from dinosaurs, whereas according to cladistics, birds *are* dinosaurs. Dinosaurs flourish today.

Results of cladistic analysis are summarized by a *cladogram*, a diagram representing lines of descent dividing in a branching pattern (Figure 14-1). Cladistic analysis makes use of *primitive characters and derived characters*. Whether a character is primitive or derived (appearing later) depends upon position in the branching pattern. For example, take feathers which are a distinctive character of the bird lineage. Feathers in the first birds were derived character because the dinosaurian ancestor of these animals did not have feathers. During later speciation events when lineages separated into owls, ostriches, etc., feathers were a primitive character because the immediate ancestors of all these birds had feathers. On the other hand, owls have enlarged sclerotic ossicles, bony plates surrounding a huge eye that cause owls to stare rigidly straight ahead. This setting of the eye is a derived character that, along with others, is used to distinguish owls from other birds.

Below are listed some phyla that are important both as fossils and amongst living organisms. These phyla existed throughout most of the Phanerozoic (Table 14-1), Figures 14-2, 14-3 and 14-4 illustrate prominent examples.

Phylum Protozoa One-celled aquatic organisms. Fossil examples have external shells of calcium carbonate ($CaCO_3$) or silica (SiO_2). Marine and nonmarine; mostly planktonic. Most common fossil phylum.

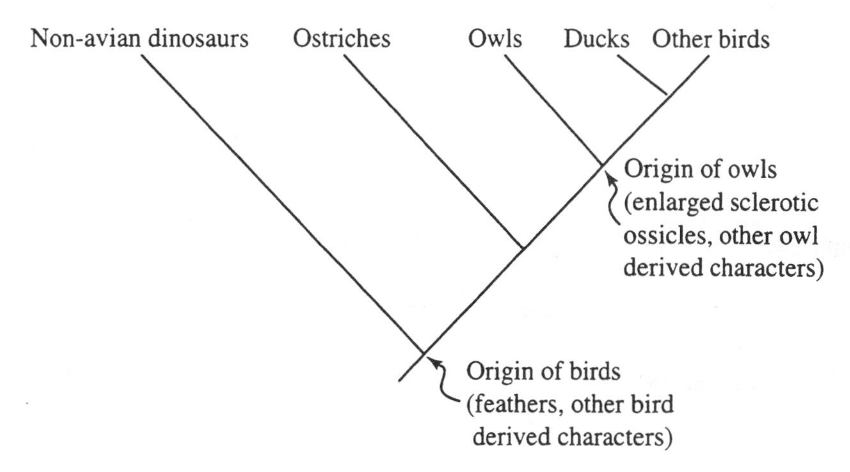

Figure 14-1. Cladogram

Phylum Porifera	Sponges. Silica or calcium carbonate skeletal elements appear in fossil record. Mostly marine.
Phylum Cnidaria	Animals having a hollow body with tentacles surrounding mouth. Includes sea anemones, jellyfish; common fossil representatives are the corals.
Phylum Brachiopoda	Marine animals, most with calcium carbonate shells. Look somewhat like clams, but each valve is bilaterally symmetrical. Most are attached to sea floor.
Phylum Mollusca	Most common macroscopic phylum. Includes clams, snails, octopus, and squid. Ancestors of squid having external shells are important as fossils. Shells generally calcareous. Mostly marine; also fresh water and terrestrial.
Phylum Arthropoda	Includes insects and crustaceans (crabs, lobsters, ostracods, shrimp, barnacles). Trilobites are the most important fossils. All have segmented chitin exoskeleton, and molt periodically. Marine, freshwater, terrestrial. Most populous phylum.
Phylum Echinodermata	All marine; commonly have five-sided radial symmetry and calcareous plates forming exoskeleton. Starfish, sea urchins, sand dollars, brittle stars, and sea cucumbers are representatives; crinoids are common fossils.
Phylum Hemichordata	Includes the extinct *graptolites*, colonial pelagic marine organisms with slight development of a dorsal stiffening rod. Remains consist of small chitinous, sawblade-like films that resemble pencil marks on the rocks.
Phylum Chordata	Mobile animals with a dorsal nervous system and a notochord or vertebral column. Major subphylum is the Vertebrata which includes fish, reptiles, amphibians, birds, and mammals.
Phylum Conodonta	Extinct phosphatic microfossils that are very useful in correlation, but until recently of unknown zoological affinity. Recent discoveries indicate a possible relationship to the chordates.

Most of the organisms described above exhibit one of two fundamental types of body symmetry, which is a property useful in identification. In organisms with **bilateral** symmetry, a central plane divides right and left halves which are mirror images of one another. The external body form (but not the internal organs) of a vertebrate animal, such as you or I, has bilateral symmetry. In contrast, lines drawn from the center to an extremity of a jellyfish, or a starfish (echinoderm) are radii of a circle. Organisms whose bodies are distributed uniformly around a central point are said to have **radial** symmetry.

BASIC PRINCIPLES OF STRATIGRAPHY

Geological analysis of a region or a continent is complete only when events, such as periods of sedimentation, erosion, structural deformation, and igneous activity, have been arranged in chronological order. In recent years, procedures to determine the ages of geologic events, based upon decay of radioactive isotopes in rocks, have become highly sophisticated. Several of these ages appear in the *Geologic Time Scale*, Table 14-1.

Historically, establishing a sequence of events (relative dating) has been accomplished through the study of rock body relationships and the fossils the rocks contain. Principles used in such studies are detailed below:

- **Superposition**—This fundamental principle of sedimentary rock study is very simple. It states that in a sequence of sedimentary rocks piled up on the earth's crust, the oldest stratum will be buried the deepest. Exceptions to this rule are uncommon, but do occur where rocks have been deformed by folding or faulting.
- **Original Horizontality**—This principle states that most sedimentary materials settle under the influence of gravity and thus initially form horizontal layers. The implication here is that layers which are tilted or folded have been deformed subsequent to deposition.

- **Cross-cutting Relationships**—This principle formalizes the common-sense observation that faults or intrusive bodies must be younger than the rocks they cut. Where a fine-grained igneous body is concordant with sedimentary layers, the distribution of baked contact zones must be examined in order to distinguish between a sill and a buried flow.
- **Faunal Succession**—Use of fossils as an indication of geologic age depends upon two assumptions of organic evolution. The first assumption is that organisms change over time and that a specific body plan is never repeated. This is another way of saying that any given time in history is the sum of all the events that preceded it, and therefore impossible to repeat in exactly the same way. The second assumption is that anatomical features that can be traced through the fossil record to the older strata represent the primitive condition of the organisms. Thus, faunal succession combines the laws of history with the law of superposition to provide a reliable key to the stratigraphic position of the rock layers.

◄ Carbonized impression of palm frond in fresh water shale, Bellingham, Washington. (Photo by Shannon O'Dunn.)

Fossil pelecypods (clams) ► show two types of fossilization: actual remains, and external mold. Marine sandstone, Capitola Beach, California. (Photo by Roland Brady.)

◄ Shell material and molds of high-spired gastropod (snail) in marine sandstone, Los Angeles County, California. (U.S.G.S. Photo.)

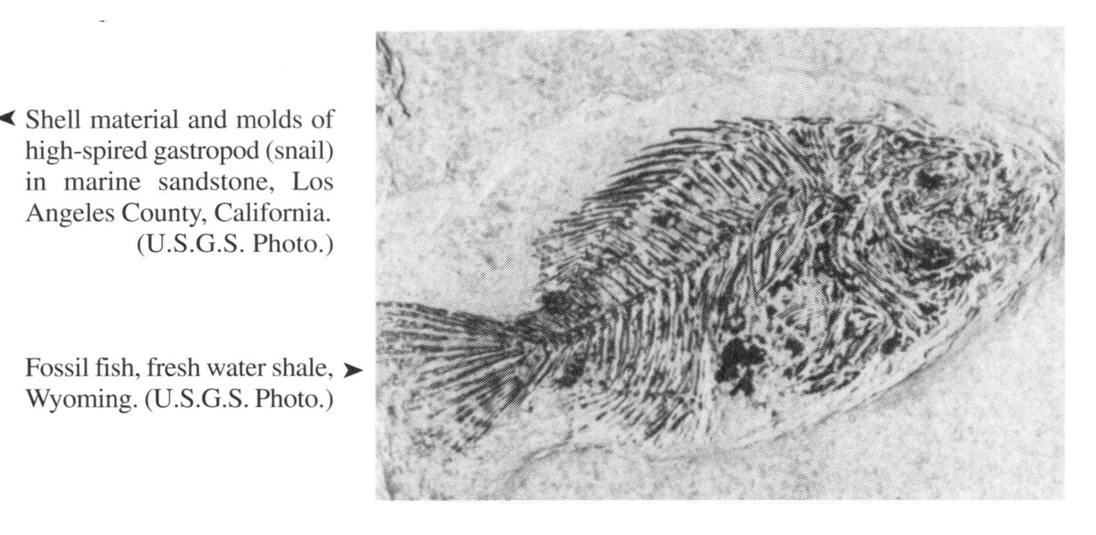

Fossil fish, fresh water shale, ► Wyoming. (U.S.G.S. Photo.)

d 14-1. Fossils

Table 14-1a. *The Geologic Time Scale*

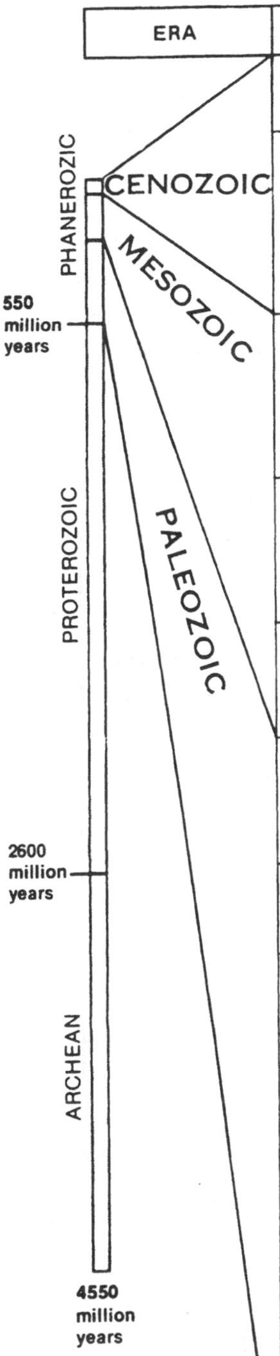

ERA	PERIOD	EPOCH	IMPORTANT LIFE FORMS	TYPICAL FOSSIL
CENOZOIC	Quaternary Q	Holocene	Existing life forms; man dominates.	
		Pleistocene	Modern man, giant land mammals.	
	Tertiary T	Pliocene	Tool-using primate; mastodons, rhinos, camels.	
		Miocene	Furred marine and grazing mammals, *Homo* ancestors.	
		Oligocene	Primates diversify; terrestrial mammals expand.	
		Eocene	Whales, bats, horses appear; fish, insects common.	
		Paleocene	Large flightless birds, small mammals, corals.	
		66		
MESOZOIC	Cretaceous K		Abundant gastropods. Dinosaurs climax and become extinct, as do almost all shelled cephalopods. Modern fish expand. Modern echinoderms. First deciduous trees and flowering plants. Terrestrial snails appear. Insects flourish. Calcareous plankton abundant. Placental mammals diversify.	
		146		
	Jurassic J		Abundant pelecypods, cephalopods, echinoderms. Massive herbivorous dinosaurs on land; carnivorous forms in all environments. Birds debut. Freshwater snails appear.	
		202		
	Triassic TR		Shelled cephalopods expand and diversify; modern corals and echinoderms develop. Many small, bipedal terrestrial reptiles, including the first dinosaurs. Rodent-like true mammals appear. Coniferous land plants.	
		251		
PALEOZOIC	Permian PM or P		Diverse reptile populations develop; amphibians also common. Shallow marine animals experience many extinctions, including all the trilobites and most molluscs and brachiopods. Fusulinid foraminifera abundant and typical.	
		290		
	Pennsylvanian IP		Insect populations expand as wetland forests (coal swamps) spread over low-lying areas. Rapid plant evolution; some trees grow to 30 m tall. Coniferous plants appear. Earliest reptile fossils.	
		323		
	Mississippian IM		The "Age of Crinoids." Other calcium carbonate secreting organisms abundant, such as planktonic protozoa, brachiopods, corals.	
		353		
	Devonian D		Corals, fish, cephalopods, brachiopods, trilobites, and gastropods are dominant marine fauna. Diverse land plants; terrestrial arthropods, amphibian vertebrates. Pelecypods enter fresh water.	
		409		
	Silurian S		Massive coral reefs, large (to 8 feet) arthropod predators, explosive evolution of the fishes. Brachiopods, echinoderms, trilobites, silica sponges are common marine invertebrates. Simple plants invade the land; possible terrestrial arthropods.	
		441		
	Ordovician O		Graptolites, trilobites, brachiopods, solitary and colonial corals are common. Cephalopod molluscs become diversified and large (to 20 feet); pelecypod and gastropod molluscs present, but less abundant. Clear evidence of primitive fish in Colorado.	
		513		
	Cambrian €		All major phyla are represented. All are aquatic organisms. Tribolites, worms, sponges, brachiopods, and corals are common. Possible vertebrate remains from Wyoming.	
		550		
	Precambrian p€	Million years	Fossils rare; include bacteria, blue-green algae, green algae, and organisms of unknown affinities. All marine, mostly microscopic free-floating organisms. Calcareous algal reefs present in Grand Canyon rocks.	

PHANEROZOIC

550 million years

PROTEROZOIC

2600 million years

ARCHEAN

4550 million years

Table 14-1b. *The Geologic Time Scale*

NORTH AMERICAN TECTONICS	REPRESENTATIVE UNITS
Western U.S. shears against Pacific Plate causing widespread tectonism. Appalachians rejunventated. Equator achieves present day position.	Scattered volcanism (Crater Lake formed, Mt. St. Helens erupts repeatedly); alluvial deposits in valleys. Mississippi delta forms, Atlantic coastal sediments deposited.
Batholithic intrusion and composite volcanic activity continue to accompany subduction in the west. The continent is completely emergent, with coastlines much like today. Modern physiographic provinces develop. Atlantic completely open.	Wasatch Formation (pink sandstone cliffs of Bryce Canyon). Volcanics in Yellowstone, Columbia Plateau, Cascades, San Juan Mts., CO. Isolated sialic plutons, Green River, WY. Lake beds (oil shales) famous for fossil vertebrates. Goldbearing veins of the Black Hills. Continental deposits of lignite and bituminous coal. Oil and gas in Gulf coast, southern California and offshore. Diverse metallic ores of Colorado Rockies.
Early in this period, the continent is mostly emergent, but later the western seaway floods into the mid-continent leaving an emergent mountain chain formed by the force of Pacific Plate/North American Plate collision. The Atlantic Ocean is open except at northern end.	Formation in Rocky Mtns. and to the east include primarily marine Dakota Sandstone, Mancos Shale, Mesaverde group, Fox Hill Sandstone; The Dakota is an aquifer, and some of the sandstones contain coal. Intrusion of Sierra Nevada and other sialic plutons. Gold-bearing veins of Sierra Nevada. Possible barrier reef off Atlantic coast. Extensive limestone formation along Gulf coast.
At first, the continent is mostly emergent, with volcanic islands in the western seaway. Later, the seaway expands into the central continent. Granitic intrusions from subduction in the west.	Navajo cross-bedded sandstone of the Colorado Plateau. Deep-water marine Franciscan group of northern California. Morrison Formation of Colorado Plateau and Rockies. Gulf coast acquires its present form; salt deposits in Gulf of Mexico. Mafic intrusive (now serpentinite) and andesites in California.
Eastern and central North America are above sea level. In the far west, shallow sea bottom surrounds island volcanoes, and fault-controlled basins and ranges develop offshore. The southern Atlantic Ocean begins to open up.	Felsic to mafic intrusives from Oregon to Alaska. Newark red beds, Palisade basalts, Moenkopi/Chinle red sandstones and shales of the Colorado Plateau. Chinle in Arizona contains agatized tree trunks of the petrified Forest. Dockum red beds in Texas.
Eastern U.S. largely emergent land. Volcanic islands indicate continuing subduction in the west. Mid-continent regions collect carbonates, evaporites, and terrestrial red sandstones and shales. Pangaea separates; North America begins to move westward.	Upper 2,000 feet of the Grand Canyon including Kaibab Limestone rimrock. Phosphoria of northwest U.S. Dunkard red beds in West Virgina. Extensive reefs in Texas and New Mexico, including limestone of Carlsbad Cavern. Extensive salt deposits in Kansas.
Northern proto-Atlantic Ocean closes, completing uplift of the Appalachians and Ouachita, formation of the supercontinent Pangaea. Volcanic activity along western continental margin. Extensive coal deposits formed.	Fountain Arkose of Rocky Mountain Front Range; Paradox Basin evaporites of Utah. Metamorphic Calaveras sequence of western Nevada to Alaska. Cyclic deposition of coal beds from northern Illinois to West Virginia.
Proto-Atlantic ocean closes in the southern part as Africa collides with southeastern North America, creating the southern Appalachian Mtns. Widespread shallow seas collect limestone and shale.	Many cliff-forming limestones in the Rocky Mountains, Mississippi Valley, and southern Appalachians. Clastic sedimentary units followed the carbonates.
Emergent mid-continent areas are drowned later in the period by shallow seas. North America and Europe again collide, pushing up Appalachians. Continuing subduction in far west creates north-south mountains from Nevada through Canada.	Temple Butte limestone of Grand Canyon. Devil's Gate carbonates, Nevada. Oil-bearing carbonate reefs of the Williston Basin in the northern Rocky Mtns. Extensive delta sediments of the Catskill Mountains.
Appalachian highlands and western U.S. volcanos are islands in North American shallow sea. Organic reefs ring mid-continent basins collecting evaporites (gypsum, halite).	Limestone of the Silurian Hills, Mojave Desert; some fossiliferous units in the northern Sierra Nevada and Klamath mountains. Granitic intrusions in northern Appalachians, Niagara Falls series of limestone and shale. Michigan Basin evaporites.
Gentle warping of Precambrian basement and sediment cover to form basins and arches. Shallow seas still cover most of North America. Ancestral Pacific Ocean floor is being subducted under western North America. North America and Europe push together uplifting Appalachians.	Granite and marine basalts in Alaska produced by subduction. Pure quartz sandstones moved westward from emerging crystalline basement to form Eureka Quartzite of Basin and Range. Harding sandstone of Colorado, deep water melange sediments in Vermont and Newfoundland. Deep water marine shales in far west and east.
Partially emergent Precambrian crystalline rocks centered on Hudson Bay region are surrounded by marine waters grading from shallow to deep near present coastlines. Nearshore sandstones are flanked by shallow limestones and deeper water shales. Equator bisects North America from north to south.	Marine sandstones, as the Tapeats of Grand Canyon, the Prospect Mtn. Quartzite of Basin and Range, and the Potsdam of New York. Marine carbonates, as the Noonday Dolomite of southeast California. Marine shales along the western and eastern margins of the continent.
Continental crust is formed by mantle differentiation. Several glaciation events. Southern continents clumped together (Gondwanaland); Europe and North America close together.	Stillwater, MT chromite deposit. Grand Canyon inner gorge crystalline and sedimentary rocks. Great iron ore deposits on Lake Superior. Sudbury nickel-copper deposits.

Table 14-2. *Fossil Information Chart*

Name	Composition of original	Diagnostic features	Age range	Phylum	Comments
Algal fruiting body	Aragonite	Spherical	Precambrian to Recent	Chlorophyta	These photosynthetic organisms are the source of much carbonate mud.
Sponge	Silica, calcite, protein	Commonly tube- or fan-shaped.	Cambrian to Recent	Porifera	Sessile, chiefly marine, lack definite tissues and organs. Internal skeleton of calcareous, siliceous, or organic spicules. Commonly in rocks just as little spicules. Your samples include a lithistid sponge and a modern soft sponge.
Coral	Calcite, aragonite	Septae evident. Many species grow as colonies.	Cambrian to Recent	Cnidaria	Your samples are "rugose" coral, and scleractinian coral similar to those living today. Coral reefs are commonly very diverse communities, sensitive to environmental change. We see only a small fraction of them in the rock record because most are broken down into carbonate sand and mud.
Echinoid	Calcite	Five-fold symmetry	Cambrian to Recent	Echinodermata	Your sample is a mobile form. We see similar forms in the sand dollars at the Gulf Coast. Some varieties have very long spines. Neither echinoids, nor the related sessile crinoids, tolerate brackish water.
Bivalve	Calcite	Bilateral symmetry *between* the "valves"	Cambrian to Recent	Mollusca	Mainly marine, but some are freshwater or land-living. Highly organized with head and foot differentiated; generally has an external calcareous shell. Found abundantly in the fossil record.
Gastropod	Mainly aragonite	Conical tube; generally coiled	Cambrian to Recent	Mollusca	Mobile, marine, freshwater and land snails. Many species graze on algae in shallow marine environments of varying energies. Commonly preserved as steinkerns (internal molds).

Table 14-2. *(continued)*

Name	Composition of original	Diagnostic features	Age range	Phylum	Comments
"Ammonite"	Calcite	Coiled in a horizontal plane	Devonian to Cretaceous	Mollusca	Closest relative is the coiled *Nautilus*. Early groups are important indicators of the passage of time. Partitions between their internal chambers intersect the outer shell along complex lines known as sutures.
Brachiopod	Calcite	Bilateral symmetry *across* the two valves	Cambrian to Recent	Brachiopoda	Sessile, marine, very common in Paleozoic rocks. The pedicle (the brachiopod "foot") requires a firm surface for attachment.
"Fusulinid"	Calcite	Sized and shaped like a rice grain	Mississippian to Permian	Protozoa	Distinctively shaped zooplankton with important widespread distribution in marine rocks. Lived in shallow waters, but quite distant from shore.
Shark tooth	Complex calcium phosphate	Variably-sized triangular teeth	Middle Paleozoic to Recent	Chordata	Mobile, aquatic (other Chordate groups such as ourselves are terrestrial). Chordates have internal backbone of some sort (a cartilaginous skeleton in the case of sharks). Shark fossils are rare except for teeth.
Wood	Lignin and cellulose	Internal organization may be growth rings or bundles of tissue.	Silurian to Recent	"Tracheophyta"	Vascular plants contain organized water- and nutrient-conducting tissues. When the plant dies, these structures allow easy infiltration by water with dissolved minerals such as silica. Vast swamp forests of the Mississippian and Pennsylvanian Periods formed the organic source for coal deposits.
Bone, teeth	Complex calcium phosphate and collagen (a scleroprotein)	Distinctive structure of bone, differentiated teeth, specialized teeth for particular tasks	Late Paleozoic to Recent	Chordata	These are mammal bones. Vertebrate skeletons are rarely preserved as complete specimens (remember the bone "pile" at the Museum). The most frequently fossilized portion is the hardy tooth, especially if we are looking at terrestrial mammals.

Table 14-3. *Chart shows how various fossils are used as date indicators throughout the geologic time scale. The black areas show the time of maximum utility for correlation; the full bars indicate the total geologic range.*

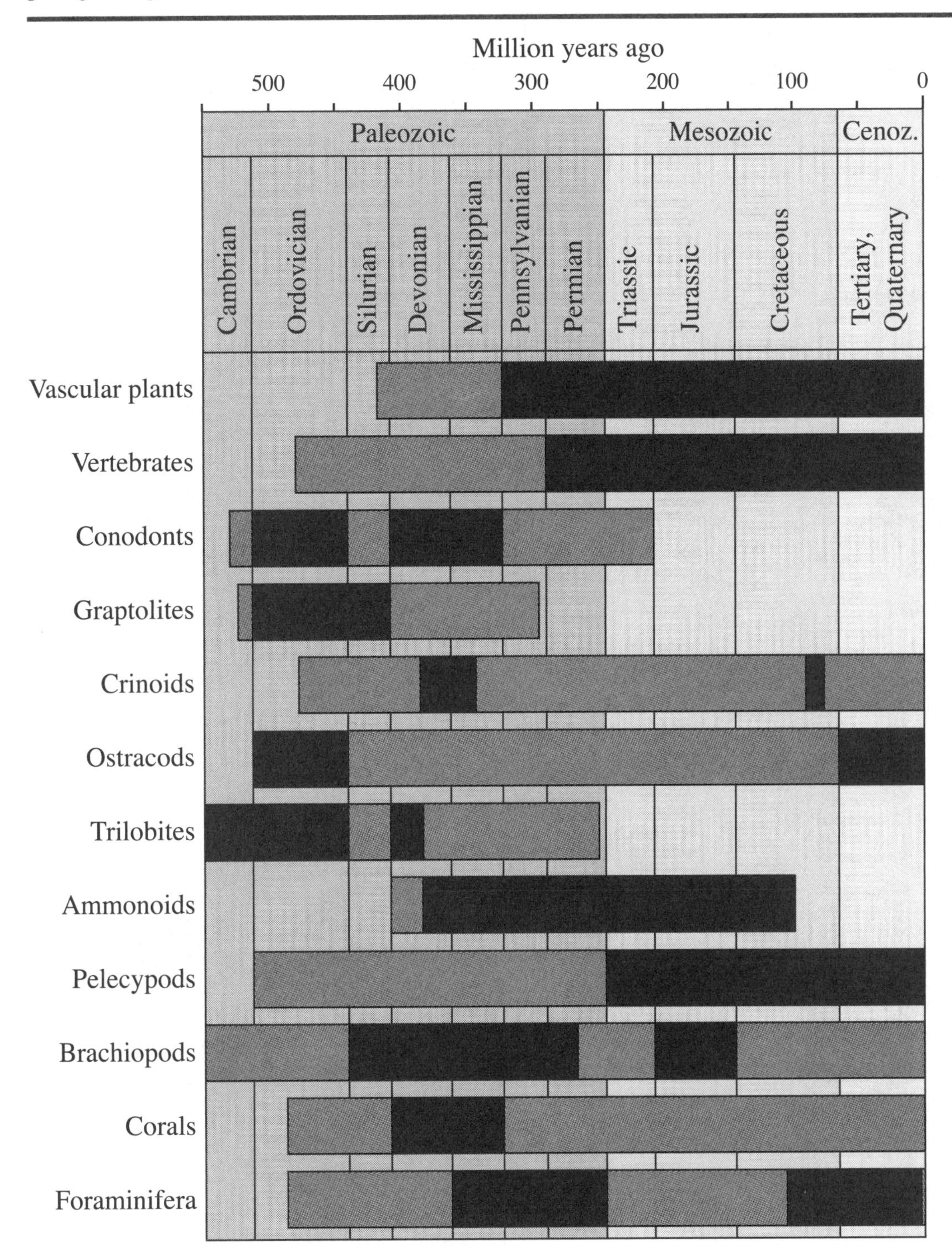

PHYLUM PROTOZOA

Foraminifera

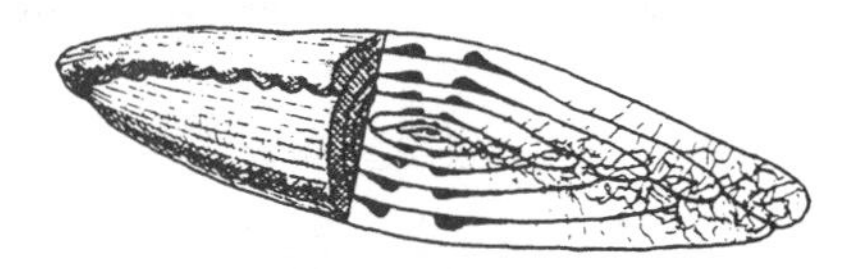

Fusulinella
Penn.

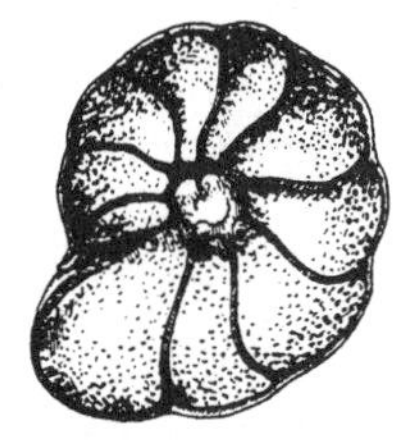

Cibicides Pachyderma
Eoc.

Textularia
Jur.-Rec.

DIVISION CHLOROPHYTA

Porocustis Globularis
(Algal Fruiting Body)

PHYLUM CNIDARIA

Solitary Corals

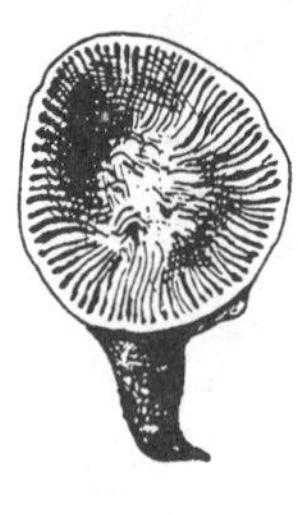

Zaphrenthis
Dev.

Amplexizaphrentis, Sp.
Miss.-Penn.

Colonial Corals

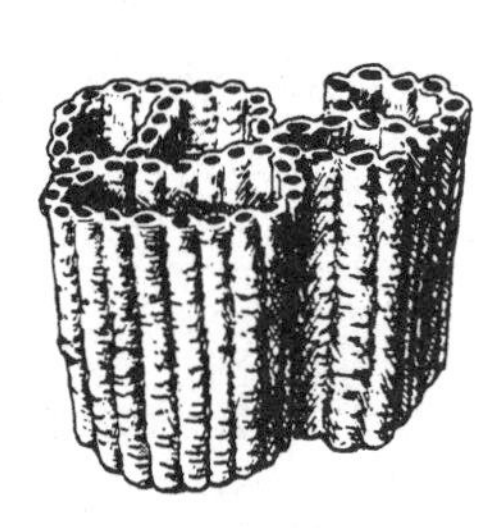

Halysites
Ord.-Sil.

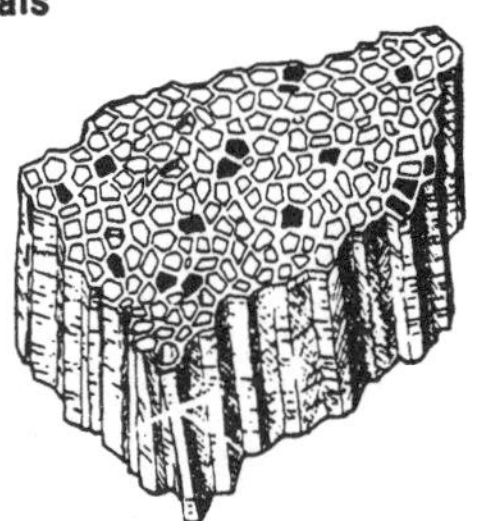

Favosites
U. Ord.-M. Dev.

PHYLUM BRACHIOPODA

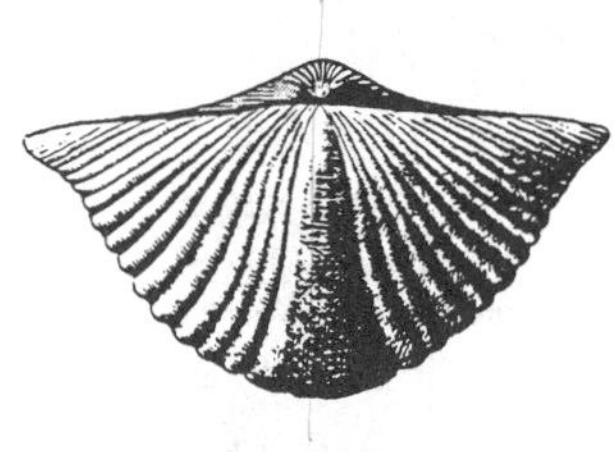

Mucrospirifer
Dev.

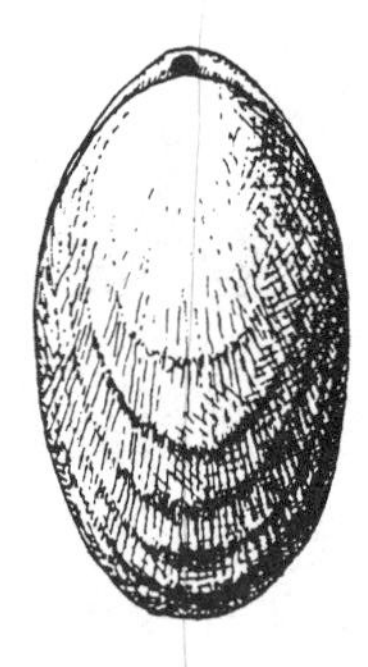

Terebratula
Cret.-Tert.

Echinoconchus
Miss.

Rhynchotreta
Miss.

Figure 14-2. Fossils

CHAPTER 14:
Fossils and Geologic Time

Name: ______________________________

Section: ______________________________

QUESTIONS FOR FOSSILS LAB

Introduction

Paleontology, the study of the geologic history of life on earth, is a very diverse subject. In this lab you will become acquainted with several of the most commonly preserved groups of fossil organisms, and investigate some applications of the science. Paleontology is used in the *horizontal* sense and in the *vertical* sense.

Horizontal refers to sedimentary environments (marsh, lagoon, open marine, etc.) that may exist side-by-side at the same moment of time. A particular assemblage of organisms may survive and flourish in one environment, but not in the others. By studying the sediment and the fossils, we may infer what the environment was.

Vertical refers to a stacked sequence of sedimentary strata, from older at the bottom to younger at the top, as demanded by the Law of Superposition. Some groups of organisms have persisted for tens, or even hundreds of millions of years without much change, but most have changed significantly with time. Some have experienced very rapid evolutionary change, such that a particular species may have lived for only a brief interval before going extinct or evolving into something different. The latter, called *index fossils*, are especially useful for assignment of the strata to a precise position in the geologic time scale. If an organism had been broadly distributed geographically, it is also useful to *correlate,* or determine the equivalence, of sedimentary strata in widely distant places.

Exercise

1. The trays contain examples of fossils of diverse groups of Phanerozoic organisms. Use the Fossil Information Chart; the drawings of fossils from the Walnut Clay of Cretaceous age (separate handout), and Figures 14-2 to 14-4 as an information base to complete the worksheet labeled "Fossils."
2. Fossils inform us about *paleo*environments (ancient environments). On each lab table are sets of fossils labeled *A*, *B*, and *C*. They were collected from sedimentary rocks of Pennsylvanian age (late Paleozoic) near Brownwood, Texas. About 300 million years ago, much of the region was covered by a sea, but land lay nearby. Rivers fed sediment into deltas (march environment, stream channel sand). In places there were shallow lagoons with brackish water (mixture of fresh and salty). Normal marine environments offshore had sandy or muddy bottoms, some shallow and some too deep to be agitated by waves.

   The three environments represented are:
   (i) stream channel, probably in a delta (freshwater environment)
   (ii) marine, fairly deep water (low energy), mud or sand
   (iii) marine, very clear water, probably high-energy.

Collection A

Two groups of organism are prominent in this collection; one is a large entire organism, and the other consists of numerous small fossils that look like grains of rice cemented together (inspect them with a hand lens). What are the microfossils?________________________________

In the large specimen, note a structure consisting of septae (partitions) that radiate from a central point. Between the septae were chambers that accommodated the soft tissue of the animal. To what group do these specimens belong?________________________________

Were these two types of organism tolerant, or intolerant of diverse environments? ____________

Were they fresh water, brackish water, or marine?________________________________

Collection B

The specimens consist of what kind of sedimentary rock? ________________________________

Inspect the grains with a hand lens. What is the chief mineral?________________________________

What are present: body fossils or trace fossils? ________________________________

What are the fossils?________________________________

Collection C

The collection contains three major groups. What are the organisms that look like small nuts? (Hint: they are bilaterally symmetrical.) ________________________________

The fossils that look like a meshwork, or like a pin cushion pricked with tiny holes are marine colonial animals called bryozoa. The third group consists of fragments that look like columns of beads strung together. Refer to Figure 14-4 to identify this animal. ________________________________

Was the environment fresh water, brackish water, or marine?________________________________

Did the organisms swim, burrow, or live fastened to the bottom?________________________________

3. Because life on earth is constantly changing, the assemblages of organisms that lived during a particular period of geologic time are both distinctive, and characteristic of that time interval. Each species of organism is fossilized throughout an interval called its *stratigraphic range,* and for the many thousands of fossil species there are thousands of overlapping ranges, each one different. We may use fossils to assign the strata to a position in the geologic time scale (see below).

   A certain set of strata contains five kinds of fossil organism that have scientific names, but which we will call "squares," "circles," "triangles," "stars," and "ovals" for simplicity. Their ranges are:

   squares: middle Permian until late Jurassic
   circles: late Cambrian until today
   triangles: middle Triassic until end of Cretaceous
   stars: late early Triassic until early late Triassic
   ovals: all of the Mesozoic Era

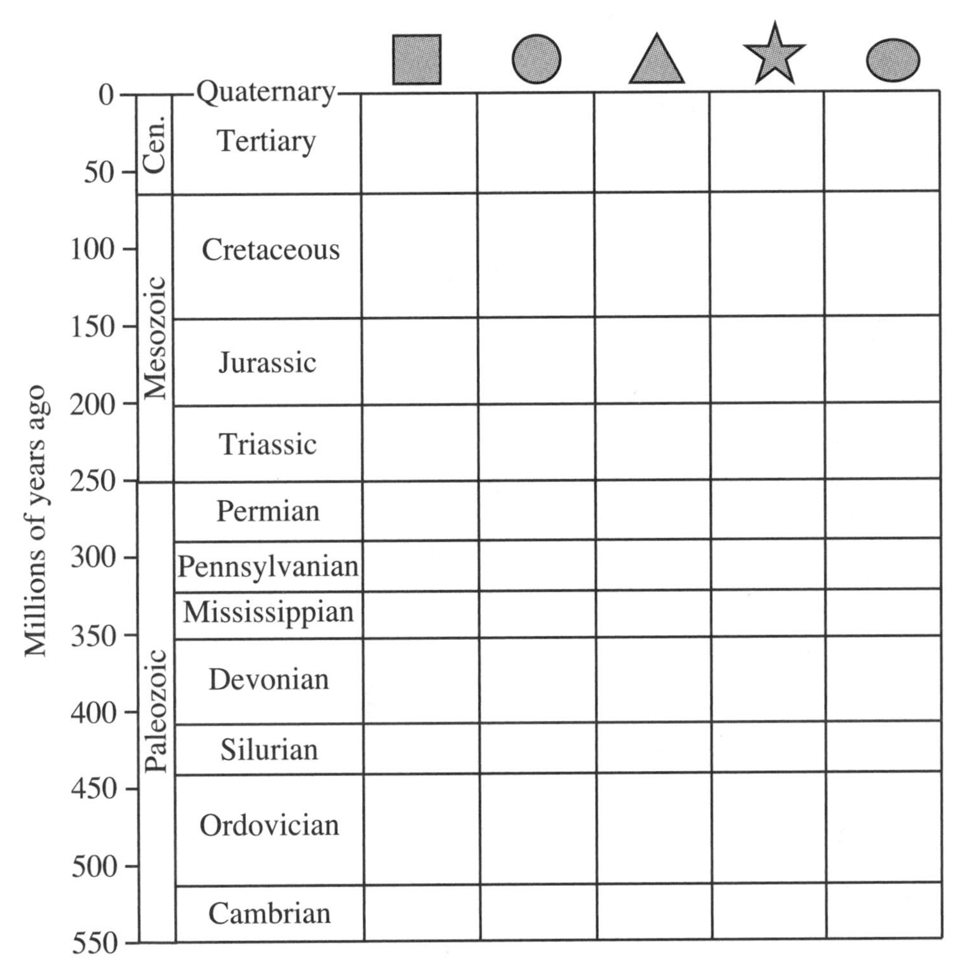

   Plot vertical bars on the geologic time scale above, to correspond to these ranges. Which fossil is the least useful to tell the age? ________________

   Which organism best qualifies as an index fossil? ________________

   Which organisms (more than one kind) were already living before dinosaurs first appeared?

   ____

   Which organism became extinct when the dinosaurs did? ________________

   What is the age of the strata containing squares, circles, triangles, stars, and ovals? (Be as specific as the data permit.) ________________

4. Why are fossils of insects or jellyfish so rare?______________________________

   What would this kind of fossil bias be called?______________________________

   Under what conditions might fossils of the delicate or soft-bodied organisms mentioned above be preserved?

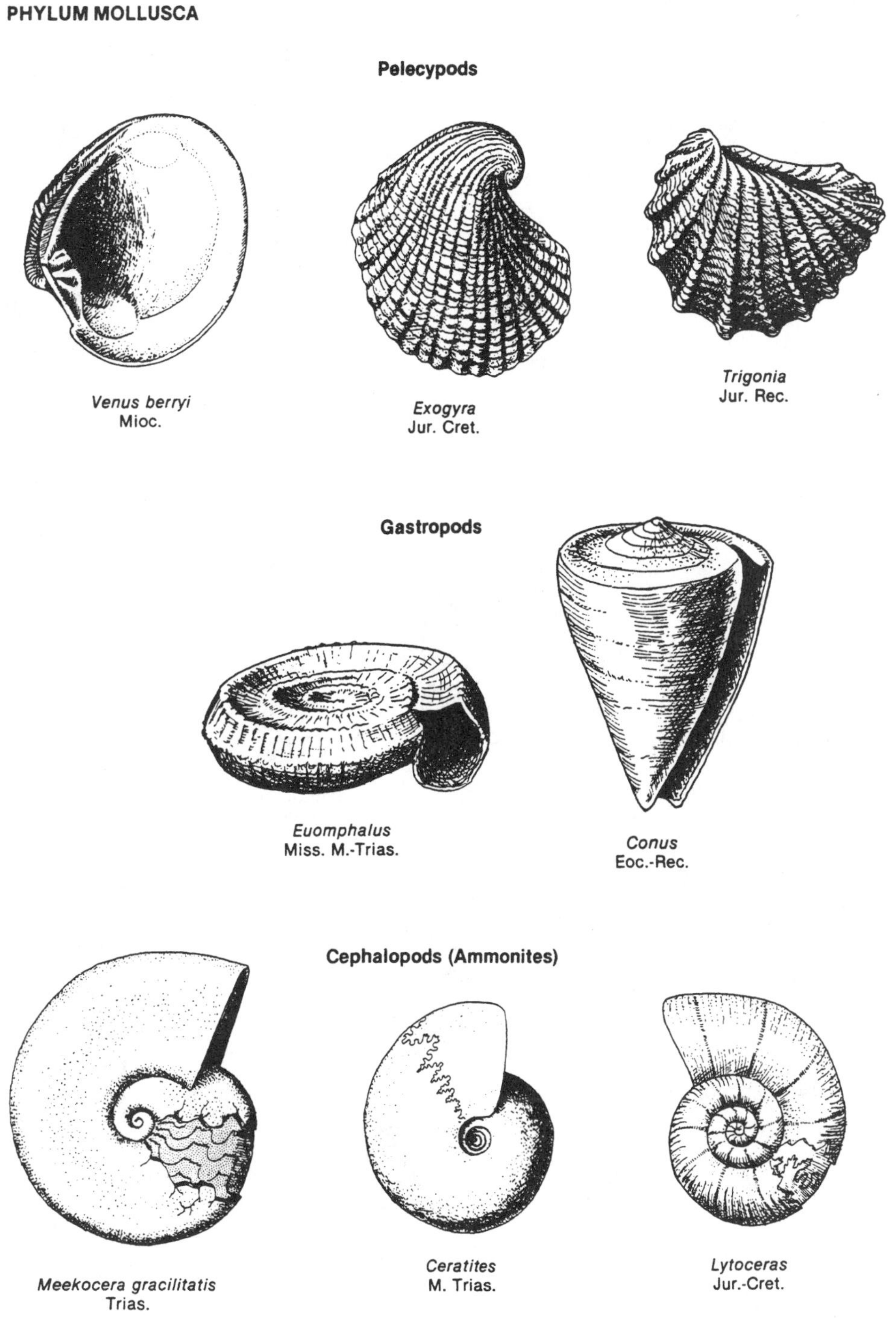

PHYLUM MOLLUSCA

Pelecypods

Venus berryi
Mioc.

Exogyra
Jur. Cret.

Trigonia
Jur. Rec.

Gastropods

Euomphalus
Miss. M.-Trias.

Conus
Eoc.-Rec.

Cephalopods (Ammonites)

Meekocera gracilitatis
Trias.

Ceratites
M. Trias.

Lytoceras
Jur.-Cret.

Figure 14-3. Fossils

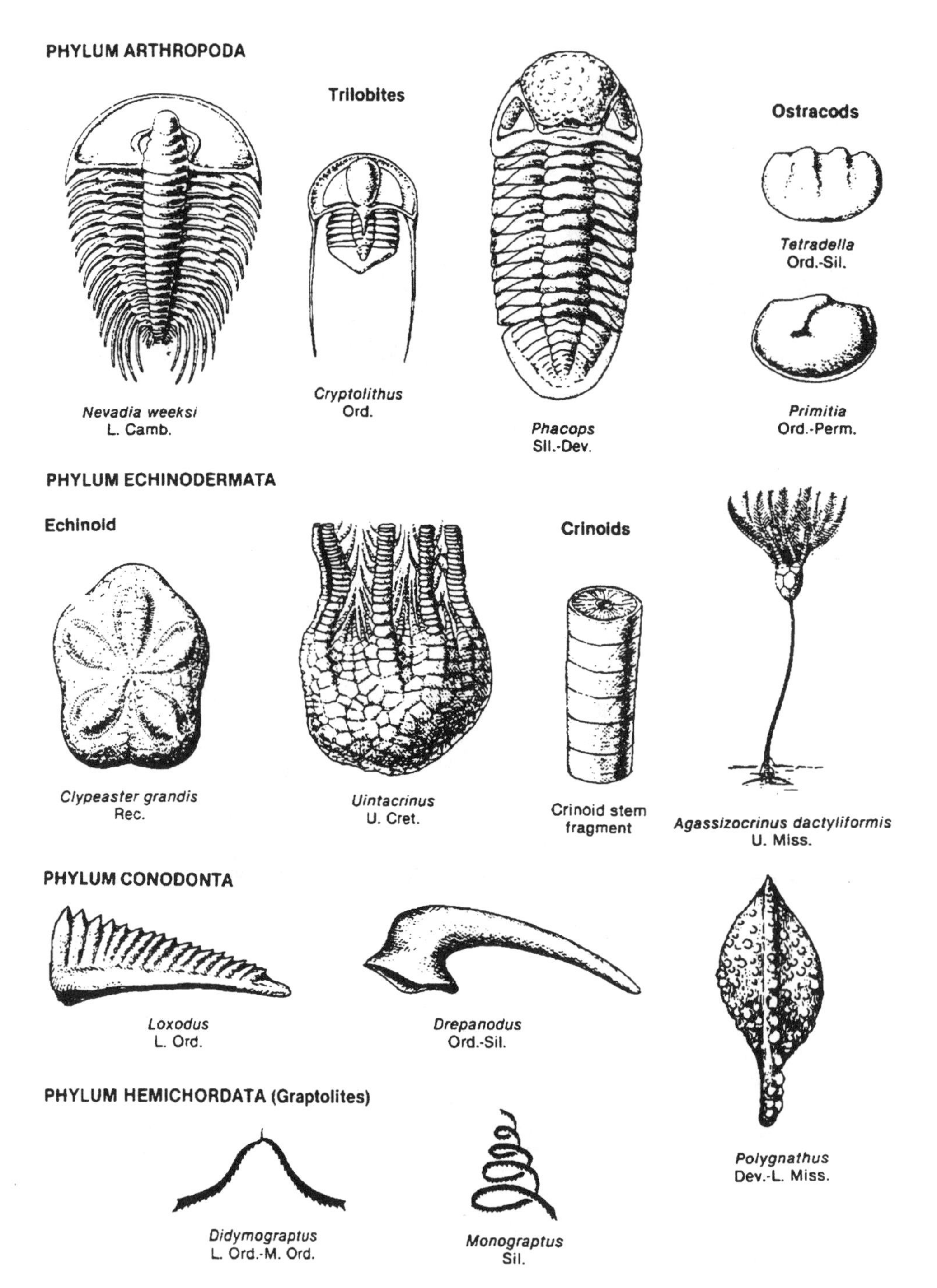

Figure 14-4. Fossils

PRESERVATION OF FOSSILS

Fossils **without alteration** are preserved most often in relatively young sediments. An extreme example is a frozen or mummified mammoth carcass. Much bone of Pleistocene or Recent age is not altered. Fossil shell material with original pearly luster is common. *Amber* is hardened tree sap that may trap and preserve insects, bits of plants, or occasional small vertebrate animals.

Fossils preserved **with alteration** have experienced some chemical or physical change.

- Replacement. Original material is replaced atom-by-atom by minerals (such as calcite, quartz, pyrite) carried to the site and precipitated by groundwater. If woody material has been replaced, thus becoming petrified, it has actually become a rock and it feels heavy.
- Preservation by **permineralization** involves partial, not total replacement. Groundwater has deposited mineral matter into the pore spaces, but much of the original hard-part material is also preserved. Most fossil bone is permineralized, and in petrified wood the original open voids are filled with silica (permineralized) while the cell walls are completely replaced.
- A **compression** forms when soft parts (leaves, animal tissue) are pressed into fine-grained sediment. Volatile substances escape, leaving a thin film of brown or black carbon. Plant remains such as ferns are commonly preserved this way.
- Fossils may be preserved as a **mold** or **cast** after sediment has surrounded or infiltrated the hard part, and subsequently lithified (hardened). An external mold is a hollow in the sediment that had lithified *around* the fossil hard part that later dissolved. If sediment has lithified *inside* the hard part—for example, the interior of a snail shell or a dinosaur skull—the result is an internal mold.
- Making a cast necessitates a more complicated series of events. First, a mold forms and the original hard part is destroyed. Then sediment fills the mold and lithifies to produce a cast. An external cast is a three-dimensional object that preserves information only about the exterior of the original mold. It is not a replacement (no internal details such as cell structure are preserved), nor is it the result of permineralization (none of the original material is preserved).

Trace fossils preserve, not some remnant of the organism but rather, signs of its activity. These fossils include footprints, tracks, trails, and burrows. *Gastroliths* are smooth pebbles swallowed by reptiles or dinosaurs to aid in digestion by grinding up food, for the same reason that chickens swallow gravel. *Coprolite* is dung fossilized by mineral replacement. When crocodile coprolites, which are very abundant, are cut and polished, they may show internal patterns similar to those in agate. A popular sale item in rock and mineral shows, polished corpolite proves that if anything sticks around long enough, it gets to be worth something.

BIAS IN THE FOSSIL RECORD

If an assortment of fossils is not fully representative of the once living community of organisms, the fossil record is said to be biased. **Preservation bias** results if some organisms (or parts thereof) are more readily fossilized than others. For example, soft tissue of an organism is more likely to decay or be eaten than are the hard parts. Fossils are more likely preserved in marine environments (where deposition is common) than in continental environments (where erosion prevails). Other biases of geologic origin include mixing of faunas of different geologic ages during transport and deposition, and deformation during metamorphism. **Collector's bias** can result if a paleontologist's objective is to collect only the most spectacular specimens for a museum display, or only the fossils of one group of organisms for specialized anatomical study.

THE GEOLOGIC TIME SCALE

The principles described above have been combined through application to develop the chronology of geologic events and organic succession as shown in Table 14-1. Many more facts are known than are detailed in the diagram, which is provincial to North America, and emphasizes familiar life forms. A simplified representation of a typical fossil is given for each period.

EXERCISES IN HISTORICAL GEOLOGY INTERPRETATION

The following exercises will draw upon your knowledge of elementary paleontology, rock origins, and the principles of stratigraphy. In geologic interpretation, try to keep in mind the basic meaning of the principle of *uniformitarianism*; that the present is the result of the past, and that geologic processes have remained essentially the same throughout geologic time. Continents and ocean basins may move about the face of the earth, but limestones still form primarily in two or three environments, and reverse faults are always the result of compressional forces. Drawings of representative fossils are included (Figures 14-2, 14-3, and 14-4) for comparison with laboratory specimens and for working out the stratigraphic range exercise.

Fossils and Geologic Time

- **Paleontology** - study of the geologic history of life
- **Fossil** - any evidence of past life
- **Body fossil** - the remains of a part of the organism
- **Trace fossil** - evidence of of an organism's behavior or activity
- **Conditions that promote fossilization**:
  1. low-energy environment of deposition
  2. fine-grained sediment
  3. rapid burial
  4. possession of hard parts

Linnean Classification System

- Plants and animals are grouped in hierarchical order according to their degrees of similarity

Kingdom --Animalia
Phylum-- Vertebrata
Class--Mammalia
Order --Primates
Family---Hominidae
Genus ---------------------------------------*Homo*
Species----------------------------------*Sapiens*
Individual organism--------------Dr. Long

Cladistics

- Clade: all the members of a group of related organisms extending back through geologic time to their earliest common ancestor
- Cladistics: a procedure based upon comparisons of numerous characteristics of living and fossil organisms to interpret the relationship of their lines of descent (clades) through time

Body Plans (symmetry)

- Spherical, radial: the organism is symmetrical around a central point. Examples: algal fruiting body, some types of coral
- Pentagonal: five-fold symmetry. Example: some echinoids
- Coiled:
  - coiling in vertical plane. Example: some gastropods
  - coiling in a horizontal plane. Example: some ammonites
- Bilateral • oyster, clam
  - bivalves: plane of symmetry passes between the valves, hence each valve is a mirror image of the other valve.
  - brachiopods: plane of symmetry passes through the center of each valve, hence one-half of each valve is the mirror image of the other half.

Types of Fossilization

- Fossilization *without* alteration – trapped in amber, frozen mammoth, mummification
- Fossilization *with* alteration
  - **Replacement:** atom-by-atom replacement (petrified wood)
  - **Permineralization:** minerals deposited in pores (fossilized bone)
  - **Compression:** carbon residue left behind from soft-part alteration
  - **Mold:** fossil surrounded by hardened sediment is dissolved, leaving a cavity in the shape of the original fossil
  - **Cast:** forms when the mold is filled with sediment (which then hardens)
- Trace fossils - include only *signs* of the organism's activity; examples include footprints, coprolite (fossilized dung; glauconite), and burrows.

Principles of Stratigraphy

1. **Superposition:** in an undisturbed sequence of strata (layers), younger strata overlie older strata (a law).
2. **Original horizontality**: sediments are initially deposited in horizontal strata (a principle generally observed).
3. **Cross-cutting relationships:** faults and igneous intrusions must be younger than the rocks they cut (a law).
4. **Faunal succession:** there is a regular, definite progression of fossil forms in going from lower (older) to higher (younger) strata. This fossil succession is unique, and cannot be repeated in the same manner during another episode of geologic time (principle).

Index Fossils, Bias in the Fossil Record

- Index fossils are:
  - abundant
  - geographically wide-ranging
  - readily preserved
  - identifiable with a specific interval of geologic time
    - useful in estimating relative ages of rock bearing fossils
    - helpful in correlating rocks bearing similar fossils
- Bias introduced into the rock record:
  - preservation bias
  - collector's bias

Geologic Time Scale

- Divided into Archean and Proterozoic (both Precambrian), and Phanerozoic **eons**
- Phanerozoic divided into 3 major **eras**:
  - Cenozoic (most recent)
  - Mesozoic
  - Paleozoic (most ancient)
- Eras divided into geologic **periods**

Major Geologic Events
(younger to older)

- Pleistocene: Ice Ages
- End of Cretaceous (K): extinction of non-bird dinosaurs
- End of Permian (Pm): largest of all mass extinctions (trilobites go extinct)
- Silurian: plants move to land
- Cambrian: all major animal phyla represented

15

A Bestiary of Vertebrates

"Very well then, hands up all those who propose to become birds."
[©PUNCH, *LONDON*]

During the Middle Ages, when explanations of natural phenomena scarcely resembled what we call scientific, the bestiary was a favorite literary device. A bestiary, or book of beasts, is a collection of fables in which the habits of animals are used to teach moral values (Figure 15-1). We use phrases such as "eager beaver," "stupid ass," "slothfulness," etc. to describe human behavior by referring to some other animal. This chapter, although not about moral principles, is like an old-time bestiary, containing stories that serve as illustrations of vertebrate evolution. As these wonderful creatures, which are the animals with backbones, march or swim or fly across the pages of geologic history, they illuminate the principles of organic evolution discussed in previous chapters.

Vertebrate fossils have been a favorite subject for many of us (yes, we are vertebrates too) ever since we were children in primary school. Finds of spectacular vertebrate fossils often make international news. There is nothing like the discovery of some weird extinct animal to excite our imaginations about what things were like in ancient times (Figure 15-2). It is unfortunate that generally the only fossil material that is preserved consists of permineralized bones and teeth. Only rarely is a fossil compression (carbonized film) discovered of an entire body outline, possibly with indications of soft internal organs. Even so, study of the bone itself provides valuable information about soft parts. Bone contains attachment points for muscles, and it is laced with openings that once accommodated nerves or blood vessels.

We postulate that the vertebrates, and indeed all life, originated by evolution. All organisms are related through common ancestry, however remote may be the degree of similarity or time of origin. If the evolutionary postulate is correct, then we can test it by making certain predictions. These are not predictions of the future, for no one knows the future, and even if we thought we did, our lives are too short to witness the outcome of any process that moves at the slow pace of geologic time. No—these are predictions projected back into the past, which is the peculiar style of geology, a historical science. A worthy geologic theory must be capable of being validated, not only by real-time experiments in the laboratory but even more by hindsight (the fossil record) and by comparisons of degrees of similarity among living vertebrates.

For example, consider the role of time in evolution. During much of the inconceivably long Precambrian episode, a typical living organism was tiny and single-celled. Vertebrate animals go back only to the early Paleozoic fossil record, originating about 500 million years ago, after nearly 90% of geologic

Figure 15-1. People in the fifteenth century were also concerned with the origin of vertebrates. One famous bestiary explained the annual appearance of migratory geese that were never observed to mate (their Arctic breeding grounds were then unknown) in this way: The goose embryos matured within the shell-like fruit of a certain tree growing near the seashore. In another version, the embryos grew like barnacles on floating logs. Somehow the two themes were later merged into the Barnacle Goose Tree. [*After J. D. Bernal*, The Origin of Life, *The World Publishing Company, Cleveland, 1967.*]

a

b

c

Figure 15-2. (*a*) An unusually complete specimen of *Dimetrodon*, a grotesque reptile with a huge, spiny "sail" on its back, was discovered in Texas. [*Courtesy A. S. Romer.*] (*b*) Still embedded in sedimentary matrix, a similar specimen was swathed in protective burlap and plaster for the trip to the preparation lab at the museum. (*c*) The reassembled skeleton is displayed in a lifelike position. Missing parts are "dubbed in" by reference to bones that are preserved on the animal's symmetrical other side, and by careful study of comparative anatomy and the general form of the animal. [*From A. S. Romer*, Man and the Vertebrates, *University of Chicago Press, Chicago, 1941.*]

time had already gone by. Vertebrates were among the last of the major groups in the animal kingdom to appear. And so our first prediction is that because the Precambrian time interval was longer, the greatest diversity of life should have evolved during the Precambrian. Biological evidence supports this prediction, for diversity is profound among prokaryotes and single-celled eukaryotes (Chapter 12), organisms of great antiquity, compared to diversity among living or fossil vertebrates. Surprising though it may be, the different body plans of vertebrate animals are comparatively minor variations on a central theme.

Secondly, we anticipate that relatively simple vertebrates should have originated before those that are more complex. Recall that evolution is defined as descent with modification, the implication being that the simpler structure is the ancestral one. An example would be the evolution of the bodies of fish, the original vertebrates. Earliest fish had no internal hard skeleton, no jaws, no teeth, only the most rudimentary brain, and no paired fins that serve as control surfaces for agile maneuvering. Only later did these standard fish structures appear. Even when evolution proceeds in the opposite direction, as it occasionally does, the progression that led up to the point of simplification was from simpler to more complex, and it is a *structure* that is simplified, not a *function* that is lost.

Evolution of the vertebrate lower jaw illustrates one of the more complicated trends. The earliest fish lacked jaws, then fish with jaws appeared and all the later groups—amphibians, followed by reptiles, followed by mammals—have jaws. Lower jaws of early vertebrates consisted of a number of bones fused together, whereas the lower jaw of a mammal contains but a single bone that nevertheless works just as effectively as the jaw with many bones. In fact, not even all of the original bones were lost. During the transition from reptiles to mammals, four reptilian jaw bones migrated into a new position and function in the skull where they transformed into delicate bones of the mammalian middle ear.

From time to time, evolutionary development opens the possibility to colonize a new environment (while previous environments continue to be occupied, of course). Our third prediction is that not only the vertebrate organism itself but the diversity of the entire community should become more complex through geologic time. This prediction too is supported by the fossil record, since the earliest vertebrates were exclusively water dwellers, later to be joined by animals that inhabit both land and water but which always stay close to the water, and finally vertebrates appeared that can live virtually anywhere on the land. In accord with the watery origin of life itself, the fossil record of *in*vertebrate phyla also displays a water-to-land pattern.

Why was water the earliest habitable environment? It is true that there is more oxygen in air than dissolved in water, and it is easier to see through air which is highly transparent, but these advantages of the land environment were relatively minor. Think how intensely hostile the land must have been 500 million years ago. In the absence of vascular plants, there was nothing there to eat except bacteria, algae, and perhaps mosses. There were not even any insects until the Paleozoic Era was well underway. Meanwhile, the fossils of the Burgess Shale (Chapter 13) show that the water environment already contained an ecologically balanced, rich diversity of invertebrate animals by the middle of the Cambrian Period, the first period of the Paleozoic Era. Organisms that evolved into vertebrates lived in the water environment, and so naturally the vertebrates themselves originated there.

Even today, living on the land surface presents a formidable challenge. There is no overhead layer of water to shield against the sun's fierce ultraviolet radiation. Land animals, or their eggs or their young, are subject to drying out or dying of thirst. Buoyancy can support a water animal of an unrestricted large body size as seen, for example, in certain giant species of whale. A land animal must use its own sturdy bones and muscles as support against the force of gravity, and all the more so if the animal flies. It is more difficult to cope with changes of temperature on land, which tend to vary between greater extremes than in the water. According to the fossil record, a sequence of great milestone developments had to occur before animals could move out of the watery abode and up onto land.

BEASTS WITH BACKBONES

What do vertebrates have in common? As the name implies, the animal has a segmented backbone running down its long axis. It has a head and (typically) a tail, and its skeleton is bilaterally symmetrical with ribs and paired appendages that might be fins, flippers, arms, legs, or wings (Figure 15-3). During the embryonic stage the backbone develops from a flexible, rod-like structure called a *notochord.* In a few organisms such as the tunicate, or sea squirt, an embryonic notochord is present that does not eventually become a backbone. For this reason the vertebrate animals are classified into subphylum Vertebrata, the largest group within a more inclusive phylum, Chordata.

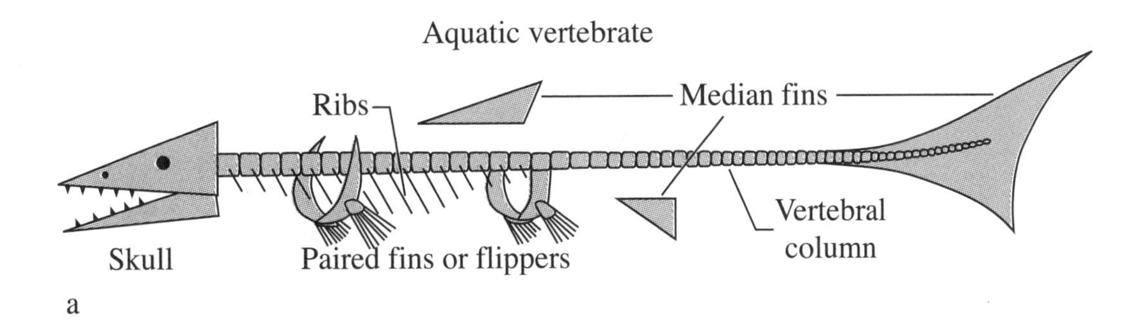

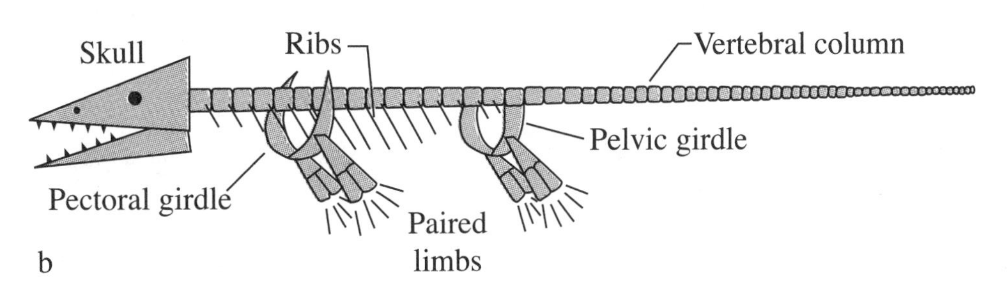

Figure 15-3. (*a*) Aquatic vertebrates typically have median (centrally located) fins, and paired fins or flippers. (*b*) Land-living vertebrates have shed the median fins, but kept the appendages that correspond to paired fins in their aquatic relatives. [*After E. H. Colbert and M. Morales,* Evolution of the Vertebrates, *4th ed. Copyright © 1991. By permission of John Wiley & Sons, Inc., New York.*]

All vertebrates have well-developed nervous systems including at least a primitive brain. Nostrils, eyes, and ears clustered together in the skull serve as a guidance system; these active animals are "always going somewhere." Vertebrate animals are quite exceptional in possessing such elaborate sensory and navigational apparatus. Blood circulates through a network whose plan is basically similar in each organism. All vertebrates are covered by naked skin or by secondary structures such as scales, hair, or feathers that grow out of the skin. All possess gills or gill-like structures which the aquatic vertebrates use for exchange of oxygen and carbon dioxide between their bodies and the water medium. In land vertebrates, the gill structure is present only during a period of development of the embryo. Vertebrate embryos are so similar that it is difficult to distinguish a fish from a bird or mammal during the early stages (Figure 15-4).

It is no great matter to transform one vertebrate skeletal form into another. Long ago the biologist D'Arcy Thompson pointed out that if a square grid pattern is laid, for example, over the outline of a human skull, a bit of coordinated squashing or stretching can change the pattern into the shape of a chimpanzee or dog skull (Figure 15-5). This could be accomplished by mutations of the genes that control the relative growth rate of different parts of the skeleton. In contrast, body forms of other animal phyla are more fundamentally different. No amount of stretching or squeezing can make the body plan of an insect (arthropod) or cuttlefish (mollusk) correspond to that of a vertebrate animal.

Classification of the vertebrates raises some sticky problems about their origins. In the traditional hierarchy devised by Linné (Chapter 12), a phylum, which is a very broad category, includes smaller divisions that contain yet smaller ones, and so on down to the level of a single species. Although this classification is compatible with ideas of evolution, it does not of itself show the evolutionary connections. For example, living reptiles are cold-blooded, whereas birds and mammals are warm-blooded, which suggests that birds and mammals could have had a common origin. On the other hand, birds have feathers but mammals have hair; birds lay eggs but only the monotreme mammals (platypus and echidna) lay eggs. Most mammals have teeth, but no modern bird does. Most birds can fly, but so can bats, which are mammals. After considering a long list of similarities and differences, we conclude that it is indeed

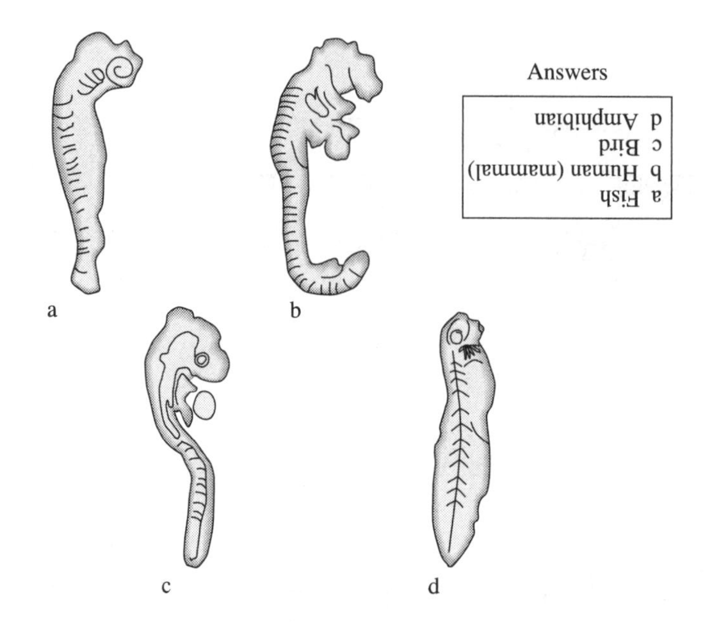

Figure 15-4. Vertebrate embryos are look-alikes. Which embryo is destined to become a fish? A frog? A fowl? A furry animal? Turn the book upside down.

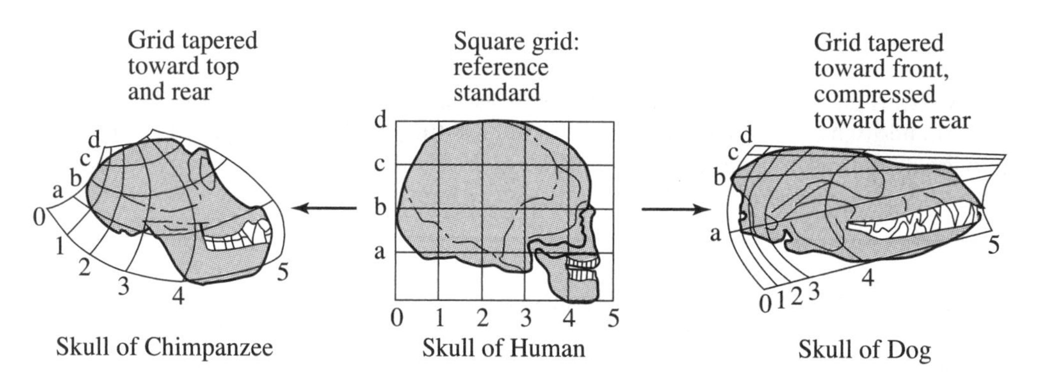

Figure 15-5. A human skull overlain by a square reference grid (center) transforms into the skull of a chimpanzee (left) or dog (right) by a systematic distortion of the grid. The shape of a human skull more resembles that of the chimpanzee, and all the elements correspond, bone for bone and tooth for tooth. A few of the dog's teeth and head bones do not correspond to those of a human. [*After D'Arcy W. Thompson*, Growth and Form, *Cambridge University Press, New York, 1942.*]

legitimate to distinguish birds from mammals, but this still does not establish whether birds came from mammals, or the other way around, or perhaps reptiles, birds, and mammals all came from a common ancestor. Fossil evidence helps to trace that thread of connection through geologic time.

Figure 15-6(*a*), known as a "bubble diagram," depicts the geologic history of subphylum Vertebrata which is subdivided into eight smaller categories (classes). It may come as a surprise that various kinds of fish comprise four of the classes (some authorities propose even five fish classes). Actually, the differences among diverse groups of fish are greater than the differences between a frog and a human being! In the fossil record are some early fish that are so bizarre by modern standards that it is not certain how they originated or what their living descendants could be, if there are any. The width of each bubble in the diagram is an attempt to picture the number of species (*not* the number of individuals) living at any moment in time, from vertebrate origins in the Cambrian Period until the present day. Of course, the fossil record is so incomplete that many estimates of numbers of species may be more like educated guesstimates. In spite of these deficiencies, we have enough data to show that during most of the Paleozoic Era, fish and amphibians predominated at the top of the food chain, and that during the Mesozoic Era the reptiles, not the mammals, held this type of domination. We mammals like to think of today as the Age of

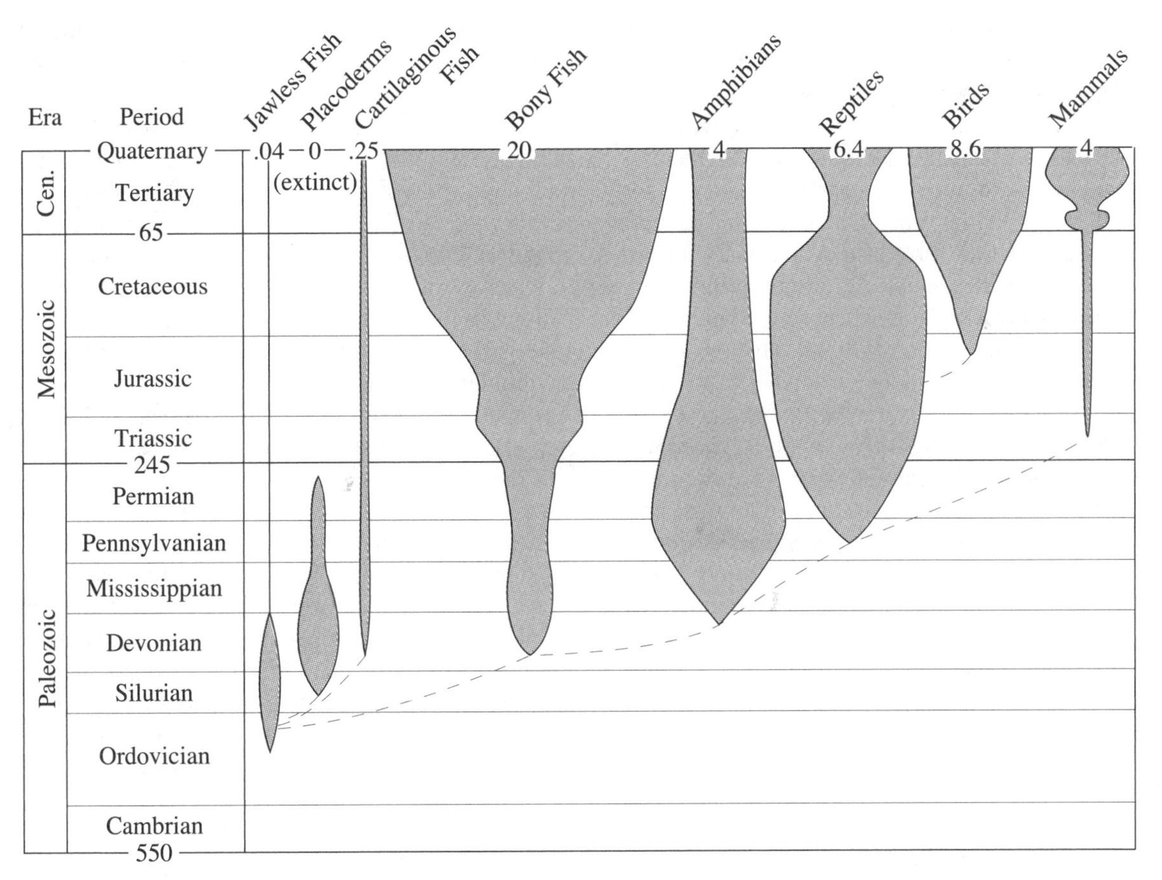

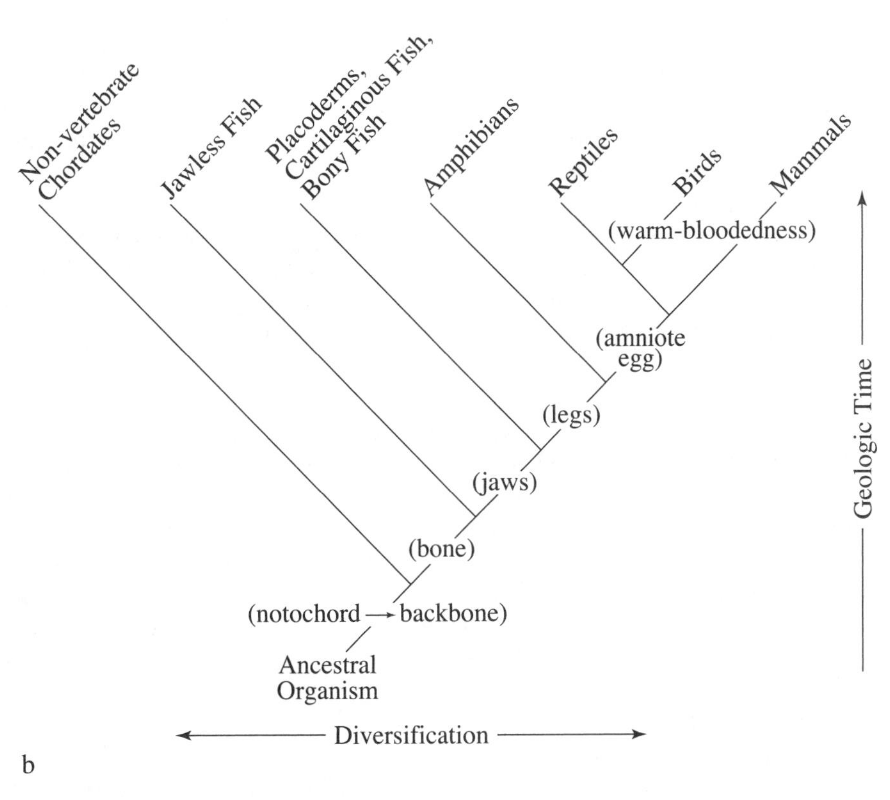

Figure 15-6. (*a*) A bubble diagram depicts how the classes of vertebrate animals have fared through geologic time. The width of each bubble corresponds to an estimated number of species, and at the top is stated the number of species living today (in thousands). (*b*) A cladogram indicates the relationships of the vertebrate lineage, and significant "milestones" of evolution along the way.

Mammals, but the diagram shows that the number of mammal species has actually diminished in the latter part of the Cenozoic Era, whereas the number of species of bony fish has steadily increased. Clearly, today is the Age of Bony Fish.

Let's review some ideas about evolution that are displayed in the tree of life (Figures 12-14 and 13-21). These diagrams show that with the passage of time, a single ancestral species of a vertebrate animal may split into different descendant species. Certain ones of its *primitive characteristics*, such as the bilaterally symmetrical skeleton with a backbone, are inherited by all of the descendants. As new groups branch off, they introduce evolutionary novelties, or *derived characteristics*, for example various types of skin covering (scales, feathers, fur). The common ancestor and all of its descendants together comprise a *clade*. In the grandest sense, you and I and all other living things belong to the prokaryote clade. This very odd statement that ties us to bacteria and blue-green algae emphasizes the oneness of life, but more to the point, there are smaller clades included within larger.

One of these is the vertebrate clade with its own smaller branches. A clade classification is rather like the Linnéan nesting of phyla, classes, orders, etc., except that clades explicitly connect the line of descent through geologic time. According to the fossil record, tetrapods (four-legged animals) evolved from fish, and so all of the land vertebrates are members of the fish clade. Figure 15-6(*b*) summarizes the relationships by means of a *cladogram* which resembles the tree of life though somewhat less artistic. In words, the cladogram states that certain fish gave rise to tetrapods, certain of the tetrapod clade evolved to become amphibians or amniotes (referring to an egg with complex internal structure), and certain members of the amniote clade were ancestral to birds, and others became mammals. Birds and mammals are not sister clades, however. The diagram shows that birds and other reptiles are closely related groups, whereas mammals are more distant. Mammals, birds, crocodiles, turtles, lizards, and snakes survive today, but some other large clades have become extinct. Many paleontologists consider that the dinosaurs also were not conventional reptiles, but a distinctly separate clade closely akin to the birds.

PARADE OF VERTEBRATES

With all of this as a preamble, let's examine the magnificent geologic history of vertebrate animals. What animal phylum is most closely related to the Phylum Chordata? That is a difficult question because a vast gulf of dissimilarity separates the various phyla. Backbones, and many of the vertebrate muscles are segmented, and so are the bodies of annelid worms, and members of the arthropod phylum which includes insects, lobsters, and trilobites. But here the similarity ceases, as the digestive, nervous, and circulatory systems of chordates, annelids, and arthropods are radically different. Comparisons of biochemistry and embryo development suggest that chordates are allied most closely to echinoderms whose living members include the sea urchin and starfish. Whatever the chordate ancestry may have been, the origin of the clade is lost in obscurity, long before animals began to manufacture readily fossilized hard parts. A certain soft-bodied organism fossilized in the Burgess Shale looks intriguingly like a chordate, and its Middle Cambrian age predates that of the oldest known fish skeletons.

Jawless Vertebrates

The first vertebrates were small creatures, rarely more than a few centimeters long. Essentially they were mobilized gill baskets, lacking jaws, and propelled by a muscular tail with awkward tadpole-like motions. Unlike most modern fish, these animals were obliged to use their gills both for breathing and feeding. A common life style was to grovel through the mud, sucking it up through a vacuum-cleaner mouth and passing it back to the gill structure which filtered out particles of food (Figure 15-7). Early jawless fish introduced a major milestone of vertebrate evolution, the development of a *bony skeleton*. Many species were adorned with a massive head shield in which bony scales butted against one another as in a brick pavement, or overlapped like roof shingles. Exterior armor plating, which was to be a common theme in later vertebrates, was all the bone that the early jawless fish had. An internal skeleton, if present, must have been made of soft cartilage that does not fossilize.

Why bone? Perhaps the highly active life style of most vertebrates was aided by the existence of bone. This complex material contains crystals of calcium phosphate knit together by tough fibers of collagen. When an animal puts out an occasional great burst of energy, the levels of both calcium and phosphate in the blood quickly change. Early in vertebrate evolution, bone may have served as a storehouse of chemicals from which the animal could borrow in times of urgent high physical demand, and restore during times of resting. Only later did the excellent rigid internal support provided by bone become important.

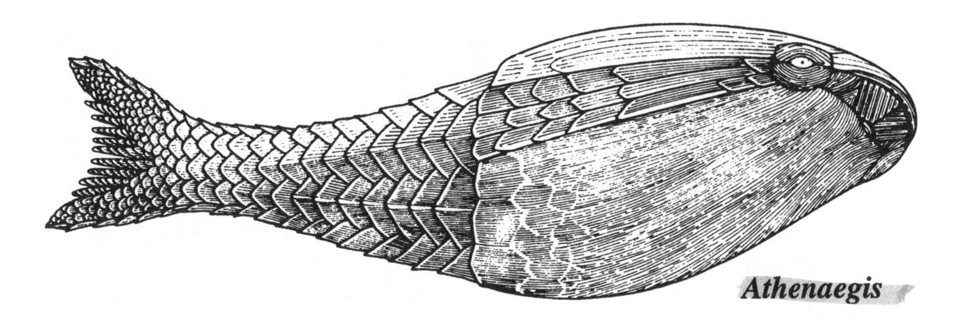

Figure 15-7. Primitive jawless vertebrates differed from familiar modern fish in several important ways. The head of this 2-inch-long animal is covered by a shield, behind which a somewhat flexible body is sheathed by scales that overlap like shingles. Its jawless, toothless mouth surrounded by bony plates could be used to scoop, nibble, or scrape. No well-defined pairs of fins protrude from the sides of the body. [*After K. L. Soehn and M. V. H. Wilson, "A Complete, Articulated Heterostracan from Wenlockian (Silurian) beds of the Delorme Group, Mackenzie Mountains, Northwest Territories, Canada,"* Journal of Vertebrate Paleontology, *vol. 10, no. 4, p. 415 (1990).*]

Jawless vertebrates became highly diversified by Devonian times, then went into eclipse when more "advanced" fish took possession of their niches and habitats. It is unfortunate that the fossil record of the fascinating, largely soft-bodied, jawless fish is so poor. Today the only survivors of the lineage are the lamprey and the hagfish which occupy a forlorn niche as scavengers and parasites in the underwater world.

Jawed Fish

Our next great milestone, which took place in the Devonian Period after at least 60 million years of vertebrate evolution, was an explosive radiation of fish that possessed paired appendages and *jaws* [Figure 15-6(*b*)]. And what a difference jaws made, for with them came the first carnivorous vertebrates able to hang on to squirming, uncooperative prey. Jaws may have developed initially to serve another function, however. Fossil evidence is incomplete, but supplemental information from the anatomy and embryonic development of modern fish suggests a plausible scenario for the origin of jaws. We begin with the support arches in the gills of fish, a primitive structure consisting of V-shape bony or cartilaginous strips arranged like so: (rear body)<<<<(head). Inspection of a modern salmon or trout impresses one that a fish jaw looks rather like a modified gill arch. If a gill arch of a jawless vertebrate [Figure 15-8(*a*)] were to be uncoupled at its center point, the two sides of the "V," now hinged, could function as a rudimentary jaw (*b*), whose function is further improved as an additional gill arch is propped against the hinge point to buttress it (*c*). By this simple modification a fish could flex its jaws, pumping water forcibly through the gills and speeding up gas exchange. Many modern fish "supercharge" the oxygen level in the blood stream in just this manner. Of course, jaws are used for a multitude of other purposes ranging from catching prey to delivering a lecture about geology. Jaws and teeth are specialized for probing, pecking, shearing, grinding, crushing, sucking, gnawing, nipping, to name only a few things that vertebrates do. No wonder that so many shapes and sizes, structures of joints, and muscle attachments have evolved, as we shall see.

Placoderms, the earliest of the jawed fish to appear, have been described as "a series of wildly impossible types which do not fit any proper pattern." Placoderms had no teeth, but the sharp edges of

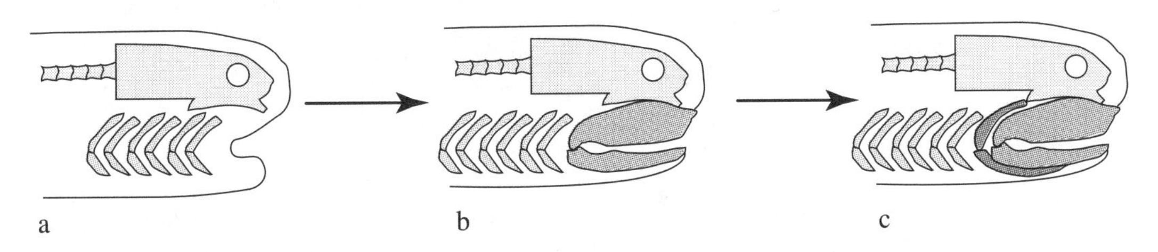

Figure 15-8. Fossils that exhibit suggested stages (*a*) and (*c*) in the evolutionary development of jaws are well known, but stage (*b*) is rather conjectural, currently based only upon indirect evidence.

the jaws of some of them were vicious slicing surfaces (Figure 15-9). Many species had flattened bodies, suggesting that they were dwellers on the sea floor. There were predatory forms that grew a set of stiff, rather immovable spines, perhaps to discourage even fiercer predators from attempting to swallow *them*. The heavily armored placoderms disappeared without descendants, and since there are no modern armor-plated fish to serve as an example, we find it difficult to imagine how the placoderms or the armored jawless fish must have lived.

In the competition for survival, placoderms went extinct but their contemporaries, the *cartilaginous fish,* flourish today. Skeletons of sharks, skates, and rays (Figure 15-10) are composed of cartilage, the springy material that gives shape to a person's nose and external ear. It is no surprise that the fossil record of cartilaginous fish is poor except for fossil teeth which are composed of very hard material indeed. Sharks and their cartilaginous kindred have occupied marine waters for hundreds of millions of years with relatively little change. Modern sharks deserve to be called "living fossils," so similar is their form to that of Mesozoic sharks, and even to their earliest ancestors of Paleozoic age.

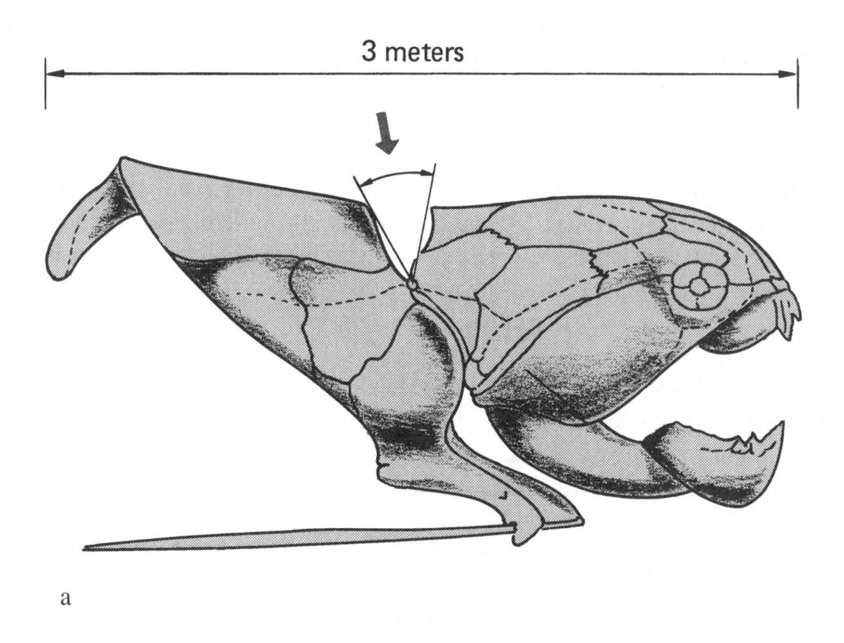

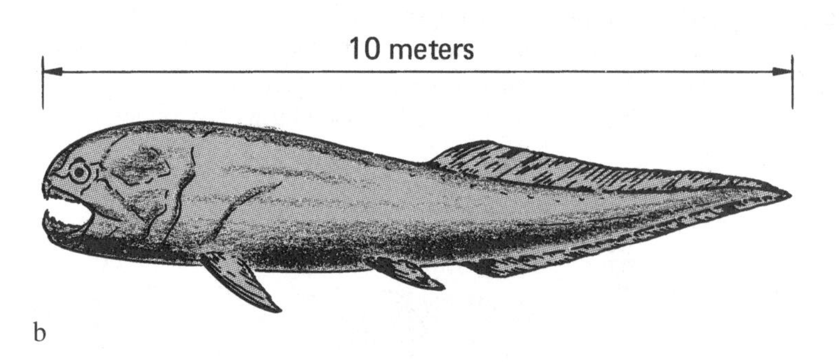

Figure 15-9. (*a*) Jaws of this placoderm fish, the first giant vertebrate, were armed with awesome cutting edges (not teeth). A hinged joint (arrow) permitted the skull to tilt up as the lower jaw tilted down. What sort of prey would have necessitated such an enormous gape? (*b*) Shown in its entirety, the fish grew as much as 10 meters long.

If the conservative cartilaginous fish survived by maintaining a small number of species that never varied much, the *bony fish* have succeeded in the opposite manner. They have continued to diversify by evolutionary radiation into every sort of underwater niche and habitat. Somehow the bony fish have managed to avoid the great mass extinctions that later were to wipe out so many of the tetrapod species from time to time.

Early bony fish, though not encapsulated in rigid armor, were covered by row upon overlapping row of thick scales surfaced by a shiny enamel. As the millions of years went by, the bony fish evolved thinner and more flexible scales, thus trading the safety of a tough coating for the security to be gained by agile maneuverability (Figure 15-11). Most importantly, as their name implies, these fish grew an ossified (bony) internal skeleton. The braincase became a complicated assortment of bones representing ossified cartilage, united with bones borrowed from the ancestral armor plate. Vertebrae developed as simple "spools" enclosing the notochord. Other bones—hundreds of them—took shape, as anyone who eats fish knows.

From water onto the land To continue our story of the vertebrates, we now focus on a finny character that would have seemed inconsequential when bony fishes first came to prominence in mid-Paleozoic times. In the structure of *ray-finned* fishes, a fan-shaped arrangement of thin bones (fin rays) is attached directly to the body wall [Figure 15-12(*a*)]. Ray-finned fish are by far the dominant sort, comprising more than 99.9% of modern species, and with regard to evolution, the ray-fins have done very well by just being conventional fish that stay in the water.

Before vertebrates could invade dry land, many conditions had to be fulfilled to make survival there possible. No land vertebrate lives in isolation; it can avoid extinction only by having assured sources of food and water, success of reproduction, and ability to breathe the air, move about on the surface, see and hear keenly, etc. In the mid-Paleozoic Era, the region of Europe and Greenland had been prepared for

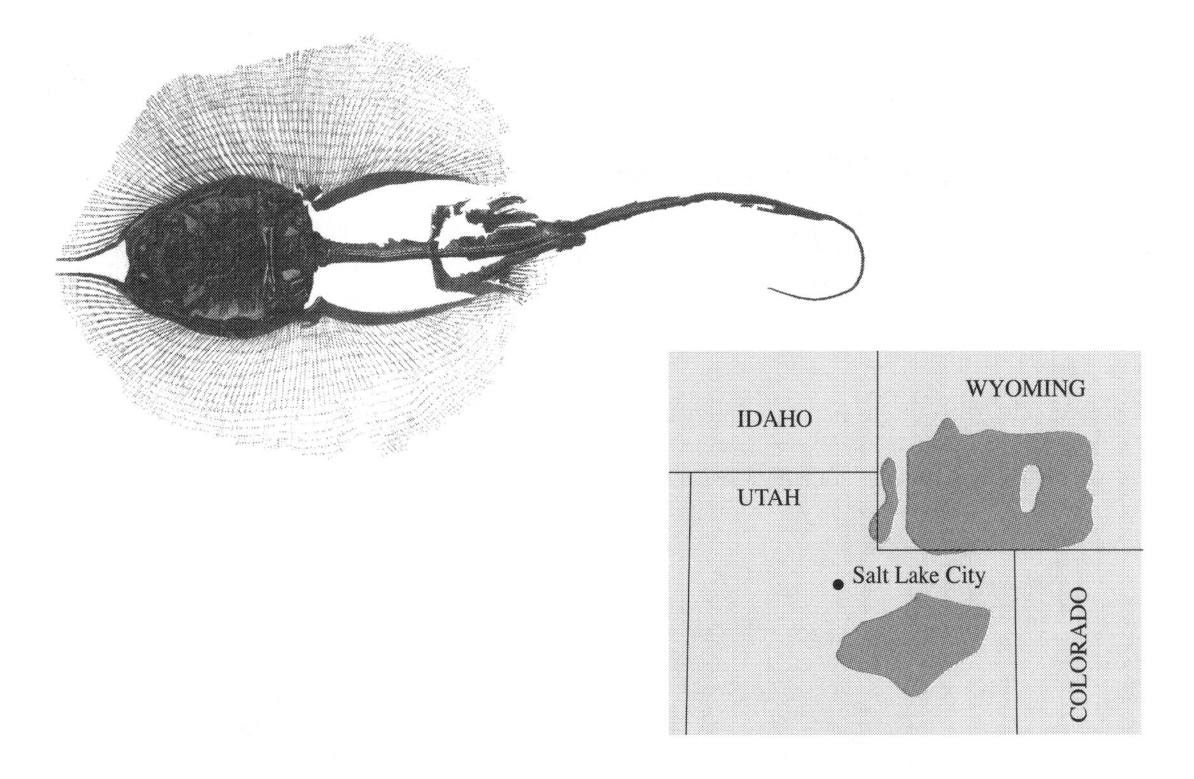

Figure 15-10. Because the soft cartilage of a shark or ray quickly rots, a completely preserved fossil skeleton is one of the rarest of finds. This specimen of a ray comes from lake sediment. During the Eocene Epoch, a group of freshwater lakes in Wyoming and Utah (inset map) supported a balanced fauna and flora. Certain bedding planes contain numerous fish of all kinds, ages, and sizes, evidently killed catastrophically. By counting fossils in the mass-death communities, paleontologists have established that herbivorous fish greatly outnumbered the carnivorous fish, just as expected. [*American Museum of Natural History photograph.*]

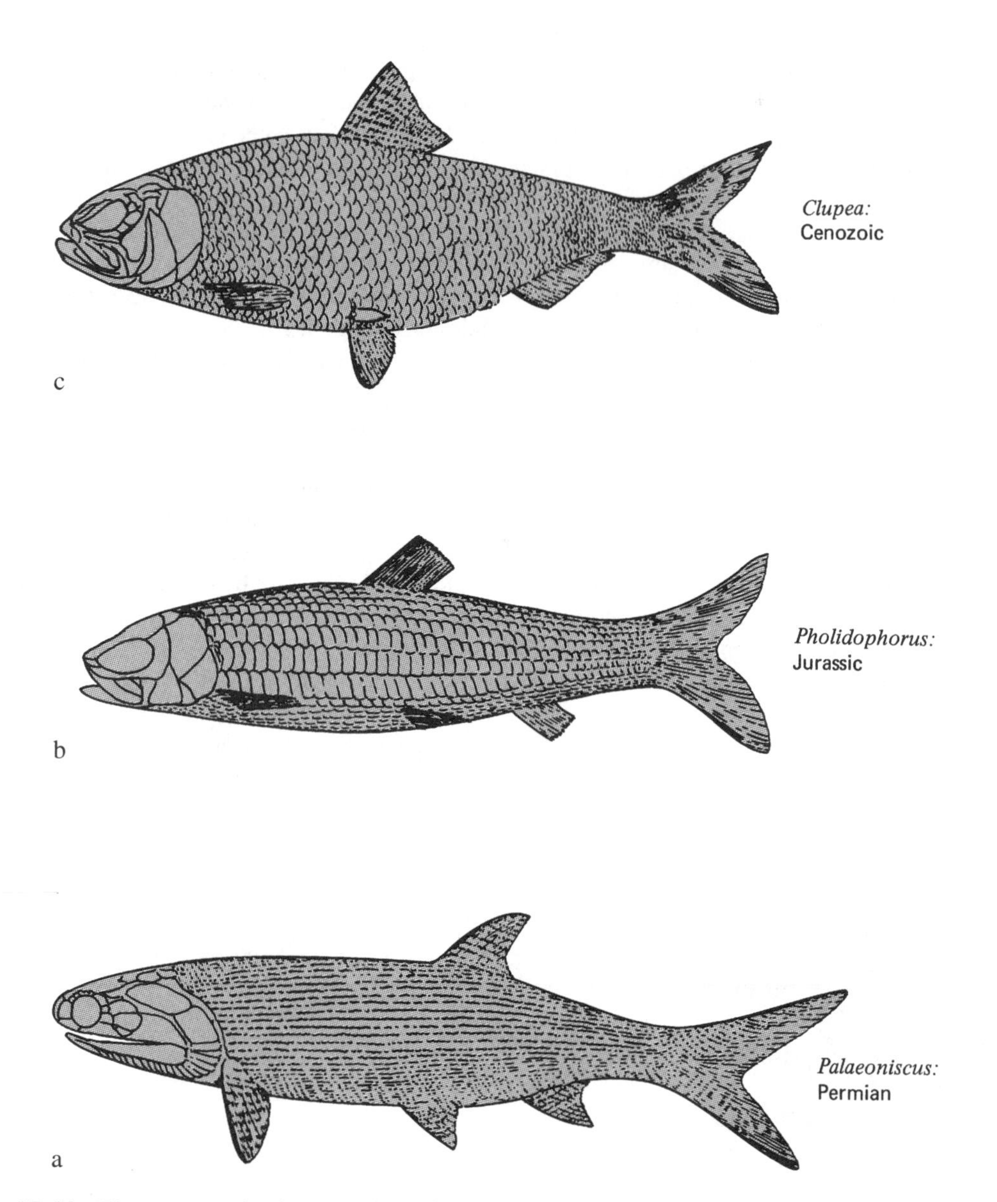

Figure 15-11. Three stages in the evolution of bony fish show that with time, the scales became thinner and more rounded, the tail became more symmetrical, and the shape of the skull was modified extensively. Only a handful of modern fish species survive as living fossils representing types (*a*) and (*b*). [*After E. H. Colbert and M. Morales*, Evolution of the Vertebrates, *4th ed. Copyright © 1991. By permission of John Wiley & Sons, Inc., New York.*]

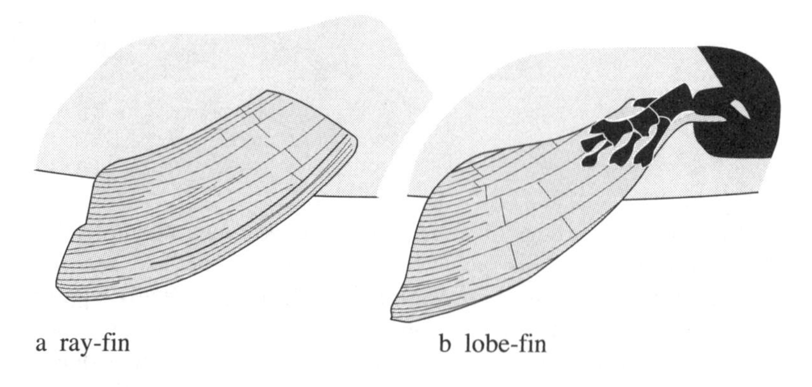

Figure 15-12. (*a*) Ray-fins connect directly to the body wall of a fish, whereas (*b*) lobe-fins include a fleshy appendage containing sturdy bones (black).

land vertebrates. A later chapter describes the evidence that continental land masses rift and drift, sometimes colliding, and in doing so the geography of the earth continually changes. In fact, in the late Devonian Period northern Europe was joined to Greenland (there was no Atlantic Ocean) and both were situated near the Equator. A major mountain range was being eroded, its sediment shed into a vast delta complex of streams, freshwater lakes, and swamps. Primitive land plants had appeared and had already diversified into understory and treetop-canopy ecosystems. Arthropods and worms sucked plant juices or fed on rotting vegetation, or they ate one another. It was an arthropod's paradise as never before or since, in which spectacular giant scorpions, cockroaches with a 2-foot wingspan, and millipedes up to 6 feet long flourished.

In this setting lived another group of fish that were contemporaries to the early ray-finned fishes. They were the *lobe-finned* fishes, of which only four species are still living today, in the Southern Hemisphere. Fin rays in these fish project out of a muscular stump, or lobe containing stout internal bones, that in turn connects to the body proper [Figure 15-12(*b*)]. Lobe-finned fish qualify as living fossils even better than sharks do. Perhaps a modern lobe-fin, the lungfish, can furnish insight into the life habits of its Devonian ancestors. Lungfish inhabit streams in the harsh tropics, and when summer drought parches the land the lungfish burrows into the mud, there to subside into a state of torpor until revived by the next rainy season. We know from fossil burrows containing lobe-finned fish that they have lived in this manner for at least 300 million years. Both the modern lungfish and the Devonian lobe-fins, called *Crossopterygians* (Figure 15-13), could breathe using gills just as any other fish does, but when necessary they could use a lung. (The swim bladder is a modified lung in many fish.) Crossopterygians were transitional, being true fish but also able to gulp the air, or live for long periods completely out of contact with water. They were to be the forebears of our next class of vertebrates, the amphibians.

Tetrapods

One of the early changes in the next milestone of vertebrate evolution was apparent in an odd animal that occupied a halfway position between fish and tetrapods (Figure 15-14). It was covered by scales and its teeth had peculiarly infolded enamel, like those of its fish ancestors. Adult individuals still retained gills and an unmistakable fish-like shape, apparent especially in the finny tail. But the animal, *Ichthyostega*, also crawled about on four feet. The transition from fish to true land animals was not a simple process, nor quickly achieved because of the major problem of self-support out of water. Lobe-fin bones of a crossopterygian could "float" unconnected to other bones (Figure 15-13), but it will not do for the skeleton of a large land animal to be so flimsy. Its body must be supported off the ground to give the lungs

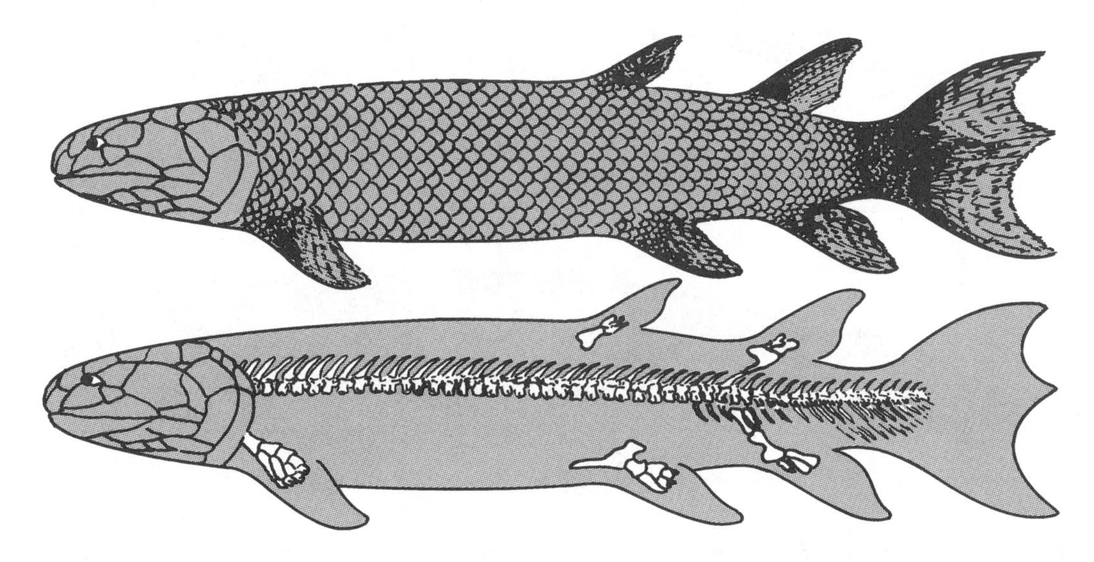

Figure 15-13. Lobe-fins were located not just on the underside of a Devonian crossopterygian fish but also on its back. Only the paired fins underneath were to be modified by later evolutionary development. [*After I. I. Schmalhausen*, The Origin of Terrestrial Vertebrates, *Academic Press, Inc., New York, 1968.*]

space to breathe, and so that it can walk. Leg bones of *Ichthyostega* were connected to the spine via stout shoulder and pelvic girdles (Figure 15-14).

Sensory organs had to be adapted to the rarefied air medium. Fish do not require sound amplification, as roughly 10 percent of the energy penetrates through the skull, but a skull in the air directly transmits only a negligible fraction of sound energy. The fossil record shows that a marvelous adaptation of the vertebrate ear commenced with the amphibians. Recall that in the evolution of the jaw of fishes, a bone is propped against the braincase at the jaw hinge [Figure 15-8(*c*)]. This prop had begun as a gill arch, then it became part of the jaw, and now it would be changed again just slightly and pressed into its *third* form of service as a conductor of sound. One end of the bone penetrated directly into the inner ear cavity, while the other end extended through a notch in the skull to touch a primitive "eardrum" consisting of stretched skin.

Considering that amphibians commonly live in swamps, one would expect to find a richly preserved fossil record. In fact it is disappointingly sparse, likely because acid waters in a swamp tend to dissolve bony material. None of the earliest amphibians resembled the familiar frogs, newts, and salamanders which appeared only much later. Long eel-like or snake-like species with tiny legs were aquatic; other species were terrestrial, built to catch insects on the forest floor. Although the amphibians and early reptiles were air-breathing tetrapods, their legs sprawled out of the sides of the body as the ancestral lobe fin had done. As they ran, their bodies whipped rapidly from side to side in a fish-like motion, each step compressing the left lung, then the right, rendering both lungs unable to function as long as running continued (Figure 15-15). It is for the same reason that lizards, which are modern reptiles, are obliged to make short dashes with frequent stops to catch a breath.

With further evolution toward the amniote condition, the number of bones in the skull was reduced (Figure 15-16), its shape became more narrow and deep, and the rowing motion of the limbs was modified toward a more efficient, downward and straight ahead, walking motion. Evolution was so gradual that it is quite arbitrary whether to regard the skeleton of some of these transitional creatures as amphibian or reptilian.

Amniotes

During these Mississippian and Pennsylvanian times [see Figure 15-6(*a*)], much of the "land" was also transitional, consisting of vast swamps. Ecological relationships were highly unbalanced from today's

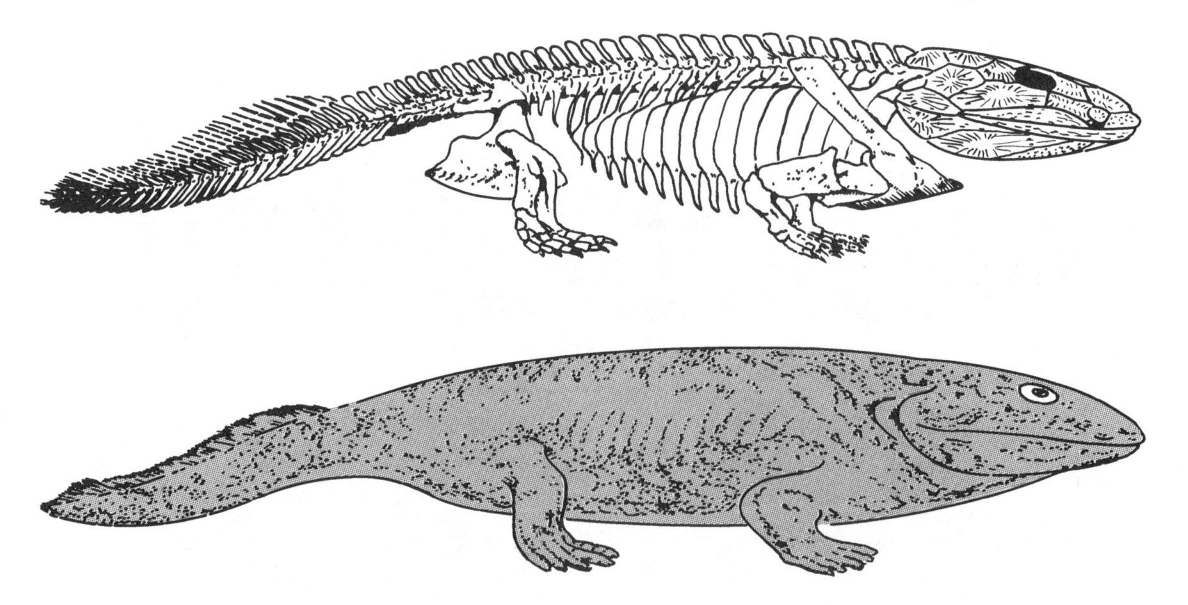

Figure 15-14. *Ichthyostega,* a primitive Late Devonian amphibian, has with equal justification been called a "four-footed fish." The animal probably walked on the underwater bottom much as a modern frogfish does, and it is doubtful that the limbs of *Ichthyostega* could support its body out of water for long. Millions of years were to pass before full-fledged land animals appeared in the fossil record. [*After E. Jarvik, "Ichthyostegalia,"* Traité de Paléontologie, *Tome V. Masson & Cie, Paris, 1955.*]

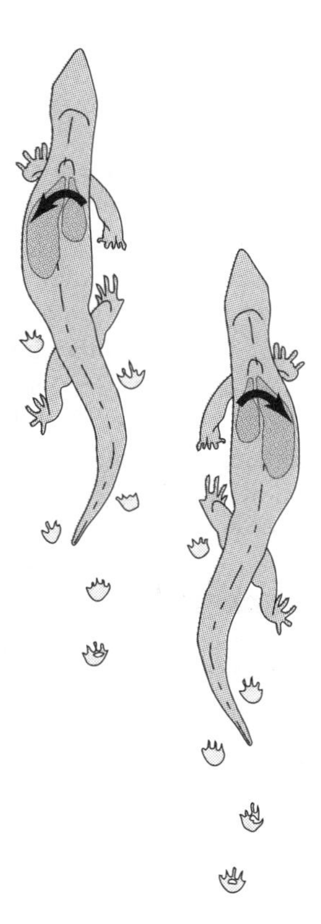

Figure 15-15. While a primitive vertebrate was walking or running, air in its lungs (shaded) would be squashed from side to side, but not in and out. Inability to breathe while walking would greatly reduce the animal's stamina. Fast swimming actually improved the stamina of its fishy ancestors by forcing water through the gills with a ram-jet effect.

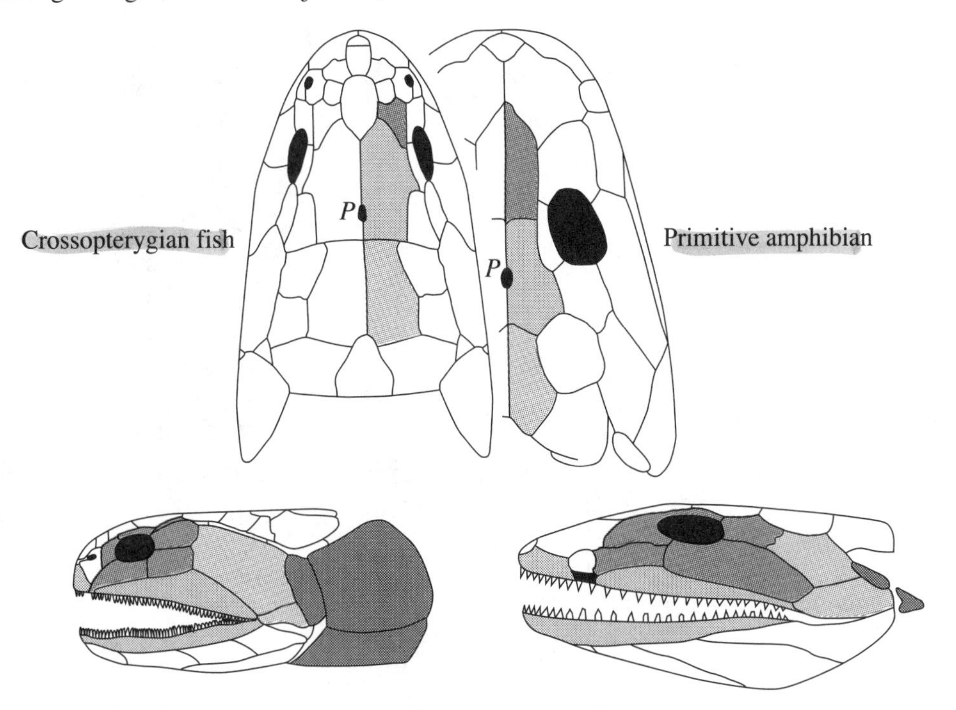

Figure 15-16. Shading denotes the equivalent bones in a crossopterygian fish and its descendant, a primitive amphibian. The 50 bones visible in the top view of the fish skull were diminished to 35 bones in the amphibian, and they were modified in size and shape. An opening for the third, pineal eye (*P*) persisted in the first amphibians. [*After E. H. Colbert and M. Morales,* Evolution of the Vertebrates, *4th ed. Copyright © 1991. By permission of John Wiley & Sons, Inc., New York.*]

point of view. Amphibians and early amniotes ate fish, insects, and one another. All of them were predators by inheritance, even though surrounded by an endless supply of vegetative food. Some amniotes (and even a few amphibians) were to become vegetarians, which required a modification of the gut and its enzyme biochemistry in order to cope with large volumes of low-calorie roughage. Temperature fluctuations are greater on the land surface, and there is evidence that early amniotes could cope with this problem to some extent.

Most importantly, the amniotes introduced a new method of reproduction. Amphibian eggs are small and must be kept moist, hatching into gill-breathing tadpoles that later metamorphose into lung-breathing adults. Only a few of the spewed-out amphibian eggs survive through the tadpole to adult stage. Amniotes circumvented the need for water breeding by introducing the *amniote egg* (Figure 15-17), so named because the embryo floats in a fluid-filled sac, the amnion. What a liberating innovation the amniote egg was! In this watery microenvironment which mimics the ancestral pond, the embryo could develop at leisure, nourished by a yolk food supply, serviced by a waste disposal unit, and protected by a porous shell through which oxygen and waste carbon dioxide are exchanged. Through the amniote egg, the descendant organisms were equipped to spread across the face of the continents.

A limitation imposed by the *square-cube law* relates to the maximum size that an amniote egg or any other animal structure may attain. Everyone knows about the fossil bones of giant dinosaurs that once trod the land, and we might expect such an animal to have laid a proportionately giant egg. This hypothetical egg would have been the size of a household refrigerator, and yet no fossil egg has ever been discovered larger than a mature cantaloupe. Consider the formulas for the volume and surface area of a sphere, whose shape approximates that of an egg. Volume equals $4\pi r^3/3$, in which r is the radius, and surface area equals $4\pi r^2$. Suppose that we double the value of radius r, from 1 unit to 2 units. By what factors do the area and the volume increase? Because the formula for area contains an r-squared term, the area increases in proportion to $2^2/1^2$, or 4 times. Volume, with an r-cubed term, increases in proportion to $2^3/1^3$, or a factor of 8 times. According to the square-cube law, when the size of an object changes, its

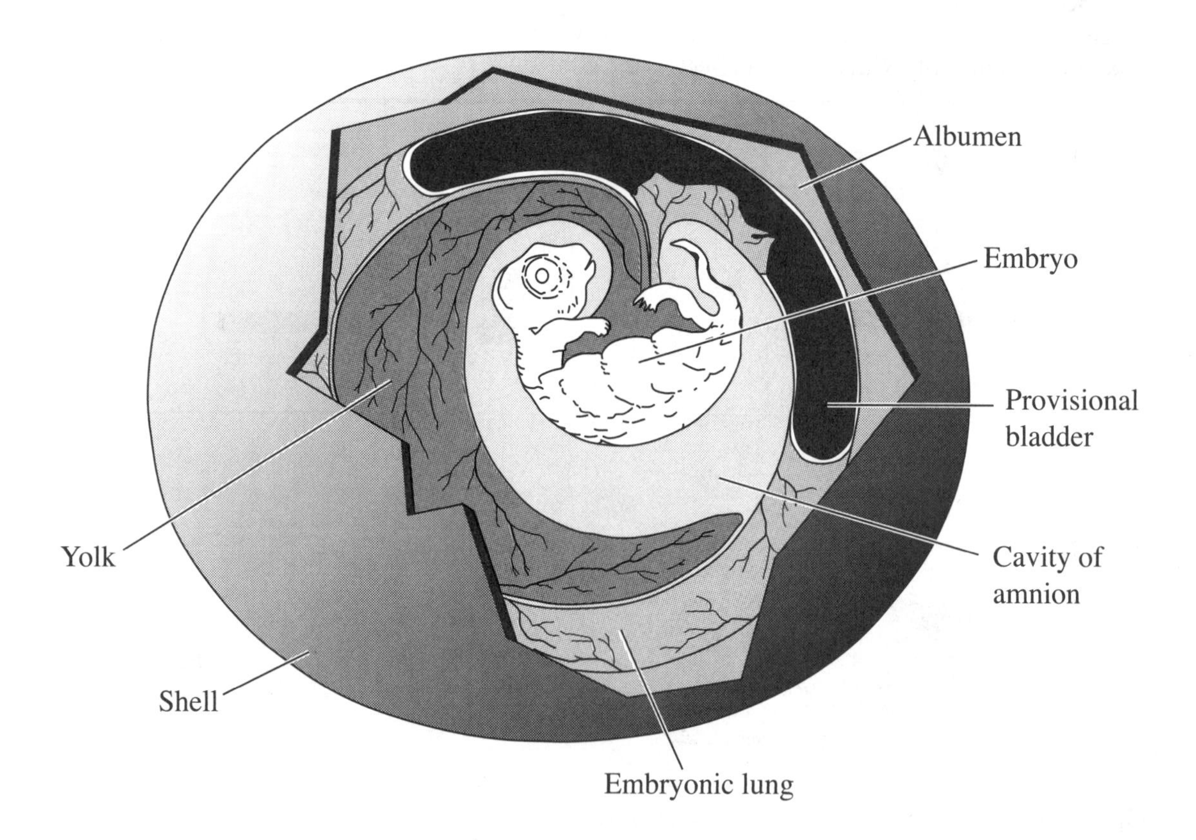

Figure 15-17. The amniote egg can survive a considerable drought. At the moment of hatching, the infant reptile is fully prepared for life on its own. [*After A. S. Romer*, The Procession of Life, *The World Publishing Company, Cleveland, 1968.*]

volume changes much faster than its surface area. The size of an embryo is proportional to the volume of the egg, but breathing occurs by exchange of oxygen and carbon dioxide through the surface of the porous shell. In growing beyond a certain modest volume, the embryo would suffocate for lack of sufficient surface for gas exchange.

A late Paleozoic animal, *Dimetrodon* ("two long teeth") suggests another illustration of the square-cube law. Long vertebral spines held up a bizarre stiff sail on its back (Figure 15-2), possibly for the purpose of heat exchange. The amount of heat to be transferred is proportional to the volume of the body, but the heat must be transmitted through an area of skin. *Dimetrodon's* sail was a thin plate whose surface area is large in comparison to volume. In the same manner, electronics engineers cool a power transistor by fastening heat-dissipating fins onto its casing. Possibly the sail was an early evolutionary "experiment" in regulation of body temperature, which is a characteristic of birds and mammals.

Synapsids Certain late Paleozoic reptiles, called synapsids in reference to a detail of the skull structure, were primitive and yet in many regards they were mammal-like. One of them was *Dimetrodon* whose stiff sail would scarcely remind one of a mammal. But *Dimetrodon* had differentiated teeth much as you and I have a variety for purposes of grinding, stabbing, or shearing. *Dimetrodon's* limb structure also resembled that of mammals (Figure 15-18).

Dinosaurs People are often curious why the dinosaurs, or "terrible reptiles," never lose their power to fascinate children and many of us grown-up children. Perhaps it is the appeal of frightening monsters that lived in unapproachably distant places and times. As someone has pointed out, we love dinosaurs because they are "big, fierce, and dead." (However, individuals of some dinosaur species never grew larger than a chicken.) Originating in the Triassic Period, the dinosaurs flourished for more than 140 million years during the remainder of the Mesozoic Era, then suddenly became extinct 65 million years ago at the end of the Cretaceous Period, under circumstances that are highly controversial.

For all of their varied forms and life styles, dinosaurs share a common set of similarities that make them easy to recognize. Occasional preservation of mummified skin proves that dinosaurs were covered by scales or, in some species, the skin was studded with bony knobs that functioned as armor plate. For obvious reasons of fossil preservation, dinosaurs are classified chiefly upon the basis of the skeleton. Dinosaur legs, tucked in under the body, are suited for efficient walking or running. In the skull are two

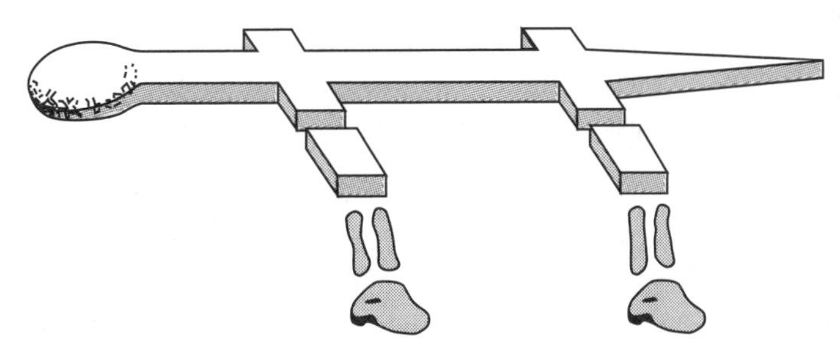

Primitive terrestrial vertebrate

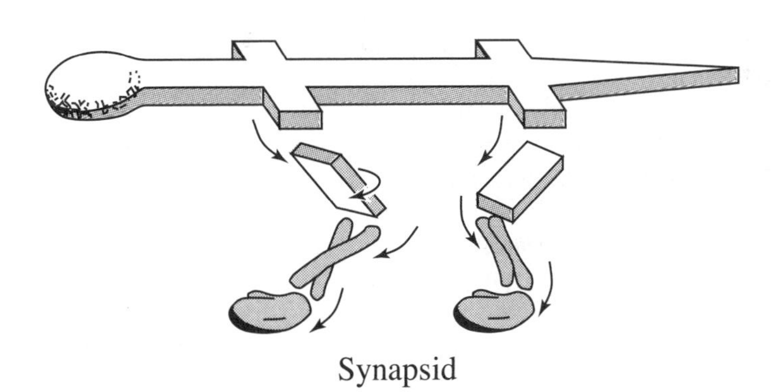

Synapsid

Figure 15-18. A sprawling posture of an early terrestrial vertebrate was modified to become more upright in a synapsid.

other openings next to the eye cavity, present probably to economize on weight and provide space for muscles to bulge when the jaws were shut. Dinosaurs were "bird-hipped" or "reptile-hipped" according to the arrangement of bones in the pelvis. All of the bird-hipped forms were herbivores and they were either quadrupedal or bipedal, the latter walking with only the two hind legs just as modern birds do. Reptile-hipped species were more diverse, being bipeds or quadrupeds with all manner of diet in various combinations. Small sizes of the brain cavity suggest that intelligence was not of high priority, yet some dinosaurs engaged in complex group behavior that includes herding, communal nesting, and shared parental care of the young.

By far the best known dinosaurs are species of gigantic herbivorous quadrupeds with pillar-like legs, a long neck, and a small head endowed with pencil- or chisel-shape teeth [Figure 15-19(*a*)]. These species of *sauropod* ("reptile feet") dinosaurs ate large quantities of coarse food that fermented in an enormous gut, or they swallowed stones that were passed into the gizzard to grind food. New fossil finds reveal ever more colossal animals that have been dubbed "supersaurus," "ultrasaurus," or "seismosaurus" (a real ground-shaker). It is so expensive to dig out and prepare the bones of such monsters that we do not yet have complete skeletons. Estimates based upon available data suggest an individual weighing more than 100 tons, with a body that would stretch half the length of a football field.

Where could such a horrendous beast have lived? Once it was believed that its weight could be supported only if buoyed up by immersion in water; hence these big dinosaurs had to be swamp or lake dwellers. Then it was noted that if a long-necked dinosaur had snorkeled with just its head showing, the water pressure would have prevented the rib cage from expanding and it could not draw a breath. Life on land is also difficult because, according to the square-cube law, the weight of an animal is proportional to its volume but its ability to bear the weight is proportional only to the cross-sectional area of its leg bones. To reduce weight without much sacrifice of strength, the bones of these monsters were deeply hollowed out, analogous to an I-beam girder in a skyscraper.

Certain other basic themes of body plan were common among dinosaur species. *Stegosaurus* ("roofed reptile") and its fellow stegosaurid species are so named from the bony plates arrayed along the back [Figure 15-19(*a*)]. An adult *Stegosaurus* was a 30-foot-long herbivore weighing close to 2 tons, with a brain the size of a prune. This creature could have browsed on the ground, or higher on trees by rearing up on its hind legs. The defensive purpose of the nasty tail spikes is obvious enough, but not so the rows of back plates. Inspection shows that they are covered with fine grooves that carried small blood vessels. The plates were not likely used for defense, but were devices to regulate heat balance, similar to the sail of *Dimetrodon*. Tests in a wind tunnel demonstrate that the plates were ideal to shed heat in a breeze, but not to soak up heat by basking. If *Stegosaurus* had a cooling problem, this implies that it was warm-blooded.

Two other famous groups were contemporaries in the final days of the dinosaurs. *Ceratopsian* dinosaurs [Figure 15-19(*b*)] were stocky herbivores, similar in size, appearance, and life style to the modern rhinoceros. Like the rhino, species of these dinosaurs had variously one to several horns, but the back of the skull flared out into a heavy bony frill. Protection of the neck is one obvious purpose of a frill, but it could also have served as an offensive weapon, or for sexual display during mating season. Expeditions to Mongolia, in central Asia, have unearthed a complete suite of ceratopsians, from ring-shaped clutches of eggs with embryos inside, to hatchlings, and so on to elderly adults. A full-grown beast would not have hesitated to charge its enemy, the ferocious tyrannosaurid dinosaur.

Most fearsome of all land predators were *Tyrannosaurid* dinosaurs [Figure 15-19(*b*)], especially *Tyrannosaurus rex* ("king tyrant reptile") whose mouth was filled with teeth that are serrated like steak knives. *T. rex* grew more than 40 feet long and weighed 6 to 7 tons. Paleontologists speculate that this monster was too ponderous to have sustained a prolonged chase. Its massive skull suggests that it ran headlong into its prey, the shock of the collision being absorbed by the skull bones. Whether *T. rex* killed outright or scavenged rotting carrion, its powerful neck muscles enabled it to tear apart mouthfuls of meat by swinging the head violently from side to side. A notable feature is the ridiculously small arms and two-clawed hands of *T. rex*. Although in principle the animal could pick up several hundred pounds with its forelimbs, they were not long enough to reach its mouth.

Dinosaurs had to do energetic things that we never expect of conventional reptiles such as snakes, crocodiles, or turtles. For example, how does a heart pump blood a height of several stories up to the head of a giant long-necked dinosaur? How did dinosaurs survive in huge numbers in both Arctic and Antarctic latitudes? Even if worldwide Cretaceous climate were mild, high latitudes would have experienced winter

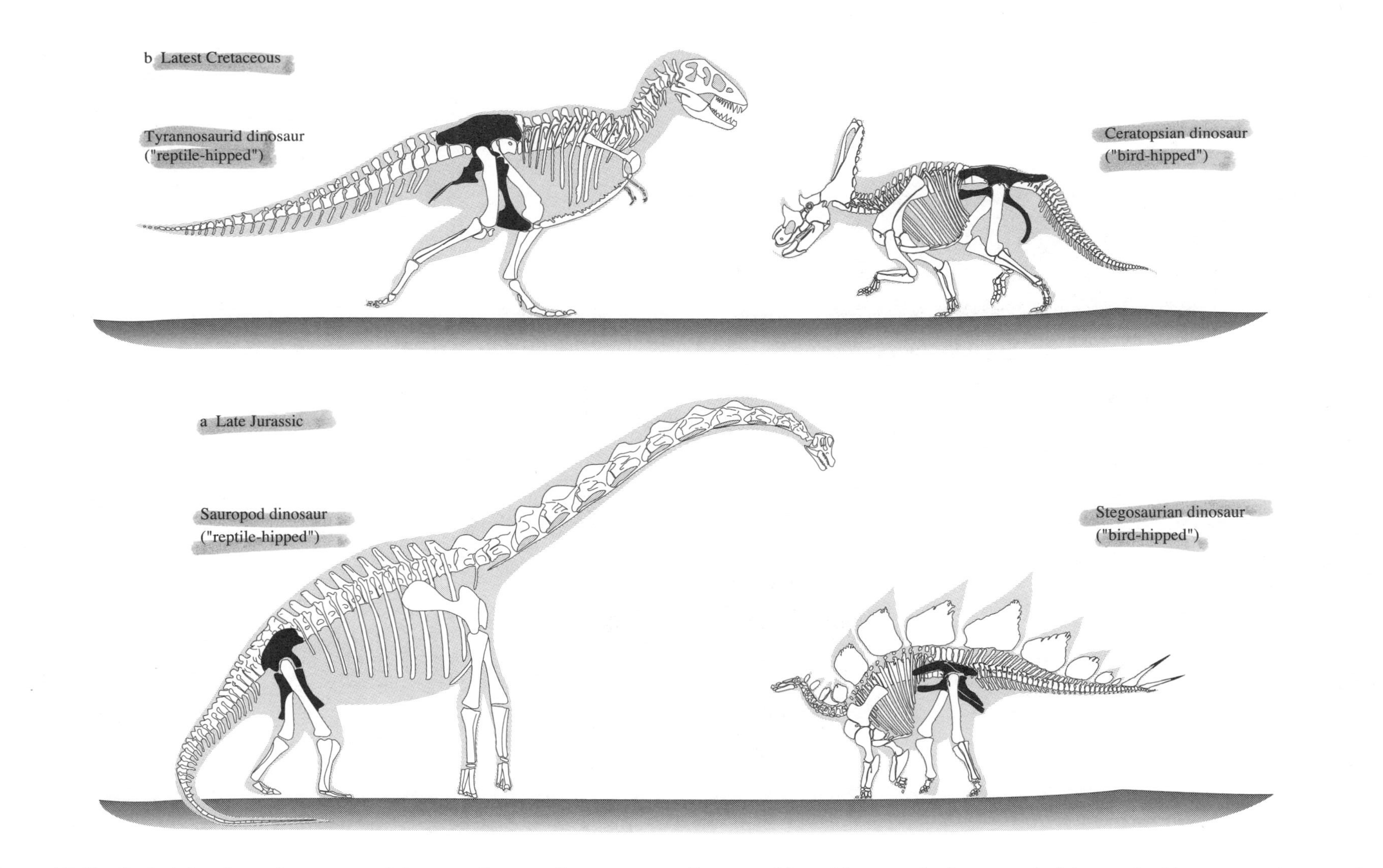

Figure 15-19. Scaled drawings show some of the more famous dinosaur types. Stegosaurids and long-necked sauropods (*a*) were herbivorous contemporaries during the late Jurassic. Carnivorous tyrannosaurids and herbivorous ceratopsians (*b*), also contemporaries, came much later at the very end of the Mesozoic reign of dinosaurs.

Figure 15-20. Although only fragments of "Supersaurus" have been discovered, they are sufficient to convey a sense of the animal's enormous size. The son of vertebrate paleontologist James Jensen, discoverer of the fossil, is more than 6 feet tall. In this photograph he is stretched out the length of the dinosaur's shoulder blade. [*Courtesy James Jensen.*]

darkness just as today, during which the plants stopped growing. In preparation for winter, large Arctic mammals either hibernate (polar bear) or migrate south (caribou). Did herds of dinosaurs annually migrate vast distances? A warm-blooded lion has to eat 10 times as much as a cold-blooded crocodile of the same size. The voracious appetite of a warm-blooded dinosaur predator could be satisfied only if there were a large ratio of prey animals to predators, as suggested by fossil census. These intriguing observations and many others indicate, but do not prove, that dinosaurs were highly active animals that could sustain and regulate an elevated body temperature. Perhaps dinosaur physiology was something between the warm-bloodedness of mammals and the cold-bloodedness of modern reptiles.

Swimming and flying reptiles During the Paleozoic Era, predatory sharks fed upon fish and cephalopods, invertebrate animals ancestral to the modern squid and octopus. In early Mesozoic times, reptile predators took to the sea where they forced a violent reorganization of the food chain, just as their relatives were doing on land. Aquatic reptiles became extinct at the end of the Mesozoic, relinquishing the top of the marine food chain to the ever-present sharks and to Cenozoic mammals, the whales.

Prominent among marine reptiles were *ichthyosaurs* ("fish reptiles"). Magnificent fossils of ichthyosaur bones, body outline, and even internal organs establish that these dolphin-shaped animals with large eyes were too highly specialized to have climbed out of the water to lay eggs, as marine turtles do. Figure 15-21 shows how ichthyosaurs solved the problem. Eggs laid under water would have suffocated, so these animals gave direct birth, evidently to quite large broods of young.

At about the same time, other reptile lineages developed a unique specialization for flight. A wing membrane was stretched, rather like the tissue of a kite, between the body and an enormous elongation of the animal's fourth finger. Once thought to shuffle clumsily on land, many flying reptiles could probably tuck the wing against the body as they walked. Conquest of the air is a formidable task because according to the square-cube law, the weight of a body, which is proportional to its volume, must be powered skyward by wing muscles whose strength is proportional only to their cross-sectional area. Flying reptiles were light and delicate, possessing hollow bones, and their skins were covered, not by heavy scales, but *fur*. Clearly they were not conventional reptiles. Various species ate insects, sifted tiny plankton from the water with comb-like teeth, speared fish with spiky teeth, or simply gulped the fish down whole, pelican-style. In size they ranged from little larger than a pigeon up to the largest flying creature ever to live. Fossils of the latter were discovered (where else but?) in Texas. With a wing span of 45 feet (14 meters), this giant must have resembled a small airplane (Figure 15-22).

The great dying At least twice in the 550 million years of Phanerozoic history, life on earth experienced great dyings. In the Permian Period, which terminated the Paleozoic Era, the most devastating of mass extinctions wiped out 95% of all marine species. Only slightly less destructive was a second dying at the end of the Mesozoic Era when all remaining flying and swimming reptiles, dinosaurs, and many bony fish, mollusks, planktonic organisms, and land plants abruptly disappeared. Oddly, the extinction did not include birds, mammals, or surviving reptiles (snakes, lizards, etc.), all of which were present during the Mesozoic. How could this "angel of death" destroy an assortment of large and small

a

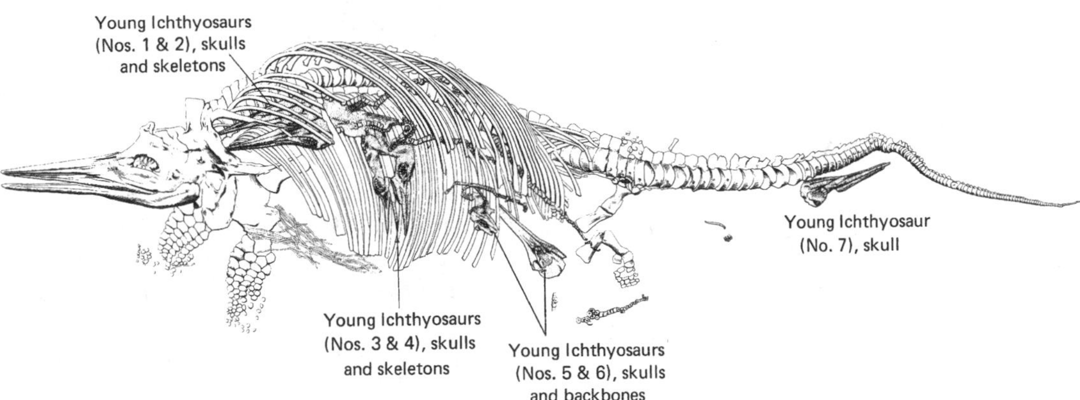

b

Figure 15-21. The fish-like ichthyosaur, actually a reptile, apparently delivered fully developed offspring not encased in a shell, just as certain snakes do today. Several embryos are visible inside the well-preserved skeleton of this female. [*American Museum of Natural History photograph.*]

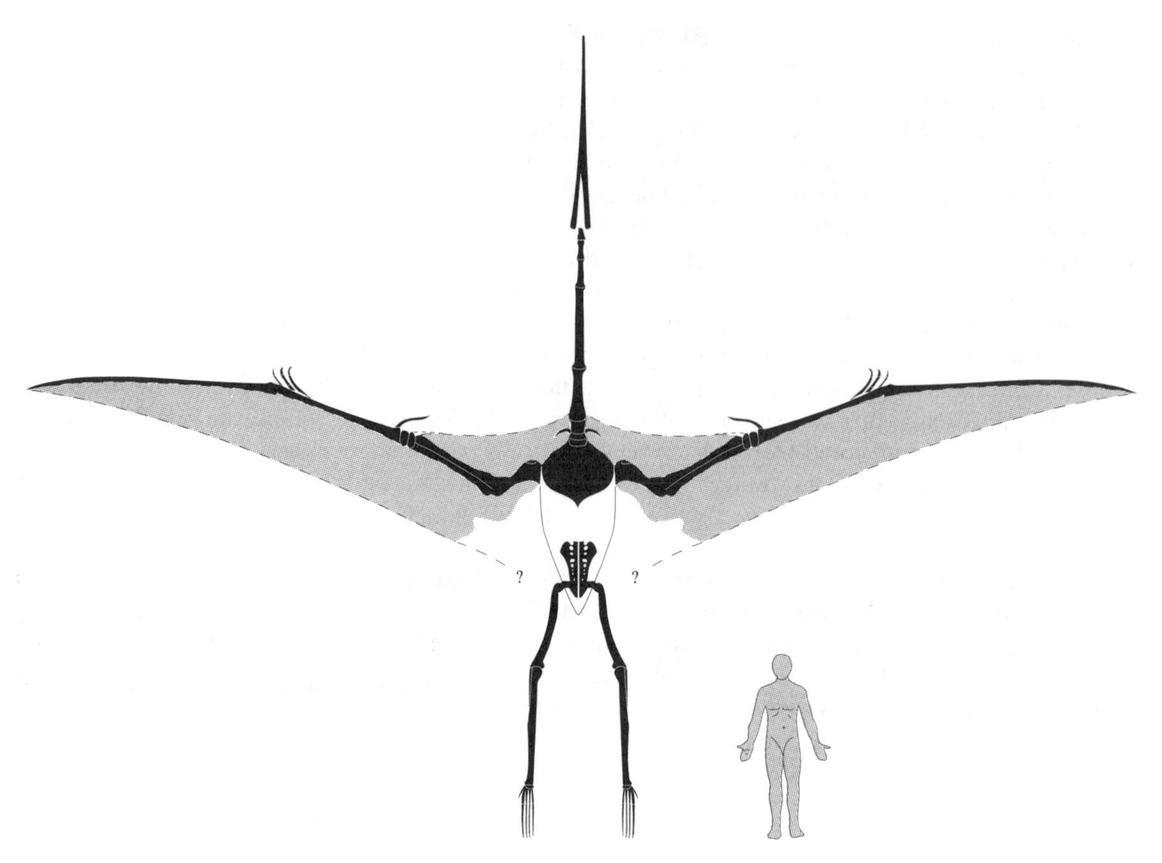

Figure 15-22. Although of huge size, this flying reptile was built lightly. Bones connected from its breastplate to the shoulder bone where the wing attaches to the body, and thence to the backbone, forming a sturdy box-like arrangement somewhat like struts in a hang glider. Perhaps the animal used its pointed jaws and long neck to probe the stinking body of a dead dinosaur or other carrion. [*Courtesy Wann Langston.*]

organisms on both land and sea, yet capriciously pass over closely related species? So sudden was the event, which defines the transition from the Cretaceous Period to the Tertiary Period, that the point in the sedimentary record is named the *K-T boundary.* (Cretaceous is designated with "K" to avoid confusion with other "C" words for periods of geologic time.)

Of course, the most spectacular aspect of the K-T event was the rapid departure of the dinosaurs. Paleontologists dispute whether the event lasted only months or tens of thousands of years which is also very brief on the geologic time scale. Long earlier, the number of dinosaur species had been gradually dwindling, perhaps due to climatic changes, but there was a dramatic final cataclysm. It could have been a side effect of volcanism which was unusually intense at the time. Another possibility is seen in a thin layer of clay that occurs at the K-T boundary in widely scattered parts of the world, which contains an abnormally high abundance of the rare chemical element iridium. Most plausibly the iridium was deposited when a nickel-iron meteorite slammed into the earth 65 million years ago in what is Yucatán today, in the Caribbean region. Even if such a cosmic projectile were to strike the ocean, it would have bored a hole to the bottom in a fraction of a second. An immense cloud of debris, lofted into the high atmosphere, obscured the sun for weeks to months, and pollution was aggravated by unchecked wildfires. Surface temperatures plummeted while photosynthesis on both land and sea shut down. Large carnivores and herbivores starved or froze to death, but small animals, which reproduce faster and which could live underground off stored roots or seeds, survived. Whatever the causes of the K-T extinctions, we shall have to rethink the standard notion of plodding, sustained uniformity of geologic processes. Overwhelming catastrophes occur, and no matter how well adapted to their normal environments the unlucky K-T species may have been, they could not cope with this degree of violence.

Birds

Among the survivors were those dinosaur-like creatures, the birds, which had already appeared by mid-Mesozoic times. In fact, the dinosaurs in a sense live on; we call them birds today. During the Jurassic Period, carbonate mud was precipitated in a quiet tropical sea that occupied what is now southeastern Germany. Quarries at the village of Solnhofen have long been excavated by hand for fine-grained lithographic limestone. During careful inspection of each slab of rock, the quarrymen discovered many remarkable fossils including some that are easily the most rare and precious known to science. One is a crow-sized animal [Figure 15-23(*a*)] that would have been mis-identified as a bipedal dinosaur except that along with its bones are preserved the imprints of feathers. Other fossils of *Archaeopteryx* ("ancient wing"), in which the evidence for feathers had been lost, were later recognized in collections. Several structures of the body of this excellent transitional animal are more reminiscent of a dinosaur than a bird [Figure 15-23(*b*)]. When feathers originated, they were probably yet another device by which dinosaurs regulated body temperature. Useful in the beginning as heat insulation, feathers were to be employed by birds to generate lift for sustained flight. Paleontologists have not firmly concluded whether or not *Archaeopteryx* could fly.

With continuing evolution, birds lost their teeth, and the long reptilian "rudder" tail shrank to a mere nub. Reduction of the tail increased maneuverability and shed unnecessary weight, but at a price of instability. Notice how perching birds constantly make corrective motions in order to keep their balance. Quick reflexes originate in the hindbrain which is enlarged and highly sophisticated. Birds radiated into all manner of habitats and niches including some that were vacated by the demise of large predatory dinosaurs. Cenozoic species included flightless forms that towered as much as 10 feet (3 meters) tall. If evolution had taken a slightly different turn, the most feared carnivores of the Cenozoic would have been birds, not mammals.

Mammals

Distinguishing characteristics of mammals (for example warm-bloodedness, hair, external ears, mammary glands, and milk-nourished devotion to the young) are not preserved, but the record of fossil bones is beautifully documented. Several important modifications, notably in the head and teeth, took place as reptiles gradually evolved into mammals. The restless, intelligent mammals were served by bigger brains, especially the cerebrum where decisions are made. Typically the mammal teeth were reduced in number but diversified in function, permitting many mammals (ourselves included) to eat a generalized diet. Teeth are so well preserved and so useful to our understanding that mammal specialists must become experts in "toothology." Modification of the joints and suspension of the lower jaw to permit a sliding or stroking motion enabled infant mammals to suck. At the same time, bones that once occupied the rear of the reptilian ancestral jaw migrated into the middle ear to become the delicate "hammer" and "anvil" bones that amplify sound vibrations (Figure 15-24).

As long as dinosaurs were around, they had filled most of the niches and habitats available to land animals. Mesozoic mammals were tiny creatures the size of a rat or shrew, that were probably also nocturnal to avoid direct contact with the terrifying ruling reptiles of the day (Figure 15-25). Even in respect to diet, the insect-eating primitive mammals avoided competition with dinosaurs. Cenozoic mammals promptly filled the niches left vacant by the K-T extinctions. Many mammals of the Paleocene Epoch (see Figure 13-13) were heavily built, "experimental models" that were replaced in a second, Eocene explosion of mammal evolution (Figure 15-26). The oldest known examples of modern mammals including bats, whales, true primates, dogs and cats, horses, rhinos, pigs, and many others are represented by Eocene fossils. So punctuated was the early Cenozoic radiation that it is difficult to find fossils that illuminate a transitional stage. For example, it has long been proposed that four-legged ancestral animals returned to the water to become the highly specialized whales. This notion is supported by a fossil record in the Sahara Desert of Egypt in which primitive whales possess tiny, remnant hind limbs. With time the fossil record increasingly resembled the modern assemblage, of which more than 50% of mammal species are rodents, and more than 20% of the species are bats.

Mammal reproduction is finely graded from that of the rather reptilian monotremes that lay eggs, to marsupials whose immature fetuses develop in a pouch, to placentals whose newborns are highly developed. Paleontologists debate whether these groups of mammals had a common ancestor, or multiple origins. Whatever the case, marsupials and placentals have tended to live separated on different continents. While the great Mesozoic supercontinent (a later chapter) was still breaking up into drifting

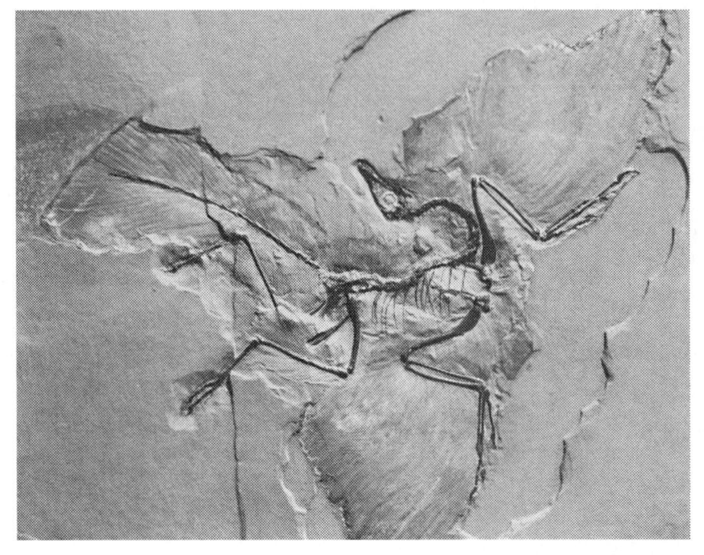

a

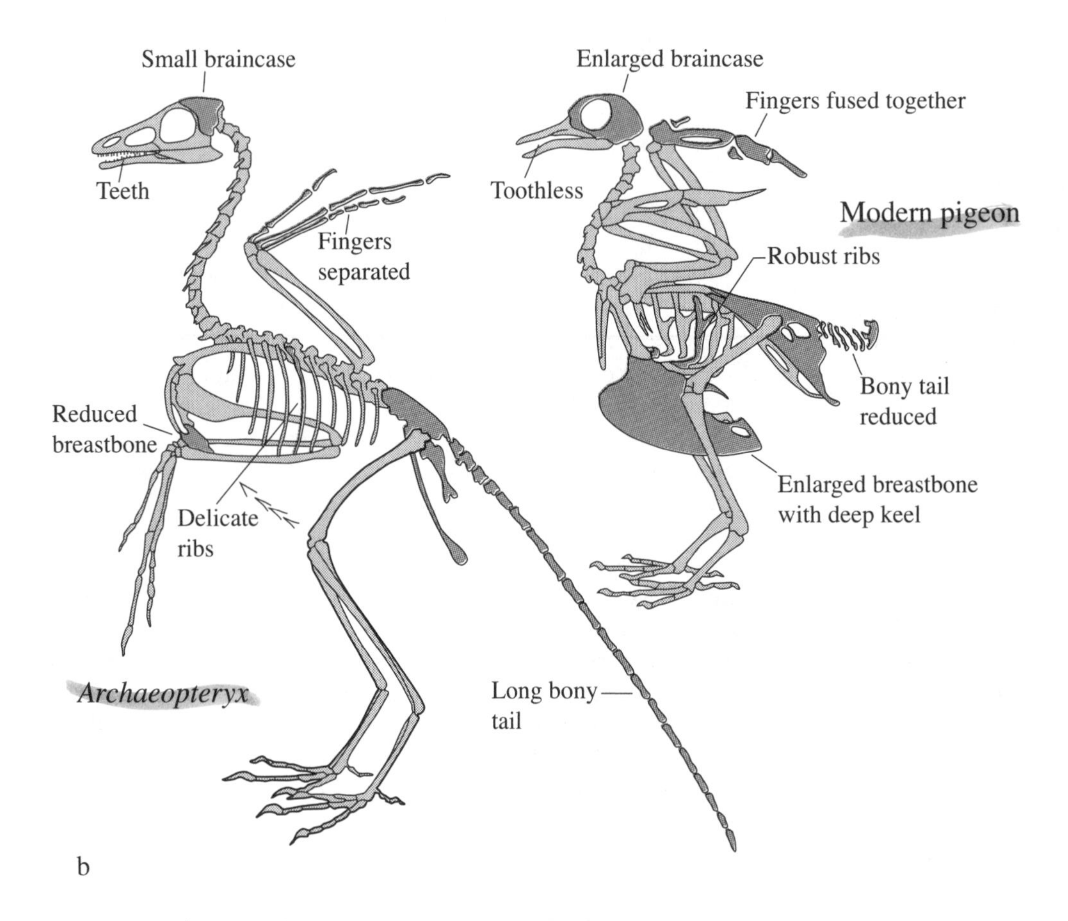

b

Figure 15-23. (*a*) Even after centuries of quarrying at Solnhofen, Germany, only six skeletons and one solitary impression of a feather of *Archaeopteryx* have been discovered. This complete skeleton shows the creature with neck arched back—a sign of rigor mortis. [*American Museum of Natural History photograph.*] (*b*) Corresponding structures in *Archaeopteryx* and a modern pigeon (not to the same scale) are emphasized in color. In every instance, the skeletal features of *Archaeopteryx* are more nearly reptilian. Many dinosaurs and all modern birds have hollow bones, but *Archaeopteryx* did not. [*After E. H. Colbert and M. Morales*, Evolution of the Vertebrates, *4th ed. Copyright © 1991. By permission of John Wiley & Sons, Inc., New York.*]

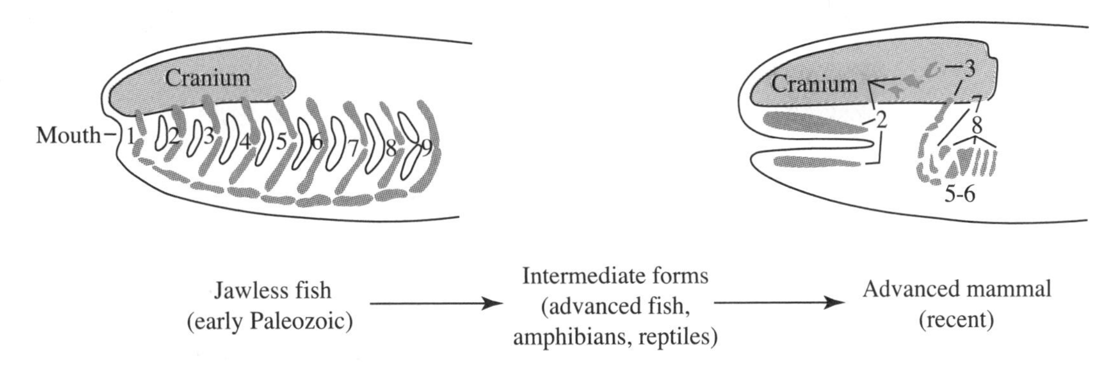

Figure 15-24. Nine primordial gill arches, present in jawless fish, were to become lost or modified for some other function in advanced mammals. In one current view, the arches became: (1) lost; (2) lower and upper jaw, further modified to become the "anvil" and "hammer" bones of the inner ear; (3) jaw prop, later to become the "mallet" bone of the inner ear; (4) lost; (5, 6) thyroid cartilage of larynx; (7) epiglottis, which protects the larynx during swallowing; (8) cartilage rings supporting the trachea; (9) lost.

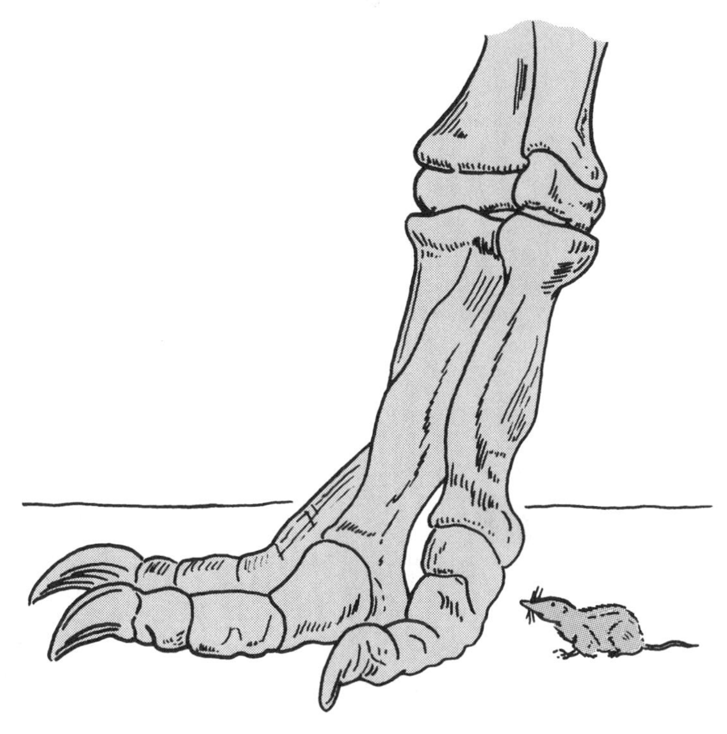

Figure 15-25. Size is not everything, but it is easy to see why a typical Mesozoic mammal would have felt intimidated at the feet of a ruling reptile, *Tyrannosaurus*. [*After D. Cohen*, The Age of Giant Mammals, *Dodd, Mead & Company, Inc., New York, 1969.*]

fragments, marsupials could migrate among the land masses, later to become isolated completely. A marsupial population was stranded in Australia, the only placentals being lately arrived rodents and widely traveled bats. Niches that placental mammals occupy elsewhere were vacant, to be filled by Australian marsupials that mimic lions, moles, anteaters, wolves, flying squirrels, mice, or wolverines. Occupation of equivalent niches by look-alike placentals and marsupials was a spectacular example of *convergent evolution*. Both groups flourished apart, and when they have occasionally been brought into contact it has generally spelled disaster for the marsupials.

More dyings One such ruination is in progress today as humans, accompanied by the usual placental pets, livestock, and vermin, have invaded Australia. Another took place in South America where marsupials had managed to prosper for more than 60 million years in a mixed population that included

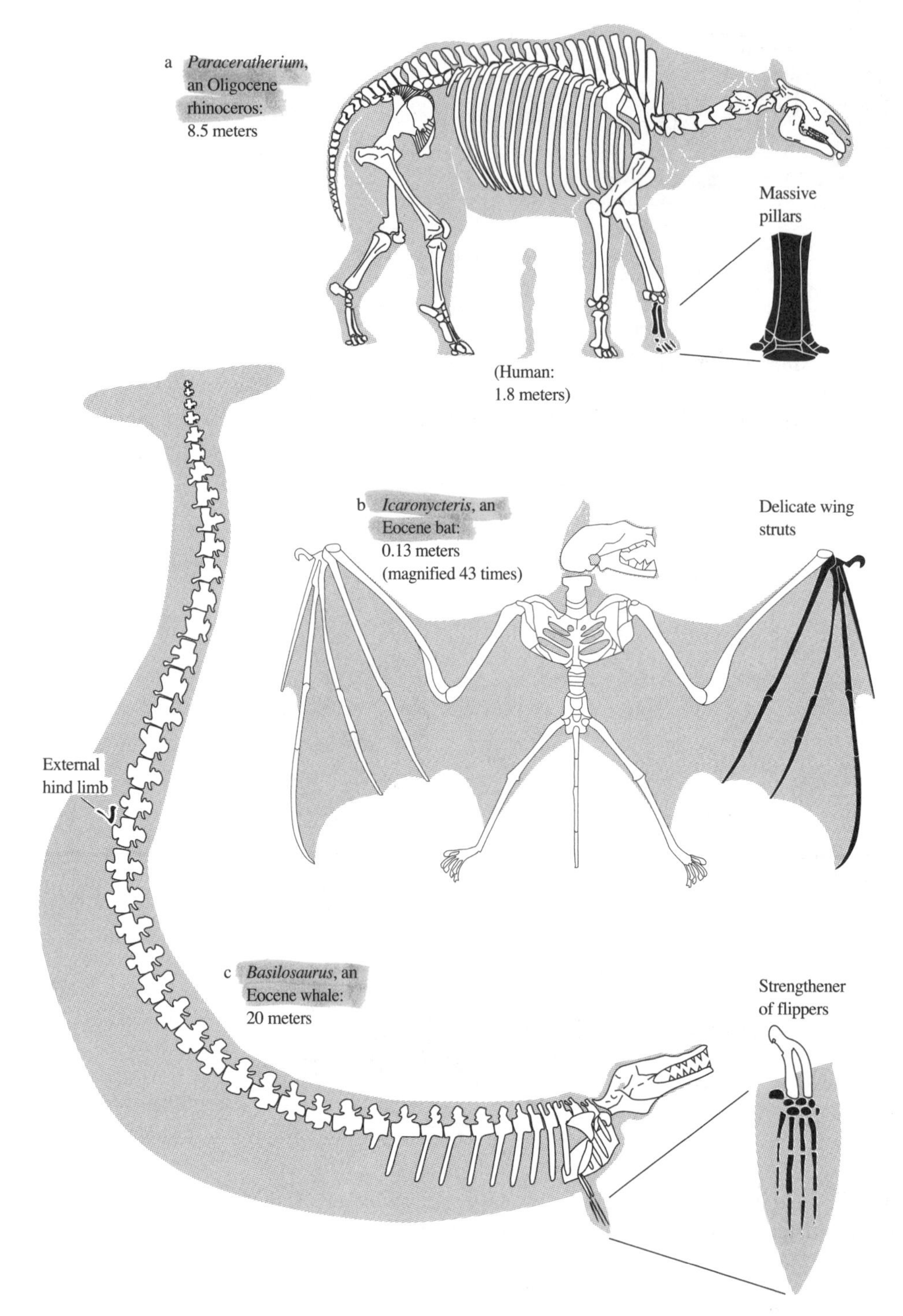

Figure 15-26. Two-thirds of the geologic history of mammals had already transpired by the end of the Mesozoic Era. Dinosaur extinctions had left unoccupied niches and habitats to be filled by evolutionary radiations of mammals. Through modification, corresponding bones of the mammalian "hand" were adapted to serve radically different purposes. (*a*) A massive column of bone was necessary to support the estimated 12-ton weight of *Paraceratherium*, one of the largest land mammals ever to live. (*b*) Petite bats use the hand bones for flight. Bones and teeth of modern bats differ significantly from those of *Icaronycteris*, the oldest known fossil bat, despite superficial similarities. (*c*) Tiny external hind limbs of early whales, though containing the customary thighbone, kneecap, etc., could not possibly have enabled the animal to move about on land. Nevertheless, their presence points to land-living ancestors of whales. Certain modern whales have functionless vestigial *in*ternal hind legs, not attached to the rest of the skeleton.

a variety of placentals. About 3 million years ago the hitherto drifting "island" of South America docked with North America, prompting a massive exchange across the Isthmus of Panama. Advanced North American placentals penetrated South America, eventually to exterminate and replace many browsers, grazers, and predators. Of the South American marsupials, only the opossum was able to thrive in the hostile North. That should be no surprise, as the opossum will eat almost anything.

World climate gradually became stratified into contrasting zones throughout the Cenozoic Era, finally climaxing in the cruel advance of ice sheets across vast regions (Chapter 24). Here was a major environmental challenge to survival that is reminiscent of the Mesozoic endtime. Another Great Dying occurred, especially during the Pleistocene Epoch when mammoths, saber-tooth cats, giant sloths, and North American horses and camels disappeared forever. Without that great natural refuge, Africa, we would have little except dry bones and cave paintings to remind us of the grandeur of these large mammals. A question widely debated is whether human hunters or deteriorating climate contributed the most to these extinctions. As our own single species expands, we may look forward with confidence and sadness to the final exit of whales and perhaps all of the large land animals. Is the Age of Mammals drawing to a swift close?

A PERSONAL POSTSCRIPT

A biologist of the previous century, T. H. Huxley, compared the outreach of evolution to filling a barrel, first with apples, then with pebbles among the apples, then with sand among the pebbles and apples, and finally all remaining pore spaces with water. Just so, from the microscopic beginnings of life, ever more niches and habitats came to be occupied with living creatures. Eventually vertebrates appeared having bone, then jaws, then quadrupedal locomotion, lungs, and the amniote egg, each innovation opening new possibilities of lifestyle until, in the Biblical metaphor, vertebrate life became abundantly "pressed down, shaken together, running over" (Luke 6:38). Have all potentialities been realized? Millions of years from now, what new group with biochemistry or body structure that is yet unknown will make even the mammals appear clumsy and archaic? What will they have that we don't? Wouldn't you like to know?

And haven't you ever wished that we could "bring 'em back alive" as the zoo keepers say? Perhaps advances in techniques to manipulate DNA give us reason to nurture this fantasy. Certain fossils, including bone, contain fragments of the information-rich molecules, protein and DNA. If only we could splice together broken bits and pieces of fossil DNA, then clone copies of the molecule, then implant the molecular code in cells, then . . . Wouldn't you like to see a real live *Stegosaurus* or *Archaeopteryx*? What were they *really* like?

SUMMARY

Vertebrate fossils consist chiefly of permineralized bones and teeth. Diversity among different vertebrates (animals with backbones), which originated early in the Paleozoic Era, is minor compared to diversity among organisms that originated during the much longer Precambrian interval. Bilaterally symmetrical vertebrates, both terrestrial and aquatic, have a head and (typically) a tail, ribs, paired appendages, and a backbone that developed from the embryonic notochord. Evolution of vertebrate body structures and functions has generally progressed from simpler to more complex. An existing structure (for example, a bone in the lower jaw) may be modified and relocated to perform some new function (become bone in the middle ear that amplifies sound vibrations). Throughout Phanerozoic time the community of vertebrates continued to expand into new niches and habitats, from life in the water, to transitional water-land, to life on land and in the air. This expansion depended upon the coevolution of other life forms.

A clade includes all the groups that descended from the same ancestral organism; each clade has retained certain ancestral primitive characteristics and has introduced novelties, or derived characteristics. Vertebrates seem to be most closely related to the echinoderm phylum. According to the fossil record, certain jawless fish evolved into groups of fish with jaws, which include placoderms, cartilaginous fish (sharks, skates, rays), and bony fish which are by far the most abundant individuals and species. Certain bony fish became amphibians, of which certain species became reptiles. Different ancestral groups of reptiles evolved independently into birds or mammals. Dinosaurs may have been a separate clade closely related to birds.

Earliest jawless fish introduced bone which was entirely an external skeleton. Initially, bone may have functioned not so much for support as for maintaining a chemical balance in the blood. Jaws appeared tens of millions of years later, most probably by a modification of V-shape gill arches. Many placoderms, the earliest jawed fish which also lacked a bony internal skeleton, were carnivores. Cartilaginous fish are poorly fossilized except for teeth, and their evolution has remained conservatively stable.

Mid-Paleozoic bony fish developed into two prominent groups: ray-finned fishes which are the dominant type today, and lobe-finned fishes that were ancestral to amphibians. Vertebrate transition from the water to land habitat was accomplished by modification of lobe fins into legs, and of the swim bladder into lungs. Other modifications were of the vertebrate eye and ear, and of the leg structure to permit the animal to breathe while walking. All of the earliest amphibians and reptiles were carnivores. Reproduction by reptiles and later groups was by the amniote egg, which enabled them to inhabit generally any of the land surface.

According to the square-cube law, as the size of an object changes, its volume changes much faster than its surface area. The sail on the late Paleozoic animal, *Dimetrodon*, may have been a means to radiate or absorb excess heat through a structure whose ratio of surface area to volume is large. Similarly, the volume of an egg is limited by the amount of surface area through which the embryo exchanges oxygen and CO_2.

Dinosaurs ruled during most of the Mesozoic Era, diversifying into numerous but distinctive sizes, shapes, and lifestyles. Certain herbivorous sauropod dinosaurs became the largest land animals ever to live (somehow coping with the consequences of the square-cube law); others became the largest land carnivores ever to live. Some dinosaurs were capable of complex group behavior including herding and caring for the young. Dinosaurs also may have been able to regulate body temperature to some extent. According to indirect evidence, some of them maintained high energy levels associated with warm-bloodedness.

Synapsid reptiles exhibited numerous mammal-like characteristics. Various Mesozoic reptiles became adapted to the marine environment, including fish-like ichthyosaurs that breathed air and gave direct birth (no egg). Delicate, hollow-boned reptiles of many different sizes could fly using a wing membrane that was stretched from the body across to an elongated fourth finger. *Archaeopteryx*, a Jurassic fossil from Germany, was a nearly ideal transitional reptile-bird that had feathers but also shared dinosaurian characteristics.

All remaining dinosaurs, swimming and flying reptiles, and many distantly related land and water organisms abruptly became extinct at the end of the Cretaceous Period, in the K-T event. Whether the K-T environmental stress was a consequence of volcanism, or whether it was a beclouding of the atmosphere with the debris of a meteorite impact, it was cataclysmic and deadly. However, many vertebrates survived the K-T extinctions, including Mesozoic mammals and birds, and snakes, crocodiles, turtles, and lizards.

Mammals could not fill many ecosystems until they were vacated by extinction of the dinosaurs. Then mammals radiated in two early bursts, the second (Eocene) one giving rise to most modern forms. Marsupials and placentals have coexisted throughout the Cenozoic, but whenever brought into contact, the placentals have dominated over marsupials. In their separate development, many marsupials and placentals exhibit convergent evolution, looking and acting similar because they occupy similar niches. Many large mammals have died out in the late Cenozoic, due partly to the onset of cold (even glacial) climate and more recently as humans have hunted them and preempted their habitats.

16

Force Fields

Sophisticated and complex though many geophysical instruments may be, they are based upon very simple principles. For example, a coiled metal spring measures the force of gravity. Variations in this force cause the spring to rotate as its stretches or contracts. An image of the rotation is greatly magnified by a light beam reflected from the mirror attached to the base of the spring. This instrument can measure differences in gravity as little as 1 part in 10 million. [*Gulf Research & Development Company photograph*]

In their interpretations of the earth, geologists make use of whatever data are available. Thus far we have examined igneous, sedimentary, and metamorphic rocks, and noted how natural radioactivity and the fossil record have revealed geologic history. Another way to probe the earth is through study of the several kinds of *force* that are present in and about it. Gravity is the familiar force by which every object with mass attracts all other masses. Another type of force is manifested when stress causes rocks to become deformed. Magnetic force can move a compass needle, and the magnetic force apparently can be sensed by certain organisms though not by humans. Gravity holds the earth together and makes rivers flow downhill, to mention just two of its many roles in nature. Stress causes rocks to crumple during the uplift of mountain ranges. In contrast, the magnetic force has little to do with shaping the earth. But as we shall see in a following chapter, earth magnetism does contain *information*, rather like the storage of data in magnetic form on a computer disk.

A convenient way to describe force is through the notion of a *force field*—a region of space in which the force is present. From point to point within this volume, the strength of a force and the direction in which it is exerted may vary. Or to put it another way, the field has a "shape." Gravitational and magnetic fields occupy both the earth's interior and the space surrounding the earth, whereas a stress field is confined entirely within solid material. Suppose that the force causes an object to move a certain distance. For example, a boulder tumbles downhill, or a magnetized compass needle rotates on its pivot point. It takes *energy* to move an object. We may state a mathematical relationship among energy, force, and distance as

$$\text{energy} = \text{force} \times \text{distance}.$$

Fundamental concepts of energy, force, distance, mass, time, temperature, etc., are ingredients of *geophysics*, a scientific discipline that provides special insight into our planet. By observing the force fields that are present in the earth, geophysicists can infer the nature of its remote, forever inaccessible interior. Thus in one sense geophysics is a quantitative science based upon sophisticated measurements whose data are manipulated by powerful computers. Yet we cannot visit the depths of the earth to make direct observations, and because of this limitation we are obliged to devise mathematical models to explain the measurements. All models fall short of a complete description of reality, with the result that some geophysical problems are equally well "solved" by many models, in some situations an infinite number of them! It then becomes necessary to use common sense and experience, or additional data of another type, to decide which implausible models to discard. Geophysicists must combine science and mathematics with a good bit of artistic latitude in their work.

SHAPE OF THE WORLD

For example, consider the earth's shape. Even the ancients had correctly concluded that to a first approximation it is a *sphere*, which is a shape described by a simple mathematical formula. In 220 BC, Eratosthenes estimated the size of the earth rather accurately by arranging for a camel to trudge across Egypt between Alexandria, a northern city on the Mediterranean Sea, and Syene (the modern Aswan) whose latitude was known to be 7.2° to the south. From the duration of the camel's journey, Eratosthenes calculated the distance to be 5000 stadia, or in modern units of measurement, about 926 kilometers. He used these data to arrive at the earth's circumference. A full circle contains 360°, which is 50 times greater than the angle of 7.2° between the two Egyptian cities. Therefore a full circumference is 50 x 926 kilometers, or 46,300 kilometers. As it turned out, this early estimate was incorrect by only a few percent, accomplished through the brilliant feet of the camel.

Other geophysical calculations employ a more refined model of the earth's shape. Earth's daily rotation slings the equatorial region into a bulge as the polar regions are flattened and drawn in closer to the center (Figure 16-1). The discrepancy from a sphere is by approximately 0.3 percent, easy to measure though probably too small for an orbiting astronaut to detect by eye. Moreover, early differentiation of the earth has caused layers of more dense material to sink beneath less dense layers. A better approximation to the true shape is the *spheroid* which corresponds to a rotating, density-stratified earth in which the topmost layer is water, a universal ocean of uniform depth. Of course the real world contains land masses, but in comparison to the whole, even the loftiest mountain departs only slightly from this idealized surface. If the earth were scaled down to an object the size of a basketball, the roughness of the Rocky Mountains would feel like fine sandpaper.

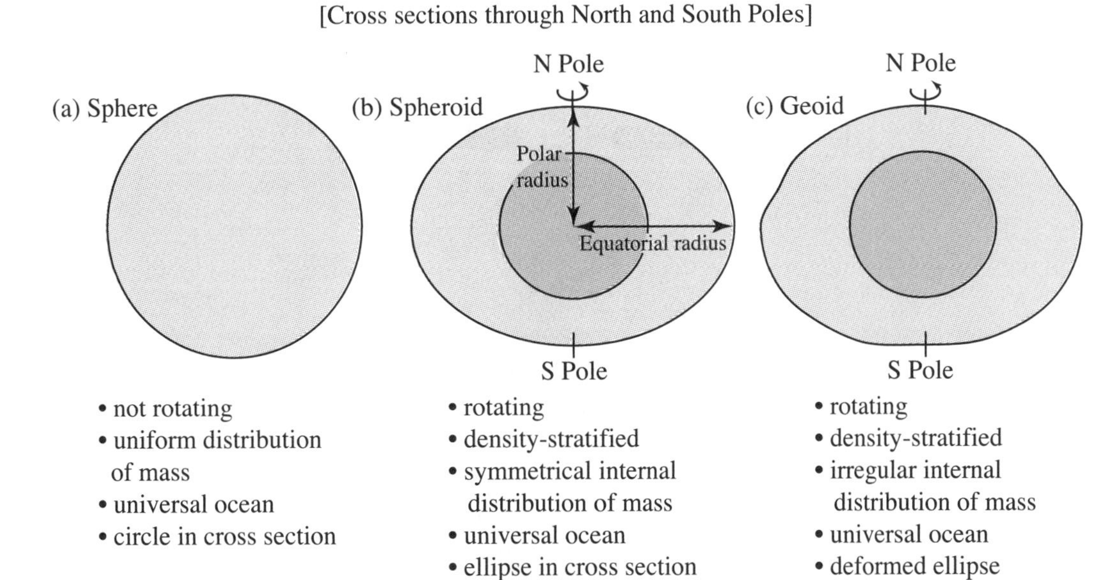

Figure 16-1. The eastward rotation of the earth, pictured here in cross section, deforms an otherwise spherical shape. As drawn, the flattening of the polar regions and bulging of the Equator are highly exaggerated. In fact the polar radius is only 21 kilometers (0.33 percent) shorter than the equatorial radius.

According to calculations, the observed polar flattening would result if the earth acts as a rotating ball of fluid suspended in space. At first this conclusion seems preposterous, for although ocean water is a fluid, the stuff comprising the continents and ocean floor is solid rock, strong enough to uphold towering vertical cliffs. Solid rock hardly seems like a fluid, but here too it is a question of scale. Think of a volume of rock, for example a cube buried deep within the earth. *Stress* is defined as *force per unit area,* in this example the pressure applied by the enclosing rock to the sides of the cube. Our selected volume of rock could respond to the stress by experiencing *strain,* or *deformation* which is defined as a *change of shape or volume*, or both (Figure 16-2).

Compression of the rock at great depth makes it stronger, but the associated high temperature at depth makes the rock weaker even if the rock is not hot enough to melt. As a sum result of these competing factors, solid material acts in dramatically different ways depending upon circumstances. At low pressure and temperature, and especially if stress is applied rapidly, the rock acts as a *brittle* substance. It develops fractures and it is commonplace to see a rock shatter when hit by a hammer. But when confined at high pressure, with modest though relentless application of stress, the rock responds by flowing in a *ductile* manner. Under these conditions the rock bends but does not break; it is deformed by folding, not by faulting, as in Figure 16-2(*d*). Either the rock would not fracture, or the fracture would heal itself by a creeping of the rock walls back together again. Beneath an outermost rind of strong, rigid, brittle rock, the substance of the earth is a fluid unable to hold a permanent shape. On a whole-earth scale of size, rock is so weak that gravity can draw the planet into a sphere with a slight rotational bulge.

Already we have illuminated an important property of rocks through geophysical modeling, but there is more. How successfully does the shape of the spheroid describe the 70% of the earth's surface that is covered by ocean? Satellites covered with mirrors have been placed into orbit to facilitate even more accurate measurements of the earth's size and shape. As the satellite passes overhead, a ground station flashes very short bursts of a laser light off one of the mirrors and back to the point of origin. Distance to the satellite is calculated from knowledge of the speed of light and the delay of the returned signal. Processing of millions of observations by the global network of laser-ranging stations enables geophysicists to pinpoint the orbit of the satellite within an accuracy of a few centimeters.

A satellite responds to the force of gravity by falling, except that it falls *around* the earth, not *into* the earth. To put it scientifically, the satellite orbit is positioned upon a surface of uniform gravitational

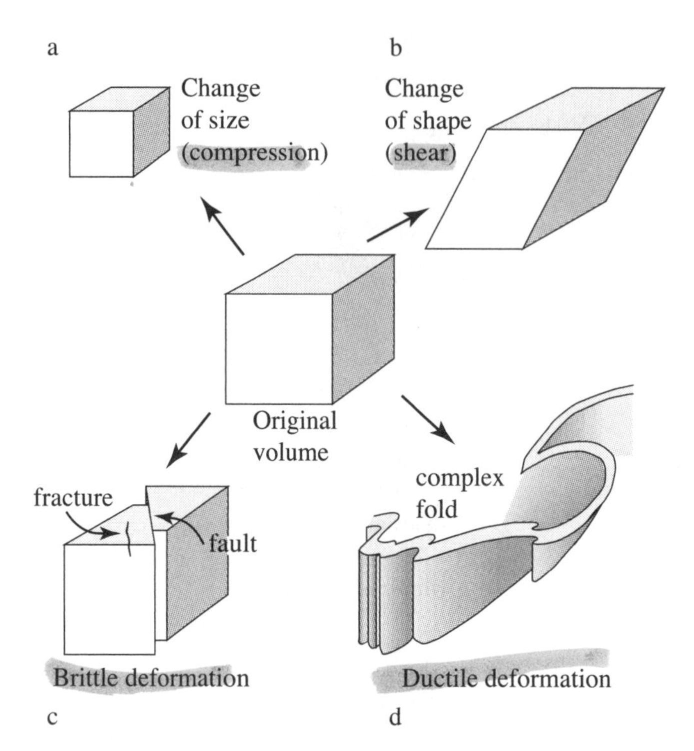

Figure 16-2. Upon being subjected to low stress, a volume of rock (in this example, a cube) will spring back to its original size and shape when the stress is released. Pure compression, in which stress is applied equally to all sides of the cube (*a*), reduces its size but does not change its shape. Pure shear, in which stress is not applied uniformly (*b*), changes shape but not size. If the stress exceeds a certain threshold, the deformation becomes permanent even after the stress is released. Stress applied rapidly fractures the rock, and a fracture may experience offsetting fault movement (*c*). Stress applied slowly causes ductile deformation (*d*) rather than fracturing or faulting. Many rocks now at the earth's surface have been intricately faulted and folded as they were previously involved in internal movement under conditions of deep burial.

potential. Water molecules in the ocean act similarly, also moving freely under the influence of gravity, and thus sea level defines another surface of uniform gravitational potential. Whether low on the ocean or high in an orbit, the surface is level and a weight on a string would hang perpendicular to such a surface in all places. (Do not confuse "level" with "flat," which is simply the local appearance of a level surface. In fact, sea level wraps around the curvature of the earth.) Orbits of satellites are used to map the level surface of the ocean, both being controlled by the force of gravity.

We call the shape of the ocean surface the *geoid*. More accurately, the geoid is a surface that coincides with sea level in the absence of tides, currents, or waves. On the continents the position of the geoid at any particular locality is the level that water would seek if a narrow slot canal were to be connected between that point and the ocean (Figure 16-3). Now we are ready for our third (but not final) approximation to the true shape of the earth. Whereas the spheroid is a mathematically regular surface, the geoid is a bit warped and irregular (Figure 16-4). The spheroid is symmetrical but the geoid is slightly pear-shaped, the Southern Hemisphere being a trifle larger than the Northern.

Why the bumps and depressions in the geoid? Geophysicists are still working on this question. To some extent the information is ambiguous, for the geoid depicts the force of gravity whose variation depends upon the distribution of earth mass that cannot be observed directly. High points of the geoid correspond to places where tectonic plates (a subject of Chapter 22) are in collision as in the Andes of South America, or they are "hot spots" of current or recent volcanism, as in Yellowstone Park in North America, and especially Iceland in the North Atlantic. Conversely, sags in the geoid occupy cool spots, inert or ancient highly stable regions such as the Precambrian shields (Chapter 11) of Canada, Africa, Asia, and Australia.

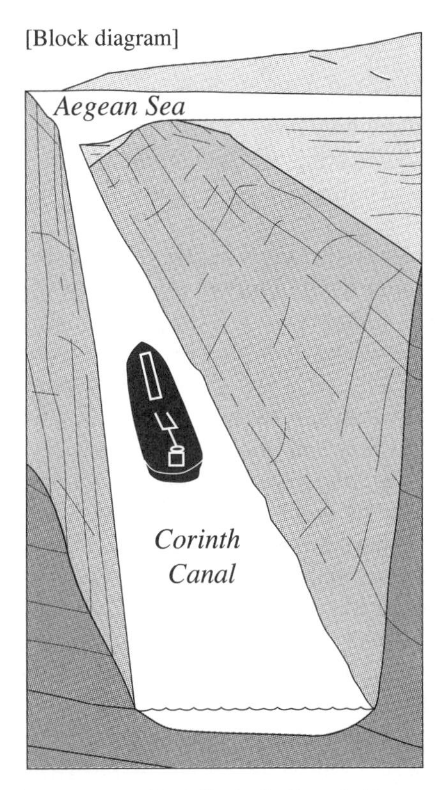

Figure 16-3. At its eastern end the steep-walled Corinth Canal, Greece, connects to the Aegean Sea (in the distance). The boat rests at sea level while being surrounded by land. A slot canal illustrates in principle how the geoid, which corresponds to sea level, can be mapped even in the midst of a land mass.

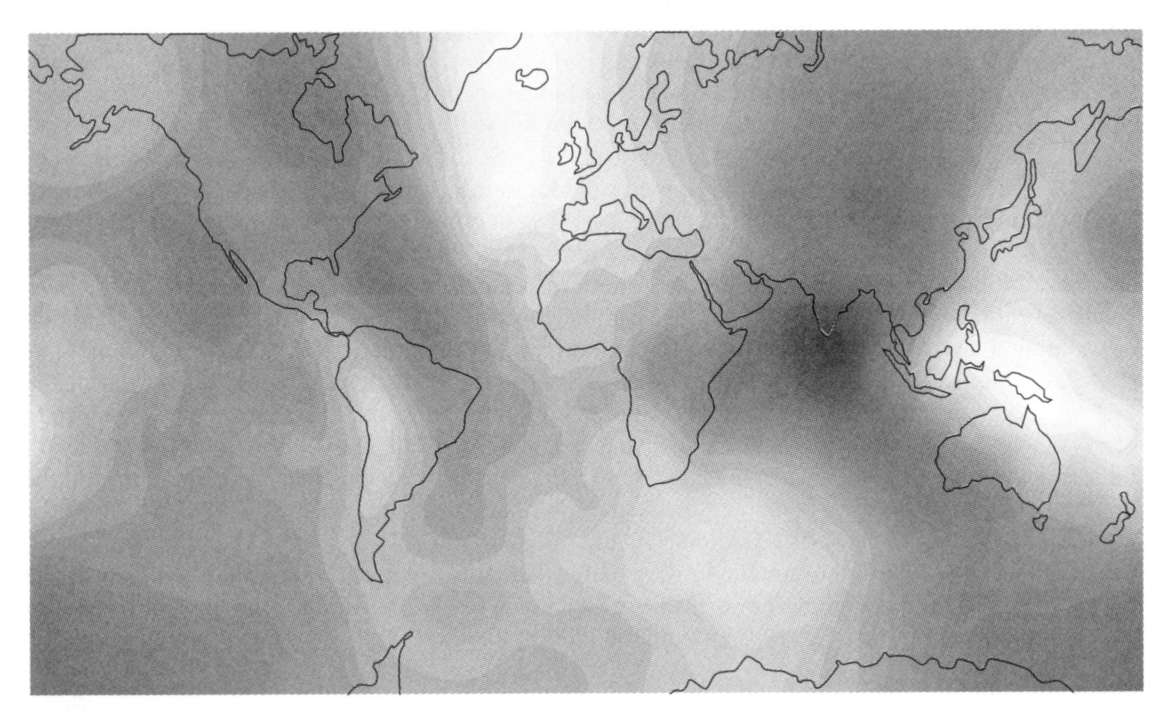

Figure 16-4. A contour map depicts highs (light areas) and lows (dark areas) of the geoid relative to the spheroid which is symmetrical. Especially prominent is the huge deep depression off the tip of India. From the highest to the lowest point on this hypothetical ocean surface, the difference in elevation is approximately 150 meters (500 feet). Contours of the geoid bear little relationship to positions of surface features such as continents and oceans. Rather, the geoid is governed by the distribution of mass very deep in the earth.

SEISMIC WAVES

One of the most urgent tasks of modern geophysics is to understand *seismic*, or earthquake phenomena better. Seismic information is vital to three basic objectives: to probe the character of the deep interior (a scientific objective), to image the layering of rocks in the uppermost several kilometers in prospecting for oil and gas (commercial), and to forecast the location, timing, and severity of earthquakes (social and political).

Of these, the art of earthquake prediction is perhaps the most important and by far the least successful. Earthquakes and volcanism go hand-in-hand (review the worldwide distribution of volcanoes in Figure 5-3), but intense earthquakes may occur unexpectedly in areas once thought to be stable. One such area, along the Mississippi River just north of Memphis, was devastated by a series of intense shocks in 1811 and 1812. Fortunately the region was lightly populated at the time. Chinese seismologists, recognizing the peril of frequent giant quakes to their country's very dense population, have become prediction specialists. Sometimes an impending earthquake will give warning signs. As stress builds up not quite to the point of triggering a major rupture, countless microfractures pop open. Animals with sensitive ears become agitated, the ground tilts, and water levels in wells suddenly change, some wells even spouting. Seismologists have proposed that, as the rock experiences this preliminary slight expansion, seismic waves from distant, unrelated earthquakes begin to travel more slowly through the zone that is about to experience an earthquake. A swarm of small earthquakes may precede the big one. According to theory, the longer these alarming signals persist, the bigger the earthquake will be.

In 1975 the Chinese government, in consultation with seismologists, decided to put the enormous risk of earthquake prediction to the test. All the danger signs were present near the city of Haicheng in northeast China. On a bitterly cold February morning the citizens were evacuated, and that evening a powerful earthquake struck. The seismologists were elated to have averted the loss of human life in a situation where 90% of the buildings were destroyed, and they felt proud and confident of their predictive powers.

But their euphoria was not to last for long. The following year, almost without warning, the nearby city of Tangshan abruptly disappeared from the face of the earth, demolished by a violent whipsawing motion of the ground. A million persons were asleep at 3:42 a.m. on July 28, and 10 seconds later 160 thousand of them were dead and more than a half million were injured! Instantly Tangshan was transformed into a replica of Hiroshima after the atomic bomb, and no wonder, for the energy released was equivalent to a blast of 400 Hiroshima bombs (800 million tons of TNT). Up to a few hours before the event, there had been no recognized precursors—no foreshocks, no warping of the ground, no changes of water level, no crazed animals scurrying about. More recently, damaging earthquakes in southern California were precipitated by movements on buried faults that no one knew existed. Seismologists regret that our ability to make reliable earthquake forecasts is about nil.

According to a scale devised by the American seismologist Charles Richter, the great 1976 Tangshan earthquake was of magnitude 7.8. Magnitude measures the amplitude (or distance) of motion of the ground, hence the destructive power of an earthquake. Amplitude depends in part upon the substrate, as illustrated in Jesus' story about the wise man whose house built upon rock remained during the destruction of the foolish man's house built on sand. A building anchored to bedrock may survive while one situated next door on quivering soft sediment is torn apart. Amplitude also drops off sharply with increasing distance from the quake. In taking these variables into account, the calculation of magnitude on the Richter scale is based upon measurement, by a standard seismic detector, of the motion of the ground at a standard distance of 100 kilometers (62 miles) from the earthquake. As earthquake magnitude increases by 1 unit, the amplitude of shaking increases 10 times. For example, compare the Tangshan earthquake (magnitude 7.8) with one of magnitude 4.8—that is, 3 units smaller. The difference in amplitude is by a factor of 10 x 10 x 10, or 1000 times.

Faults

What causes earthquakes? Numerous legends, scientific and otherwise, are the heritage of every group of people who have to contend with serious earthquake hazards. Ancient Japanese entertained themselves with accounts of the thrashing body of a giant underground catfish. Famous in American earthquake lore are stories of the killer that leveled much of San Francisco in 1906, and it was this traumatic event that led to understanding how fault activity triggers a quake. You recall that the earth has been relatively displaced on the two sides of a fault. Along some faults the offset is tiny; for others the displacement is thousands of kilometers. A fault may be active or completely dead, plainly visible or concealed beneath sediment or ocean waters. Fault motion may be a continual slow creep, or occasional violent lurches (earthquakes).

Each different type of stress pattern produces a characteristic type of fault motion. For example, during the Tertiary Period (Chapter 13) an unusually high flow of heat from the earth's mantle under the western United States caused a large region to expand by bulging upward. As the overlying crust became stretched and thinned, it broke into long slivers separated by steeply inclined faults. Pull-apart, or *tensional* stress permits a block of earth called a *graben* (German for "ditch") to break away and drop down from the adjacent high-standing block, or *horst* (German for "high place"). A *normal*, or *gravity* fault is the result, in which the graben block is permitted to gravitate down the plane of the fault [Figure 16-5(*a*)]. Fluids may migrate easily through the shattered rock in the vicinity of a fault plane, where they precipitate valuable ore minerals. Once miners have excavated the ore from the fault zone, they have sufficient room to stand erect on the fault plane (even though steep). Beneath their feet is the *footwall* fault block, and over their heads looms the opposing fault block, the *hanging wall* [Figure 16-5(*a*)].

Regional uplift and normal faulting may operate on a grand scale of several kilometers of vertical displacement. In the Sangre de Cristo Range of Colorado and New Mexico, a spectacular front of lofty mountains (the horst) overlooks the adjacent valley (the graben). Uplift is always accompanied by erosion; as the mountainous block rises, streams are carving canyons into it, and dumping the sediment into the graben.

Just as compression is the opposite of tension, the motion on a resulting *reverse* fault is opposite to that on a normal fault. Compression forces the hanging wall block to ride *up* the plane of a reverse fault, contrary to the pull of gravity [Figure 16-5(*b*)]. Still another style of faulting develops under even more extreme compression. A large sheet of rock that might be as much as kilometers across becomes detached, and slides over the underlying block along a *thrust* fault. Unlike a reverse fault which is steep, the plane of a thrust fault is horizontal or at a shallow angle [Figure 16-5(*c*)]. In the Alps and Himalayas the rocks are arranged in a series of sheets that were folded and thrusted, one over the other, then eroded. These mountain structures remind us of a rug that is wrinkled into folds when skidded over a polished floor, or a mass of snow that is broken and telescoped together into a thick mound when bulldozed by a plow. Impressive as the vertical pile-up of these rocks may be, the distance of horizontal transport was greater by far.

Yet another type of stress produces a lateral wrenching action. Offset along a *strike-slip* fault is also chiefly horizontal, but side-by-side rather than over-the-top as in a thrust fault [Figure 16-5(*d*)]. It was strike-slip motion on the famous San Andreas Fault system in California that destroyed San Francisco in 1906 (Figure 16-6). As the seismologist H. F. Reid examined the data of repeated surveys across the trace of the San Andreas Fault, he noticed that from the viewpoint of an observer on one side of the fault, the ground on the far side is moving slowly toward the right. That is, the San Andreas is a *right-lateral* fault in which the ground on the east side of the fault is moving south with respect to ground on the west side.

Reid used this information to propose the *elastic rebound* theory of earthquakes. Suppose that we construct straight parallel lines across the fault (fences will do) to serve as reference markers [Figure 16-7(*a*)]. As strain builds up, the earth is distorted into an "S" shape (*b*), but the sides of the fault remain locked together by friction. The hang-up may be confined to just a few small areas called *asperities*, or "sticking points." Suddenly the asperities can resist the stress no longer; they become the *focus* of earthquake rupture, locally relieving the strain and allowing a fence row (and the earth beneath) to snap back into a straight line. For just an instant, intense compression develops between the rock that has rebounded elastically and adjacent rock that is still distorted (shaded areas, *c*). Immediately the fault "unzips" in both directions at a rate of 3 to 4 kilometers per second. Moments later, all the fence rows are straight again but offset (*d*), ready for the cycle to repeat the next time and the next.

During an earthquake the earth may rupture at the surface, or at some depth (Figure 16-8). In the latter instance a map of the surface would not locate the focus which lies buried in the third (vertical) dimension. Instead, the earthquake map depicts an *epicenter*, the point on the surface directly above the focus. In general, epicenters are of greatest interest to us because we live on the earth's surface.

Strain can accumulate [Figure 16-7(*b*)] only as long as the sides of the fault stick together. Because the strength of rocks is finite, there is an upper limit to the buildup of stress at any one spot before it ruptures, but in principle there is no limit to the length of a fault that can be torn apart as the rupture propagates. The amounts of energy released by different earthquakes vary over an enormous range.

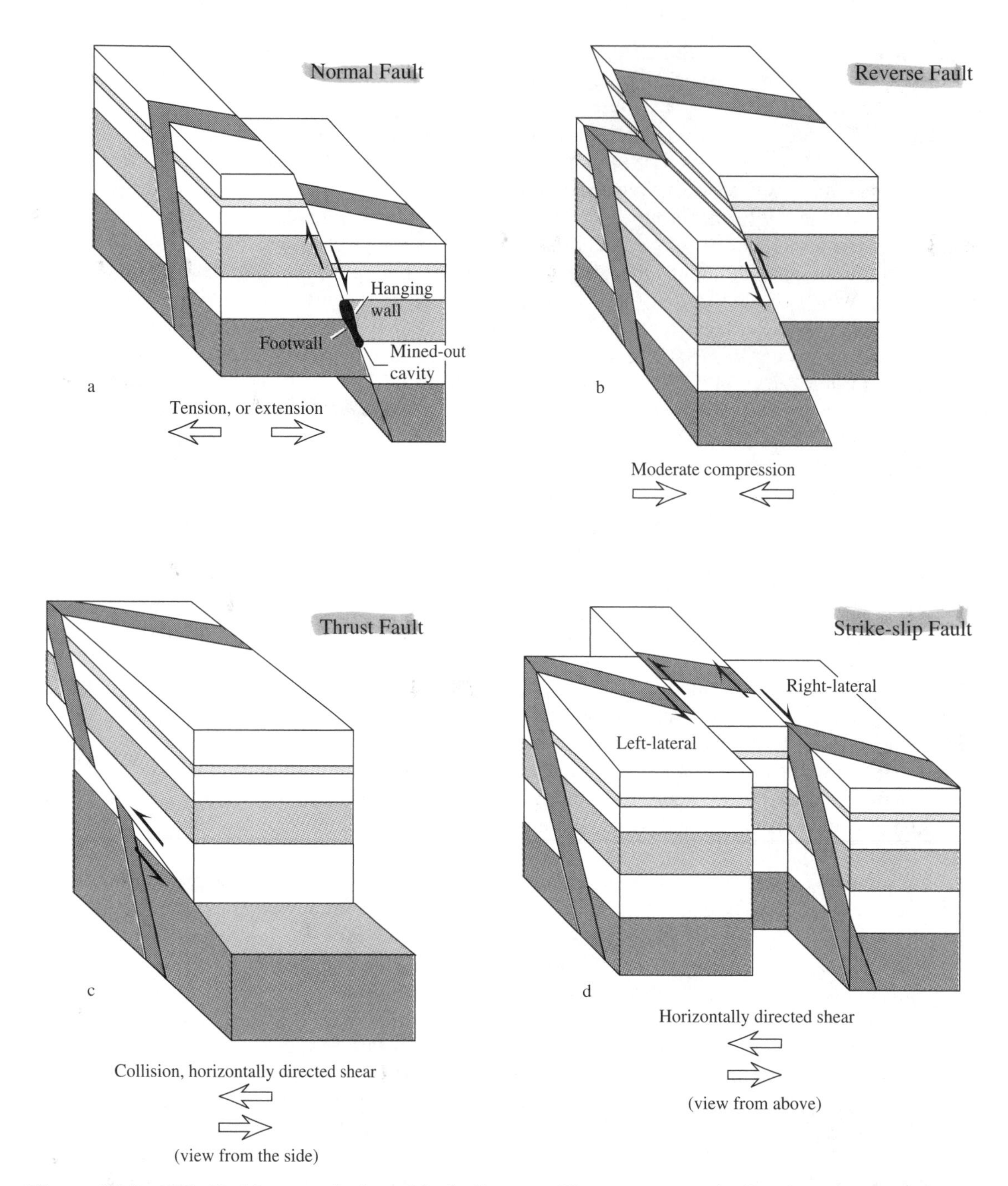

Figure 16-5. Filled half-arrows in these block diagrams illustrate types of offsetting motion along a normal fault (*a*), reverse fault (*b*), thrust fault (*c*), and right- and left-lateral strike-slip faults (*d*). Hollow arrows indicate the directions of opposing forces that cause failure of the earth along fault planes. On a right-lateral strike-slip fault (*d*), the ground on the far side of the fault moves to the right with respect to the ground on the near side; for a left-lateral fault, the ground on the far side moves relatively to the left. These descriptions of strike-slip movement are unambiguous and do not depend upon which side of the fault the observer is positioned.

Magnitude of the 1906 quake at San Francisco was 8.25, and significant damage occurs at magnitude 5.5 or above. The largest earthquake ever experienced, at magnitude 9.5, rocked the mostly uninhabited desert of Chile in 1960, and the second largest earthquake hit Anchorage, Alaska on Good Friday, 1964. In fact, just these two earthquakes together account for nearly 25% of the energy released from all of the millions of earthquakes ever recorded!

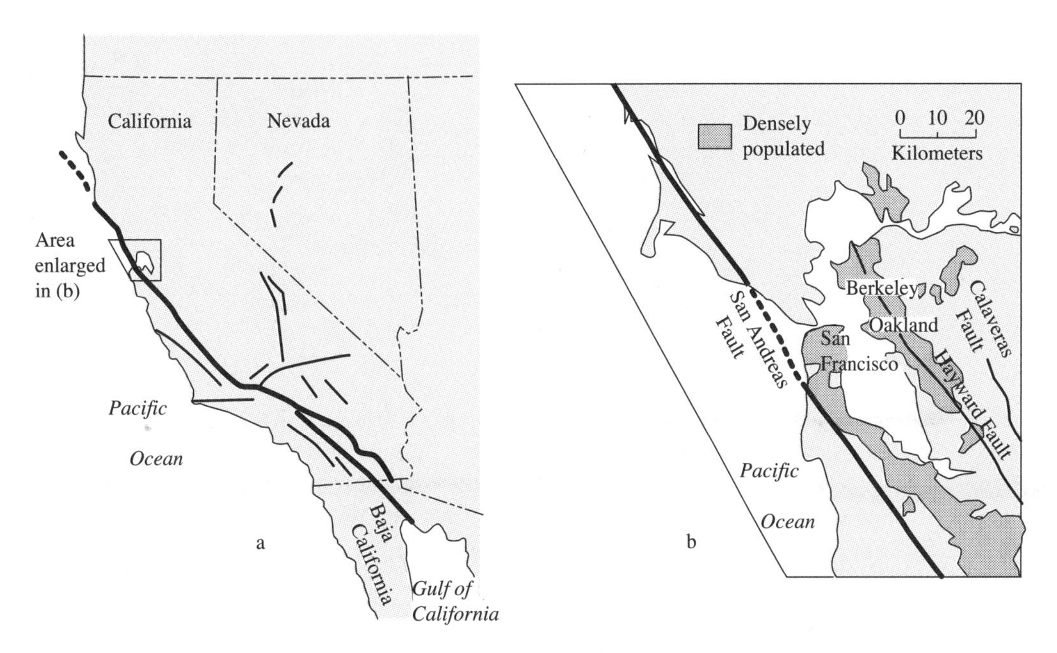

Figure 16-6. (*a*) The San Andreas Fault system (heavy line) intersects North America at the head of the Gulf of California and continues through most of the length of the state of California. It includes a number of subsidiary faults (thin lines). (*b*) Small lakes and deeply indented bays mark the trace of the San Andreas Fault near San Francisco. Earthquake damage in 1906 was greater in areas of unconsolidated fill, or "made land," which shook more violently than did tracts of solid bedrock. Since 1906 the Bay Area population has mushroomed, creating a land shortage. Developers have constructed housing subdivisions directly across the active faults, in which foolish landowners now live at their peril.

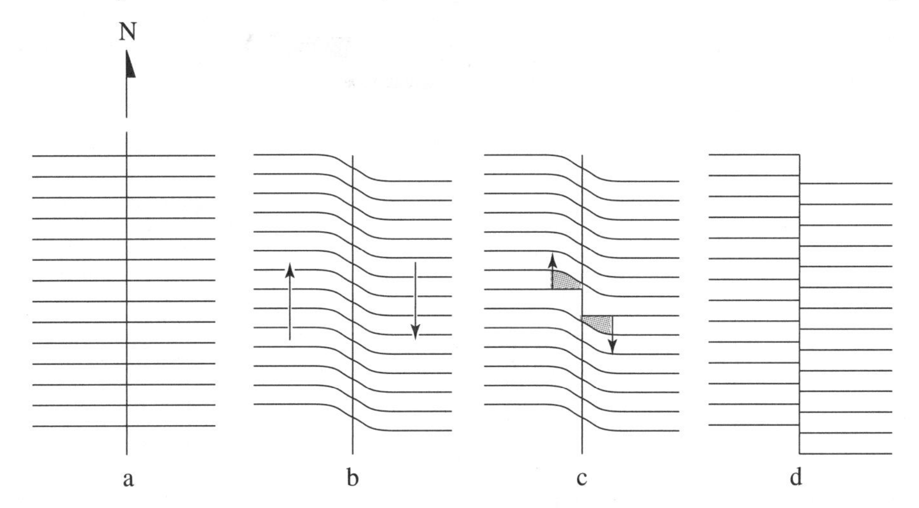

Figure 16-7. Map views indicate stages of strike-slip (horizontal) motion on the San Andreas Fault system. (*a*) Reference lines are established across the fault just after an earthquake has relieved previously accumulated strain. (*b*) Continued right-lateral movement (arrows) distorts the ground. (*c*) Immediately after initial rupture, intense local compression (shaded areas) causes fault movement to propagate. (*d*) Reference lines are again straightened but they are offset, awaiting repetition of the process.

Types of Seismic Wave

In some regards, the behavior of a wave is opposite to the behavior of a steady current. A stream flowing through a waterfall is an example of a steady current, in which the *substance* (the water) travels, but the *form* (the shape of the waterfall) remains stationary. In contrast, for a seismic wave it is the form, not the substance, that travels. After vibrating momentarily, the atoms comprising the medium return to their

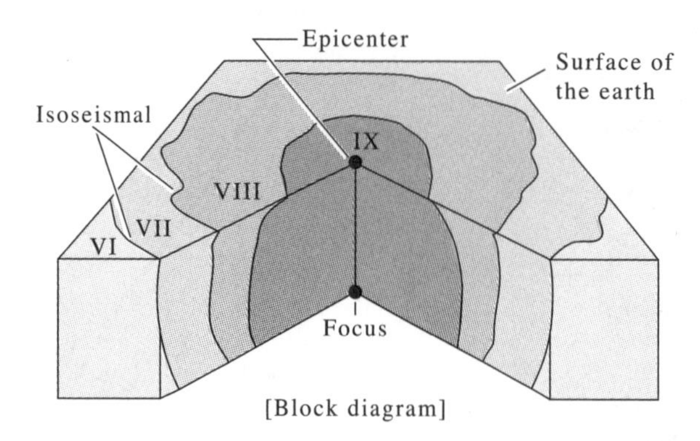

Figure 16-8. *Isoseismals,* or lines of equal earthquake intensity, form a bull's-eye pattern indicating that intensity diminishes away from the epicenter. Intensity could be described by the quantitative Richter magnitude scale or by the more descriptive Mercalli scale (roman numerals) based upon damage to human psyches and constructions. For example, sleepers are awakened (Zone V, not shown), windows and dishes are broken (Zone VI), large bells ring (Zone VII), chimneys collapse (Zone VIII), general panic prevails (Zone IX), etc.

original positions. An earthquake includes a disturbance of both form and substance. Only along the fault does the substance of the earth actually break, whereas seismic waves carry the message throughout the earth beyond. The rupture is permanent, but the vibration is temporary. Violent offsetting motion of the ground is an obvious source of damage, but the seismic waves that radiate out from large earthquakes can cause destruction many hundreds of kilometers from the epicenter.

A pebble dropped into a pond will help to illustrate the nature of seismic waves. Ripples spread outward from the point of impact, wrinkling the water's surface into a series of ridges and troughs (Figure 16-9). Each expanding concentric circle illustrates a *wavefront*—the shape of the wave form. Another way to describe wave motion is to trace a *ray path*, the line along which an infinitesimal

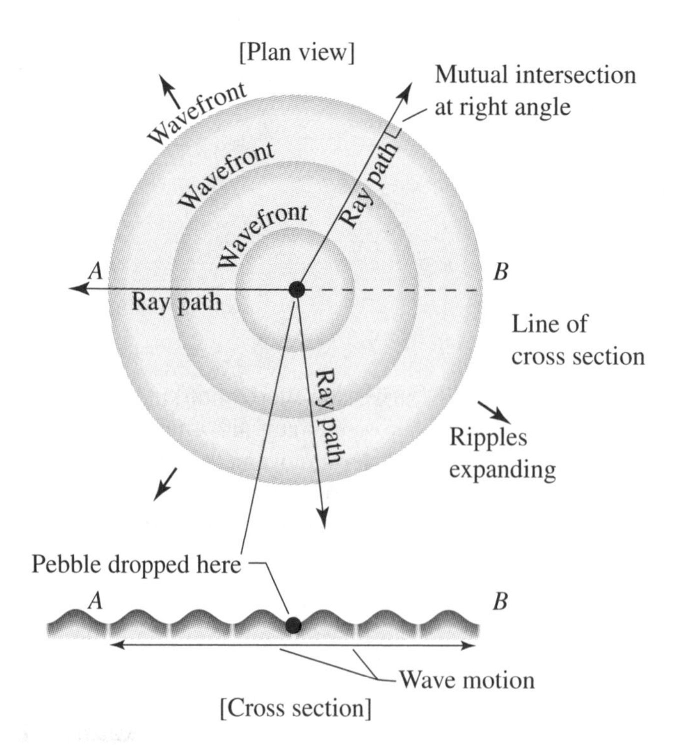

Figure 16-9. Three representative ray paths are shown out of an infinite number of possibilities. Ray paths intersect wavefronts at right angles.

"packet" of energy travels away from the focus. In the pond example, there are an infinite number of ray paths that are radii of the circular wavefronts. Ray paths intersect wavefronts everywhere at right angles.

Wavefronts and ray paths of seismic waves are a bit more complicated. Pond water has uniform properties throughout, whereas rocks are not homogeneous, and the shape of the three-dimensional earth is more complex than the two-dimensional surface of a pond. Moreover, an earthquake generates different kinds of seismic waves that travel at different speeds, and if these reflect off deep layers back to the surface, likely they will arrive at a distant point in a confused jumble.

During their passage, the seismic waves cause matter to deform by a momentary change of size or change of shape. Let's return to the cube of rock mentioned at the beginning of this chapter. As the cube becomes more deeply buried, the enclosing rock would exert more pressure, causing the cube to shrink. Pure *compression* would cause a change of size but not shape [Figure 16-10(*a*)]. In another setting the cube might be part of a mountain mass being deformed by thrusting. It would shear apart along numerous parallel planes, each thin slice accommodating movement, analogous to a pack of playing cards slipping past one another [Figure 16-10(*b*)]. With pure *shear*, the shape of the cube changes (it is thus no longer a cube) but its size does not change, which is an effect just the opposite to deformation by pure compression.

Let's put all this information together by considering two seismic wave types called *body waves* because they penetrate deep into the earth's interior (Table 16-1). One of them, the *primary*, or *P* wave, travels faster and is the first to arrive at a distant point. Suppose that atoms joined by chemical bonds were symbolized as a chain of little spheres connected together by springs [Figure 16-11(*a*)]. When a sphere is rammed against its neighbor, the spring located ahead of it is compressed while the spring behind it is extended. P waves are *compressional*, causing alternate zones of compression and extension to travel through the rock [Figure 16-12(*a*)]. As this occurs, the atoms move back-and-forth in a direction that is *parallel to* the direction the wavefront is traveling. Because the interaction between atoms is directly head-on, P-wave motion can be transmitted not only through a solid, but also through a liquid or gas in which chemical bonds are weak or almost absent.

Another body wave is the *secondary*, or *S* wave, so named because it travels more slowly, arriving later at a distant point (Table 16-1). S waves are *shear* waves in which the atoms vibrate in a plane that is *perpendicular to* the travel direction of the wavefront. In our analogy of a horizontal string of spheres

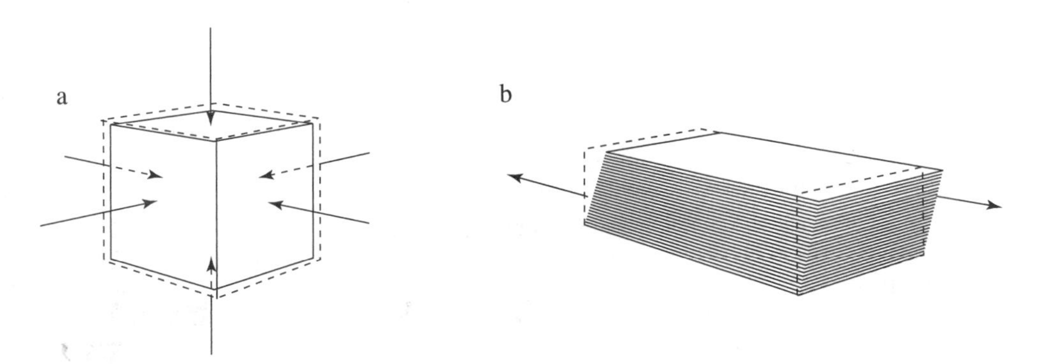

Figure 16-10. (*a*) Pure compression acting upon a volume of material would cause its size to shrink, but not change its shape. (*b*) Pure shear is illustrated by a pack in which playing cards slide past one another. Because each card maintains a constant volume, the shape of the pack changes but its size does not.

Table 16-1.

Body waves: travel *through* the earth
    P (primary, also compressional, *push-pull*: travels through any material)
    S (secondary, also *s*hear, *s*hake: travels only through solids)
Surface waves: travel *around* the earth
    L (for *long* wavelengths; includes Love and Rayleigh waves)

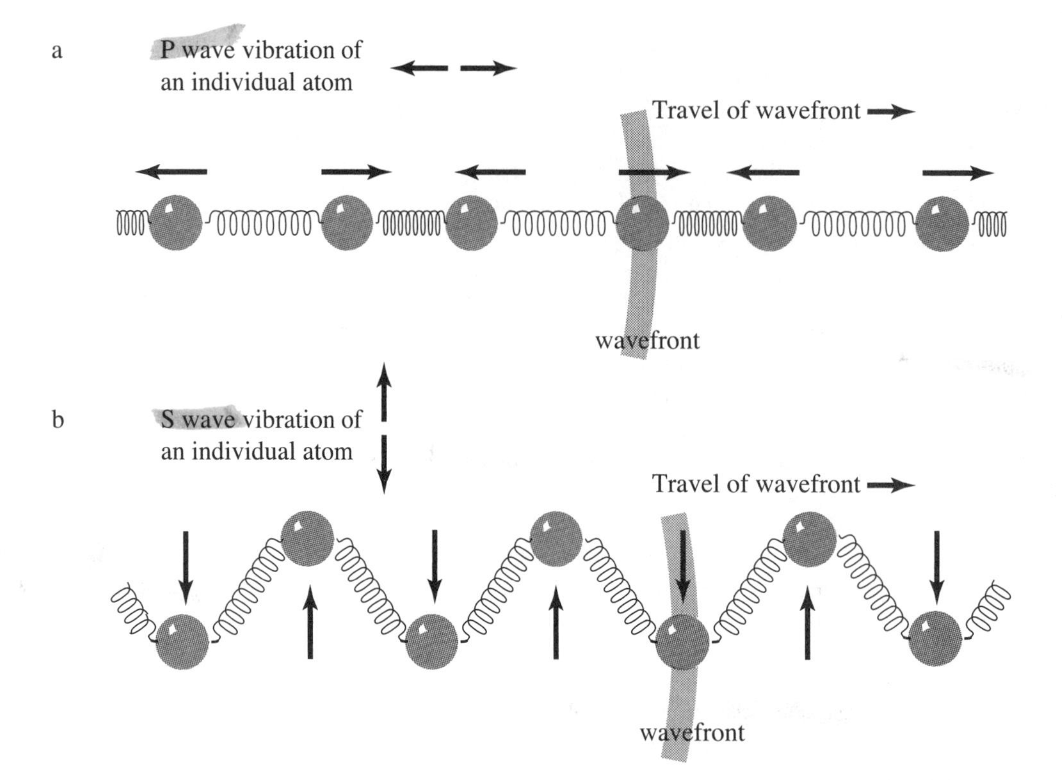

Figure 16-11. In this ball-and-spring analogy to atoms and chemical bonds in a material, a small segment of a wavefront (gray band) pictures the travel of wave energy from left to right. In solids, the atoms are connected to one another by strong chemical bonds, but in liquids and gases the bonds are weak to almost nonexistent. Ability of a substance to transmit P or S waves depends upon strengths and types of interaction of the bonds.

(atoms) connected by springs, as a sphere travels up or down the springs attached to it are stretched, pulling the adjoining spheres up or down [Figure 16-11(*b*), Figure 16-12(*b*)]. This interaction, being more side-by-side than head-on, can occur only if the springs (chemical bonds) are quite strong. Thus seismic S waves are transmitted *only through solid material.* Liquids and gases have no strength to resist being torn apart by shear. How much effort does it take to cut water using a pair of scissors?

A third type of wave motion is confined to the outermost part of the earth, the amplitude of shaking being sharply diminished at depth. These *surface waves* are also termed *L waves* because of their long wavelengths. One type of L wave, named after the British mathematician A. E. H. Love, causes matter to whipsaw horizontally rather like the motion of a sidewinder snake. Another type, the Rayleigh wave, causes the atoms to move through the form of an ellipse. In summary, body waves (P and S) travel *through* the earth and surface waves (L) travel *around* the earth.

Although surface waves travel more slowly than body waves, the concentration of L-wave energy near the earth's surface, coupled with large amplitude, can be highly damaging. Arrival of a P wave is experienced as a sharp jolt, whereas surface waves cause a prolonged swaying. If the rhythm of swaying of a large building is "in tune" with the period of surface-wave motion, the building may collapse.

Finally, a large earthquake may cause the entire earth to reverberate as a bell does when struck. In these *free oscillations*, the earth may expand and deflate like breathing in and breathing out, or it may experience more complicated motions. A strainmeter (Figure 16-13) measures the very long-period waves that require many minutes or even longer for a single vibration.

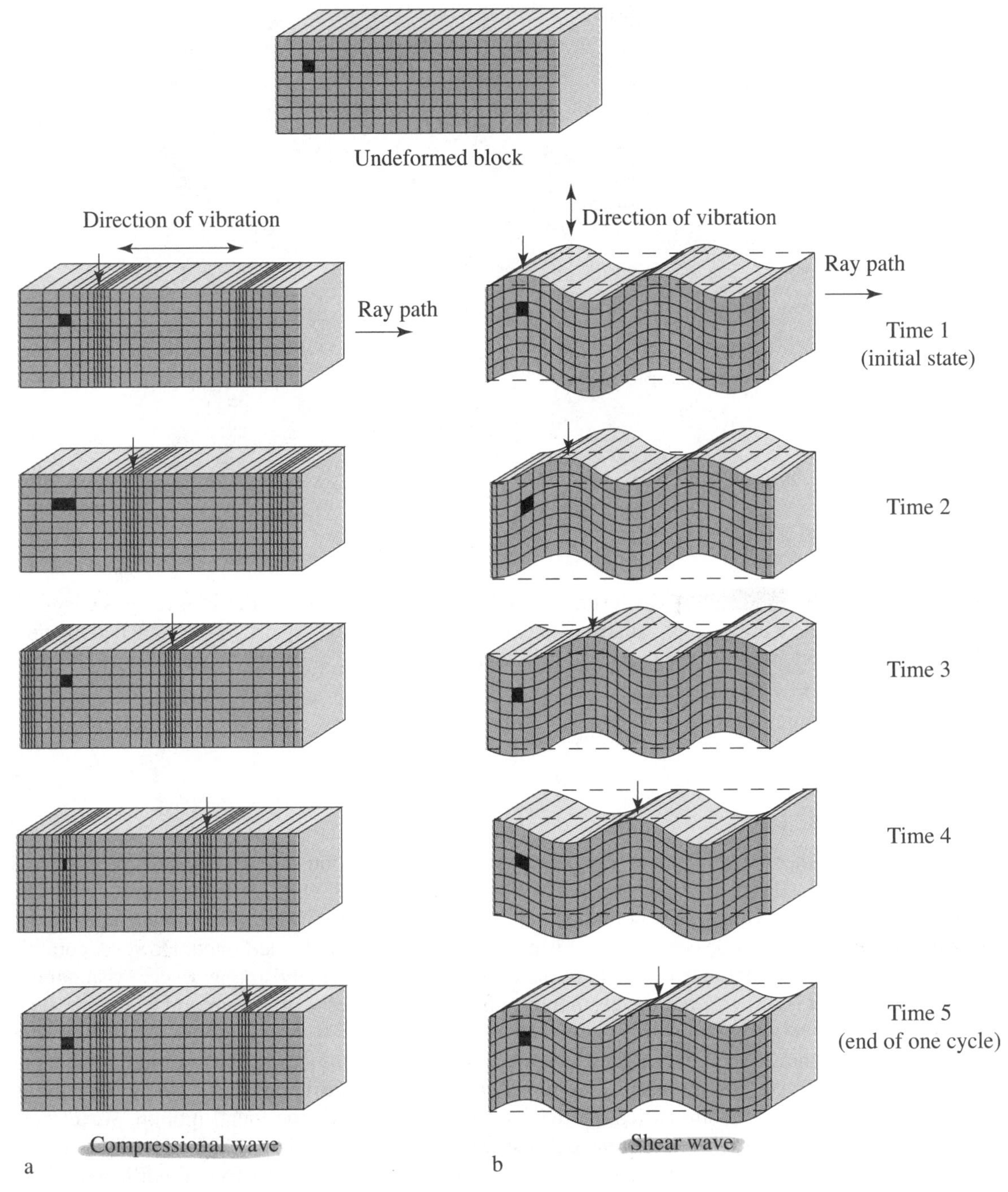

Figure 16-12. (*a*) As a compressional wavefront (vertical arrow) moves to the right, a small reference cube (black) undergoes alternate expansions and contractions. Both its volume and shape vary as the wave form sweeps by. (*b*) The shape, but not the volume, of a small reference cube changes when it is deformed by a shear wave. [*After O. M. Phillips*, The Heart of the Earth, *Freeman, Cooper, & Co., San Francisco, 1968.*]

Figure 16-13. In this strainmeter which is mounted in a tunnel in bedrock, a detector records changes of as little as 1 part in a billion in the distance between two piers. A long quartz rod is attached to one of the piers, and motion is measured between the other end of the rod and a reference point on the second pier. [*Teledyne Geotech photograph.*]

Detecting Seismic Waves

To our knowledge, the first earthquake wave detector was invented about AD 132 by a Chinese man of genius, Chang Heng (Figure 16-14). Although it was a crude affair that responded only to violent motions, at least it could indicate an approximate direction toward the epicenter. Only much later did the *seismograph*—a device that detects and records earth motion—begin to be perfected. However complicated the modern instrument may be, its principle of operation is extremely simple. Every seismograph contains a mass that is suspended in space, therefore free to move relative to the ground (Figure 16-15). Its supporting framework is bolted to a heavy concrete slab or directly into bedrock. When a seismic wave arrives, everything shakes except the isolated mass which remains steady, thus setting up a relative motion between the mass and its suspending apparatus. As Figure 16-15 indicates, one instrument is designed to measure and record vertical motion; another detects only horizontal motion. Wavefronts approaching a seismograph station at some oblique angle would activate both kinds of motion. A well equipped station would contain three instruments to receive motions in the east-west, north-south, and vertical directions.

Locating Distant Earthquake Epicenters

As earthquake waves sweep past a station, the seismograph makes a *seismogram,* a permanent record of the time of arrival and the amplitude of wave vibration. Whether the motion is registered directly in visual form, or electronically for computer processing, the seismogram reveals information about the earthquake itself and the nature of the earth through which the waves have traveled. First let's examine how to locate the epicenter of the earthquake. An actual seismogram obtained over a 24-hour period at Alert, a remote station in Arctic Canada, illustrates the procedure. In the instrument at Alert, the seismogram was recorded on paper as a line that winds round and round a drum, one revolution of the spiral for each hour of the day. Uncurled, the drum chart exhibits rather straight lines indicating quiet, except where interrupted by violent wiggles when the seismograph was thrown into motion [Figure 16-16(*a*)]. Every minute, a dot was imprinted on the chart to keep track of the passage of time [Figure 16-16(*b*)].

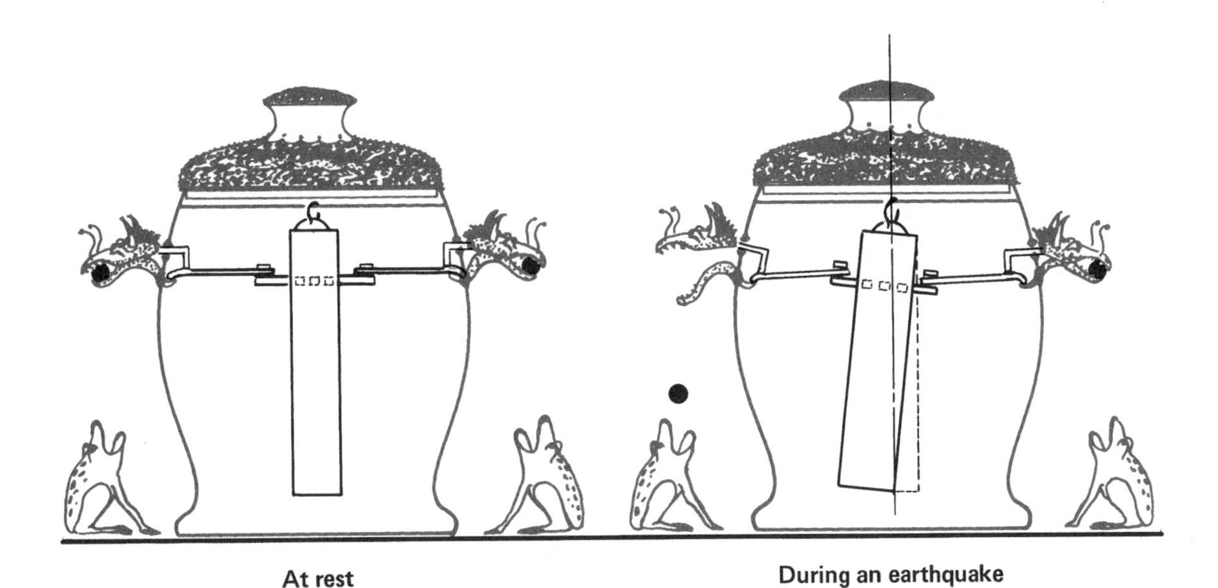

Figure 16-14. Inside a bronze jar was suspended a pendulum (vertical rod) attached to a wheel with eight spokes. When an earthquake shook the jar, the pendulum moved certain of the spoke levers depending upon the direction of swinging, causing a ball to drop out of the mouth of the dragon into the eager waiting mouth of a frog below. This device indicated the direction of motion of the ground, which provided information about the direction toward the earthquake epicenter. [*After J. T. Wilson, "Mao's Almanac,"* Saturday Review, *Feb. 19, 1972.*]

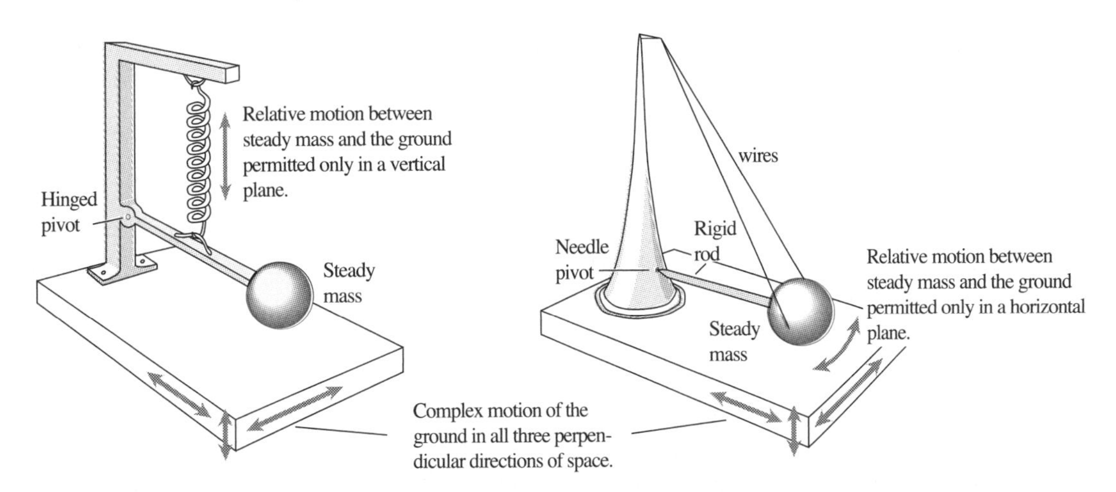

Figure 16-15. Simplified models illustrate how vertical or horizontal motions create a relative movement between a steady mass and the remainder of the apparatus. Different instruments are tuned to respond to longer or shorter frequencies of vibration, typically in the range of a few seconds to a fraction of a second.

Consider a simple case, an earthquake whose focus is near to the earth's surface. All three seismic wave types are generated together and at the same time, but the P wave promptly speeds ahead of the others while the L wave lags behind. A seismograph located even a short distance away would record three separated wave arrivals: P, followed by S, and finally L. A more distant seismograph would record later arrivals, and longer time separations between them. We can distinguish which station is relatively far or near, but exactly how distant?

Not only is the earth approximately spherical but its internal layers are also concentric spheres like the layers of an onion (review the crust, mantle, and core in Figure 2-16). In view of this symmetry, the

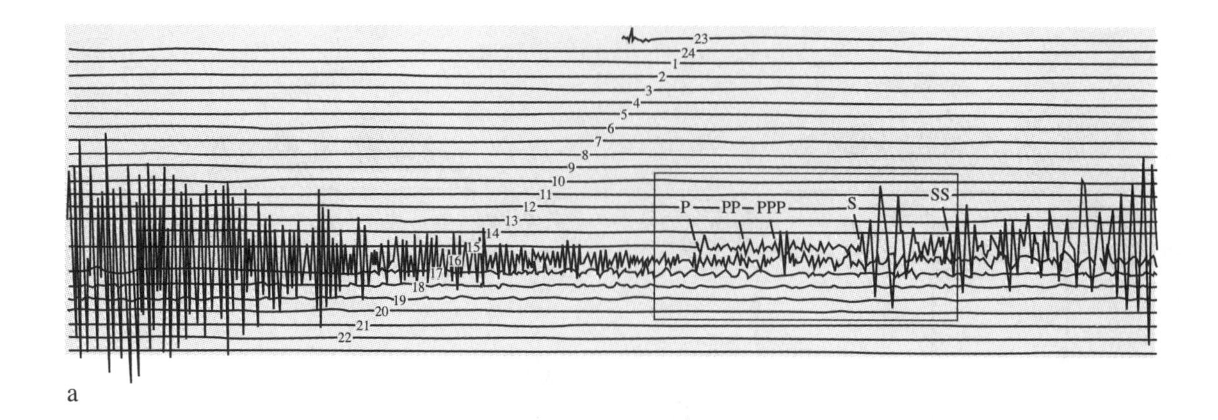

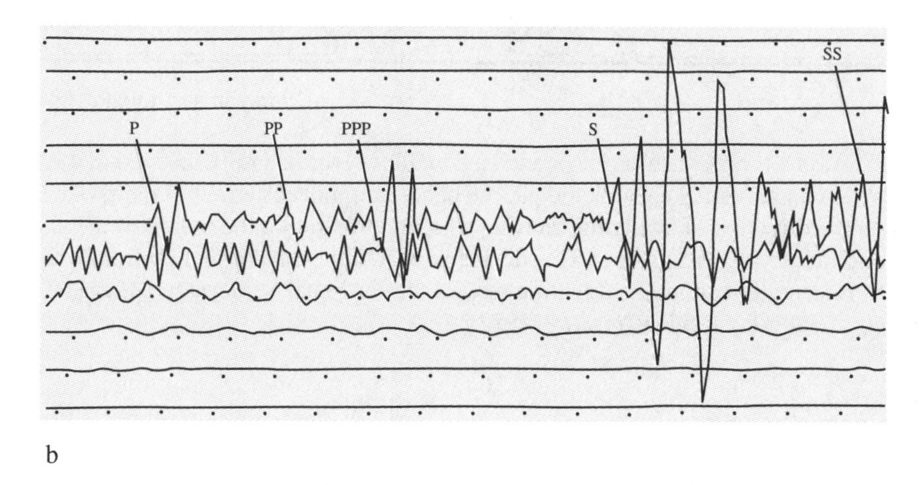

Figure 16-16. (*a*) The seismogram for May 18, 1962, at Alert was recorded on a chart, one line for each hour of the day. (*b*) Wave arrivals are seen more distinctly in an enlarged part of the record (enclosed by the box above). Dots register the passage of each minute. *PP*, *PPP*, and *SS* are P and S waves that had previously reached the earth's surface at a distant point, only to be reflected down and back up again one or two times. [*After J. H. Hodgson*, Earthquakes and Earth Structure, *Prentice-Hall, Inc., Englewood Cliffs, NJ, 1964.*]

ray paths along which body waves and surface waves transmit energy are similar for an earthquake occurring at any arbitrary time or place. This permits us to construct a globally valid *time-distance graph* to describe the travel characteristics of P, S, and L waves [Figure 16-17(*a*)]. It is based upon observations of waves generated by earthquakes and large explosions whose times and locations were known, and now we may use the information in the inverse sense to locate an earthquake (or atomic bomb blast) whose timing and epicenter are initially unknown.

Point (0,0) in Figure 16-17(*a*) refers to the time of the earthquake and position of the epicenter. Note that the P and S curves flatten out with increasing distance and travel time, whereas the line for L waves is straight. As P and S waves descend into the body of the earth they encounter material whose dramatically different elastic properties cause the waves to speed up. In contrast, surface waves penetrate only the outermost part of the earth where the elastic properties are approximately uniform; therefore L waves travel at roughly constant speed. (More precise analyses reveal variations of two percent or so in the time-distance curves for different parts of the earth. For example, body waves speed through the mantle beneath the Canadian Shield faster than through the mantle beneath Hawaii, and surface waves traverse the ocean floor more rapidly than through continental crust. These tiny deviations provide further clues to the structure of the earth's crust and mantle, to which we shall return.)

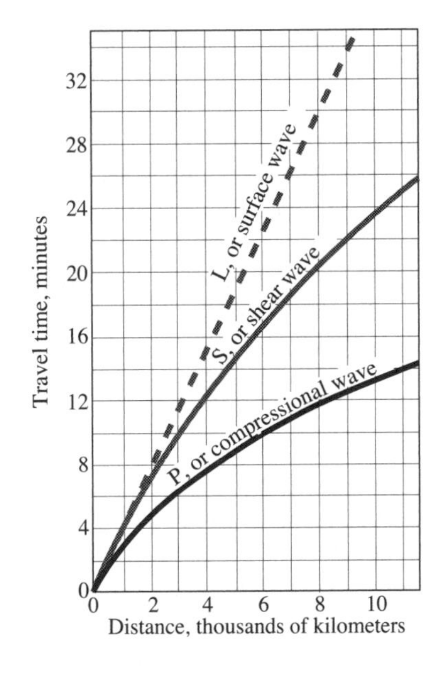

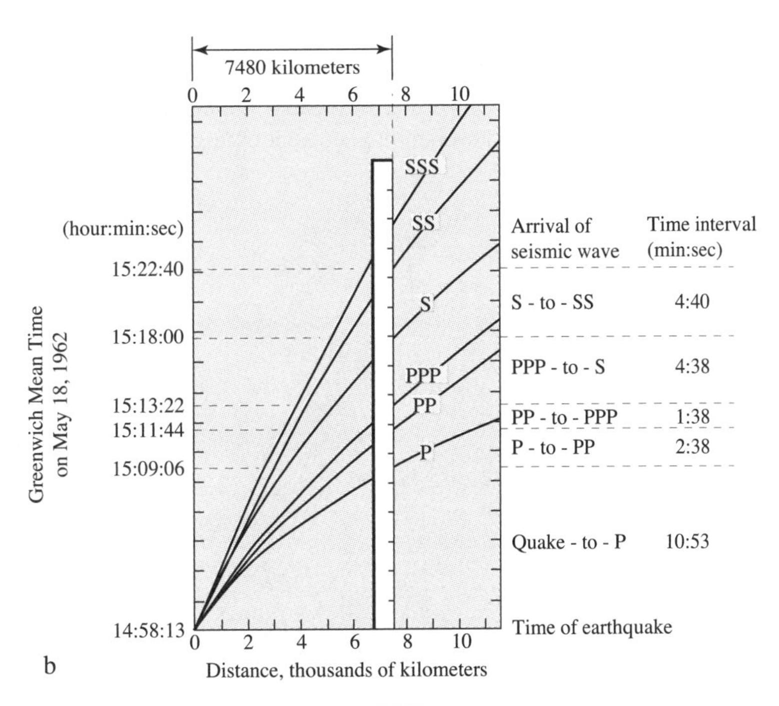

Figure 16-17. (*a*) To a first approximation, a time-distance graph describes the travel of P, S, and L waves for earthquakes at all times and all places. (*b*) In this more elaborate time-distance graph, the wave arrivals from the May 18, 1962, earthquake are recorded. Time intervals observed between arrivals of the various waves at Alert must be the same as the time intervals between curves, given by the time scale along the vertical axis of the graph. A good match corresponds to a distance of 7480 kilometers between Alert and the epicenter. The entire graph may "float" up or down to adjust the beginning of wave travel to the time of day when the earthquake occurred, which in this case was 14:58:13 Greenwich Mean Time.

Consider the sequence of observations at a distant seismograph station such as the one at Alert. Seismic waves began to travel out from the epicenter at "time zero," but several minutes were to elapse before the arrival of the P wave alerted the Canadian seismologists that an earthquake had occurred. Once the S wave had swept by, 8 minutes and 54 seconds later, the seismologists (and we) are prepared to calculate the distance to the epicenter. It is the distance that corresponds to a delay between arrivals of P and S equal to 8 minutes, 54 seconds. We may use the time axis of Figure 16-17(*b*) to transfer an interval symbolizing this duration of time onto a loose strip of paper. Then we slide this little piece of the vertical scale along the P curve to the point where it just fills the gap between the P and S curves. On the time-distance graph, the match-up corresponds to a distance of 7480 kilometers (4650 miles) from the epicenter. Other time intervals such as between arrivals of S and L, or between P and L, would have served the calculation just as effectively.

What about direction? The epicenter could lie on any point of a circle, centered upon Alert, whose radius is 7480 kilometers. The same is true of a circle that is centered on some other seismograph station for its appropriate station-to-quake distance. Seismologists in Pasadena, California, determined the distance to be 2690 kilometers, and those in Palisades, New York, found it to be 3605 kilometers (Figure 16-18). All three distances are simultaneously correct where the circles intersect in west-central Mexico. Large earthquakes may register at a hundred or more stations around the world, thus providing statistical information to obtain a precise "fix" on the epicenter.

Finally, the time that the earthquake occurred is easily obtained once the distance is known. According to Figure 16-17(*b*), the P wave had been traveling 10 minutes, 53 seconds before arriving at Alert at 15:09.06 Greenwich Mean Time (GMT). Subtracting, we find that the earthquake occurred at 14:58.13 GMT. Analyses of seismograms at Pasadena and Palisades, although indicating different distances to the epicenter, provided the same answer for the timing of the quake.

Deep-Focus Earthquakes

As mentioned, the earth's bulging equator and flattened polar regions imply that rock in the interior has almost no strength. Deep material should deform continually, rather than storing up the strain that is released suddenly during an earthquake. But seismologists kept noting peculiar signals from some earth-

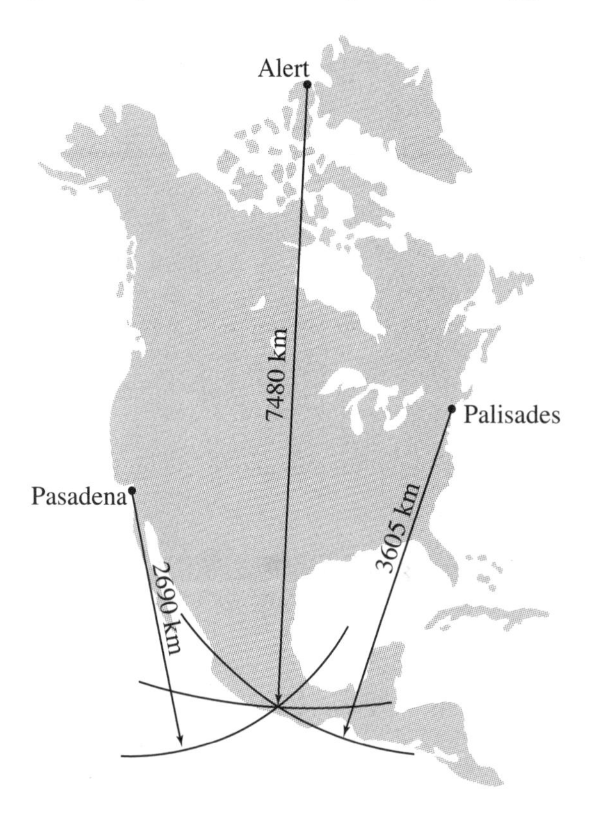

Figure 16-18. Stations in Alert, Canada, in Pasadena, California, and in Palisades, New York, recorded the shock on May 18, 1962. Circles, whose radii correspond to distances calculated in a similar manner for each station, intersect in west-central Mexico, a region of active faulting and volcanic activity. This unusually severe earthquake killed 3 people, injured 16 others, and caused extensive damage to property. [*After J. H. Hodgson,* Earthquakes and Earth Structure, *Prentice-Hall, Inc., Englewood Cliffs, NJ, 1964.*]

quakes that contradict this expectation. Surface waves were weak or absent, and distance calculations revealed that *no* station was very close to the focus, even in regions with many quakes and many stations. Damage to structures might be slight (though widely distributed) even for very powerful events. All of these symptoms could be explained only by postulating *deep-focus* earthquakes, as deep as 690 kilometers (420 miles) beneath the surface. Deep-focus earthquakes are peculiarly concentrated into narrow belts, especially around the margin of the Pacific Ocean. Intensive research has failed to explain the earthquake mechanism, which definitely is not triggered by elastic rebound as described for the San Andreas Fault. Possibly the deep-focus earthquakes involve the sudden collapse of mineral structures into more densely packed arrangements of atoms.

PROBING THE DEEP INTERIOR

Now that we can locate seismic disturbance, what more can we learn about the deep earth through which the P and S energy has traveled? To get started, let's examine some other aspects of the behavior of wavefronts and ray paths, described above for water ripples in a pond (Figure 16-9). As P and S waves pass downward into the earth, they encounter a more and more *dense* medium. Deep material is composed of dense ferromagnesian minerals, and the weight of overlying rock compresses it to an even higher density. Review Figure 16-10 which illustrates how a substance can be deformed by pure compression or pure shear. Deep material is highly *incompressible*; it is already so compressed that it is resistant to being compressed even more. It is also highly *rigid*, resistant to deformation by shearing. Incompressibility and rigidity are mechanical properties that describe the physical strength of a material. If increasing density were the only influential factor, the P and S waves would slow down, but associated increases in rigidity and incompressibility cause the waves to speed up. As a net effect of these opposing factors, the waves speed up as they go deeper.

Let us represent incompressibility by the quantity *B*, rigidity by the quantity *G*, and density by the Greek letter *rho* (ρ). Velocity of a shear wave (v_{shear}) is given by the simple formula

$$v_{shear} = \sqrt{\frac{G}{\rho}}.$$

Liquids or gases have no shear strength (no rigidity); G = 0, and therefore according to the formula, $v_{shear} = 0$. We have already noted that shear waves do not travel through a substance that lacks rigidity. In contrast, P waves travel through any material, with a velocity ($v_{compressional}$) given by the formula

$$v_{compressional} = \sqrt{\frac{B + \frac{4}{3}G}{\rho}}.$$

A value of *B* or *G* is either zero or some positive number. Thus the formulas state what we have already learned, that P waves *must* travel faster than S waves. Fortunately the situation is quite simple, because these velocities depend upon *B*, *G*, and ρ which refer only to properties of the material. Whether the waves originated naturally from earthquakes or artificially from explosions, whether they are large or small in amplitude, and whether they have traveled a long or short distance does not matter. By comparing wave velocities in the earth with velocities determined in the laboratory for basalt or other familiar rock types, we may deduce what kinds of rock likely occupy the depths of the earth.

A wavefront expands downward as a three-dimensional "shell," but the speeding-up process causes the deepest part of the wavefront to go faster and farther. Thus the wavefronts become elongated downward, and ray paths, which cross wavefronts at right angles, are gentle curves (Figure 16-19). P and S energy descends into the earth along these ray paths, then returns to the surface. Some seismic energy skims shallowly through the earth, and some travels via steeper and deeper ray paths and so, in principle, the entire planet can be "sampled" by the passage of seismic waves.

Core, Outer and Inner

By the first part of the 20th Century, seismologists had constructed the time-distance graph and were locating epicenters worldwide. Soon they discovered a signature of far-traveled seismic waves that provides

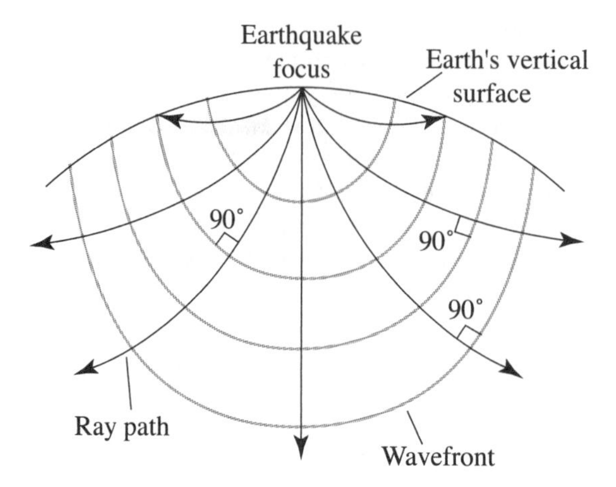

Figure 16-19. Wavefronts in the earth are elongated downward; ray paths are gentle curves.

remarkable evidence for the existence of a central core. Body-wave arrivals are registered up to a distance of about 103° (or 11,500 kilometers around the circumference of the globe) from an earthquake epicenter, but more distant seismograph stations receive neither P nor S waves. A ray path that emerges at 103° must have barely avoided a deep obstruction, the core [Figure 16-20(*a*)]. Wave energy that descends along a more steep ray path will encounter the core, there to be sent off in some other direction.

In fact, S is absent from 103° all the way to the far side of the earth at 180° [Figure 16-20(*a*)]. Shear-wave energy cannot pass through the core, and since these waves travel through solids only, we conclude that the core must have the properties of a liquid. At first thought this seems impossible because how can a liquid core, having no shear strength, support a solid mantle? It is density, not strength that counts. For example, liquid water supports floating solid ice simply because the water is more dense.

Very high pressure at the core-mantle boundary, which is 1.4 million atmospheres (20 million pounds per square inch), cannot cause the material of the core to be liquid. On the contrary, application

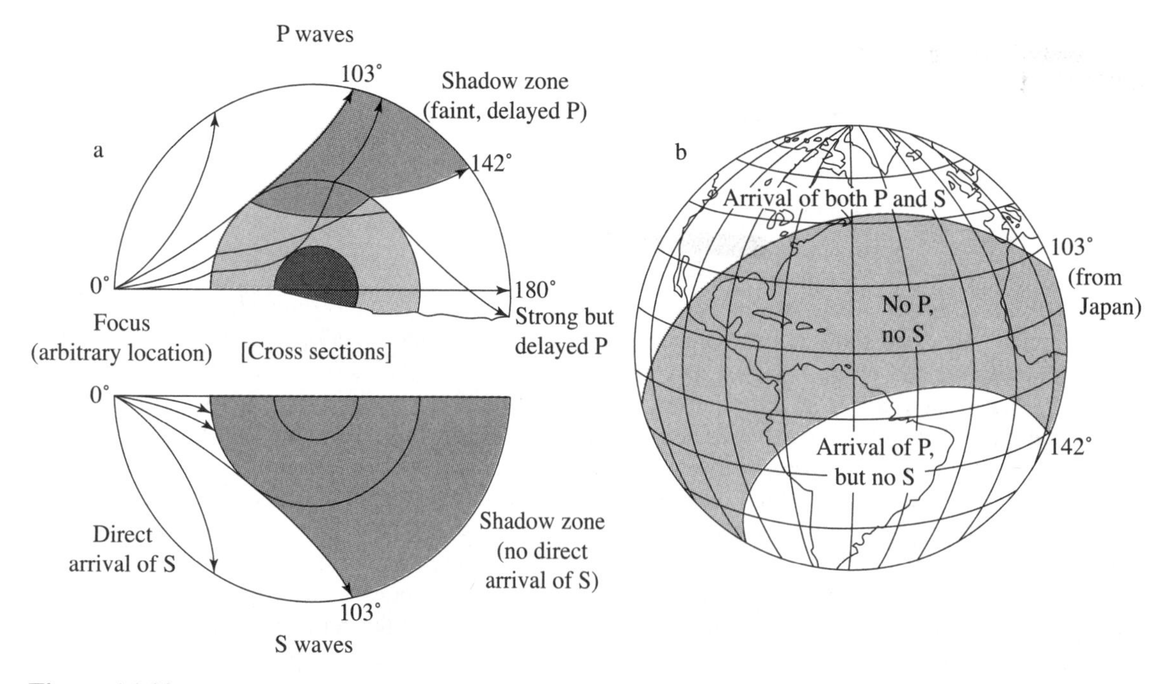

Figure 16-20. (*a*) Cross sections picture certain of the P and S seismic ray paths coming from a focus at the surface of the earth. (Only half of the symmetrical earth is shown.) Ray paths that intersect the core are either stopped (S waves) or diverted from the shadow zone except for very weak P waves (color) that are refracted by the inner core. (*b*) The earth's core casts this shadow zone in the path of seismic waves originating in Japan.

of pressure would have the opposite effect, transforming a liquid into a solid. (This is because freely moving atoms in a liquid tend to remain far apart. At high pressure the atoms are forced into tightly locked positions characteristic of a solid.) Meanwhile the mantle material remains solid even at a white-hot temperature estimated to approach 4000°C. The mantle and core do not differ because of the environment, but because they are composed of different substances.

Inasmuch as the core occupies a substantial 1/6 of the volume of the earth, it would plausibly consist of a material that is generally abundant in the solar system. This substance at high temperature and pressure must be a liquid with a density of about 10 g/cm^3. Experiments show that the silicate or oxide minerals common in stony meteorites (Chapter 2) would not be nearly dense enough even under such enormous pressure, but the alloy of iron-nickel meteorites would actually be a bit too dense. If just small amounts of lighter elements such as oxygen or silicon were mixed with this alloy, the density and the liquid condition would be nicely explained. These ingredients could come from silicate or oxide constituents of the mantle that are slowly dissolving into the core material. A molten core made of iron-nickel alloy is our best hypothesis, and it holds some other interesting possibilities. For one thing, it would be a good conductor of electricity.

P waves, which are compressional, can travel through a liquid but as they pass from solid lower mantle into liquid outer core, they abruptly slow down. A law of optics states that if the speed of a wave changes as it passes from one medium into another, the ray path is bent, or *refracted*. Just as a glass lens refracts light waves, the core acts as a giant lens that refracts seismic waves. Ray paths that pass through the core are kinked, and they even may cross one another [Figure 16-20(*a*)]. At the earth's surface between 103° and 142° from an earthquake epicenter there is a belt, called a *shadow zone*, that receives neither P nor S waves [Figure 16-20(*b*)]. The core diverts the P-wave energy away from the shadow zone, and focuses it instead into a circular region capping the earth at the far end, 142° to 180° distant from the epicenter.

Years after the core was discovered, improved seismographs demonstrated that P waves, very faint and late in arrival, in fact were getting into the shadow zone. This observation is explained by the presence of an *inner* core occupying the central 15 percent of the core (or less than 1 percent of the volume of the entire earth). Presumably the inner core is also made of iron-nickel alloy, solidified by the intense pressure of up to 3.6 million atmospheres at the center of the earth. There is evidence that crystals in this solid material are aligned in one direction (rather like foliation in a metamorphic rock), and that the inner core is actually spinning more rapidly than the earth's daily rotation. The molten outer core effectively blocks the seismic signals, making it very difficult to obtain data about the inner core.

During the journey of seismic wave energy throughout the earth, some is *reflected* from deep layers up toward the surface, or even from the surface back into the depths. Pathways may be quite complicated, for instance for a P wave that is refracted as it enters the outer core, then reflected off the surface of the inner core, then refracted again as it re-enters the mantle on the return to the surface. Arrivals of multiple reflections and refractions may clutter the seismogram, but they also bear subtle information. For example, they indicate that vigorous chemical and physical interactions are taking place in a complex layer at the contact between the core and mantle.

Mantle, Upper and Lower

Although the mantle almost everywhere lies below the bottom of the deepest drill hole, nature has put mantle rocks within our reach in a few places. In Oman, a desert nation in the southeastern corner of the Arabian Peninsula, thick slices of oceanic crust with a bit of attached mantle have been shoved up over the continent along thrust faults. Entire mountain ranges of this once-deep material are exposed there by erosion. Elsewhere, especially in the Southern Hemisphere, "belches" of gas from the mantle have explosively drilled vertical pipes up through the crust. These are filled with a rubble of crustal and mantle fragments, and some of them contain diamonds which can form only at a high pressure not attainable except in the mantle.

About the time that evidence for the core was first recognized, the seismologist A. Mohorovicic (Mo-hoaro-VEE-chik) noted peculiar double arrivals of P and S waves at stations near an earthquake in his native Croatia. He concluded that the waves had echoed off an interface, or internal surface at a depth of some 50 kilometers (30 miles). By today, countless seismograms generated by earthquakes and explosions have enabled geophysicists to map the *Mohorovicic discontinuity* (or simply "Moho" to all of us lazy tongue-tied people). Present throughout most of the world, the Moho is the buried boundary between crust lying upon mantle. P waves abruptly speed up as they descend through the Moho into mantle rock of higher density, incompressibility, and rigidity. In places the Moho is almost knife-sharp;

elsewhere it is a broader transition zone. Oman provides a fascinating insight where a sharp Moho boundary is exposed on mountain slopes. Dark, dense mantle rock beneath the Moho is seen to be *ultramafic*, composed of little else besides olivine and pyroxene which are ferromagnesian minerals.

To understand the deeper mantle, we use laboratory simulations and geophysical data to supplement these meager scraps of direct observation. The crust and uppermost mantle are rigid, strong, and relatively cool. Increasing temperature at depth would cause material to melt, whereas increasing pressure inhibits melting. Beginning at a depth of tens of kilometers under an ocean, and 150 or so kilometers under a continent, is a *low-velocity layer* in the mantle. In this region the opposing influences of pressure and temperature are delicately balanced such that the mantle is just at the verge of melting (Figure 16-21). It takes only a fraction of a percent of melted material to weaken the mantle and slow down the passage of body waves, and in fact, high-frequency S waves almost fail to get through this zone. Presence of a low-velocity layer raises some other intriguing possibilities. Basaltic magma originates through slight melting of the ultramafic mantle rock in the low-velocity layer. There is also opportunity for the rigid external part of the earth to slide laterally over this weak material which acts as a "lubricant."

Several more abrupt discontinuities are found deeper in the mantle, a prominent one being at 690 kilometers which happens also to be the maximum depth of any earthquake. Experiments suggest that these changes of seismic properties are created by high pressure which causes the oxygen atoms in silicate minerals to rearrange into a more tight packing. Four oxygens surround a silicon atom in the silicon-oxygen tetrahedron (Chapter 3), but at very high pressure, six oxygens crowd around a silicon. Figure 16-22 summarizes density and other physical characteristics of the mantle and core.

Crust, Oceanic and Continental

From a geophysical point of view, the crust is hardly more than a thin "scum" coating the earth. Truly the crust is the daughter of the mantle. Basaltic magma has ascended from the mantle to build the ocean floor, and even the numerous varieties of continental rock initially were mantle material that has gone through repeated differentiations, sortings, and recyclings.

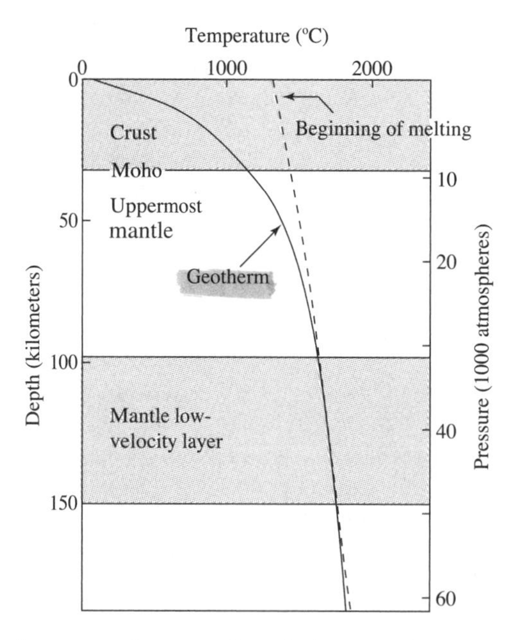

Figure 16-21. The *geotherm* is a curve that describes the increase in temperature with increasing depth in the earth. Just beneath the surface the temperature increases sharply, continuing to rise somewhat more gradually at greater depth. A broken curve shows that at greater depth (greater pressure), a higher temperature is needed for rocks to begin to melt. At shallow depth the rocks are not hot enough to melt, whereas at great depth, high pressure prevents melting. In the low-velocity layer the temperature and pressure factors are balanced such that hot but solid rock is weakened, or a tiny fraction of it is actually melted. Figure 16-22 shows how narrow the low-velocity layer is in whole-earth perspective.

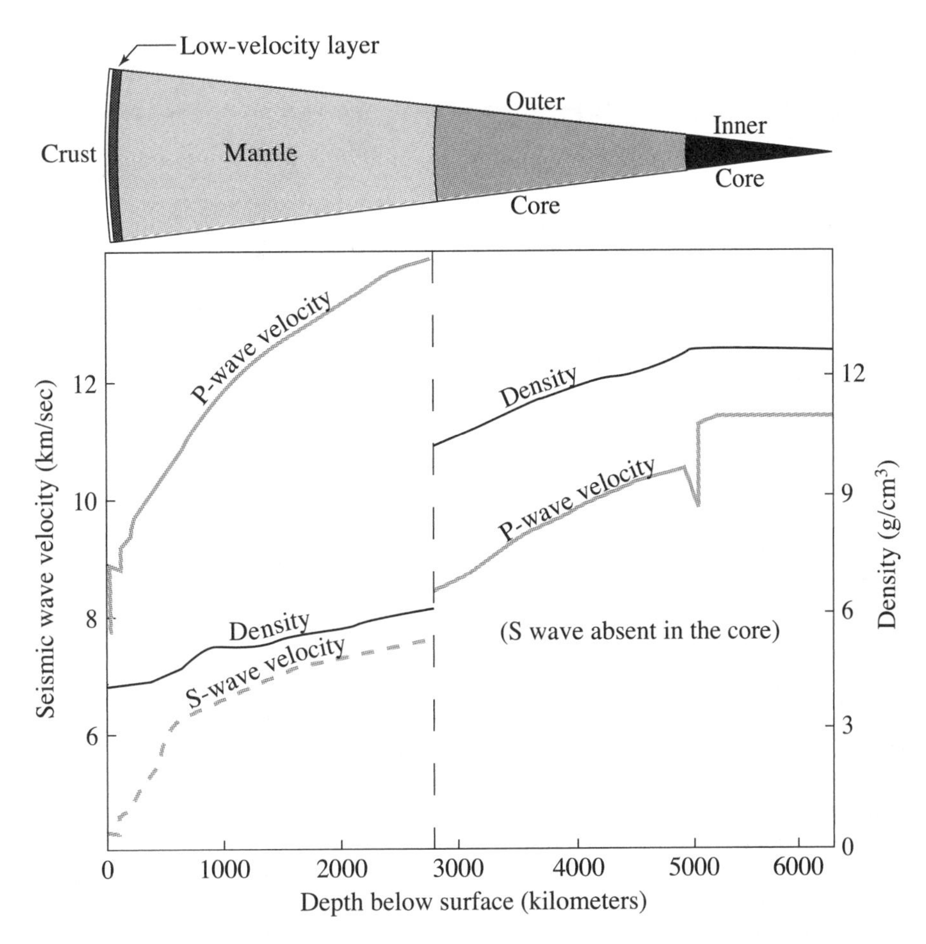

Figure 16-22. Density of the earth and velocities of seismic waves increase downward in the mantle. Below the mantle-core boundary, S waves disappear, P waves slow down abruptly, and density jumps up.

At the base of oceanic crust (Figure 16-23) is a layer consisting of *gabbro*. Gabbro is an intrusive igneous rock (cooled slowly at depth, therefore coarse-grained) having the same composition as basalt which is an extrusive rock (rapidly cooled, therefore fine-grained). When the gabbro was yet a liquid, it filled a chamber that fed magma up through a swarm of conduits, and out onto the ocean floor where it rapidly chilled as underwater basalt flows. Chapter 5 describes how basalt forms characteristic "pillows" when erupted underwater. In oceanic crust, a 5 kilometer thick gabbro layer and dike swarm is capped by a 1.5 kilometer thick layer of pillow basalt, above which lies a layer of sediment, typically between 0.2 and 2 kilometers thick out in mid-ocean. Closer to the continents whose erosion is a source of sediment, the sand and mud on the ocean floor is a much thicker accumulation. Finally, this package of about 7 kilometers of oceanic crust is covered by a layer of sea water about 5 kilometers deep (with considerable variation), and so the Moho lies about 12 kilometers beneath the ocean surface.

Depth to the Moho under continents is much greater—typically 30 to 40 kilometers—but in places it varies from 20 to 75 kilometers. The Moho is deepest where mountains are the highest; beneath the Andes, Himalayas, and other great mountain systems there are counterpart "root zones" of low-density crust. Upper continental crust consists of the familiar wide diversity of igneous, sedimentary, and metamorphic rock types. Ironically, it is easier to visit upthrusted outcrops of oceanic crust than to obtain samples of deep continental crust. Chunks of lower crust are brought up in the diamond-bearing pipes mentioned above, and there is an exposure of upended lower crust in South Africa at the site of a very large meteorite impact. These direct observations, and seismic imaging of layers, reveal that the lower continental crust is also highly diverse. Much of it is high-grade metamorphic rock from which H_2O has been expelled. Heat supplied by deep injections of basaltic magma has partially melted the metamorphic rock to form magma of granite or granodiorite composition. Pockets of this magma have migrated to

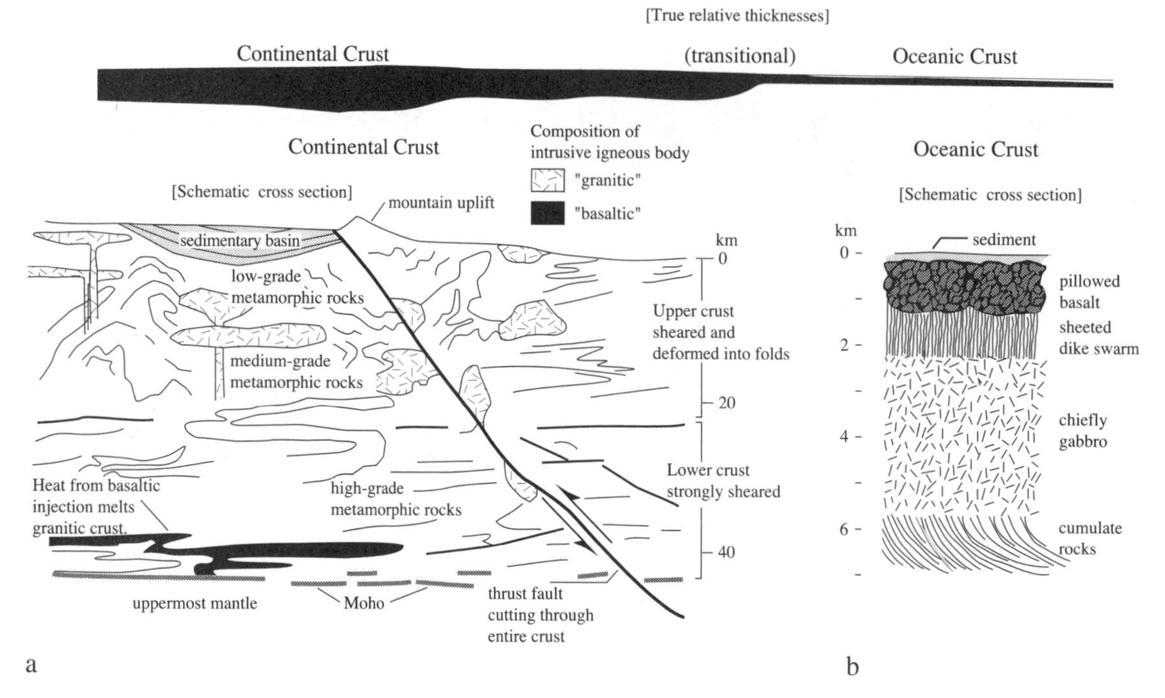

Figure 16-23. (*a*) Poorly-known lower continental crust consists of intensely sheared, high-grade metamorphic rocks from which H_2O has been mostly expelled under high temperature. Large igneous intrusions derived from the mantle stagnate upon reaching the lower crust, unable to rise higher because basaltic magma is of high density. Heat from the intrusions melts the lower crustal rocks, generating low-density magma of granitic composition which ascends higher into the crust. (*b*) Oceanic crust is 5 to 10 times thinner than continental crust (note the two scales of depth), and is composed almost exclusively of gabbro and its fine-grained extrusive equivalent, basalt. A magma chamber, fed from the mantle beneath, in turn feeds basalt liquid up through dikes crowded together (sheeted dike swarm) to emerge as lava on the ocean floor. Sediment has slowly accumulated after completion of the igneous stage.

higher levels where they froze into bodies of intrusive igneous rock. Much smaller amounts emerged to the surface as rhyolite flows or explosive outpourings of ignimbrite (Chapter 5).

Thus the differences between the geology of continents and oceans are profound in every important respect. Thick continental crust rises above sea level, whereas thin oceanic crust lies submerged. Higher-density oceanic crust is of basaltic composition, whereas average lower-density continental crust is of granitic to granodioritic composition. Continental crust is recycled by erosion, metamorphism, melting, etc., but recycling is incomplete and so continental rocks of many ages, from recent to more than 4 billion years, have survived. In a following chapter we shall see that oceanic crust is recycled wholesale, such that no part of it has survived longer than the latest 4 percent of earth history.

GRAVITY AND ISOSTASY

With some basic ideas about the crust and mantle in mind, we may now gain a deeper insight into the role of gravity. In 1686, Isaac Newton announced that "Every particle of matter attracts every other particle in the universe with a force that is directly proportional to the product of their masses, and inversely proportional to the square of the distance between them." In mathematical terms, if the masses are m_1 and m_2, and r is the distance between them (more accurately, between their centers of gravity), and the force is F, then

$$F \text{ is proportional to } \frac{m_1 \times m_2}{r^2}$$

Mass must not be confused with *weight.* Mass is a fundamental property of a piece of matter no matter where it is located. An astronaut on the moon weighs less than on earth, but this is because the mass of the moon is less than the earth's mass, and not due to any difference in the astronaut in the two places. In the formula above, m is mass and F is weight. Let's apply the formula to the same person located at sea level at the Equator or at the North Pole. We have seen that the polar radius is shorter than the equatorial radius (Figure 16-1) and, since r is in the denominator of the formula, one would weigh a trifle more at the Pole. Another factor is centrifugal force associated with the earth's rotation which tends to "levitate" objects off the Equator but not the Pole. A combining of these effects would make a 100-kilogram person weigh about 0.5 kilogram more at the Pole, which would hardly be noticed. It would make an enormous difference to a sensitive gravity meter, however.

Suppose we fly the gravity meter over the Himalaya Mountains in northern India, continuing at the same altitude over the Ganges River floodplain at the base of the mountains. Our formula would predict the force of gravity to be greater over the mountains whose mass looms high into the sky, nearer to the flight path. Surprisingly, the measured variations of gravity are much smaller than expected, bearing little relationship to the topography. This is also apparent in the absence of an abrupt step or discontinuity in the smooth slope of the geoid (Figure 16-4) at the site of the Himalayas.

It is noteworthy that India was to become the setting for the first serious consideration of the earth's gravity field, long before the day of airplanes and gravity meters. During the 1840s, the British, who had a strong political presence in India, decided to conduct a topographic survey of that country. Surveying parties had used conventional but extremely accurate methods of triangulation to measure the distance from a point in Kaliana, a village situated at the foot of the Himalayas, due south to another point in the town of Kalianpur. Careful surveyors were confident that their measurement error was a remarkably small 0.2 meters (or less) over a distance of 600 kilometers.

Because the two end points lay exactly north-south, the survey result could be checked by an independent technique using astronomy. Suppose that we measure the angle between a star and a vertical line, the latter established by dangling a heavy lead weight (a plumb bob) on the end of a string, just as a carpenter would do. Presumably the plumb bob would point toward the center of the earth whether in Kaliana or Kalianpur, such that the differences in angle between the star and a vertical line would be due to traveling around the curvature of the earth's surface. To put it another way, the two end points of the survey lie at different latitudes, which in turn can be equated to a length of the survey line.

A distressingly huge discrepancy of about 150 meters between the results of the conventional survey and the astronomical measurements caught the attention of the Rev. J. H. Pratt, Archdeacon of Calcutta. Pratt immediately and correctly identified the problem as lying with the astronomical technique. Rather than pointing to the earth's center, the plumb bob was attracted sideways toward the mass of the Himalayas. The disturbing effect should be greater at Kaliana located immediately adjacent to the mountains. In a lengthy paper, Pratt computed the gravitational attraction of the plumb bob as though the Himalayas consist of an "extra" mass perched upon the crust. To his dismay, the calculations argued that the plumb bob should be deflected about three times more than it actually is. Pratt then had to modify this plausible but incorrect hypothesis into the following more successful model of earth structure.

In Pratt's mental image, mountain uplift is like a batch of rising bread dough. Just as fermenting yeast generates carbon dioxide which causes the dough to expand, the Himalayas similarly had been "puffed up." Mountain uplift is chiefly vertical, accomplished as high-density material expands to become a larger volume at reduced density. Regions of low or high topography are floating in equilibrium upon a more dense substratum [Figure 16-24(*a*)]. Whether in a lowlands or a highlands, a given area of the earth is underlain by an equal amount of mass everywhere. Hence the concept of ***isostasy*** (eye-SAH-stah-see), which is Greek for "equal standing."

Pratt's report was noted by the British astronomer G. B. Airy who offered an alternative explanation. Airy's mental image was of logs floating in a pond, all of the logs being of the same density but varying in diameter. Thicker logs sink farther down into the water than thinner logs do, and also rise farther above the water surface. Similarly, lowland regions are underlain by thinner crust, and mountainous regions by thicker crust of the same density [Figure 16-24(*b*)]. Where the surface rises higher, the base of the crust plunges deeper. This mirror-image relationship pertains only to a regional scale, not beneath every hill and valley. Obviously, the crust has mechanical strength that is able to support local irregularities. A more realistic analogy would be floating logs lying upon a flexible rubber sheet that helps to hold them together and restrains their vertical movements somewhat.

Which is correct—Pratt's variable-density crust or Airy's crust of uniform density but variable thickness? Figure 16-23 shows that, on a very large scale of continents *vs.* oceans, both models are vindicated. Pratt's model emphasizes that low-lying oceanic crust is composed of dense basalt and gabbro,

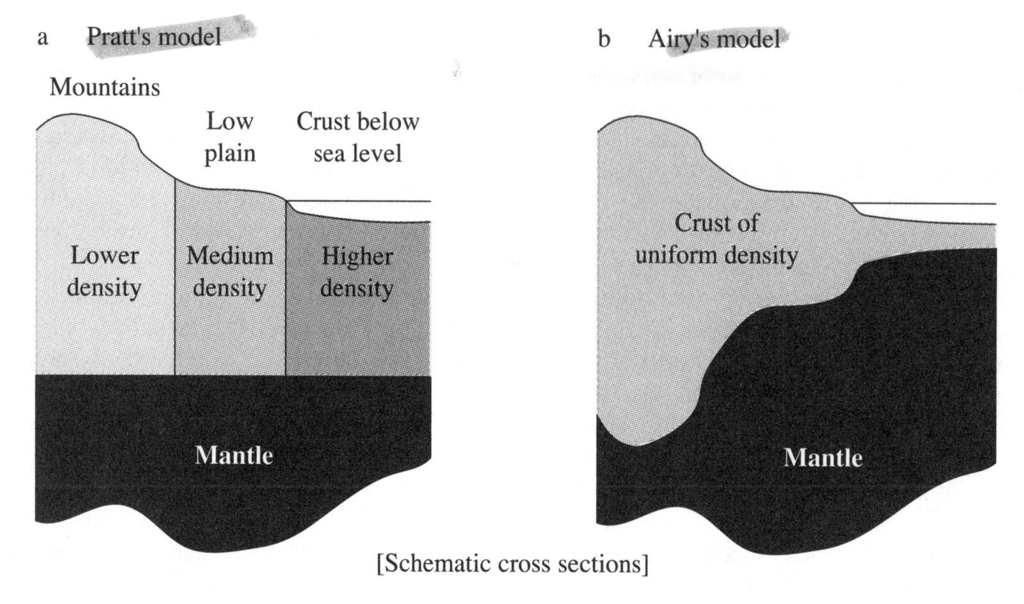

Figure 16-24. (*a*) According to Pratt's model of isostasy, a plate of initially uniform density and thickness is permitted to expand upward, becoming less dense but retaining the same amount of mass at all points through a vertical cross section. (*b*) Airy's model postulates crust of uniform density but variable thickness. In both models, less-dense crust floats upon more-dense material at depth.

in contrast to high-standing continental crust whose average composition is of granodiorite, a less dense rock. Airy's model correctly asserts that thicker continental crust rises topographically above thinner oceanic crust. How well do the models explain a balance between the Himalaya Mountains and the adjacent low plains to the south? Both of these regions are comprised of continental crust of similar density, and in fact most of southern India consists of deeply eroded Precambrian basement, deformed rocks that had once been part of mountain ranges perhaps similar to the modern Himalayas. Pratt's model fails to describe this situation, whereas Airy's model requires that the Himalayas be supported by a thick "root" of low-density material, as indeed they are.

It is ironic that Pratt's more self-evident model accounts for only about one-third of isostatic equilibrium on a worldwide basis, while Airy's model gets two-thirds of the credit. Seafloor sediment occupies the summit of Mount Everest, the highest peak on earth. Of course mountains have been uplifted vertically, as assumed by Pratt! Airy's model allows for vertical uplift, but as we shall see in a following chapter, the scale of horizontal motion has been vastly greater. Indeed, how could the mountains and their root zones have originated if this required continental crust to be stuffed down into and displace mantle rock of higher density? We shall address this counter-intuitive notion in Chapter 22. Pratt's concept applies quite well where thermal expansion has caused the crust to be uplifted, as beneath the East African Rift Valleys or in the Basin-and-Range Province of western North America.

Mountains eroding All the while, mountains are actively being destroyed and nowhere on earth is erosion more vigorous than in the Himalayas. Estimates are that rivers draining this part of the world carry four times more sand and mud than do all other rivers combined! For simplicity, suppose that construction of mountains having a root zone (Airy's model) had ceased. Much as a floating log would pop up when its top is shaved off, the mountain range responds to erosion by uplifting vertically. As the low-density root material ascends, mantle rock flows inward to replace it [(Figure 16-25(*a*)]. Later, the process of uplift and erosion slows down, when only a much diminished root with less buoyancy remains [(Figure 16-25(*b*)]. Ultimately, when both the mountain range and its supporting root have disappeared, the outcome is a low plain composed of deformed igneous and metamorphic rocks brought up to the surface from great depth [(Figure 16-25(*c*)]. Vast Precambrian shields (Chapter 11), the "nuclei" of continents, have originated in this manner. Perhaps mountains cannot persist forever, but thanks to isostatic uplift their existence is prolonged by a factor of about three times. Most of us who enjoy the beauty of mountains are grateful for that.

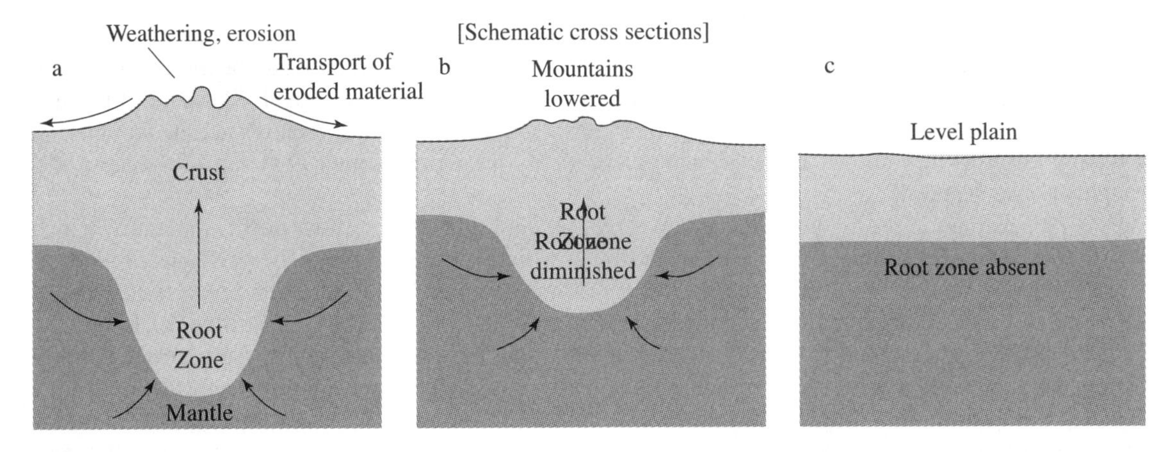

Figure 16-25. (*a*) Mountains and supporting root zone ascend in response to erosional unroofing. (*b*) As these processes continue, the rate slackens in a sort of "erosional half-life" analogous to half-life for radioactive decay (Chapter 11). Typically, about 40 million years are required to reduce 8,000-meter mountains to half of that elevation, but an equal length of time is needed to reduce a terrain from 80 to 40 meters elevation. (*c*) At the end stage, both the mountains and root zone have disappeared, leaving a plain of low elevation and topographic relief. The rate of erosion approaches zero.

SUMMARY

By analyzing a force field—a region of space in which a force is present—geophysicists may infer the deep internal structure of the earth. In a series of closer approximations, the shape of the earth is described by a sphere (homogeneous, non-rotating), spheroid (a modified sphere that is density-stratified, and rotating with an equatorial bulge), and geoid (all of the preceding but also warped, corresponding to the ocean surface or a projection of sea level into the interior of a land mass). The slightly irregular shape of the geoid corresponds to an irregular distribution of mass (and its associated gravity field) deep within the earth.

On a whole-earth scale of size, rocks have almost no strength. Deformation (or strain) causes the original shape or volume of an object to change. Solid rocks deform by developing fractures (brittle behavior) in response to short-term stress at low pressure and temperature, but they flow (ductile behavior) in response to sustained stress under deep burial. Rocks are commonly broken and offset along faults during brittle behavior; during ductile behavior they deform into folds.

Geophysicists use seismic (earthquake) information to probe the earth's deep interior, form images of buried strata in the search for oil and gas, and forecast earthquakes. Currently, even after much research, earthquake prediction is unreliable. Earthquake magnitude on the logarithmic Richter scale describes the amplitude of shaking, hence release of energy and potential for destruction. Most earthquakes occur by elastic rebound, during which rocks on opposing sides of a fault remain locked together even while stress causes them to become distorted. Eventually the accumulating stress overcomes friction, and the fault asperity (hang-up point) suddenly ruptures. The point of initial rupture is the earthquake focus, and a point on the earth's surface directly above a buried focus is the epicenter. Deep-focus earthquakes occur in abundance in a belt around the Pacific Ocean, at any depth to a maximum of 690 kilometers. Their mechanism is unknown, but definitely not by elastic rebound.

The style of fault motion is a consequence of the pattern of stress. In normal (or gravity) faults, which occur where tensional stress is pulling a region apart, a fault block (graben) slides down a steep plane separating it from an adjacent high-standing block (horst). An opposite sense of motion occurs on a reverse fault in an environment of moderate compressional stress. Intense compression may drive a sheet of rock horizontally (or nearly so) over the underlying rock along a thrust fault. Relative motion along a strike-slip fault is also chiefly horizontal, but it is a lateral or side-by-side offset.

A seismic wavefront depicts the shape of the wave form at a given instant in time. A seismic ray path is the pathway by which an infinitesimal "particle" of seismic energy travels through the earth. Wavefronts and ray paths are mutually perpendicular. P, or primary waves, are compressional, transmitted through any state of matter. S, or secondary waves, are shear waves that travel only through solid material, and more slowly than P. During passage of a P wave the atoms vibrate in a direction parallel to the direction of wave travel, whereas for an S wave the atomic vibration is perpendicular to wave travel. Slowest of the wave types are L, or surface waves having long wavelengths. Body waves (P and S) can penetrate the interior, traveling faster as they go deeper, but L waves travel only through the outermost part of the earth at a roughly constant speed.

In a seismograph, a disturbance sets up a relative motion between most of the apparatus, which is vibrating, and a mechanically isolated steady mass which is not vibrating. The permanent record of wave motion, a seismogram, indicates precisely timed arrivals of P, S, and L (and also reflected and refracted waves). With increasing distance of a seismograph station from an earthquake focus, the arrivals of P, S, and L are more delayed and the time intervals between wave arrivals are greater. A time-distance graph displays the travel times of seismic waves worldwide. By combining information from a seismogram and the time-distance graph, one may calculate the timing of the earthquake and the focus-to-station distance. Seismogram data from three or more stations are sufficient to determine the geographic location of the focus.

At the core-mantle boundary, P-wave ray paths are refracted (kinked) and S waves are totally reflected, or transformed into P waves. The result is a shadow zone, between 103° and 142° around the circumference of the earth from the earthquake focus, that receives neither direct P nor direct S. P waves emerge to the surface between 142° and 180° from the focus. Seismic information, density data, and consideration of meteorite compositions suggest an outer core consisting of liquid Fe-Ni alloy containing minor abundances of lighter elements. A small inner core, presumably also Fe-Ni alloy, is solid.

Indirect geophysical evidence and rare occurrences of mantle rock at the surface suggest that the mantle is ultramafic, consisting chiefly of the ferromagnesian minerals olivine and pyroxene. At a shallow depth is a low-velocity layer where mantle material is softened or even a fraction of a percent melted. Abrupt changes in seismic properties at still deeper levels are consistent with high-pressure collapse of the atomic structures of silicate minerals to more densely packed arrangements.

The Moho is the worldwide boundary between mantle and crust. Relatively thin (~7 kilometers) and dense basaltic oceanic crust is submerged beneath ~5 kilometers of ocean water. High-standing continental crust is relatively thick (~35 kilometers) and less dense, consisting of high-grade metamorphic rocks containing no hydrous minerals in the lower part, and highly diverse rock types in the upper part. On average, upper continental crust is of granodioritic to granitic composition.

The force of gravity is directly proportional to the product of two masses, and inversely proportional to the square of the distance between them. Nevertheless, regional variations of gravity tend to be small or unrelated to variations in the earth's surface topography. This observation is explained by a condition of isostasy—flotational equilibrium amongst large segments of the earth's crust. In Pratt's model of isostasy, higher topography is underlain by expanded, lower-density crust whereas lower topography is underlain by condensed, higher-density crust. In Airy's model, crust of uniform density is thicker under mountainous regions, thinner under low-lying regions. Both of these explanations correctly describe isostatic balance in different situations, but Airy's model is more generally applicable. With continuing erosion of mountains underlain by a root zone, the mountains respond by uplifting vertically as the root zone ascends (becomes diminished), and the ultimate product is a low plain consisting of once deep-seated deformed igneous and metamorphic rocks.

17

Topographic Maps

Information taken from topographic maps (discussed in this chapter) was converted into digital form for display in this relief map of the lower 48 States. A Shuttle orbiter has gathered data from which to make similar high-quality relief maps of almost all of the world's land area.
[*U.S. Geological Survey.*]

INTRODUCTION

A well-constructed topographic map provides an excellent way to present many different kinds of information. The informed reader can accurately determine the location of a point on the earth, the height of a mountain, the distance between two points, the surface area of a lake or city, the steepness of a hiking trail, the distribution of water and vegetation, road placement, and the shape and character of the land itself.

The purpose of this chapter is to acquaint you with the theory and language of topographic maps necessary to *prepare and read* them. Developing map-reading skills will make you more comfortable with using maps for driving, wilderness exploration, locating property accurately, and many other activities. For those planning careers in the areas of earth science, marine science, engineering, land development, city planning, water resources, environmental studies, aviation and the military, knowledge and understanding of topographic maps is essential. The principles discussed here will be applied in later exercises on geologic maps.

MAP TYPES

You may have had occasion to sketch directions to your house for a friend, showing streets, local landmarks, and the desired destination. Such a map is a **planimetric** map, as are road maps published by oil companies and automobile clubs, political maps, and even so-called treasure maps. These maps portray the locations of cultural and natural features such as roads, cities, political borders, rivers, shorelines, and mountain peaks in a two-dimensional display. Planimetric maps vary in detail and accuracy, and are generally designed for destination-oriented tasks or to delineate land-control boundaries.

For more technical use, such as in the career areas mentioned above, the portrayal of *relief* and *topography* (land elevation and shape) is essential. A **topographic map** contains contour lines with specific elevations that demonstrate the vertical (or third) dimension of the land, in addition to the planimetric data. Topographic maps therefore maximize available information, and it is with these maps that we will be concerned for most of this chapter.

MAP PROJECTIONS

Because the earth is a sphere, all maps printed on a flat piece of paper are distorted in some respect. The map *projection*, or type of inherent distortion will be determined by what the map is to be used for, and what area of the globe it represents. The **Mercator** projection, used chiefly in navigation, assumes that lines of latitude and longitude are everywhere perpendicular; therefore, this type of map becomes progressively more distorted toward the poles, where the land masses appear to be several times their actual relative size. An **equal-area** projection maintains correct relative sizes of areas, but distorts their shape; a **conformal** projection has just the opposite effect. One of the best compromises is the **polyconic** projection used by the United States Geological Survey (U.S.G.S.) in making topographic maps.

MAP GRIDS

One of the primary functions of a map is to establish the location of a point or an area so that this position may be found at a later time, communicated in writing or speech, or recorded for legal purposes.

The most efficient way to establish location is by means of a *grid* or *network of reference lines* crossing at right angles which are numbered from some designated point. A person giving directions such as "*two blocks north and one block east from here*," is using intersecting streets for a grid, and the designated point is the location where the person is standing. Similarly, the x-axis and y-axis of the Cartesian coordinate system make up a grid use of plotting (x, y) points, with the origin (0, 0) as the designated point.

Topographic maps primarily employ the **latitude** and **longitude** grid system, which is an international location net using the Equator and Prime Meridian as reference lines. Lines of latitude (or parallels) are rings around the earth parallel to the Equator, which is at 0° latitude. Because there is one-quarter of a circle (90°) from the Equator to a Pole, lines of latitude are numbered from 0° to 90° north or south of the Equator. Lines of longitude, also called meridians, are circles that pass through both Poles. The Prime Meridian, 0° longitude, runs through Greenwich, England (a neighborhood in London) and longitude is counted in degrees eastward or westward to 180° at the International Dateline. Latitude and longitude thus form a grid on the earth's surface that can be used for locations on land or water (Figure 17-1). All professionally produced maps are oriented with north to the top.

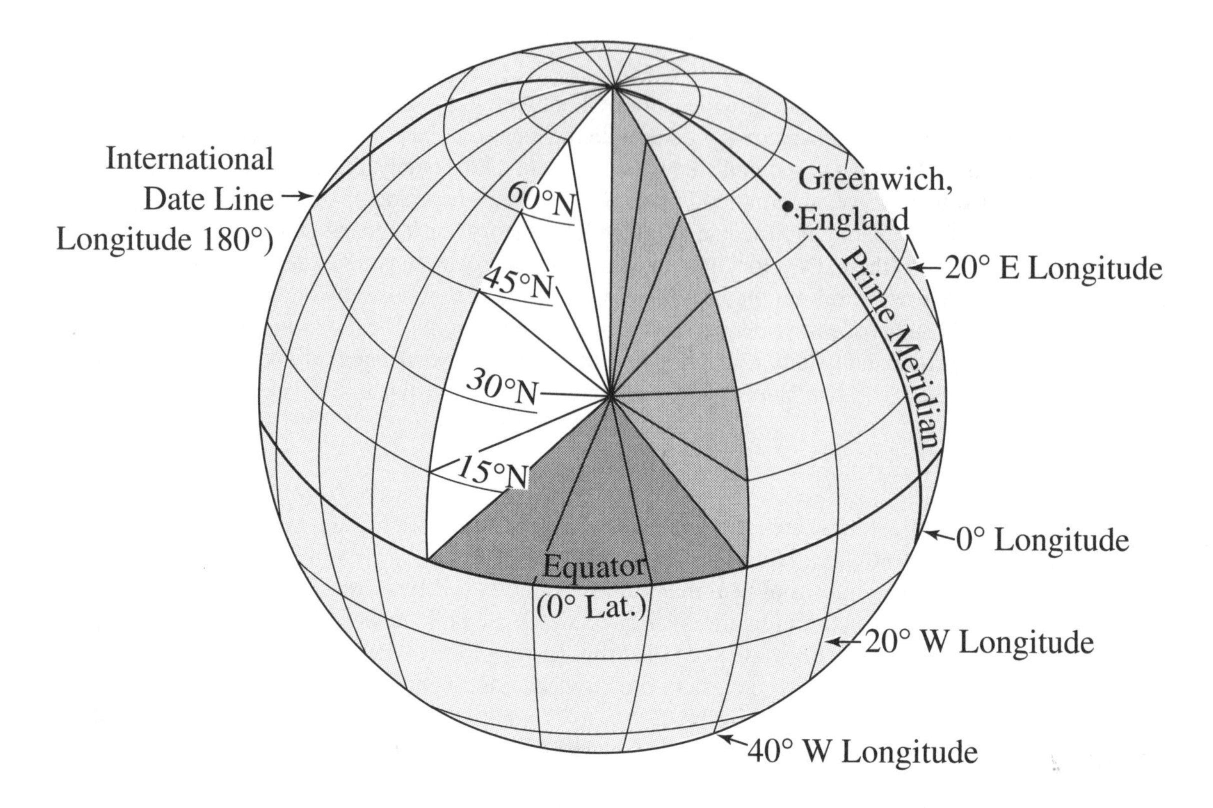

Figure 17-1. Latitude and Longitude Grid System

Latitude and longitude lines are circles, which is why they are calibrated in degrees. A degree can be broken down into smaller units of minutes and seconds in the same manner that the time unit of one hour is subdivided. There are 60 minutes (') in a degree (°), and 60 seconds (") in a minute. The correct designation for 1.5 degrees would be 1°30'; adding one-quarter minute to this would give 1°30'15".

MAP SCALES

The fundamental usefulness of maps derives from the fact that they represent the reduction of vast areas down to a piece of paper we can easily handle. In order to interpret a map successfully, we must know the amount of this reduction, and know how a unit measured on the map relates to actual distance on the ground.

The amount of reduction is expressed on maps as the **ratio scale**; i.e., the distance on the map is a certain fraction of that on the ground. Note that any system of units may be used, as the ratio scale is unitless. A 1:24,000 scale means that any one linear unit measured on the map is equal to 24,000 of those same units on the ground. Using one inch for the unit, one inch on such a map would represent a distance of 24,000 inches, or 2,000 feet, on the ground. So for all maps printed at a ratio scale of 1:24,000, the relation of map to ground units, the **verbal scale**, is one inch equals 2,000 feet, 1" = 2,000'.

A graphic scale or **bar scale** is a plot of the verbal scale on the map. This scale, which is printed at the bottom center of all U.S.G.S. maps, is actually a ruler for measuring map distances. This scale will still be valid if the map on which it is printed were to be reduced or enlarged photographically, although the verbal scale and ratio scale will not be correct after transformation of the size of the map. A 1:62,500 bar scale looks like this:

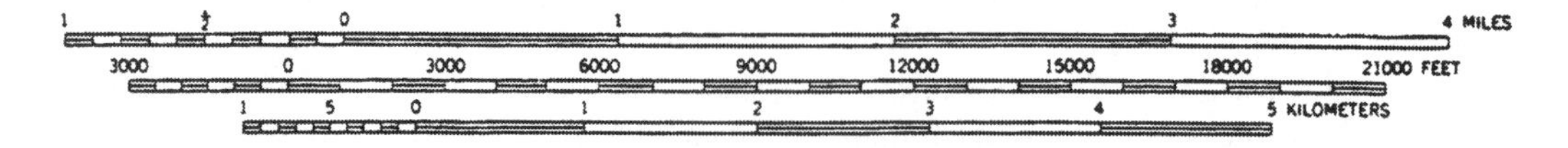

CONTOUR LINES

Contour lines are used to depict three-dimensional features (topography) on a flat piece of paper. Literally, topography refers to the "top of" the land surface. Contours show the shapes of hills, mountains, and valleys, as well as their altitude. A **contour** is an imaginary line on the ground, all points of which are at the same altitude, or, put another way, *a contour line is a line connecting all points of equal elevation.* The zero contour is the shoreline of the ocean midway between high tide and low tide (mean sea level). All points 10 feet above sea level would lie on the 10-foot contour; all points 20 feet above sea level would lie on the 20-foot contour, and so on. Similarly, underwater contours refer to depth below mean sea level.

In the example above, the *contour interval*, which is the difference in elevation between two adjacent contours, is 10 feet. A contour interval is chosen to match the relief of the landscape and the scale of the map; it is selected to show as much information as possible about relief without cluttering the map with lines bunched too closely together. Commonly used intervals 10, 20, 40, 80, and 100 feet. Very coarse contour intervals of 500 or 1000 feet are used for maps of remote, poorly-known parts of the world. These reconnaissance maps are rapidly being supplanted by modern topographic maps as all parts of the earth's land surface come under close scrutiny, but much of the ocean floor is yet unmapped.

Relief is the difference between the local highest and lowest points of elevation. Look for the highest point along divides or summits of hills or mountains, and the lowest point along a stream or body of standing water. Finding the highest and lowest spots on a map may take some searching.

In Figure 17-2, a map of a hill is depicted by contour lines drawn at 10-foot intervals. Above the map, a topographic profile shows a vertical "slice" through the hill along a line of profile, A–A'. Horizontal lines in the profile correspond to elevations of 0, 10 feet, 20 feet, etc.

At each intersection of a map contour with A–A', a dashed line is projected up to the equivalent elevation on the topographic profile. Finally, the smooth outline of the hill is drawn through these projection points. Although the contour map does not contain exact information about the elevation of the summit, the profile suggests a value of approximately 38 feet.

Figure 17-3 shows contour lines drawn on a natural landscape. If this imaginary area complete with contour lines were photographed from above, the resulting photo would be a topographic map. In fact, modern topographic maps are created by sophisticated computer processing of vertical aerial photographs.

Listed below are some rules, summarizing the basic nature of contour lines, that should be used when constructing or interpreting a topographic map:

1. On truly level ground, or on a surface of standing water, there are no contours.
2. The spacing of contours reflects the gradient, or slope:
   a. contour lines that are far apart indicate a gentle slope.
   b. contours that are close together indicate a steep slope.
   c. contours that merge indicate a vertical slope. Truly vertical cliffs, or overhangs, are exceedingly rare.

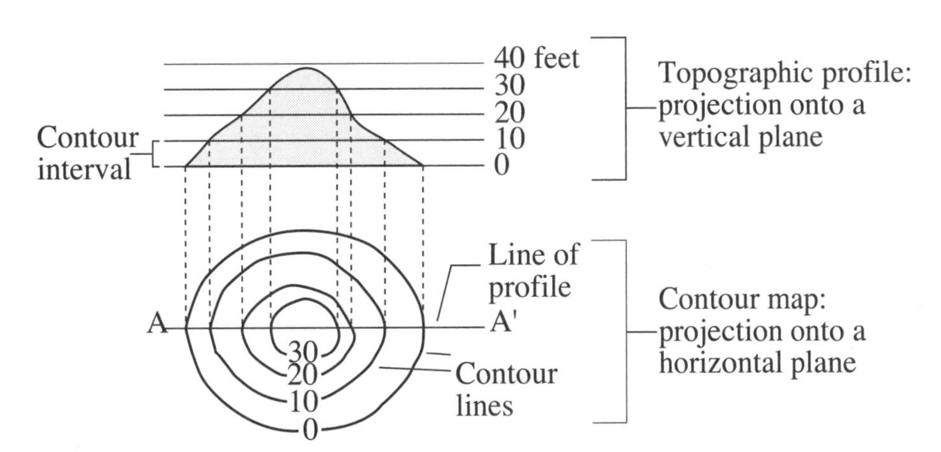

Figure 17-2. Contour Map and Topographic Profile

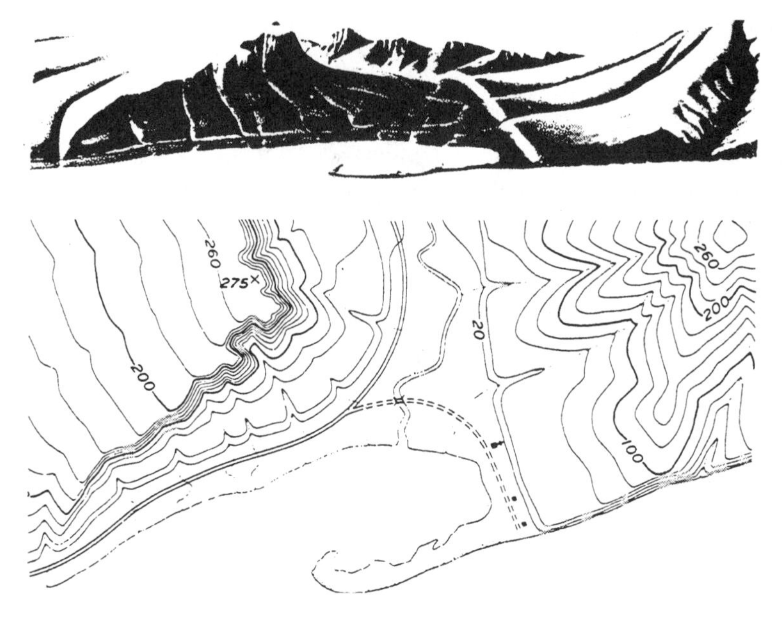

Figure 17-3. Landscape with Contours

3. Contours do not cross one another, nor branch, nor terminate. However complex the shape of a contour line may be, it is still a closed loop. Of course, a contour line may run off the edge of the map, but if all adjacent maps were assembled the closure would be evident.
4. All solid-line contours are multiples of the contour interval; e.g., if the contour interval is 10 feet, the contours are 10, 20, 30, etc. Usually every fifth contour, called an *index* contour, is printed as a heavier line for ease of reference.
5. Dashed contour lines, which are seldom used, represent elevations of half of the normal interval, and are added in areas of low relief to increase detail.
6. Channels are downward-sloping troughs. Where a contour line crosses a channel, it forms a "V" pointing upstream.
7. Contour lines depicting jagged topography have numerous sharp angles, whereas smooth rolling landscapes correspond to gently curved contour lines.
8. Normal contours enclose an area that is higher; all points that lie within the closed contour are above the level of the contour. For example, the 30-foot contour in Figure 17-2 encloses the highest point on the hill which is nearly 40 feet.
9. Depression contours enclose areas in which water would have no outlet (closed basins). These contours are marked by hachures on the inside.

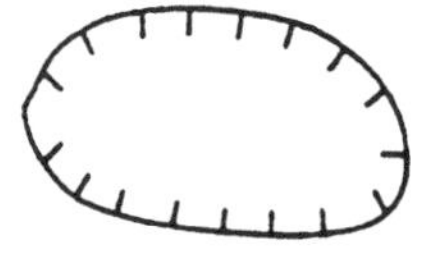

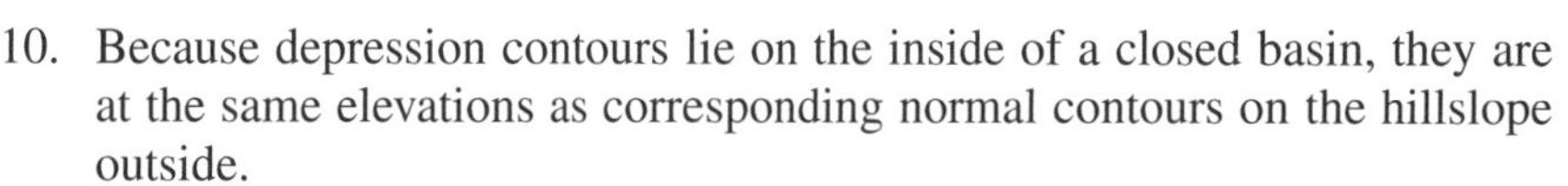

10. Because depression contours lie on the inside of a closed basin, they are at the same elevations as corresponding normal contours on the hillslope outside.
11. Contours must be counted consecutively. Thus if adjacent contours are repeated, they indicate a change in slope direction, such as in entry into a depression or crossing from one side to another of a valley.
12. Benchmarks (specially surveyed points), and spot elevations are exact values.
13. As noted above, a summit elevation lies above the highest contour shown, but not as high as the next higher contour would have been. The opposite sense applies to elevations of drainages or bottoms of depressions.
14. Elevations of points between contours may be estimated. The nearer the point is to a contour line, the more similar its elevation is to that of the contour. This generalization is not perfect because the topography may have an irrregularity of unknown form between contour lines.

U.S. GEOLOGICAL SURVEY TOPOGRAPHIC QUADRANGLES

Standard U.S.G.S. quadrangles are maps of small sections of the earth and are bounded by the same amounts of degrees or minutes for both latitude and longitude. They approach a true square only at the Equator, since lines of longitude converge toward the Poles. The sizes of maps printed by the Survey, their relation to one another, and the scales for each are given in Figure 17-4(*a*). You will primarily be working with 7.5' and 15' quadrangles. Note that a 15' quadrangle depicts four times the area of a 7.5' quadrangle, and yet may be a smaller map.

A number of important details are given in the margins of these maps. Familiarize yourself with this information as described below [clockwise from top right in Figure 17-4(*b*)]:

1. *Top right*: Name, location and size of the quadrangle.
2. *Bottom right*: Name, date of publication, road classification.
3. *Toward bottom center*: Quadrangle location on state map.
4. *Bottom center*: Scales applicable to quadrangle, contour interval.
5. *Left of center*: magnetic declination. The earth's magnetic and rotational poles do not exactly coincide, so magnetic compass readings in most places will deviate from true north. Magnetic readings must be corrected by the amount given adjacent to the right of the symbol, and in a direction opposite to the declination.
6. *Bottom left*: Details of how the area was mapped and who did the surveying, if mapped before the 1940s when aerial photography became the principal method of mapping.
7. At all corners and center of each side, in parentheses, is the name of the adjoining quadrangle and its scale if different from the map you are reading.
8. Around the periphery you will find township and range data printed in red, and intermediate minutes of longitude and latitude between corners, printed in black. (However, because Texas was never surveyed for township and range, there is no reference to township and range in Texas topographic maps.)

DATA FROM TOPOGRAPHIC MAPS

Many kinds of information may be derived from topographic maps by using simple measurements and arithmetic.

Measuring Distances: If the distance to be measured is a straight line, simply mark it off on the edge of a piece of paper and compare it to the bar scale. If the distance crosses onto a map of a different scale, figure each separately and add the results.

For irregular or curved distances, such as that along a stream course, place the corner of a sheet of paper at the beginning point and line the edge up against the first leg of the route. Put a pencil point at the end of the leg and swing the paper edge to conform with the next segment. Continue this, averaging out minor irregularities on the route, until you reach the other end of the distance being measured. Mark the end, and then compare the bar scale with the length of the edge from corner to end.

Computing Gradient: Gradient is a measure of the slope of the land. It is expressed as a ratio of total vertical drop between two points per unit of horizontal distance. For example, a certain stream drops through three 10-foot intervals along a distance of 2-1/2 miles. To calculate gradient, solve for X in the following equation:

$$\frac{30 \text{ ft}}{2.5 \text{ mi}} = \frac{X \text{ ft}}{1 \text{ mi}}$$

$X = 12$. The gradient is 12 feet per mile.

Making a Contour Map: Making a complete contour map from seemingly sketchy initial data is quite a challenge, but it is rewarding to see the shape of the land develop from isolated numbers. You will start with a base map showing spot elevations, drainages, and water bodies. Interpolating between

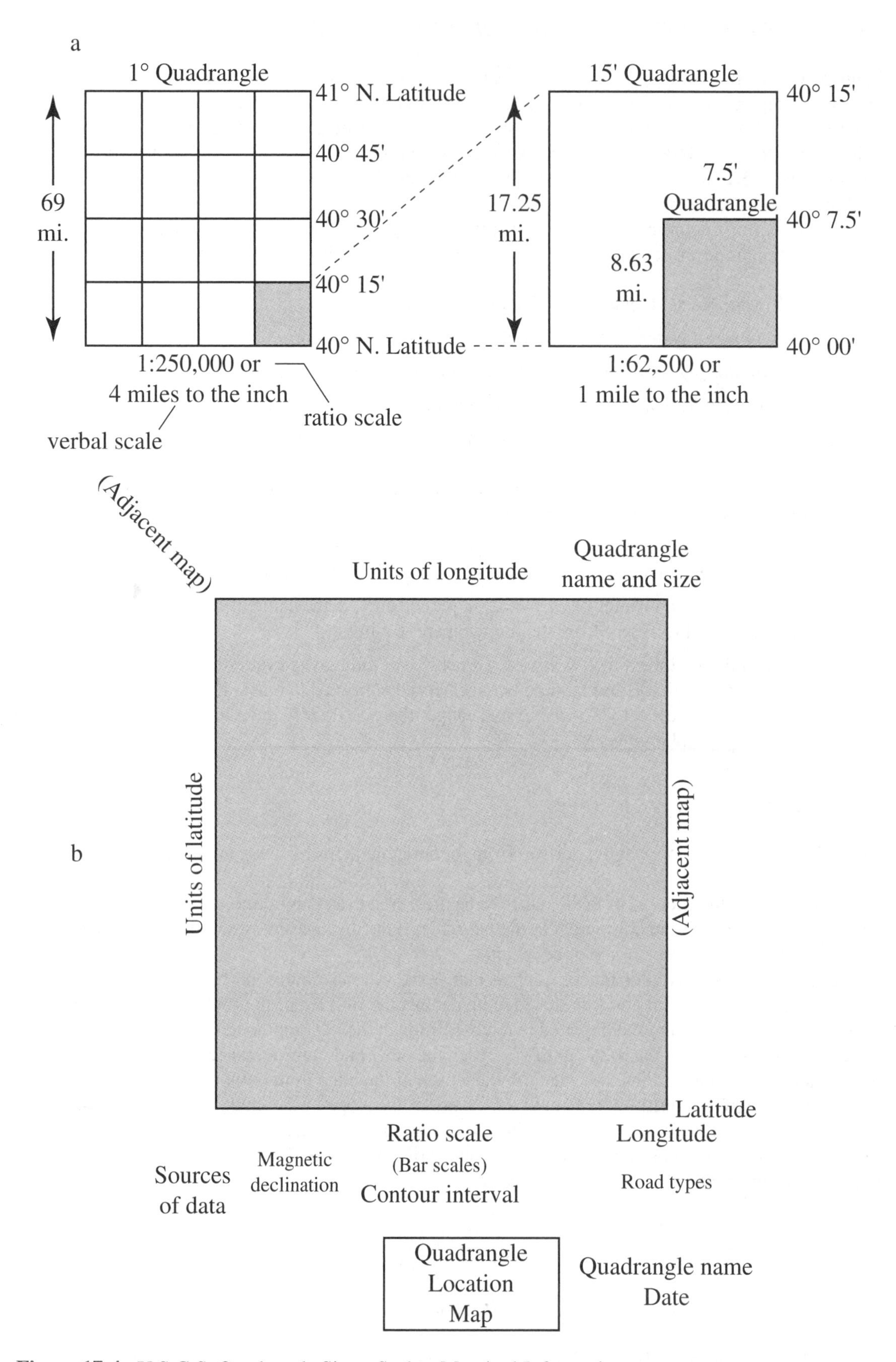

Figure 17-4. U.S.G.S. Quadrangle Sizes, Scales, Marginal Information

given elevations, find as many points as possible that correspond to full contour intervals. Then begin to connect points of the same elevation. It is best to start in one area of the map bounded by drainages and establish all contour lines within that area. Carry them forward to the next area as a group. Remember upstream Vs, the rules for depressions, and other contour rules as outlined above. In this type of exercise, where there is no opportunity to field-check the contours, variations in interpretations of data are expected, and each person's product will be somewhat different. Any interpretation is acceptable that does not break the rules of contours.

Making a Topographic Profile: Refer back to Figure 17-2. A profile is a silhouette of part of the earth's surface; it is an irregular line showing the surface in cross section. In the exercise of making a topographic map and profile, first complete the topographic map and then draw a line of profile A–A' across it. Wherever that line crosses a contour, extend a perpendicular line (dashed in Figure 17-2) to the profile line of corresponding elevation and make a dot. Extending perpendiculars from hilltops and stream bottoms would also be helpful. When all of the elevations have been projected, connect the dots to complete the profile. Make certain that the profile extends the entire length of line A–A'. Remember that streams run in gullies, the hilltops are typically rounded, and attempt to make your profile as realistic as possible.

In making a profile from a standard topographic map, place the top edge of a piece of graph paper along the line where the profile is to be made. Mark all contours, streams, and hilltops as small tick marks along the paper's edge, and label their respective elevations. Then set up the profile lines on graph paper and extend perpendiculars as discussed above.

Vertical Exaggeration of Profiles: Horizontal map distances are usually a different order of magnitude than the vertical relief along the same distance. Ten miles of horizontal distance may show only a few tens of feet of vertical change, and a profile to the scale of the map would most closely resemble a straight, flat line. For this reason, topographic profiles are usually stretched vertically, or exaggerated, in order to emphasize relief. This distortion is a valid technique as long as the amount of stretching is stated. After drawing a profile, you should be able to calculate the vertical exaggeration, as in the following example:

A profile on a 7 1/2' quadrangle (1:24,000, or 1" = 2,000') is plotted with a vertical scale of 1' = 500'. The calculation of the vertical exaggeration is:

$$\text{Vertical Exaggeration} = \frac{\text{Vertical scale}}{\text{Horizontal scale}} = \frac{1''/500'}{1''/2,000'} = \frac{2,000}{500} = 4X$$

TOPOGRAPHIC MAP SYMBOLS

VARIATIONS WILL BE FOUND ON OLDER MAPS

Primary highway, hard surface

Secondary highway, hard surface

Light-duty road, hard or improved surface

Unimproved road

Road under construction, alinement known

Proposed road

Dual highway, dividing strip 25 feet or less

Dual highway, dividing strip exceeding 25 feet

Trail

Railroad: single track and multiple track

Railroads in juxtaposition

Narrow gage: single track and multiple track

Railroad in street and carline

Bridge: road and railroad

Drawbridge: road and railroad

Footbridge

Tunnel: road and railroad

Overpass and underpass

Small masonry or concrete dam

Dam with lock

Dam with road

Canal with lock

Buildings (dwelling, place of employment, etc.)

School, church, and cemetery — Cem

Buildings (barn, warehouse, etc.)

Power transmission line with located metal tower

Telephone line, pipeline, etc. (labeled as to type)

Wells other than water (labeled as to type) — Oil, Gas

Tanks: oil, water, etc. (labeled only if water) — Water

Located or landmark object; windmill

Open pit, mine, or quarry; prospect

Shaft and tunnel entrance

Horizontal and vertical control station:

Tablet, spirit level elevation — BM Δ5653

Other recoverable mark, spirit level elevation — Δ5455

Horizontal control station: tablet, vertical angle elevation — VABM Δ9519

Any recoverable mark, vertical angle or checked elevation — Δ3775

Vertical control station: tablet, spirit level elevation — BM ×957

Other recoverable mark, spirit level elevation — ×954

Spot elevation — ×7369 ×7369

Water elevation — 670 670

Boundaries: National

State

County, parish, municipio

Civil township, precinct, town, barrio

Incorporated city, village, town, hamlet

Reservation, National or State

Small park, cemetery, airport, etc.

Land grant

Township or range line, United States land survey

Township or range line, approximate location

Section line, United States land survey

Section line, approximate location

Township line, not United States land survey

Section line, not United States land survey

Found corner: section and closing

Boundary monument: land grant and other

Fence or field line

Index contour — Intermediate contour

Supplementary contour — Depression contours

Fill — Cut

Levee — Levee with road

Mine dump — Wash

Tailings — Tailings pond

Shifting sand or dunes — Intricate surface

Sand area — Gravel beach

Perennial streams — Intermittent streams

Elevated aqueduct — Aqueduct tunnel

Water well and spring — Glacier

Small rapids — Small falls

Large rapids — Large falls

Intermittent lake — Dry lake bed

Foreshore flat — Rock or coral reef

Sounding, depth curve (10) — Piling or dolphin

Exposed wreck — Sunken wreck

Rock, bare or awash; dangerous to navigation

Marsh (swamp) — Submerged marsh

Wooded marsh — Mangrove

Woods or brushwood — Orchard

Vineyard — Scrub

Land subject to controlled inundation — Urban area

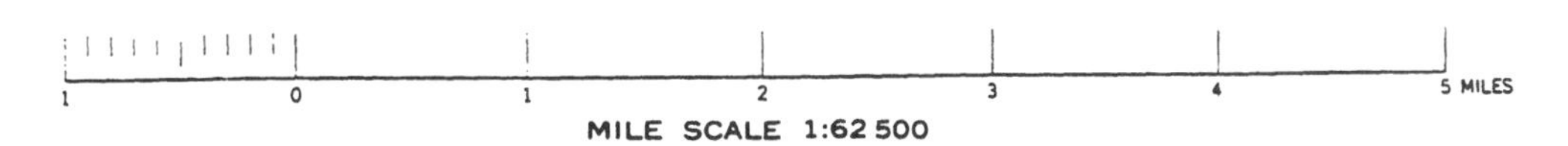

UNITED STATES
DEPARTMENT OF THE INTERIOR
GEOLOGICAL SURVEY

TOPOGRAPHIC
MAP INFORMATION AND SYMBOLS
MARCH 1978

QUADRANGLE MAPS AND SERIES

Quadrangle maps cover four-sided areas bounded by parallels of latitude and meridians of longitude. Quadrangle size is given in minutes or degrees.
Map series are groups of maps that conform to established specifications for size, scale, content, and other elements.
Map scale is the relationship between distance on a map and the corresponding distance on the ground.
Map scale is expressed as a numerical ratio and shown graphically by bar scales marked in feet, miles, and kilometers.

NATIONAL TOPOGRAPHIC MAPS

Series	Scale	1 inch represents	1 centimeter represents	Standard quadrangle size (latitude-longitude)	Quadrangle area (square miles)
7½-minute	1:24,000	2,000 feet	240 meters	7½×7½ min.	49 to 70
7½×15-minute	1:25,000	about 2,083 feet	250 meters	7½×15 min.	98 to 140
Puerto Rico 7½-minute	1:20,000	about 1,667 feet	200 meters	7½×7½ min.	71
15-minute	1:62,500	nearly 1 mile	625 meters	15×15 min.	197 to 282
Alaska 1:63,360	1:63,360	1 mile	nearly 634 meters	15×20 to 36 min.	207 to 281
Intermediate	1:100,000	nearly 1.6 miles	1 kilometer	30×60 min.	1568 to 2240
U. S. 1:250,000	1:250,000	nearly 4 miles	2.5 kilometers	1°×2° or 3°	4,580 to 8,669
U. S. 1:1,000,000	1:1,000,000	nearly 16 miles	10 kilometers	4°×6°	73,734 to 102,759
Antarctica 1:250,000	1:250,000	nearly 4 miles	2.5 kilometers	1°×3° to 15°	4,089 to 8,336
Antarctica 1:500,000	1:500,000	nearly 8 miles	5 kilometers	2°×7½°	28,174 to 30,462

CONTOUR LINES SHOW LAND SHAPES AND ELEVATION

The shape of the land, portrayed by contours, is the distinctive characteristic of topographic maps.
Contours are imaginary lines following the ground surface at a constant elevation above or below sea level.
Contour interval is the elevation difference represented by adjacent contour lines on maps.
Contour intervals depend on ground slope and map scale. Small contour intervals are used for flat areas; larger intervals are used for mountainous terrain.
Supplementary dotted contours, at less than the regular interval, are used in selected flat areas.
Index contours are heavier than others and most have elevation figures.
Relief shading, an overprint giving a three-dimensional impression, is used on selected maps.
Orthophotomaps, which depict terrain and other map features by color-enhanced photographic images, are available for selected areas.

COLORS DISTINGUISH KINDS OF MAP FEATURES

Black is used for manmade or cultural features, such as roads, buildings, names, and boundaries.
Blue is used for water or hydrographic features, such as lakes, rivers, canals, glaciers, and swamps.
Brown is used for relief or hypsographic features—land shapes portrayed by contour lines.
Green is used for woodland cover, with patterns to show scrub, vineyards, or orchards.
Red emphasizes important roads and is used to show public land subdivision lines, land grants, and fence and field lines.
Red tint indicates urban areas, in which only landmark buildings are shown.
Purple is used to show office revision from aerial photographs. The changes are not field checked.

INDEXES SHOW PUBLISHED TOPOGRAPHIC MAPS

Indexes for each State, Puerto Rico and the Virgin Islands of the United States, Guam, American Samoa, and Antarctica show available published maps. Index maps show quadrangle location, name, and survey date. Listed also are special maps and sheets, with prices, map dealers, Federal distribution centers, and map reference libraries, and instructions for ordering maps. Indexes and a booklet describing topographic maps are available free on request.

HOW MAPS CAN BE OBTAINED

Mail orders for maps of areas east of the Mississippi River, including Minnesota, Puerto Rico, the Virgin Islands of the United States, and Antarctica should be addressed to the Branch of Distribution, U. S. Geological Survey, 1200 South Eads Street, Arlington, Virginia 22202. Maps of areas west of the Mississippi River, including Alaska, Hawaii, Louisiana, American Samoa, and Guam should be ordered from the Branch of Distribution, U. S. Geological Survey, Box 25286, Federal Center, Denver, Colorado 80225. A single order combining both eastern and western maps may be placed with either office. Residents of Alaska may order Alaska maps or an index for Alaska from the Distribution Section, U. S. Geological Survey, Federal Building-Box 12, 101 Twelfth Avenue, Fairbanks, Alaska 99701. Order by map name, State, and series. On an order amounting to $300 or more at the list price, a 30-percent discount is allowed. No other discount is applicable. Prepayment is required and must accompany each order. Payment may be made by money order or check payable to the U. S. Geological Survey. Your ZIP code is required.
Sales counters are maintained in the following U. S. Geological Survey offices, where maps of the area may be purchased in person: 1200 South Eads Street, Arlington, Va.; Room 1028, General Services Administration Building, 19th & F Streets NW, Washington, D. C.; 1400 Independence Road, Rolla, Mo.; 345 Middlefield Road, Menlo Park, Calif.; Room 7638, Federal Building, 300 North Los Angeles Street, Los Angeles, Calif.; Room 504, Custom House, 555 Battery Street, San Francisco, Calif.; Building 41, Federal Center, Denver, Colo.; Room 1012, Federal Building, 1961 Stout Street, Denver Colo.; Room 1C45, Federal Building, 1100 Commerce Street, Dallas, Texas; Room 8105, Federal Building, 125 South State Street, Salt Lake City, Utah; Room 1C402, National Center, 12201 Sunrise Valley Drive, Reston, Va.; Room 678, U. S. Court House, West 920 Riverside Avenue, Spokane, Wash.; Room 108, Skyline Building, 508 Second Avenue, Anchorage, Alaska; and Federal Building, 101 Twelfth Avenue, Fairbanks, Alaska.
Commercial dealers sell U. S. Geological Survey maps at their own prices. Names and addresses of dealers are listed in each State index.

INTERIOR—GEOLOGICAL SURVEY RESTON VIRGINIA—1978

MILE SCALE 1:24 000 (2 MILES, 1, 0, 5)

FOOT SCALE 1:24 000 (1000, 0, 5000, 10000, 15000 FEET)

FOOT SCALE 1:62 500 (5000, 0, 5000, 10000, 15000, 20000, 25000 FEET)

Topographic Maps

- Map grids: coordinates of latitude and longitude for each location are unique. No two locations on the earth's surface have the same pair of coordinates.
- Latitude:
  - imaginary lines running E-W, measured N and S from the Equator. Equator at 0° latitude divides the earth into two hemispheres. Northern Hemisphere ranges from 0° to 90°N. Southern Hemisphere ranges from 0° to 90°S.
- Longitude:
  - imaginary lines running N-S. Prime meridian at 0° longitude passes though Greenwich, UK. Western Hemisphere ranges from 0° to 180° going west. Eastern Hemisphere ranges from 0° to 180° going east. International Date Line at 180° passes through the middle of the Pacific Ocean.

Different Types of Maps

- Planimetric map: locations of cultural and natural features
- Topographic map: uses contour lines to convey information about elevation
- Map projections:
  - Mercator projection - assumes that lines of latitude and longitude are perpendicular and uniformly spaced. Distortion greatest at poles.
  - Equal-area projection - maintains correct relative sizes of areas.
  - Polyconic projection- adopted by U. S. Geological Survey
- Latitude and longitude are expressed in degrees, minutes, and seconds.

  60" (seconds) = 1' (minute)
  60' (minutes) = 1° (degree)
- Mean Sea Level (reference for elevation)

Contour Lines

- Contour line: imaginary line that connects all points of equal elevation on the land surface
- Contour interval: the difference in elevation between adjacent contour lines
- Rules generally obeyed by contour lines:
  - Contour lines cannot intersect (cross one another).
  - Contour lines are closed loops, though not necessarily within a given map.
  - Contour lines cannot intersect a body of standing water.
  - Contour lines "V" up a stream valley.
  - A contour line generally runs parallel to adjacent contour lines.
  - Closely spaced contour lines indicate steep slopes.
  - Widely spaced contour lines indicate gentle slopes.
  - Contours that merge indicate a vertical slope (very rare).
- Contour lines in domes and basins:
  - Hachured lines in closed depression

Types of Map Scales

- Verbal scale (example): 1 inch = 2000 feet (1" =2000')
- Ratio scale: 1:24,000
- Bar scale: graphical representation using bar lengths with number labels. (Scale is valid even after photographic reduction or enlargement.)
  - Need to be able to convert from one type to another —
- Different ratios show different amounts of detail and area in maps. For example:
  - 1 : 63,360 — Less detail, more area
  - 1 : 12,000
  - 1 : 20 — More detail, less area

Displaying Information about Elevation

- Relief: the difference in elevation between local high and low spots
- Gradient: relief/ ("path distance")
- Slope: relief/("as the crow flies")
- Topographic profiles convey a sense of the ruggedness of an area.
- Vertical exaggeration (VE) in topographic profiles:
  - VE = vertical scale / horizontal scale
  - Example: vertical scale: 1" = 500'; horizontal scale: 1" = 2000'

$$\frac{1'' / 500'}{1'' / 2000'} = (1'' / 500') \times (2000' / 1'') = 2000'/500' = 4x$$

Topographic Map Information

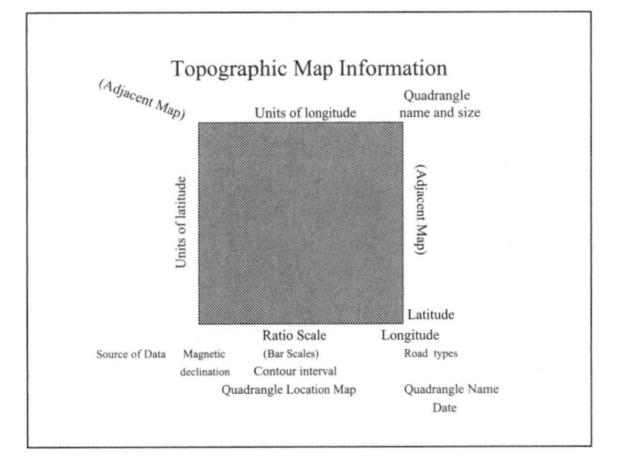

18

Structural Geology

INTRODUCTION

Many lines of evidence support the concept of a dynamic, mobile outer earth. Earthquakes and volcanic eruptions attest to current crustal activity; rocks bent or broken in earlier times demonstrate that such movement has been occurring throughout most of the earth's history.

Rocks, like artificially made materials, are of limited strength. They can be **deformed** by the application of *stress*, or *force per unit area*, that exceeds the ability of the rock to remain intact. *Deformation*, or *strain*, refers to a change of shape or size, or both, as a rock body is bent, broken, or moved from its original position. The amount of deformation will depend upon a number of factors such as the strength of the rock, the amount and duration of application of stress, temperature, depth of burial (equivalent to pressure), and the amount of water present. **Compression** (squeezing), **tension** (extension), **shearing**, and **uplift** and **subsidence** all occur in the outer earth, and these processes produce characteristic deformation.

This chapter is concerned with the geometry and terminology of the most common patterns of rock deformation or structure. Because the application of stress is an event, deciphering the consecutive development of structures in a given area will give a time sequence of events. This provides a framework for the geologic history of that area. An analysis of rock types and their probable origin will complete the historical picture. Deducing the geologic history of an outcrop or a region is a satisfying exercise in itself and is absolutely essential to the exploration, discovery, and development of petroleum and mineral deposits. Petroleum fields are almost exclusively associated with deformed sedimentary rocks. In Saudi Arabia, oil and gas are concentrated in a series of crumpled layers deformed when the Arabian Peninsula pulled away from Africa and pushed into Eurasia. A slight change in tilt between sedimentary layers served to trap oil and gas over thousands of square miles of east Texas. Petroleum deposits in southern California are commonly associated with the shearing plate boundary of that region. Solid mineral deposits cannot be efficiently exploited unless their structural setting is understood, since this strongly affects the origin, shape, and extent of such bodies.

This unit also includes explanations and exercises dealing with basic geometric concepts in the three-dimensional portrayal of structures, as well as with the more common types of specific structures. Additional exercises will focus on deciphering the history of various geologic settings.

FORCES PRODUCING STRUCTURAL DEFORMATION

The three primary stress configurations created by interacting segments of the lithosphere are compression, tension, and shearing, and each produces a characteristic set of deformation (strain) features (Figure 18-1). These configurations also represent the three generic types of tectonic plate boundaries—a subject presented later in this course.

A fourth important force is vertical uplift or subsidence (sinking) of extensive regions, which can be achieved by heating or cooling of the mantle below (causing it to expand or shrink), or by loading the crust by deposition of sediment, or unloading it through processes of erosion. Figure 18-1 also shows characteristic structures produced by vertically directed force.

Keep the causative force in mind as you learn about the various structures in more detail below. Structures will be easier to understand and deal with if you know their causes. Conversely, you will be able to tell what kinds of force have been applied to an area by interpreting existing structures.

The geologic history of any region typically consists of a series of events in which the rocks are first formed, then deformed into various simple or complex structures, and finally after a period of erosion, they are exposed at the earth's surface. As a result, part of the structure intersects the surface as **outcrop** whereas the remainder of it is buried at depth.

A block diagram of a portion of the earth (Figure 18-2) containing a geologic structure illustrates various ways to view a three-dimensional object. Most familiar to us is a **map** view, which is the pattern visible on the earth's surface, which in most places approximates a horizontal plane. Of course, in most places the earth's surface is not perfectly smooth or horizontal. A map view is projected straight down, and consequently topographic irregularities are not manifested. In this example, the structure is a deformed layer that intersects earth's surface in a "V" shape outcrop. Shaded sides of the block diagram correspond to vertical slices, each one a **cross section** of the earth that displays other parts of the structure. Cross sections as seen in a vertical cliff face, for instance, are rare in nature. One of the most chal-

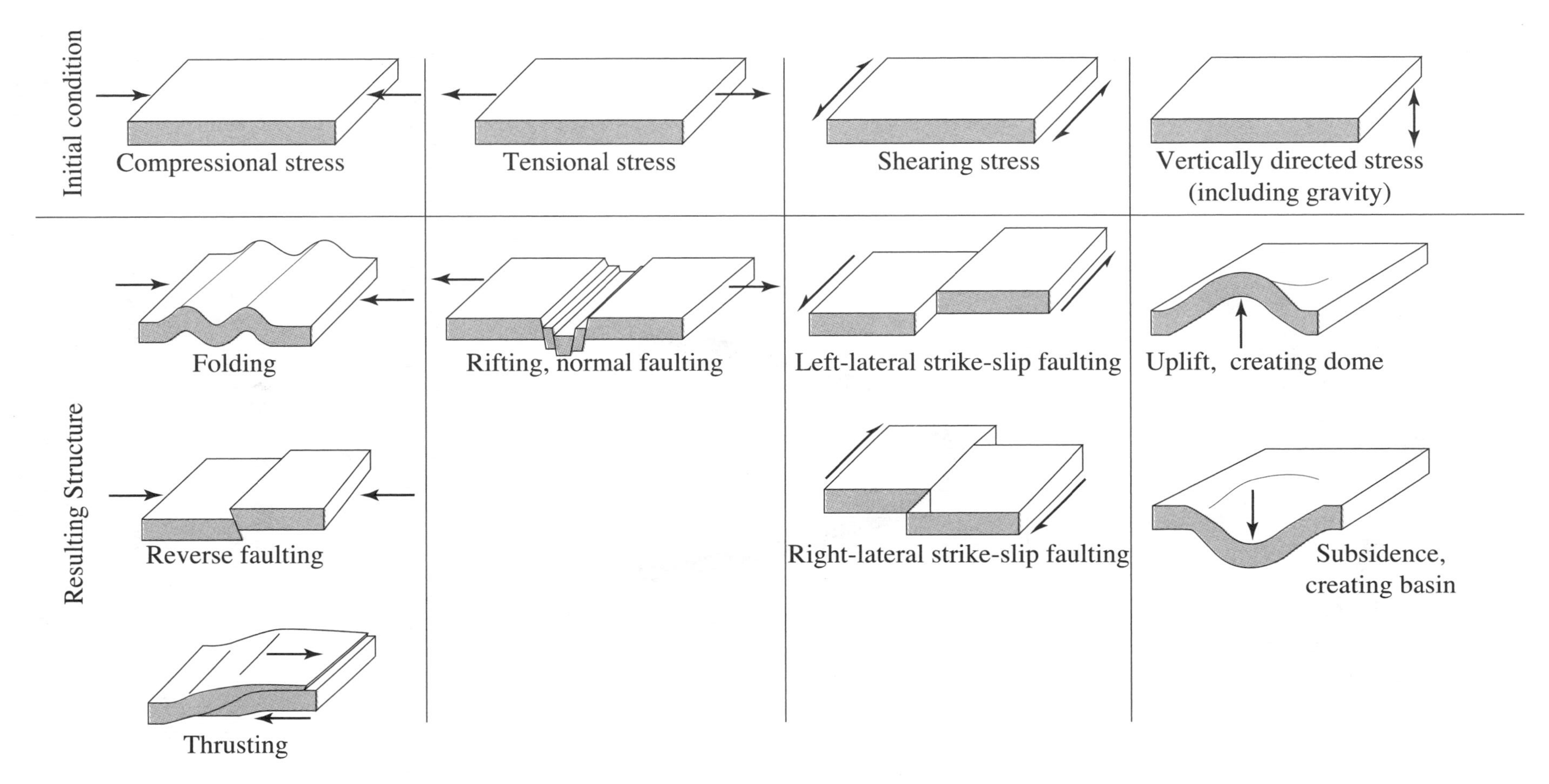

Figure 18-1. Geologic Structures and Causative Stresses

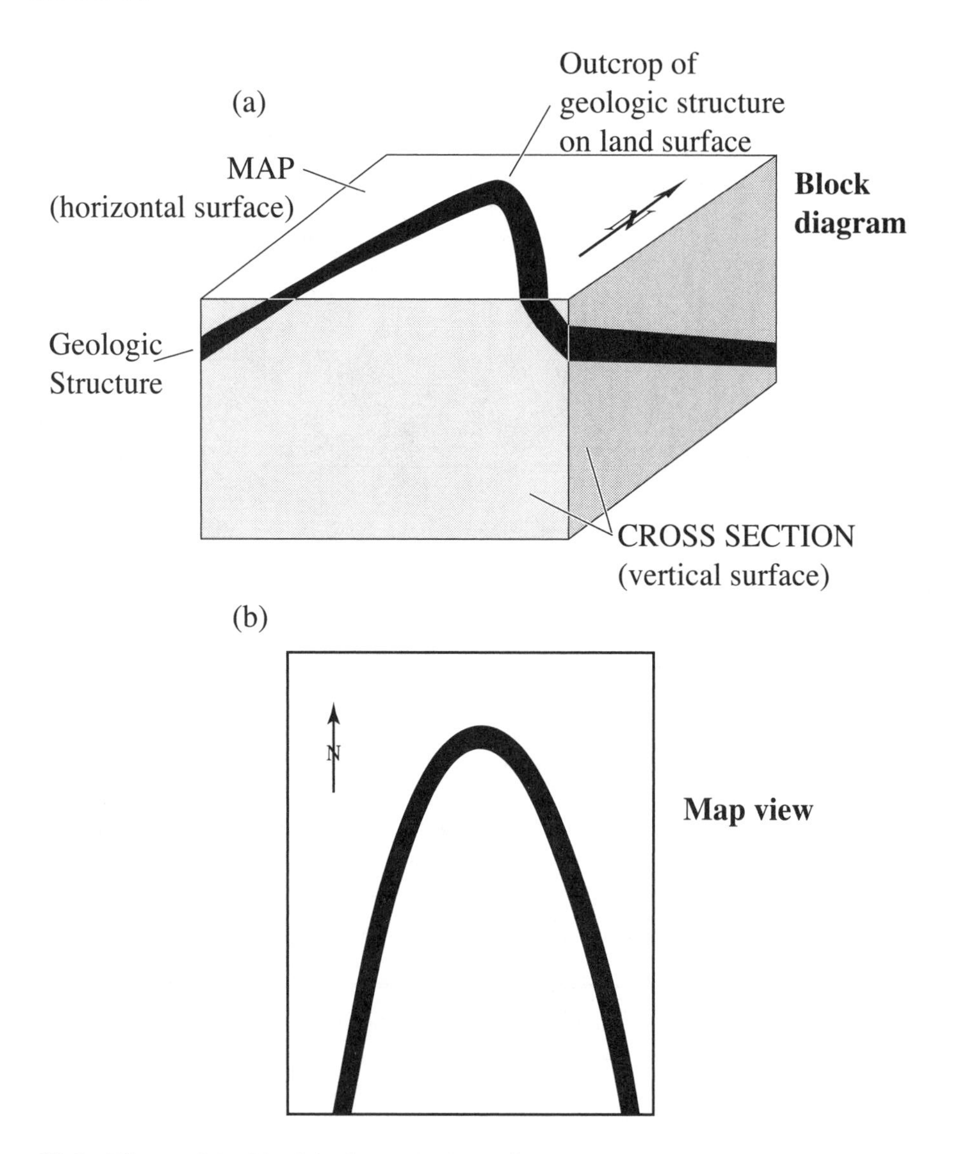

Figure 18-2. Views of the Earth in Several Dimensions

lenging tasks to a field geologist (and to us as students) is to use information available at the earth's surface to infer what a geologic structure looks like in cross section, in the subterranean depths to which there is no direct access.

STRIKE AND DIP

Geologists have devised a notion called **strike and dip** (Figure 18-3) to define the orientation of any plane in space. Specifying this orientation is an essential first step toward accurate description of deformed rock bodies.

Strike: the compass direction of a horizontal line on a tilted plane.

Dip: the acute angle between a tilted plane and the horizontal plane, measured perpendicular to strike.

Strike and dip directions are at right angles to one another. Suppose that a rock layer projects above the level of a lake, and extends beneath the water [Figure 18-3(*a*)]. The water line marks the intersection between the water (a horizontal surface) and the dipping layer, and the compass direction of the water

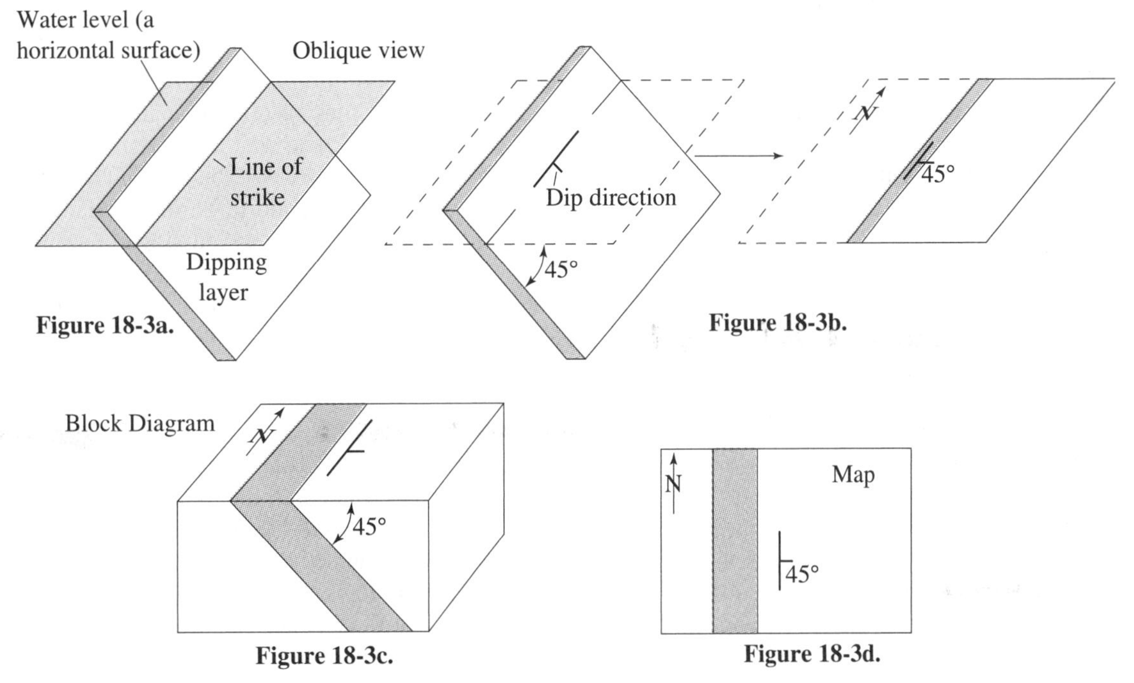

Figure 18-3a.

Figure 18-3b.

Figure 18-3c.

Figure 18-3d.

Figure 18-3. Strike and Dip

line is the line of strike. Dip is in the direction that a drop of water would slide down the surface of the rock layer.

Block diagrams, maps, and cross sections are used to portray rock bodies in this chapter. The symbol of strike and dip [Figure 18-3(*b*)], which is used on the tops of block diagrams [Figure 18-3(*c*)] and maps [Figure 18-3(*d*)], has a strike line in true compass orientation, to which is attached a short line stroke at right angles, with a number in degrees to indicate the amount of dip.

In the special case of perfectly horizontal beds, the strike is undefined, and the symbol ⊕ is used. At the other extreme, vertical beds are designed +90° or simply +.

Strike and dip may also be conveyed in written or spoken form. For example, the orientation of the layers in Figures 18-3(*c*) and 18-3(*d*) would be stated: N-S, 45°E; that is,

Direction of strike	Amount of dip	Direction of dip
N-S	45°	E

The strike line in this case is due north, or north-south. Strike orientation may be read from maps by using a protractor. Further examples are provided in Figures 18-3(*e, f, g*).

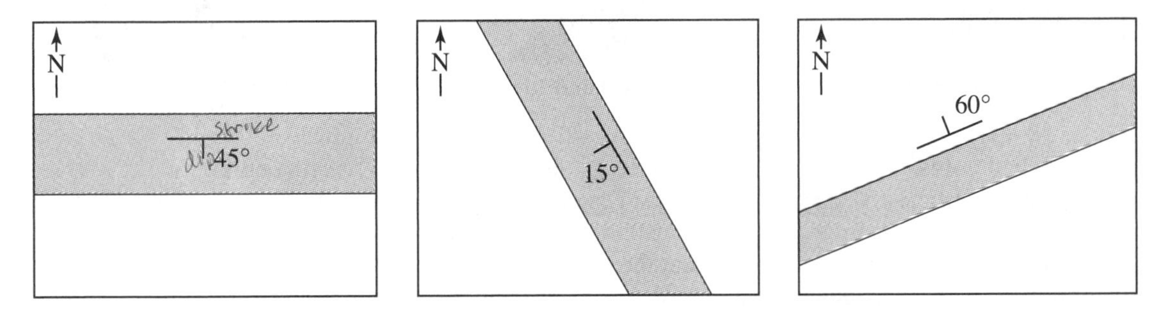

Figure 18-3e. E–W, 45°S **Figure 18-3f.** N30°W, 15°W **Figure 18-3g.** N68°E, 60°N

TYPES OF STRUCTURAL DEFORMATION

Folds

Folds in rock bodies are bends or curves in sedimentary layers, lava flows, or other planar features that demonstrate that the rock body has experienced compressional stress. Rocks that are massive, without obvious internal features such as bedding, may also be folded, but the folds would be difficult to detect. Rocks that bend, rather than break under such stress, are typically weak (said to be incompetent), or warm, or fluid-filled. Even the strongest rocks are bent into folds if stress is applied slowly over long periods.

In order to develop the concepts of fold types and orientation, we must define three elements of fold symmetry: **axial plane**, **limb**, and **axis**. An axial plane is one that cuts a fold into two symmetrical parts, or sides, each of which is called a limb. The axis is a line formed by the intersection of the axial plane and planar feature of the fold.

Let us examine two common types of folds, **anticlines** and **synclines**, in more detail. An *anticline* (Figure 18-4, bottom) is a fold in which the limbs dip away from the axial plane, and is best defined as a fold in which the oldest beds (lowest numbers, earliest to be deposited) are in the middle. Note the symmetrical distribution of numbers on opposite sides of the axial plane caused by opposite dip directions. Anticlines can serve as traps for gas and oil, and therefore are eagerly searched for by petroleum geologists.

A *syncline* (Figure 18-4, top) is a fold in which the limbs dip toward the axial plane, and is best defined as a fold in which the youngest beds (highest numbers, later deposited) are in the middle. The numbering of beds is symmetrical to the axial plane, but in reverse sequence from those in an anticline. Synclines and anticlines are commonly found to be associated as anticline-syncline-anticline, etc.

Synclines
Youngest beds are in the center of outcrop pattern.

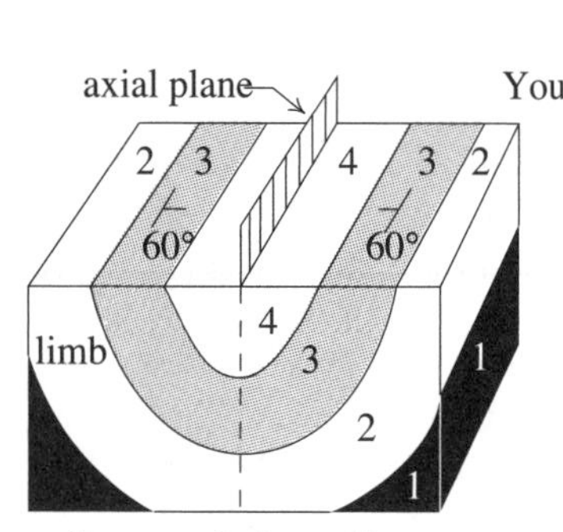

Symmetrical syncline

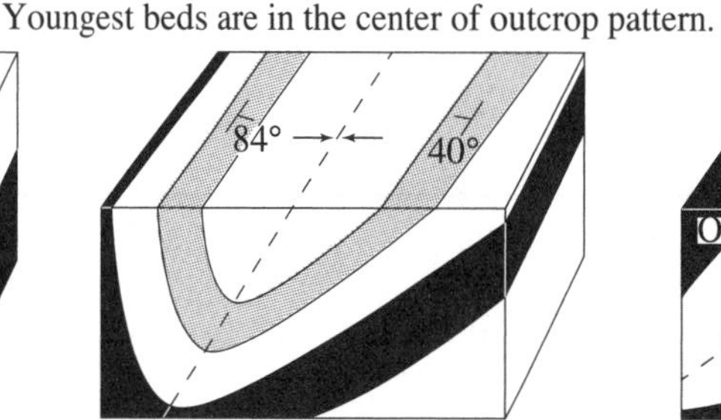

Asymmetrical syncline

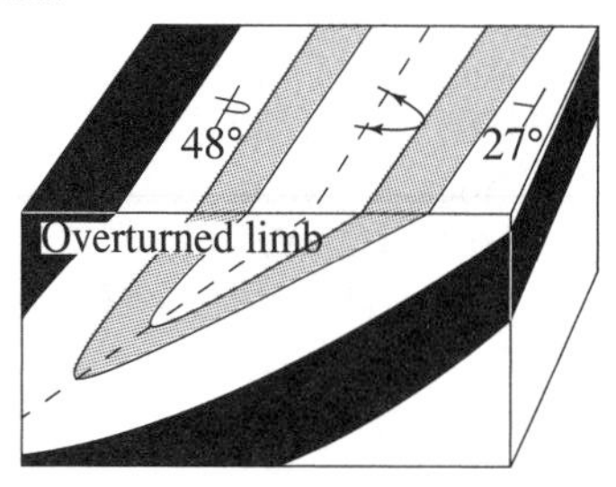

Overturned syncline

Anticlines
Oldest beds are in the center of outcrop pattern.

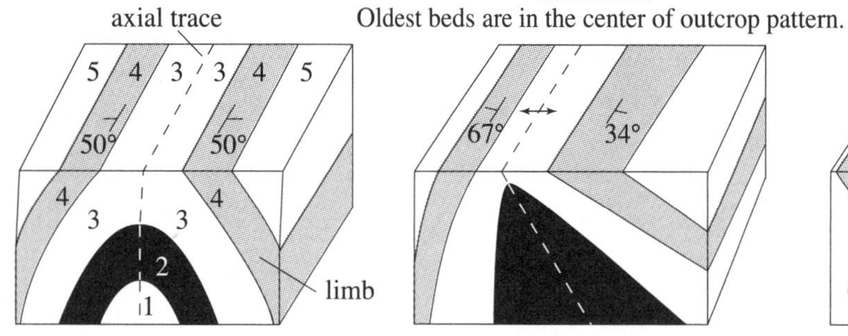

Symmetrical anticline **Asymmetrical anticline**

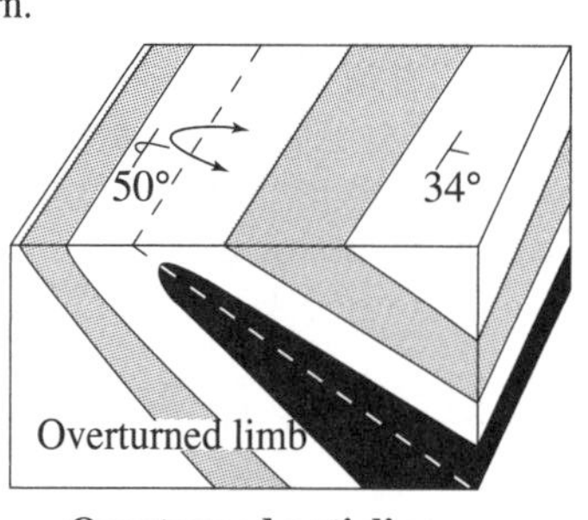

Overturned anticline

Figure 18-4a.
Symmetrical Folds
Axial plane is vertical. Surface outcrop pattern is symmetrical about the axial plane. Angles of dip of opposing limbs are equal.

Figure 18-4b.
Asymmetrical Folds
Axial plane is inclined. Surface outcrop pattern is not symmetrical about the axial plane. Angles of dip of opposing limbs are not equal.

Figure 18-4c.
Overturned Folds
Axial plane is inclined. Surface outcrop pattern is not symmetrical about the axial plane. Opposing limbs dip in the same direction.

Symmetry of anticlines and synclines depends upon the orientation of the causative stresses in the earth's crust, which in turn will determine what pattern an eroded fold makes where exposed at the earth's surface. In *symmetrical* anticlines and synclines the axial plane is vertical and the limbs dip the same amount but in opposing directions [Figure 18-4(*a*)]. In *asymmetrical* folds, one limb dips more steeply than the other [Figure 18-4(*b*)]. Axial planes of asymmetrical folds are not vertical. Under extreme conditions of compression and folding, one of the limbs may become inclined ever more steeply, then to a vertical position, and then past vertical. Because this limb has been turned upside down, the fold is said to be *overturned* [Figure 18-4(*c*)]. Ironically, in an overturned fold which is the most extreme example of deformation, the beds dip in the same direction, appearing superficially as though the rocks are not folded at all. However, the exposure of a simple sequence of dipping beds would not repeat. In contrast, the beds on either side of the axis of an overturned fold form a repeating pattern, such as 1-2-3-4-3-2-1.

If any of the folds shown above were to be tilted so that their axes were inclined to the horizontal, the result would be a **plunging fold**. Plunging fold outcrop patterns are convergent rather than parallel; their eroded exposures appear to be V- or U-shape on geologic maps. Plunging folds in series are easy to spot by the zig-zag design they form on maps and aerial photos. In a cross section perpendicular to the fold axis, plunging folds look the same as nonplunging folds.

Anticlines and synclines of any orientation may be consistently distinguished from one another by the distribution of the ages of layers. This distinction is further clarified for plunging folds by the use of plunge arrows [Figure 18-5*(a, b, c)*], which are arrows on the fold axis pointing in the direction of downward axial plunge. Note that three separate types of information are provided here that precisely distinguish anticlines from synclines: age relationships, plunge arrows, and dip-and-strike symbols. Figure

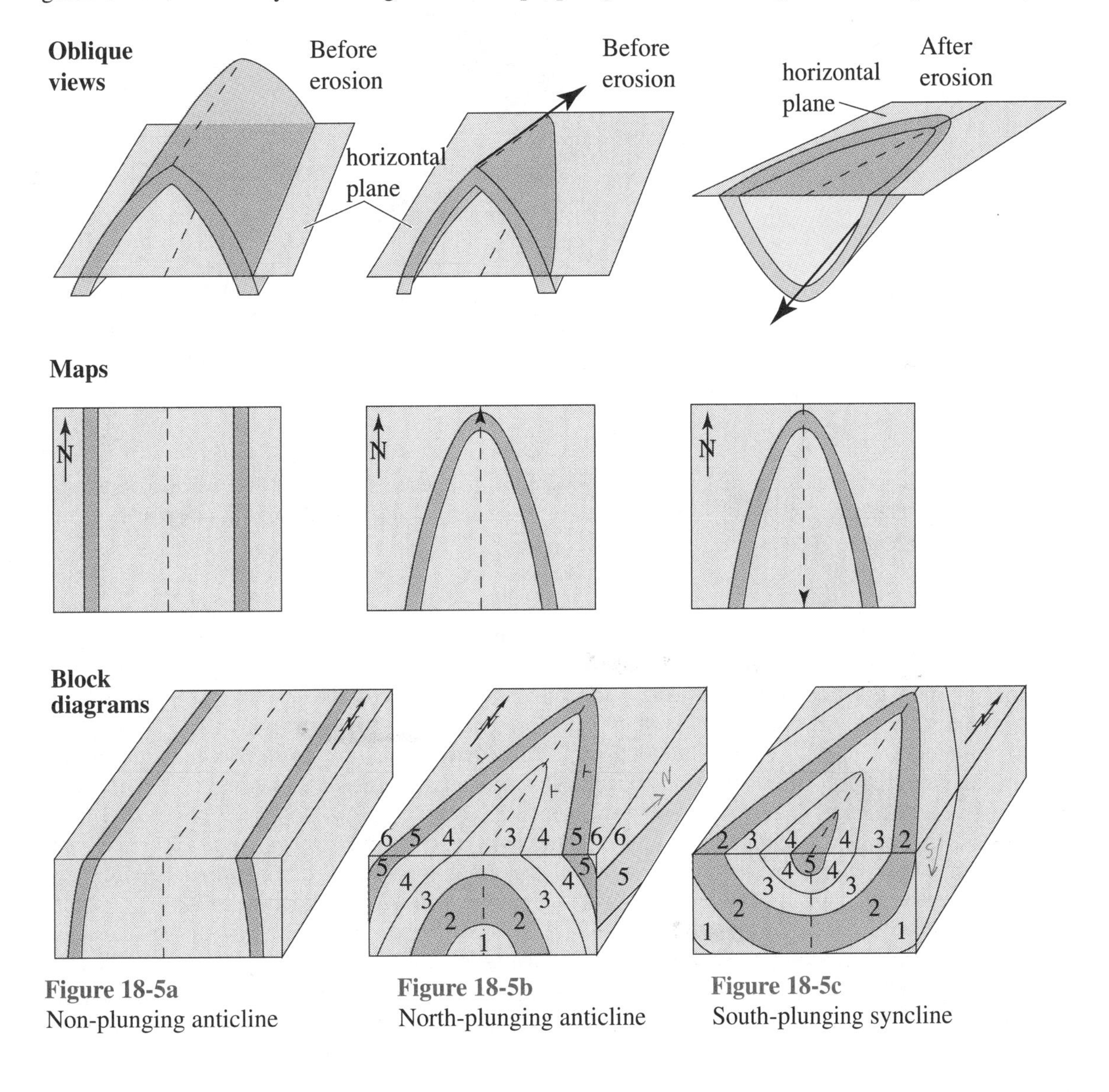

Figure 18-5a
Non-plunging anticline

Figure 18-5b
North-plunging anticline

Figure 18-5c
South-plunging syncline

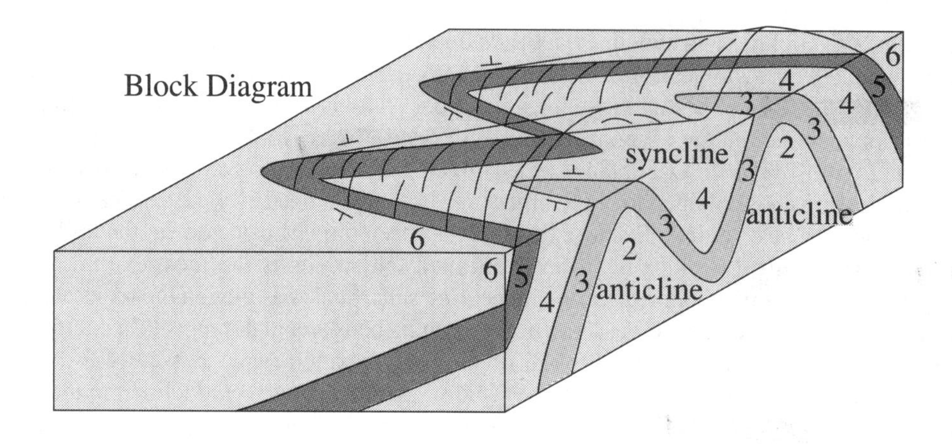

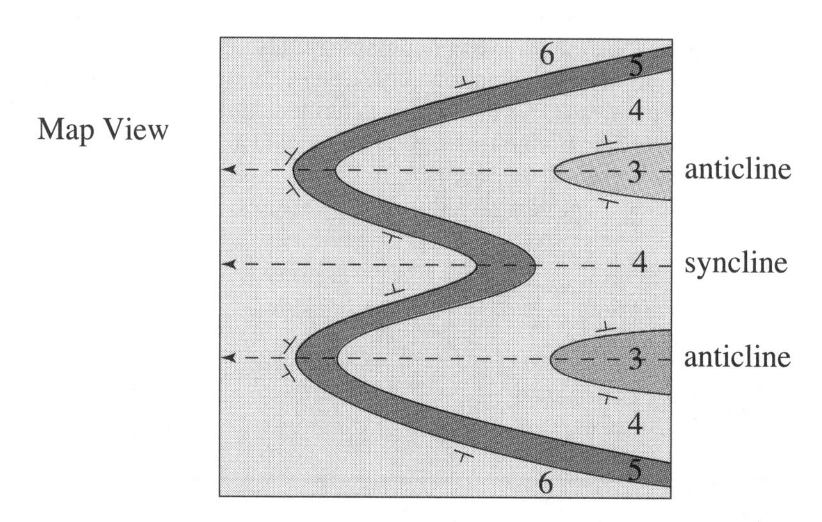

Figure 18-6. Multiple Plunging Symmetrical folds

18-6 shows a series of plunging folds with appropriate symbols. Anticlines plunge toward the closed end of the V-shape outcrop, whereas synclines plunge toward the open end.

Joints

Joints are cracks or fissures in rocks, generally without displacement, caused by overload pressure, shrinkage from cooling, expansion due to erosion of overburden, and various other factors. They occur in igneous, sedimentary, and metamorphic rocks.

Faults

A fault is a break in the earth along which there has been movement of one side relative to the other. The effect of faulting on rocks is to *separate* or *offset* formerly continuous features, such as sedimentary layers, metamorphic foliation, or dikes. It is this offset that often reveals the existence of faults in the field. Another indication of the existence of faulting is the presence of **slickensides**, which are polished surfaces, commonly with grooves or scratch marks, on the fault parallel to the direction of movement. Slickensides are the result of grinding and polishing during fault movement and, where present, may give the best clue to the actual direction of fault movement.

Rocks that break and shift, i.e., fault, under stress are generally relatively strong (said to be competent). They are able to store stress until their ultimate strength is exceeded, rather than bending progressively as stress is applied. (However, strata are commonly deformed by bending in the near vicinity of a fault, a situation known as *fault drag*.) Very large faults, with extensive offset and earthquake activity, may constitute the boundary between moving tectonic plates. Faults, as planar features, manifest strike and dip. The fault trace on a horizontal surface represents the strike, and an arrow attached at right angles shows the dip direction (Figure 18-7). This arrangement distinguishes the fault symbol from that

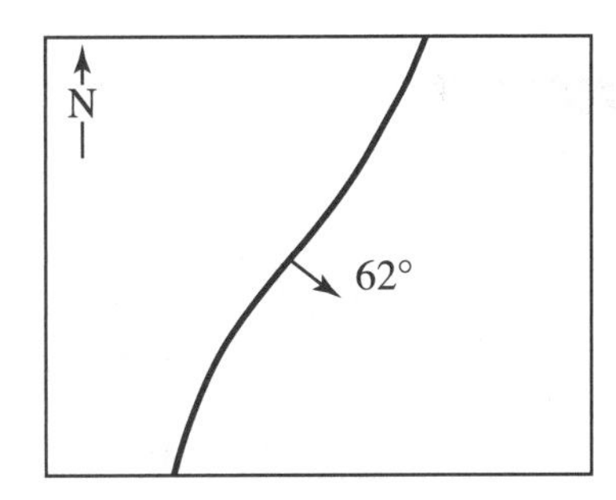

Figure 18-7. Strike and Dip of Fault

used for tilted layers, in which the ⊢ symbol is used. Let us examine two common categories of fault as classified on the basis of direction of movement of the rock bodies involved: **dip-slip faults** and **strike-slip faults**.

Dip-slip faults are those in which displacement is parallel to the dip direction of the fault surface. Rock bodies move up or down the fault surface, and slickenside grooves are perpendicular to fault strike. Three types of dip-slip faults are **normal**, **reverse**, and **thrust**.

Normal dip-slip faults are those in which the fault surface dips toward the structurally lowered side (Figure 18-8). Because we cannot know which side of the fault actually moved, we may tell only relative displacement. Pairs of half-arrows are used to express offset in cross section (a vertical plane). In a horizontal plane (map view) a **U, D** notation indicates which side of the fault had a relative *up* or *down* motion. After erosion has removed part of the structurally uplifted side, older rocks will be exposed here, while younger rocks are preserved on the down-thrown side (Figure 18-8).

Shattered and ground-up rock on a fault surface is permeable, permitting fluids to pass through carrying dissolved ions. If these fluids had deposited economically important minerals, the fault zone may have become the side of an ore deposit. Mining operations would follow the high concentration of valuable minerals near to the fault, excavating rock along the dashed line in Figure 18-8(*a*). In the old days, miners called the block on the left-hand side the **footwall** because they could stand on it (precariously!). Rock on the right-hand side, called the **hanging wall**, loomed over their heads. Along a normal fault, the footwall has moved relatively up, the hanging wall relatively down.

Normal faults are commonly the result of extensional forces in the crust, as can be seen by comparing the length of line X-Y before faulting [Figure 18-8(*a*)] to the longer line X'-Y' after faulting [Figure 18-8(*b*)]. The effect of normal faulting is to create a partial or total *gap* between the faulted portions of a particular layer. Movement on a normal fault would result if gravity simply pulled the hanging wall side of the fault down the sloping fault surface. Sets of normal faults in the crust are common over sites of mantle swelling, or where a crustal mass is beginning to split apart. In North America, the Basin and Range Province of the western United States has experienced considerable crustal extension. Crustal blocks downdropped along parallel normal faults are called **grabens** (German for "ditch" or "trench"), and uplifted blocks are **horsts** (German for "aerie," meaning "high place"). In series, they form *graben and horst topography* [Figure 18-8(*d*)].

A near-surface type of normal displacement is shown by the downhill movement of coherent blocks under the force of gravity [Figure 18-8(*e*)]. These slump-type landslides most commonly develop on incompetent rocks (shale, volcanic ash) in slope. Individual landslide events are usually triggered after heavy rains which have filled the porous material with water, making it heavy.

Reverse dip-slip faults are those in which the fault plane dips toward the structurally elevated side (Figure 18-9). On a reverse fault, the footwall has moved relatively downward, the hanging wall relatively upward. Reverse faults are the result of crustal compression, causing shortening. They are genetically akin to folding in that rock bodies are forced to take up less lateral space (and more vertical space) as a result of deformation. Note that X'-Y' [Figure 18-9(*b*)] is shorter than X-Y [Figure 18-9(*a*)]. Again, as in normal dip-slip faulting, after erosion the oldest bed is exposed at the earth's surface on the upthrown side. The difference is that in normal faulting the dip arrow points to the downthrown side, whereas with reverse faulting, the arrow points toward the upthrown side.

Figure 18-8. Normal Dip-Slip Faulting

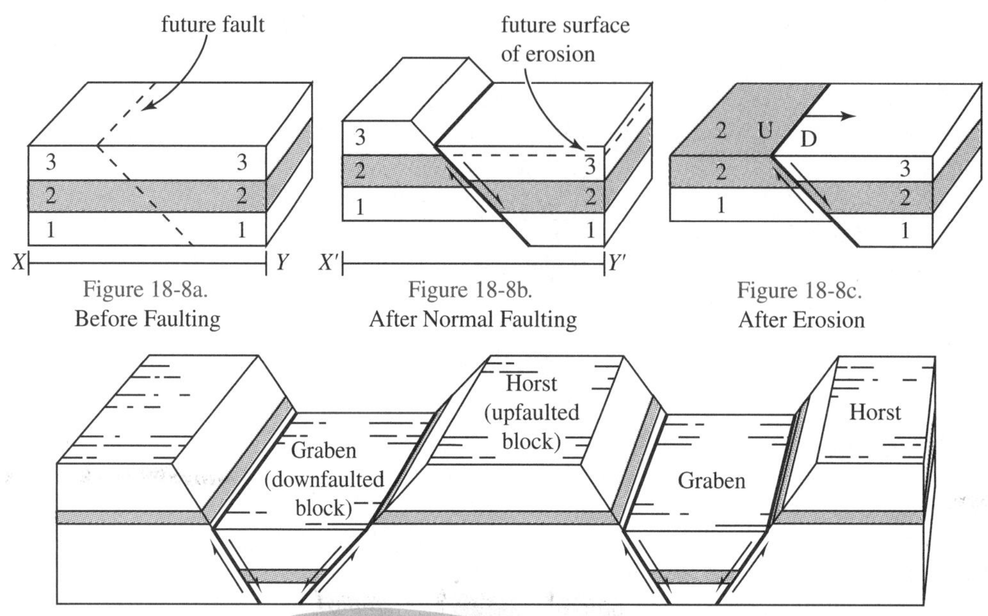

Figure 18-8a. Before Faulting

Figure 18-8b. After Normal Faulting

Figure 18-8c. After Erosion

Figure 18-8d. Graben and Horst Topography created by Normal Faulting

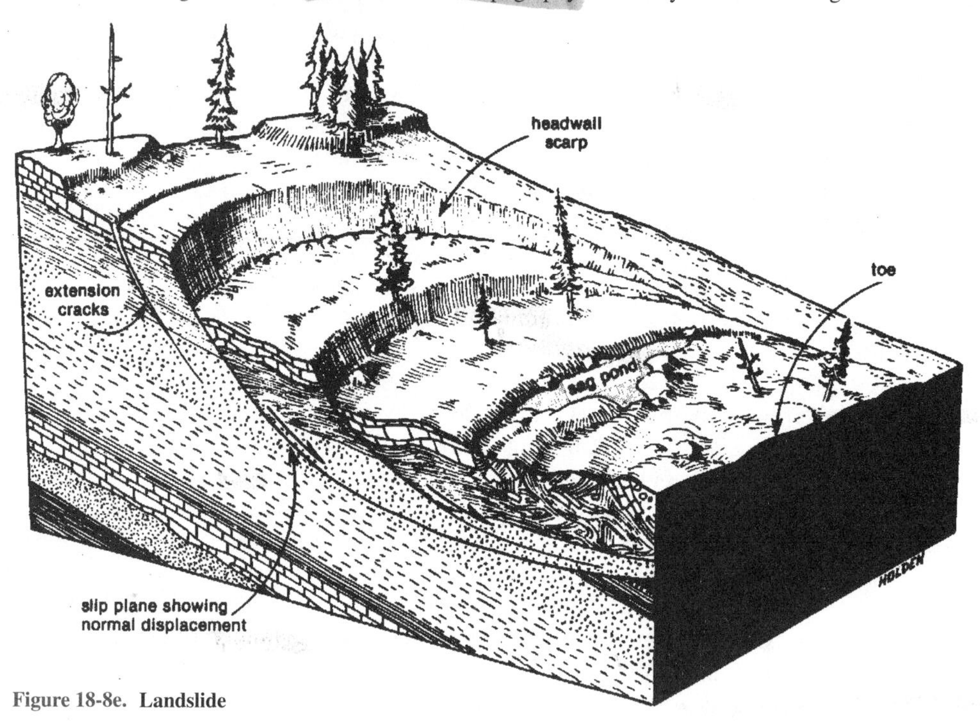

Figure 18-8e. Landslide

Figure 18-9. Reverse Dip-Slip Faulting

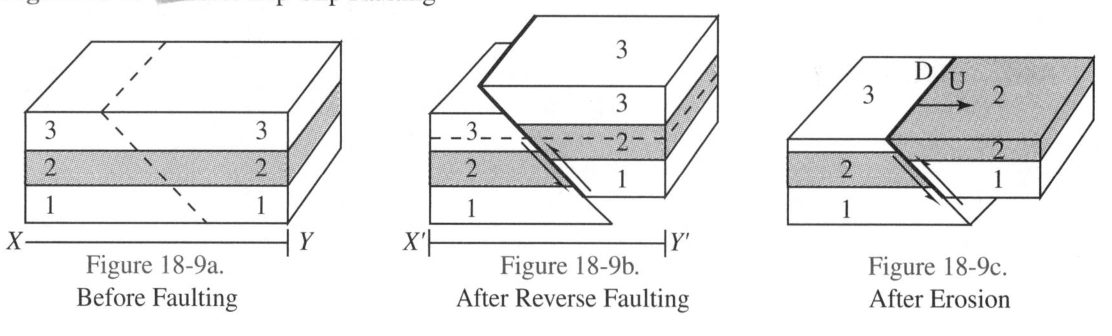

Figure 18-9a. Before Faulting

Figure 18-9b. After Reverse Faulting

Figure 18-9c. After Erosion

Thrust faults (Figure 18-10) are having low angles of dip (<45°). Many thrust faults have significant displacement (tens of kilometers). With this kind of faulting, movement as shown by the black arrow [Figure 18-10(*b*)] results in a transported segment called an overthrust sheet. On geologic maps the edge of a thrust sheet is shown by a sawtooth line with triangular teeth on the upper plate. Like the uplifted portions of normal and reverse faults, overthrust sheets are subject to erosion that often leaves isolated older rock remnants called klippen, stranded over younger rock sequences [Figure 18-10(*c*)]. A hole eroded into the upper sheet of a thrust [Figure 18-10(*c*)] is called a fenster (German for "window").

Strike-slip faults are those in which displacement is parallel to the strike of the fault surface (Figures 18-11, 18-12). Rock bodies move horizontally (laterally) past one another, and slickensides on the fault surface are horizontal. A strike-slip fault may originate as a strain feature within a crustal plate, or may constitute the boundary between two tectonic plates. Large strike-slip faulting results in greater displacements than large dip-slip faulting, in part because the chief motion of the great tectonic plates is in a horizontal sense.

Right-lateral strike-slip faults [Figure 18-11(*a, b, c*)] are those in which the block across the fault from an observer has moved relatively to the right. After crossing the fault, one would have to go to the right to find the continuation of a particular layer or dike. Study Figures 18-11 and 18-12 to convince

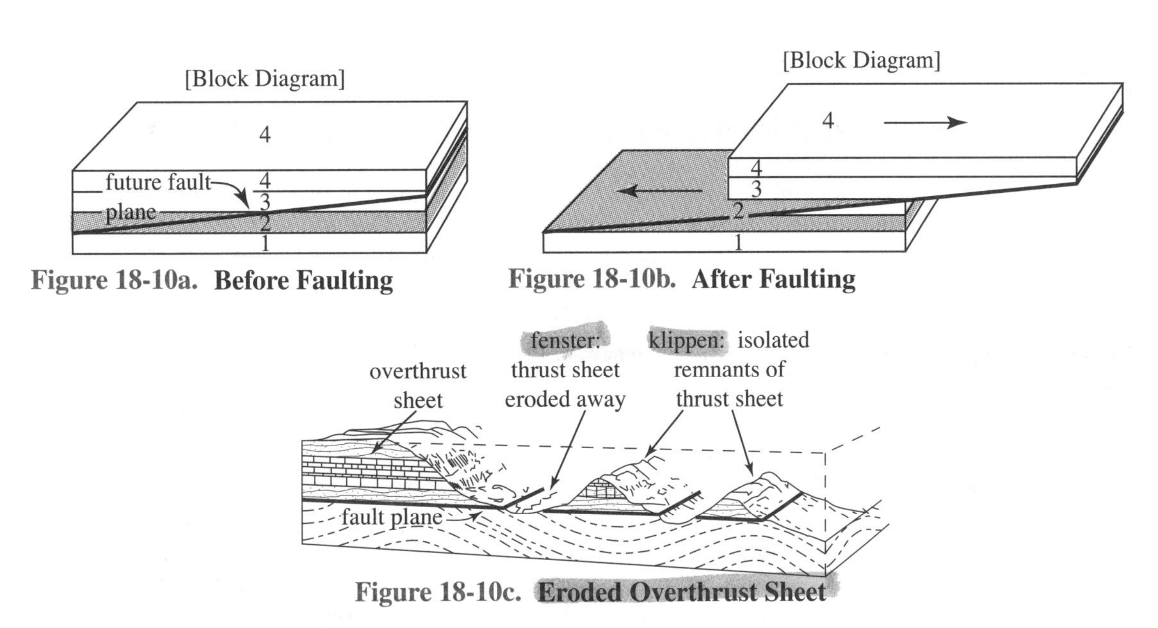

Figure 18-10a. Before Faulting **Figure 18-10b. After Faulting**

Figure 18-10c. Eroded Overthrust Sheet

Figure 18-10. Thrust Faulting

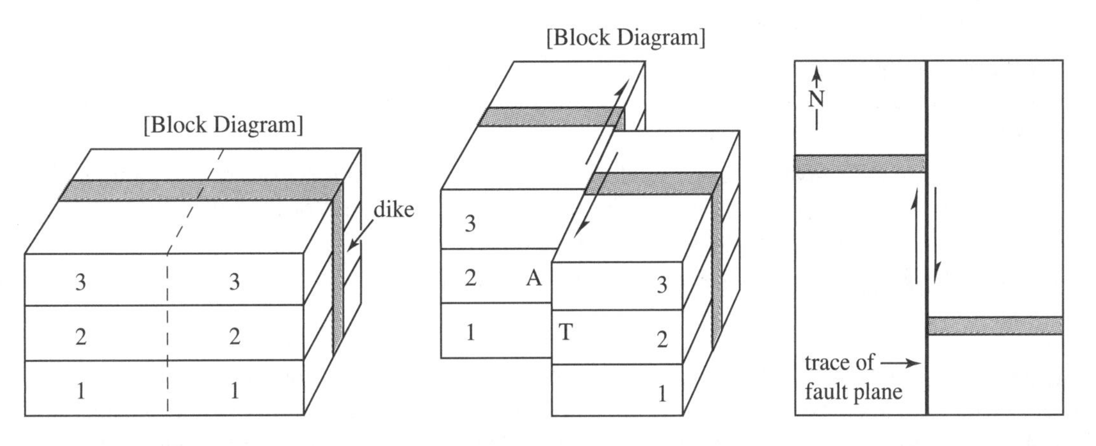

Figure 18-11a. Before Faulting **Figure 18-11b. After Faulting** **Figure 18-11c. Map View**

Figure 18-11. Right-Lateral Strike-Slip Faulting

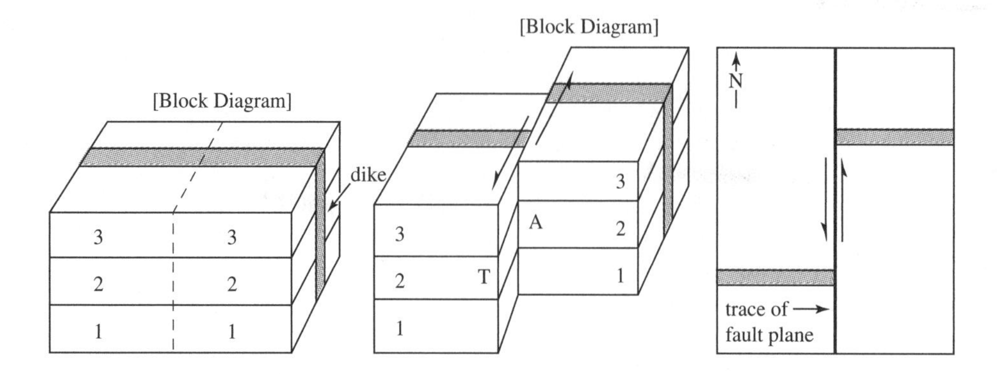

Figure 18-12a. Before Faulting **Figure 18-12b. After Faulting** **Figure 18-12c. Map View**

Figure 18-12. Left-Lateral Strike-Slip Faulting

yourself that right-lateral or left-lateral movement is unambiguous; it does not change if an observer who was first positioned on a given "near side" were to cross over the fault so that the former far side becomes the near side. The San Andreas Fault in California is a right-lateral strike-slip fault.

On left-lateral strike-slip faults [Figure 18-12(*a, b, c*)], the block across the fault has moved to the left relative to the observer, and the continuation of a feature across the fault will be found displaced to the left. Symbols have the same meaning as for right-lateral strikeslip faults.

Movement on dip-slip and strike-slip faults is indicated in opposite ways on maps and cross sections. On a map [Figures 18-11(*c*), 18-12(*c*)] half arrows indicate the relative motion of a strike-slip fault (in contrast to D and U for dip-slip faults). In cross section, the movement of a strike-slip fault block is *toward* or *away from* the observer, necessitating **T** or **A** [Figures 18-11(*b*), 18-12(*b*)]. In contrast, arrows show motion on a dip-slip fault in cross section.

Unconformities

An unconformity is a buried surface of erosion (Figure 18-13). Erosion removes previously existing rock from a given site, and consequently an unconformity signifies one aspect of recycling—the absence of part of the geologic record. Some unconformities are minor, representing erosion during perhaps only a few tens of thousands of years. Others, in which strata containing fossils of late, complex life forms directly overlie extremely ancient rocks, represent profound gaps in the geologic record. Recognition of unconformities is essential to understanding the geologic history of an area.

Three major types of unconformity are classified according to the characteristics of rock bodies above and below the erosion surface.

- **Disconformity**: Layers below and above the unconformity are parallel, having the same strike and dip [Figure 18-13(*a*)]. There was no structural deformation, such as tilting, between the formation of the lower (older) and upper (younger) strata.
- **Angular Unconformity**: Layers below and above the unconformity are not parallel [Figure 18-13(*b*)]; they have different strikes and dips because movement of the earth occurred after the lower beds were deposited, but before the upper beds were deposited.
- **Nonconformity**: The upper beds lie upon metamorphic or intrusive igneous rock [Figure 18-13(*c*)].

In general, a disconformity indicates a relatively minor duration of erosion. At the other extreme, the ancient metamorphic or igneous rock beneath a nonconformity was formed perhaps kilometers deep in the crust. An enormous thickness of rock has been eroded over a time interval of hundreds of millions, to billions of years.

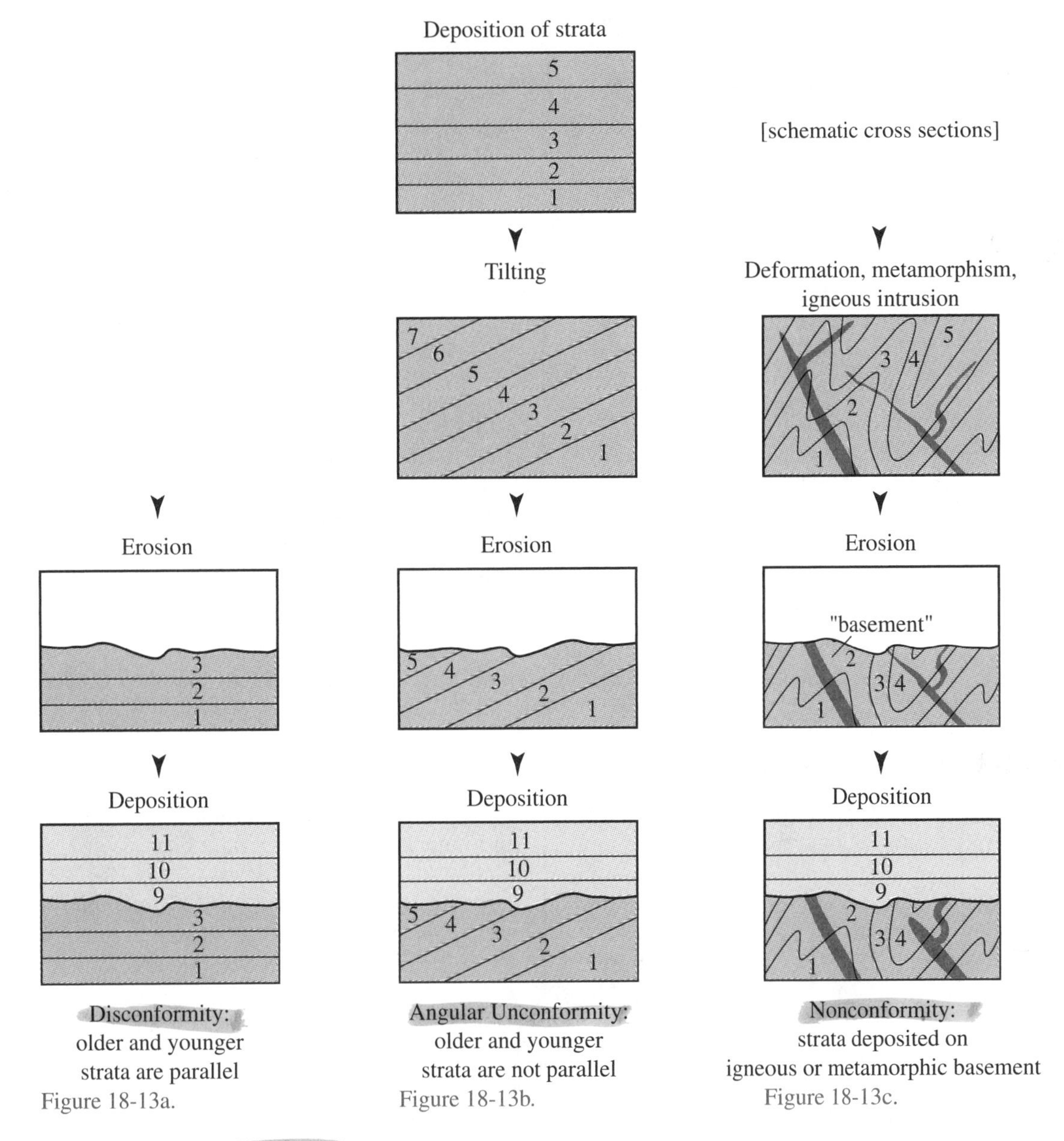

Figure 18-13. Unconformities

OVERVIEW

The preceding pages describe a variety of types of folds and faults. Folds may be symmetrical, or asymmetrical upright to overturned. Fold axes may be horizontal or plunging. Fault motion may be normal, reverse, thrust, or right- or left-lateral strike-slip. Faults may cut through dipping or folded strata that later are partially removed by erosion. The three-dimensional shapes of these deformed rock bodies, and the two-dimensional patterns of their intersection with the earth's surface may be quite complex. On the following page is a summary of dipping beds, folds, and faults.

Geologic mapping is typically the only available source of information. Mapping reveals the distribution of bedrock units, with dip-and-strike readings of the attitudes (spatial orientations) of the rocks where exposed at the surface. Our task is to use this fragmentary knowledge as a basis to understand the entire structure, and from that to deduce a history of geologic events that produced the observed final result. Following are some examples that demonstrate step-by-step procedures of how to reason through such data.

GEOLOGIC STRUCTURES

INCLINED BED OR FAULT SURFACE: the primary structural element

Strike: the compass direction of a horizontal line on an inclined plane	**Dip**: the angle down from horizontal, measured on the plane perpendicular to strike

FOLD: deformation by **bending**

Anticline (result of compressional stress) (oldest bed in center of outcrop pattern) (limbs dipping away from center)	**Syncline** (result of compressional stress) (youngest bed in center of outcrop pattern) (limbs dipping toward center)
Symmetrical anticline: outcrop of beds in parallel bands on earth's surface **Asymmetrical** anticline: beds with variable widths of outcrop **Plunging** anticline: inclined fold axis; plunge axis pointing into "V" of outcrop	**Symmetrical** syncline: outcrop of beds in parallel bands on earth's surface **Asymmetrical** syncline: beds with variable widths of outcrop **Plunging** syncline: inclined fold axis; plunge axis pointing away from "V" of outcrop
Dome (result of uplift) (limbs dipping away from center in all directions)	**Basin** (result of subsidence) (limbs dipping toward center from all directions)

FAULT: deformation by **breaking**

Dip-slip fault (movement along dip of fault plane)	**Strike-slip** fault (movement along strike of fault plane as a result of shear stress)

Normal fault (result of tensional stress)	**Reverse** fault or **Thrust** fault (result of compressional stress)	**Right-lateral:** relative movement of far side to the right	**Left-lateral:** relative movement of far side to the left

Solving a Problem of Folded Strata

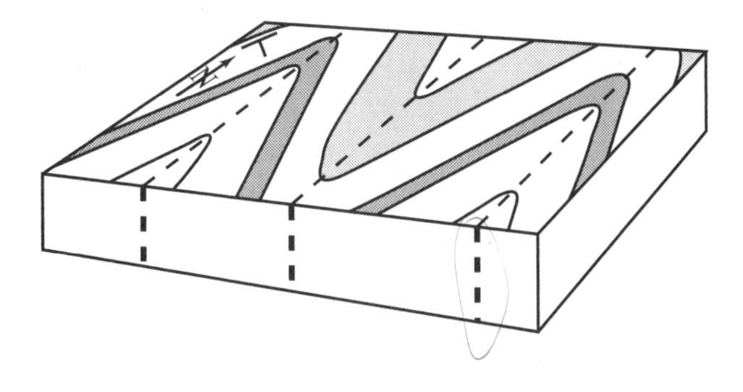

The block diagram shows the earth's surface eroded to a level plain, in which is exposed the outcrop pattern of a set of plunging folds. Dashed lines indicate fold axes. Because the pattern is symmetrical about a fold axis, the axial planes must be vertical.

We draw the intersections of the axial planes on the front vertical face of the block diagram (bold lines).

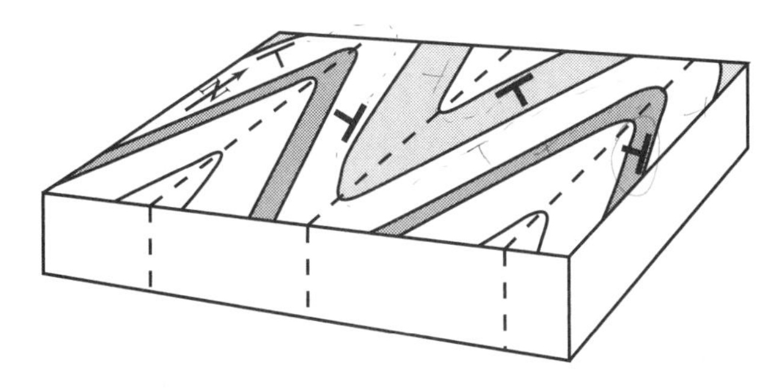

The strike-and-dip symbol in the upper left corner indicates that the bed dips toward the fold axis. The bed must also dip toward the axis on the opposite limb of the fold (the dip direction reverses).

Thus we can follow the set of beds around, and place more strike-and-dip symbols (bold) in correct orientation.

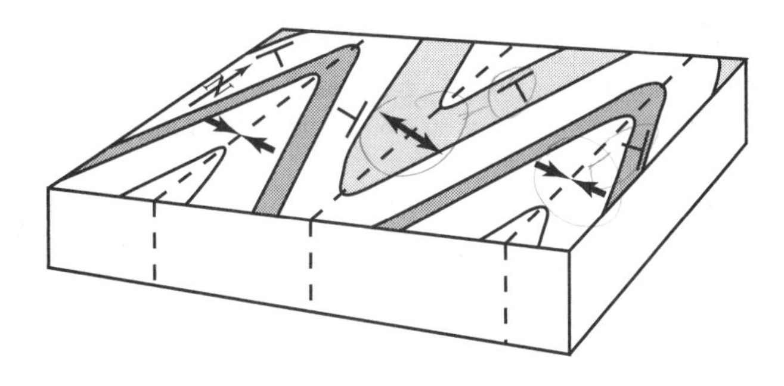

If the beds dip toward the axial plane, the fold is a syncline; if the beds dip away from the axial plane, the fold is an anticline.

We place syncline and anticline symbols (bold) on the upper surface of the block.

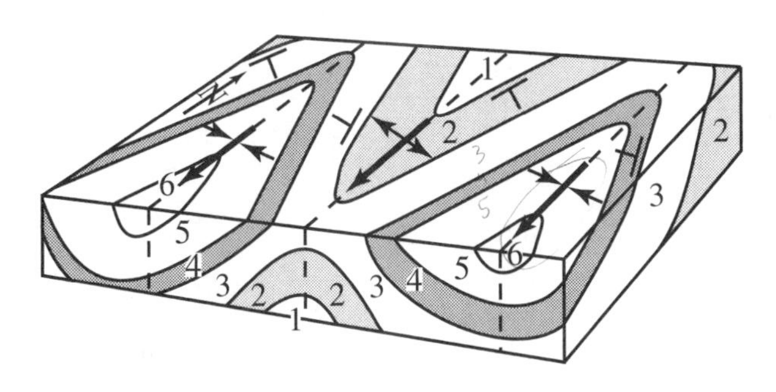

The law of superposition states that younger beds lie above older beds. We number the beds according to their relative ages (larger numbers for younger beds).

We now see that two synclines and one anticline are plunging south. We add plunge arrows (bold).

Finally, we draw and number the beds on the vertical faces and complete the shading.

Solving a Problem of Dip-Slip Fault Motion

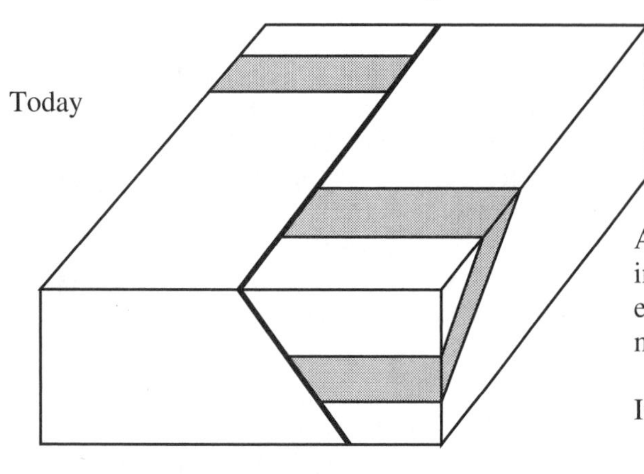

A block diagram shows dipping strata intersecting the Earth's surface. According to independent evidence, the offset on the fault (bold line) must have been by dip-slip motion.

Is it a normal or reverse fault?

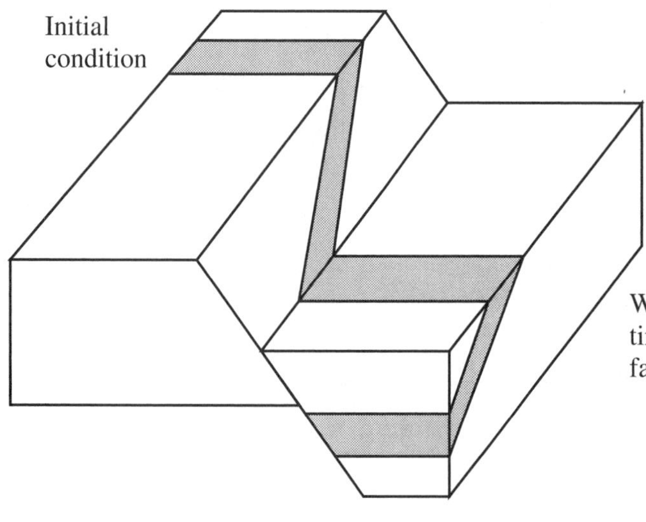

We know that initially the strata must have continued unbroken across the plane of the future fault.

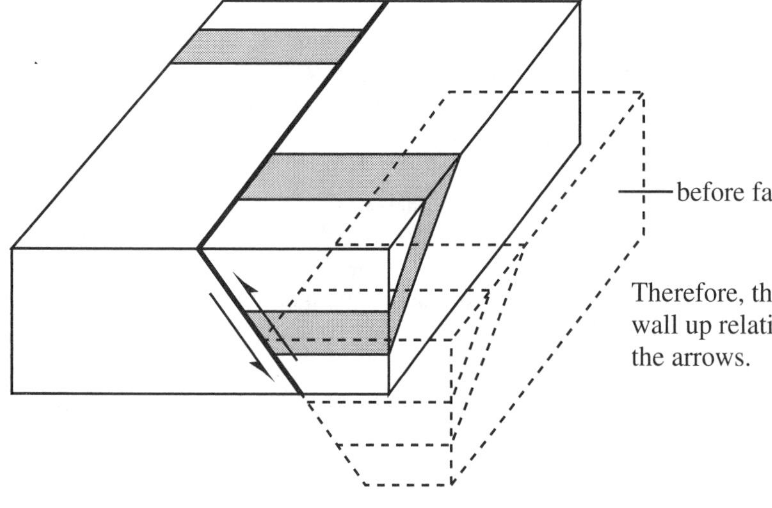

Therefore, the fault must be reverse (hanging wall up relative to the footwall) as indicated by the arrows.

Solving a Problem of Strike-Slip Fault Motion

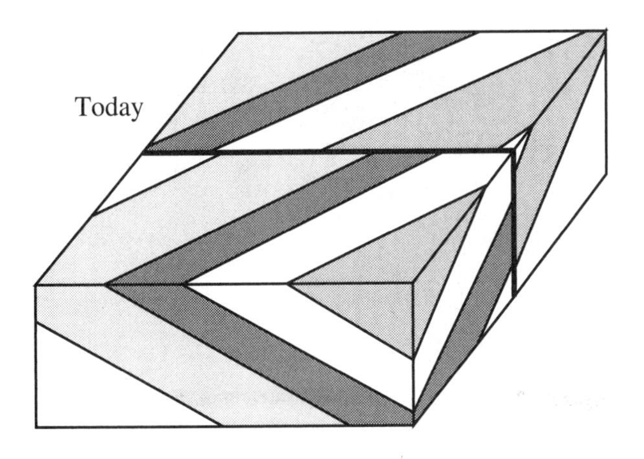

A block diagram shows dipping strata intersecting the earth's surface. According to independent evidence, the offset on the fault (bold line) must have been by lateral (strike-slip) motion.

Is it a right-lateral or left-lateral fault?

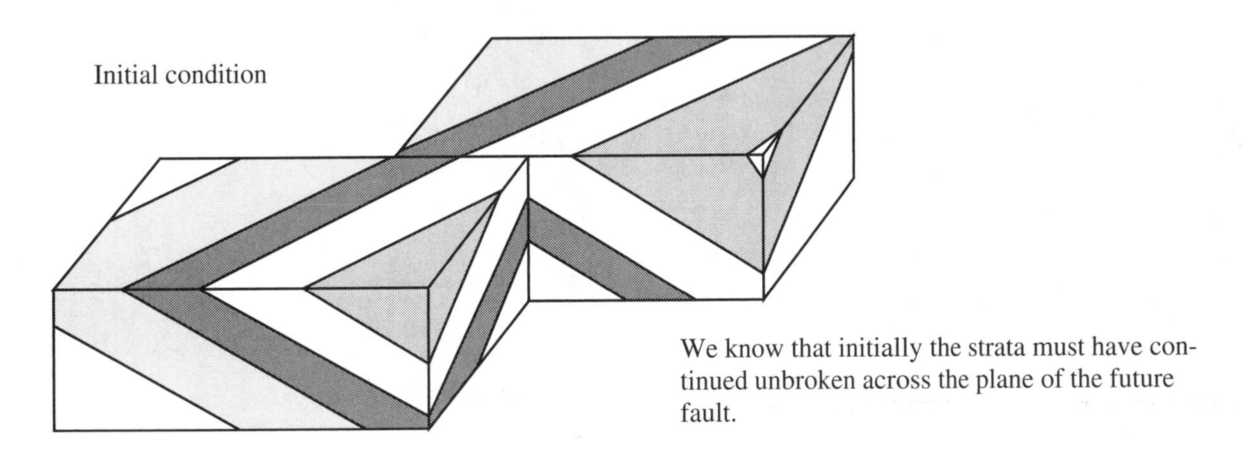

We know that initially the strata must have continued unbroken across the plane of the future fault.

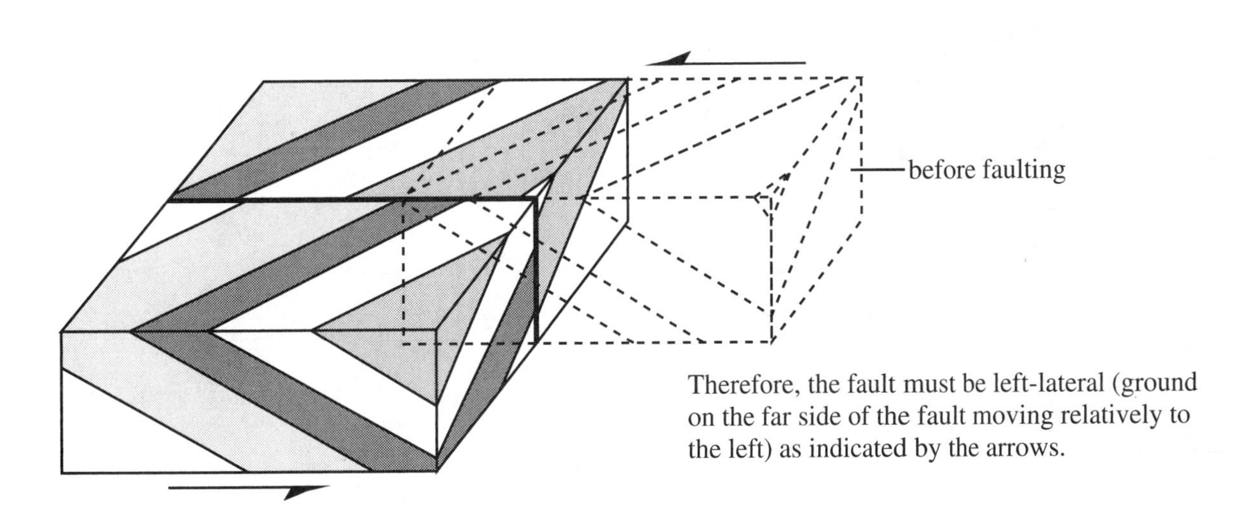

Therefore, the fault must be left-lateral (ground on the far side of the fault moving relatively to the left) as indicated by the arrows.

Tilted sedimentary layers showing strike and dip, Imperial Valley, California. (Photo by Shannon O'Dunn.)

Symmetrical plunging anticline and syncline, Calico Mountains, Mojave Desert, California. (Photo by Shannon O'Dunn.)

Symmetrical syncline beneath angular unconformity, Barstow, California. (Photo by Shannon O'Dunn.)

Overturned anticline. (Photo by John Shelton.)

Symmetrical plunging anticline. (Photo by John Shelton.)

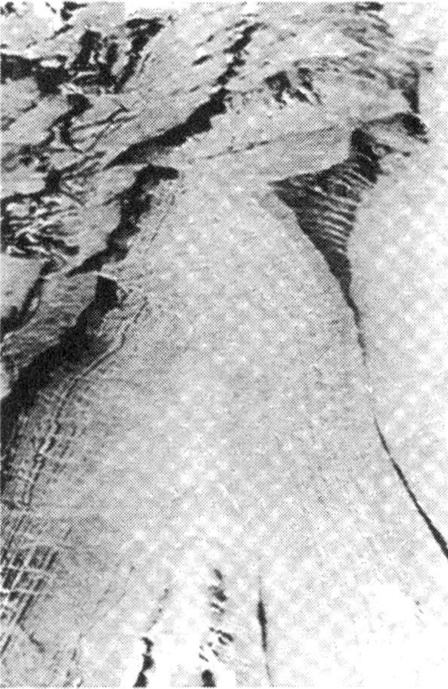

Asymmetrical plunging anticline. (Photo by John Shelton.)

Syncline plunging to right on skyline. (Photo by Shannon O'Dunn.)

Photo 18-1. Dip and Strike, Folds

Normal faulting of Columbia Plateau basalt flows, central Oregon. (Grossmont College Photo)

Vertical fault in granite shows slickensides and the non-linear character typical of many faults. San Diego County, California. (Photo by Shannon O'Dunn.)

Normal faulting in marine sandstones resulting from large-scale seaward landsliding, Del Mar, California. (Photo by Shannon O'Dunn.)

A tectonic breccia produced by great sliding force at the base of the Titus Canyon Thrust Fault, Death Valley, California. (Photo by Roland Brady.)

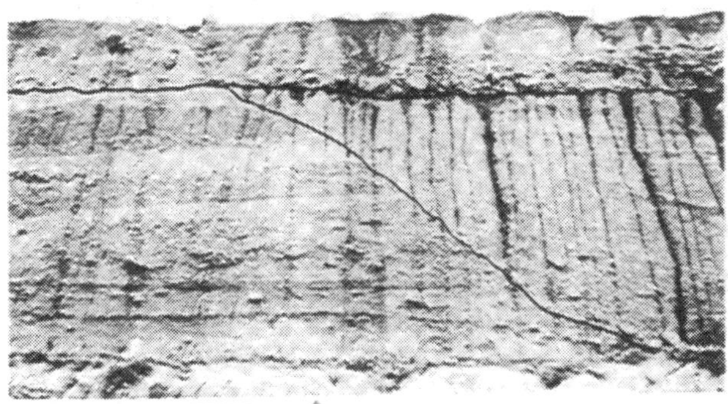

Two angular unconformities can be distinguished in these sandstone and conglomerate deposits near Ensenada, Baja California, Mexico. (Photo by Shannon O'Dunn.)

A nonconformity which represents about a billion years of missing Earth history separates crystalline rocks below from gently dipping overlying sandstone. Colorado Rockies. (Photo by Shannon O'Dunn.)

Photo 18-2. Faults, Unconformities

Table 18-1. *Geologic Map Symbols*

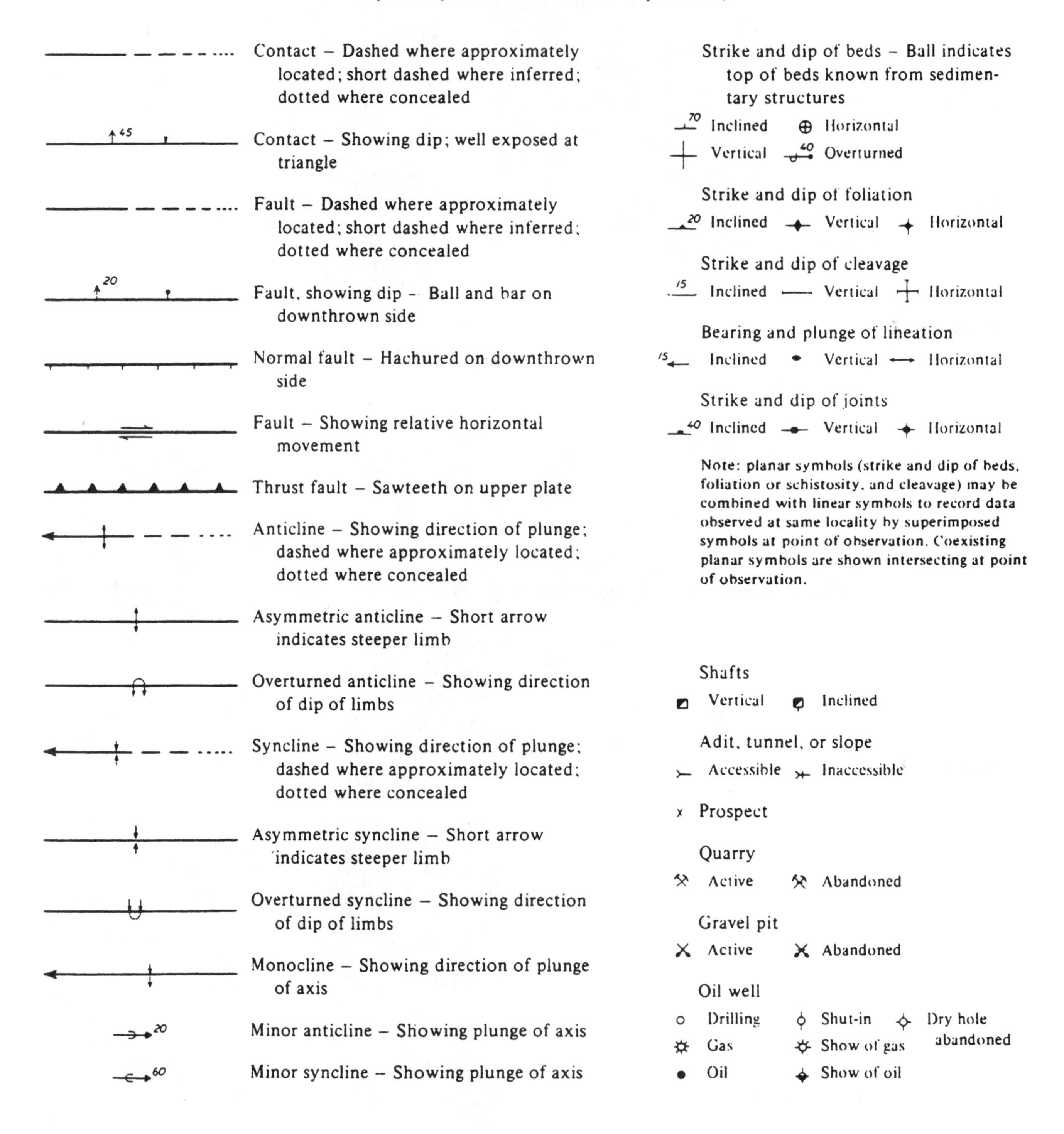

Structural Geology

- Consider different types of deformation, and using the laws (or principles) of Superposition, Original Horizontality, Cross-cutting Relationships, and Faunal Succession, to determine the geologic history.
  - Fault (fracture with offsetting motion)
  - Unconformity (buried surface of erosion)
  - Fold

Strike and Dip of a Planar Feature

- Strike: compass direction of a line formed by the intersection of a dipping plane (a stratum or fault) and a horizontal plane

N-S strike E-W strike N30°E

- Dip: measured at a right angle to the strike (true dip). The amount of dip is the angle between the dipping plane and a horizontal plane.

20° 65°

Structures Related to Stress Type

- Stress (force per unit area) causes strain (deformation).
- Tensional stress: pulling apart, extension, stretching
  - Normal fault, rift
- Compressional stress: pressing together
  - Fold, reverse fault, thrust fault (reverse fault with low-angle fault plane)
- Shear stress: tangential
  - Strike-slip fault
- Vertically directed stress: Stress up or down
  - Uplift: dome
  - Subsidence: basin

Types of Unconformity

- A buried surface representing a period of time when erosion removed part of the rock record
  - Angular unconformity: surface of erosion between nonparallel strata
  - Disconformity: surface of erosion between parallel strata
  - Nonconformity: surface of erosion between sedimentary strata above, and igneous or metamorphic rock below

Rules for Assigning Relative Age

- Superposition: in an undisturbed succession, younger strata overlie older strata.
- If beds are numbered, older beds are arbitrarily assigned numbers with smaller values.

3
2
1

- In tilted strata, older beds dip toward younger beds.

3 2 1   3 2 1

- In an eroded upfold (anticline), older rocks occupy the core in cross section and map view, whereas in an eroded downfold (syncline), younger beds occupy the core.

Views of Structure

- Map view: pattern created by the intersection of rock units with the earth's surface
- Cross section: pattern created by the intersection of rocks with a vertical plane (for example, a cliff or road cut).

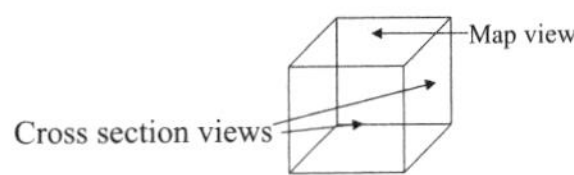

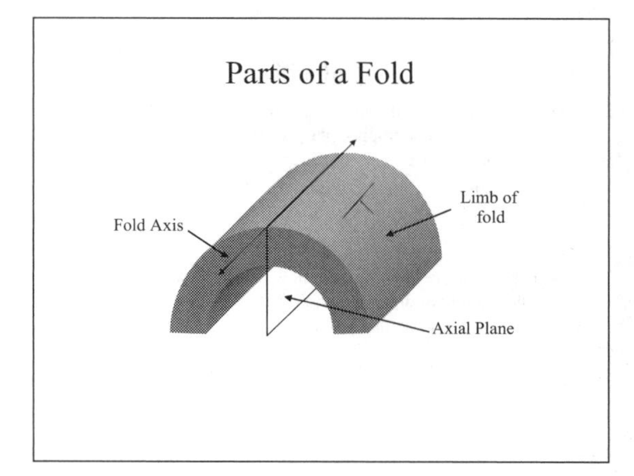

Folded Strata

- A fold results from compression as stress is applied slowly, over a long period of time.
- Anticline: up-folded structure in which the limbs dip away from the center (axial plane).
- Syncline: down-folded structure in which the limbs dip toward the center (axial plane).
  - Anticlines and synclines may be symmetrical or asymmetrical.
- Dome: results from uplift; limbs dip away from the center in all directions.
- Basin: results from subsidence; limbs dip toward the center in all directions.

Broken Rocks

- Joint: fracture with no appreciable displacement of beds (vertical or horizontal)

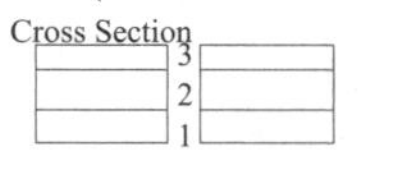

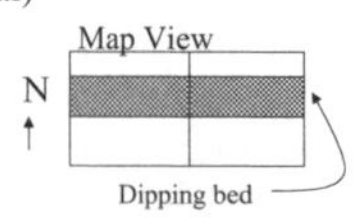

- Fault: fracture with appreciable displacement of beds along a plane that can be of any orientation

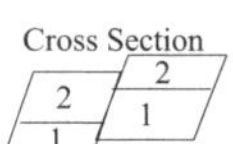

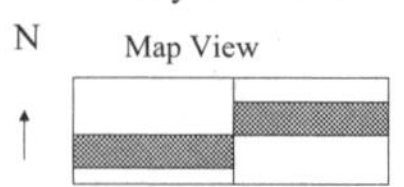

Dip-Slip Fault Terms

- Dip-slip fault: displacement is parallel to the dip of the fault plane
- Footwall: an old miner's term, used to describe the side of the fault that one could stand on
- Hanging wall: the wall that hangs above the footwall
- Normal fault: created by tension. The hanging wall moves down relative to the footwall.
- Reverse fault: created by compression. The hanging wall moves up relative to the footwall.
- Thrust fault: a reverse fault with a low-angle fault plane.

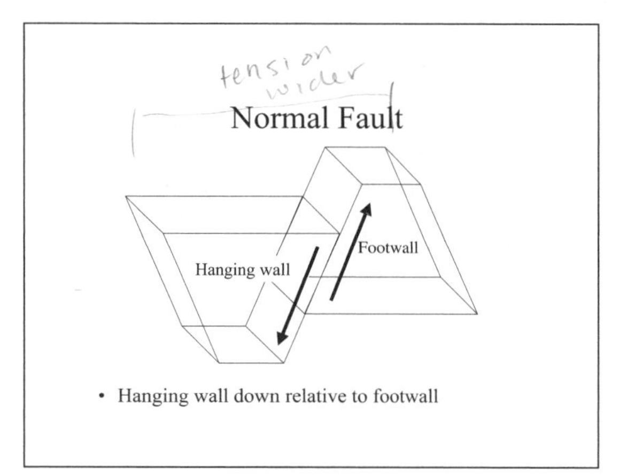

Reverse Fault (or Thrust Fault)

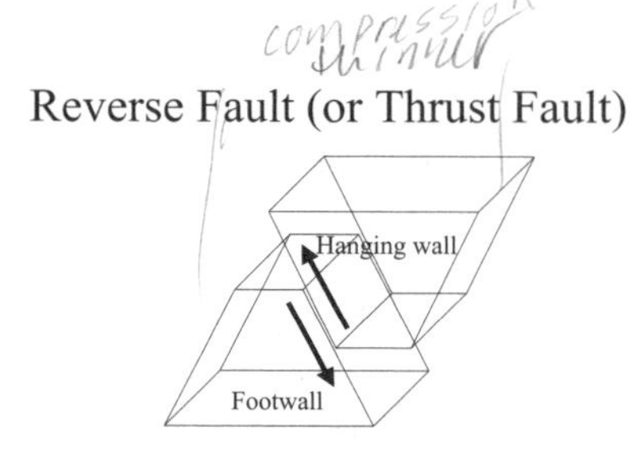

- Hanging wall up relative to footwall
- Low-angle fault plane = thrust fault

Strike-slip Fault

- Fault in which movement is parallel to the strike of the fault plane
- Left lateral:
- Right lateral:

Fault Slickensides

- Grooves on the fault face that indicate the general direction of movement
  - Horizontal slickensides = parallel to strike movement (strike-slip fault)
  - Vertical slickensides = perpendicular to strike movement (dip-slip fault)

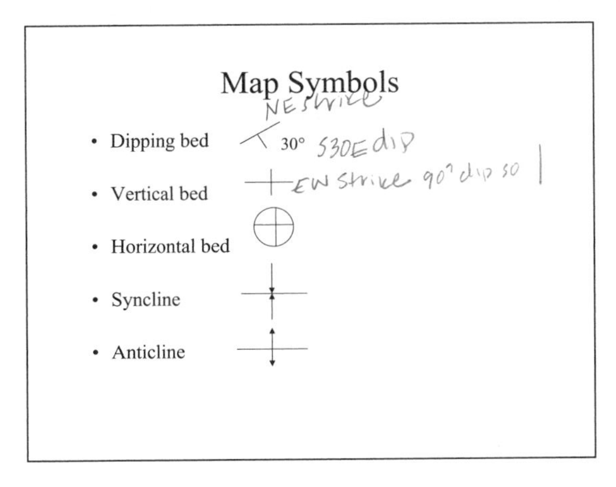

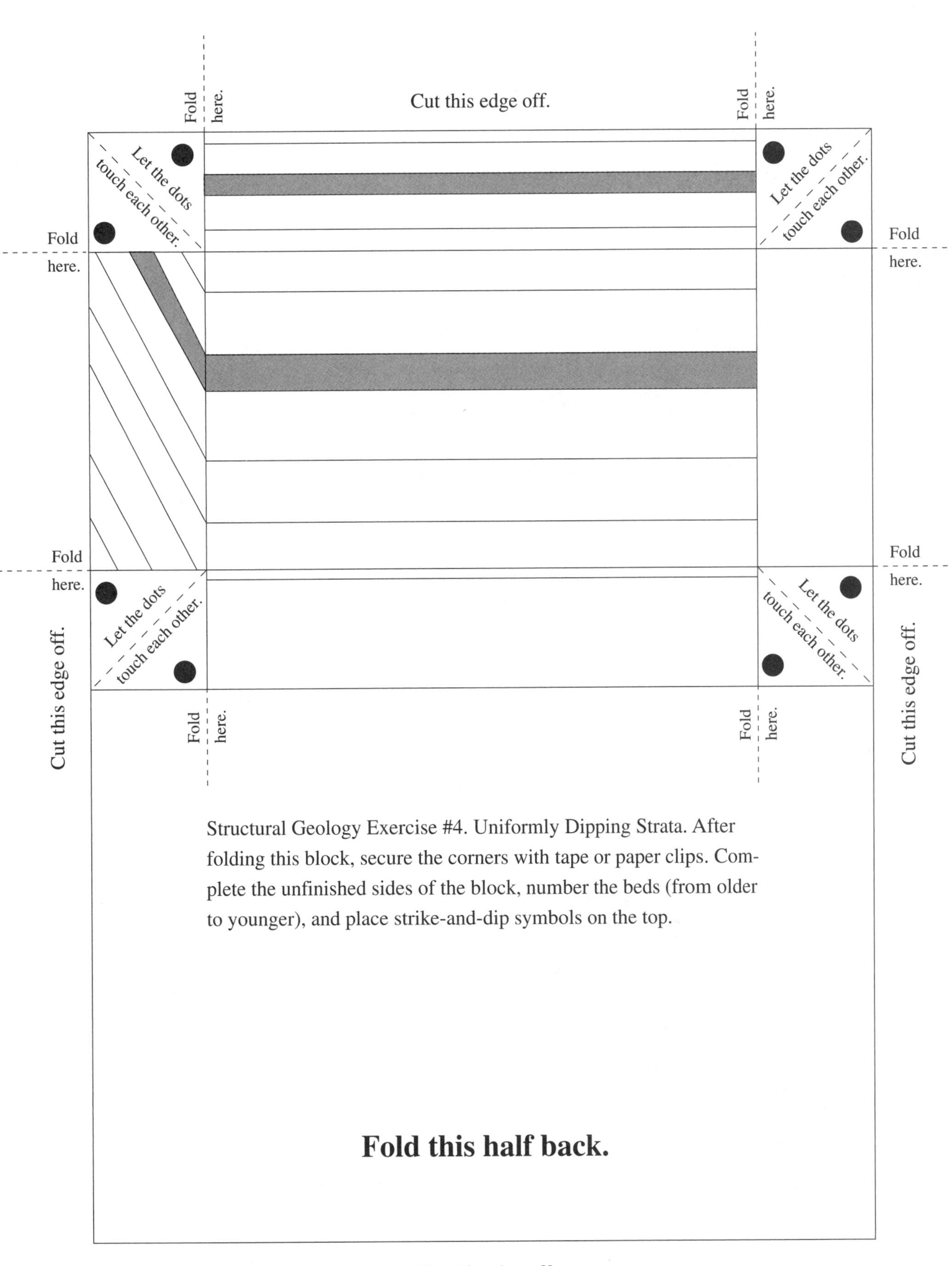

Structural Geology Exercise #4. Uniformly Dipping Strata. After folding this block, secure the corners with tape or paper clips. Complete the unfinished sides of the block, number the beds (from older to younger), and place strike-and-dip symbols on the top.

Fold this half back.

Cut this edge off.

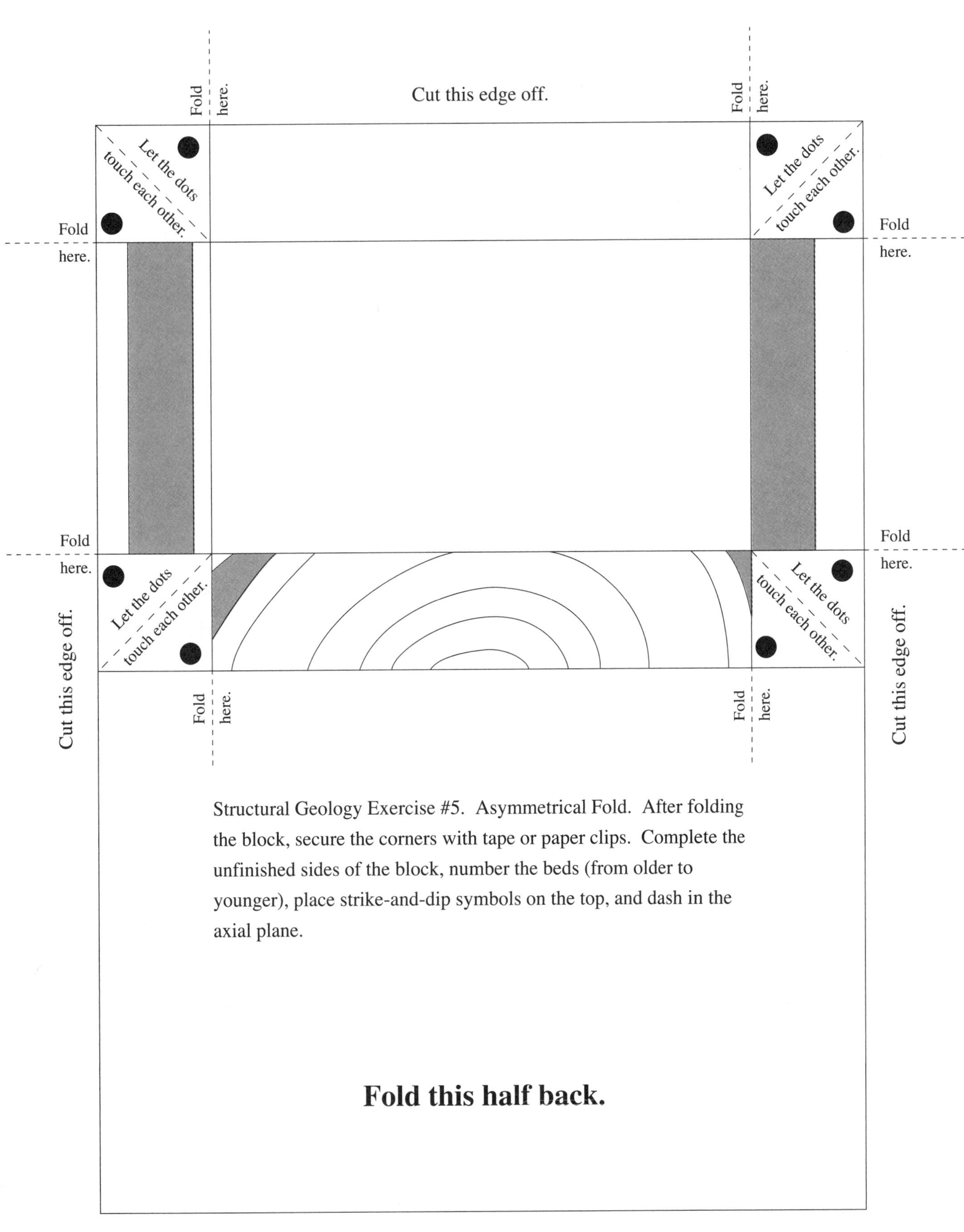

Structural Geology Exercise #5. Asymmetrical Fold. After folding the block, secure the corners with tape or paper clips. Complete the unfinished sides of the block, number the beds (from older to younger), place strike-and-dip symbols on the top, and dash in the axial plane.

Cut this edge off.

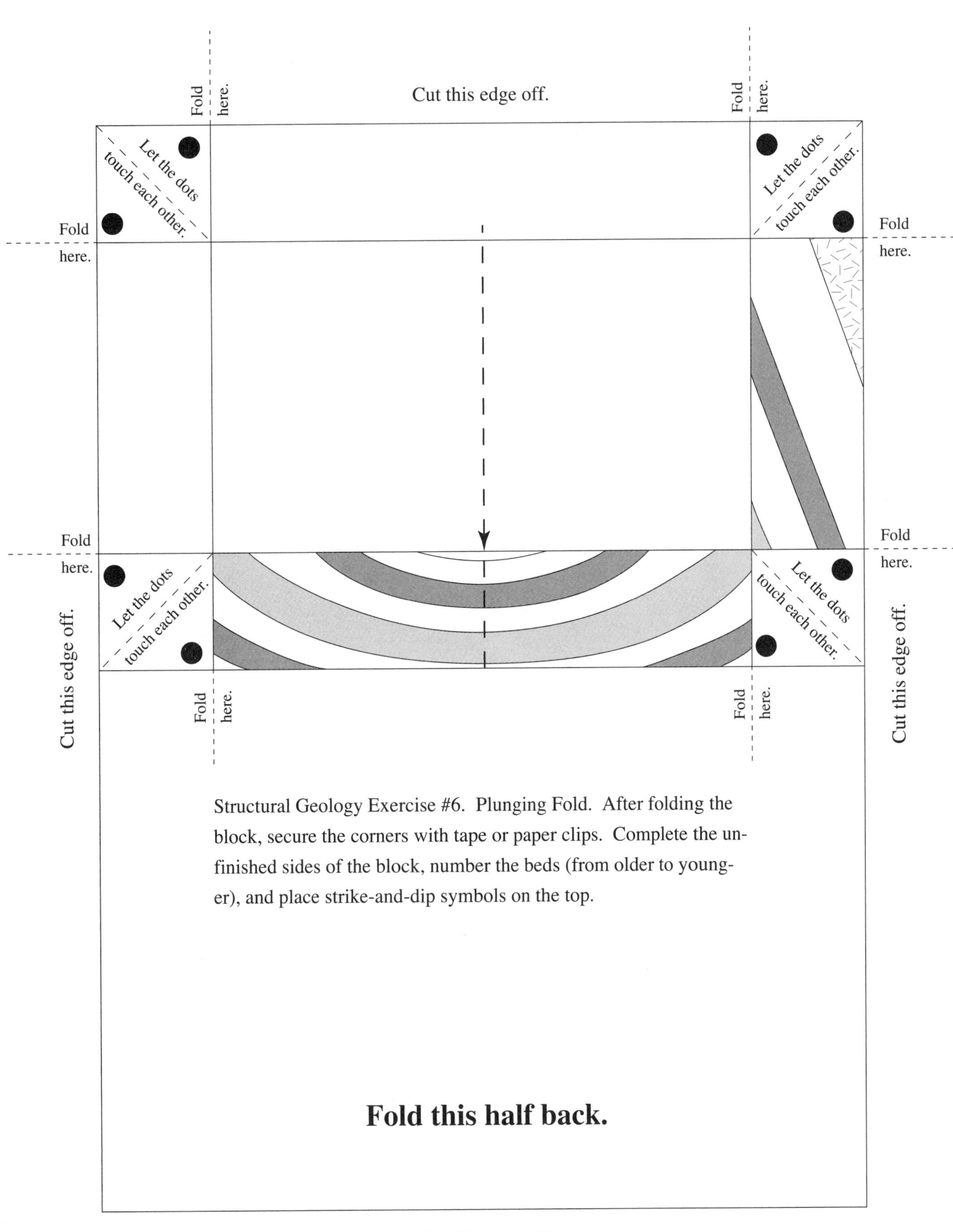

Structural Geology Exercise #6. Plunging Fold. After folding the block, secure the corners with tape or paper clips. Complete the unfinished sides of the block, number the beds (from older to younger), and place strike-and-dip symbols on the top.

Cut this edge off.

Fold here. Fold here.

Let the dots touch each other. Let the dots touch each other.

Fold here. Fold here.

Fold here. Fold here.

Let the dots touch each other. Let the dots touch each other.

Cut this edge off. Cut this edge off.

Fold here. Fold here.

Structural Geology Exercise #7. Fault and Dipping Strata. After folding the block, secure the corners with tape or paper clips. Complete the trace of the fault on the side panel. Then complete the beds on the unfinished sides of the block, place a strike-and-dip symbol on the top on each side of the fault, and place arrows on the side panels to show fault motion

Fold this half back.

Cut this edge off.

Name: ______________________________

Section: ______________________________

STRUCTURAL GEOLOGY EXERCISE #8: FOSSILS AND STRUCTURAL INTERPRETATION

The use of fossils as relative age indicators will often enable a geologist to establish the correct structural interpretation of a deformed sequence of layers. In these problems below, use the fossil symbols from the Geologic Time Scale (Table 14-1a) just as you used numbers on layers in this chapter to establish dip direction (i.e., assume that layers dip toward the youngest bed).

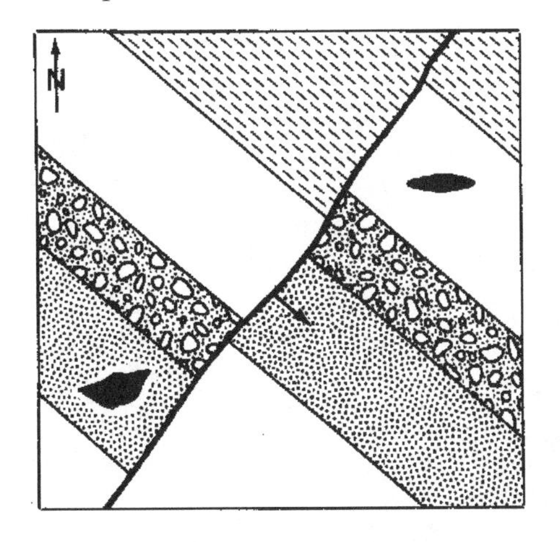

1. What is the compass direction of dip of these layers?

   ____

2. What is the youngest rock unit shown? ____________

   ____

3. Assuming dip-slip movement, what specific kind of fault is shown here? ____________

4. Assume strike-slip motion; name the fault. ____________

   ____

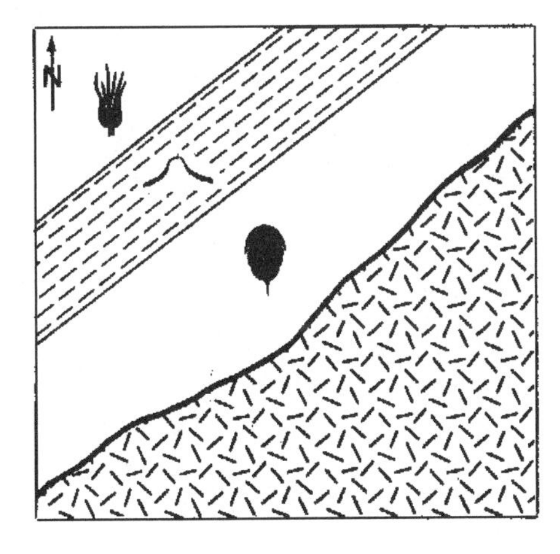

5. What kind of unconformity separates the fossiliferous and nonfossiliferous units?____________

   ____

6. What is the probable age of the granite? ____________

   ____

7. Put dip and strike symbols on the sedimentary layers.

8. Write out the strike and dip of the layers. ____________

   ____

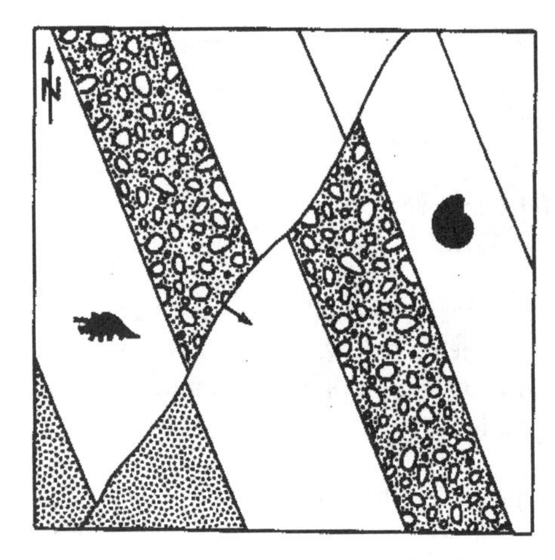

9. What is the dip direction of the layers? ____________

____

10. Mark the oldest layer with an X.

11. Assuming strike-slip motion, name the fault. ________

____

12. Assuming dip-slip motion, name the fault. _________

____

Name: ______________________

CHAPTER 18: Structural Geology

Section: ______________________

REVIEW QUESTIONS

1. What is the fixed angular relationship between dip and strike? ______________________

____

2. Anticlines, synclines, and ______________ faults are caused by compression.

3. What type of fold has the most economic significance to geologists?

____

4. ____________________ folds form U- or V-shape outcrop patterns on the surface.

5. The best indicators of actual fault movement directions are ____________________.

6. 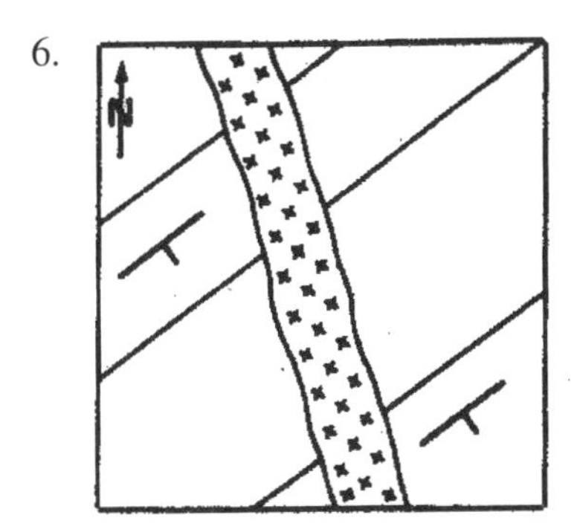

Put numbers on the beds to show relative ages. Assume that the land is flat, and that the beds have not been overturned.

7. 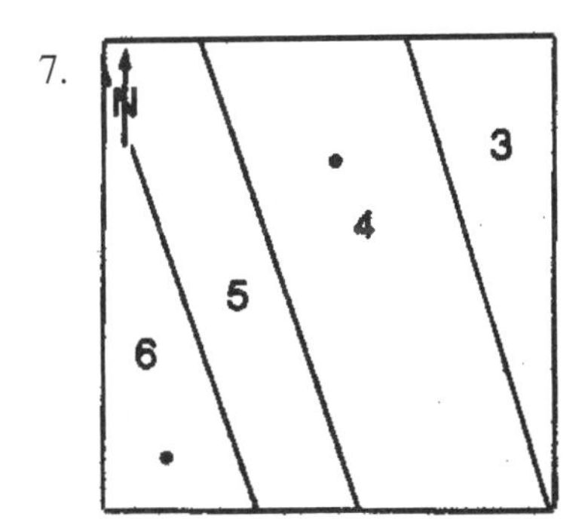

Put dip and strike symbols on the beds at the dots. Use the same assumptions as Question #6.

8. 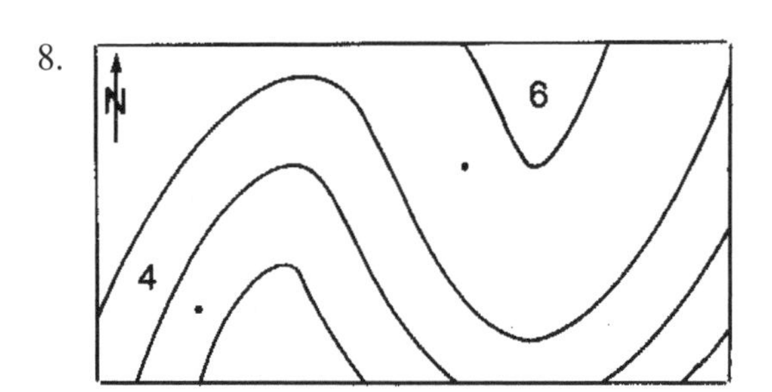

Place plunge arrows on the map, and dip and strike symbols at the dots.

9. What general kind of structure dominates this region? ______________________

10. Complete the block diagram below. Outline the geologic history of this area using specific terms for the rock types and structures. Refer to Table 14-1a for symbols, displayed below, of geologic periods.

Geologic History

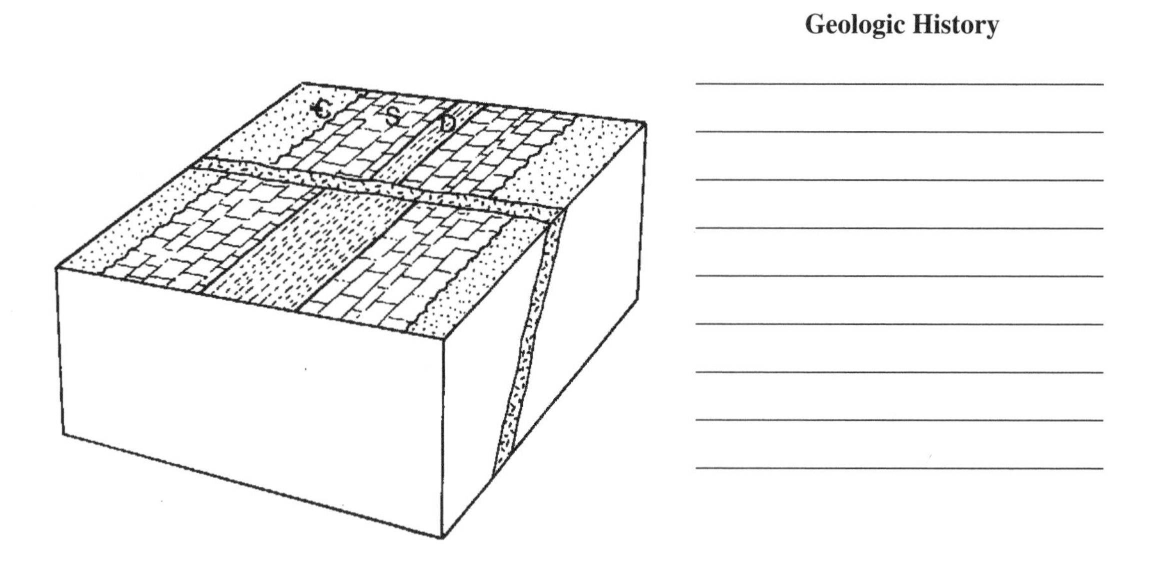

11. How would you distinguish between a disconformity and an angular unconformity on a geologic map? ____

____

Name: ______________________

CHAPTER 18: Structural Geology

Section: ______________________

MORE CHALLENGING QUESTIONS

1. What kind of unconformity would be most difficult to identify in the field? ______________________

2. What is the difference between stress and strain? ______________________

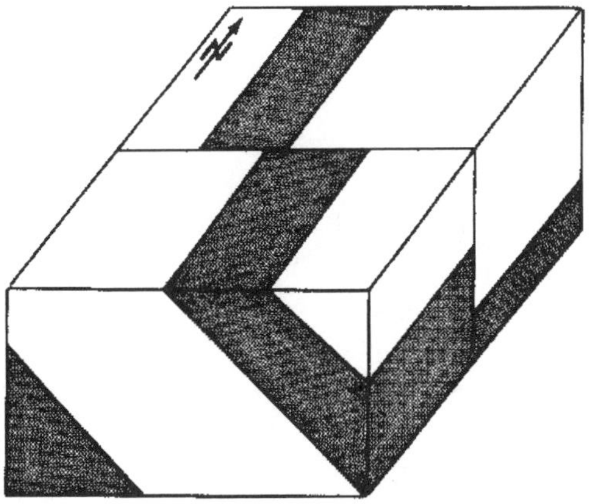

3. a. Place the appropriate symbols on the map (top of the block).

   b. Write out the strike and dip for the dipping layers.

   ____

   c. Write out the strike and dip for the fault plane.

   ____

4. Under compressional stress, some rock bodies bend (fold) and other break (fault). What conditions might determine which strain pattern develops?

   a. Folding ______________________

   b. Faulting ______________________

5. In studying asymmetrical folds, we saw that the outcrop (map) width of a given layer of uniform thickness may vary depending upon ______________________________.

6. This is a map view of an eroded plain.

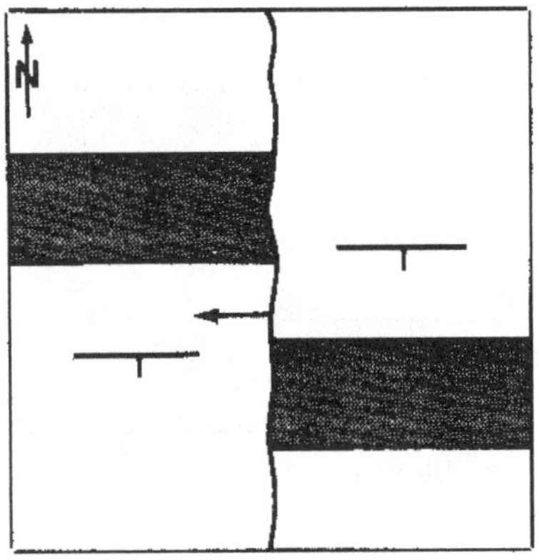

N

a. Assuming horizontal slickenside grooves, name the fault:

____

b. Assuming vertical slickenside grooves, name the fault:

____

7. What is the difference between a nonconformity and an igneous intrusive contact?

____

____

____

____

19

Geologic Maps

INTRODUCTION

Geologic maps portray the distribution of discrete rock bodies and geologic structures. Planimetric details such as roads, buildings, and spot elevations are normally included. Geologists create these informative and often colorful maps by plotting the location and structural orientation (i.e., strike and dip) of bedrock exposures on a topographic base, using data from the field, photo imagery, and subsurface work where available. Boundary lines between distinct rock units are drawn to show how the area would look with the surface cover stripped away, and structural symbols are plotted. Vertical slices (cross sections) showing subsurface distribution of rock bodies and structures may be produced from map and field data.

In making a geologic map, the geologist must define discrete rock bodies that are mappable units in an area, resolve the age sequence of the rocks, identify the structural features and patterns present, and extrapolate the distribution of rock units and structures where they are obscured by a surface cover of soil, vegetation, water, and human cultural features (roads, buildings, etc.). This process draws upon a geologist's knowledge of petrology, paleontology, structure, topographic maps, and interpretation of aerial photography. Similarly, your ability to derive information from geologic maps in this chapter will greatly depend upon your comprehension of material covered in preceding chapters.

ROCK UNIT SYMBOLS AND CONTACTS

A discrete mappable rock unit, or geologic **formation**, is defined on the basis of rock type, age, fossil content, and internal structure or texture. On a geologic map, each formation is distinguished by a unique letter symbol, and color or pattern. It is standard procedure to name a geologic formation after the proper name of a locality where the formation is well exposed or was first defined. Examples of local formations are the Buda Limestone, after the town of Buda south of Austin, the Smithwick Shale, after a small settlement in the Llano Uplift west of Austin, and the Valley Spring Gneiss, a metamorphic unit named after the village of Valley Spring in the Llano Uplift. An abbreviation of the name of a formation includes an upper-case letter that symbolizes the geologic time period when it originated (for example: Precambrian, Cretaceous) and lowercase letters for the name itself. Cretaceous is abbreviated as "K" to avoid confusion with Cambrian and Carboniferous, two other "C" names for periods of geologic time. For the formations just cited, we have:

Formation	Age of origin	Abbreviation
Buda Limestone (bu)	Cretaceous (K)	Kbu
Smithwick Shale (sm)	Pennsylvanian (IP)	IPsm
Valley Spring Gneiss (vs)	Precambrian (p€)	p€vs

Note that in the list, the older formation (Smithwick Shale) is positioned below the younger formation (Buda Limestone), and Precambrian Valley Spring Gneiss is at the bottom. This is to acknowledge the law of superposition, which states that younger strata rest upon older in an undisturbed sequence.

GEOLOGIC CONTACTS

A geologic **contact** is the line (on a map) or interface (in the real world) between adjacent rock units. Three fundamental types of contact are **depositional**, **fault**, and **igneous intrusive**. Depositional contacts lie between adjacent sedimentary strata, lava flows, etc., or between the metamorphosed equivalents of these rocks. Along fault contacts, the rocks have been displaced by dip-slip or strike-slip motion, or a combination of the two. Igneous intrusive contacts refer to the margins of bodies of granite, gabbro, etc. that have invaded the host rock. Refer back to Table 18-1, which provides standard symbols for various types of contact where they are exposed or concealed beneath soil or vegetation. Note that unconformities, which are a type of depositional contact, have no special symbol. Existence of an unconformity is verified by age relationships, and commonly by discontinuities in type and orientation of the rocks above and below the buried surface of erosion. Because the erosional surface of an unconformity is typically irregular, it is symbolized in cross sections by a wavy line. On the other hand, a map view must display an unconformity exactly as it intersects the land surface.

PERIPHERAL INFORMATION ON GEOLOGIC MAPS

Every geologic map must be accompanied by an **Explanation**. All rock units on the map are identified by age, name, symbol, and color. Structure symbols used on the map are also identified.

Study of the map may raise questions about the relationships of rock bodies at depth, shapes of buried portions of structures, etc. Many geologic maps are supplemented by one or more cross sections that are located on the map along lines designated A-A', B-B', etc. Cross sections portray the third (vertical) dimension and are very helpful in developing a comprehensive picture of the geology.

Occasionally other information is included in order to point up a special or important geological feature. Examples are detailed descriptions of rock units, reconstructions of geologically ancient topography, or additional maps that emphasize particular structures, units, economic mineral deposits, or information about groundwater.

OUTCROP PATTERNS ON GEOLOGIC MAPS

Geologic maps may be visually simple or complex depending upon the number of rock units present, structural complications, and degree of dissection of the topography by erosion. We may generalize that simple-appearing geologic maps correspond to a coincidence of topography and structural trends, with few rock units present. Geologic maps are complex where many rock units, structures, and dissected slopes are present, and the slope of the land differs considerably from regional dips. Diagrams in Figure 19-1 show some of these variables, and demonstrate how a geologic map compares in cross section with the geology.

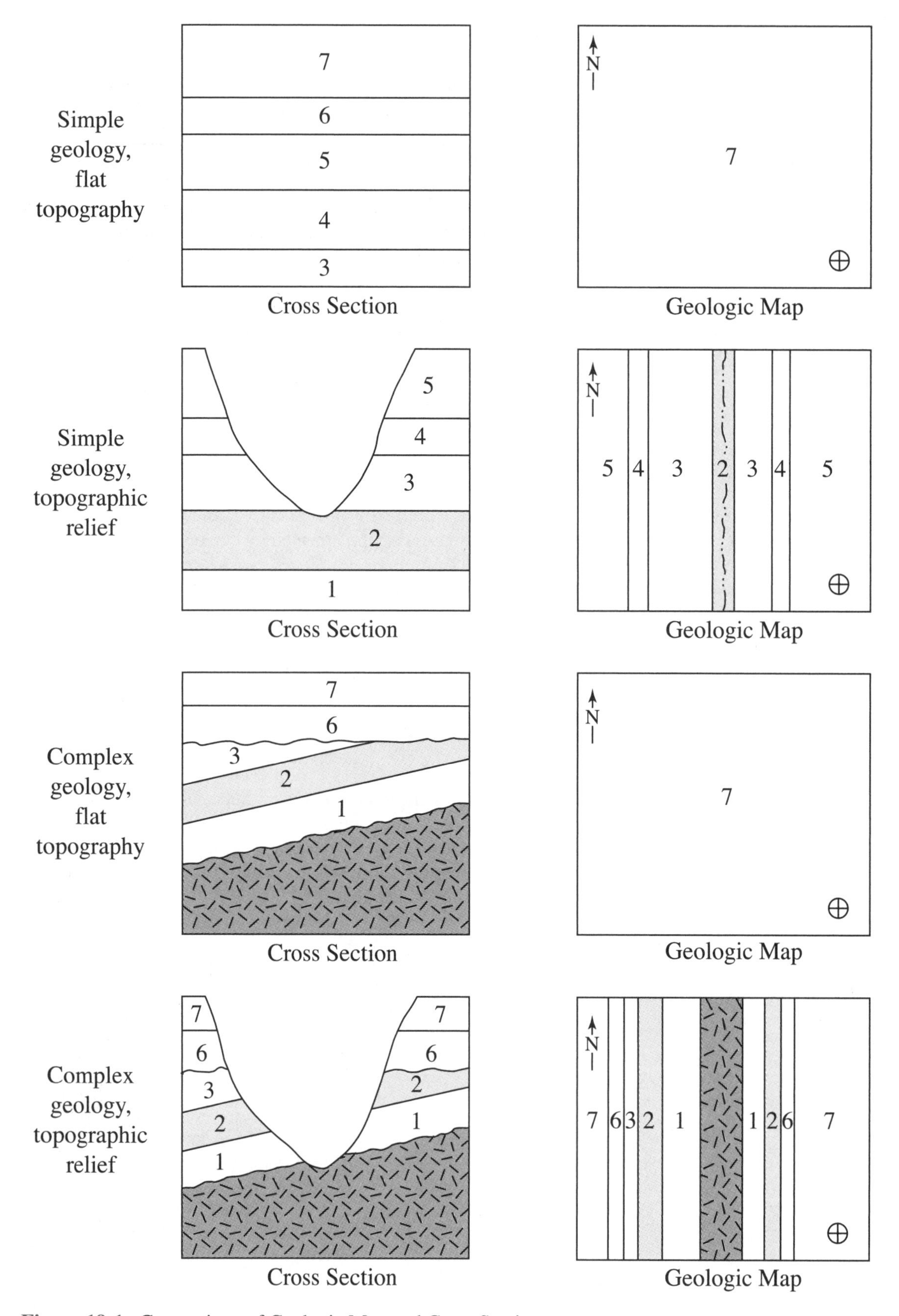

Figure 19-1. Comparison of Geologic Map and Cross Section

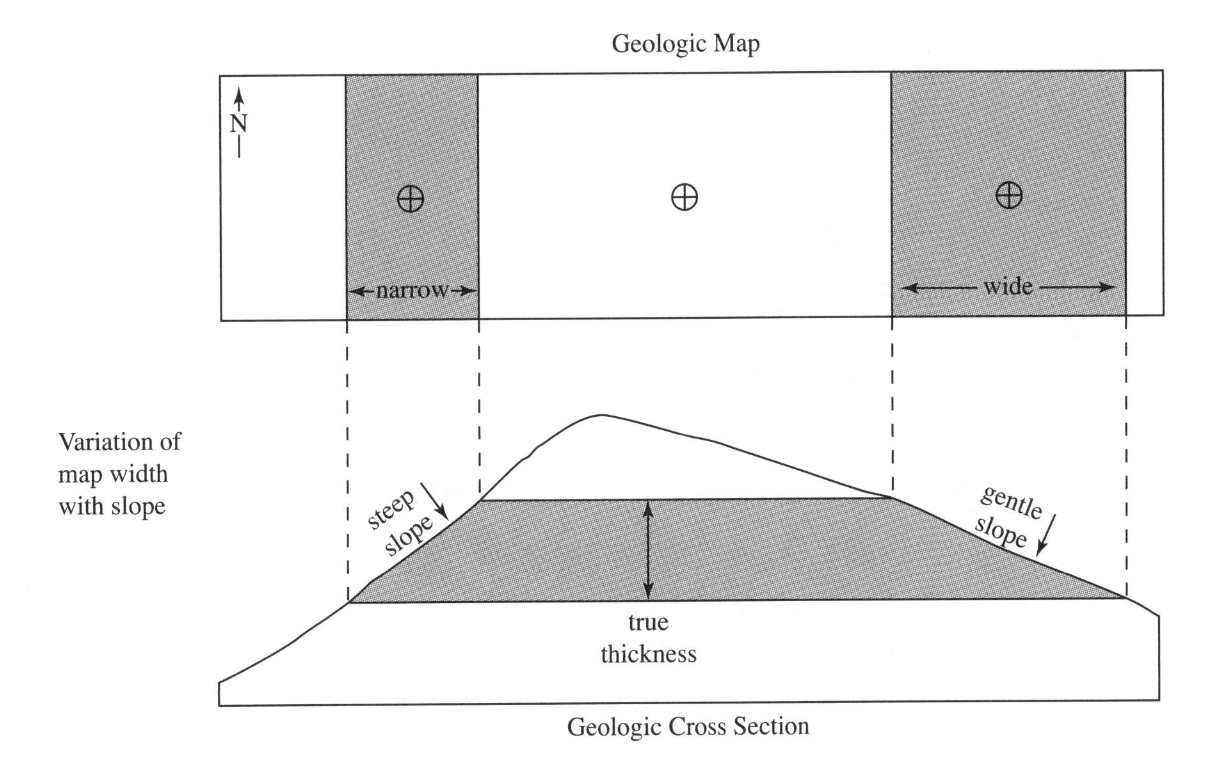

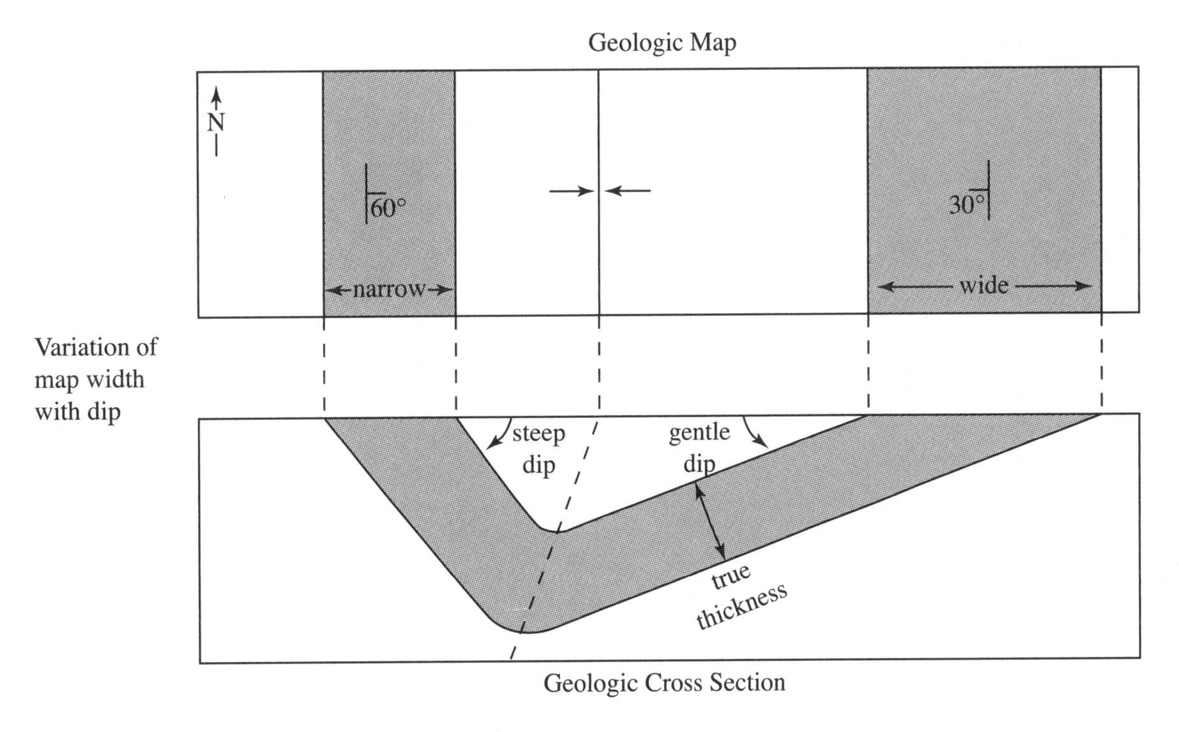

Figure 19-2. Variation of Map Width with Slope and Dip

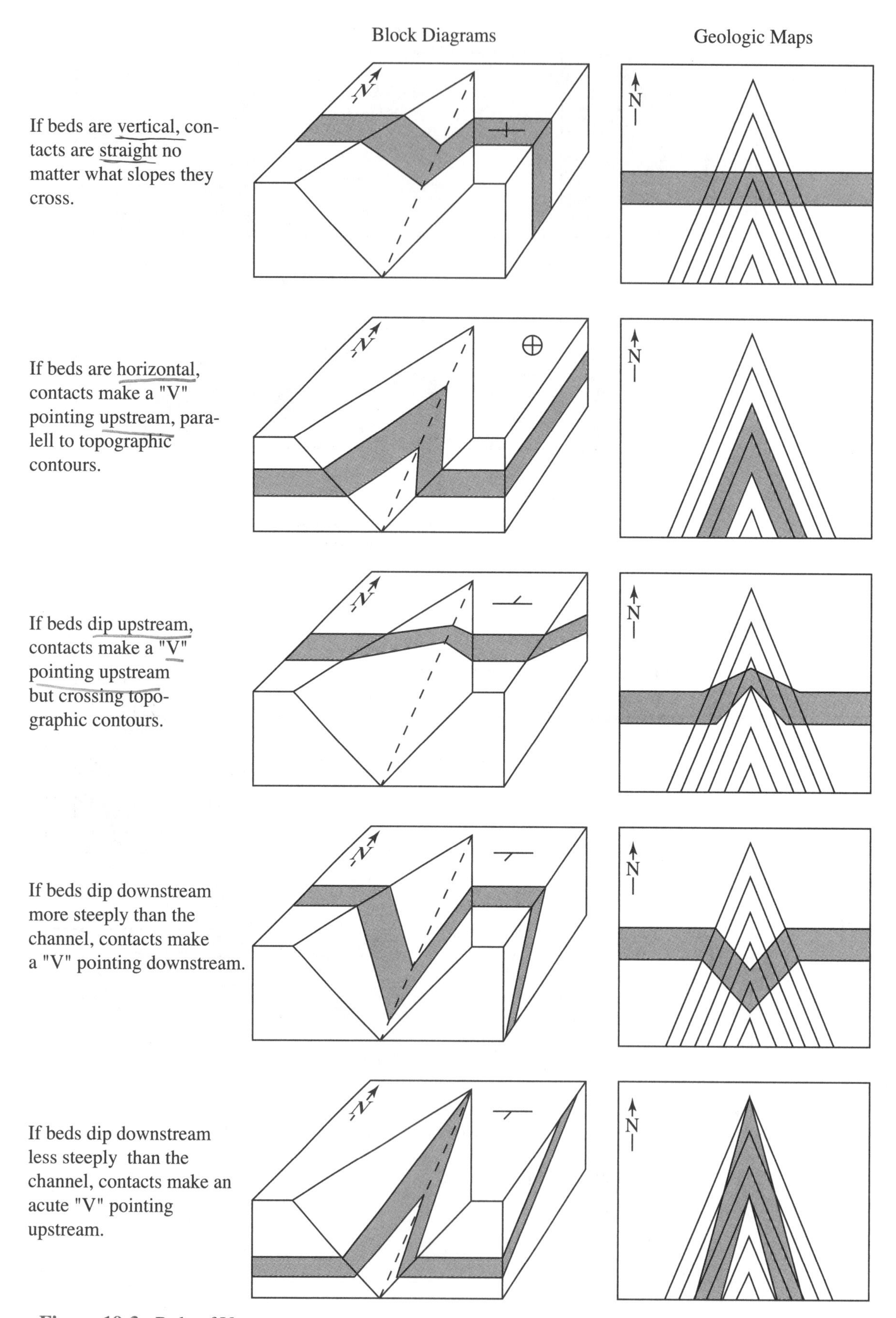

Figure 19-3. Rule of Vs

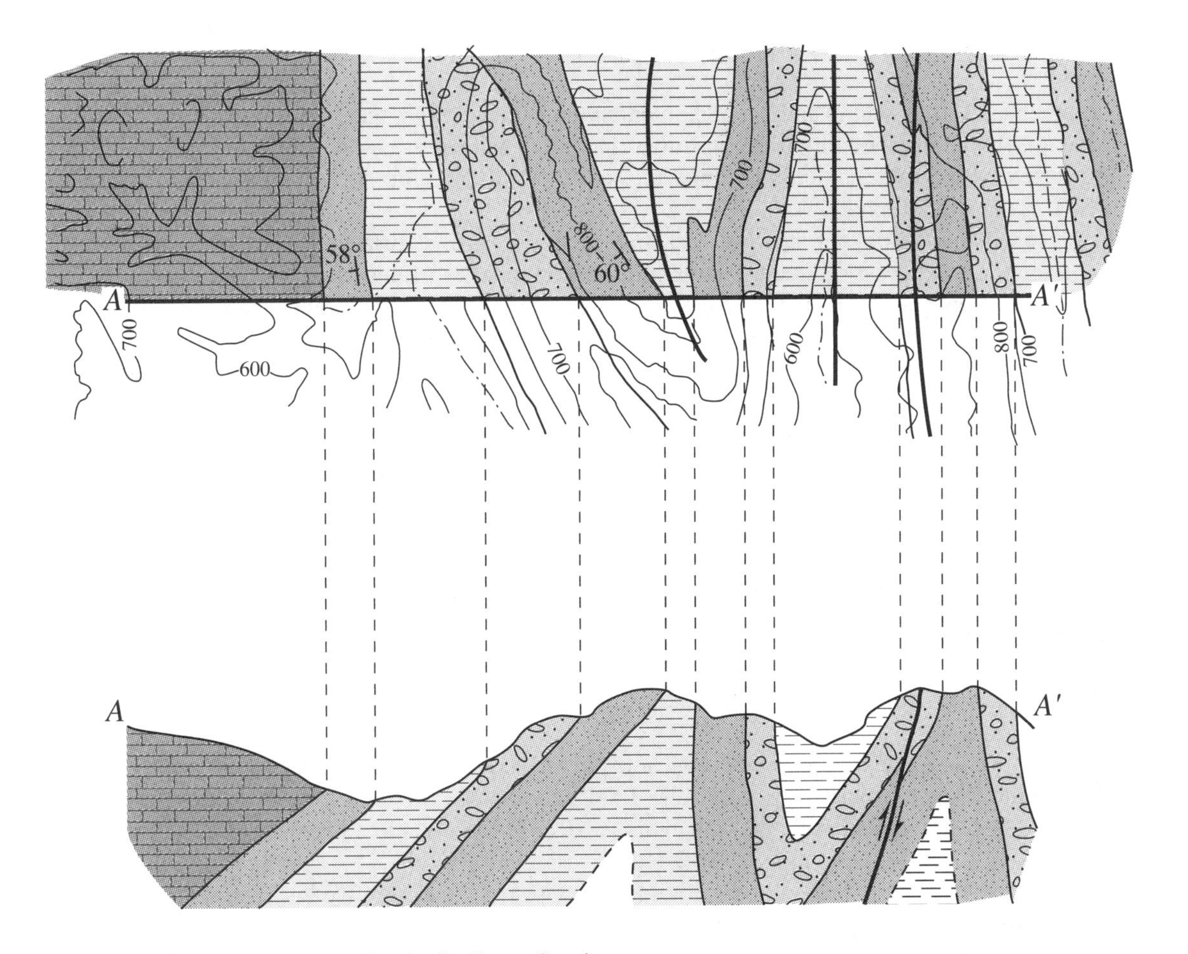

Figure 19-4. Constructing a Geologic Cross Section

CONSTRUCTING A GEOLOGIC CROSS SECTION

If a geologic cross section is not provided for a mapped area, it is possible to construct one by following the steps given below. You have already made a number of geologic cross sections in Chapter 18 by completing front and side portions of block diagrams. The only essential difference here is that we will be combining topographic profiles and more complex geological relationships to produce more sophisticated and realistic cross sections. Constructing a geologic cross section is particularly satisfying because you create a view of a geologic setting that did not exist before and there is room for intelligent speculation as well as straight transfer of data.

1. Select a line of cross section to be oriented as nearly perpendicular as possible to major geologic trends such as contacts, fold axes, and fault traces.
2. Construct a topographic profile along the line of section, following procedures developed in Chapter 17.
3. Transfer all pertinent geologic data (contacts, fold axes, faults) to the profile by marking them as points along the top edge of the profile paper, and then projecting straight down to the profile line (Figure 19-4).
4. Where dips are known, extend contact and fault planes down into the profile using a protractor to measure angles.
5. Tie together all outcrops of the same rock unit using a logical extension of dip directions, as you did to complete the block faces in Chapter 18. Remember that most rock units maintain a fairly uniform thickness, and that units normally do not match up across a fault.
6. Complete the cross section by placing letter symbols on rock units and displacement symbols on faults.

INTERPRETING STRUCTURE FROM A GEOLOGIC MAP

A geologic map shows granite and three sedimentary units that contain index fossils. A vertical exposure of these units at another locality illustrates the principle of faunal succession. The unit with "star" fossils is at the bottom (oldest), and the unit with "oval" fossils is at the top (youngest). We assign this sequence to the stratigraphic column.

A fault plane (bold) that dips 60° east, intersects the earth's surface. The irregular map contact between granite and lowest sedimentary unit indicates an older erosion surface; the sediment rests nonconformably upon granite. In the stratigraphic column we position the granite beneath sedimentary rocks, and draw a wiggly line in between to symbolize this surface.

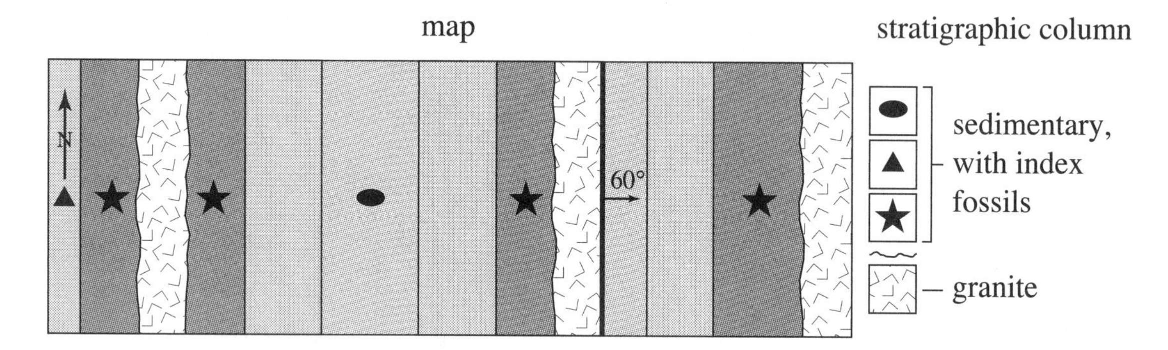

Below, we assign a numbering system (bold) to the sequence of rocks, beginning arbitrarily with "1" for granite. Note the symmetry of 1-2-3-4-3-2-1 near the central part of the map, and the interruption of symmetry associated with the fault. This is because the units had been offset by faulting, then eroded.

In an eroded syncline the youngest stratum is exposed in the center. We insert strike-and-dip symbols (bold) showing strata dipping inward toward the axis of the syncline, and apply different shadings to rock units as an aid to identification. On the east side, the strike-and-dip symbol is similarly consistent with the sequence of strata.

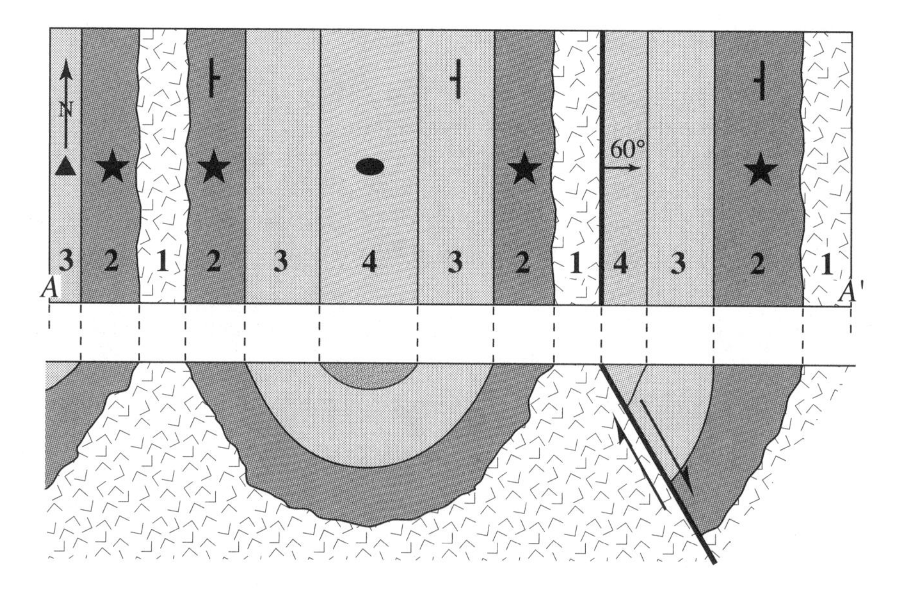

Now we are ready to draw a cross section for A to A', an interpretation of the structure where it is concealed beneath the surface. We extend dashed guidelines from the map down to the cross section. In the cross section we project the rock units below the surface in accordance with local dip.

Once this is completed, the pattern demands that the fault be a normal fault (hanging wall has moved down with respect to the footwall).

Geologic Maps

- Determine the structure of rocks from the pattern created by the intersection of dip-ping layers with the (level) land surface.
- Use strike, dip, and other map symbols to determine structure.
- Formation: discrete mappable rock unit
- Map notation of a formation. Example:
  - formation name age notation
  - Buda Limestone (bu) Cretaceous (K) = Kbu

Geologic Contacts

- Line (on a map) or interface (in the real three-dimensional world) between adjacent rock units (formations)
  - Depositional contact: between adjacent sedimentary strata, lava flows, etc., or their metamorphic equivalents
  - Fault contact: between rock units that have strike-slip or dip-slip displacement
  - Igneous intrusive contact: between host rocks and an invading igneous body
- Geologic contacts between unfolded horizontal strata follow contour lines.

Interpreting Structural Forms in Geologic Maps

- Look for omission or repetition of beds.
- Omission of beds may signify the presence of an unconformity or fault.
- Symmetrical repetition of beds may indicate the presence of a fold: anticline or syncline.
- Anticline: repetition is in the form of younger-older-younger.
- Syncline: repetition is in the form of older-younger-older.

Outcrop Width

- Variation related to slope of the land surface:
  - Steep slope: more narrow outcrop pattern
  - Gentle slope: broader outcrop pattern
- Variation related to dip of strata:
  - Steep dip: more narrow outcrop pattern
  - Shallow dip: broader outcrop pattern
    - The more shallow the dip of the bed, the broader the outcrop width. Hence for a dipping bed, outcrop width is greater than the true thickness of the bed for any angle of dip more shallow than 90°.
- For a vertical bed (90°), the outcrop width equals the true thickness of the bed.

Plunging Folds

- Fold whose axis is inclined to the horizontal
- N-plunging anticline S-plunging syncline

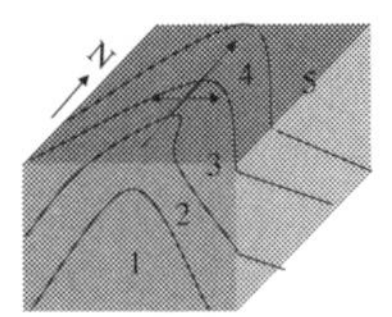

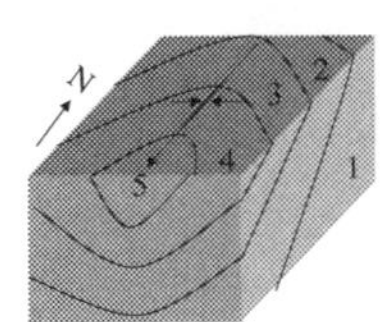

Outcrop Patterns

- Non-plunging folds:

Symmetrical

N

3	2	1	2	3

Asymmetrical

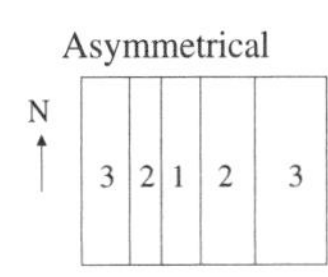

- Plunging folds:
  - Plunging anticline: closure points toward the direction of plunge.
  - Plunging syncline: closure points opposite to the direction of plunge.

More Patterns

- Faults: asymmetrical repetition may be due to faulting.

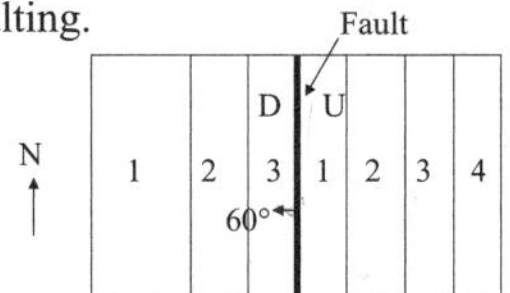

- Dome: doubly plunging anticline
- Basin: doubly plunging syncline

Rule of Vs

- The pattern created where a bed crops out in a stream channel.
- Allows us to determine the dip of the bed.

Map Symbols

- Strike and dip 30°
- Horizontal bed
- Vertical bed
- Anticline
- Syncline
- Plunging anticline
- Plunging syncline
- Fault, and dip of the fault plane
- Thrust fault

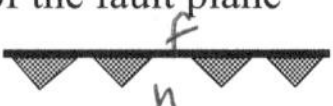

Maps Symbols (continued)

- Light solid line: depositional or igneous intrusive contact
- Light dashed or dotted line:
  - where contact is uncertain
- Heavy solid line: fault
- Heavy dashed or dotted line:
  - where location of fault is uncertain

Name: ______________________________

CHAPTER 19: Geologic Maps

Section: ______________________________

REVIEW QUESTIONS

1. How does the letter symbol for a given rock unit express the age of that unit? Use a specific example. ______________________________

2. Define "true thickness' and map width. ______________________________

   ____

   ____

3. Explain, using a cross-section sketch, how a flat-lying layer might have a *greater* map width than its true thickness.

4. Explain, using a cross-section sketch, how a flat-lying layer might have a *smaller* map width than its true thickness.

5. How do map width and true thickness of a vertical layer compare where it crops out on a horizontal surface?

   ____

Earthquakes

This aerial view shows the San Andreas Fault where it crosses the Carrizo Plain in California's Central Valley. (*U.S. Geological Survey photo by R.E. Wallace*)

INTRODUCTION

Earthquakes are one of the most terrifying geologic events. They occur suddenly, usually without warning, and in less than five minutes may cause destruction and human suffering on a scale difficult to comprehend. Ironically, earthquakes usually do not damage the land or even seriously change its topography, but destroy only those things that are built on top of the land. At present we cannot control earthquakes or even predict them within an acceptable time frame. Our methods of coping with earthquakes include avoiding living in areas where they may occur, or designing structures that can withstand earthquake motion. A map of the 48 contiguous United States (Figure 20-1) gives an idea of where earthquakes are most likely to occur. Note that the map does not indicate probable magnitudes of earthquakes. We should remember that in this region, the most powerful earthquake in historic times took place in Missouri.

MEASURING EARTHQUAKE MAGNITUDE AND INTENSITY

Two scales are commonly used to describe the intensity of earthquakes. The Richter Scale, named after the seismologist Charles Richter, is a scientific scale that requires special instruments to make measurements. This is a scale of the amount of shaking, or amplitude of motion of the ground, during an earthquake. It is a logarithmic scale, each integer number representing a factor of 10 times larger or smaller than an adjacent integer. For example, an earthquake of magnitude 7 is ten times more powerful than one of magnitude 6, and an earthquake of magnitude 8 is a thousand times ($10 \times 10 \times 10$) more powerful than an earthquake of magnitude 5. The largest recorded earthquakes are approximately of magnitude 9; serious damage to structures begins at around magnitude 5.5.

A more popularized description, the Mercalli Scale, is based upon damage to human structures and psyches. In evaluating earthquake intensity according to the Mercalli Scale, we would use some of these observations:

I. Not felt.

II. Felt by persons at rest, on upper floors, or favorably placed.

III. Felt indoors. Hanging objects swing. Vibration like passing of light trucks. Duration estimated. May not be recognized as an earthquake.

IV. Hanging objects swing. Vibration like passing of heavy trucks, or sensation of a jolt like a heavy ball striking the wall.

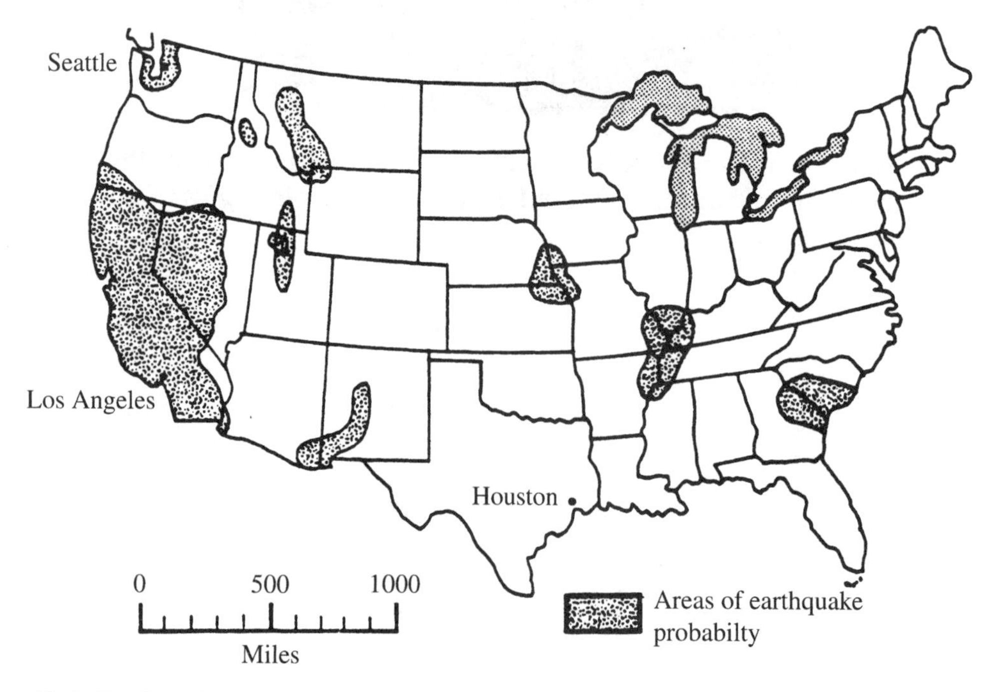

Figure 20-1. Earthquake Probability Map

V. Felt outdoors; direction estimated. Sleepers wakened. Liquids disturbed, some spilled. Small unstable objects displaced or upset. Doors swing, close, open. Shutters, pictures move.

VI. Felt by all. Many persons frightened and run outdoors. People walk unsteadily. Windows, dishes, glassware broken. Furniture moved or overturned. Weak plaster and masonry D (weak masonry) cracked. Small bells (church, school) ring.

VII. Difficult to stand. Noticed by drivers of vehicles. Hanging objects quiver. Furniture broken. Damage to masonry D, including cracks. Weak chimneys broken at roof line. Fall of plaster, loose bricks, stones, tiles, cornices, unbraced parapets, and architectural ornaments.

VIII. Steering of driven vehicles is affected. Damage to masonry C (ordinary masonry); partial collapse of masonry D. Some damage to masonry B (good masonry); none to masonry A (excellent masonry). Fall of stucco and some masonry walls. Twisting or falling of chimneys, factory smokestacks, monuments, towers, elevated tanks. Changes in flow or temperatures of springs and wells.

IX. General panic. Masonry D destroyed; masonry C heavily damaged, sometimes with complete collapse; masonry B seriously damaged. General damage of foundations. Frames cracked. Serious damage to reservoirs. Underground pipes broken. Conspicuous cracks in ground. In alluviated areas, sand and mud ejected; earthquake fountains, sand craters.

X. Most masonry and frame structures destroyed with their foundations. Some well-built wooden structures and bridges destroyed. Serious damage to dams, dikes, embankments. Large landslides.

XI. Rails bent greatly. Underground pipelines completely out of service.

XII. Damage nearly total. Large rock masses displaced. Lines of sight and level distorted. Objects thrown into the air.

LOCATING EARTHQUAKE EPICENTERS

The exact place within the crust of the earth where an earthquake occurs is called its **focus**. The spot on the surface of the earth directly above the focus—the zone at the surface that is nearest and therefore the most affected—is called the earthquake **epicenter**. An epicenter is located by determining the time intervals between arrivals at a seismograph station of compressional, or **P waves**, which travel the fastest, and **S waves**, which are more slowly traveling seismic shear waves. Data from arrivals of seismic **L waves**, whose effects are confined to near the earth's surface and which travel most slowly of the three types, are used in the same manner.

Time intervals between wave arrivals can be used to calculate the distance, but not the direction, from the seismograph station to the epicenter. We know only that the epicenter lies somewhere on a circle whose radius is the distance from station to epicenter. To establish the precise location of an epicenter, we need distance data from at least three seismograph stations. Three circles are plotted, each centered upon the corresponding seismograph station. At the epicenter, all circles are simultaneously correct; they all intersect at a single point.

Procedure:

1. We note the arrival times of P, S, and L waves on the record of seismic vibrations, called a seismogram. Each arrival is announced by a sudden sharp jolt, as demonstrated by a fictitious simple seismogram (Figure 20-2). To determine a time interval between arrivals, we hold the

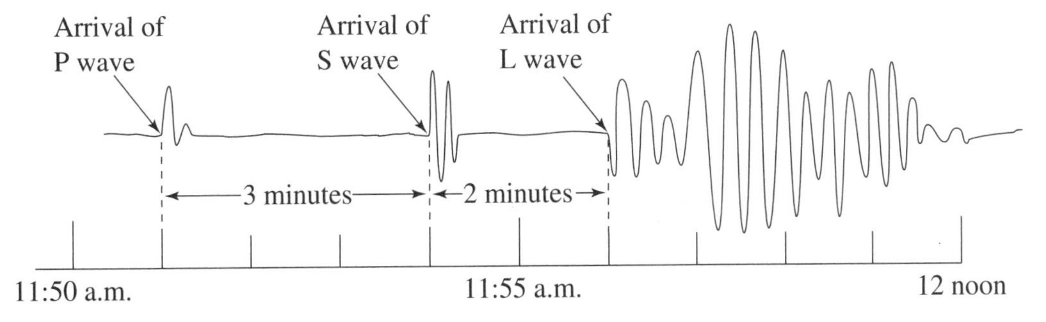

Figure 20-2. Fictitious Seismogram

straight edge of a piece of paper against the seismogram, place a tick mark at each arrival, then slide the edge against the seismogram time scale to make accurate measurements. In this example, the P wave arrived at 11:51, the S wave at 11:54, and the L wave at 11:56 a.m. Three minutes had elapsed between arrivals of P and S waves, and 2 additional minutes had elapsed before the arrival of L waves (5 minutes elapsed time between arrivals of P and L).

2. Next, we refer to the calibration of seismic-wave travel, summarized by a time-distance graph (Figure 20-3). To a first approximation, the time-distance graph describes the behavior of seismic waves originating at any arbitrary time, at any arbitrary point on the earth's surface. Seismic waves start out together from the epicenter (distance zero) at the time of the earthquake (time zero). As time passes (vertical axis), the three types of wave travel farther distances from the epicenter (horizontal axis). A vertical line on the graph corresponds to the sequence of observations at a seismograph station at a fixed distance from the epicenter. We see that as time goes by, first P, then S, then L waves sweep by the station. With increasing distance from the epicenter, the three waves arrive later and the time intervals between arrivals become larger.

A practical way to determine the distance of a station is to use a movable strip of paper containing the time axis of the graph. In the provided example, we place tick marks on the movable strip corresponding to 3 minutes (P-to-S interval) and 5 minutes (P-to-L interval). [Caution: the time axes of the graph and of the seismogram may be scaled differently. For instance, a time interval of 5 minutes could be one inch on the seismogram but only one-half inch on the time axis of the graph. In transferring data, we count minutes or seconds of time, not inches or centimeters on a piece of paper.] We position the strip on top of the time axis of the graph, then slide it along the P curve while keeping it vertical—i.e., parallel to the time axis. A time interval of 3 minutes between arrivals of P and S, and an interval of 2 minutes between S and L correspond to a *unique* distance from the epicenter. We drop a line to the horizontal axis of the graph, to read the station-to-epicenter distance.

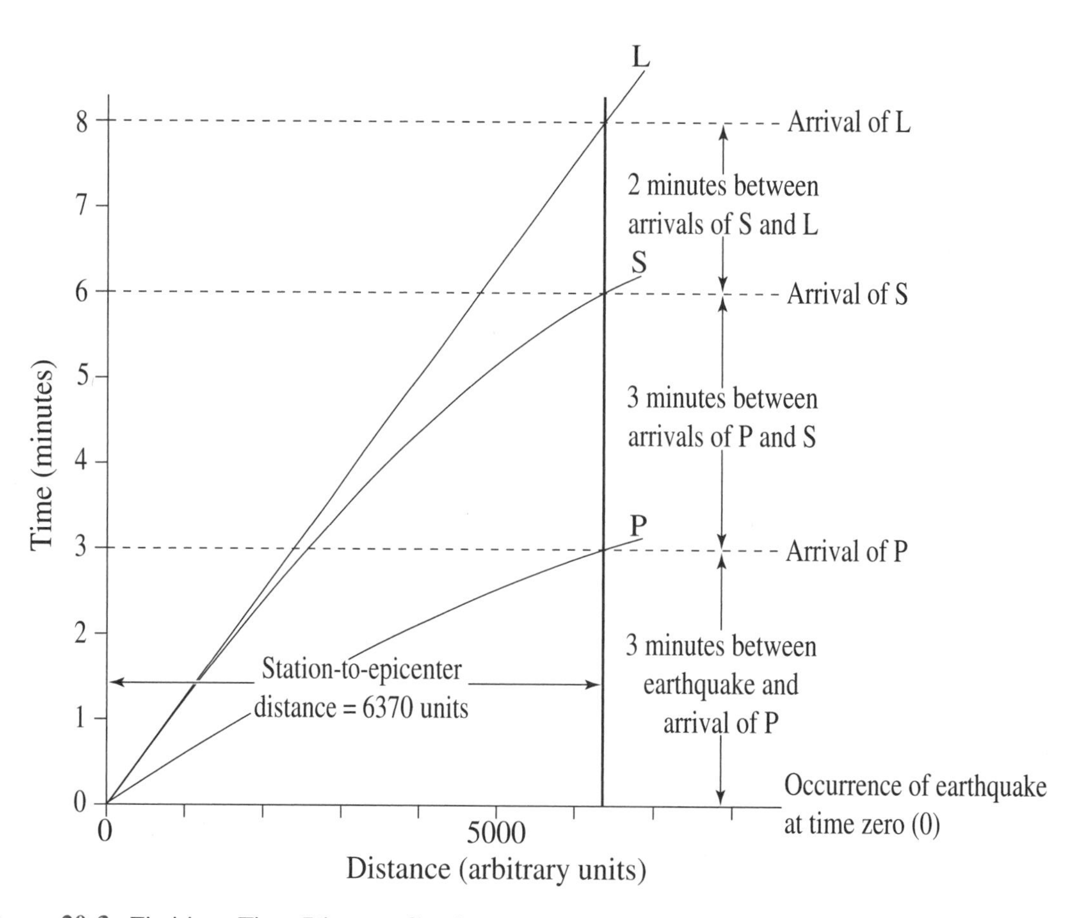

Figure 20-3. Fictitious Time-Distance Graph

3. We repeat steps 1 and 2 above for data gathered at the second and third seismograph stations.
4. The position of each station is symbolized by a dot on a map. We draw a circle centered about a dot, whose radius corresponds to the station-to-epicenter distance for that station. Three circles will intersect at one mutual point, the position of the epicenter.
5. Once we know the distance of a station from the epicenter, we can calculate the time of day that the earthquake occurred. In the example, we see that the P wave had been traveling 3 minutes before arriving at the station at 11:51 a.m. Thus the earthquake occurred at 11:48 a.m.

Consistency of results is a good indication that we are doing steps 1 through 5 correctly. Distance can be calculated by using data from wave arrivals in any combination: P and S, P and L, or S and L. For three stations, there are 9 wave arrivals. In principle, we could calculate the station-to-epicenter distance 9 times and get the same consistent result. Similarly, we could count back the number of minutes from each of 9 arrivals, to calculate the same time of day of the earthquake over and over. If the results do not agree, generally it is because data were incorrectly transferred from the seismogram time axis directly to the graph time axis without allowing for differences in scale. Another common error is to slide the base of the movable time axis of the time-distance graph along the horizontal axis of the graph, rather than along the P curve.

Name: ______________________________

Section: ______________________________

EARTHQUAKE EXERCISE #1: LOCATING AN EARTHQUAKE EPICENTER

Instruction: Data provided below include seismograms for Stations 1, 2, and 3 (Figure 20-4), a time-distance graph (Figure 20-5), and a map of the Southwest Pacific region (Figure 20-6). In contrast to the simplified fictitious diagrams used above as examples of the procedure, the following seismograms and time-distance graph are appropriate for the real earth. Seismograms 1, 2, and 3 (Figure 20-4) are given in terms of Greenwich Mean Time (GMT) so that no corrections need to be made for the fact that the seismograph stations are located in different time zones. Below the map (Figure 20-6) are provided a time scale that is the same as the vertical axis of the time-distance graph (Figure 20-5), and a distance scale for use with the map. Tear these two scales off the page to enable you to slide them around. Use the distance scale as a crude, but adequate paper compass for drawing arcs of circles on the map.

The objectives are to locate the earthquake epicenter and specify the time of day when it occurred, by following steps 1 through 5 in the preceding discussion. Everyone will obtain slightly different results because any series of steps that involve placing tick marks, positioning a piece of paper, or reading a graph, introduce errors of measurement. For simplification, this exercise has been set up such that seismograph stations 1, 2, and 3 are some exact multiple of 500 kilometers from the epicenter. That is, the distance from a given station to the epicenter will be exactly 4000 kilometers, or exactly 4,500 kilometers, etc. You should obtain an answer that is obviously very close to one of these possibilities.

What is the distance of Station 1 from the epicenter? __________ kilometers

What is the distance of Station 2 from the epicenter? __________ kilometers

What is the distance of Station 3 from the epicenter? __________ kilometers

In what country, or Australian state, is the epicenter located? ______________

At what time of day did the earthquake occur? __________ Greenwich Mean Time

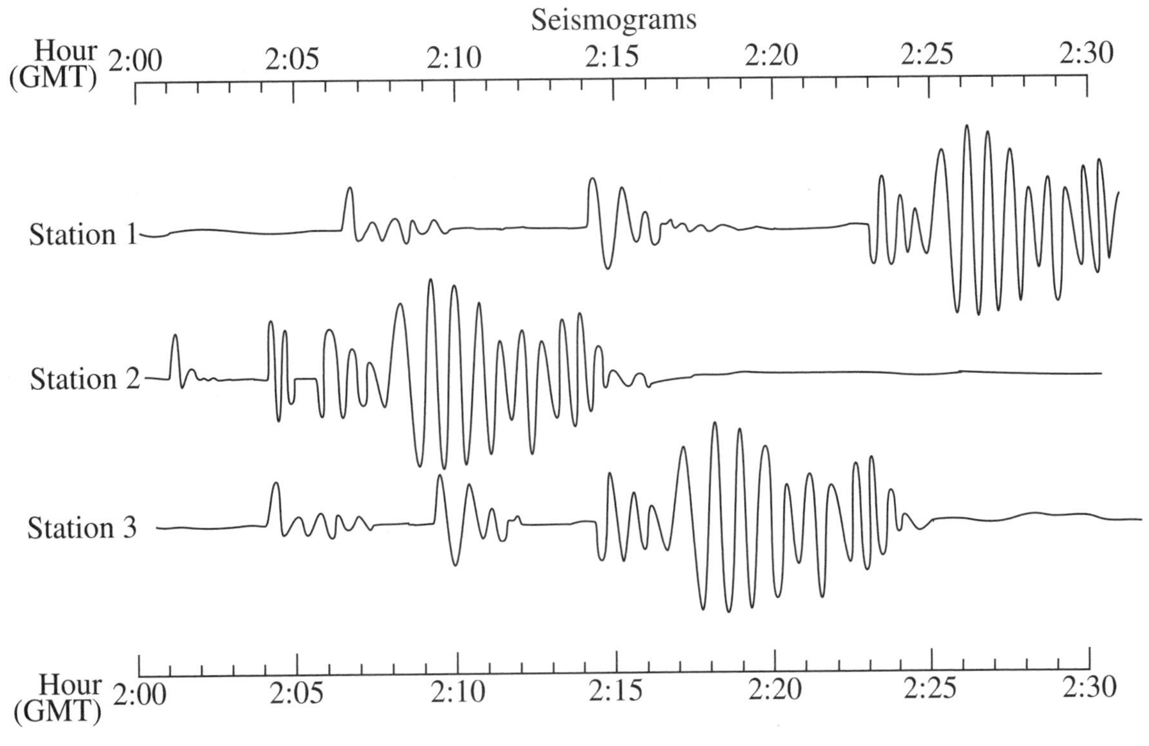

Figure 20-4. Seismograms

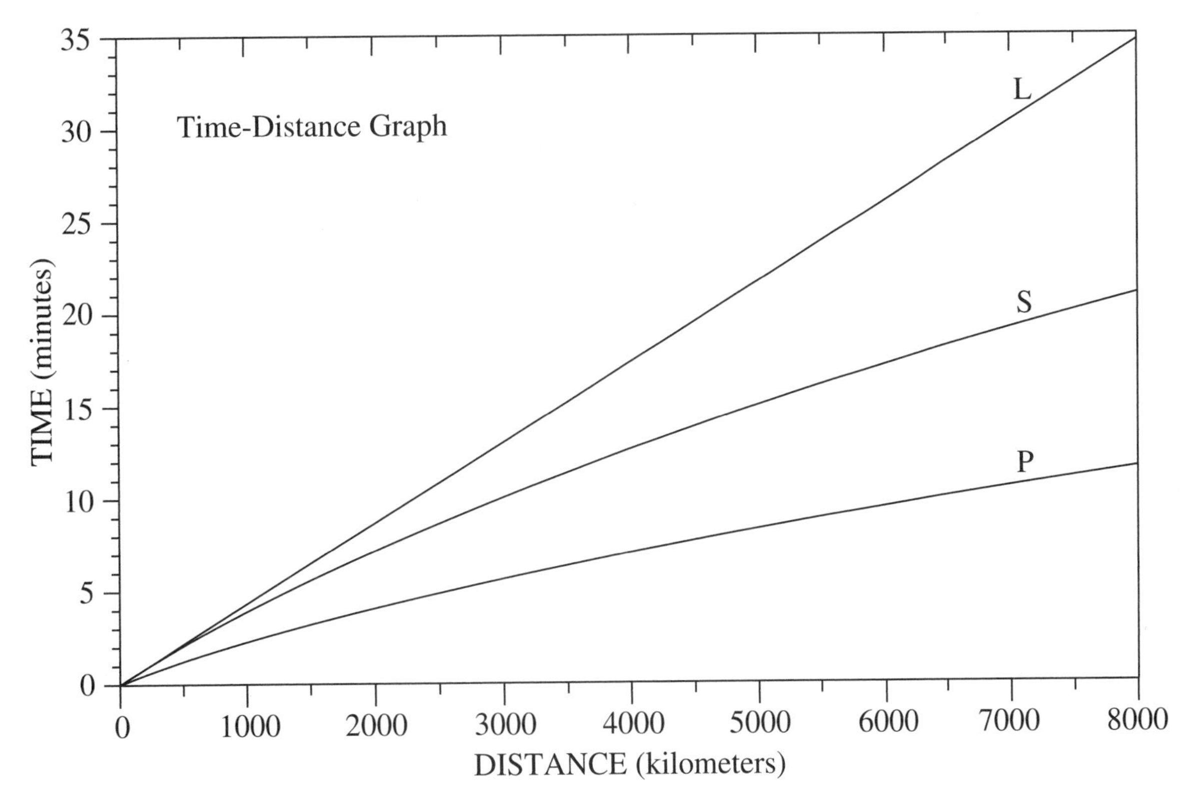

Figure 20-5. Time-Distance Graph

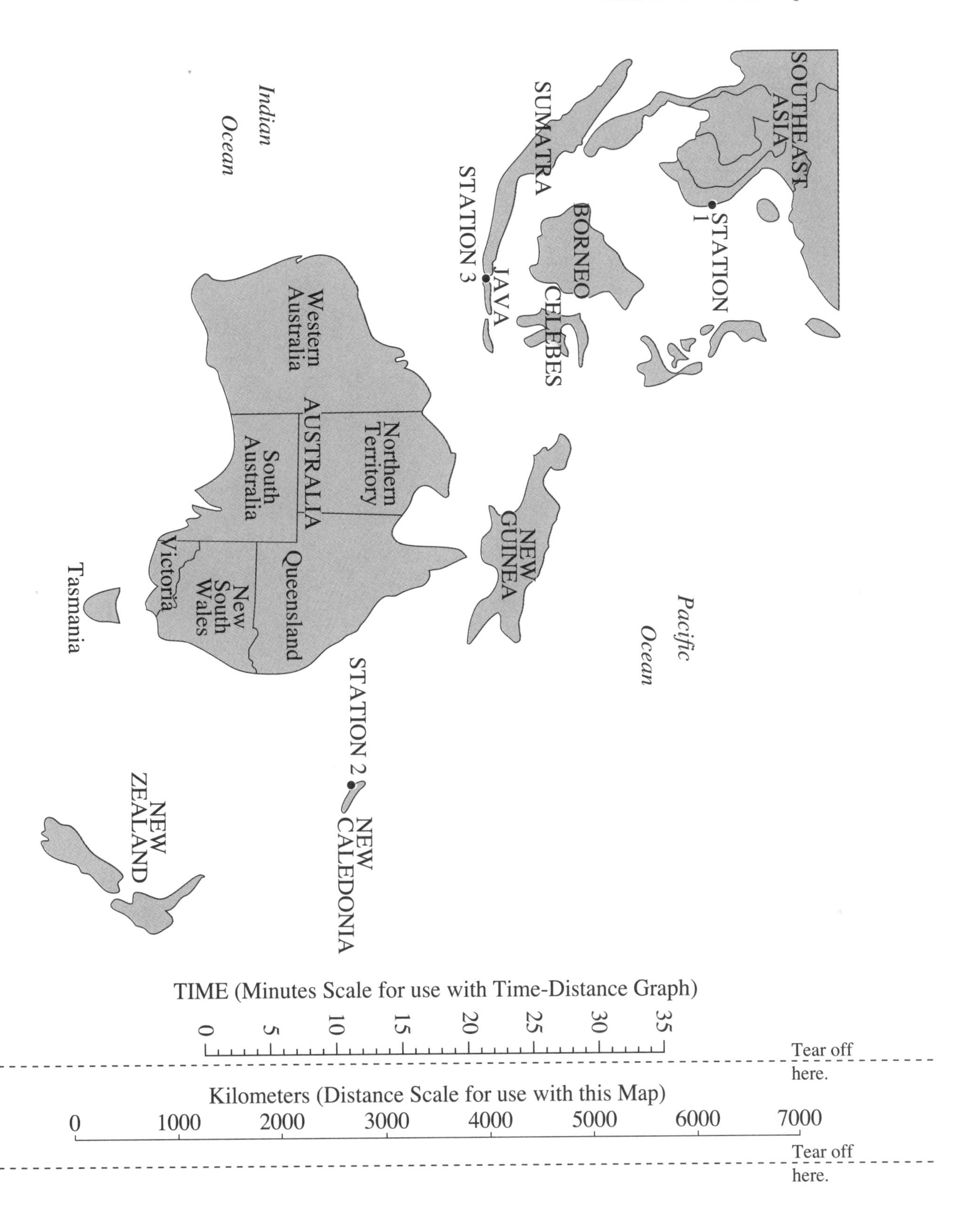

Figure 20-6. Seismograph Stations in the Southwest Pacific

21 Preparing for the Grand Synthesis

A scene in the Alps. The Italy-Switzerland border lies on the skyline to the north. [*Courtesy Earl Verbeek*]

In a preceding chapter we used the concept of a force field as an indirect means to examine the earth's deep interior. Our goal is to combine this information with many other subjects—indeed nearly everything already discussed in this book—to synthesize a "big picture" of the earth and how it operates. In working toward the Grand Synthesis, let's first explore how magnetism, which is yet another phenomenon that can be described by a force field, contributes to an understanding of the earth.

EARTH MAGNETISM

In 1918, the mathematician C. Hansteen poetically observed that "[t]he earth speaks of its internal movements through the silent voice of the magnetic needle." Earth magnetism is a geophysical recorder of happenings in the remote interior, and also in the remoteness of geologic time. Faint imprints of magnetism in the rocks tell a story so astonishing that many geologists were long reluctant to accept its implications. What is this mysterious force that unfailingly draws a suspended magnetic needle into a northerly bearing, and what is the origin of magnetism in the earth?

For centuries, people thought that the North Star, "which does not move around the axis of the heavens as do the other stars," had somehow imparted "virtue" to the needle. Already by AD 1600, enough was known about earth magnetism for a British physician, William Gilbert, to summarize his own and others' experiments and observations in a substantial book, *De Magnete*. He noted that the *magnetic field* surrounding the earth is similar to the field associated with a permanent magnet shaped as a sphere. Gilbert correctly recognized that the source of magnetism lies not with the North Star or other heavenly object but, rather, deep inside the earth.

Magnetic Fields

A magnetic field is commonly represented by *magnetic lines of force*. Although such lines are actually only a convenient bit of fiction, we can see something resembling them by dumping iron filings onto a magnet. As the tiny needle-like particles of iron become aligned parallel to the magnetic force, they clump together into slender threads, or "lines." Magnetic lines of force depict the *strength* and *direction* of the field. No matter how complexly twisted a line of force may be, each is a closed loop. Some lines of force lie entirely inside the earth, and some extend through its interior into the surrounding space (Figure 21-1). In principle, if we were to visit all regions of the earth's internal and external space, we could map the field using a magnetized needle which everywhere aligns itself parallel to the direction of the local line of force.

These lines converge toward north and south *magnetic poles,* which can be distinguished because one end of the magnetic needle is attracted to the North Pole while being repelled away from the South Pole (Figure 21-1). Unlike the force of gravity that only attracts, the magnetic force is characterized by both an attraction and a repulsion, a "pull" and a "push." To a close approximation, the earth's magnetic field is *dipolar* (containing two poles). Its strength is symbolized by the degree to which the lines of force are crowded together. Although the lines are present everywhere at the earth's surface, Figure 21-1 indicates that the field is about two times stronger in the polar regions than at the Equator.

Soon the assertion of Gilbert's classic publication, that the earth behaves as a giant permanent magnet, met serious challenge. For one thing, the magnetic poles do not quite coincide with the rotational poles that mark the earth's axis of spin. Yet the magnetic poles are only about 11° (approximately 1200 kilometers) distant from the rotational poles, near enough to suggest that production of the magnetic field is somehow connected with the earth's rotation. The North and South Magnetic Poles are not exactly 180° opposite one another; the axis of symmetry of the magnetic field does not pass through the center of the earth. Moreover, continued monitoring reveals that both the directionality and the strength of earth magnetism are changing. At present, the field is steadily weakening so rapidly that it will disappear within about two thousand years unless it picks up again. Observatories distributed widely throughout the world record a steady drift in local compass direction. All of this sounds very *im*permanent indeed. Where and how does earth magnetism originate?

Origin of Magnetism

Magnetism results from the organized movement of electrical charges. We may visualize electrons as charged particles that spin on their axes as they move about the nucleus of an atom. In an electron shell (Chapter 3) the electrons are commonly paired, each member of the pair sharing all the same properties

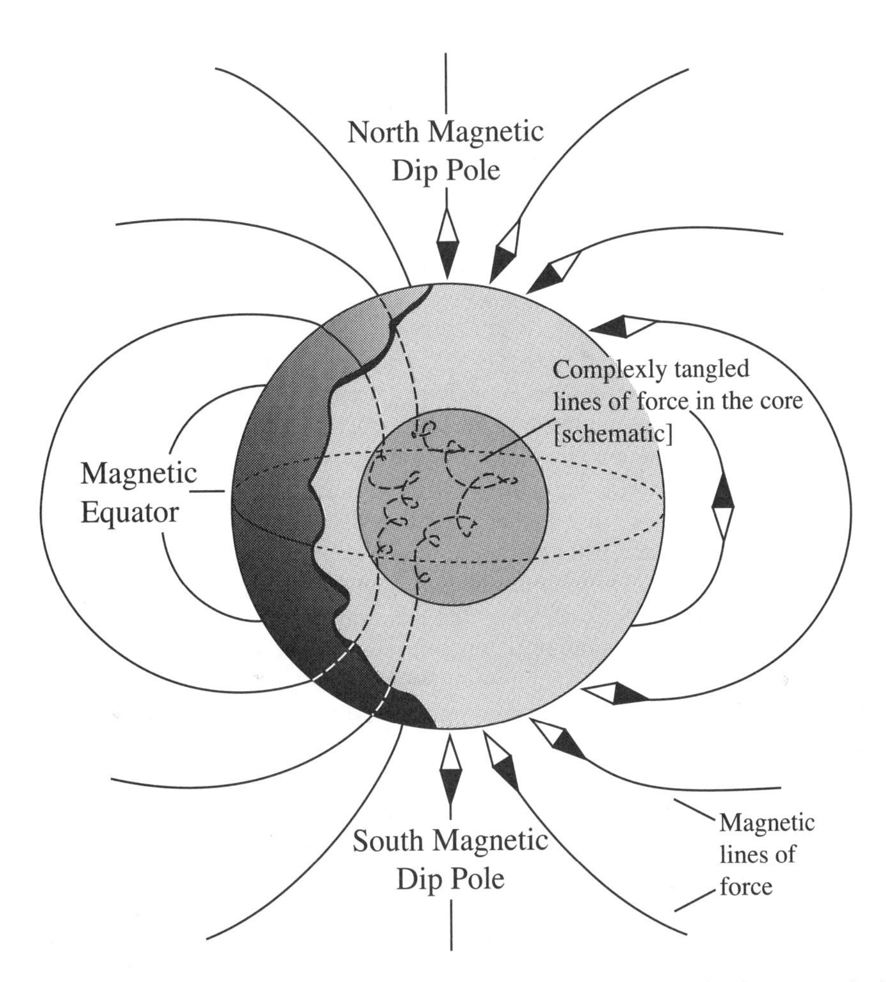

Figure 21-1. Hypothetical magnetized needles trace the lines of force in the magnetic field external to the earth. The field exhibits polarity, the colored end of a needle being attracted toward the North Pole and the white end toward the South Pole. At the poles where the field is stronger, the lines of force are more densely crowded. Lines of force embedded within the earth's molten outer core are stretched and tangled together, and in constant motion, transported by equally complex internal motions of the core material.

of energy, etc., but they are spinning in opposite directions. If one electron is spinning clockwise, the spin of its partner is counterclockwise. Because the effects of the opposite spins cancel one another, the substance that contains the electrons does not dramatically respond to a magnetic field, nor does it create one. In a strongly magnetic mineral such as magnetite (Fe_3O_4: Chapter 3), not all of the spinning electrons are paired. More electrons are spinning in one direction than in the other, and in this sense there is an organized net movement of electrical charge.

In an electromagnet, a coil of wire conducts an electric current, which is a flow of electrons that is also an organized motion. When the current is shut off, the magnetism of an electromagnet disappears, whereas in magnetite the electrons continue to spin indefinitely. Thus magnetite is an example of a permanent magnet, whereas an electromagnet is not permanent.

Just as moving electrical charges create a magnetic field, the opposite is also true. That is to say, the motion of a magnet (and its associated field) can create an electric current. Let's compare a dynamo, which makes electricity, with a motor that uses electricity. As energy is applied to spin the shaft of a dynamo at the power station, causing its internal magnets also to spin, the motion of the magnetic field generates an electric current. This current is sent to your home where it enters an electric motor. Here the electric current, coupled with a field generated by internal magnets, transforms the electromagnetic energy into the mechanical rotation of a shaft. Dynamos and electric motors, which are so-to-speak the opposite sides of the same coin, share three things in common: (i) mechanical motion, (ii) an electric current consisting of an organized motion of electrons, and (iii) an associated magnetic field.

Origin of the Earth's Magnetic Field

Of course, deep in the earth there are no wires or rotating shafts, but rocks do contain crystals of magnetite and other magnetic minerals. Could permanently magnetized minerals account for the earth's general field, as William Gilbert had surmised? We may answer this question by observing what happens as basaltic lava cools and crystallizes. Melt of basalt composition emerges from the ground at approximately 1200°C, and by the time it has cooled to 900°C (still red-hot), it has already fully solidified into its most common minerals, pyroxene and plagioclase feldspar, with the occasional grain of magnetite. Because atoms and their electrons are strongly agitated at such a high temperature, the directions of electron spin are chaotic and disorganized, unable to generate magnetism. Only as the basalt cools through a critical point called the *Curie temperature*, which is 580°C for magnetite and approximately 680°C for hematite (Fe_2O_3: Chapter 3), can a mineral begin to acquire a permanent magnetism. As noted in Figure 16-21, temperature in the earth increases sharply with depth, such that rock temperatures in the mantle and possibly in the lower crust are much hotter than the Curie temperature for any magnetic mineral. No minerals in the deep, hot earth are magnetic, and permanently magnetized minerals in the cool uppermost crust are of such minor abundance that they account for only about 2 percent of the earth's field.

If permanent magnetism is not the chief source, could there be a dynamo that somehow combines the ingredients of mechanical motion, electric current, and magnetism? To perform as a dynamo, a portion of the earth must be able to conduct electricity, and there must be a source of energy to propel an *internal* motion (not simply the daily rotation of the entire earth). A splendid candidate for such a dynamo is the outer core which is believed to consist of liquid Fe-Ni alloy (Chapter 16).

We postulate that this molten alloy sustains a complex overturning, or *convective* motion, powered by heat energy. In slightly warmer zones that consequently are expanded (less dense), the liquid core material streams upward, whereas in cooler regions there is a flow path of descending, more dense material. Heat is supplied by radioactive decay, some heat is residual from the formation of the core, and some comes from slow crystallization of the alloy. Atoms in a solid are less energetic than the same atoms in a liquid at the same temperature. Or, to put it another way, heat energy is released as liquid changes into solid, even without a change in temperature. Crystals of metal grow in the midst of the earth's outer core, and rain down onto the solid inner core. Billions of years from now, when the outer core has frozen completely, there can be no more dynamo.

Calculations support the notion of a dynamo, but no one really understands it in detail. According to the theory, the liquid alloy wafts along at a rate of several centimeters per minute, the internal electric current is on the order of billions of amperes, and the central magnetic field is intense, only a tiny portion of it "leaking" up to the earth's surface. Magnetic lines of force, entrained in the core fluid, become stretched and twisted like elastic cords. They appear to be dragging on the solid inner core, causing it to spin more rapidly than the earth's daily rotation. At the surface we observe continual changes in the strength and directionality of the magnetic field. And yet, because the earth's rotation controls the pattern of convection in the outer core, to a good approximation the magnetic field surrounding the earth also has a rotational symmetry. Magnetic lines of force (Figure 21-1) would look the same if they were rotated about an axis projected through the magnetic poles.

Energy associated with the earth's magnetic field is *potential*, being manifested only when there is a change of directionality or strength. It is about the same as the energy contained in a thousand or so atomic bombs, which is not much considering that it is distributed over the huge volume of the earth and surrounding space.

Reading the Magnetic Record in Rocks

Although the motions of core material and of its resultant magnetic field are turbulent, ever-changing, and poorly understood, certain systematic patterns of behavior are hidden in this apparent chaos. We may extract precious information about past conditions of the earth from the magnetic record imprinted in rocks. Let's begin with the cooling basalt flow discussed above. Already by the time that temperature has dropped through the Curie temperature for its magnetic minerals, they are frozen securely in place, not free to rotate physically as a compass needle can do. Nevertheless, with further cooling the mineral grains acquire magnetic lines of force that are parallel to the lines of force in the earth's local magnetic field. In many situations, the minerals retain the original magnetic signature (becoming a magnetic "fossil") that does not change even though the earth's field may change later on.

To measure the direction of fossil, or *remanent* magnetism, we must first acquire a carefully oriented sample, usually by extracting a small core out of the outcrop using a portable gasoline-powered drill. Before removing the sample, we scratch a marker line on the side of the core, and measure its orientation. We collect at least 10 samples from each flow to obtain statistically better data (recall the old slogan "There's safety in numbers."). Back in the laboratory, the sample must pass a series of tests to determine whether its original magnetic record has been firmly retained. An instrument then measures the direction of magnetism in the sample relative to the scratch mark, and hence relative to the earth as a whole.

Orientations of magnetic lines implanted in a basalt flow depend upon its geographic location. The flow could lie anywhere between the Equator [0° latitude: Figure 21-2(*a*)] and the North or South Pole (90° latitude). Suppose that we map the earth's lines of force using a specially designed compass whose needle rotates in a vertical plane. It would show that the lines run parallel to the earth's surface at the magnetic Equator [Figure 21-2(*c*)]; they trend vertically to the surface at a magnetic pole, and they intersect the earth at some intermediate angle in every other place. Just so, the remanent lines of force are implanted horizontally in basalt that had cooled at the Equator, and if the basalt had erupted at a pole the frozen-in lines of force would be vertical. If you enjoy trigonometry, you can explore the simple formula (comment box, following page) that relates a sample's latitude to the orientation of its lines of magnetic force.

Apparent Polar Wander

Measurement of remanent magnetism provides the magnetic inclination, which is the direction in a vertical plane that is related to magnetic latitude (see the comment box), and magnetic declination, which is the east-west direction measured in a horizontal plane. These data and a calculation using spherical trigonometry provide the position of the ancient magnetic pole. Today the rotational and magnetic poles lie near one another, although not occupying precisely the same spot. Were these two types of pole closely associated in past times? Suppose that we analyze remanent magnetism in basalt flows that erupted within the last tens of thousands of years, which is recent geologically speaking. The data plot as a splatter of points (Figure 21-3), each point an instantaneous "snapshot" of the position of the magnetic pole when a particular sample acquired remanent magnetism. The position of the magnetic pole must be constantly changing, and note that the distribution of points is centered upon the *rotational* pole, not the current magnetic pole. The latter (the black dot) is just a typical data point, a momentary value similar to all the others. The magnetic pole is like a moth at night, flittering randomly about a candle

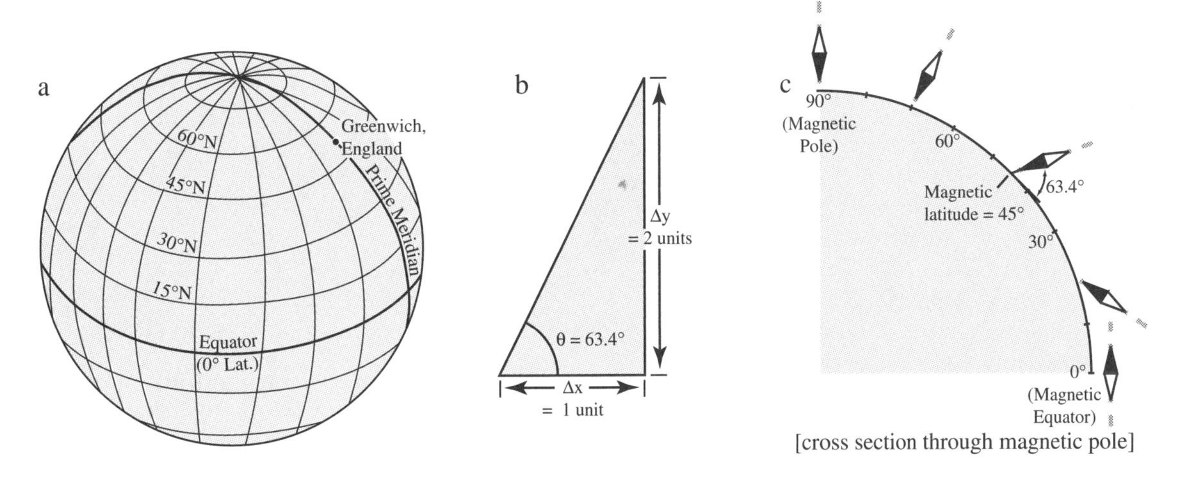

Figure 21-2. (*a*) Representative lines of latitude and longitude. (*b*) In a right triangle, the tangent of angle θ (Greek theta) is defined as distance *y* (side of triangle opposite angle θ) divided by distance *x* (adjacent side of triangle). In the example of θ = 63.4°, distance *y* is 2 times distance *x*, and thus the tangent of angle θ = 2. (*c*) Magnetic lines of force are parallel to the earth's surface at the magnetic equator, becoming ever more steeply inclined toward a magnetic pole where they intersect the surface vertically. Halfway between the equator and the pole, at a latitude of 45°, a magnetic line of force intersects the earth's surface at an angle of 63.4°.

Let us define the *magnetic inclination* as the angle between a magnetic line of force and the earth's surface. Inclination and magnetic latitude are related by the formula:

$$\tan I = 2 \tan\lambda,$$

where I is inclination and λ (Greek lambda) is latitude. For example, suppose the sample is located at latitude 45° (halfway between the Equator and a Pole). Figure 21-2(*b*) reminds us of the definition of the tangent of an angle, which for an angle of 45° is simply 1÷1, or 1.0. Thus, according to the formula, $\tan I = 2 \tan\lambda = 2 \tan (45°) = (2)(1) = 2$. For what angle I does its tangent = 2? The answer is inclination $I = 63.4°$, as shown in Figure 21-2(*b*, *c*). Use the formula to verify that at latitude 0° the lines of force are horizontal ($I = 0°$), and at latitude 90° the inclination is vertical ($I = 90°$).

Note that we can determine only the latitude, *not* the longitude of a sample. Latitude is defined with respect to the earth's axis of rotation [Figure 21-2(*a*)]. Definition of longitude is arbitrary (degrees east or west of an observatory in Greenwich, England), not related in any necessary way to the geometry or motion of the earth.

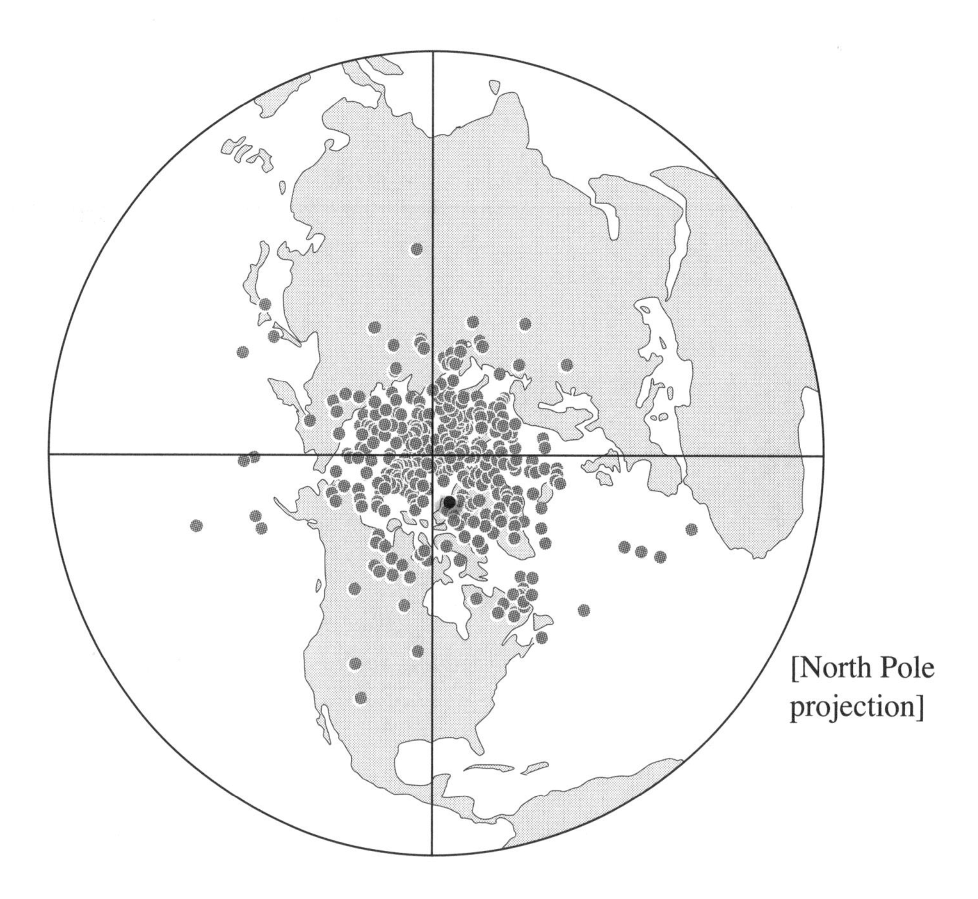

Figure 21-3. Roughly two-thirds of the data points that correspond to recently formed rocks are located within 12° (1350 kilometers) of the rotational pole, not symmetrical about the magnetic dip pole whose current position (black dot) is transitory. Some of the more distant points could be erroneous data due to equipment failure or (heaven forbid) blundering researchers! [*After R. Doell, "History of the Geomagnetic Field,"* Journal of Applied Physics, *vol. 40, 1969.*]

(rotational pole), always keeping near the flame although never exactly in it. Whatever may be the complex turbulent motions within the core dynamo, these motions are symmetrical about the earth's spin axis over a long-term average of thousands of years.

This tight connection permits us to use ancient magnetic pole positions (*paleo*magnetic poles) as a reasonably good proxy for ancient rotational pole positions. To our surprise, some of these positions turn out to be very distant from the modern North or South Pole, possibly even lying in the tropics. Moreover, analyses of rocks of many ages show that, with the passage of geologic time, the poles have moved along defined pathways known as *apparent polar wander paths,* which we shall explore in more detail in the Grand Synthesis (Chapter 22). Fascinating questions come to mind. Did the poles move with respect to a fixed continent, or was it the continent that had moved, or had both moved? In fact, earth magnetism provides powerful evidence that continents have drifted.

Magnetic Reversals

An inconstant magnetic field generated by a mysterious internal dynamo may seem complicated enough, but there is more. Consider a stacked sequence of basalt flows, such as those visible in a hillside in British Columbia (Figure 21-4). Although each flow would have been exposed for a time at the earth's surface, there is almost no weathering. Another eruption must have promptly buried (and protected) the flow beneath, and so on for the next eruption, and next.

A short time scale can be confirmed by use of the potassium-argon (K-Ar) isotopic age method (Chapter 11) to date the flows. In a typical situation (Figure 21-5), the interval between eruptions is only hundreds to a few thousand years. The earth's magnetic poles would not have changed very much during such a short length of time. Consequently, the embedded magnetic lines of force, symbolized by compass needles, are oriented parallel from flow to flow. But the magnetic lines of force also exhibit *polarity.* We have noted that one end of a compass needle (let's color it black) is attracted toward the magnetic North Pole whereas the other end (color it white) is attracted toward the magnetic South Pole. Studies of volcanic sequences have revealed an amazing situation, that occasionally the earth's magnetic poles must have reversed. Today's magnetic field is said to be "normal" and the other state, in which South and North Poles have exchanged positions, is a "reverse" polarity. Such labeling is arbitrary, of

Figure 21-4. Stacked flows of basalt exposed in this hillside were probably erupted within a short interval of geologic time. [*Geological Survey of Canada photograph.*]

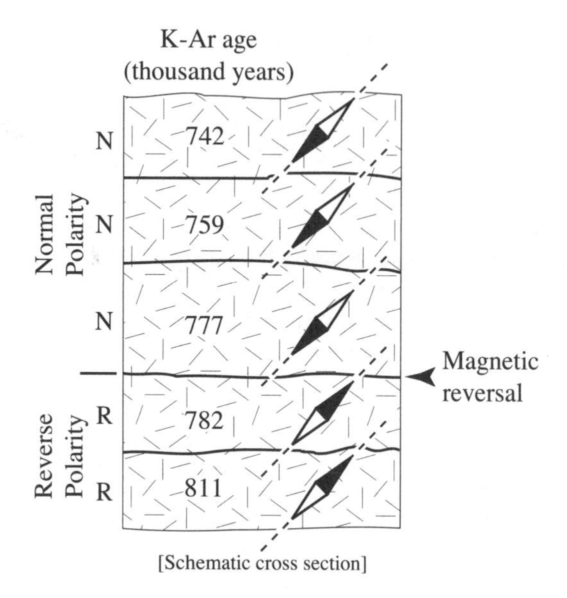

Figure 21-5. Potassium-argon ages of basalt flows indicate a magnetic reversal between 782 thousand years ago (youngest flow that is reversely magnetized) and 777 thousand years ago (oldest flow that is normally magnetized). Although this sequence is hypothetical, it realistically depicts how the most recent major magnetic reversal, which occurred 779 thousand years ago, could be dated at this locality within narrow limits.

course, just a bit of scientific whimsy. (After all, everyone knows that *we* are normal—it is the other guy who is reversed!) In Figure 21-5 the lower two flows are reversely magnetized, and the more recent upper flows are normally magnetized. A magnetic reversal must have occurred some time between the eruptions of the 782- and 777-thousand-year-old flows.

Detailed examination of rocks that were forming at the exact moment of a magnetic reversal shows that such events are extremely rapid. In just a thousand years or so—a mere blink of an eye in the vastness of geologic time—the earth's magnetic field "goes crazy," dropping to low intensity as the poles race to their new positions. Except for polarity, the normal and reverse states of the magnetic field cannot be distinguished, both of them experiencing short- and long-term fluctuations in strength and local position of the magnetic poles (Figure 21-6). It is yet another example of the unstable behavior of the earth's central dynamo.

As mentioned, the strength of the earth's magnetic field is currently diminishing. Is the magnetic field about to reverse, or will it maintain normal polarity as its strength recovers? No one knows, because magnetic reversals are unpredictable. It is a behavior illustrated by shaking a small pebble vigorously in a glass jar. After the pebble has bounced off the walls many times (like an ever-changing yet stable normal or reverse magnetic field), suddenly and without warning the pebble breaks a hole in the glass and

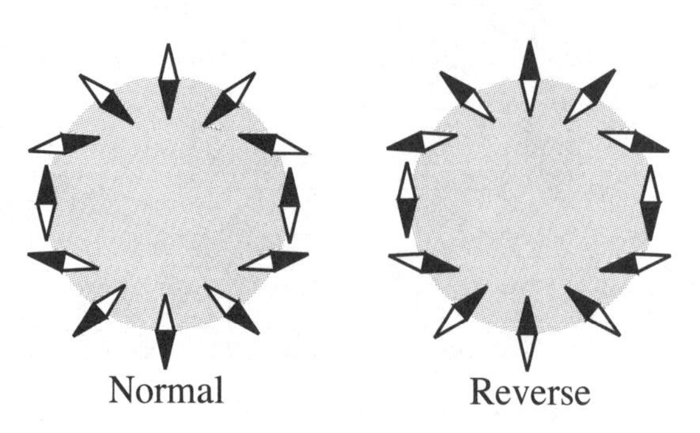

Figure 21-6. Behaviors of normal and reverse magnetic fields are identical except for polarity.

shoots through (magnetic reversal). Normal and reverse states are of randomly long or short duration, typically persisting for tens of thousands, to tens of millions of years. A normal or reverse magnetic direction is imprinted wherever in the world a volcanic eruption may be cooling. As sedimentary particles settle through a quiet body of water, their magnetic directions become oriented with the earth's field. Normal or reverse polarity can also be determined in samples of sandstone or mudstone.

With a sufficiently large number of magnetic direction measurements on rocks that are also dated by the K-Ar method, we may pinpoint the times of magnetic reversals quite accurately for the most recent several million years (Figure 21-7). Timings of more ancient reversals are dated indirectly through magnetic measurements on ocean-floor basalt and its sedimentary cover, as we shall see in Chapter 22. The earth's magnetic field has reversed more than 300 times within the past 160 million years, the most recent major reversal occurring about 0.78 million years ago. Magnetic reversal chronology is rich in useful information, analogous to wide or narrow tree rings, or the string of zeros and ones in a computer code, and this too will be used in the Grand Synthesis.

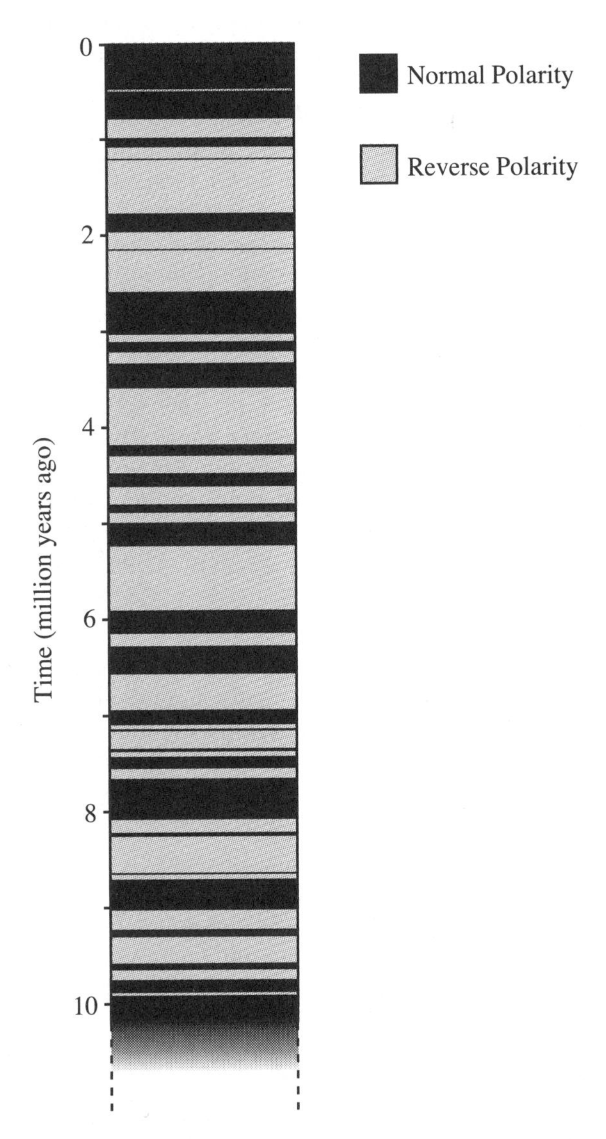

Figure 21-7. Potassium-argon ages, measurements of normal or reverse polarity, and observations of the magnetic record in ocean basins (Chapter 22) were used to construct a time scale of geomagnetic reversals during the most recent 10 million years. Times of magnetic reversal seem to be completely random. [*After S. C. Cande and D. V. Kent, "A New Geomagnetic Polarity Time Scale for the Late Cretaceous and Cenozoic,"* Journal of Geophysical Research, *vol. 97, no. B10, 1992.*]

THE WORLD OCEAN

Some years ago, Thomas Kuhn wrote *The Structure of Scientific Revolutions*, an influential book describing how scientific enterprises make progress. He observed that scientific discoveries do not operate like some great war tank pressing relentlessly forward. Rather, they advance by fits and starts, even convulsions. Mostly there are long periods of "doing normal science" during which our understanding of geology or some other discipline is steadily enriched and deepened. Scientific research is guided by *theory*, which is a set of postulated explanations for observations or experiments. Some explanations are so well supported by data that they have become a *paradigm*, meaning that everyone now takes them for granted. For example, a paradigm established long ago is that ordinary matter is made of atoms that are comprised of protons, neutrons, and electrons. However, sometimes conflicting new data appear suggesting that the established paradigm is wrong or inadequate. With further testing, the researchers regard the new findings with skepticism, then with keen interest, and finally with alarm, recognizing that something is amiss with the prevailing theory but not yet knowing how to revise it. This uneasy condition may persist for decades until some genius proposes a radically new way to interpret old data, or new technology enables an entirely different kind of data to be gathered. Then the discipline launches into a frenzy of rethinking its standard assumptions, and an exciting scientific revolution is underway.

Beginning in the 1960s, geology experienced such a revolution, whose results have been assimilated into a new era of "normal science." This revolution has produced a satisfying general explanation for the origin of all the major features visible on the face of the earth. Seeing that geology emerged as a discipline back in the 1700s, why was the revolution so long in coming? In large part it is because we had lacked the technology to explore the world ocean which covers 70 per cent of the globe. Impetus for this new technology came during World War II when submarine warfare demanded accurate maps of the ocean floor. Up until that time, geologists had paid attention only to the continents, remaining ignorant about the largest feature on earth!

Even today, the topography of the ocean floor is far less well known than the topography of Venus or the moon, distant objects. The most accurate data are provided as ships make continuous measurements of ocean depth, but there are large areas where ships never go, one such blank region being as large as the state of Oklahoma. Recently, data from satellites have supplemented the ship soundings. In Chapter 16 we saw that the orbits of satellites are used to map the geoid, which coincides with the surface of the ocean. Tiny but detectable "wrinkles" in the geoid correspond to the ups and downs of seafloor topography. Data from satellites, which now orbit over all parts of the earth, were instrumental in the discovery of a cluster of more than 40 huge volcanoes submerged in a remote part of the Pacific Ocean.

Some Generalizations

In reality there is only one worldwide, interconnected ocean that is composed, in order of decreasing size, of the Pacific Ocean, which occupies 1/3 of the earth's surface, and the Atlantic, Indian, and Arctic Oceans (Figure 21-8). The Southern Ocean is a convenient label for those parts of the Pacific, Indian, and Atlantic Oceans that encircle Antarctica. In addition, there are a number of small basins that are floored by oceanic crust (Chapter 16), examples being the Mediterranean Sea and Sea of Japan.

In many ways the underwater seascape is easier to interpret than a continental landscape whose original features may have been destroyed by erosion. Even where a gentle rain of fine sediment has obscured the ocean's basaltic basement, this situation is no obstacle to geophysical exploration. Geophysical research vessels have drilled thousands of holes in the floor of the world ocean, from which core samples of sediment and igneous basement were retrieved. A ship equipped with a battery of air guns can send a powerful acoustic ping through the water and into layers of sediment below. The deeper a buried horizon, the longer is the delay before the sound is echoed back to specialized receivers (hydrophones). Information from returned signals is assembled by computers into a profile of both the buried basement and overlying strata (Figure 21-9).

Seeing that the ocean floor is the lowest elevation on the surface of the planet, geologists had expected to find thick sediment containing a fossil record dating back perhaps to the very beginning of life. It was thus a great surprise to discover that the sedimentary blanket is typically less than one kilometer thick. Deposition is slow in oceanic areas distant from land, the only available material being windblown dust, micrometeorites, and the shells of tiny organisms such as foraminifera. Special applications of isotopic dating confirm that rates of deposition are indeed low, about 1 to 10 meters per million years. Even at this incredibly slow pace, the observed thickness would have accumulated in a hundred million years or so.

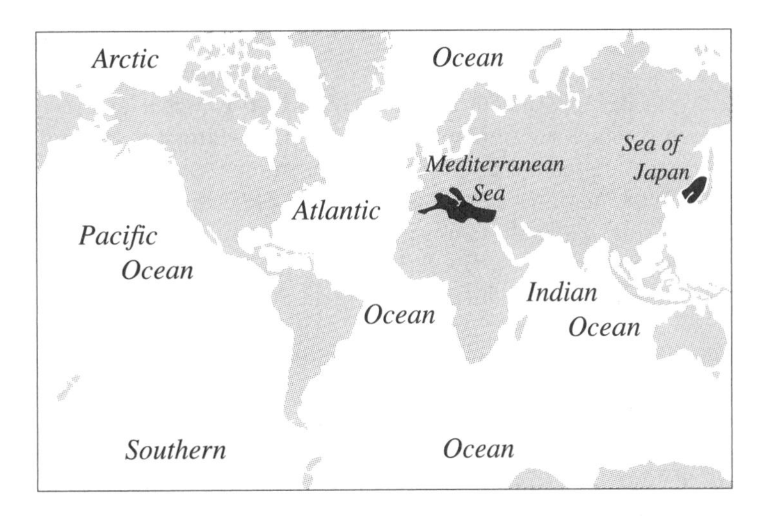

Figure 21-8. The world ocean consists of major basins, and small basins including the Mediterranean Sea, Sea of Japan, and several others that are virtually landlocked.

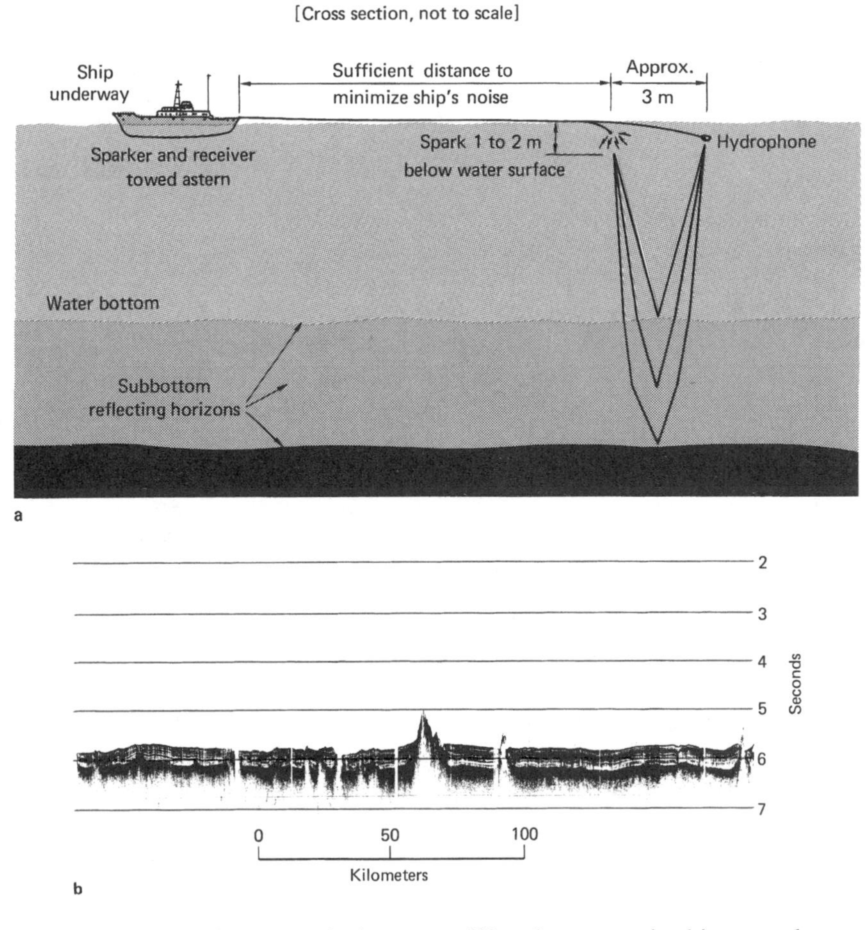

Figure 21-9. (*a*) Frequent miniature explosions, set off by air guns or, in this example, a potent electric spark, send sound waves down through the water column and into the ocean floor beneath. Sound energy reflected back to the surface is picked up by hydrophones trailed behind the geophysical research vessel. (*b*) A continuous profile is built up of myriads of thin vertical lines recorded as the ship sails along. Units of the vertical scale are the number of seconds before the sound is reflected off a buried surface and back to the hydrophones, proportional to depth. This record from the equatorial Pacific shows a rough basement masked by strata that lap against buried hills. Here and there, naked volcanic peaks project above the general level of the sediment. [(*b*) *after J. I. Ewing, "History of the Ocean Basins as Recorded in the Sediments,"* Governor's Conference on Oceanography, *Lamont-Doherty Earth Observatory, Palisades, N. Y., 1967.*]

No oceanic fossils are older than late Jurassic (approximately 150 million years ago). And yet, fossils much older than Jurassic are contained in deposits of shallow continental seas that had been in communication with the world ocean. Ancient rocks, as old as 90 per cent of the age of the earth, are preserved in the continents, which are vulnerable to recycling by erosion. Ironically, in no part of the ocean floor, which receives the products of erosion, is the sediment older than the latest 3 or 4 per cent of geologic time! How can the marine water mass actually be older than the ocean floor beneath it? Our Grand Synthesis will surely need to address this puzzling observation.

Continental shelf, slope, and rise Bordering the world's land masses is a zone of shallow water known as the *continental shelf*, whose width averages about 80 kilometers but with variations from zero to as much as 1500 kilometers off the northern coast of Asia. The shelf is a vast region, in area equal to the sum of Europe and South America. Intensive geophysical exploration for oil and gas reveals that continental crust extends offshore beneath the shallow waters of the shelf. It is as though the ocean is a little bit too full and "slops" over the edges of the continents.

At a water depth of around 130 meters (also with much variation), the shelf merges into the *continental slope*, which leads toward the abyss (Figure 21-10). Beneath the slope we find the transition from

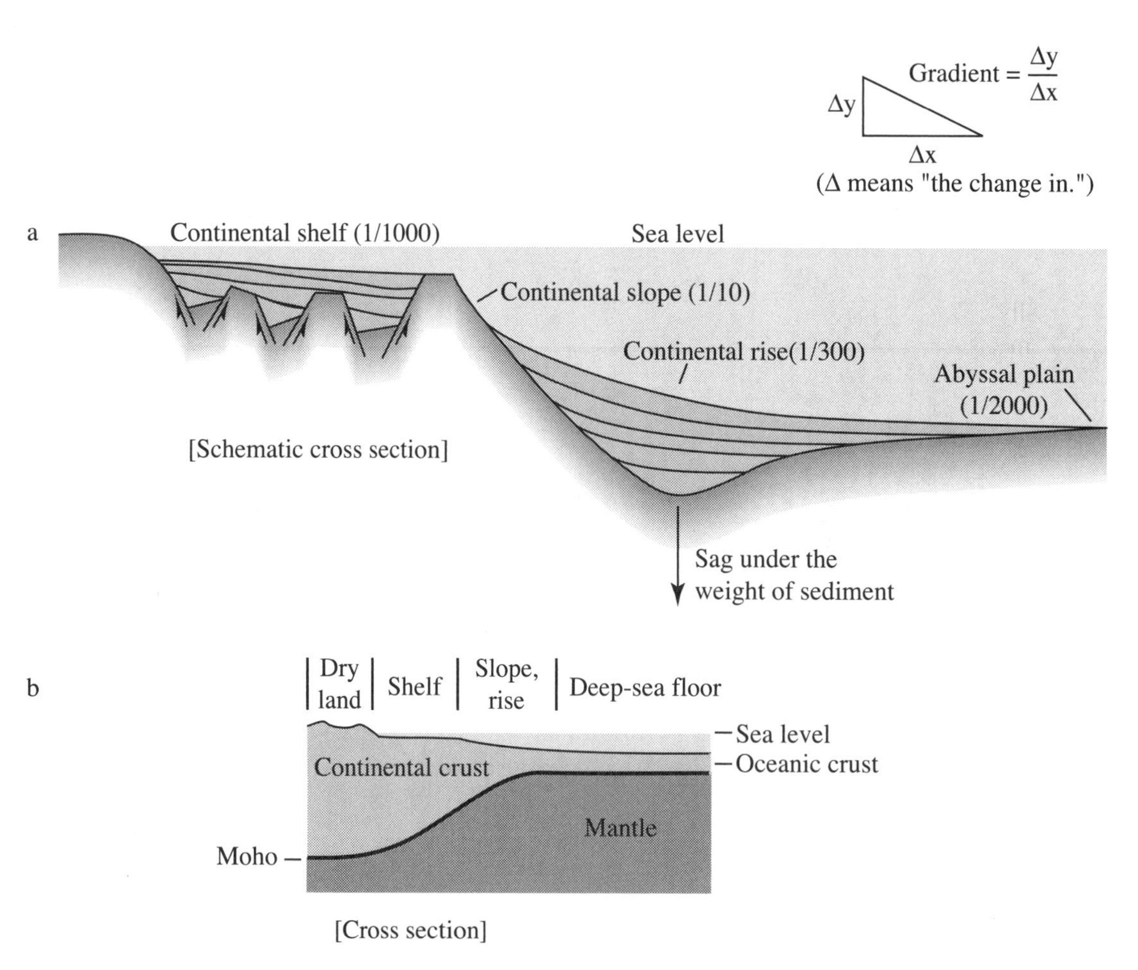

Figure 21-10. (*a*) A cross section (with vertical exaggeration) depicts the relationship of shelf, slope, and rise. Continental basement beneath the shelf may be a complexly faulted "borderland" such as along the coast of southern California, partly buried by sediment. Oceanic crust beneath the rise off the Atlantic Coast of the United States is sagged downward under the weight of accumulated sediment that may exceed 12 kilometers in thickness. (*b*) Transition between continental and oceanic crust occurs in the region of the continental slope and rise. The crust thins by oceanward descent of the floor and, more especially, by ascent of the Moho (Chapter 16) from deep beneath the continent to shallow beneath the ocean.

continental to oceanic crust, commonly buried under thick sediment and for this reason extraordinarily difficult to study even with seismic probes. In places, the continental slope is cut by submarine canyons, some of them outrivaling the greatest canyons on dry land. Typically, the decline of the continental slope is about 5 degrees, but where rivers have poured forth a great mass of sediment, as in the Bay of Bengal that borders India on the east, the shelf and slope merge together as one enormous, gently inclined plane. This is quite in contrast to underwater topography off the west coast of Florida where the continental slope is a bold escarpment.

Submarine canyons that extend across the shelf nearly to shoreline, as along the coast of California, provide an efficient means to channel the flow of sediment into the depths. Fan-shaped masses of sediment accumulate at the base of the slope, and strong bottom currents may distribute the sediment laterally. The result is a thick sediment wedge, the *continental rise*, banked against the slope and tapering seaward into the thin sediment of standard deep-ocean floor (Figure 21-10).

Ocean ridge system Until the mid-20th Century it was widely believed that the ocean floor is a flat, monotonous plain, as indeed much of it is. The existence of a continuous, 75,000 kilometers long *ocean ridge system* that nearly encircles the globe, still awaited discovery. Let us begin an imaginary journey along the ridge system, noting its characteristics along the way. We commence where the ridge intersects the wide continental shelf north of Siberia (Figure 21-11, point *A*). The ridge crosses the Arctic Ocean, and swings southward to extend the length of the Atlantic (*B* to *C*). Here the ridge has a symmetrical form occupying the central one-third of the Atlantic basin, rising some 2 kilometers above the floor of the deep abyss [Figure 21-12(*a*)]. Incised into the crest of the ridge is a continuous deep cleft, the *medial valley* [Figure 21-12(*b*)].

Geologic processes in Iceland, the largest island situated atop the ridge, are representative of the system as a whole. Iceland consists of a complex of basalt flows, dikes, and active and extinct volcanoes. As seen in its continuation through Iceland, the medial valley is bounded by normal faults (Chapter 16), indicating that the earth is in tension, being pulled apart. As groundwater descends along faults, it comes in contact with hot basalt, later to issue forth as hot springs and geysers. About 85 per cent of the housing in Iceland utilizes geothermal heating, though one borehole encountered not hot water but molten lava!

Throughout its length the ocean ridge system is cut into numerous segments, each segment stepped off laterally to the right or left. The longer offsets are *fracture zones* in which the rock is heavily sheared by movement along strike-slip faults (Chapter 16). Large fracture zones are bounded by imposing undersea escarpments where the entire thickness of oceanic crust, and even a bit of the mantle beneath, can be visited by submersible vessels. Fault movement along the medial valley and in the fracture zones is expressed as numerous, exclusively shallow, low- to medium-energy earthquakes. Very weak quakes (microearthquakes) are attributed not to slippage on faults but to the movement of basaltic magma under the medial valley. Figure 21-13 summarizes the geology along the crest of the Mid-Atlantic Ridge.

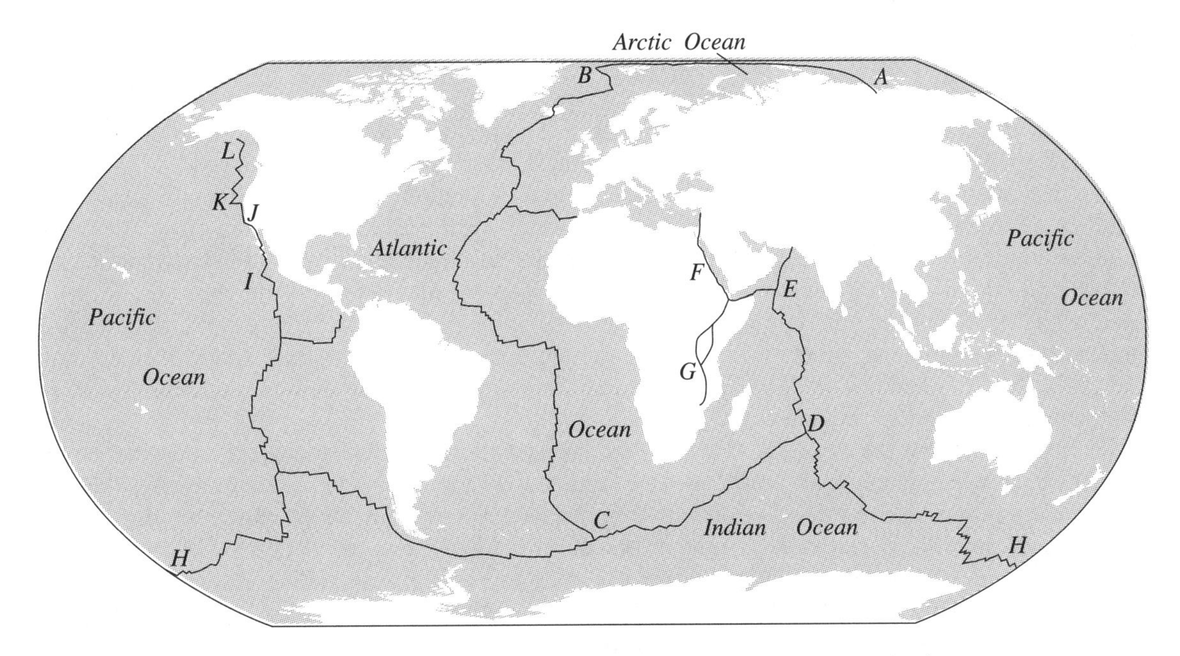

Figure 21-11. The ocean ridge system extends through all of the major ocean basins.

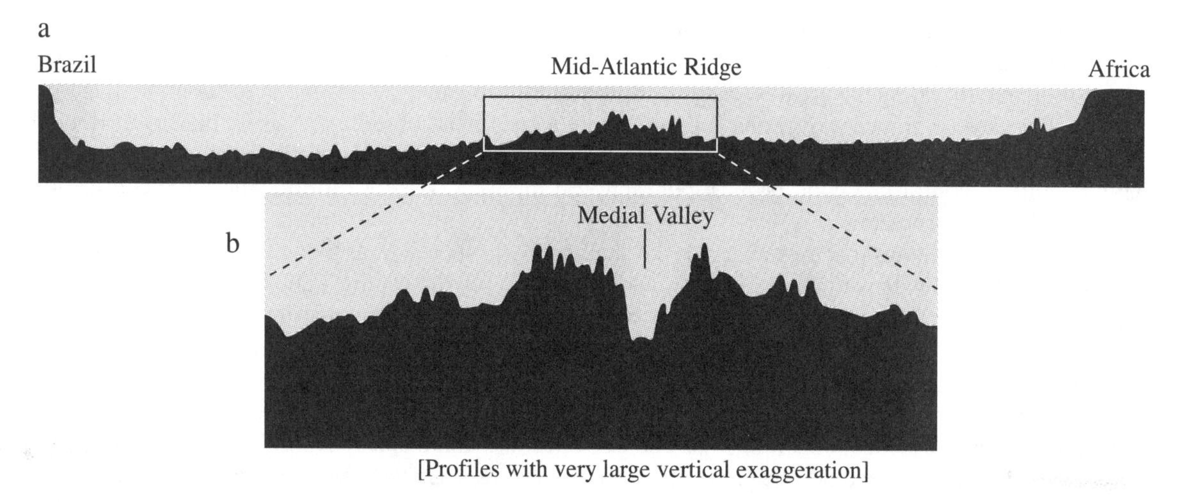

Figure 21-12. (*a*) A cross section shows the general symmetry of the Mid-Atlantic Ridge between Brazil and western Africa. (*b*) A close-up view of the ridge crest emphasizes the prominent medial valley.

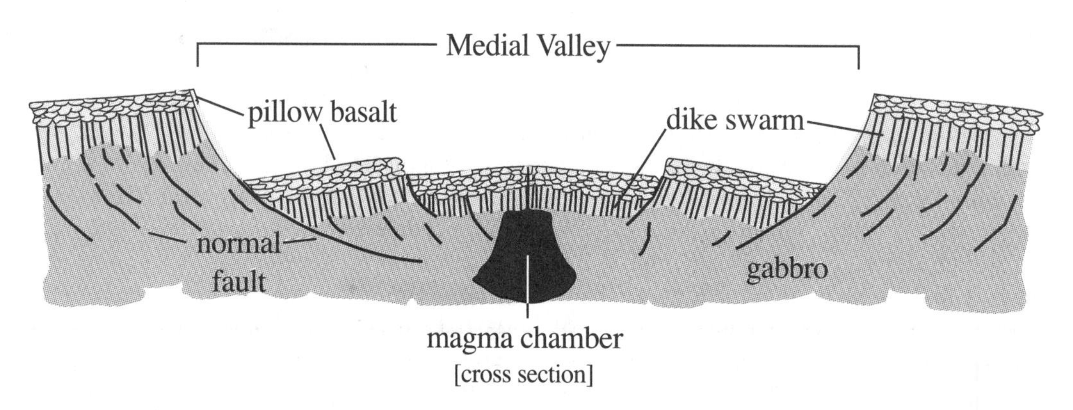

Figure 21-13. A magma chamber below the medial valley feeds liquid basalt up into fractures where it freezes, forming a mass of igneous dikes. Magma that oozes through fractures onto the ocean floor is chilled by the sea water, forming a covering layer of pillow basalt (Chapter 5). Magma that remains at depth cools slowly, forming coarsely crystalline gabbro.

Near the Equator, where the trend of the ridge is sharply kinked, it continues to maintain a position midway between the Old and New World (Figure 21-14). Here the ridge is cleaved into short segments that are strongly offset along fracture zones. Studies of earthquakes in the fracture zones raise another surprising apparent contradiction that our Grand Synthesis will need to resolve. By noting whether an earthquake sets the first pulse of ground motion toward or away from a seismograph station, and compiling the "first-motion" analyses for many stations, we may determine the direction of movement along the fault plane. In Figure 21-15, the segment of the ridge on the far side of the fracture zone appears to have moved relatively to the left, as though displaced along a left-lateral strike-slip fault. However, the first-motion studies indicate precisely the opposite sense of motion, as though the offset segments of the ridge are moving closer together.

Passing through the Southern Ocean below Africa, the ridge system proceeds into the central Indian Ocean where it splits into two branches (Figure 21-11, point *D*). One branch traverses the Gulf of Aden (*E*), beyond which it forks yet again. A branch with a prominent medial valley continues up the axis of the trough-like Red Sea (*F*). Another branch of the ridge system heads south through Africa where it appears as the *East African Rift Valleys* (*G*). Nestled in the valleys are lakes, some of them with bottoms lower than sea level. These valleys must have been dropped down along faults, not carved by rivers which cannot erode to an elevation lower than sea level. In the same region are volcanoes whose unusual low-silica lavas could have ascended along faults from sources deep in the mantle. In origin,

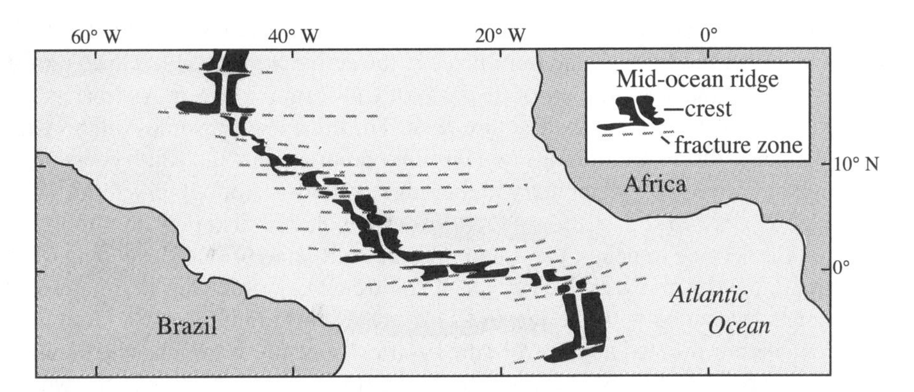

Figure 21-14. Broad stripes separated by a narrow gap symbolize the crest of the Mid-Atlantic Ridge with its medial valley. The ridge is severed into many small offset segments where it bends sharply between Africa and South America. [*After W. J. Morgan, "Rises, Trenches, Great Faults, and Crustal Blocks,"* Journal of Geophysical Research, *vol. 73, no. 6, p. 1964, 1968, Copyright by American Geophysical Union.*]

[Schematic block diagram]

Figure 21-15. A common-sense interpretation of the history of these segments of the ridge system is that they have been offset along a left-lateral strike-slip fault, as indicated by the black arrows. However, according to seismic first-motion studies, the movement (colored arrows) is precisely the opposite!

rock composition, size, and topographic profile (up-arch with a downdropped block [a graben] at the crest), a typical East African Rift Valley distinctly resembles its oceanic counterpart.

Returning to branching point *D* (Figure 21-11), we follow the ridge as it passes through the Southern Ocean midway between Australia and Antarctica, thence into the Pacific. Here, the position and topographic form of the ridge system are uniquely different. The *East Pacific Rise* wanders along a gently sinuous path far off-center almost to South America, there turning northward toward the west coast of Mexico (*H* to *I*). Fracture zones and volcanic seamounts are present, but no rugged topography and only a hint of a medial valley. The Rise is more a low bulge equal in area to South plus North America, of relatively shallow ocean depth.

Seismic waves travel much more slowly through magma than through solid rock. Seismologists have used this property to detect the presence of molten basalt in the ridge system. A narrow magma body (only a kilometer or so wide) resides just beneath the crest of the East Pacific Rise. Magma chambers in the Mid-Atlantic Ridge are smaller and rather sporadically distributed. Even so, three times more magma is erupted in the ocean ridge system than in all other volcanic areas of the world combined. Most eruptions occur deep below the waves and are never observed!

As sea water seeps through fractures in the mass of hot basalt, the water becomes chemically corrosive, attacking the basalt. Superheated water spews out onto the ocean floor in *black smokers*, submarine hot springs. The "smoke" is actually a fine dispersion of sulfides and other minerals, instantly precipitated when ion-laden water at 300°C is chilled against ordinary sea water at 2°C.

To resume our journey, at point *I* the ridge system heads up the long slot of the Gulf of California. As in Africa, the ridge "runs aground," and terminates in the active *San Andreas Fault System* (*J*, Figure 21-11) that passes through the western part of the state of California. The San Andreas is identified not as the crest of the ridge but as an offsetting fracture zone. The crest itself resumes offshore in the Pacific (*K*), from there advancing through more jogs to a terminal point against the south coast of Alaska (*L*).

Ocean trench system Complementary to the ridge system—a topographic high—is a system of the most spectacular depressions on earth, *ocean trenches*, which will also play an important role in our Grand Synthesis. In the deepest trenches, the ocean floor lies farther *below* sea level than Mount Everest, the highest mountain, towers *above* it. Nearly all of the trenches border the perimeter of the Pacific Ocean where they are associated with the Ring of Fire volcanoes (Figure 21-16). Even the Indian and Atlantic Ocean trenches are situated not far from the Pacific. Stupendous trenches lie parallel to western Central and South America just offshore. If only the ocean water were not present, the world's grandest mountain front would be visible along South America: 14 vertical kilometers (46 thousand feet) of continuous ascent from trench depths to Andes heights.

As viewed in a map, trenches come in a variety of shapes from straight furrows, to sharply hooked at one end, to graceful open curves, or arcs. Trenches in the northern and western parts of the Pacific lie more distantly offshore and are typically bordered by island chains called *volcanic arcs*, an example being the string-of-pearls-like Aleutian Islands (Figure 21-16). Volcanoes associated with trenches erupt a variety of lava types ranging from dark-colored, high-density basalt to light-colored, low-density rhyolite (Chapter 5), but especially great quantities of lava whose composition is midway between basalt and rhyolite. The latter is called *andesite*, after the Andes Mountains. (Recall that the much more abundant magma of the ocean ridge system is basaltic.)

The very existence of ocean trenches invites more Grand Synthesis questions such as, How do trenches form? If rivers are transporting sediment into nearby offshore trenches, why are they not clogged to the brim? What explains the pattern of powerful earthquakes?

Consider the Tonga-Kermadec Trench in the southwest Pacific. Cross sections (Figure 21-17) depict a profusion of earthquake foci viewed along (*A-A'*) and across the trench (*B-B'*). Earthquake foci populate a dipping plane, from the most shallow depth at the trench floor to deep-focus earthquakes (Chapter 16) as much as 690 kilometers below the earth's surface. The plane of earthquake foci dips westward toward Australia. In trenches along the east side of the Pacific, similar planes of earthquakes

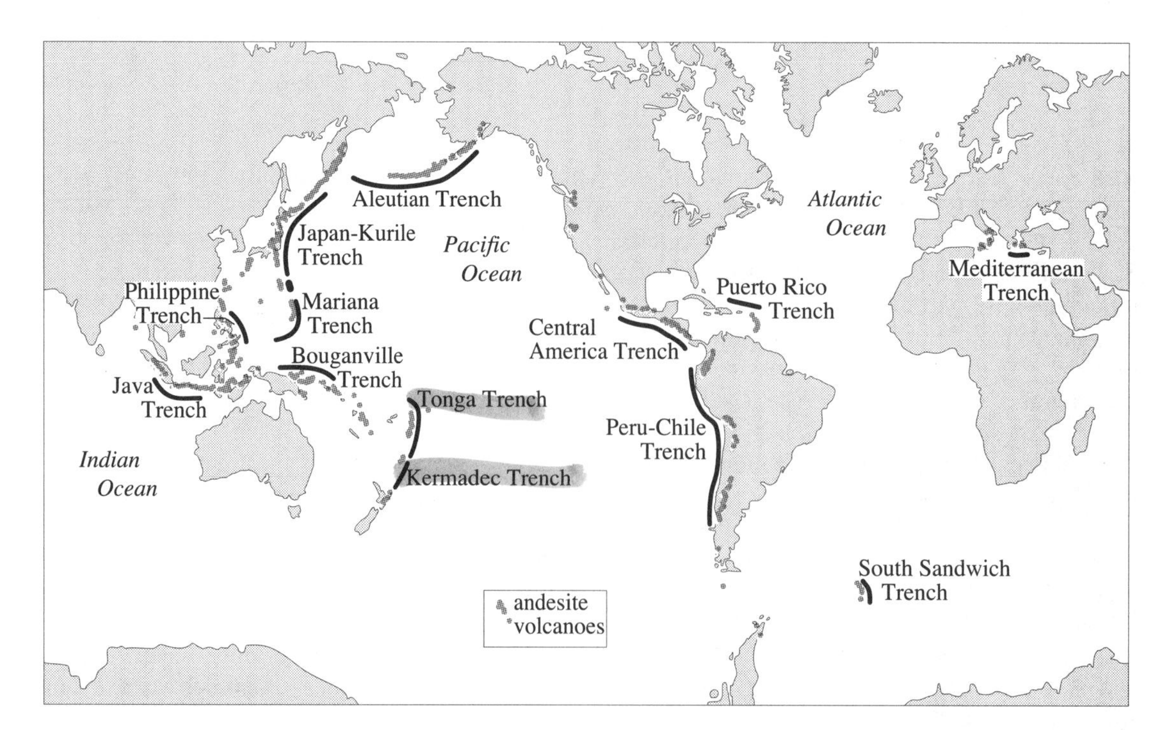

Figure 21-16. Major ocean trenches rim the Pacific Ocean, and occupy nearby parts of the Indian and Atlantic Oceans. Dots are associated andesite volcanoes.

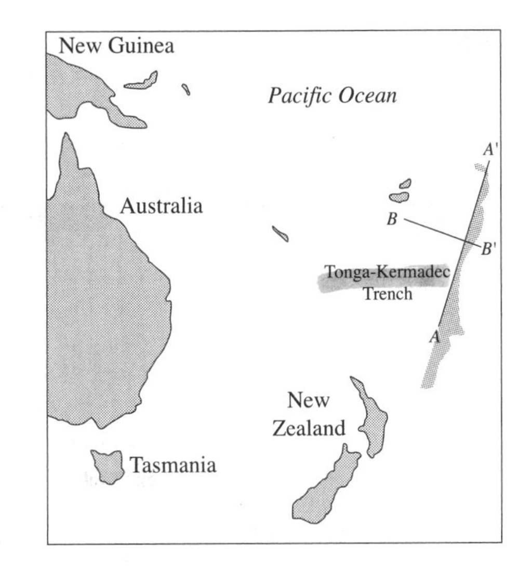

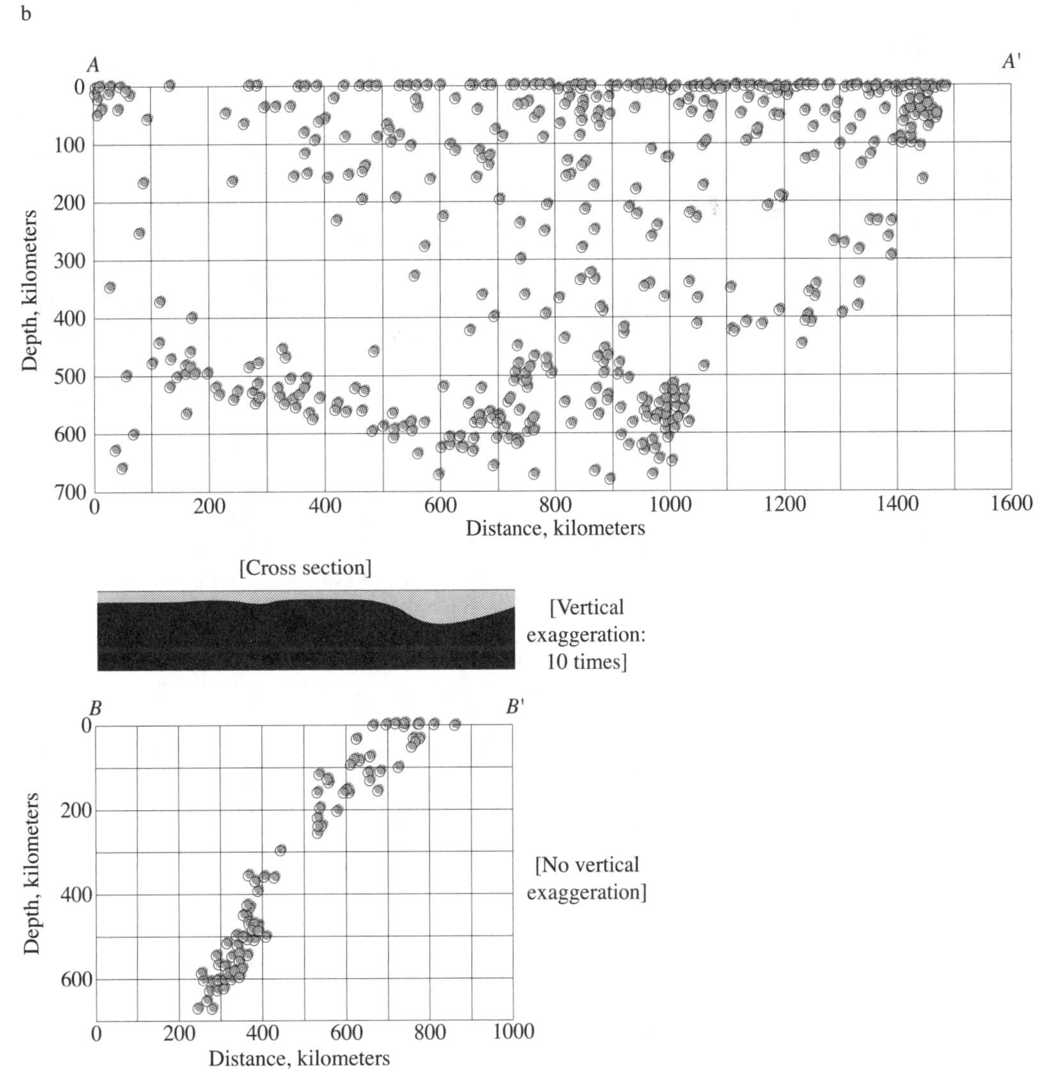

Figure 21-17. (*a*) An index map locates the Tonga-Kermadec Trench (shaded where water depth exceeds 5 kilometers), and cross sections *A-A'* along its length and *B-B'* across its width. (*b*) Earthquake foci (dots) extend the length of the trench axis, and to a depth approaching 700 kilometers. About half of all deep-focus earthquakes occur in the Tonga-Kermadec Trench alone. As seen in cross section *B-B'*, the foci define a dipping plane that descends steeply from the trench floor. [*After L. R. Sykes, "The Seismicity and Deep Structure of Island Arcs,"* Journal of Geophysical Research, *vol. 71, no. 12, pp. 2982, 2994, and 2996, 1966.*]

dip eastward under South America; planes of earthquakes dip northward in the north Pacific, and westward in the west Pacific, in all of these cases dipping toward the nearest continent. Typically they dip at about 45°, but the angle of dip varies from 30° to almost vertical.

Smaller features Figure 21-9 shows the typical deep-ocean floor in which a dead-flat veneer of sediment conceals the more minor irregularities of the basement. Poking above the sediment layer as much as a few hundred meters are relatively small topographic highs, *abyssal hills*. Ocean basins contain an estimated 1.5 million abyssal hills which are easily the most abundant topographic feature on earth. *Seamounts* are larger, projecting at least a kilometer above the floor. Loihi Seamount, and an estimated 30 thousand other seamounts in the Pacific, are mostly of volcanic origin. Because Loihi is conveniently located a short distance off the south shore of Hawaii, its active volcanic construction and its numerous earthquakes can be closely monitored. Loihi is already a giant although it must build up yet another kilometer to break above sea level, many thousands of years from now. It seems destined to fuse against the flanks of the great volcanoes that comprise Hawaii, themselves already the largest mountains on earth.

Of more obscure origin are the strange, coral-encrusted *atolls* of the southwest Pacific. Rising steeply from the ocean floor, an atoll culminates at sea level in a broad, shallow lagoon hemmed in by a reefy barrier. Deep drilling in Enewetak and Bikini atolls penetrated a kilometer or two of limestone of shallow-water origin before entering a volcanic basement. These findings vindicated the idea of a pioneer in the study of atolls, Charles Darwin. He proposed that an atoll was once a volcanic island that began to subside. At first, he said, the reefs merely fringed the island's rocky shores, but with sufficiently slow subsidence the coral and other carbonate-secreting organisms were able continually to build a platform upward to sea level. Eventually the entire volcanic summit became submerged beneath a thick limestone cap topped by an active reef.

Atolls are similar to *guyots* (GHEE-oes) which were discovered by World War II surveys of the Pacific. Guyots are seamounts whose flat tops lie as much as 2 kilometers below sea level. Dredge hauls bring back fossils of extinct Cretaceous or Cenozoic reef organisms adapted to life in shallow water, and rounded basalt pebbles tumbled and polished by wave action. Apparently guyots too had subsided deeply, but, for reasons that are not fully understood, the upward-building reef organisms were unable to keep pace.

MOUNTAIN BELTS

Any successful global hypothesis must be able to account for major features of continents as well as oceans. A frequency diagram (Figure 21-18) summarizes the distribution of the earth's surface according to its elevation above or below sea level. The nearly 75 per cent of the land surface that rises no higher than one kilometer above sea level is unlikely to have much spectacular scenery. Geologists love

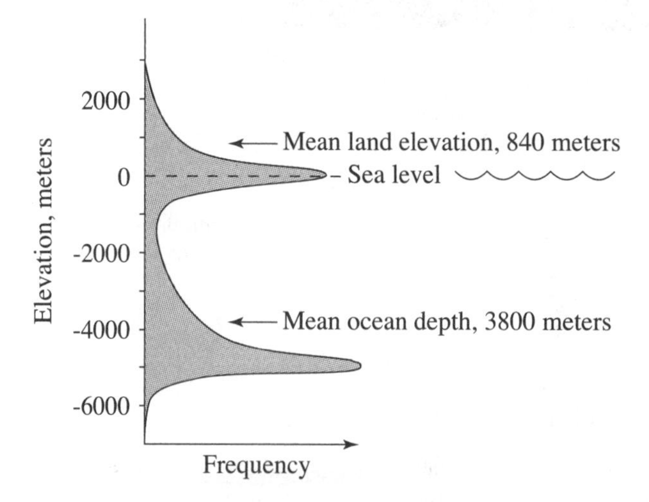

Figure 21-18. Elevations of continental and oceanic crust are sharply distinguished. The two maximum points of the curve signify the most frequent (*not* the average) elevations. Erosion has degraded most of the continental elevation down nearly to sea level. Ocean floor is typically about 5 kilometers below sea level.

to visit the mountainous regions, not just to enjoy their natural beauty as any other person would, but also to analyze complex internal structures that are exposed in such places. Mountain chains are perpetually crumbling into ruins from the moment they begin to be uplifted. Erosional destruction has gone nearly to completion in Precambrian shields (Chapter 11) where only low plains remain of what formerly were mountain ranges. Familiarity with modern mountains serves to guide a geologist who is studying some ancient eroded mountain remnant.

Mountain chains are so gigantic that their structures may become apparent only after the assembly of years of field studies. It was decades before skilled geologists in Switzerland understood the complexities of the Alps in that small country. Even then, some major controversies were to be settled only after tunnel construction permitted a look into the deep interiors of these mountains. Field mapping, aided by photographs taken from satellites, is still in its initial stages in remote areas such as Antarctica, the high Andes of western South America, and the plateau of Tibet in southeast Asia.

Mountains may be of diverse origins and somewhat arbitrary definition. What is an impressive mountain to most of us may seem like a mere hill to someone from the Himalayas. Mt. Rainier, near Seattle, and Fuji, near Tokyo, are volcanic edifices; the Grand Tetons of Wyoming were uplifted high along faults; a plateau in West Virginia appears to be mountainous but in a negative sense, because erosion has carved deep valleys into it. We shall focus on the mountains that comprise the earth's two great systems (Figure 21-19). One mountain belt nearly encircles the Pacific Ocean and includes the prominent Andes of South America. A second chain extends eastward from southern Europe (Alps, and others), through the Middle East, and into northern India and neighboring countries (Himalayas). Let us examine the Alps as an excellent case study of features that are common to many mountain systems worldwide.

Mountains in four dimensions What is so special about the Alps? In order to understand any mountain belt, we must know its three-dimensional structure and be able to reconstruct its development in the fourth dimension, geologic time. Thousands of geologist-years of investigation have made the Alps the best known of all mountain ranges. The geologic setting of the Alps is ideal for such studies. Teams of geophysicists have created images of the mantle and deep crust. Field geologists can trace distinctive sedimentary strata across mountain slopes even where the strata are metamorphosed and severely contorted. Abundant fossils facilitate dating the deposition of the strata. Uplift was especially vigorous 20 to 40 million years ago, providing sufficient time since then for erosion to carve out a magnificent 3 kilometers of vertical relief without yet having destroyed all the key evidence.

Long earlier, other mountains had stood in the same spot, and indeed the modern Alps are just one piece of a European "jigsaw puzzle," a collage of regions of different ages and geologic histories. Small remnants of 470 million year old basement (early Paleozoic) are preserved, and larger patches of volcanic rocks intruded by granite whose isotopic ages are around 300 million years. Not much evidence remains concerning these ancestral cycles of mountain-making.

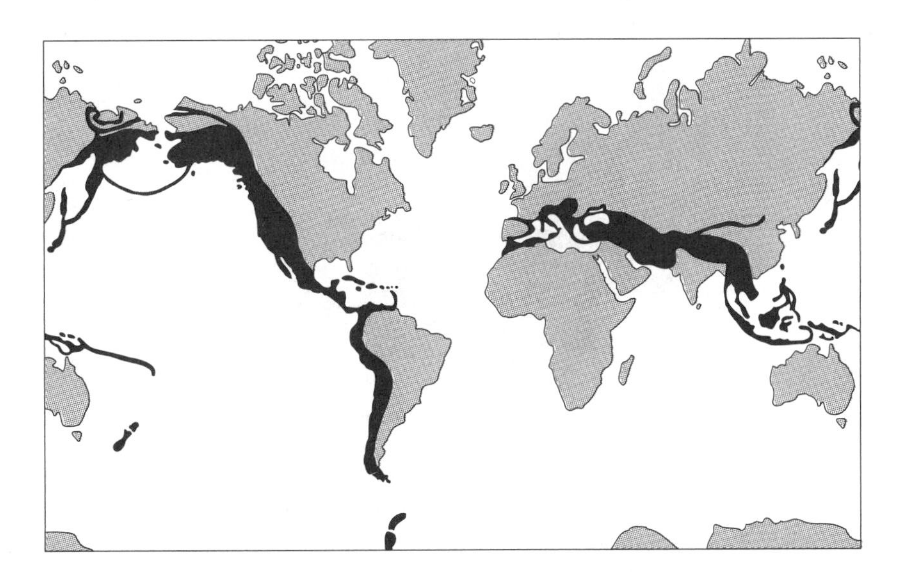

Figure 21-19. The earth's great mountain systems are organized into two major belts.

The modern episode began during the Mesozoic Era, when to the south of Europe there lay a substantial seaway, much larger than the modern Mediterranean Sea. Tensional stress extended the earth's crust, causing it to become thinner and to subside. Sediment derived from the continent was deposited into these nearshore basins, eventually accumulating to an enormous thickness. Then the application of stress was reversed, becoming compressive, collapsing the sedimentary basins, squeezing the sediment into a series of submarine ridges and island chains separated by deep troughs. Occasionally the soft sediment would slump back into a trough, then become involved again in deformation somewhat cannibalistically. These underwater events were just the opening phase in transforming the Alps into a towering landscape.

Let's visit that landscape in Switzerland in a climb up a spectacular peak, the pyramid-shaped Matterhorn. Near its base, somewhat metamorphosed Triassic and Jurassic strata lie in an almost horizontal position. Correlation with equivalent rocks elsewhere indicates that an original accumulation of thousands of meters has been thinned and stretched to 20 to 30 meters at the Matterhorn, to only about 1 per cent of the original thickness. What is more, Jurassic rocks are succeeded upward by Triassic rocks (which are older), and at the summit is a massive block of pre-Triassic basement. The entire sequence is upside down!

From this and numerous other observations, a unified picture of the Alpine structure emerged. The earth's crust, squeezed laterally as though clamped between the jaws of a vise, was buckled into folds tens of kilometers across. Because rocks are not especially strong on this gigantic scale of size, the folds tipped over and slid forward as transported sheets, termed *nappes* by French geologists. The nappes probably flowed down a gentle incline so that gravity aided their forward movement. Fold after fold arose until a stack several nappes deep had formed, each one extending farther to the north than the one beneath it, like folds of cloth drapery. At times a deforming mass ruptured along a nearly horizontal plane and continued to be shoved laterally along a *thrust fault* (Figure 21-20). The net result of these movements was to crumple the earth's crust, thickening and shortening it. According to one estimate, a region initially 450 kilometers across became compressed into a mountain belt only one-fourth as wide. Imposing though mountain heights may be, the vertical movements were almost trivial compared to the horizontal transport.

The mass of piled-up nappes rises and falls in broad undulations along the length of the mountain chain. In no one locality is the entire structure visible, but erosion has exposed various lower and higher levels, permitting a reconstruction in three dimensions (Figure 21-21). On the south side of the Alpine heap is a zone where once horizontal layers now stand vertically (Figure 21-22). They are the deformed and metamorphosed "roots" of the nappes, containing fragments of basaltic ocean crust and its ultramafic mantle, along with rocks of other origins. Further south in Italy, another pile of nappes is overturned in the opposite direction, such that the total structure resembles a flower with outwardly-pointed petals (Figure 21-23).

Recent seismic probing confirms that far more than just the sediment at the surface was involved in deformation. Generally a seismic profile passes from upper continental crust down through lower crust, across the Moho into mantle beneath (Chapter 16). There are as many as three stacked-up repetitions of

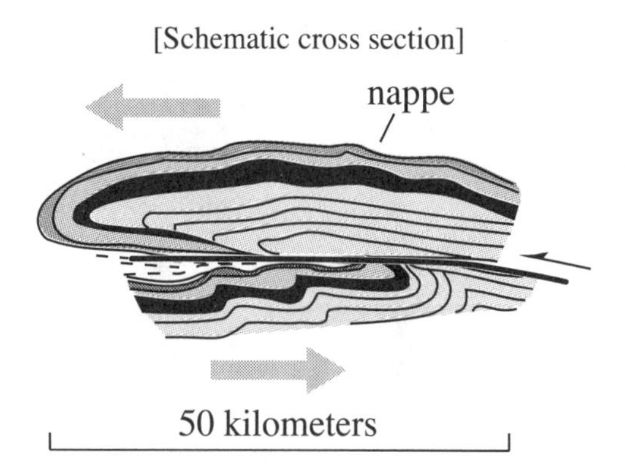

Figure 21-20. A cross section shows that flat-lying structures in compressional mountains are driven by forces acting in a horizontal direction. As deformation intensifies, a nappe may become smeared out and greatly elongated, or a nearly horizontal fault plane may break through the rocks, permitting the upper slab to continue sliding over the lower. After erosion, the only remnant may be the upside-down strata that had comprised the underside of a nappe, as at the Matterhorn.

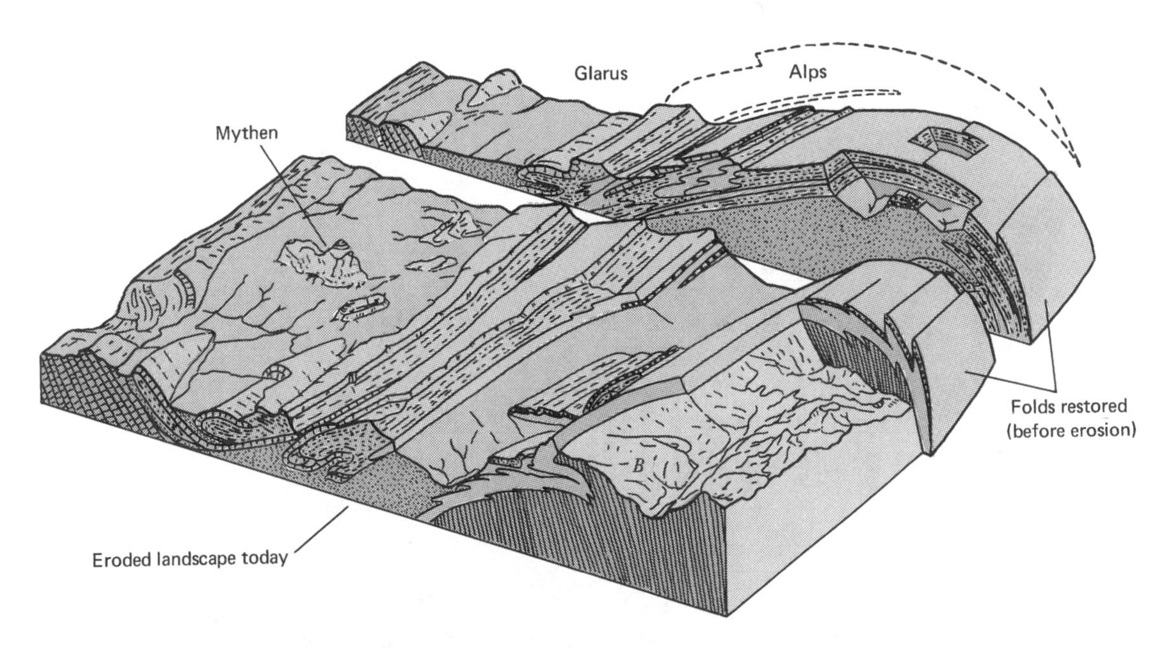

Figure 21-21. This block diagram of a region near Lucerne, Switzerland, shows ancient basement rocks draped over by folds of deformed sedimentary rocks. The Mythen are gigantic blocks of limestone carried along within an advancing nappe. Now that the enclosing rocks have been stripped away, we find Cretaceous rocks (the Mythen) resting "rootless" upon Eocene strata that are younger than Cretaceous. The offset block shows similar structures in the Glarus region of the Alps. [*After J. H. F. Umbgrove*, Symphony of the Earth, *Martinus Nijhoff, The Hague, 1950.*]

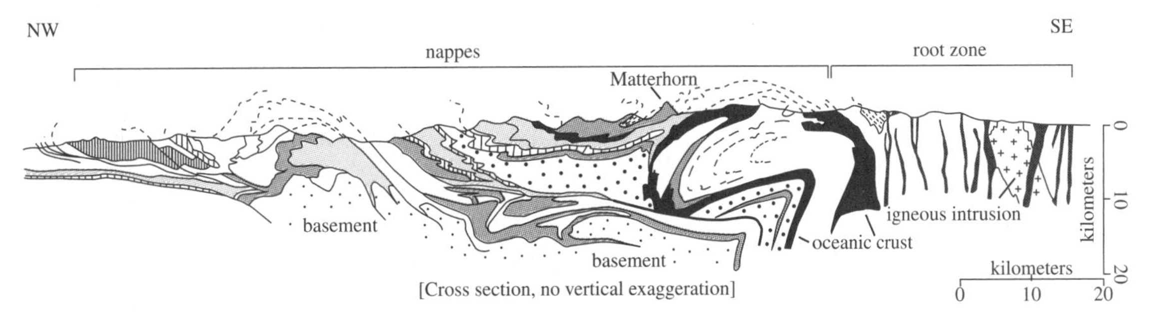

Figure 21-22. A cross section through the western Alps, displayed with no vertical exaggeration, shows basement, sedimentary cover, and ocean crust involved in a massive pile-up of nappes, some of them transported along thrust faults. Dashed lines indicate structures inferred to have existed before erosion. [*After J. Debelmas, A. Escher, and R. Trumpy, "Profiles through the Western Alps,"* Profiles of Orogenic Belts: Geodynamics Series Vol. 10, *American Geophysical Union, 1983.*]

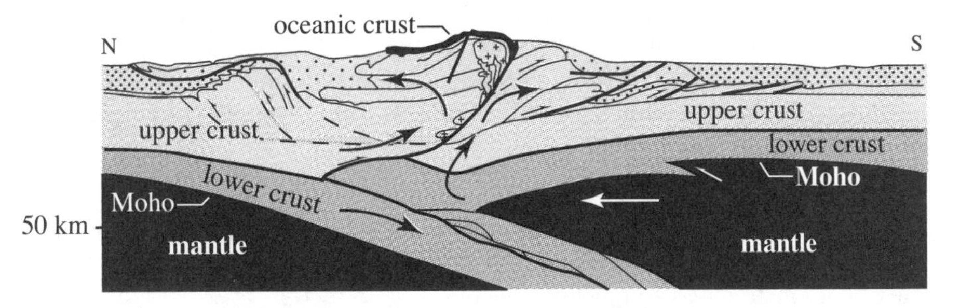

Figure 21-23. Geophysical studies show that a wedge of crust and upper mantle approaching from the south had jammed into, split apart, and crumpled the rocks lying to the north. As material comprising the uppermost few kilometers was compressed, it thickened into piles of folds (nappes) that advanced toward the north in Switzerland and toward the south in Italy. [*After A. Pfiffner, "Alpine Orogeny," in* A Continent Revealed: The European Geotraverse, *Cambridge University Press, 1992.*]

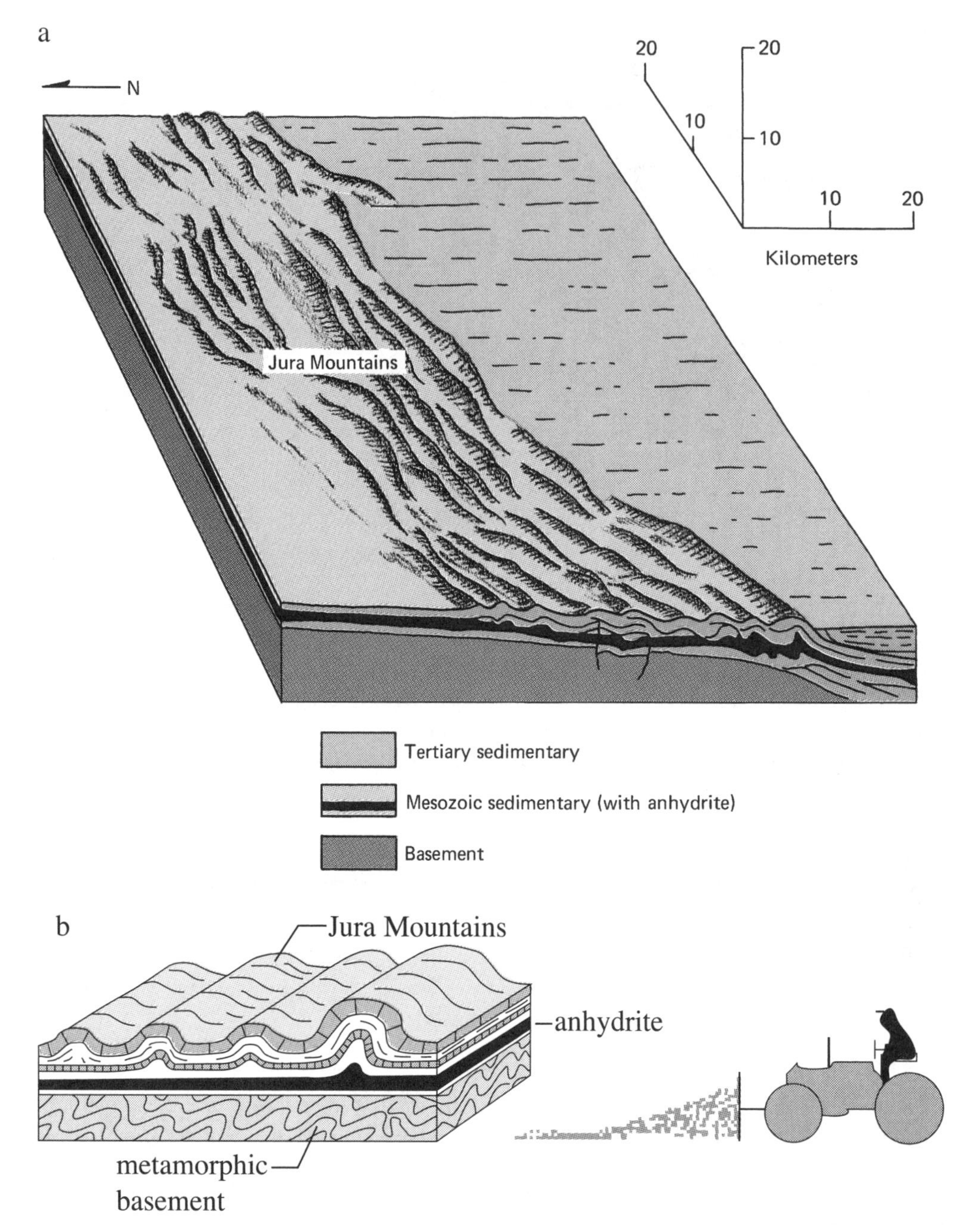

Figure 21-24. (*a*) A block diagram of northern Switzerland shows the Swiss Plain and the wrinkles of the Jura Mountains. (*b*) In the Jura Mountains the superficial sedimentary beds became detached from the basement, then slid over it. This was accomplished by a push from the side, analogous to the way a bulldozer blade heaps up snow in front of it. A similar relationship between basement and covering strata is found in the folded Appalachians—the long ridges and valleys so prominent in Pennsylvania and West Virginia. [*After J. H. F. Umbgrove,* Symphony of the Earth, *Martinus Nijhoff, The Hague, 1950.*]

this sequence under the Alps, as though the entire crust and uppermost mantle had been jammed together and interleaved by a horrendous collision (Figure 21-23). Aftermaths of the collision are felt even now, but the main phase of deformation was completed long ago.

Effects at the fringe All this pushing and shoving was certain to transmit stress through rocks lying to the north and west, in front of the Alps. In this region the Jura Mountains, namesake of the Jurassic Period, are comprised of strata folded into a bundle of parallel valleys and ridges. Significantly, these beds lie above deposits containing the soft evaporite mineral anhydrite ($CaSO_4$), which in turn lies upon metamorphic basement that is nowhere exposed. A wealth of data from tunnels and boreholes reveals the situation. As the upper strata were pushed laterally they became "unglued" and slid over the weak, slippery anhydrite substratum [Figure 21-24(*b*)]. They acted like a rug that becomes wrinkled as it is skidded across a polished floor, or like snow that becomes detached when shoved ahead of an advancing plow blade. Mechanically strong basement rocks did not participate in folding deformation.

The ridge-and-valley province of Pennsylvania and West Virginia provides another spectacular example of this type of structure. This region is part of a much longer compressional chain, the Appalachian Mountains that trend down the Atlantic seaboard of Canada and the United States. At their southern end the Appalachians are concealed beneath younger sediments, but the trend continues farther west as the Ouachita Mountains of Arkansas and Oklahoma, thence in concealment under central Texas. The Appalachian-Ouachita chain, which formed in late Paleozoic time, is similar in many ways to the Alps.

Immediately adjacent to the main Alps lies the Swiss Plain, a trough that has been filled with sandstone and conglomerate of mid-Tertiary age (Figure 21-25). These sediments were stripped off and dumped in front of the rising mountains, then partially buried beneath the advancing thrust sheets.

Today the same processes that constructed the Alps are active in other areas. Offshore of southeast Asia, sediment is just beginning to be compressed into submarine ridges and troughs. Thrust faulting is proceeding at full intensity in the Himalayas, which are in mature development. Coarse sediment like that beneath the Swiss Plain is cascading into deep basins off the coast of Venezuela. Sediment in the East China Sea is tearing loose and crumpling before the advancing Taiwan bulldozer, as happened in the Jura Mountains. These examples raise questions to be addressed by the Grand Synthesis: What is the source of energy? What determines where mountain uplift will occur? Why is compression directed chiefly in a lateral direction?

SUMMARY

Magnetic lines of force, closed loops that can have complicated shapes, symbolize the direction and strength of a magnetic field. The earth's field is essentially dipolar, having North and South Magnetic Poles toward which the lines of force converge, and where the strength of the field is greatest. One end of a compass needle is attracted toward the Magnetic North Pole, and the other end toward the South Pole. The axis of the earth's magnetic field stays near to, though not exactly coincident with, its spin axis, and the direction and strength of the field continually change; currently its strength is weakening.

A magnetic field is created by an organized motion of electrons, for example flowing as an electric current, or having an aligned direction of spinning in a permanently magnetized material. Magnetite (Fe_3O_4), hematite (Fe_2O_3), and other common minerals can act as permanent magnets, but only if they are cooler than the Curie temperature pertaining to that mineral species. Above the Curie temperature, thermal agitation disorganizes the directions of electron spin, destroying magnetism. In the core (source of 98 per cent of the earth's magnetism) and in the mantle, the temperature far exceeds the Curie temperature for any mineral, and thus most of the earth does not act as a permanent magnet. Liquid Fe-Ni alloy that comprises the outer core can conduct electricity. This property, and internal convective motion of core material, are believed to generate an (as yet) poorly understood dynamo that has an associated magnetic field.

As a basalt flow cools, it acquires remanent or "fossil" magnetism containing information about the former polarity and orientation of the earth's local magnetic field. The inclination of remanent lines

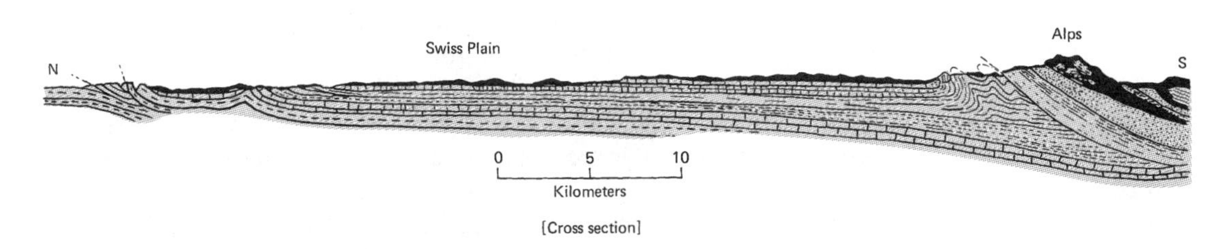

Figure 21-25. As the giant sheets comprising the main Alps advanced northward, they crumpled and overrode their own erosional debris. [*After J. H. F. Umbgrove,* Symphony of the Earth, *Martinus Nijhoff, The Hague, 1950.*]

of force is related to magnetic latitude, which in turn is a good proxy for geographic latitude. Analyses of remanent magnetism in rocks of many geologic ages indicate that the poles had wandered along pathways that may be very distant from the modern pole positions.

Moreover, the analyses indicate numerous reversals of the earth's magnetic field. The usual inconstant behavior of the magnetic field is the same during normal and reversed episodes, except that the North and South Poles have exchanged positions. A reversal occurs very rapidly, geologically speaking. Numerous potassium-argon ages of basalt are used for precise dating of magnetic reversals during the past few million years, which are shown to be intervals of randomly short or long duration.

Exploration of the 70 percent of area of the earth occupied by the world ocean has led to a revolution in geologic understanding. In the ocean, water about 5 kilometers deep is underlain by basaltic oceanic crust, whereas water in a sea is typically shallow and underlain by continental crust. A few seas are actually small ocean basins. Specially equipped research vessels make accurate measurements of water depth, and images of ocean-floor sediment resting upon igneous basement. Data from satellites assist in mapping of submarine topography, especially in remote regions. Far from land, the sedimentary blanket is less than one kilometer thick, and nowhere older than late Jurassic (150 million years), which is only 3 to 4 percent of the age of the earth.

Fringing the land masses is a seaward extension of continental crust, the shallowly submerged continental shelf. Submarine topography descends into the abyss in the adjacent continental rise, occupied beneath by the transition from continental to oceanic crust. In many areas the shelf and rise are underlain by very thick accumulations of sediment.

The ocean ridge system is a 75,000-kilometer-long, continuous topographic high that trends through all the major basins of the world ocean. Composed of basalt and gabbro (intrusive equivalent of basalt), the ridge is a locus of frequent, shallow, weak to moderate earthquakes. Ridge segments are offset laterally, the larger offsets being seismically active fracture zones. The ridge system is symmetrically centered throughout the length of the Atlantic Ocean, approximately centered but with branches in the Indian Ocean, and asymmetrically positioned far to the eastern side of the Pacific Ocean. Sporadic shallow basalt magma chambers feed a system of dikes topped by pillow basalt in a prominent, fault-bounded, medial valley at the crest of the Mid-Atlantic Ridge; below the East Pacific Rise there is a narrow but more continuous magma chamber, and no medial valley. Black smokers (submarine hot springs) are fed by sea water that was heated as it circulated through the ridge. A branch of the Mid-Indian Ridge intersects Africa, where it is manifested as the East African Rift Valleys whose profile and geology closely resemble the characteristics of their oceanic counterparts. Another intersection of the ridge system with California corresponds to the San Andreas Fault System.

Nearly all members of the ocean trench system lie around the perimeter of the Pacific Ocean where they are associated with andesite volcanoes of the Ring of Fire. Volcanic arcs typically accompany the more distant offshore trenches. Trenches are sites of frequent powerful earthquakes that are positioned upon a plane that intersects a trench floor and dips toward the nearest continent. Earthquake foci may be shallow, or as deep as nearly 700 kilometers beneath the surface.

Smaller ocean-floor topographic features include more than a million abyssal hills less than 1 kilometer high, to thousands of seamounts higher than 1 kilometer, mostly of volcanic origin. In an atoll, $CaCO_3$-secreting organisms maintain upward reef building near to sea level, while the foundational seamount subsides. The flat, reef-encrusted top of a deeply submerged guyot suggests that organisms had failed to sustain upbuilding as the seamount subsided.

Erosion is vigorously attacking mountains, and has already reduced most of the continental surface to an elevation less than 1 kilometer above sea level. Mountains may be of diverse origins and sizes, but in the earth's two truly great mountain belts—the Pacific Ring of Fire and the Alpine-Himalayan system across southern Europe and Asia—they are of compressional origin.

During construction of the well-studied Alps, a region initially under tension, experiencing subsidence and deposition of sediment, later became involved in compression that deformed the sediment, underlying basement, and some ocean crust into huge recumbent folds (nappes). Stacked-up nappes were ruptured by thrust faults, and further transported laterally. Images created by geophysical techniques show that the entire crust and uppermost mantle participated in crumpling and thickening, with the result that lateral transport of material far exceeded the extent of vertical uplift. Ahead of the Alpine bulldozer, the sedimentary cover broke loose from its basement and wrinkled into the ridge-and-valley Jura Mountains. Coarse sediment, eroded off the rising Alps, was deposited immediately in front, then partially overridden by thrust sheets. All of these processes are currently in progress in other parts of the world.

Plate Tectonics: The Grand Synthesis

In southern California, the spectacular San Andreas Fault marks the boundary between two moving tectonic plates. [*U. S. Geological Survey photograph by Robert Wallace*]

The essence of doing science is to gain a deep understanding of the workings of nature. Geologists are not content simply to accumulate data, but rather to assemble all those innumerable geologic facts into a satisfying larger picture. We now proceed to a Grand Synthesis called *plate tectonics*, an explanation of the mutual relationships of all the major features of the earth, from its surface to its core. A deep understanding indeed!

CONTINENTAL DRIFT

A favorite metaphor to symbolize our notion of stability is "terra firma"—solid earth, something we can count on to endure forever. Geologists had long worked under this assumption, but bits of puzzling evidence began to appear suggesting that the continents may not be fixed immutably in place. To imagine continents as drifting is counter-intuitive, and initially the idea was widely disbelieved. The geologists were facing the same predicament that makes science so difficult for many other people. They were confronting evidence pointing to the un-thinkable, something contrary to our intuitive notions of what is possible or not possible. It took much debate, and discovery of more confirming evidence such as that described below, and especially the development of plate tectonic theory to explain how continental drift can occur, for the community of researchers to accept what had been formerly regarded as nonsense.

Some Puzzling Data

Sizes and shapes of landmasses Intriguing information had already appeared by the early 1500s when the Atlantic coastlines were mapped. The jutting corner of South America seems to fit so nicely into the opposite "bite" taken out of Africa. Could the Old and New Worlds formerly have existed as a united landmass, a supercontinent, later to be rifted apart and drifted into their current positions? If so, the Atlantic would be new ocean filling the gap between the receding landmasses. Alfred Wegner, an early 20th Century German meteorologist and ardent proponent of continental drift, pointed out that the mutual fit is improved by matching, not coastlines, but edges of the continental shelf, which marks the true limit of continental crust. In an updated map of the proposed supercontinent (Figure 22-1), we see a poor correspondence of the coastline of Argentina against that of South Africa, whereas the broad submarine shelf fills the gap well between these countries. Near the Equator is a region where Africa would overlap South America if the two continents were to be restored. In fact, this possible discrepancy is not a problem; the overlap is the delta of the Niger River, new African land built out into the Atlantic after the continents had parted. Fit of continental shelves along the North Atlantic is also excellent after a bit of tweaking, for example if Iberia (Spain and Portugal) had formerly been rotated clockwise up against France. The fit of shapes and sizes of continents, like the fit of irregular pieces of a jigsaw puzzle, is powerful if not compelling evidence for continental drift.

Distribution of fossils Also recognized by the early 20th Century was the fact that fossils of the same extinct species may be distributed in continents that are very remote from one another today. To qualify as evidence, the organism must have been landlocked, not able to swim, fly, or drift across an ocean. Broad dispersal of fossil sharks, migratory birds, or seeds and spores might be consistent with the hypothesis, but explained just as easily without appeal to continental drift. A celebrated example of such fossil evidence is the genus *Lystrosaurus*, an extinct reptile found in early Triassic strata (approximately 200 million years old) from South Africa across Asia to China. It was thus a gratifying surprise to discover fossils in Antarctica, not only of *Lystrosaurus* but also of many other animals that are associated with it elsewhere. Species of *Lystrosaurus* lived exclusively on land, a typical animal being built rather like a hippopotamus with nostrils positioned high on the skull (Figure 22-2). We can picture this creature lazily half-submerged in a river waiting for prey to come by. There is no way that an animal adapted to life in a floodplain could have swum across the stormy waters that now intervene between South Africa and Antarctica. *Lystrosaurus* must have roamed freely about upon a continuous land surface that was later disrupted.

Numerous other examples of fossil distributions are helpful to reconstruct ancient geography. Deserts, extensive bodies of water, or mountain ranges are barriers to the migration of land-living organisms, just as any landmass is a blockade to movement of marine organisms. A habitat may be confined against the barrier or, if a barrier is erected in the midst of a habitat, the living population is broken into isolated sub-populations that continue to evolve in different directions. Later these populations may be reunited. For example, South and North America are narrowly connected by the Isthmus of

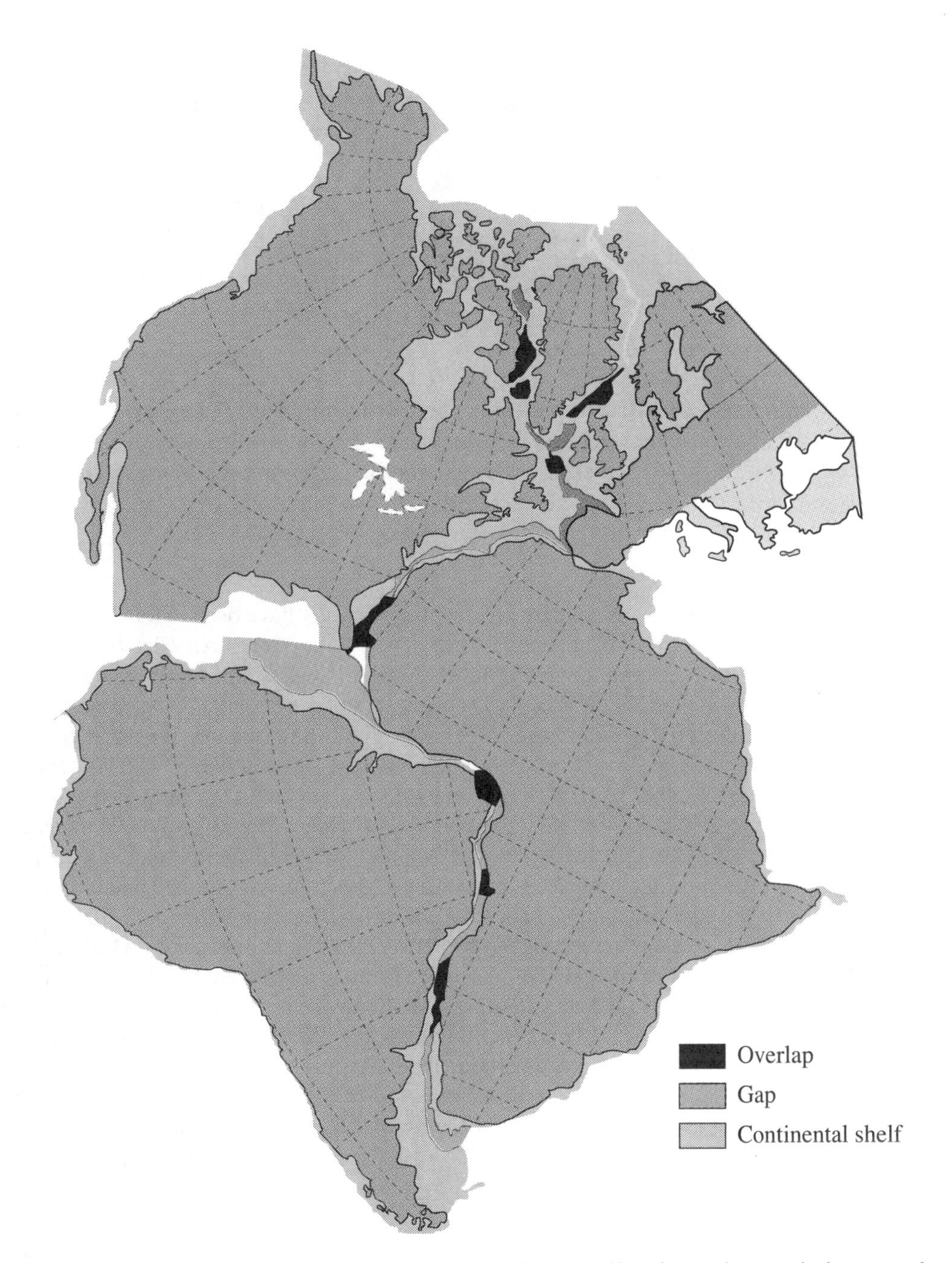

Figure 22-1. If the 1000-meter-deep water contour, not the shoreline, is used to mark the true edge of continental crust, the shapes and sizes of the Old and New Worlds would fit together quite well. A major apparent discrepancy, where Africa would in principle overlap South America, is not a problem because the Niger River built its delta off the coast of Africa *after* the continents had separated. Small bits and pieces of continental crust must have occupied the geologically complex region of today's Mexico, Central America, and the Gulf of Mexico and Caribbean Sea. Information is still too scanty to justify reconstruction of landmasses in this blank spot on the map. Locations of the Great Lakes, Canadian Arctic islands, etc. are only for reference, not to imply that these were geographic features 200 million years ago. [*After E. C. Bullard and others, "The Fit of the Continents around the Atlantic," in* A Symposium on Continental Drift, *Philosophical Transactions of the Royal Society, Vol. 258A, London, 1965.*]

Figure 22-2. Distributions of fossils of long-extinct organisms, of which *Lystrosaurus*, an early Mesozoic reptile, is a spectacular example, can be explained only by invoking continental drift. [*After* The Age of Reptiles *by Edwin H. Colbert, by permission of W. W. Norton & Company, Inc. Copyright © by Edwin H. Colbert.*]

Panama. Beginning in the Mesozoic Era, these continents apparently have been in touch and out of touch several times. A unique assemblage of marsupials had developed in South America during a period of isolation. Following the most recent rejoining, about 3 million years ago, North American placental mammals invaded South America where they wiped out most of the marsupials. Only one hardy marsupial, the opossum, was able to extend its range from native South America into the north.

Isotopic age patterns furnish yet another line of evidence for continental drift. If continents are like pieces of a jigsaw puzzle, the age patterns are analogous to the picture printed on its surface. Both the pieces and the picture should reassemble into a continuous whole. Deeply eroded Precambrian basement rocks in western Africa are matched across the Atlantic with equivalent rocks in Brazil. Isotopic ages refer to times of mountain-building accompanied by regional metamorphism and emplacement of igneous bodies. When the continents are viewed in a pre-drift restoration (Figure 22-3), we see a zone of 0.55 to 0.7 billion year ages cutting across the corner of Brazil, continuing into Africa. Adjacent on either side of this belt, much more ancient ages that exceed 2 billion years are preserved in the basement rocks on both continents. Not only the age pattern but rock types and even individual structures continue seamlessly across from one continent to the other. For example, the Pernambuco Shear Zone in Brazil connects to the Adamaoua Shear Zone in Cameroon, a west African nation.

Similarly, Europe and North America were once joined together. The Appalachian Mountains trend up the eastern seaboard of North America, heading out to sea off the coast of Newfoundland. A continuation known as the Caledonian Mountains resumes in the British Isles, passing through

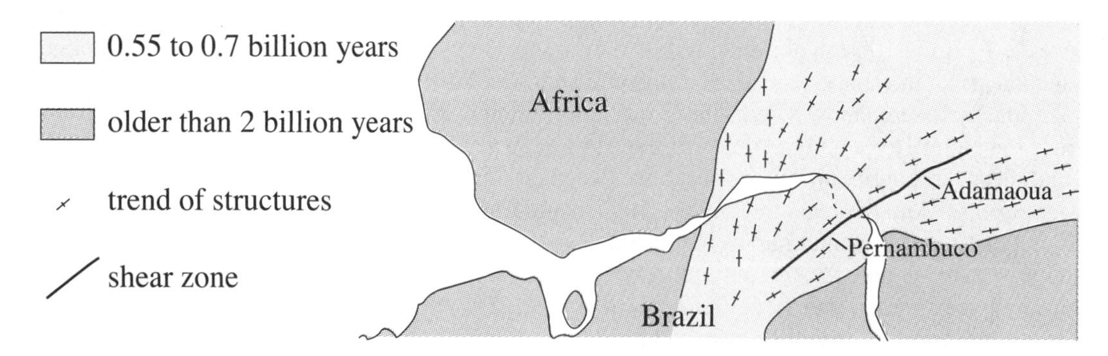

Figure 22-3. Isotopic ages of basement rock correspond to ancient mountain-building events accompanied by igneous intrusion and regional metamorphism. In this part of Africa and South America, the uplift of a mountain belt from 0.7 to 0.55 billion years ago affected rocks that had already existed for more than a billion years. Since that time, all of these mountains have been deeply eroded, forming a Precambrian shield (Chapter 11).

Scandinavia on the east and Greenland on the west, and on to Spitzbergen in the Arctic Ocean (Figure 22-4). In this mountain system too we find a correspondence of rock types, fossils, ages, and structures.

Apparent polar wandering paths provide information about the timing and directions of continental drift. Recall that, on average, the earth's magnetic and rotational poles occupy the same position (Chapter 21). Moreover, the direction of remanent magnetism in a rock indicates where the magnetic (and thus rotational) poles were located when the rock formed. Later events of heating, deformation, or chemical change may have overprinted the magnetic record, and so each sample must pass stringent tests that it has retained its original magnetic signature. Suppose that we analyze remanent magnetism in many rock samples from northwestern Europe, whose ages range from 0.45 billion years up to the present day [Figure 22-5(*a*)]. During that time interval the pole appears to have approached its current position, wandering along a curved pathway starting in the Southern Hemisphere. Was it the pole that had wandered [Figure 22-5(*a*)], or had the landmass drifted with respect to a fixed pole [Figure 22-5(*b*)], or perhaps had both moved? Because only the relative positions of pole and landmass can be measured, any one of these possibilities explains the paleomagnetic data equally well.

Next, let's compare apparent polar wandering pathways for rocks in both Europe and North America for the interval 0.4 to 0.16 billion years ago (just before breakup of the supercontinent). The pathway for North America has a similar shape but it is offset to the west of the European pathway [Figure 22-6(*a*). Imagine Europe sliding westward to be joined with North America, closing the Atlantic Ocean and reuniting the Appalachian and Caledonian mountain chains. Europe's polar wandering curve would also glide westward to coincide with the curve for North America [Figure 22-6(*b*)]. Regardless of whether or not the pole had moved, Europe and North America must have drifted apart.

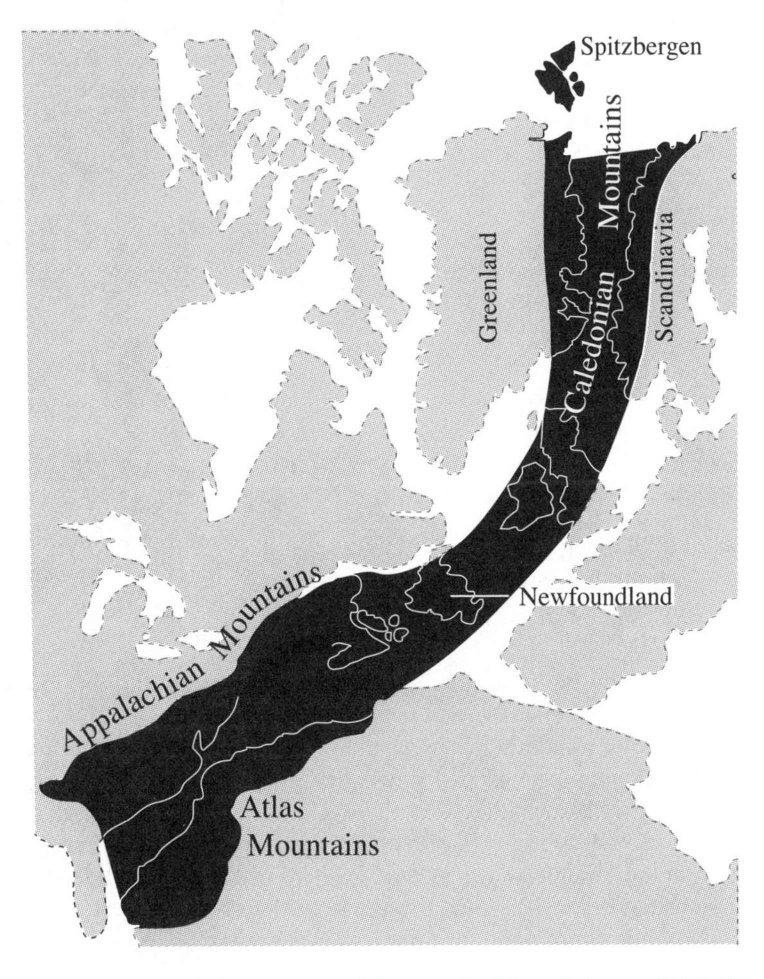

Figure 22-4. Today, deeply eroded remnants of the Appalachian, Atlas, and Caledonian Mountains trend along the margins of the North Atlantic, but they were once united into a single early Paleozoic mountain system. Dashed lines serve only as familiar modern landmarks, not as the actual distribution of land and sea 400 million years ago.

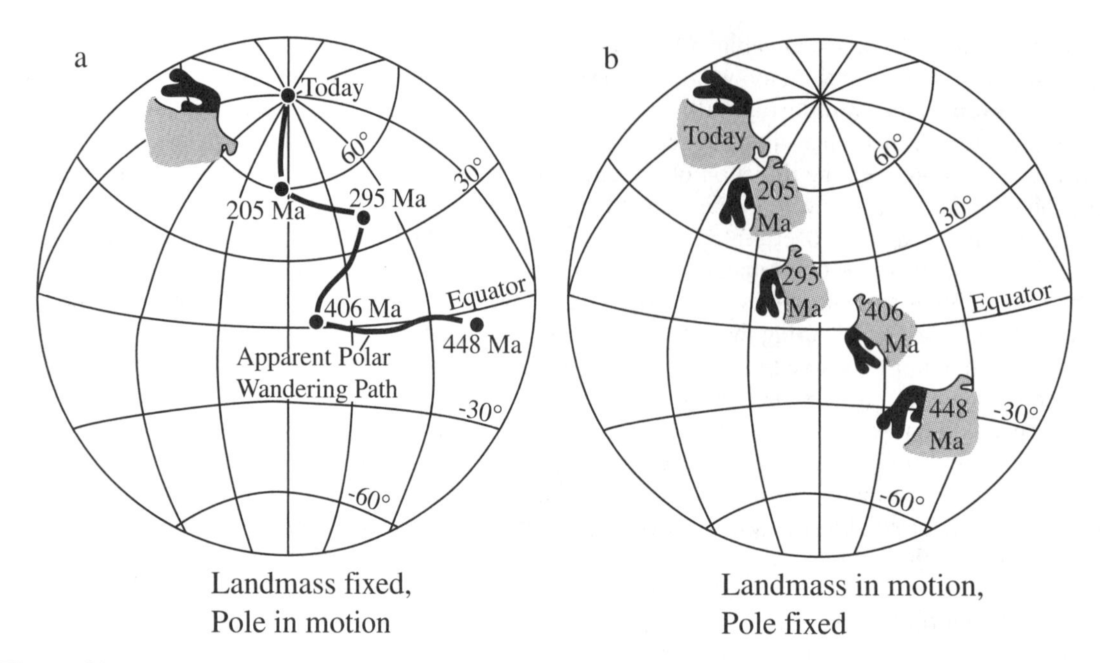

Figure 22-5. (a) In this scenario, northwestern Europe (Norway, Sweden, and Finland colored black for reference) remains fixed. From the viewpoint of the landmass, the magnetic pole appeared to have wandered throughout Phanerozoic time (Ma = million years ago). (b) Alternatively, the pole could have remained fixed while the landmass drifted across the face of the globe. Interpretations (a) and (b) explain the paleomagnetic data equally well. [*After R. Van der Voo,* Paleomagnetism of the Atlantic, Tethys and Iapetus Oceans, *Cambridge University Press, 1993.*]

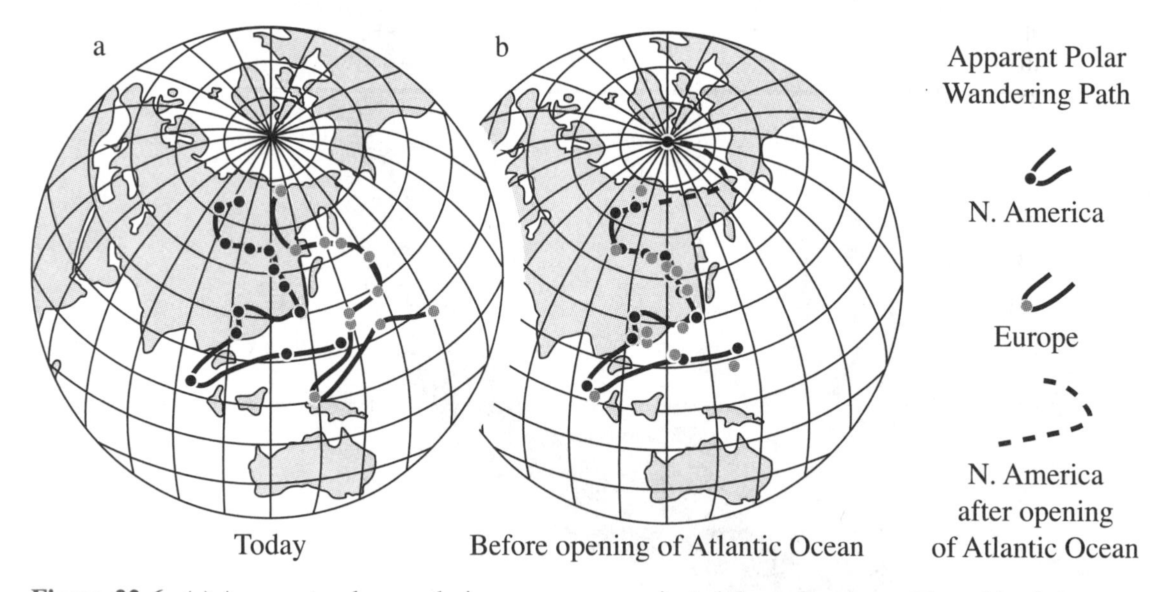

Figure 22-6. (a) Apparent polar wandering curves are projected through pole positions (dots) that pertain to selected points in geologic time. The pathways for Europe and North America are systematically offset, implying that regardless whether the pole or a landmass or both had moved, at least North America (and its magnetic record) must have drifted westward with respect to Europe, opening the Atlantic Ocean. (b) Before the Atlantic Ocean existed, the two pathways coincided because formerly both landmasses had moved as one unit, locked together in a supercontinent. [*After R. Van der Voo,* Paleomagnetism of the Atlantic, Tethys and Iapetus Oceans, *Cambridge University Press, 1993.*]

Polar wandering paths reveal that during the latter part of the Paleozoic Era, all of the continents were united into a great supercontinent known as Pangea (literally "all the earth"). A world ocean, of which the modern Pacific Ocean is a shrunken remnant, enveloped the rest of the globe. More accurately, two supercontinents had joined together to comprise Pangea. A northern landmass named "Laurasia" (from Eurasia + the Laurentian Highlands of Canada) had previously assembled consisting of North America, Greenland, Europe, and Siberia. To the south, "Gondwana" (after the Gonds, an ancient tribe of India) included Antarctica, South America, Africa, Madagascar, Australasia, and the subcontinent of India which now lies in the Northern Hemisphere. Rifting of Pangea commenced in the Mesozoic Era, and drifting has continued to this day.

What causes continents to drift? Those who wrestled with the concept speculated that the moon had separated from out of the body of the earth, or that there was a meteorite impact, or that the earth is shrinking, or expanding, or that the earth's rotation provides the energy. A popular analogy was the continental "ship" plowing through the mantle "sea." Supposedly the mantle resisted the forward motion of the continent, causing it to wrinkle into mountains at the leading edge. Serious objections attended all of these proposals, leading to bewilderment and skepticism. Some geologists concluded that, because we did not know how to explain continental drift, it therefore did not occur! Yet there are at least thirty other types of independent evidence for drift in addition to the four discussed above. What was lacking was a theory adequate to make sense of the data. Having a scientific theory is like voyaging on a secure ship, and as Thomas Kuhn (Chapter 21) pointed out, even when we know our ship is sinking, we will not abandon it unless a rescue vessel is passing by. In the midst of this dilemma one of the pioneering geophysicists, Bruce Heezen, exclaimed "We can't explain anything. We can't analyze our data; we can't write our papers because we can't decide whether the basins of the oceans are formed by drift or whether they are permanent, and if you can't decide that, you can't do anything." On a personal note, I recall a seminar when I was a graduate student (long ago) in which Prof. Walter Bucher stated that he "had heard about the mid-Atlantic ridge but had no idea why it is there or what it is doing." Given the then-current state of knowledge, the eminent Prof. Bucher did not understand one of the key elements of plate tectonics.

PLATE TECTONICS

So what about this unifying theory that was to appear in the late 1960s? Plate tectonic theory has become so well supported by evidence that it is now the ruling paradigm. Let's begin with a world map of more than 200 thousand earthquake epicenters recorded since 1963 (Figure 22-7), each epicenter located using the timings of P-, S-, and L-wave arrivals as explained in Chapter 16. Earthquakes may occur anywhere,

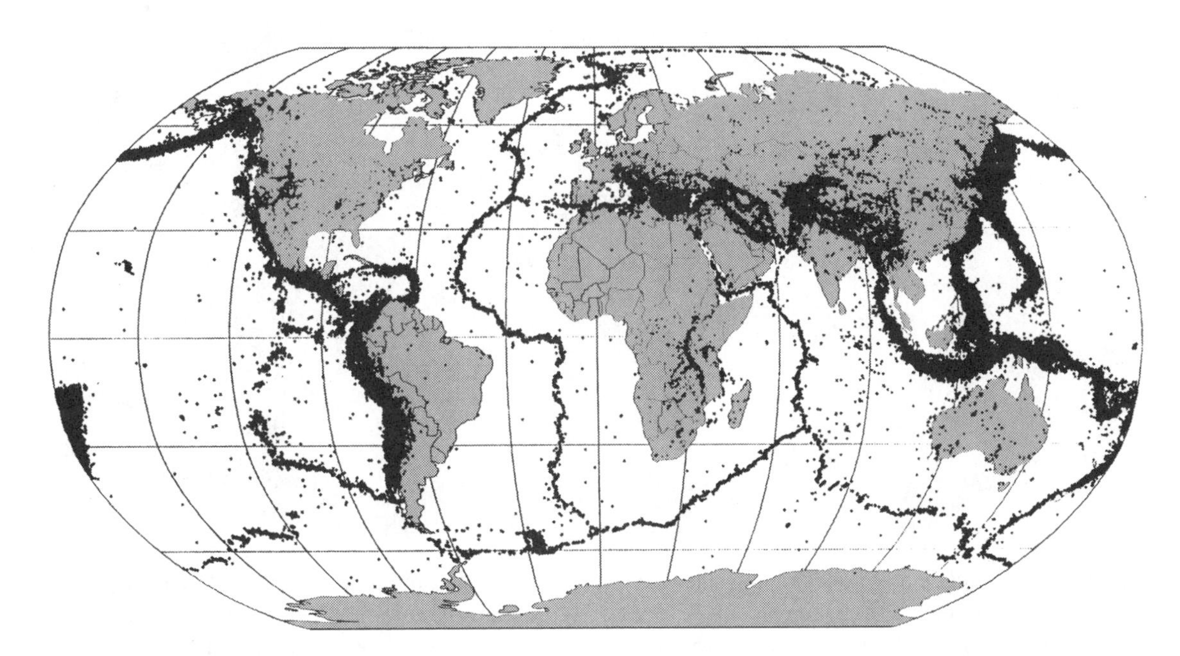

Figure 22-7. More than 200 thousand epicenters of earthquakes are situated mostly in narrow zones that coincide with the ocean ridge system, the ocean trench system, and the earth's major mountain belts. [*After J. Yates and others, "A digital tectonic and volcanic activity map,"* Geological Society of America Abstracts with Programs, *vol. 30, no. 7, 1998.*]

but by far most of them are located in three distinct zones with which we are already familiar. A sprinkling of shallow, modest earthquakes is confined very precisely to the crest of the worldwide mid-ocean ridge system. Abundant, often powerful earthquakes are associated with the ocean trench system, chiefly around the perimeter of the Pacific. These earthquakes appear to be scattered more broadly, but that is partly an artifact of their display on a two-dimensional map. In the third (vertical) dimension the earthquake foci are distributed upon dipping planes, an epicenter being the projection from a focal point up to the earth's surface. Another rather diffuse zone of earthquake epicenters coincides with the system of compressional mountains that runs from southern Europe through southeast Asia. Also common in these zones are volcanoes, yet another manifestation of the earth's internal energy. Earthquakes and volcanism tell us "where the action is."

We postulate that belts of earthquake epicenters outline the margins of half a dozen large *plates*, a similar number of much smaller plates, and a dozen or so "microplates" (Figure 22-8). The plates are curved, conforming to the earth's spherical shape much as curved plates fit together in the shell of a turtle. Moreover the plates are in motion in diverse horizontal directions, vigorously interacting along their edges, whereas their interiors tend to be stable and inert as indicated by a general absence of earthquakes and volcanism in these places. (However, note how diffuse some of the earthquake belts are [Figure 22-7]. A completely rigid plate is only an idealization, and in fact about 15% of the area of the plates is experiencing internal deformation.) Thus, "plate" is the noun and "tectonics" refers to these interactions. An imperfect analogy would be pieces of floating pack ice colliding and separating as they are wafted by water currents. Continents are embedded in the plates, drifting passively.

Note that plate margins do not necessarily coincide with the familiar continents and oceans that were mapped centuries ago. Plate boundaries are more subtle; they could not be mapped until 20th-Century technology made it possible to locate earthquake epicenters precisely. Within the North and South American plates are included those two continents and the western half of the Atlantic Ocean. The African plate contains a continent, and Mediterranean Sea and parts of the Atlantic and Indian Oceans. The Australian plate encompasses Australia, some of the Indian and Pacific Oceans, and India but not the remainder of Asia. The Pacific plate, largest of them all, is entirely oceanic except for the sliver of Baja California and the western portion of the State of California that are continental. Plate boundaries slice through oceans and continents indiscriminately, as though they make no difference. Therefore, plates

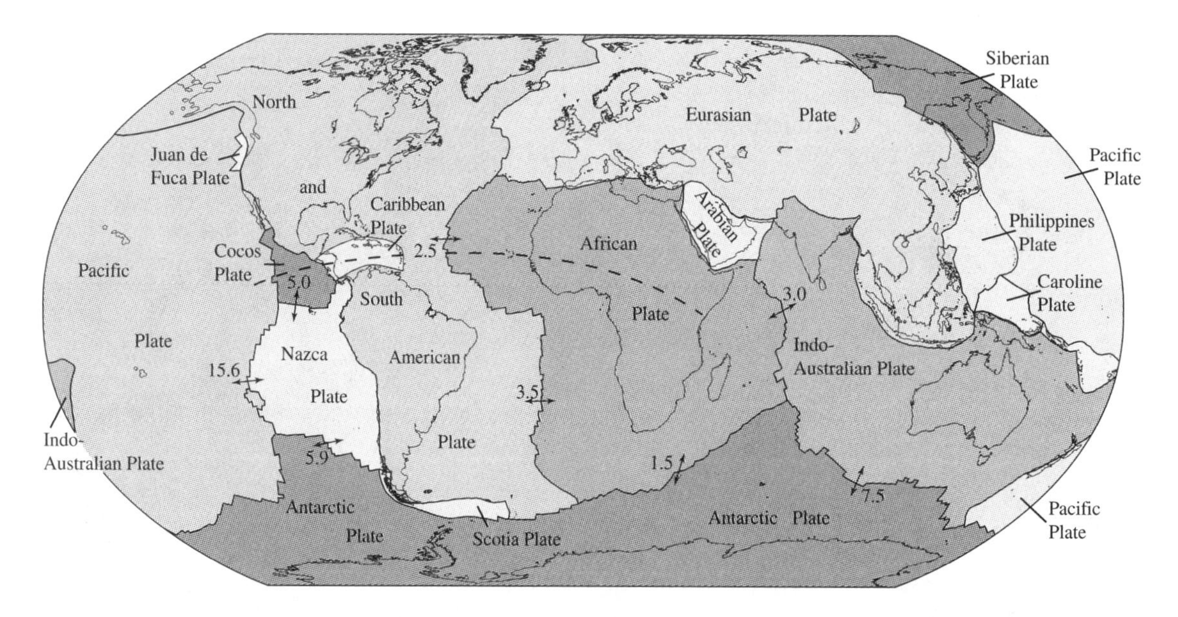

Figure 22-8. Especially in oceanic regions, the boundaries of tectonic plates correspond to belts of densely concentrated earthquake epicenters seen in Figure 22-7. Geologic mapping assists in identifying plate margins in regions of compressional mountains where earthquake epicenters are spread more diffusely. Labeled arrows indicate rates (cm/yr) and directions of seafloor spreading. Dashed line: position of the cross section through the mantle shown in Figure 22-23. [*After J. Yates and others, "A digital tectonic and volcanic activity map,"* Geological Society of America Abstracts with Programs, *vol. 30, no. 7, 1998.*]

must be thicker than either continental or oceanic crust, incorporating whatever type of crust and at least some of the mantle.

What forms the top, bottom, and sides of a plate? The top surface is either land being eroded or a body of water receiving the deposition of sediment. As for the bottom, recall that with increasing depth in the earth, increasing temperature would promote melting but increasing pressure inhibits melting (Figures 16-21 and 16-22). In a region of the upper mantle where these competing influences are in balance, the rock is softened, even a trifle melted locally. This zone, the *asthenosphere* (from the Greek "asthenes": mechanically weak), provides a sort of lubricating layer upon which the overlying plates can move. The asthenosphere is identified as the seismic low-velocity zone, traversed by dramatically slowed-down P and S waves. Above it lie the plates comprised of either continental or oceanic crust, the Moho, and the uppermost mantle, also known collectively as *lithosphere* (from the Greek "lithos": stone, implying a substance that is mechanically strong and rigid). Depth to the asthenosphere varies from more than 300 kilometers beneath the most ancient Precambrian shields, to virtually zero at the crest of a mid-ocean ridge (Figure 22-9). In fact, oceanic asthenosphere may transform into lithosphere simply by cooling.

Logic permits three possible types of interaction at the margins of plates (Figure 22-10). (i) Zones where adjacent plates are *pulling apart* from one another are identified with the mid-ocean ridge system, or with rifted regions within continents. We shall see that new oceanic *crust is created* at this type of plate boundary. (ii) In zones where plates are *colliding*, the style of interaction depends upon which type of crust is involved. In case (ii*a*), if one or both colliding plates contain relatively thin and dense oceanic crust, an oceanic plate bends downward and descends beneath the opposing plate in a process of *subduction* (from the Latin "to lead under"). Subduction occurs in the ocean trench system, where *crust is consumed* in the sense that it disappears deep into the earth. Alternatively, in case (ii*b*), both colliding plates could contain thick continental crust which because of its low density would resist being dragged or pushed down into more dense mantle. This encounter results in a spectacular system of compressional mountains such as the Himalayas in which the crust is crumpled and thickened, but not subducted.

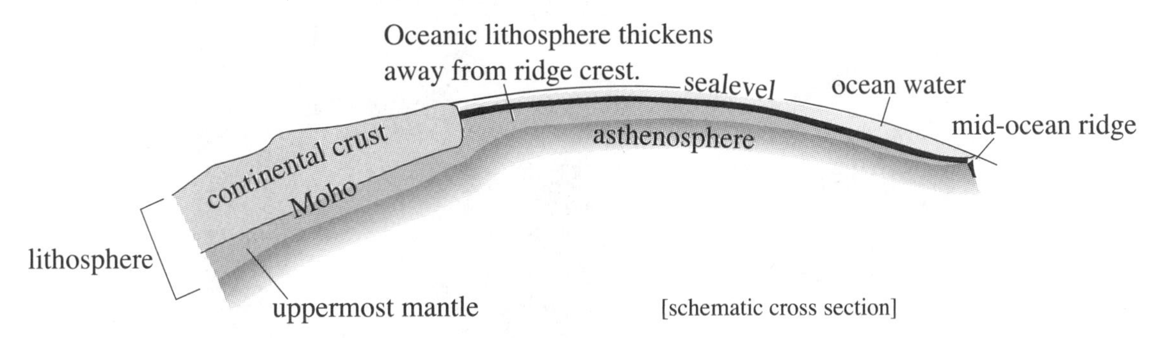

Figure 22-9. Lithosphere, which includes both crust and the uppermost mantle, is thicker beneath continents than beneath oceans.

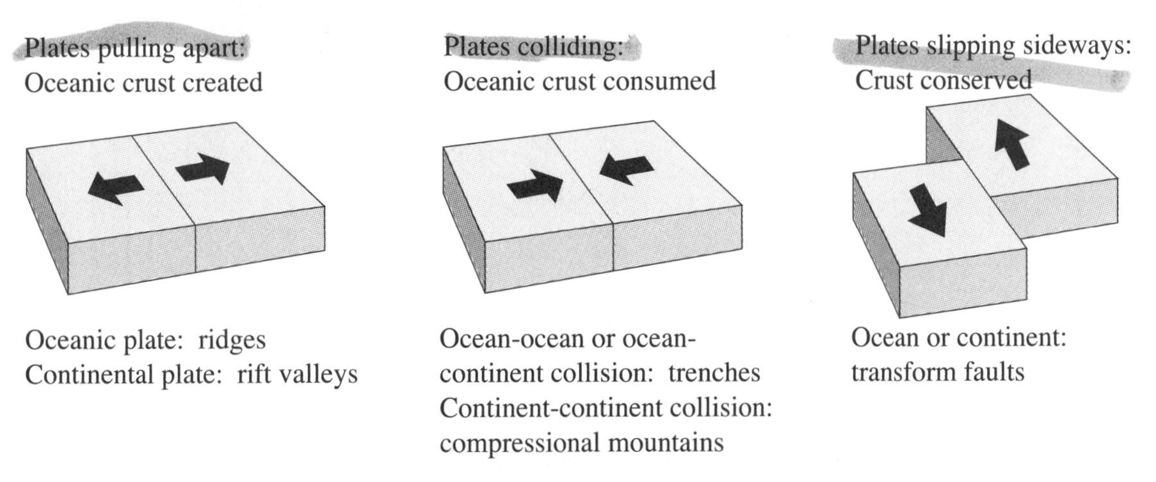

Figure 22-10. Three Logical Types of Interaction Between Adjacent Tectonic Plates.

(iii) Where plates are *slipping sideways* past one another, *crust is conserved*, being neither created nor consumed. This style of interaction occurs in fracture zones that connect the offset segments of mid-ocean ridge, some fracture zones actually crossing part of a continent as in the San Andreas Fault System of California. Let's examine these three kinds of plate interaction in more detail.

Plates Pulling Apart

A passing astronaut captured a magnificent photograph of the Arabian Peninsula and neighboring Africa (Figure 22-11), which serves as our starting point. Suppose that a supercontinent is lying over a zone of mantle rock that becomes abnormally hot. The latter will expand, bulging up the continental crust into a broad arch while stretching and thinning it. Eventually the crest of the uplift breaks apart into a rift valley bounded by normal faults. Volcanoes deliver mantle magma up through the fault conduits while the valley begins to fill with sediment eroded off its walls. Ever since originating in this manner about 25 million years ago, the East African Rift Valleys (Chapter 21) have sputtered along with insufficient energy to bring them into a more advanced stage of development. Meanwhile, farther north the supercontinent had split apart in three directions, like an ugly wound in a person's flesh. Deep rupturing along two of the branches permitted the Arabian Peninsula to break away from mainland Africa to which it was formerly attached. New seaways, the Gulf of Aden and the Red Sea, filled in behind the receding Arabian plate (Figure 22-11). The third branch, the system of East African Rift Valleys, is called a *failed arm*

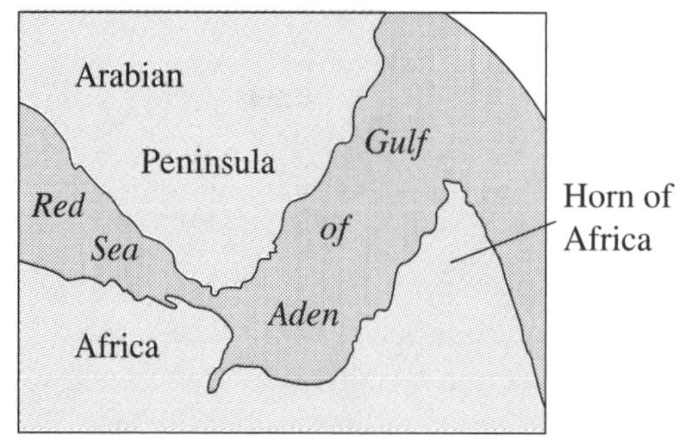

Figure 22-11. This photograph was taken from an orbiting spacecraft. A sketch map locates prominent geographic features.

because it never became a seaway (Figure 22-12). It is common for a supercontinent to break up initially along one "failed" and two "successful" arms. Failure may ultimately become success as the East African Rift System continues to propagate southward, possibly one day to sever the whole of east Africa away from the remainder of the continent.

Seafloor spreading To view more of the spreading process, let's visit the mid-Atlantic ridge, which is in a mature stage of development. Hot asthenosphere is ascending just beneath the crest, and as pressure is reduced at shallow depth the material is able to expand. This permits some of it to melt, forming little pods of basalt magma. Once the magma has collected into a connected network, it suddenly drains upward, opening and invading a fracture where it freezes as a dike as described in the preceding chapter (Figure 21-13). Some of the liquid may ooze out as pillow lava onto the ocean floor. In order to accommodate a new dike, the countless preexisting dikes move laterally to either side. New oceanic crust is created in this manner, while *seafloor spreading* carries the older crust away from the crest of the ridge. Throughout the mid-ocean ridge system, a "scab" of crust continually solidifies onto the trailing edges of plates along a pull-apart boundary that has been called "the wound that never heals."

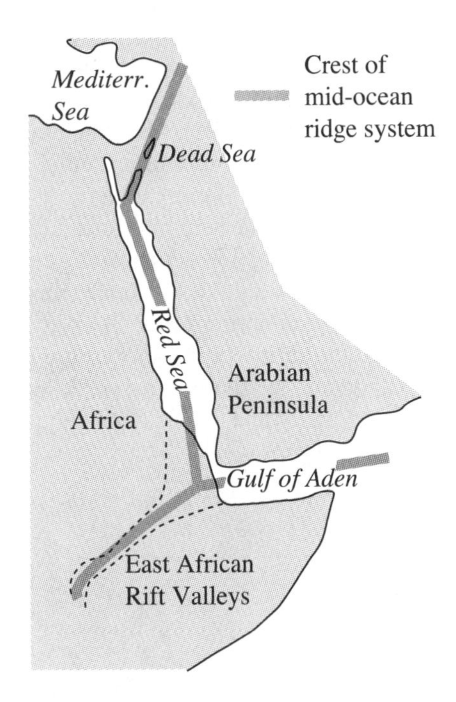

Figure 22-12. The Red Sea and Gulf of Aden are two "successful" pull-apart arms of the rift system. The East African Rift Valleys comprise a "failed" arm that is manifested as valleys containing volcanic edifices, bordered by spectacular fault escarpments.

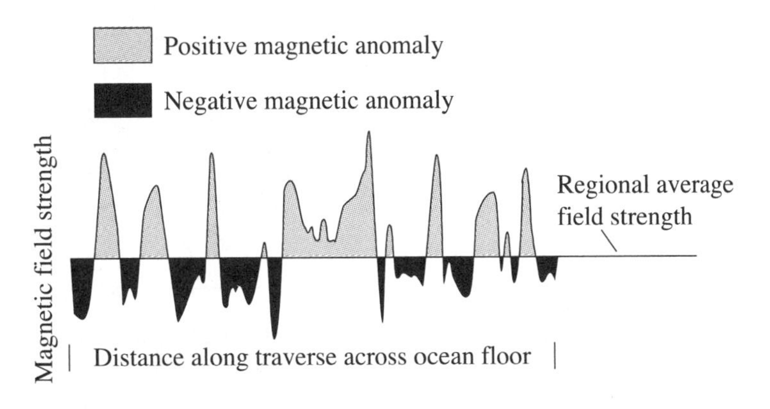

Figure 22-13. Measurements of the strength of the earth's magnetic field along a traverse perpendicular to the mid-ocean ridge show alternating highs (positive magnetic anomalies) and lows (negative anomalies).

How rapid is seafloor spreading? An early study that was centered upon the Mid-Atlantic Ridge near Iceland illustrates how to answer this question. Geophysicists already knew that the strength of the earth's magnetic field varies from point to point across the ocean floor, and they had suspected a relationship between the magnetic pattern and mid-ocean ridges. Researchers from Columbia University arranged for a specially equipped plane to fly more than 50 tracks back and forth perpendicular to the ridge, measuring only the strength (not the direction) of the magnetic field along these traverses. The record for a typical traverse (Figure 22-13) is a line that wiggles above and below the horizontal line which corresponds to the regional average field strength. A high point on the wiggly line represents a *positive* magnetic anomaly where earth magnetism is abnormally strong; conversely, a low point indicates a *negative* magnetic anomaly, an abnormally weak magnetic field.

An amazing pattern unfolded when the data were assembled (Figure 22-14). Records for the traverses are aligned, positive wiggle for positive, and negative for negative. Figure 22-15 depicts the information as a series of stripes, coded in shades of color for regions of positive magnetic anomaly and unshaded for negative anomalies. Stripes are of various widths, reminiscent of a sequence of broad and narrow tree rings. Moreover the pattern is parallel to the trend of the ridge, and symmetrical in either direction away from its crest.

The following interpretation of the striped pattern is perhaps the most innovative idea in all of the Grand Synthesis. While injections of basalt magma are perpetually healing the ridge's "open wound," the earth's magnetic field occasionally reverses (Chapter 21). As a batch of magma crystallizes and the rock cools below the Curie temperature of a magnetic mineral (for example, magnetite), the rock acquires permanent magnetism. Suppose that cooling occurred during an episode of normal magnetic polarity, the present day being such a time. In this instance, permanent magnetism in the basalt is oriented in the same direction as the field being produced by dynamo action in the earth's core. Magnetic fields originating in the core and in oceanic basalt add together, resulting in a stronger magnetic field—a positive anomaly. Conversely, magnetism in basalt that had cooled during a time of magnetic reversal is oriented in a direction opposite to magnetism coming from the earth's core today. These two magnetic fields partially cancel one another, creating a negative anomaly, an abnormally weak magnetic field. Thus the stripes in Figure 22-15 correspond to alternately normally and reversely magnetized oceanic crust.

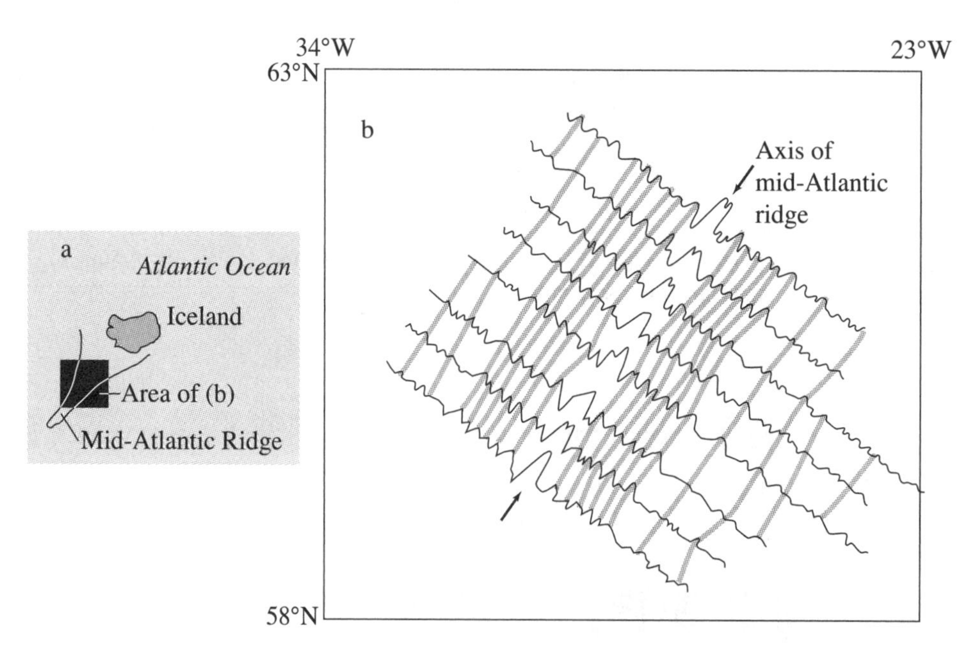

Figure 22-14. (*a*) Numerous traverses back and forth across the Mid-Atlantic Ridge were made in order to measure magnetic field intensities in the area of the black square. (*b*) Correlated profiles indicate that whatever is responsible for the magnetic anomalies is arranged in strips parallel to the ridge crest. [*After M. Talwani and others, "East Pacific Rise: The Magnetic Pattern and the Fracture Zones,"* Science, *vol. 150, no. 3700, pp. 1109–1115, 1965. Copyright 1965 by the American Association for the Advancement of Science.*]

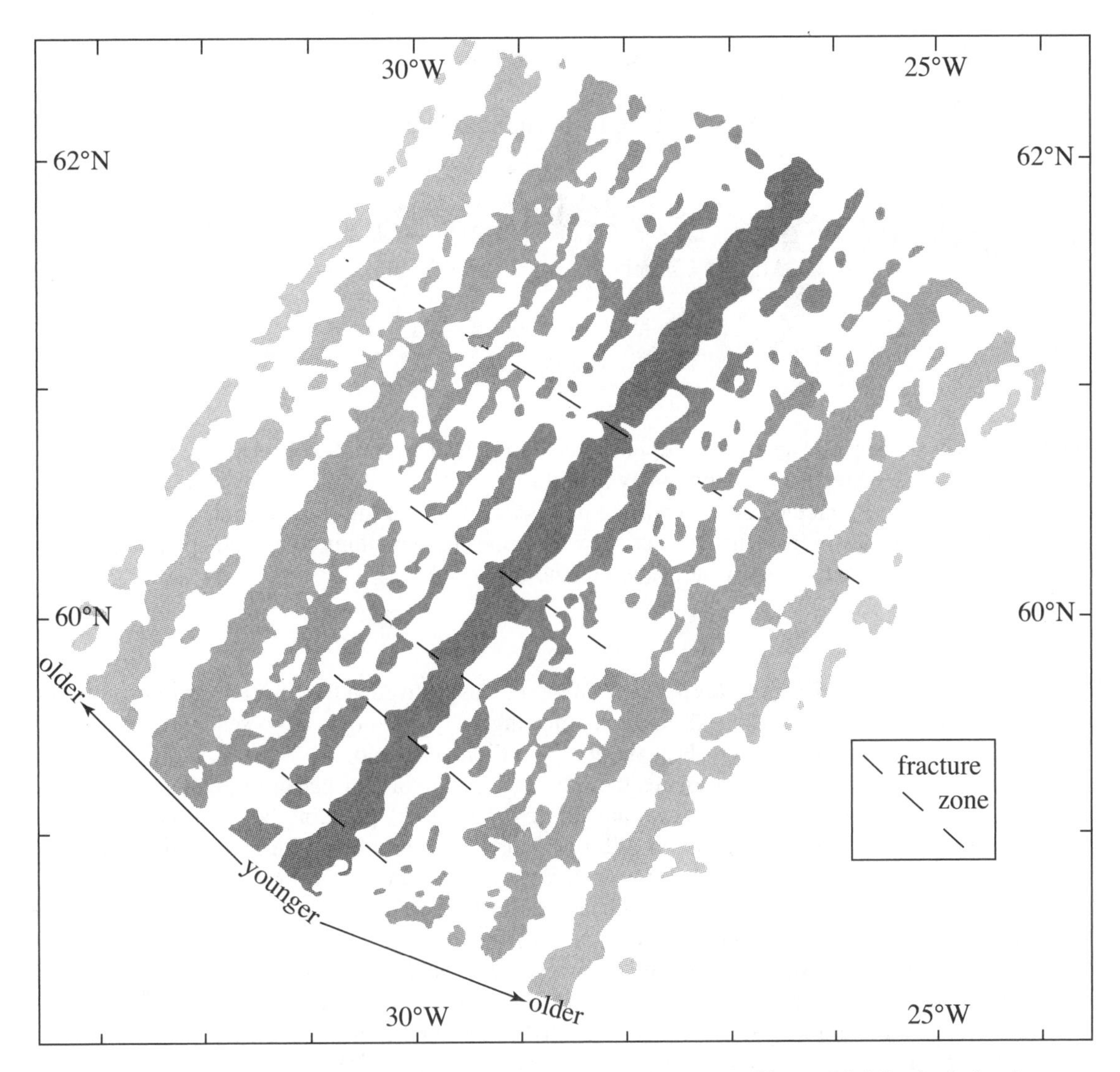

Figure 22-15. In this map of the area indicated by the black square (Figure 22-14), shaded stripes pertain to ocean crust with positive magnetic anomalies. Shaded stripes alternate with other stripes (not shaded) that have negative magnetic anomalies.

If the rate of seafloor spreading remained steady, a broad stripe would correspond to a prolonged interval of normal or reverse magnetic polarity, and a narrow stripe would correspond to a brief interval. For the most recent several reversals, there is excellent correspondence between the width of a stripe and duration of the magnetic episode as determined by the potassium-argon method (review Figure 21-7). This permits us to count stripes going away from the crest of the ridge, and to assign an age to each of them (Figure 22-16). The speed of seafloor spreading is equal to distance (of a stripe from the ridge crest where it originated) divided by time (age of the stripe).

Only a few of the more than 300 reversals that occurred within the life span of the oldest oceanic crust have been dated directly, but we can obtain further information from the magnetic record in ocean-floor sediment. Sediment immediately begins to accumulate when new crust is created. Just as the basaltic crust contains magnetized stripes that are progressively older away from the ridge, the sedimentary blanket becomes thicker (and older at its base) away from the ridge. Ocean sediment also acquires a magnetic directionality during deposition. Using a geophysical research ship, we may drill the ocean floor and retrieve a core sample of this sediment. In proceeding up the core from older to younger sediment, we encounter randomly thick or thin intervals that are labeled alternately with normal and reverse magnetic directions. Suppose that the sediment contains tiny single-celled fossils named

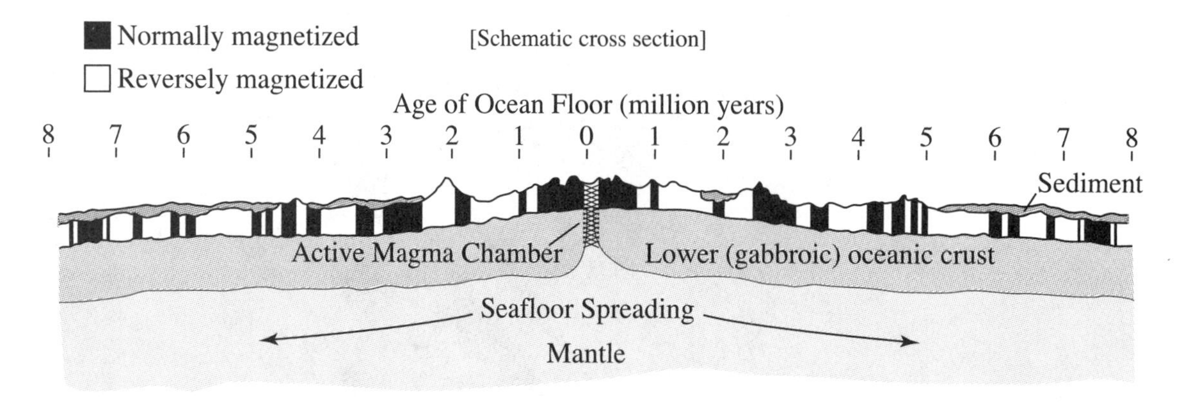

Figure 22-16. The magnetic anomalies are interpreted to indicate normally or reversely magnetized ocean-floor basalt. As the crust is continuously manufactured at the crest of the ridge and spreads laterally to either side, it is "labeled" with a normal or reverse magnetic imprint. Oceanic crust is progressively older going away from the ridge crest, each stripe corresponding to a magnetic polarity episode that was dated by the K-Ar isotopic age method.

Microstaurus chiastius and *Rotelapillus laffittei*. These organisms lived at the time of transition between the Jurassic and the Cretaceous Period, and, by referring to the geologic time scale (review Figure 13-13), we could pinpoint these reversals at about 146 million years ago.

If continents are situated on two plates that are separated by a mid-ocean ridge, how rapidly are they drifting apart? We must double the calculated rate for seafloor spreading because *both* plates are engaged in the process. Rates of separation differ by more than an order of magnitude from ocean to ocean, from as little as 1.2 centimeters per year across the ridge in the Arctic Ocean, to 16 cm/year between the Pacific and Nazca plates in the southeast Pacific Ocean. The most common rate is 4 cm/year (1.6 inch/year), which is about how fast your fingernails grow. Continental drift sustained at this rate creates profound changes in world geography that are very rapid, geologically speaking. For example, the South Atlantic opened at a rate of 4 cm/year, reaching its current width in less than 3% of geologic time.

Recent techniques utilizing satellites have enabled us to establish a geographic position anywhere on earth within an error of one centimeter or less. Given such incredible accuracy, only a few years would suffice to monitor the widening gap between New York and London, or the shrinking distance between San Francisco and Tokyo. After all the decades of fierce controversy, we have confirmed continental drift by direct observation! It is astonishing that today's "instantaneous" rates and directions of plate motion established through satellite data are in such good agreement with the values averaged over millions of years, determined by analysis of seafloor magnetic anomalies. Plate tectonics must be a stable, steady process.

Magnetic anomalies extend throughout the world ocean (printed on the back cover of this book), the most complete record being in the large Pacific plate where the age of the crust varies from zero at the East Pacific Rise to mid-Mesozoic offshore of Japan. But notice that the pattern is not fully repeated to the east of the Rise, only a little being preserved adjacent to South America, and none at all beyond the intersection of the Rise with North America. A minimum of 13,000 kilometers of Pacific Ocean floor must have been "gobbled up"! This brings us to the next type of boundary where plates are in collision.

Plates Colliding

Oceanic plates in collision If the earth maintains a constant size, for which there is strong evidence, then plate material must be destroyed elsewhere at the same rate that it is created in the ridge system. Plates are consumed in the ocean trench system, not absolutely but through subduction which recycles their substance back into the mantle. In Figure 21-17 we noted a plane of earthquake foci dipping downward from the floor of a trench. Deep earthquakes mark where a plate containing oceanic crust is descending into the depths (Figure 22-17), with spectacular consequences both for the plate and everything in its vicinity. The plate consists of ocean-floor gabbro and basalt, some asthenosphere that had frozen onto its underside, and accumulated sedimentary cover. It had cooled during millions of years while migrating

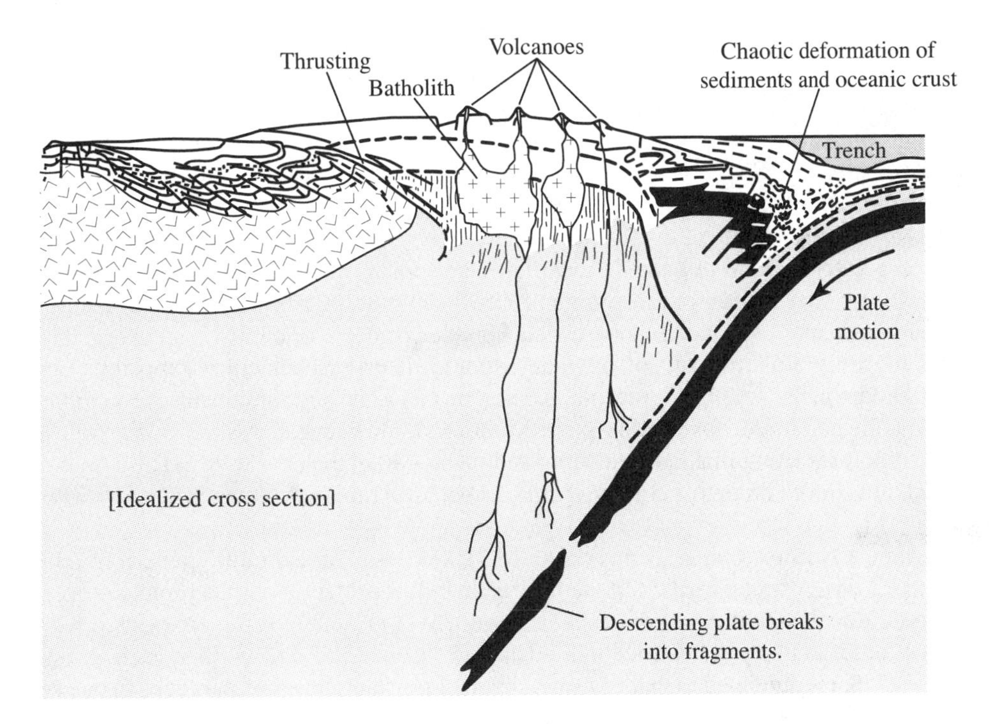

Figure 22-17. Beneath a continent, a plate containing oceanic crust is actively subducting, descending into the depths of the mantle. In the process, the leading edges of both plates are deformed, creating compressional mountains in the continental plate (as in the Andes), and crumpling and offscraping of sediment from the oceanic plate. At greater depth, partial melting generates magma that is emplaced upward as batholiths. [*After J. F. Dewey and J. M. Bird, "Mountain Belts and the New Global Tectonics,"* Journal of Geophysical Research, *vol. 75, no. 14, p. 2638, 1970. Copyright by American Geophysical Union.*]

across an ocean basin, becoming more dense and thickened as shown in Figure 22-9. In fact, by the point of subduction its density exceeds that of the mantle beneath—an unstable situation. A dense subducting plate sinks into the less dense mantle chiefly of its own accord. Gravity also gives a boost by pushing the plate downhill into the subduction zone from its point of origin high upon a mid-ocean ridge.

More millions of years will pass before this cold, rigid plate has absorbed enough heat from its surroundings to reach thermal equilibrium. Even before that time, some plates will have plunged to the limit of the deepest earthquakes nearly 700 kilometers beneath the surface. What happens to a plate beyond this limiting depth of earthquake foci? There is indirect evidence that a plate can descend perhaps all the way to the core-mantle boundary. P and S waves from unrelated earthquakes travel more rapidly through subducted plates, which are cooler and more rigid than surrounding mantle, and the waves lose less energy while in transit. Seismologists have analyzed the waves that have traveled from many earthquakes along many different pathways, some through subducted plates and some not, and they are mapping a "graveyard" of old, dead plates lodged very deep in the mantle.

In the trench, some of the ocean-floor sediment is scraped off against the leading edge of the overriding plate. The material accumulates as a pile of deformed sediment sliced by a multitude of thrust faults (Figure 22-17). Other sediment that is subducted to great depth is metamorphosed, often so quickly that there is little opportunity for it to heat up. Unusual metamorphic minerals develop that are stable at high pressure but relatively low temperature. The sediment also contains sea water, and hydrous minerals such as clay that yield H_2O when decomposed by heating. This water penetrates into the overriding plate and, because H_2O is so effective in breaking chemical bonds, it acts to lower the temperature of melting. Bodies of magma accumulate in the wedge of mantle rock lying overhead. If two oceanic plates are in collision, the magma feeds a string of andesitic volcanoes such as in the Aleutian island arc (Chapter 21). Volcanism also accompanies the encounter between an oceanic and a continental plate, as along the Andes Mountains where gigantic andesite volcanoes are perched on the skyline.

Much of the magma does not reach the surface, however; it crystallizes as batholiths, deep masses of intrusive igneous rock consisting of granite or granodiorite (Chapter 5).

In some cases the contents of an oceanic plate are not entirely subducted during a collision. Diverse fragments had rifted away from the edge of Gondwana, the former southern supercontinent, during its initial stages of breakup. Seafloor spreading carried these bits of continental crust across the Pacific Ocean and slammed them against the west coast of North America where they were grafted onto the continent as *exotic terranes*. Pieces of continent that have traveled halfway around the globe are exotic, and so is the even greater volume of oceanic material incorporated into such terranes. The latter includes island-arc volcanic rocks, deep-ocean sediment rich in marine microfossils, and in a few localities, basaltic ocean crust and associated mantle called *ophiolite*. Indeed, ophiolite is so exotic that its origin was recognized only after the advent of plate-tectonic theory. Spectacular exposures occur in the Sultanate of Oman, in the Arabian Peninsula, where one can scale a mountainside through the ophiolite sequence—mantle peridotite, upward across the Moho, and into oceanic crust consisting of gabbro, then basalt dikes, pillow lava, and finally ocean-floor sediment—all in the dry desert! Dense ophiolite should be subducted, not shoved up onto a continent, and all but an estimated 0.001 per cent of oceanic crust is in fact subducted.

Westernmost North America, from Alaska to Mexico, is a "crazy quilt" pattern of added-on terranes (Figure 22-18). After an exotic terrane has made initial contact, continued plate movement tends to smear it out into a long sliver against the host continent. Ten such terranes are nestled within a short span of 120 kilometers in central Alaska, faulted against or on top of one another, each terrane having a geologic "style" that is unrelated to that of its neighbors. For example, all of the rocks in one terrane may have formed in the mid-ocean, whereas a nearby terrane contains sediment derived from a continent. Magnetic polar wandering data show that some terranes had traveled thousands of kilometers from their points of origin, perhaps from the Southern Hemisphere to a docking against Alaska in the far north. Recall (Chapter 21) that paleomagnetic data refer only to latitude, not longitude. We can infer how far

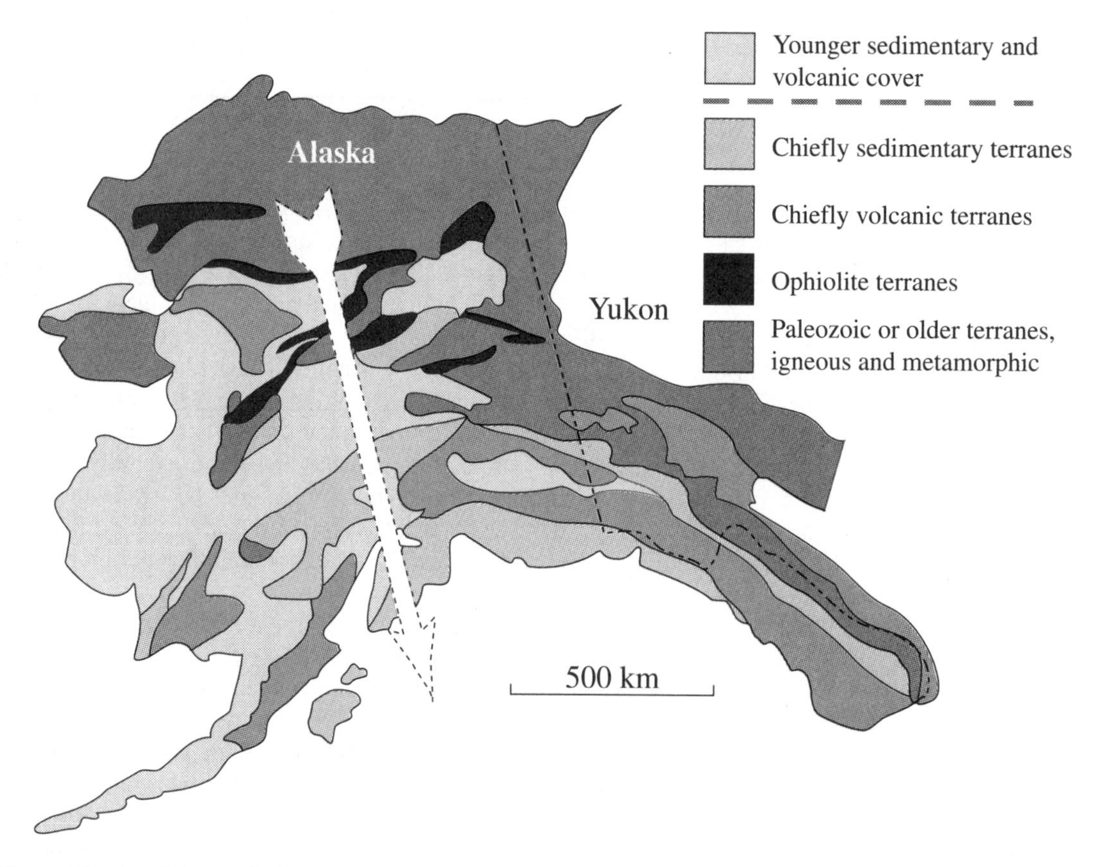

Figure 22-18. Much of Alaska consists of far-traveled exotic terranes that have accreted (welded against) the North American continent. Accretion proceeded from the north toward the south as indicated by the arrow.

an exotic terrane had traveled in a latitudinal north-south direction, while the unknown extent of its longitudinal east-west travel could have been far greater.

Continental plates in collision A stupendous collision in progress between India and Eurasia has given rise to the Himalaya Mountains (the world's highest) and adjacent lofty Tibetan Plateau. Both opposing plates in this region contain thick, buoyant crust that can jam together and crumple, but not subduct. The initial encounter of continent against continent slivered the Indian plate, and then most of it bent downward and slid underneath the Eurasian plate. Crustal thickness is about 55 kilometers beneath the Himalayas, increasing to 70 kilometers—double the customary thickness—beneath the Tibetan Plateau. Structures such as nappes, thrust faults, and stacked-up repetitions of the Moho, like those we noted in the Alps (Chapter 21), are also characteristic of the Himalayas.

Plates Slipping Sideways

Early in the development of plate tectonic theory, the Canadian geophysicist J. T. Wilson pointed out that plate boundaries discussed above (mountain ranges, trenches, segments of mid-ocean ridge) commonly end very abruptly. Consider the Pacific plate being created along the East Pacific Rise and disappearing down trenches along its northern and western edge. We have defined the trailing and leading edges of the plate, but what about its sides? If the plate is to move, there must be faults along the sides to permit the plate to slip laterally past its neighbors. Wilson coined the term *transform fault* indicating that, at its two ends, such a fault "transforms into" (is connected onto) the terminal point of some other type of plate margin. A transform fault is our third type of plate boundary, one in which crust is neither created nor consumed.

In most places, a transform fault occupies the fracture zone that lies between offset segments of a mid-ocean ridge (review Figures 21-14 and 21-15). Figure 22-19 shows a typical short stretch of the Mid-Atlantic Ridge, with two possible interpretations. Before the advent of plate tectonic theory, the only plausible interpretation would have been diagram (*a*) which implies that a formerly continuous length of ridge had been broken and offset by a left-lateral strike-slip fault. In either case, whether the ridge is apparently offset by left-lateral slip (as illustrated) or right-lateral slip, the seismic first-motion

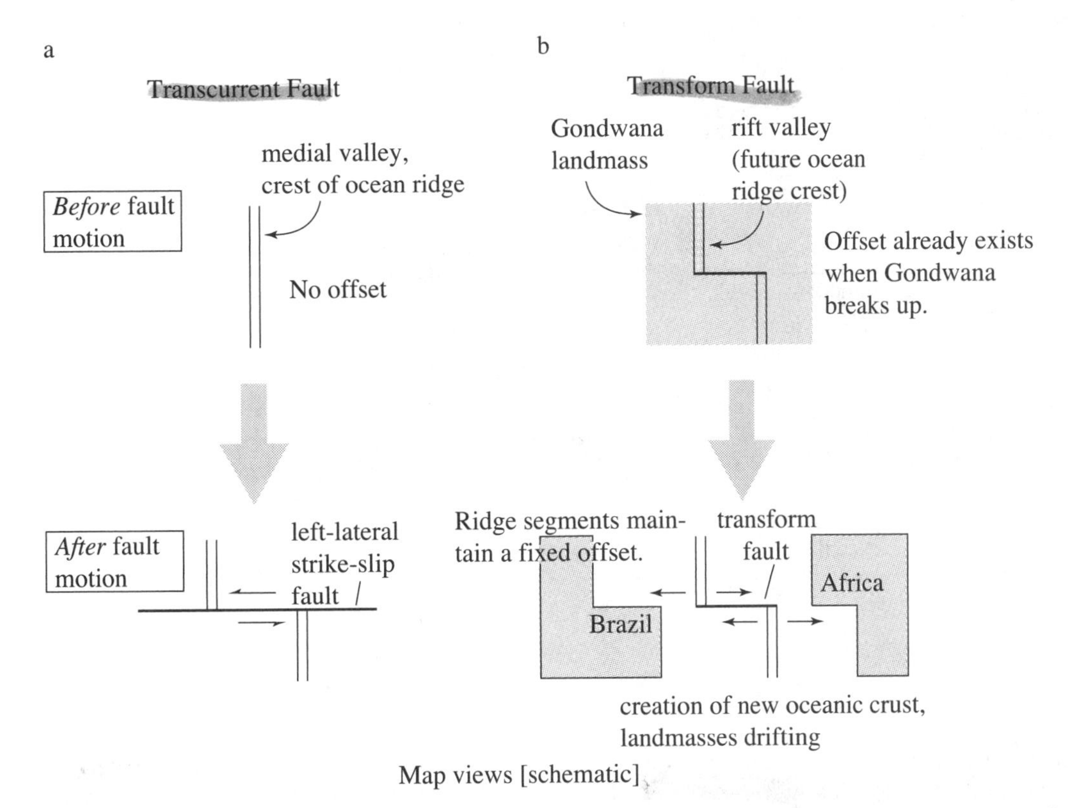

Figure 22-19. Two Interpretations of the Origin of Offset Segments of the Ocean Ridge System. Only the transform fault interpretation is consistent with the motion of the plates indicated by seismic data.

studies described in Chapter 21 would be in direct contradiction, indicating a sense of motion that is opposite to the apparent motion.

A correct (and more subtle) interpretation (*b*) reconciles the seismic data and also accommodates the process of seafloor spreading that is ignored in interpretation (*a*). When the supercontinent rifted, giving birth to the Atlantic Ocean, the ridge segments were initiated *already* offset from one another, and their positions remain fixed. As pictured in (*b*), new oceanic crust is spreading laterally to either side. Along the transform fault offset between the segments, the crust is moving in opposite directions with right-lateral motion. In regions beyond this zone, the crust is continuing to move in the same direction, toward the right on the east side and toward the left on the west side.

Throughout most of the length of the mid-ocean ridge system, the ridge dominates and transform-fault offsets are relatively minor. In the Gulf of California there is an opposite pattern, in which short segments of ridge are connected by lengthy transform faults (Figure 22-20). The longest of them, the San Andreas and its associated faults, cuts through western California and its right-lateral sense of motion (review Figure 16-5) accommodates the northwesterly drift of the Pacific plate past the North American plate.

Hotspots, Mantle Plumes

Boundaries along which plates are spreading, converging, or slipping sideways are not quite the entire story of plate tectonics. We noted that the interiors of plates are mostly "dead," but there are some spectacular exceptions to this rule, as in the Hawaiian Islands. Located in the middle of the vast Pacific plate, the Hawaiian volcanoes are vigorously spewing out lava (Chapter 5). They are situated above a *hotspot*,

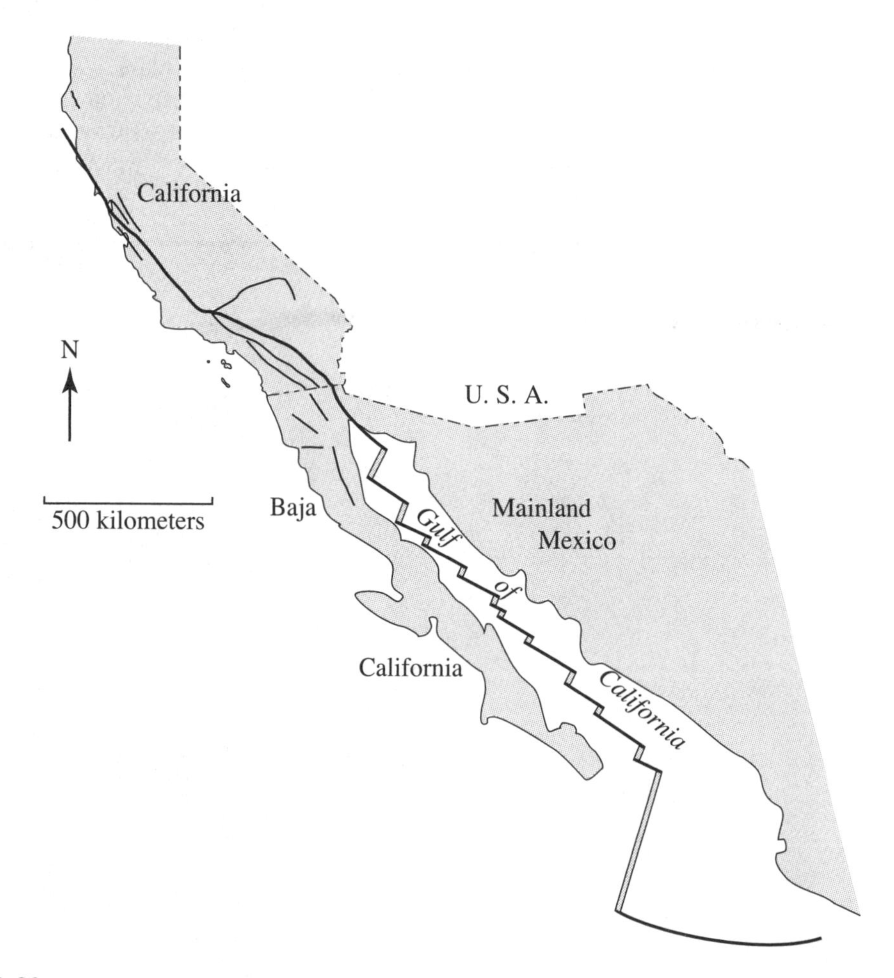

Figure 22-20. In the Gulf of California, the ocean ridge system consists of short ridge segments (double lines) offset by lengthy transform faults. The San Andreas and its associated faults in the State of California are part of this system where it runs across the continent. The transform faults accommodate right-lateral motion as the North American plate slips sideways past the Pacific plate.

a narrow zone of anomalously hot mantle material that is streaming upward as a *mantle plume*, possibly from as deep as the core-mantle boundary. Mantle peridotite in the plume melts as it approaches the earth's surface for the same reason that ascending mantle melts along ocean ridges, the difference being that a plume feeds volcanoes localized within a small area.

Forty or so prominent hotspots have been identified, many of them distant from any plate boundary. They may be oceanic as beneath Hawaii or Iceland, or continental as beneath Yellowstone National Park, famous for its geysers and hot springs. Evidence for a very deep-seated origin is that hotspots do not participate in plate motion, but rather they remain stationary (or nearly so) as a plate passes overhead. In the Hawaiian Islands, the site of a very long-lived hotspot, the effect is analogous to a chimney belching puffs of smoke that are swept downwind. Magma from the hotspot perforates the Pacific plate, building a volcano that drifts away from its hotspot source, which shuts down the volcano, and the process repeats (Figure 22-21). There are frequent large eruptions in the "big island" of Hawaii at the end of the chain, and just offshore in the Loihi seamount (Chapter 21). Maui, the next island to the northwest, sustains infrequent small eruptions and beyond Maui, all of the volcanoes are extinct. K-Ar ages of volcanism are systematically older in a northwesterly direction, and the islands become smaller and more deeply eroded, then continuing underwater as a chain of seamounts.

From time to time, hotspots have furiously built immense volcanic fields of flood basalt (Chapter 5) whether on land or on the ocean floor. One such series of flows poured out in Siberia 251 million years ago at the moment of the greatest mass extinction ever to occur, that ended the Paleozoic Era. Mass extinction of dinosaurs and associated organisms at the end of the Mesozoic Era corresponded to another mega-eruption about 66 million years ago in India. A popular explanation attributes the latter extinction to general chaos following a meteorite impact (Chapter 15), but the timings of these great eruptions were too coincidental to ignore. Eruptions could have suddenly injected volcanic gases into the atmosphere

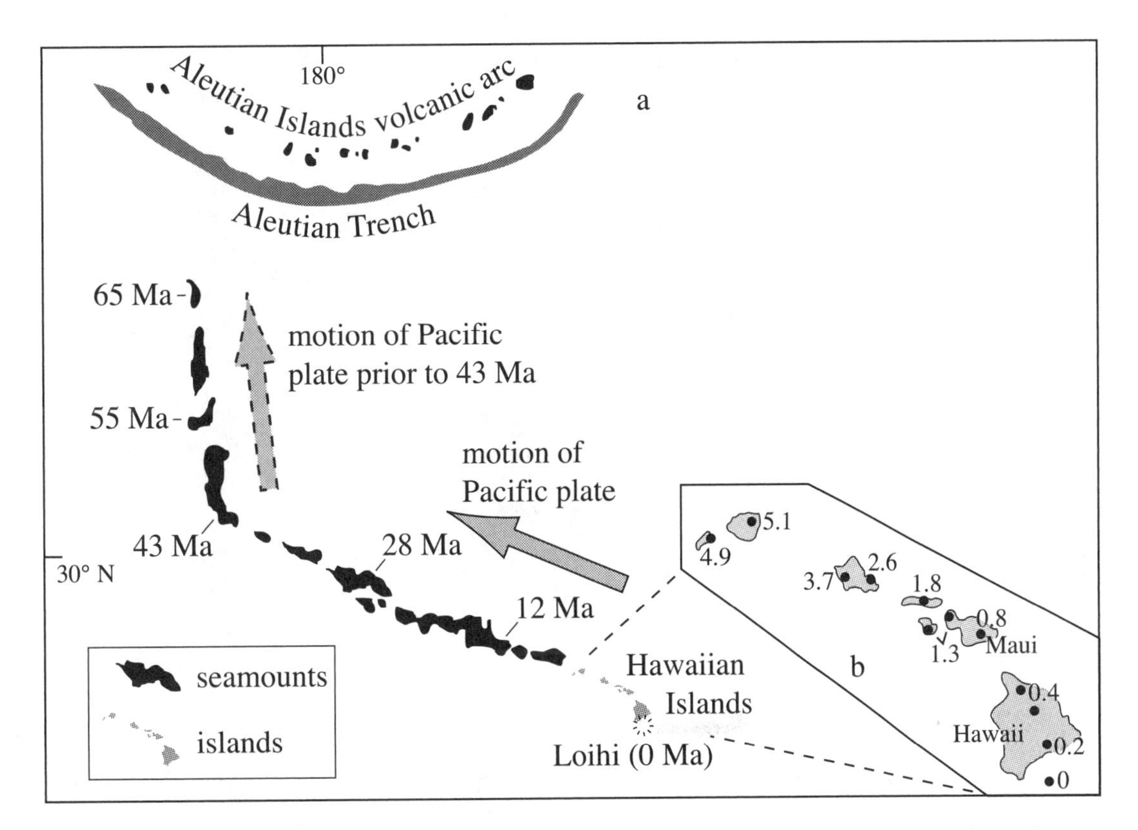

Figure 22-21. A chain of seamounts (submerged volcanoes) trends northwest from the Hawaiian Islands, thence through an "elbow" into a more northerly trend. Ages of volcanism steadily increase along this trend. All of the volcanoes originated over the long-lived Hawaiian hotspot and were drifted away from their source by plate motion that earlier had a northerly bearing. At 43 million years ago (Ma), the plate motion changed to its current direction. (*b*) Enlargement showing progression of K-Ar isotopic ages (Ma) of volcanism in the Hawaiian Island chain.

triggering catastrophic changes in world climate (Chapter 24), or toxic volcanic gases could have poisoned the organisms.

Before Pangea

What would happen if current plate tectonic motions were to continue? The Arctic, Atlantic, and Indian Oceans would widen while the Pacific shrinks by encroachment of surrounding landmasses. After a supercontinent rifts apart, its fragments drift around the globe, there to reassemble into another supercontinent, thus completing one plate tectonic cycle. It is fairly obvious and straightforward to reassemble Pangea which, geologically speaking, broke apart only recently (Figure 22-22*a*). Restoration of

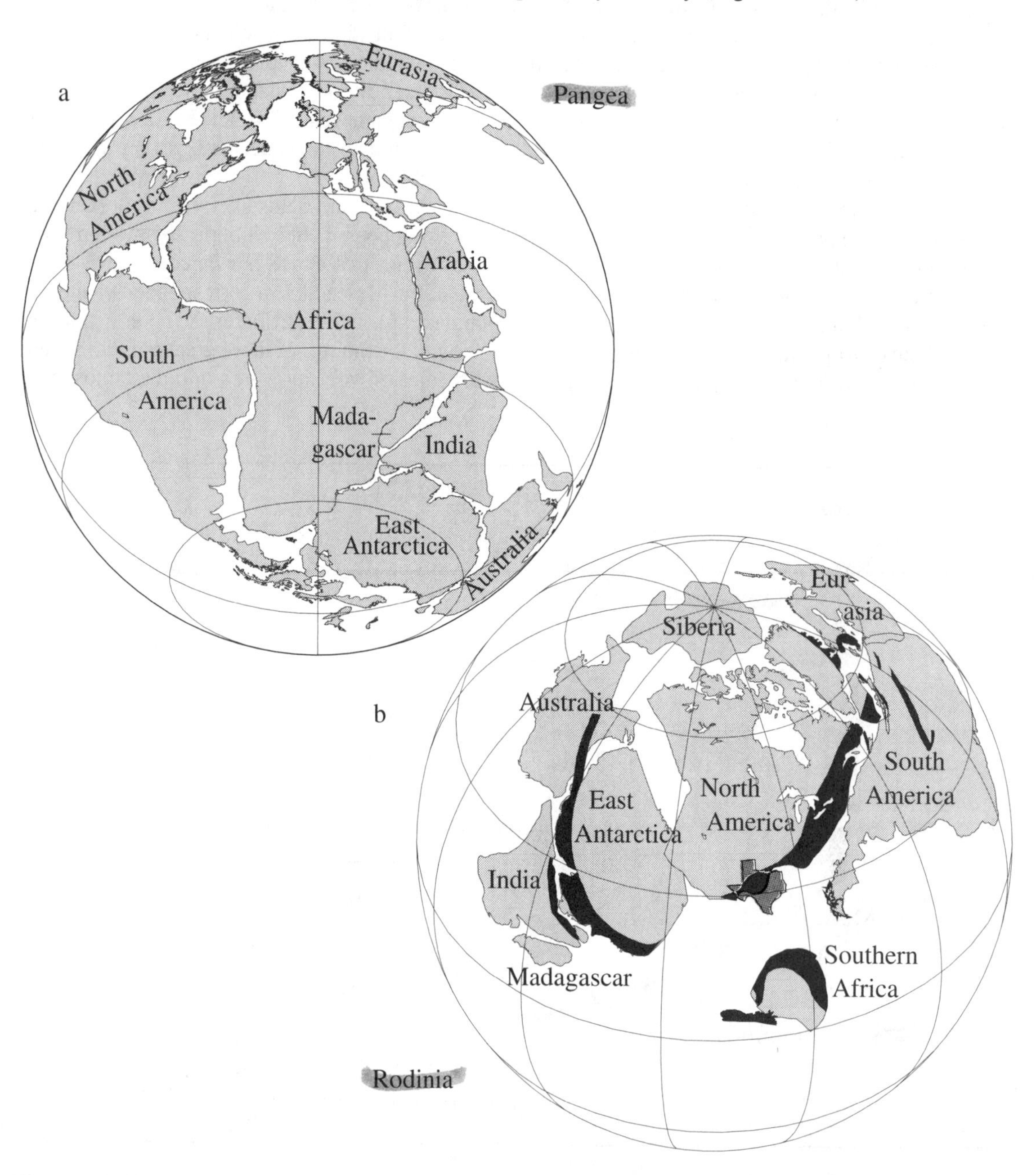

Figure 22-22. Pangea (*a*) refers to the most recent, Paleozoic age supercontinent composed of pieces broken and dispersed from a yet earlier supercontinent, Rodinia (*b*). Rodinia landmasses were oriented using an ancient mountain range as a “tracer,” here reassembled into a nearly continuous black band. The mountain belt trended through what is Texas today (outlined in the center). [*Courtesy of Ian W. D. Dalziel and Lisa M. Gahagan, PLATES Project, University of Texas Institute for Geophysics.*]

earlier cycles is much more difficult because no oceanic crust of such antiquity remains with its tell-tale magnetic anomalies, and the landmasses have since been fragmented along different lines, jostled about, eroded, deformed, metamorphosed, etc.

Only a few scraps of evidence remain to challenge the plate tectonic experts in reconstruction of the predecessor to Pangea, a supercontinent named Rodinia. We have seen how matching of trends of ancient eroded mountain belts was useful to correlate landmasses now located on either side of the Atlantic (Figures 22-3 and 22-4). In a reassembly of Rodinia, a dominant mountain chain of 1.3 to 1.0 billion years age forms a continuous sweep [black band, Figure 22-22(*b*)]. The world of Rodinia scarcely resembles today's geography, as pieces of the mountain belt have become distributed amongst India, Australia, Antarctica, Africa, South and North America, and Europe. Note that in Rodinia, nuclear North America lay between South America and Antarctica!

The Great Heat Engine

Processes of plate tectonics at the earth's surface—compositions of plates, interactions at their margins, continental drift—are quite well understood, but fundamental questions remain. What source of energy drives plate tectonics? If mantle material ascends at a mid-ocean ridge, is incorporated into a plate that travels laterally, then is subducted, how does flow in the deep mantle complete the circuit back to the starting point? Does the zone of flow extend no deeper than the deepest earthquakes, or is the entire mantle involved in internal motion? These are the issues of current research in geodynamics, the science of the earth's deep interior.

Ultimately, it is internal heat energy that drives the plate tectonic engine. Heat is supplied by radioactive decay, and some "original" heat still persists from 4.55 billion years ago when the earth's substance accumulated and separated into a core and mantle. Long-lived radioactive isotopes of potassium, uranium, and thorium are highly concentrated into the continental crust, so we would expect heat to be flowing up from the interior much faster through the continents. It was thus a surprise to discover that heat flow is the same, on average, in the continents and in ocean basins whose crust is nearly barren of radioactivity. There must be another, much deeper source of heat under the ocean.

Heat energy is conveyed through the earth by *conduction* and *convection.* In conduction, the energy is transferred by vibrating atoms that are connected by chemical bonds. Heat diffuses through the material which itself is not transported. The process of convection, in which hotter, less dense regions of material are rising and colder, more dense regions are sinking, can transport heat far more rapidly and efficiently. With increasing depth in the earth, the temperature rises so sharply that we would expect the mantle to be molten at a shallow depth, contrary to the observation that the mantle conducts seismic S-waves which travel only through solid material. Inasmuch as the mantle is not melted, there must be a way to transport heat rapidly upward for disposal at the earth's surface, and only convection is efficient enough to do this. Convective motion in the interior accompanies the motion of plates at the surface.

Seismologists are mapping the deep interior using seismic waves that travel through it in many directions, somewhat as one may use a CAT scanner to map the interior of a human body by sending x-rays through it in many directions. A cross section through the mantle (Figure 22-23) depicts slight deviations in the local speed of S-wave travel. The deeper the shade of gray, the faster the waves travel compared to the average speed at a given depth, and conversely the green tones refer to anomalously slow travel speed. Although several factors may influence the speed, the chief one is temperature: rapid travel through colder, more rigid material (gray) and slow where the material is abnormally hot. Hot patches denote the East Pacific Rise and Mid-Atlantic Ridge, and mantle plumes beneath the East Africa Rift System and the Cape Verde Islands which are volcanic hotspots. Exceptionally cold regions include the thick lithosphere of Africa and a slab descending beneath the Caribbean Sea, the latter consisting of the vast oceanic plate that is almost entirely subducted, that once lay on the east side of the East Pacific Rise.

This amazing picture provides strong evidence for a connection between activity in the deep mantle and tectonic plates at the surface. It suggests that plate tectonics involves the entire mantle, not just its uppermost few hundred kilometers. The earth is a heat engine on the grandest scale. Eventually much of the heat energy simply escapes the earth. Of that which is used to propel internal motion, about 90 per cent is expended on processes of making, moving, and destroying plates; the remaining 10 per cent goes to develop mantle plumes.

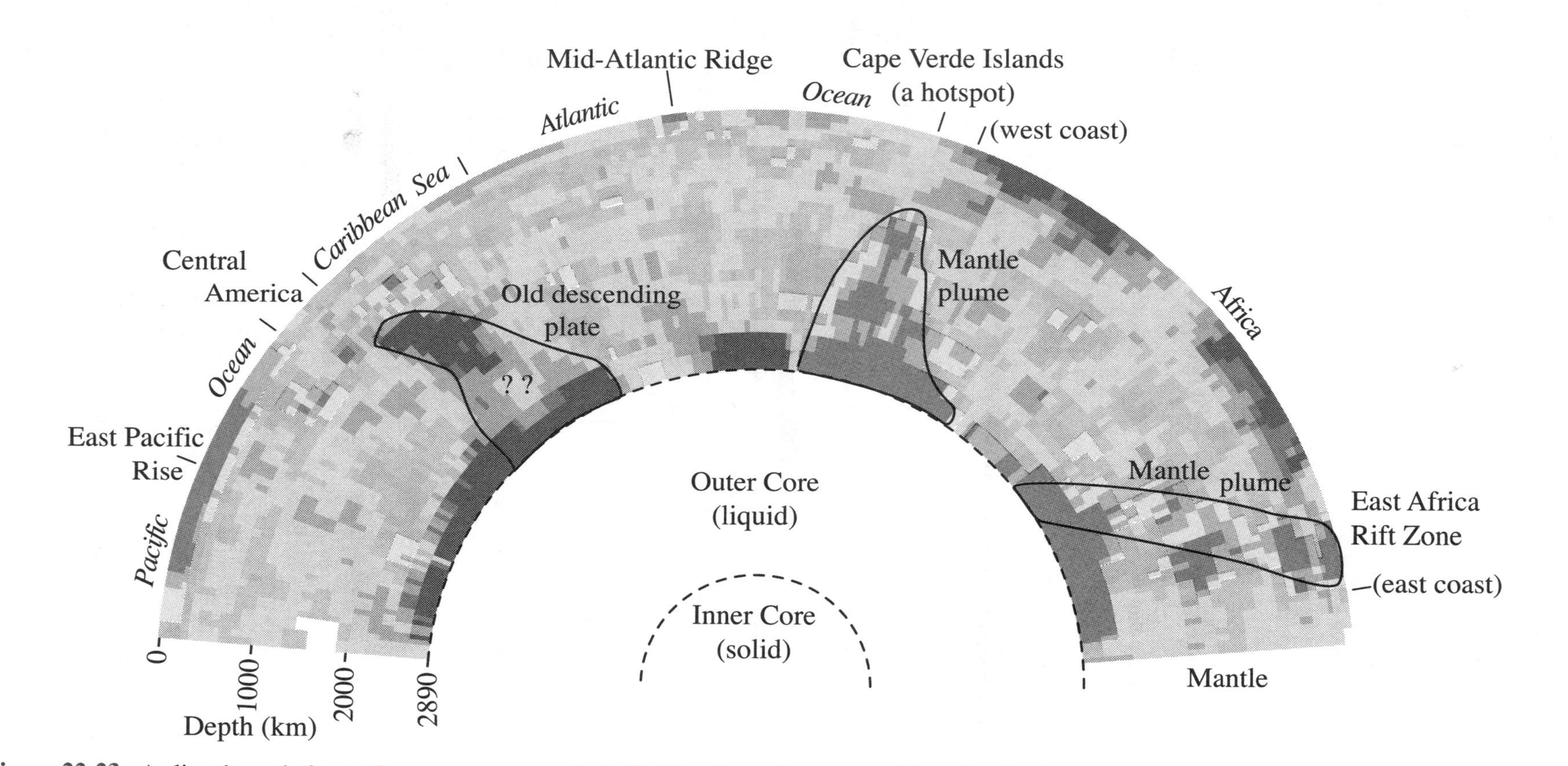

Figure 22-23. A slice through the earth encompasses nearly half of its circumference, positioned at the dashed line in Figure 22-8. Continental and oceanic crust is too thin to indicate on this scale. Deep sources of heat energize the upwelling of mantle plumes (the conduit up to the Cape Verde hotspot may be too narrow to detect by seismic means). At the crests of the Mid-Atlantic Ridge and East Pacific Rise, the hot regions are not connected to a deep source. Melting of asthenosphere to produce ocean-floor basalt is a passive process due more to release of confining pressure than to input of heat. An exceedingly complex, inhomogeneous, and poorly understood zone lies at the core-mantle boundary. [*Courtesy Stephen P. Grand.*]

SUMMARY

Several lines of evidence suggest that by the end of the Paleozoic Era, a single supercontinent (Pangea) had assembled by the joining of a northern supercontinent (Laurasia) to a southern supercontinent (Gondwana). A universal ocean, of which the Pacific Ocean is a remnant, occupied the remainder of the earth's surface. Pangea began to rift and drift apart in the Mesozoic Era and the fragments—today's landmasses—have continued to disperse except for a few areas where they are in collision.

Examples of evidence for continental drift include the following. (i) Shapes and sizes of rifted landmasses mutually correspond. For example, the jutting corner of Brazil, as defined by the edge of the continental shelf, fits against the embayment of west Africa except for the overlapping region of the Niger delta which built out into the Atlantic Ocean only after the two continents had separated. (ii) Fossils of the same species of extinct organism (for example, the early Mesozoic reptile *Lystrosaurus*) may be located in landmasses now widely separated (for example, Africa and Antarctica), thus arguing for a formerly continuous landmass. To serve as convincing evidence, the organism must not have been able to perform intercontinental travel on its own. (iii) Isotopic age patterns, rock types, faults and folds, and metamorphic zones correspond between the two edges of a formerly continuous landmass. For example, isotopic age zones correspond between western Africa and eastern South America. The Appalachian Mountains, whose North American trend terminates in Newfoundland, resume as the Caledonian Mountains in the British Isles. (iv) Analyses of magnetic directions in rocks of many ages from a single landmass define an apparent polar wandering path. From this information alone one cannot distinguish whether the magnetic and rotational poles had wandered, or the landmass had wandered, or both. However, a different apparent polar wandering path will be observed for some other landmass, thus establishing that the two landmasses had moved with respect to one another.

Continental drift is just one manifestation of a more inclusive process called plate tectonics, according to which the earth's surface is divided into small-to-large plates that are in motion, interacting with one another along their margins. Plate boundaries are marked by zones of volcanoes and earthquake epicenters, whereas interiors of plates are (almost) inert as indicated by general absence of volcanic and seismic activity. The boundaries correspond, not with the edges of continents and ocean basins, but rather with the mid-ocean ridge system or continental rift valleys (where plates are pulling apart), compressional mountain belts or the ocean trench system (where plates are colliding), and major strike-slip fault zones (where plates are slipping sideways past one another). A plate includes either oceanic or continental crust, the Moho, and uppermost mantle, collectively known as lithosphere, and it moves over a deeper, softened zone of mantle rock, the asthenosphere.

Seafloor spreading occurs at the crest of the ocean ridge system. As the tectonic plates continually pull apart, basaltic magma streams into the opened space where it freezes, forming new oceanic crust. At random time intervals the earth's magnetic field abruptly reverses, imprinting magnetic directions in the basalt that are oriented in opposite directions. This is registered as a set of magnetic stripes in which the magnetic field is anomalously strong (positive anomaly above normally magnetized sea floor) alternating with stripes with a negative magnetic anomaly where the ocean floor is reversely magnetized. Broad and narrow stripes correspond to longer or shorter episodes of magnetic polarity which have been dated by the K-Ar method. This information provides calculations of the speed of seafloor spreading (and continental drift) which varies between 1 and 16 centimeters/year in different ocean basins. Today's instantaneous rates of plate motions measured using satellite data agree very well with plate motions averaged over millions of years obtained from the striped magnetic anomaly pattern. Magnetic signatures in overlying ocean-floor sediment are also compatible with all of these data, and the associated fossils permit the age of oceanic crust to be dated back to the oldest surviving remnant in the Pacific plate near Japan (about 150 million years).

Oceanic crust older than mid-Mesozoic has been subducted back into the mantle along margins where plates are in collision. Descending plates in active subduction zones are marked by foci of earthquakes (some very powerful) along dipping planes, to depths of as much as 700 kilometers. Ocean trenches are located where a plate bends over, beginning its descent. H_2O incorporated within a plate encourages melting which is manifested as andesite volcanoes (extrusive) or as batholiths (intrusive). Mountains ranges (for example, the Andes) are created where an oceanic plate collides with a continental plate. Where both colliding plates contain low-density continental crust, subduction cannot occur. Instead, the crust is telescoped together and thickened, as in the Himalaya Mountains where the crust approaches double the normal thickness.

In some instances, ocean-floor sediment is not subducted, but rather it is accreted (welded) onto a continent as an exotic terrane. Much of the western seaboard of North America consists of an amalgamation of accreted exotic terranes that include local areas of ophiolite—ocean floor basalt, gabbro, and underlying mantle.

Transform faults occupy the margins of plates that are slipping sideways. Most transform faults are identified with offsetting fracture zones in the ocean ridge system. The supercontinent initially broke apart along an offset, zigzag pattern. This pattern persists after seafloor spreading opened up an intervening ocean, consisting of segments of ocean ridge crest ("zigs") connected together and offset by transform faults ("zags"). A transform fault may cross into continental crust, as in the San Andreas Fault System in California, where the Pacific plate is slipping past the North American plate with right-lateral strike-slip motion.

Mantle plumes may originate near the core-mantle boundary, and ascend toward the earth's surface where they are manifested as volcanic hotspots. A hotspot may lie beneath an ocean ridge (as in Iceland), or beneath the middle of an oceanic plate (as in the Hawaiian Islands), or beneath a continent (as in Yellowstone National Park). As a tectonic plate drifts over a hotspot which itself remains almost stationary, volcanoes are built at the surface, then carried away by plate motion. The Hawaiian Islands and their underwater extension as seamounts are systematically older at greater distance from the hotspot located at the southeast end of the chain. Immense volcanic outpourings from hotspots in the geologic past are correlated with major mass extinctions of species.

Various lines of evidence can be used to reconstruct the most recent supercontinent (Pangea), and its predecessor supercontinent that existed 1.3 to 1.0 billion years ago (Rodinia).

Internal heat energy propels the tectonic engine. Plate motion at the surface is believed to be accompanied by convective overturn in the earth's interior. Regions of hotter, less dense mantle ascend (and inject basalt magma) beneath ocean ridges and cooler, more dense plate material descends back into the mantle in subduction zones. Seismic evidence suggests that old, dead plates are lodged deep near the core-mantle boundary.

23

Depositional Systems

Point bars on the meandering Colorado River, Texas. [*University of Texas at Austin, Bureau of Economic Geology photograph*]

The remainder of this book focuses upon geologic processes at work upon the earth's surface, where you and I live. Sedimentary rocks, which overlie much of the continents and virtually the entire ocean floor, supply about 90% of humanity's mineral and fuel resources. Urgency to find new discoveries of oil and gas has stimulated research in a variety of environments such as rivers (the *fluvial* environment), deltas, coasts, and the deep ocean [Figure 23-1(a)]. As noted in Chapters 7 and 8, sediment may be *terrigenous clastic*—transported to the site of deposition as particles eroded from an older source—or it may be *chemical* or *biochemical* sediment that was precipitated directly from dissolved ions. Our theme in this chapter is the story of sand and mud, which is terrigenous clastic sediment, and we shall use the Mississippi River, seventh largest in the world and most intensively studied of all rivers, as a case study of deposition in these environments. The Mississippi meets the Gulf of Mexico in its delta where most of the sediment is stored, but beyond which some of the sediment descends into great oceanic depth, or is distributed far along the shore.

Central interior North America is a vast lowland that slopes gently southward toward the Gulf of Mexico. Most of the drainage funnels into tributaries of the Mississippi, which carries about 40 percent of the runoff from the continental United States. This river system, its modern and ancient deltas, and the Gulf have persisted as stable areas since the Mesozoic Era, experiencing little adjustment except for that due to piling on of sediment. By now, approximately one-half of the original Gulf cavity has been filled in with sediment.

DEPOSITIONAL PROCESSES

Water flows downhill, and with it the incorporated sediment. Recall the ideas of dip and strike (Chapter 18) that are useful to describe a sloping plane. Dip is the direction that a drop of water flows downward under the influence of gravity, and the strike direction is perpendicular to dip, a line that is everywhere at the same elevation. Topographic contour lines run parallel to strike, for example. Because rivers flow down the continental surface, the fluvial depositional system is said to be *dip-fed*. Waves may waft sediment laterally along a coast, which is a horizontal region at zero elevation (sea level), and so the coastal depositional system is *strike-fed*.

The open Gulf contains yet other depositional environments [Figure 23-1(b)]. Terrigenous clastics are deposited from the muddy waters along the north and west coasts, whereas on the east and south are regions of clear water where limestone (a biochemical sediment) is accumulating. Other depositional systems, known elsewhere, are not important in the Gulf of Mexico. Among these are the glacial, the lacustrine (lake deposits), and the eolian (windblown sediment prominent in deserts). Uplift and erosion may lay bare the sediment of any origin or age on the land surface. A task of the geologist is to interpret the environment in which ancient sedimentary rocks originated.

What clues are present to guide the interpretation? Was a particular sandstone body deposited in a stream channel, in an advancing delta front, as a windblown dune, on a beach? To make sense of the ancient record, we must understand modern streams, deltas, dunes, and beaches, taking seriously Hutton's famous dictum: "The present is the key to the past." Today we are mapping both the modern and ancient environments in ever more exquisite, three-dimensional detail. Geophysical sensors are lowered into countless wells to characterize the sediment. Seismic waves, sent down into the earth, are reflected off buried strata back to the surface for analysis. Data from these sophisticated techniques are transformed into visual images projected by computers against the walls of a darkened room. It is a surreal experience to enter this room for a virtual walk through the underground. To understand how deep the strata are, their thicknesses and compositions, and where they are deformed into folds or broken by faults, is to understand where best to put the next well in search of oil or gas. Modern geophysical exploration has revolutionized the efficiency of the oil industry. Whereas the success rate for drilling a wildcat well (exploratory in unproven territory) used to be 10%, today the success rate can approach 70%.

RIVERS

Let us follow the journey of a sand grain headed down-river toward its final storage in a delta. In the soil zone, the grain may take hundreds to thousands of years to creep downhill to a stream channel. It could spend a million years in a major river system as it is picked up and laid down many times. Upon reach-

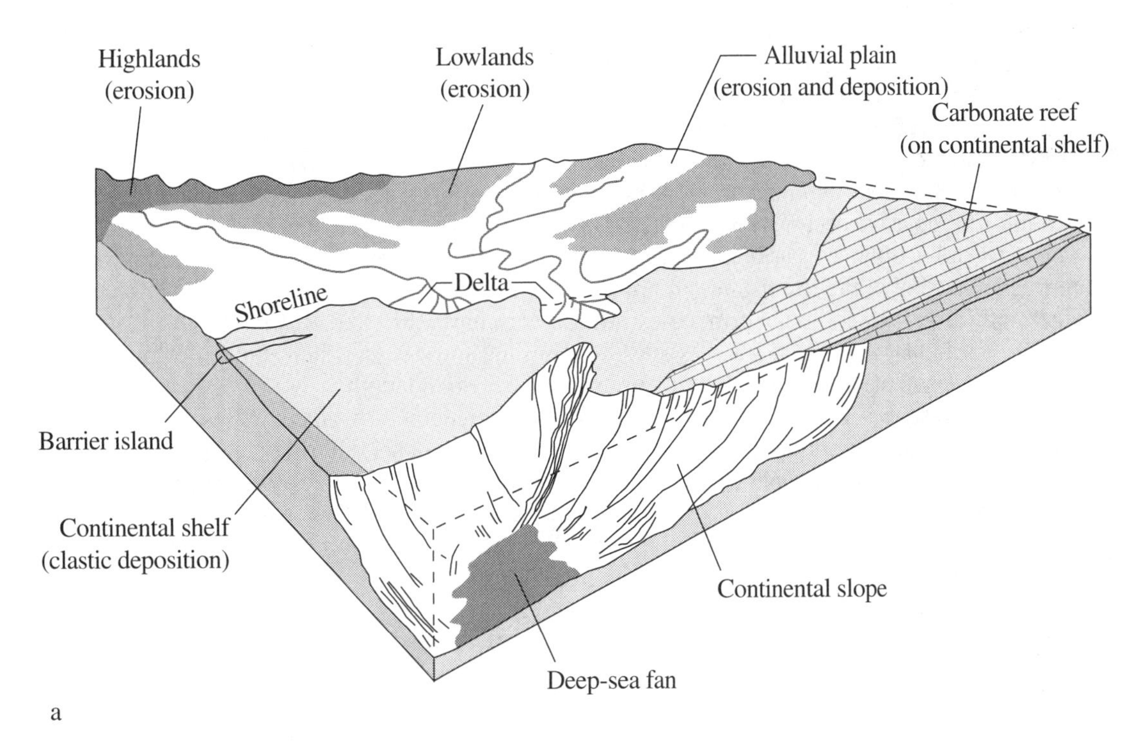

Figure 23-1. (*a*) Local environments of deposition or erosion shown here each consist of a mosaic of related sub-environments. For example, maps of sedimentary geology along the Texas coast recognize 130 distinct kinds of environment. [*Courtesy Howard Gould and ExxonMobil Upstream Technology Company.*] (*b*) Other depositional environments in shallow to deep water of an ocean basin are being vigorously explored. This map identifies a few of them in the Gulf of Mexico. [*University of Texas at Austin, Bureau of Economic Geology.*]

ing a delta it could remain for hundreds of millions of years before uplift begins the next cycle of erosion, transportation, and deposition. Erosion predominates in the uplands where hills and valleys have steeper slopes, and flowing water has more energy. Deposition predominates in regions near the sea, where slopes are more gentle and the energy level is diminished. Current research is discovering that the same relationships of slope and energy, and erosion and deposition are repeated in the depths of an ocean basin.

Large river systems consist of two parts. Streams join together to form ever larger streams in the *tributary network,* which occupies the upper reaches of the basin (Figure 23-2). Tributaries are united together like the branches and main trunk of a tree, or like blood capillaries emptying into larger and yet larger veins. Suppose we designate a stream that has no tributary as of first-order rank, and a stream that has only first-order tributaries as being of second-order rank, etc. It is a hierarchy in which each larger grouping includes all of the lower-rank groupings. On this basis, the Mississippi is a 10th- or 11th-order stream (really big!) whose major tributaries are the Missouri and Ohio Rivers (Figure 23-3). In the Mississippi's tributary network there are some 300 thousand streams, of which about two-thirds are first-order channels, each of them typically only a kilometer or two in length.

A stream system is enlarged by headward erosion, by lengthening of tributaries around the fringe of its drainage basin. Sometimes an aggressive tributary invades a neighboring drainage basin and captures streams from it. An example (not in the Mississippi system) is the Pecos River, which extended itself up through New Mexico (Figure 26-1), capturing streams that flow eastward from the Rocky Mountains. They were diverted southward into the Pecos River, leaving much of the High Plains as a "perched" surface no longer served by any through-going stream.

The Mississippi system has also extended its outreach headward, ever since the shallow Cretaceous sea retreated tens of millions of years ago and central North America became dry land. Simultaneously,

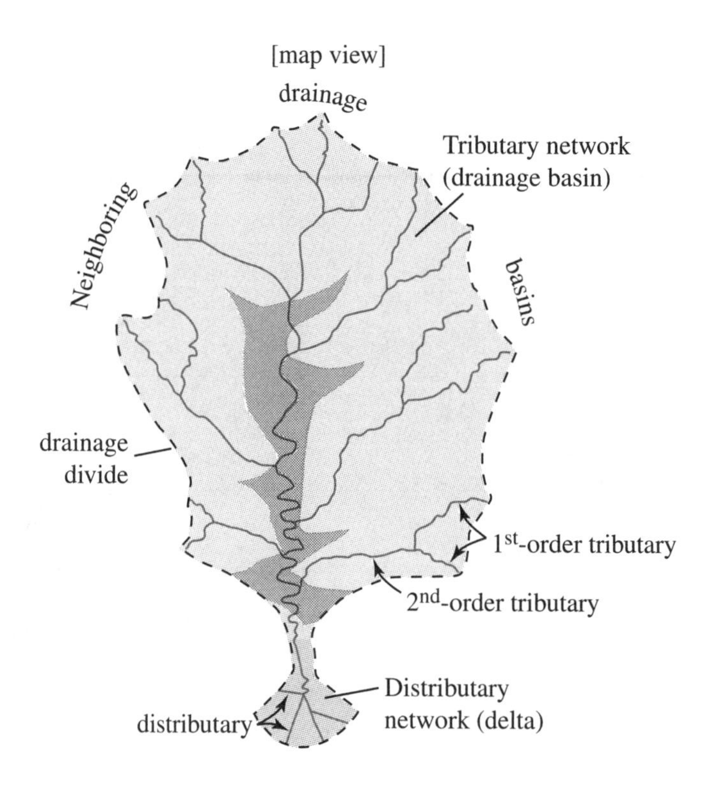

Figure 23-2. On this map, tributaries form a dendritic pattern that resembles the trunk and branches of a tree (the Greek word *dendron* means "tree"). A gray shaded area outlines the part of the basin in which precipitation runs directly into the master stream. It raises the question of effective flood control: Should we retain flood waters behind one very large dam far downstream, or retard them with many small dams placed higher up on the tributaries? The latter solution is definitely helpful, but in view of the large area that feeds directly into the master stream, it appears that *both* kinds of dams are needed.

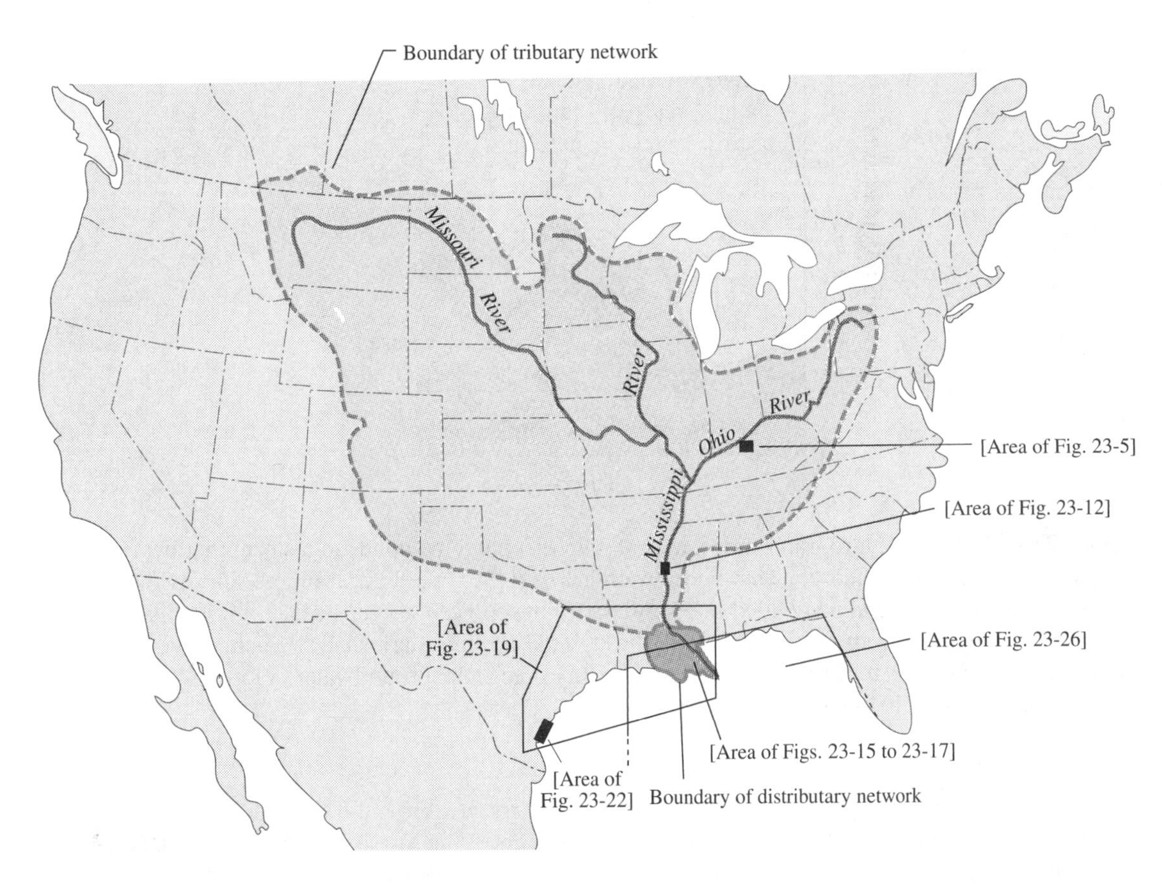

Figure 23-3. This index map locates the Mississippi River and its two largest tributaries. An ice sheet had repeatedly occupied the upper Mississippi Valley, and the close fit of the ice limit to the modern Ohio and Missouri Rivers suggests that these valleys were eroded when meltwater surged along the margin of the ice.

new land grew forward into the Gulf of Mexico as sediment was deposited at the river mouth (a process called *progradation*), thereby forcing the Mississippi to wander farther and farther to reach the sea. This is the region of the *distributary network* (Figure 23-2), where the master stream splits into smaller *distributaries* that fan out over the delta. A distributary network is invariably of much smaller area than the tributary network, in the Mississippi system having a ratio of 1 to 50.

Fluvial regimes Although every stream, great and small, experiences periods of flood and of low water, the pattern of these intervals—its flow regime—varies widely. Floods are well-known agents of geologic change, but events during the quieter but much longer intervals of normal flow are also effective, and the stream self-adjusts its channel to cope with both condition. Smaller streams respond more vigorously and quickly to storms than larger streams do. For a small stream the *discharge*, which is the volume of water passing a given point per unit time (such as cubic meters/second), rises and drops quickly, hence the familiar term "flash flood." A *hydrograph*, a plot of discharge over time, shows some of the contributions to the discharge (Figure 23-4). Streams continue to flow during dry weather, fed by water seeping laterally through the ground into the channel, and to this is added runoff directly from the land during a time of rainfall. In Figure 23-4 we see that seepage into a stream had been diminishing, and that a storm event temporarily created surface runoff while also replenishing the stored groundwater. Hydrographs for the Ohio River at Louisville, Kentucky, and for Beargrass Creek, a small local tributary, nicely illustrate contrasting stream behaviors (Figure 23-5).

The Pleistocene braided Mississippi Both the day-to-day variations in the *weather* and longer-term changes in *climate* influence the regime of a stream. Several thousand years ago during the Pleistocene Epoch, an ice sheet had overspread the northern part of the United States, pushing south approximately to the present positions of the Ohio and Missouri Rivers (Figure 23-3). Melting of this ice was catastrophically rapid, such that the Mississippi received an enormous surge of meltwater in the

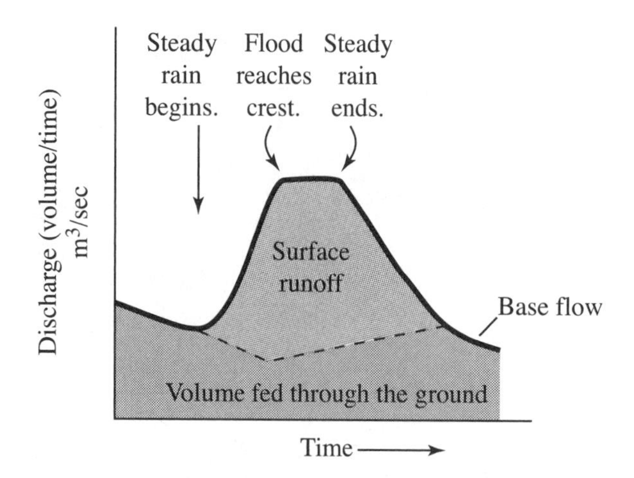

Figure 23-4. A simple hydrograph shows how stream discharge responds to a storm that begins and ends abruptly. The area under the curve corresponds to height x width, or (volume/time) x time = volume of water. The area can be divided into sub-areas that represent direct surface runoff (light shade) and water that enters the stream via baseflow through the ground (dark shade). Such a division of the hydrograph may be legally important because in many places the groundwater belongs to the private citizen, but the runoff belongs to the state.

summertime, but with sharply reduced flow during winter freezes. Both the water discharge and the load of entrained sediment fluctuated widely. In this climatic regime, the Mississippi became a *braided* stream in which small channels split and rejoined, threading in and out like strands of braided hair. During high discharge a braided stream can move anything from fine to very coarse particles, but during low discharge it cannot handle the sedimentary load, which is dumped as innumerable shifting bars or small islands of sand and gravel. Streams that drain glaciated areas are commonly braided (Figure 23-6).

Ice sheets are nourished by snowfall precipitated from humid air masses, and these in turn had evaporated from the ocean, the ultimate water reservoir. Growth of ice sheets on the continents was accompanied by a fall of sea level, and this triggered a response from the Mississippi and all other streams that enter the sea (Figure 23-7). The *long profile* is a plot of the elevation of a stream channel from its source to its mouth, typically having a steeper slope at the source and becoming gentler toward the mouth. Whatever the circumstance, the stream adjusts its long profile in order to maintain that characteristic shape. The control is *base level*, the deepest elevation to which a stream can erode, which can be no lower than the bottom of the stream channel at the mouth. If sea level were to fall, the gradient and erosive power would increase, and the stream would regain its long profile by cutting down into the landscape. If sea level were to rise, gradient and erosive power would decrease, and the stream would adjust by depositing fluvial sediment, elevating its long profile. It is amazing that a change in base level is reflected in changes upstream perhaps thousands of kilometers from the mouth.

And so it was with the Mississippi River. At the height of the recent Ice Age, the Gulf shoreline receded to the edge of the continental shelf, far seaward of today's coast, and the braided Mississippi River lengthened and entrenched (deepened) its valley. When the ice melted and sea level rose, the river backfilled its valley with alluvium. The climate also became temperate and more humid, causing the river slowly to transform into a *meandering* stream (Figure 23-8).

The modern meandering Mississippi Meanders are smooth serpentine (snaky) loops named after a stream in Turkey once known as the Maiandros (see the front photograph of this chapter). All streams are conduits of water and sediment, but the sediment is not always in motion. During prolonged stable sea level (with stable base level and long profile), the valley is not cut down or backfilled, but rather the stream spends its energy by migrating laterally across its floodplain and possibly cutting against a distant upland (Figure 23-8). In this environment, fluvial sediment moves by fits and starts, being picked up and set down again and again.

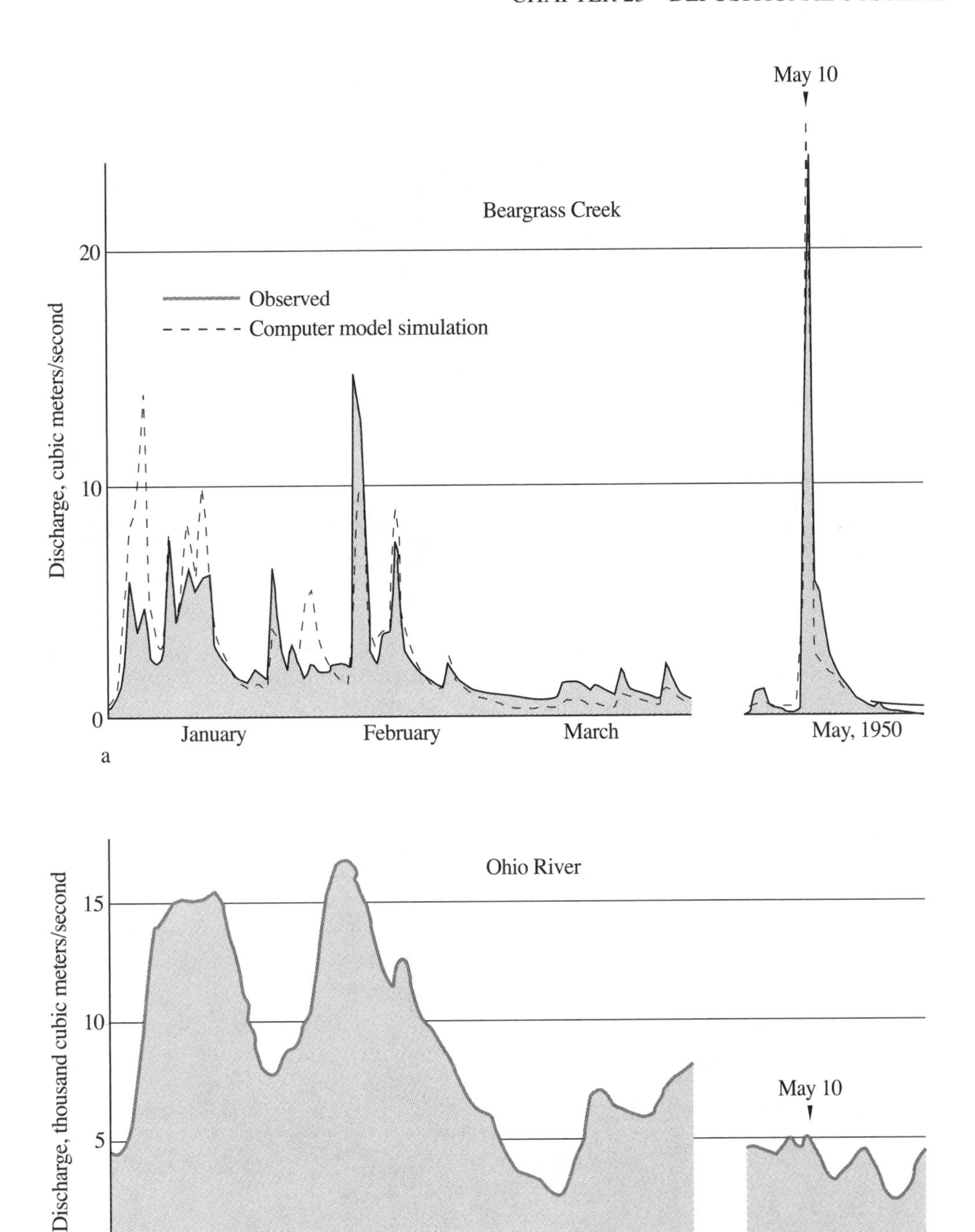

Figure 23-5. (*a*) Beargrass Creek drains a 48 km² basin in Louisville, Kentucky. Discharge *vs.* time (the hydrograph) depends upon timing and amount of rainfall, size and shape of the drainage basin, vegetation, saturation of the soil, and other factors. Its characteristics are important to the proper designing of bridges, flood-control channels, road elevations, and the like. Stanford University geologists devised a computer simulation (broken curve) that fits the observed hydrograph moderately well. [*After N. H. Crawford and R. K. Linsley, "Digital Simulation in Hydrology: Stanford Watershed Model IV,"* Technical Report No. 39, 1966.] (*b*) A gauging station on the Ohio River 8 km. downstream from the mouth of Beargrass Creek provided data for this hydrograph during the same time interval. On May 10, a local storm created a huge spike on the Beargrass hydrograph, but hardly a ripple on the Ohio River hydrograph. Note the great difference in vertical scales of the two hydrographs. [*Data from* U. S. Geological Survey Water-Supply Paper 1173, part 3, Ohio River Basin, *1953*.]

Figure 23-6. Although the Mississippi River does not occupy a rugged glaciated terrain, during the Ice Age the Mississippi would have resembled this braided stream draining Mt. Denali, Alaska. The steep gradient of a braided stream enables it to transport coarse sediment (sand-size up to large boulders) that is moved along during frequent times of high water discharge.

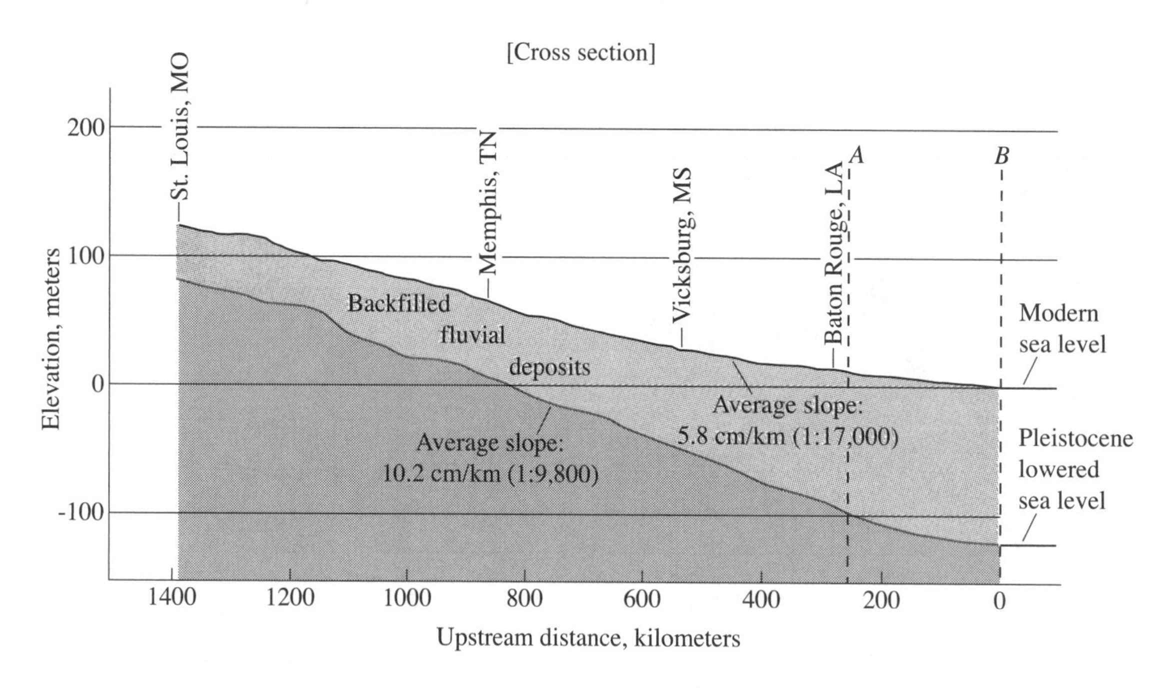

Figure 23-7. Lowered sea level during the Pleistocene Ice Age induced the Mississippi to cut a deeper and steeper long profile (lower). The Mississippi responded to today's elevated sea level by depositing sediment until it had established the upper profile. Volume of sediment placed in storage between the two curves exceeds 4000 km^3. An amazingly low average gradient (1: 17,000) of the modern stream is sufficient to enable the river to carry to its mouth more than a *million* metric tons of sediment per day! Within the past 5 thousand years, the front of the Mississippi delta has prograded approximately 200 km. from a former shoreline near Baton Rouge (vertical line *A*) to the modern shoreline (vertical line *B*). [*After H. N. Fisk*, Geological Investigation of the Alluvial Valley of the Lower Mississippi River, *Mississippi River Commission, Vicksburg, MS, 1944.*]

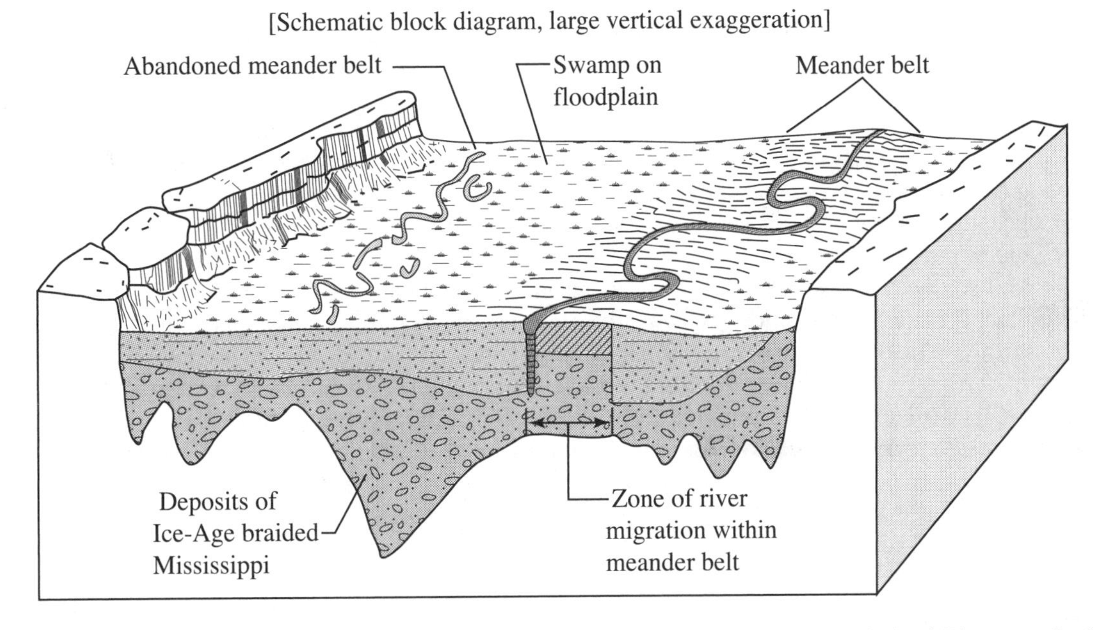

Figure 23-8. This schematic block diagram shows the modern meandering Mississippi River perched upon its meander belt whose crest lies as much as 3 meters above the level of the floodplain. Present in the floodplain are discontinuous remnants of an older, abandoned meander system. Braided sediment of the ancestral Mississippi River lies concealed beneath the recent floodplain sediment. [*After H. N. Fisk*, Fine-grained alluvial deposits and their effects on Mississippi River Activity, *Mississippi River Commission, Vicksburg, MS, 1947*]

Contained within the water mass are *dissolved* load, *suspended* load, and *bedload*. Dissolved ions (Na^+, Ca^{2+}, etc.) go directly to the sea and do not concern us here. The river water is *turbulent*, filled with swirling eddies and chaotic internal motion. Turbulence is the chief factor in eroding and transporting sediment. Turbulent water can pick up and suspend a tiny clay particle because, locally, the water is moving upward faster than the particle sinks through it. Bedload, consisting generally of sand-size and coarser particles, is too heavy to be kept suspended, and it hops or rolls along the streambed (Figure 23-9). Thus the sediment is naturally sorted, the suspended load potentially able to be swept over the top of the bank during a flood while the bedload stays confined to the channel.

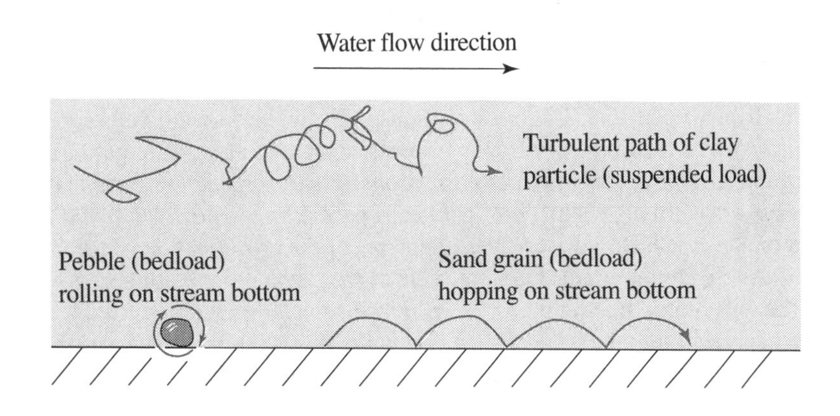

Figure 23-9. Transportation of suspended load and bedload.

Consider a meander bend and a straight channel segment of a river that is set in the midst of a floodplain (Figure 23-10). The situation is simpler in the straight segment whose cross section, and zones of maximum velocity or turbulence are symmetrical. At a bend the water hurls its force against the outer bank, scouring away the soft, unconsolidated material. Turbulence is at a maximum on the outside of the bend where erosion occurs, and at a minimum on the inside where deposition occurs. In cross section, the asymmetrical channel is deeper near the bank being undercut. A crescent-shape *point bar* composed of sand (bed material) is deposited on the inner bank. In this dynamic situation of erosion and deposition, the entire channel migrates in the direction of the outer bend, leaving an accumulation of older point bars in its wake in the inner bend.

And so, the river "snake" is writhing as meanders continually move around over the face of the floodplain. If a snake can swallow its own tail, so can a river meet itself coming and going. Suppose that a meander loop has become extremely accentuated [Figure 23-11(a)]. If the river were to breach through the narrow neck (perhaps during flood), it would abandon the old, lengthy path in favor of the shortcut [Figure 23-11(b)]. Eventually the entrances to the old loop become plugged with clay, leaving a segment of abandoned channel, an *oxbow lake*. In Chapter 25 we shall note a surface, called the water table,

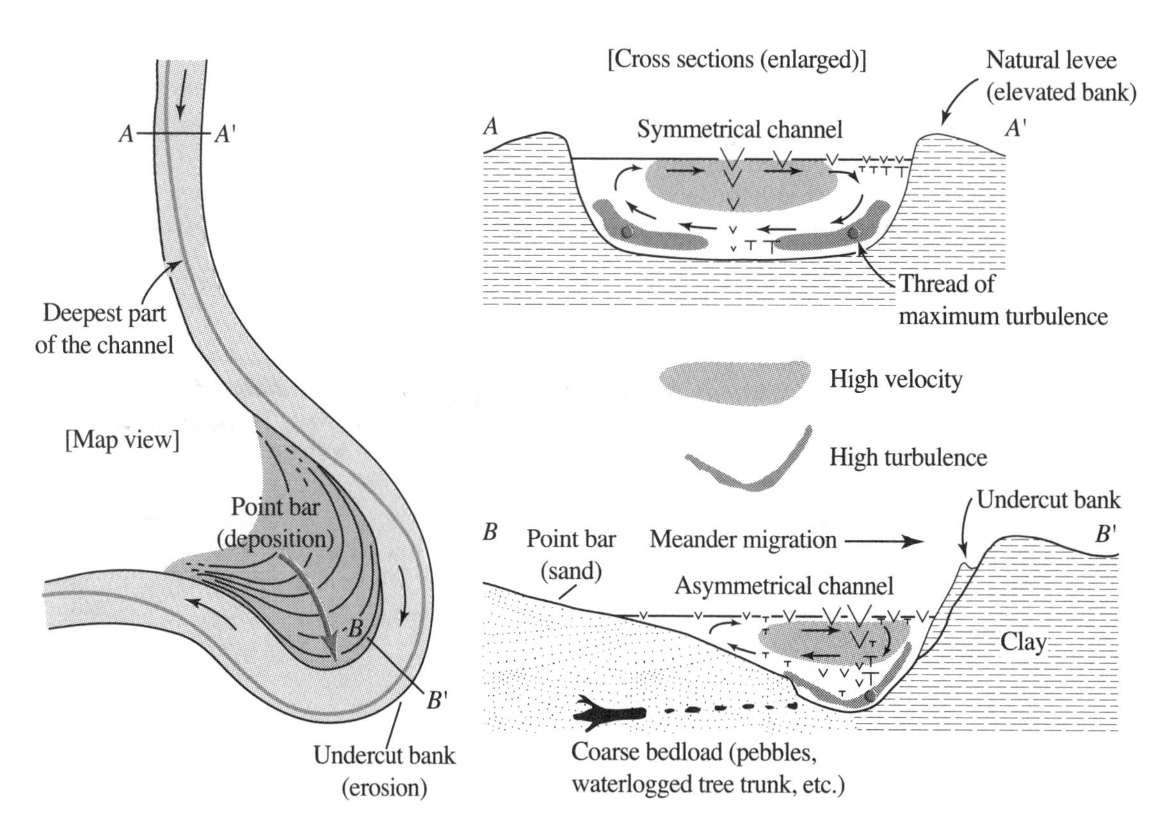

Figure 23-10. Relative sizes of *V* or *T* in cross sections indicate the forward velocity of water or degree of turbulence. Water is turbulently flowing downstream, and also participating in an overturning motion as it rounds the bend (arrows in cross sections). As the channel migrates laterally (cross section *B* – *B*´, heavy arrow in map), the point bar keeps pace with erosion also by building laterally (gray shaded area on the map). Because of the asymmetry of the cross section of the channel at a bend, the deepest part of the channel migrates from one side of the stream to the other in going from one bend to the next (heavy colored line on map). "Lag" gravels, waterlogged tree trunks, and other bedload debris are incorporated into the base of the point bar deposit. (In Triassic times, huge trees of the Petrified Forest, Arizona, were buried in a fluvial environment, then silicified.)

beneath which the ground is saturated with water. In most places the water table lies below the earth's surface, but in a lake the earth's surface lies below the water table. Eventual destruction of an oxbow lake is not by drying up (the channel lies below the water table), but rather, by becoming silted up by later flood deposits.

a

b

Figure 23-11. (*a*) At flood stage (note the standing water) the river flow threatens to breach through the narrow neck of a meander. (*b*) In another place, the stream has bypassed a meander loop (now an oxbow lake) and it has locally and temporarily established a straight channel.

Figure 23-10 also shows a *natural levee*, riverbank that is somewhat elevated above the level of the floodplain. During flooding, as water laden with suspended sediment overtops the bank, it abruptly slows down due to friction, and it drops the sediment across the floodplain and prominently upon the natural levee. A river channel seeks the lowest elevation, but the process of overbank deposition builds up the river, causing it to flow along the crest of a ridge of its own making, a *meander belt*. A tributary that is not as vigorous as the Mississippi with its high natural levee, is forced to flow a long distance in parallel before finally joining the master stream. Such a tributary is called a "Yazoo stream" after the Yazoo River in the State of Mississippi.

Buildup of natural levees also explains why the Mississippi has occasionally abandoned not just an individual meander loop but also an entire meander belt. The lower Mississippi Valley contains more than 400 abandoned meander loops, and at least 5 abandoned meander belts. If the river were to breach its natural levee during flood, it might find an alternate pathway through a distant part of the floodplain that lies at a lower elevation. This would be a disaster to farms and communities along the stretch that had been abandoned, and to those in the pathway of the relocated part. Because levees are a protection against flooding, they are artificially enhanced along the Mississippi and other rivers such as the Yellow River and Yangtze River in China. Densely populated, rich agricultural floodplain in eastern China faces chronic threat of flooding. In 1954, a flood on the Yangtze destroyed 2.2 million homes and killed 31 thousand people. It may have approximated a 100-year flood. (An area is not secure for the next entire century following a 100-year flood, but rather there is a 1% probability for such a flood in any given year.) Does an artificially elevated levee truly protect, or will it release even worse devastation when some future pent-up flood bursts through?

Engineers have long attempted to control the Mississippi River by taking advantage of its natural activity. They have directed the flow with dikes, shored up the embankments against erosion, and dredged to encourage the river to switch course into some new channel. They have made serious mistakes and learned hard lessons in a program of alteration so extensive as to transform much of the Mississippi River into the Mississippi Ditch (Figure 23-12). A lasting effect of this tampering has been to reduce the length of the river. This is good news to the river bargemen, except that the altered river dumps more sediment into shifting, shallow shoals—which is definitely not good news. With a shorter pathway and steeper gradient, the river had more energy, which it used by attacking its banks, widening the channel.

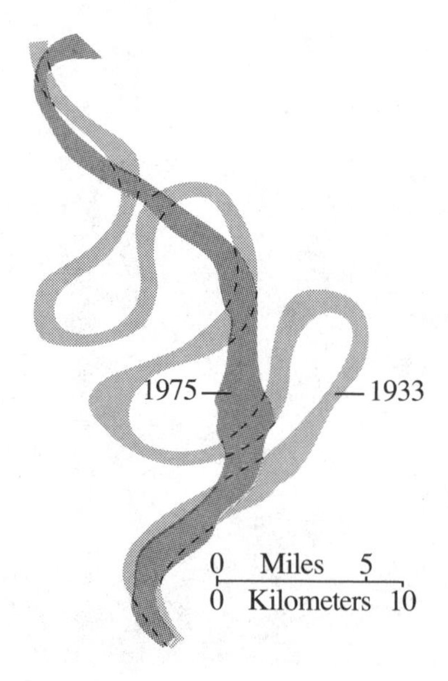

Figure 23-12. Early in the 20th Century, a certain part the Mississippi's course was extremely serpentine (gray), but since then the Corps of Engineers has "trained" the river with a series of cutoffs into a nearly straight course (colored). [*After B. R. Winkley, "Manmade cutoffs on the Lower Mississippi River: Conception, Construction and River Response,"* U. S. Army Corps of Engineers District, Vicksburg, MS, Report 300-2, *1977.*]

Viewed from high altitude, a mature floodplain such as that of the lower Mississippi River is seen to be a fantastic tangled maze of abandoned meander scars (Figure 23-13). Differences in vegetation and soil color make the structure of the floodplain more evident when viewed from above than on the ground. What are the time scales of these interesting and complex river processes? A clay particle is continually jostled as the turbulent river sweeps it around a bend in a matter of minutes to hours. A flood surge may take days or weeks to traverse the Mississippi to its mouth, and great floods recur every decade or so. Meander loops are abandoned, and new loops generated in a century or two. Pieces of land that were

Figure 23-13. Each lateral swing of a meander loop has erased an older deposit, replacing it with a new point-bar deposit. [*Tobin Research, Inc., photograph.*]

continuous when the States of Louisiana and Mississippi were created in the early 1800s are now forlornly isolated on the opposite side of the river from the mother state! Thousands of years may go by before the river switches out of one meander belt to occupy another.

Ancient fluvial sediments are important sources of petroleum and natural gas, called *hydrocarbons* because the molecules in these substances are composed chiefly of hydrogen and carbon. Initially deposited in the overbank mud or swamp of a floodplain, the organic matter transforms into hydrocarbons with burial and gentle heating. These hydrocarbons are fluids, able to migrate into the open pore spaces in sand in a point bar, but unable to leak upward because impermeable floodplain mud also lies overhead (Figure 23-14). Thus the floodplain mud is a *source* of hydrocarbons, which migrate into a *reservoir* (point-bar sand), there to be stored because mud acts as a *trap* or *seal*. Every deposit of oil or gas owes its existence to a source, reservoir, and seal.

DELTAS

About 70 percent of all terrigenous clastic sediments accumulate in *deltas*, where streams discharge into open bodies of water. The term was coined 25 centuries ago by Herodotus who was struck by the similarity between the Greek letter Δ and the triangular shape of the Nile delta. A delta is an uneasy place, an arena that is not quite land and not quite sea. As the river delivers sediment, the delta builds forward (it progrades); meanwhile, waves, tides, and longshore currents are redistributing the sediment away from the river mouth. It is a battle and, depending upon which processes are dominant, the shapes of other deltas may be different from the classic simple shape of the Nile delta.

The delta cycle Of course, the fluvial environment continues on across the part of a delta that lies above sea level (the *delta plain*). Compared to the immensity of this plain, though, even the mighty Mississippi River seems to be hardly more than a winding thread. How could the river have deposited the remote parts of the delta, as much as 250 kilometers distant? Today's situation offers a clue to the explanation. Far upstream on the delta plain, a major distributary, the Atchafalaya River, branches off from the main channel of the Mississippi, diverting flow along a pathway to the sea that is three times

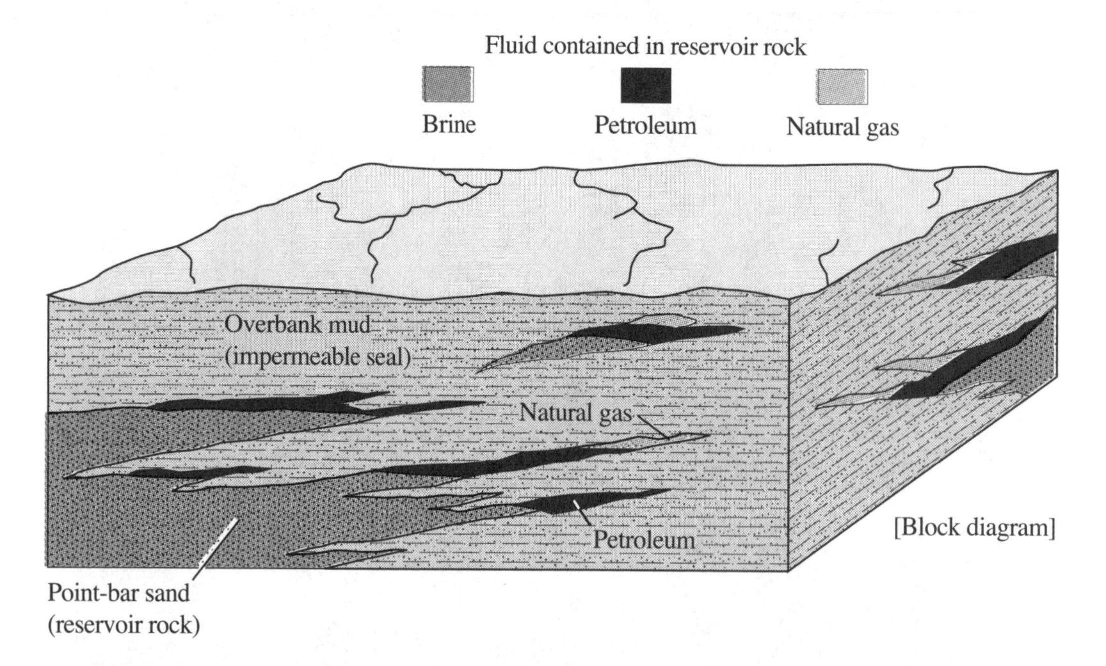

Figure 23-14. Drilling for hydrocarbons in fluvial deposits is an important, if tricky, business. The trick is to strike the highly productive, but localized, sandstone reservoirs. Not even a direct penetration guarantees success, because fluids in the buried point-bar deposits may have acted like the bubble that goes from side to side in a huge spirit level. Low-density hydrocarbons would be trapped at the upper end of the tilted spirit level, but sand in the lower end would be saturated, not with oil or gas, but with worthless brine (salt water).

shorter than that of the master stream (Figure 23-15). The Atchafalaya would capture all of the flow if engineers had not built a system of locks to limit the diversion to about 30 percent of the total. Intervention was necessary to prevent the downstream cities of Baton Rouge and New Orleans from being stranded along a stagnant, stinking slough!

Figure 23-15 summarizes what has happened again and again during the 10 thousand years before humans were present to interfere with nature's processes. Wherever the Mississippi enters the Gulf, it builds forward a projection, a *delta lobe.* Core material from numerous borings has revealed at least 17 such lobes that are grouped into 5 major lobe complexes in the modern delta. Eventually the building of a delta lobe is self-defeating, for as the river travels farther across previously deposited sediment, its gradient diminishes. More importantly, the delta plain everywhere is subsiding (sinking). Freshly deposited mud is 80 percent water that is slowly squeezed out during burial. Delivery of a million tons of sediment per day places an enormous load on the earth's crust. Just as a mountain range responds to erosion by uplifting (Chapter 16), the opposite effect occurs in a delta where the load of new sediment depresses the crust. Together, the processes of *sediment compaction* and *regional isostatic adjustment* produce subsidence that may exceed a meter per century. The Atchafalaya distributary is aggressive because it traverses old much-subsided delta lobes; its gradient is three times steeper than that of the master stream.

Dating of organic debris by the carbon-14 method (Chapter 24) shows that these abrupt diversions of the river have occurred every few hundred years. If you turn on a garden hose full force and let go, it thrashes about unpredictably, spewing water. Similarly, the mouth of the Mississippi switches about erratically within the delta while old, abandoned lobes continue to sink. Louisiana is rapidly losing land

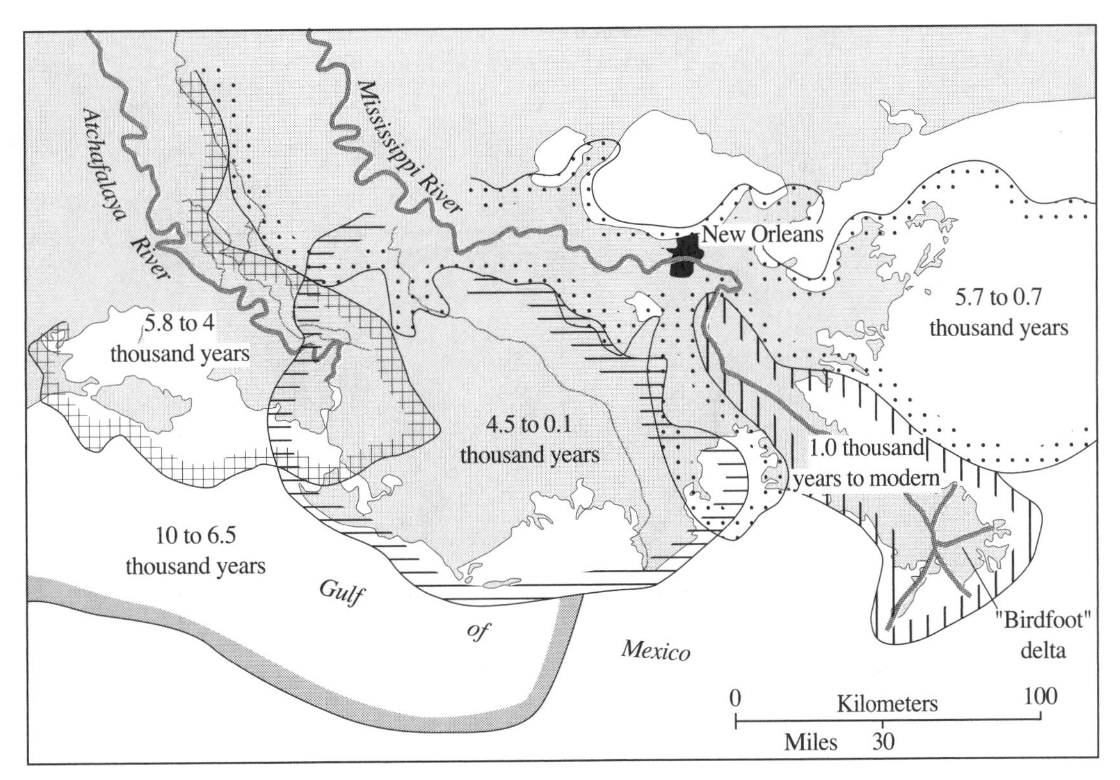

Figure 23-15. This map displays five principal delta-lobe complexes, each consisting of smaller sediment lobes, which make up the modern Mississippi delta. Periods of active progradation in each lobe are given in thousands of years before the present. At certain times, the river was feeding two lobes simultaneously. In the lobe that is active today, the master stream is the "arm" that breaks into distributaries (at the "wrist") that feed the Birdfoot delta (the "hand") in which each distributary projects "fingers" of natural levees into the Gulf of Mexico. A moth-eaten appearance of the shoreline of older lobes bears witness to subsidence and invasion by the sea. [*After D. E. Frazier, "Recent Deltaic Deposits of the Mississippi River: Their Development and Chronology,"* Transactions, Gulf Coast Association of Geological Societies, *vol. 17, 1967.*]

because subsidence is widespread while only a single small delta lobe is currently being constructed. After the small settlement of New Orleans outgrew its original perch upon the natural levee, cypress swamps behind the levee were cleared for the city to expand. Today, half of the city has sunk below sea level, necessitating that rainwater and sewage be pumped out. A great hurricane or flood would be disastrous. Life in some parts of the world is in jeopardy for geologic reasons.

The active delta lobe, called the "Birdfoot" because of its short, stubby distributaries that spread out like a chicken's toes, is about 600 years old and it contains its own smaller and more short-lived lobes (Figure 23-16). Natural levees continue across the Birdfoot and into the shallow Gulf of Mexico. Sand

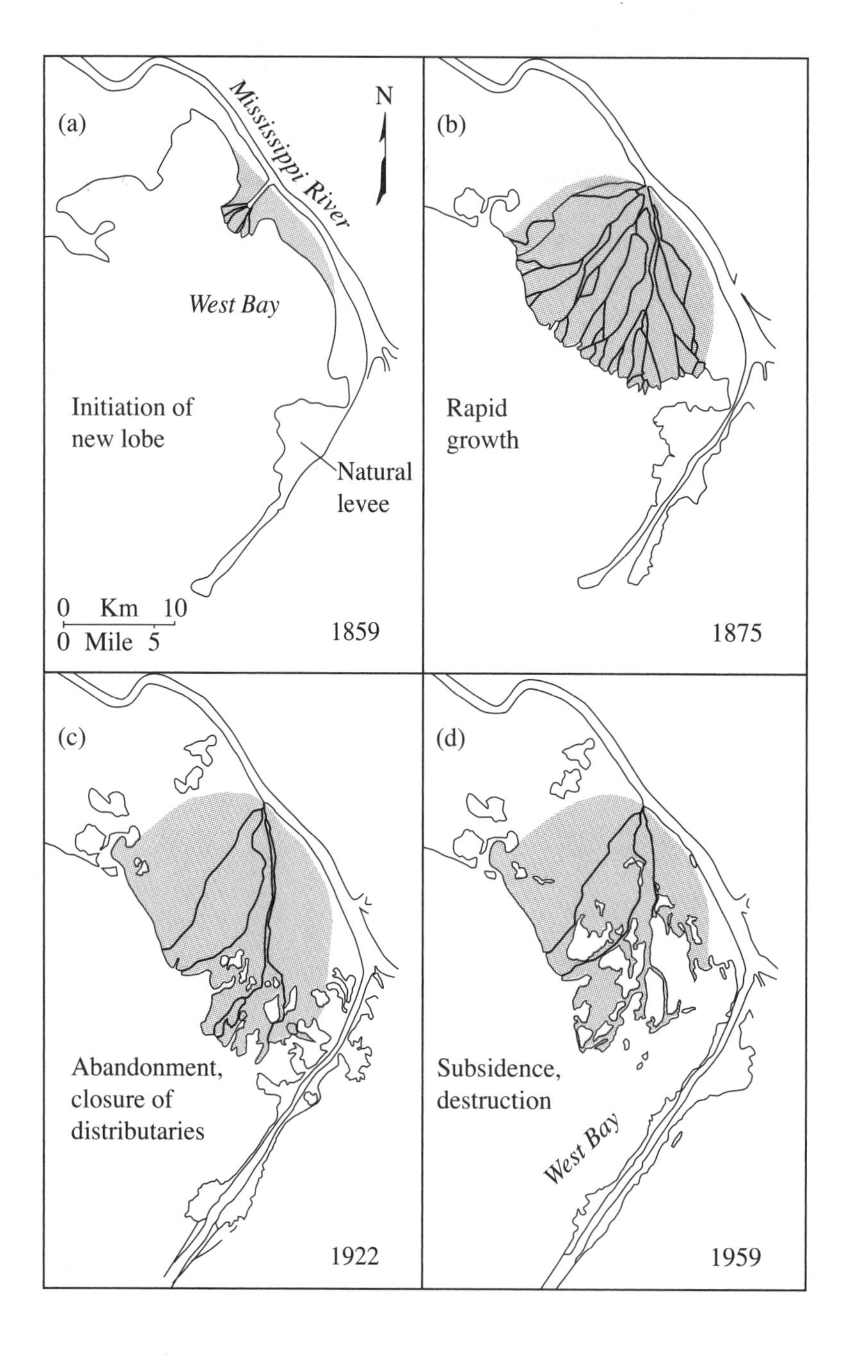

Figure 23-16. It took just one century, from 1859 to 1959, for a delta sub-lobe within the Birdfoot to bud (*a*), grow rapidly (*b*), become abandoned and malnourished (*c*), and be largely destroyed (*d*). [*After D. J. Morgan, "Geoscience and Man, Volume XVI: the Mississippi River delta: legal-geomorphologic evaluation of historic shoreline changes,"* School of Geosciences, Louisiana State University, *1977.*]

grains (bedload) are confined to the bed of a distributary channel or are deposited at its mouth (Figure 23-17). During a flood, the mud particles (suspended load) can overtop the natural levees to fill in the bays between distributaries. The distributaries deliver a plume of fresh but muddy water into the Gulf where it mixes with salt water (Figure 23-18). In the freshwater environment, each microscopic clay particle had been armored with electrical charges, causing the particles to repel one another and remain suspended. Upon reaching the Gulf, the charges on these particles are neutralized by ions dissolved in seawater, permitting the clay particles to touch and clump together. Down they go, accumulating immediately offshore as an enormous mass of *prodelta mud.*

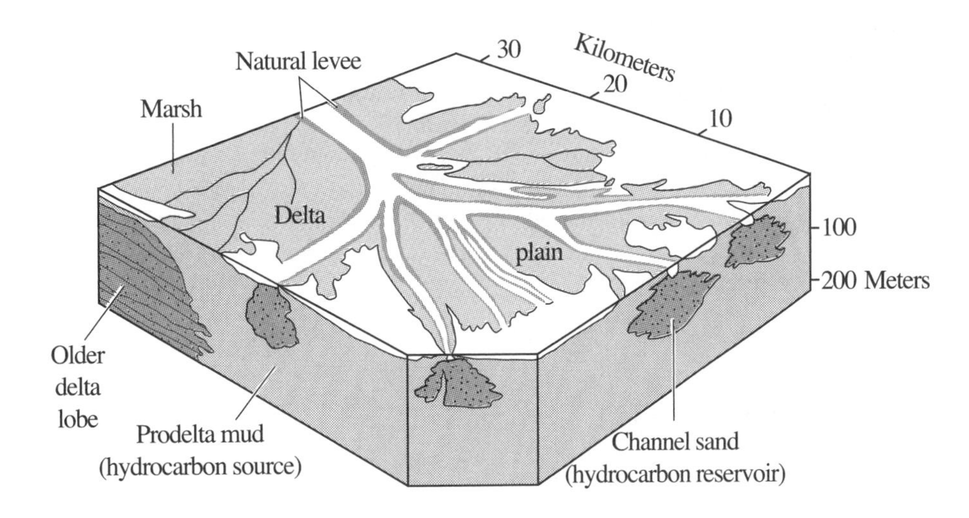

Figure 23-17. A block diagram of the active Mississippi delta lobe explains its birdfoot shape. As thick, water-saturated prodelta mud continues to compact (subside), the distributary channels become all the better able to conduct the flow of water. Hence, thick finger-like sand bodies accumulate beneath just a few well-stabilized distributary channels. [*After H. N. Fisk and others, "Sedimentary Framework of the Modern Mississippi Delta,"* Journal of Sedimentary Petrology, *vol. 24, no. 2, 1954.*]

Figure 23-18. This photograph, taken from an orbiting satellite, shows a plume of muddy Mississippi River water mixing with marine water of the open Gulf where the sediment promptly precipitates as prodelta mud. [*National Aeronautics and Space Administration (NASA) photograph.*]

And so, the delta establishes a sort of rhythm. While the river is depositing sand and mud in one lobe, the other lobes are subsiding. Eventually this causes the river to abandon that lobe to start a new one. Marine waters reoccupy lobes that have subsided below sea level, there to deposit limestone. All three of the common sedimentary rocks (shale, sandstone, limestone) accumulate in a delta environment, and the process of subsiding, depositing, switching, and stacking continues as the *delta cycle*.

Delta resources Satellite images of Egypt show dramatically that, except for the well-vegetated valley and delta of the Nile River, all is desert where nothing grows and almost no one lives. Egypt's population depends upon the fertile alluvial soil to produce three good food crops every year, and other deltas worldwide are of agricultural importance.

Another resource is the 30 percent of the world's production of oil and gas that comes from ancient delta sediments, for example in the Mississippi delta, the North Slope of Alaska, and the Gulf Coast of Texas (Figure 23-19). In the delta setting, organic-rich prodelta mud is the source of hydrocarbon molecules. The resulting fluids migrate out of the source, to be stored in the reservoir comprised of the long, finger-like bodies of sand in distributary channels (Figure 23-17). Impermeable mud in the delta cycle that overlies this sedimentary package is the seal that prevents escape of the hydrocarbons.

Nearly all of the earth's coal originated in delta marshlands. Thick deposits of peat accumulate in a saltwater marsh or (in another stage of the delta cycle) a freshwater marsh, and forests grow in delta swamplands. With progressively deeper burial the organic material metamorphoses into lignite, then bituminous coal, and finally anthracite coal.

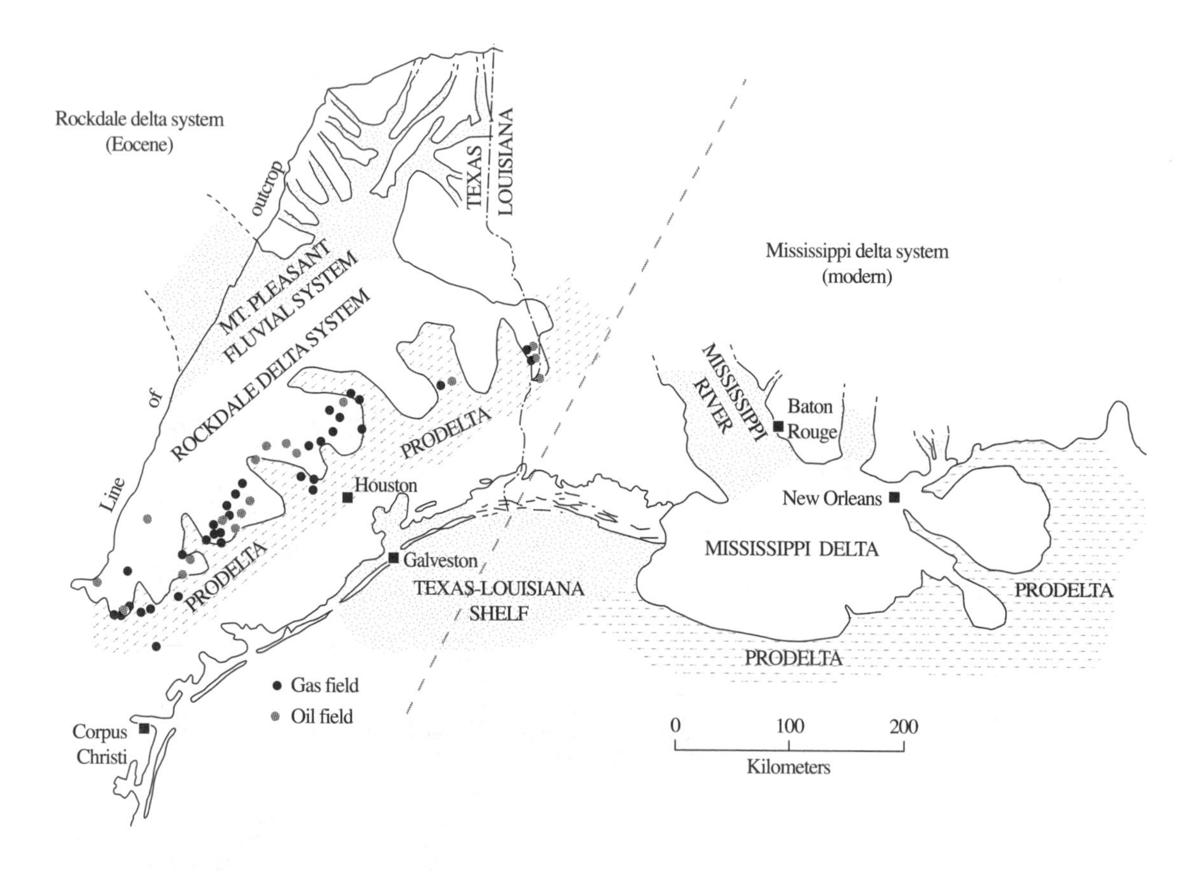

Figure 23-19. Early in the Eocene Epoch a delta system, much like the Mississippi delta in size and shape, developed along the Texas Gulf Coast (but somewhat inland from the modern coast). Today, only a little of this coastward-dipping sediment is exposed as a narrow band at the surface, the remainder being deeply buried and the source of prolific resources of oil and gas. Somewhat younger hydrocarbon-rich deltas of Miocene age lie buried beneath the modern Mississippi delta. [*After W. L. Fisher and J. H. McGowen, "Depositional Systems in Wilcox Group (Eocene) of Texas and their Relationship to Occurrence of Oil and Gas,"* Bulletin of the American Association of Petroleum Geologists, *vol. 53, no. 1, 1969.*]

COASTAL SYSTEMS

Some of the sediment is further distributed into deep water or along an adjacent coast. Attempts to classify coastal landforms are in confusion, probably because many changes have occurred in the past million years as continental ice sheets have expanded (causing sea level to fall), and melted (causing sea level to rise). Sea level is currently rising so rapidly that processes along coasts are out of equilibrium. An example of disequilibrium is a coast that contains deeply indented bays; nature at equilibrium attempts to create a rather straight shoreline.

Shoreline processes Perhaps it is surprising that, for all their energy, coastal processes cannot keep up with changing geologic conditions. Who has not stood in awe at the power of the surf crashing on a beach? Typically about 8000 waves will hammer that beach each day. However, what matters is not just the amount of energy but also how it is directed. A river, a dip-fed system, transports sediment efficiently downstream; in contrast, wave action washes sediment back and forth inefficiently on a shoreline, which is a strike-fed system.

Waves can originate in several ways. Tidal bulges in the world ocean, one on each side of the earth and traveling around it daily, might be thought of as the largest "waves." A rare wave type is the *tsunami*, incorrectly called a tidal wave, which is energized by a sudden disturbance such as an underwater earthquake. Tsunamis travel as fast as 250 meters per second, but they pass unnoticed beneath a ship at sea because of their very long wavelength. Only upon approaching a distant shore does a tsunami transform into a monster wave.

Persistent urging of the wind generates the familiar water waves whose pattern changes throughout the year according to such factors as prevailing wind direction, and whether a season is calm or stormy. In a water wave (as in a seismic surface wave) the water (or rock) is deformed only temporarily,

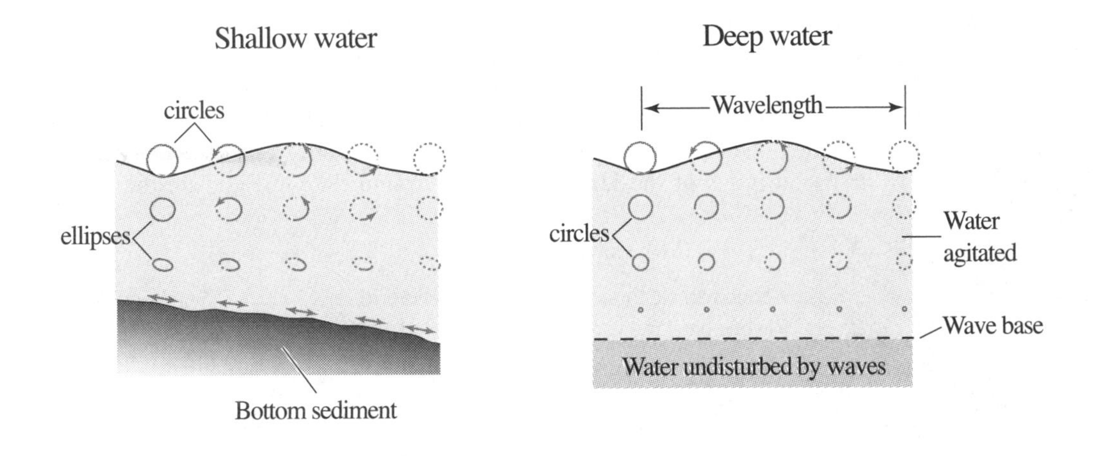

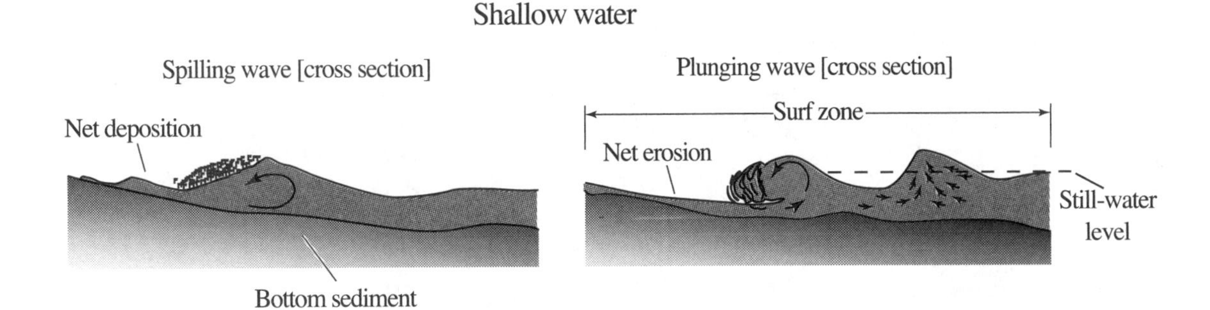

Figure 23-20. Cross sections show the motion of water molecules when a wave passes through deep water (circles) or shallow water (ellipses). All of the particles in a vertical column of water move to the right and to the left in unison (that is, in phase). Plunging waves topple violently, accomplishing net erosion during a stormy season. Spilling waves tumble more gently down into the trough ahead, accomplishing net deposition during seasons of milder weather.

each particle returning to its original position after the wave has passed by. Colored droplets of neutral buoyancy are introduced into a water tank to act as visible tracers in wave experiments (Figure 23-20). Their motions show that a water molecule at the surface describes a large circular pathway, while at greater depth the circles are smaller and smaller, ultimately shrinking to a point (no water motion) at *wave base*. Below this depth, which is around 10 meters, not even the largest waves can disturb the water. (Certain fish in the Gulf of Mexico seek shelter below wave base when they sense an impending hurricane.) As the wave enters shallow water, friction against the bottom impedes its internal motion. Water that is deeper in the wave does not move in circles, but in ever smaller and more flattened ellipses, and against the bottom it simply drags sediment back and forth. Meanwhile, the waveform at the surface continues to move forward rapidly, outdistancing the deeper part of the wave whose motion is retarded. The wave steepens in the surf zone, becoming unstable and it breaks into a plunging wave or spilling wave (Figure 23-20).

When the wind blows obliquely at the shore, some of the energy of the breaking waves goes to support *longshore drift*. A wave swashes sediment diagonally up on the beach, but the flow recedes straight down the beach face passively under the influence of gravity, and then the next wave repeats the process. Sand grains wander along the shore in an irregular saw-tooth manner, as much as a hundred or so meters in a single day (Figure 23-21). In the surf zone a few meters offshore, the water itself slowly drifts as a *longshore current* parallel to the beach. Seasonal reversals of the prevailing wind direction along many coasts cause much of the sand to drift right back where it started. Such recycling makes the sediment become more mature (particles better sorted and more rounded: Chapter 8) without much net transport.

Barrier islands Permanent changes do occur, both worldwide in response to rising sea level, and locally, for example where the Mississippi delta is prograding into the Gulf of Mexico. Mississippi delta sediment is distributed westward by longshore drift along the shores of Louisiana and Texas. Deltas of the much smaller rivers of Texas are unable to prograde into the Gulf because the powerful longshore drift promptly sweeps the sediment away. About 18 thousand years ago, during the height of the Ice Age, the shoreline had retreated to the distant edge of the continental shelf. Melting commenced, and as a rising sea transgressed rapidly across this broad, gentle surface, the waves kept pushing the sand ahead to the shoreline. Beginning about 4 thousand years ago, sea level has continued to rise but much more slowly, and this led to the construction of a system of long offshore strips of sand, *barrier islands*. Barrier islands extend along 10 thousand miles of the U. S. coastline, around the Gulf and up the eastern

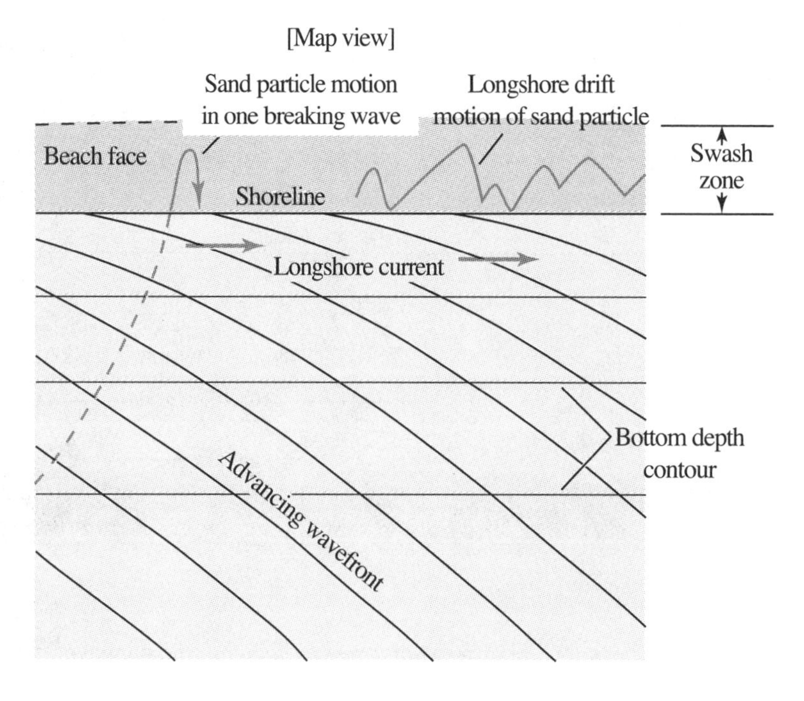

Figure 23-21. On a windy day, a sand grain "walks" many meters along a zigzag path in the swash zone of a beach, propelled by wave run-up and retreat. Offshore, the surf zone is carpeted by a fitfully drifting ribbon of sand, 100 meters or so wide and 5 to 10 centimeters thick.

seaboard to Long Island. In Texas there are two coastlines: an outer shore where barrier islands face the sea, and an inner shore on the edge of the mainland (Figure 23-22). Shallow lagoons intervene between the barrier islands and the mainland. Bays are deeply indented into the inner shore; they are "drowned" valleys that were downcut by streams during the time of low sea level.

Beware of the risk of locating a summer cottage on some lovely barrier island beach! During calm weather the waves build a beach with a gentle profile, but then comes the hurricane season. On average over the past century, a hurricane or very large storm has landed somewhere on the Texas coast about once a year. Storm waves attack the beach, steepening it and removing part of it into storage in deeper water, and your nice cottage could be destroyed or left stranded in the surf zone. Property owners are not aware that wave action will restore the beach, or are unwilling to wait for that to happen. They build walls perpendicular to the shore to intercept the drifting sand, only to deny that sand to the beach beyond. They build walls parallel to the shore that reflect the wave energy, causing the beach to be scoured away. After importing sand at great expense, they watch it become promptly removed as the waves attempt to maintain an equilibrium beach profile. No method of intervention works permanently in this very dynamic environment, and it is today's sad situation that there is not enough sand to go around. Most of the world's beaches are in erosional retreat. On a time scale of centuries or millennia, the barrier islands will eventually be joined to the mainland. Hurricanes breach through them, eroding sand that fills the lagoon. Other sand wanders offshore below wave base where it is removed from circulation.

GEOLOGY OF SALT

In the early Mesozoic Era, the Old and New Worlds were united into the supercontinent named Pangea (Chapter 22). South America was joined against the southern edge of North America, and the Gulf of Mexico did not yet exist. Then rifting and drifting of fragments commenced, opening the Gulf of Mexico and Atlantic Ocean. Initially these ocean basins were just narrow seaways whose connection with the world ocean was poorly established. High evaporation in this tropical setting caused the seawater to

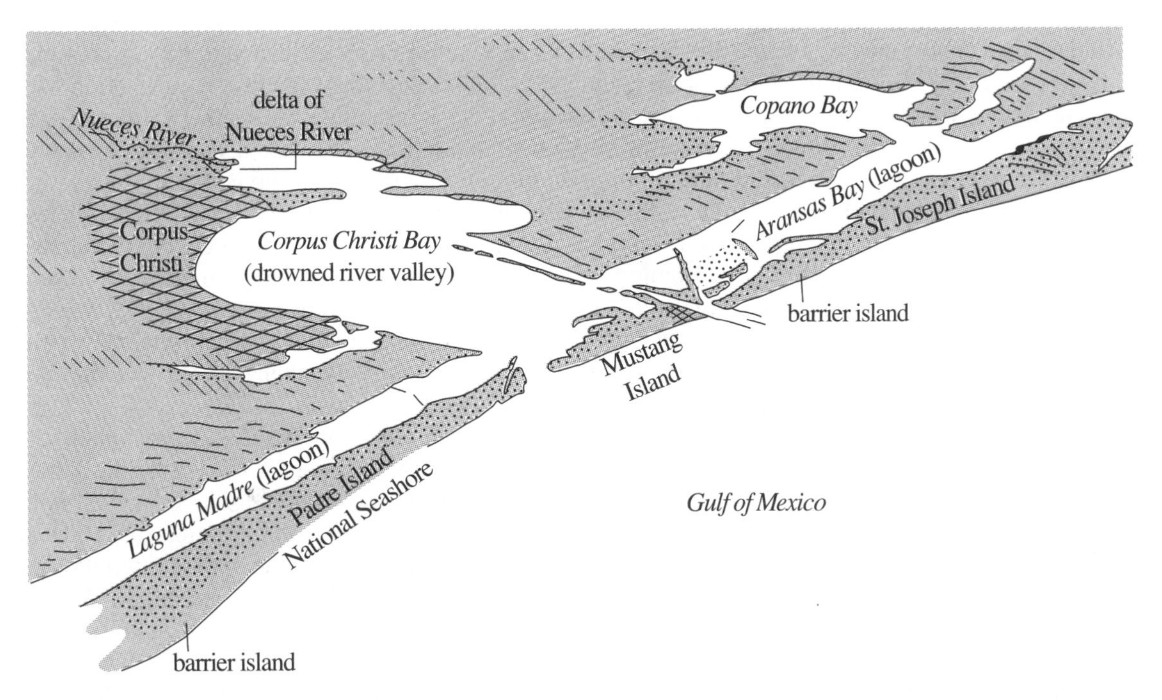

Figure 23-22. This oblique view of the south Texas coast near Corpus Christi includes four major components: barrier islands, lagoons behind the barriers, deeply indented estuaries (bays), and deltas that are filling in these estuaries. [*After J. H. McGowen and others, "Effects of Hurricane Celia: A Focus on Environmental Geologic Problems of the Texas Coastal Zone,"* Bureau of Economic Geology Circular 70-3. University of Texas at Austin, *1970.*]

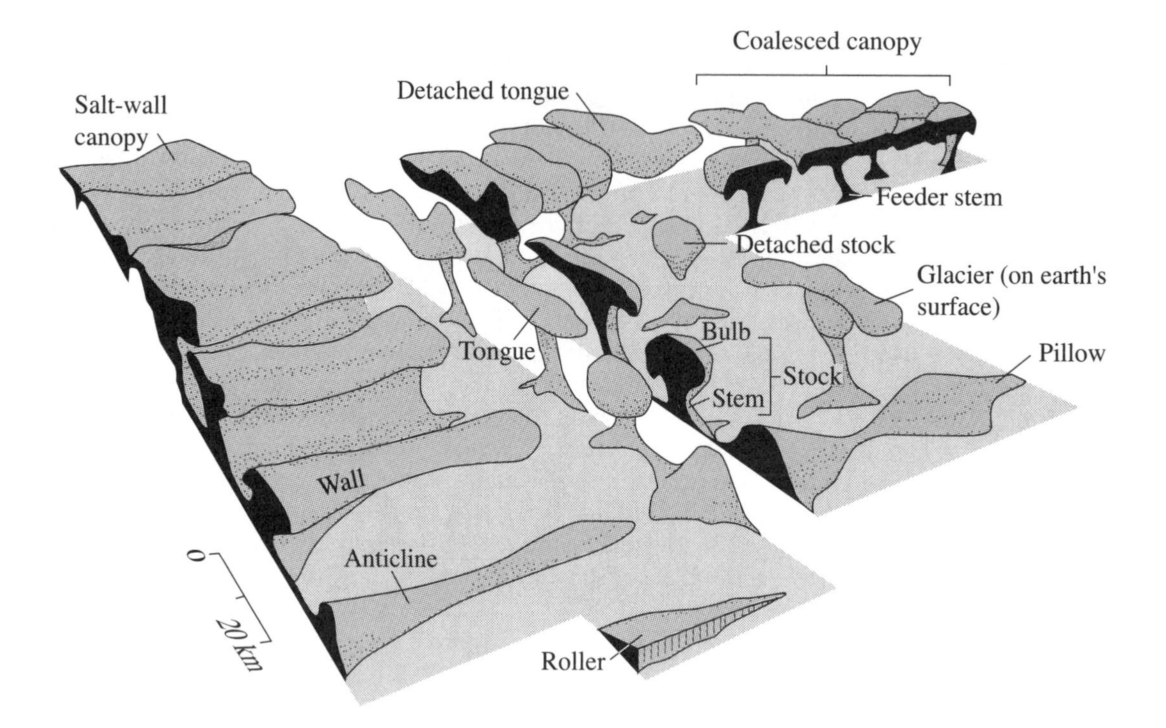

Figure 23-23. This schematic drawing depicts some shapes of salt bodies that have penetrated into overlying sediment. Only the salt is shown—not the enclosing sand and mud. [*After M. P. A. Jackson and C. J. Talbot, "A Glossary of Salt Tectonics,"* Bureau of Economic Geology Circular 91-4. University of Texas at Austin, *1991*.]

become supersaturated with salt, and then to precipitate enormous masses estimated to have been 4 to 6 *kilometers* thick in places! Further seafloor spreading eventually opened up a good communication with normal marine waters, ending the episode of salt deposition. In the meantime, the southern United States had become dry land upon which the newborn Mississippi and other rivers were depositing deltas into the Gulf of Mexico. Sand and mud prograded over the salt, placing it in deep burial.

Salt is a rather remarkable evaporite sediment. Its density, about 2.2 grams/cm^3, is significantly less than the density of compacted clastic sediment (about 2.4 grams/cm^3). Unlike mud, salt contains almost no water and it is incompressible, not becoming more dense with burial. It is a mechanically weak substance, so easily deformed that it acts almost like a fluid. An unstable situation arose in which *less* dense salt lay buried beneath *more* dense clastic sediment. The salt responded to the density inversion by penetrating through the overlying sediment. Where the salt pierced upward it assumed different shapes—pillows, tall spines, mushroomlike overhangs, or even a continuous wall (Figure 23-23).

These structures are commercial sources of halite (salt) and other commodities. Occasionally the top of a salt intrusion emerged near to the surface, as at Avery Island, Louisiana and High Island, Texas. Groundwater flushed away the easily dissolved salt, leaving a sheath, or *caprock*, of less soluble impurities, notably anhydrite ($CaSO_4$). Caprock environments may contain water, calcium sulfate, and oil and gas—all of the ingredients necessary for sulfate-reducing bacteria to flourish. One of the bacterial waste products is H_2S, which has been converted into large quantities of valuable native sulfur (S) in many caprocks. Spindletop, the first gusher in North America, burst forth when the drill punched into cavernous caprock filled with oil and gas under high pressure.

Salt basins (very thick accumulations) are located beneath the coastal plain around the northern and western Gulf of Mexico. Happenings were even more spectacular and bizarre under the deep Gulf where piled-on clastic sediment caused the salt to extrude as a "glacier" onto the sea floor. (Salt glaciers in the Iranian desert originated in this manner, being exposed today in mountain ranges uplifted by the collision of tectonic plates.) As some of the salt dissolved, insoluble impurity minerals formed an armor coating that prevented further dissolution. More sediment piled on, and the process of upward penetration and extrusion was repeated, each time forming a salt "canopy" (Figure 23-23). A canopy layer is not a normal stratum because all of the salt had been deposited deeper, then ascended and spread out at a higher level. Petroleum companies have drilled more than 400 salt structures and are intensively studying the salt canopies, seeking vast deposits of oil and gas that are trapped beneath them.

Abundant *growth faults* in the Gulf region are another manifestation of salt geology. In a conventional fault, the rock is already fully formed before being broken and offset. Activity on a growth fault is more complex, as the deposition of sediment accompanies and promotes the fault motion. Deposition may cause a given stratum to be much thicker on the downthrown side of a growth fault. In a conventional fault, the two sides remain locked together until the buildup of stress ruptures the rock, creating an earthquake. Motion on a growth fault is by continual, sustained creep in the absence of earthquakes. Growth faults commonly "bottom out" in bodies of salt at depth (Figure 23-24).

DEPOSITION IN DEEP WATER

Where the Mississippi delta has prograded out to the edge of the continental shelf, an unstable mass of sediment may suddenly slump off into deep water. Deposition is occasional and catastrophic in the deep-water environment. It may occur as a *subaqueous debris flow*, which is a dense slurry, like freshly poured concrete. A debris flow is a jumbled, unsorted mixture of coarse and fine particles whose progress downslope comes to a halt quite abruptly. In another type of deposit, a *turbidity current*, the suspension of sediment is more dilute. Mixed sediment and water in a turbidity current act like a dense, turbulent liquid that hugs the bottom beneath the less-dense water overhead. Coarser particles tend to concentrate near its base, like bedload in a river. As the current gains momentum down the continental slope, it can scour (erode) the bottom. Farther out, where the current slackens on the nearly level ocean floor, the coarse particles drop out first, followed by finer and finer particles (Figure 23-25). The result is a *graded bed*: coarser sediment at the base, grading upward into finer sediment at the top. Countless graded beds may be stacked up, each bed deposited during an individual turbidity current event.

Now that technology enables us to drill wells in very deep water, the frontier of exploration has moved into this realm where it has revealed details of the sea-floor topography and structures of the sediment. Bottom topography of the Gulf of Mexico is one of the most complex in any sedimentary basin

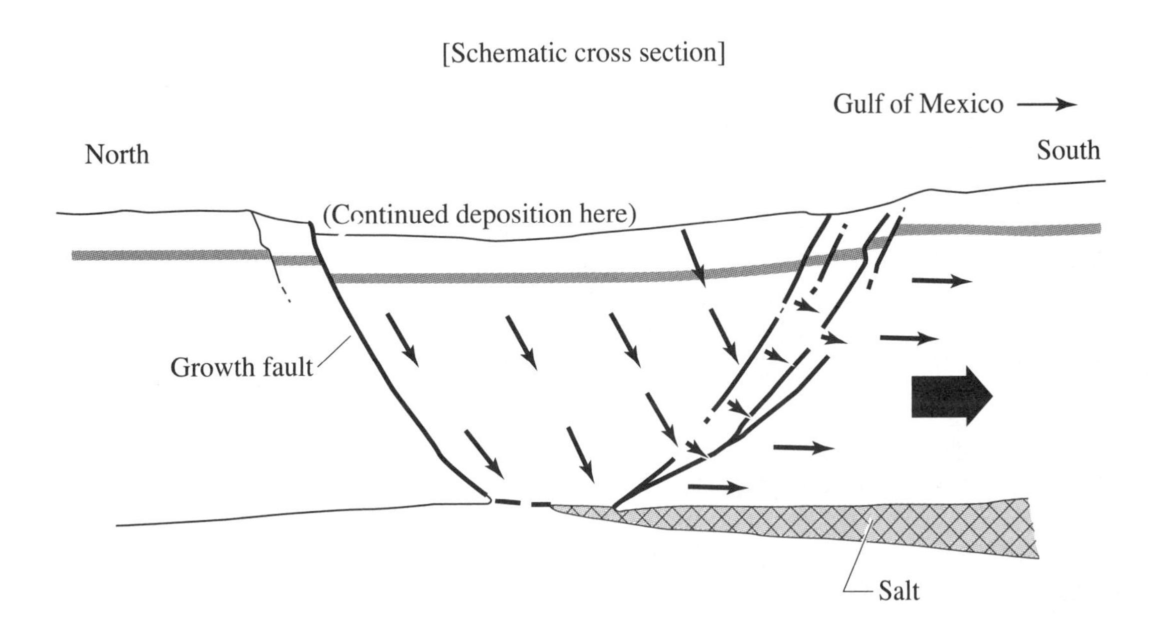

Figure 23-24. Growth faults (heavy lines) are steeper near the earth's surface, becoming more nearly horizontal at depth. One fault merges into a stratum of easily deformed, lubricating salt, above which a block slides laterally toward the Gulf of Mexico (heavy arrow).

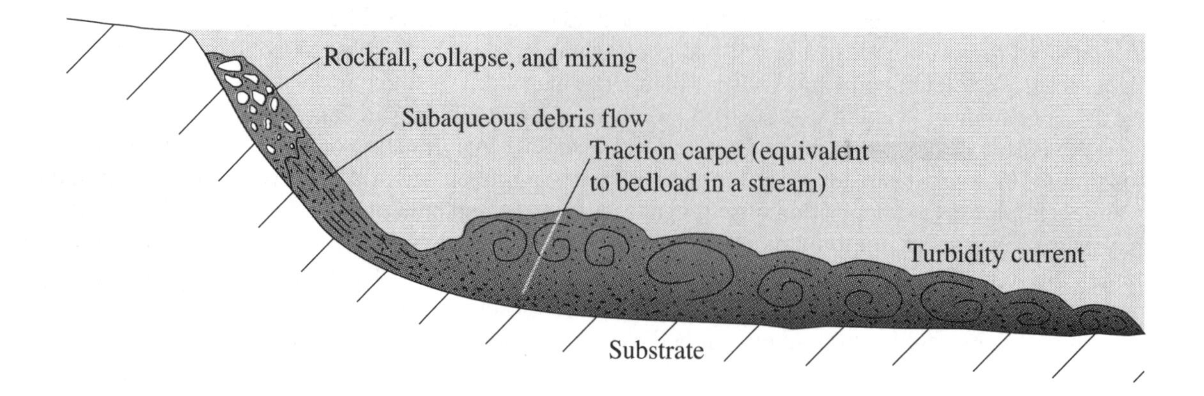

Figure 23-25. A turbidity current starting high up on the continental shelf or slope may lay a deposit with catastrophic suddenness. In 1929 an earthquake triggered a submarine slump on the Grand Banks, near Newfoundland. A number of trans-Atlantic cables were stretched across the ocean floor immediately downslope from the earthquake epicenter. One by one the cables were snapped in a regular progression. Timing of the cable breakages shows that the disturbance rushed downslope initially at a speed of 100 km/hour. It was still moving 20 km/hour when the most distant cable broke, some 750 kilometers from the region of origin. Underwater surveys revealed that a bed of sand whose area is the size of the State of Indiana was deposited by this single event.

in the world, due largely to the anomalous behavior of the buried salt (Figure 23-26). Sedimentary processes on the sea floor are astonishingly similar to those on the land surface. Counterparts of all of these familiar features are present under deep water: braided stream channel, meandering stream channel, meander belt, point bar, abandoned meander loop (oxbow lake on land), natural levee, bedload deposit, suspended load deposit, distributary, delta lobe, deposit of oil and gas including source, reservoir, and seal. Apparently, undersea turbidity currents can accomplish what rivers do on land. Artificially generated seismic waves, sent down into the strata and reflected back, are computer-processed into images. Figure 23-27 shows a meandering channel and a concentration of sand (a point bar) that would make a good hydrocarbon reservoir.

SUMMARY

Clastic sediment, chiefly sand and mud, is composed of solid particles eroded from a source terrain, and transported to a site of deposition through the agency of gravity. In a fluvial (river) system, which is dip-fed, the sediment is straightforwardly transported downslope. Along a coast, which is a strike-fed depositional system (on a horizontal plane), gravity operates more indirectly through wave activity. Erosion is more effective in uplands areas where slopes are steeper and energy of transport is greater; deposition predominates in lowlands where slopes, and available energy, are reduced.

A major river system consists of a tributary network: the drainage basin in which smaller tributaries feed into larger ones, and a distributary network: the delta where the master stream branches into smaller distributary channels that enter the sea. A river dumps its load in the delta, causing the newly deposited land to build forward (prograde) into the sea.

Stream discharge is the volume of water passing a given point per unit time, and a hydrograph is a plot of stream discharge *vs.* time. Small streams respond more rapidly and vigorously to local weather events than large streams do; the hydrograph of a small stream is "spikier." A steep gradient and extremes of high and low discharge characterize a braided stream, in which constantly shifting channels are threaded in and out amongst islands of coarse bedload (coarser, heavier particles that are confined to the channel). A gentle gradient and finer-grained sediment load are characteristic of a meandering stream. Turbulence (internal chaotic water motion) is the chief agency that keeps microscopic clay particles suspended in the water column. A stream attempts to maintain a long profile (elevation of its channel) that

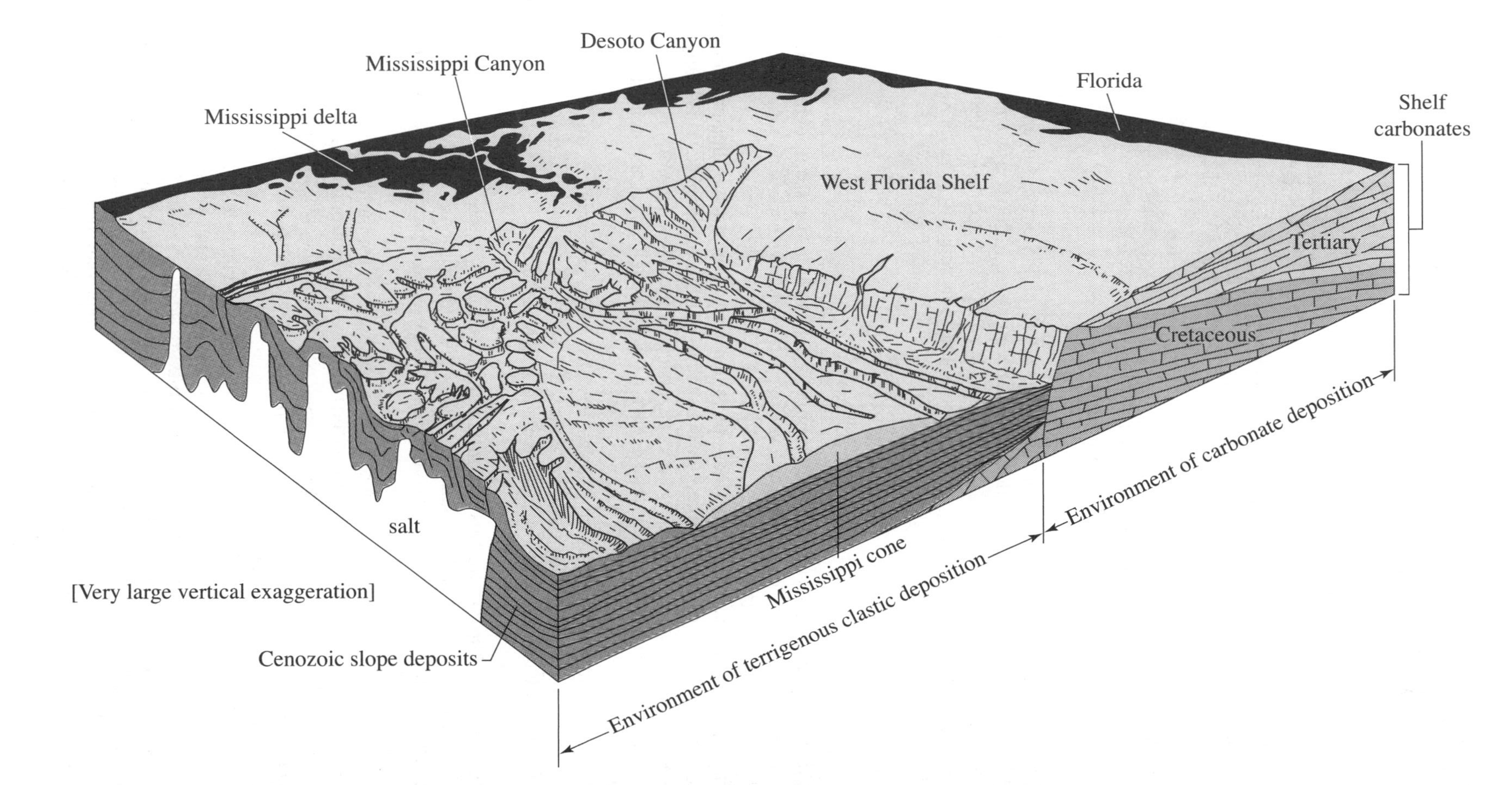

Figure 23-26. This block diagram summarizes the major features of the northeastern Gulf of Mexico. West of Florida, the broad, shallow continental shelf is bounded by one of the world's steepest slope escarpments. A colossal turbidite fan floors the Gulf in front of the Mississippi delta. Turbidity flows have cut well-defined submarine channels into the surface of the fan. As clastic sediment sank under its own weight, intrusions of buoyant salt were displaced upward through it. Bumpy seafloor topography that developed over the salt structures (left-hand side of the diagram) is shown schematically. In fact, there are more than 100 massive salt intrusions that are large enough to have been given names. [*After P. Lehner, "Salt Tectonics and Pleistocene Stratigraphy on Continental Slope of Northern Gulf of Mexico,"* Bulletin of the American Association of Petroleum Geologists, *vol. 53, no. 12, 1969.*]

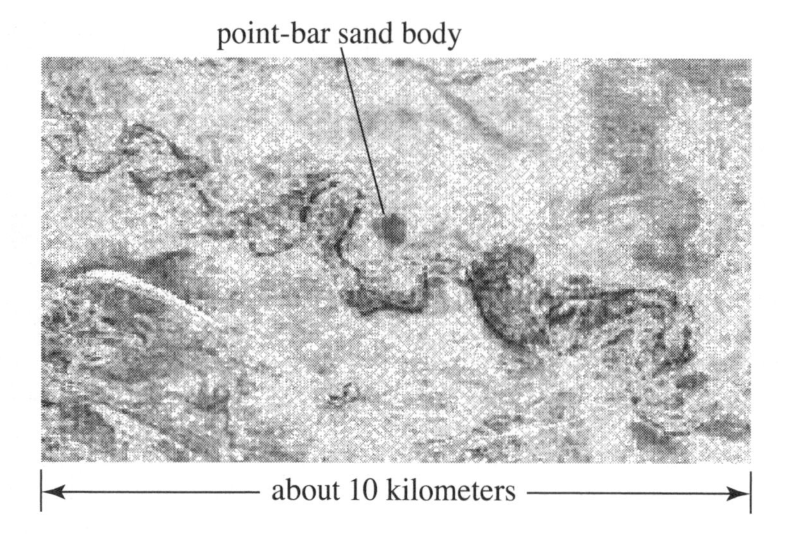

Figure 23-27. This amazing image is of a thin horizontal "slice," several kilometers deep within the sediment pile that in turn is overlain by several kilometers of ocean water. [*After W. Sikkema and K. M. Wojcik, "3D Visualization of Turbidite Systems, Lower Congo Basin, Offshore Angola,"* Deep-Water Reservoirs of the World, Society of Economic Paleontologists and Mineralogists, Perkins Research Conference, *2000.*]

is steeper at its source, and gentler at its mouth. The stream responds to a drop in sea level by cutting its valley downward, restoring the long profile. If sea level rises, the stream restores its long profile by depositing fluvial sediment in its valley.

In meanders, serpentine loops, the stream erodes the outer bank in the unconsolidated floodplain sediment, while deposition of a crescent-shape point bar occurs on the inner bank. This causes the stream channel to migrate in the direction of the outer bank, changing the size, shape, and location of the meander loop. A strongly accentuated meander loop occasionally cuts itself off, abandoning a segment of a stream channel as an oxbow lake.

During flood stage, a stream builds natural levees, elevated banks consisting of mud (suspended load), and so the entire meander belt is built up above the level of the surrounding floodplain. Occasionally, the stream may break through its bank to create a new meander belt in a distant part of the floodplain.

Hydrocarbon molecules, the constituents of petroleum and natural gas, are generated by decomposition of organic material deposited in floodplain mud. The fluid hydrocarbons migrate out of the mud (the source) into porous point-bar sand (the reservoir), from which escape is prevented by impermeable mud (the trap, or seal) lying overhead.

In a large delta such as that of the Mississippi River, distributaries are building a localized delta lobe while subsidence (sinking) continues elsewhere as the mud loses water through compaction, and as the delivered sediment weights down the earth's crust. Subsidence induces the river to switch into a more depressed area, there to build another delta lobe, and the process of switching, building, abandonment, and reoccupation by the sea comprises the delta cycle.

Fertile delta soils are important agricultural lands, and organic growth in delta swamps or marshes transforms into peat, lignite, or various grades of coal depending upon depth of later burial. Fresh, but muddy river water promptly deposits prodelta mud upon mixing with seawater. Organic material in prodelta mud is the source of hydrocarbons, which migrate into reservoirs consisting of bedload sand in distributary channels, sealed by prodelta mud of the next delta cycle that is deposited overhead.

On a coast, wind-generated waves are the chief geologic agent. Internal motion is impeded by friction as a wave enters shallow water, causing the wave to become unstable and to break in the surf zone. The wave sloshes sediment back and forth inefficiently, but if it approaches the beach obliquely, some of its energy transports the sediment laterally by longshore drift.

During the most recent Ice Age, the shoreline retreated to the edge of the continental shelf as sea level dropped, and streams responded by entrenching (deepening) their valleys. When the ice melted, sea level rose and the waves propelled long strips of sand, barrier islands, up against the coast of the Gulf of Mexico. Barrier islands, and beaches generally around the world, are currently experiencing unavoidable erosional retreat.

Early during the opening of the Gulf of Mexico, intense evaporation of seawater in the absence of replenishment caused the precipitation of enormous masses of salt. When rivers became established, their delta deposits prograded over, and buried the salt beneath clastic sediment. Low-density, incompressible, mechanically weak salt acted as a fluid, piercing upward while more dense clastic sediment descended. The salt deformed into bizarre structures—walls, spines, domes, and detached canopies—both in the mainland and under deep waters of the Gulf of Mexico. A salt structure that is partially dissolved by groundwater may develop a caprock in which chemical reactions transform the H_2S waste product of sulfate-reducing bacteria into commercial deposits of native sulfur. Cavernous caprocks also store oil and gas under high pressure. Growth faults are abundant in an environment of prolonged clastic deposition. In a growth fault, motion on the fault plane and continued deposition of sediment at the surface go on continuously, in the absence of earthquakes. Growth faults commonly merge into salt at depth.

Oversteepened, water-saturated sediment at the brink of the continental shelf may suddenly slump into very deep water as a debris flow (pasty, unsorted mass) or as a turbidity current (churned up mixture of sediment and water that acts as a dense fluid). When a turbidity current comes to rest, the coarser particles drop out first, followed by finer and finer particles, forming a graded bed. Most deposition in the deep Gulf of Mexico is catastrophic and episodic, by turbidity current events.

24

The Great Ice Ages

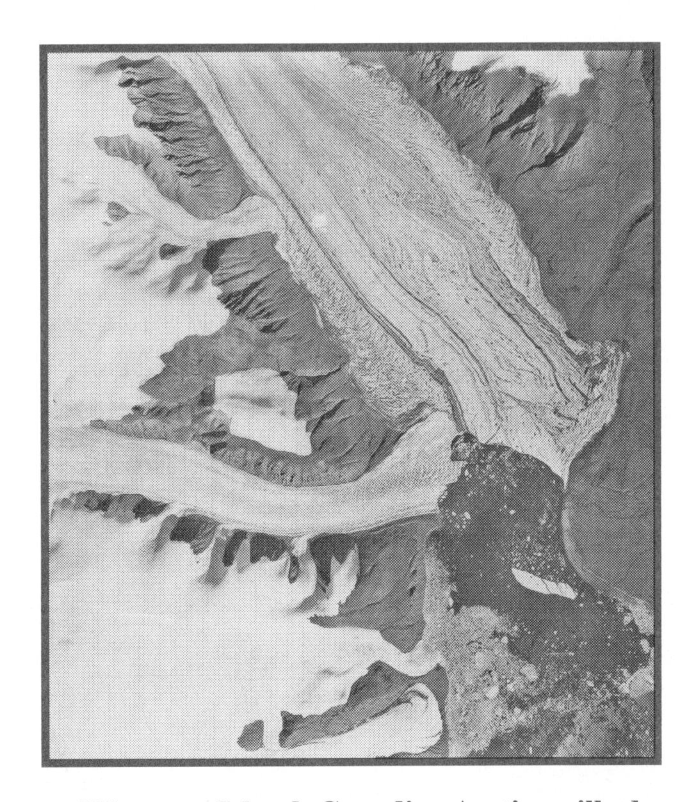

An icecap on Ellesmere Island, Canadian Arctic, spills down into valley glaciers that occupy a fjord. [*National Photo Library, Surveys and Mapping Branch, Department of Energy, Mines, and Resources, Ottawa, Canada*]

Some of the most spectacular climatic changes that the earth has ever witnessed have occurred within the past few thousand years, and the near future holds a threat of more to come. Any change—whether from wetter to drier, or colder to warmer climate, or the opposite—is a threat because human cultures everywhere are delicately adjusted to the local environment. Cultural accommodation, even to a climatic change that is "beneficial," may be stressful. World climate has switched repeatedly between two extreme states known as the "icehouse earth" and "greenhouse earth." Climate today is highly stratified, from harsh polar regions to pleasant temperate zones, to tropical rain forests, to deserts. Although nearly 98 percent of the surface H_2O is in liquid form, one continent (Antarctica) and the largest island (Greenland) are mantled by ice sheets, and thousands of smaller glaciers are scattered about. Ice covers about 10 percent of the land; we are truly living in an Ice Age, though it is not now at its maximum. Over the past million or so years, the ice sheets have expanded and retreated many times. At maximum, they covered an estimated 30 percent of the continents and locked up as much as 8 percent of the water (Figure 24-1).

And so, what of the future? Are we poised to enter a greenhouse phase of serious global warming? What if the ice sheet that covers western Antarctica were to surge rapidly into the sea? Such things have happened before, but this time human civilization would be deeply impacted.

Were it not for the abundance and remarkable properties of H_2O, earth climate would have lapsed into a permanent greenhouse mode as on Venus, or perhaps into a permanent icehouse mode as on Mars,

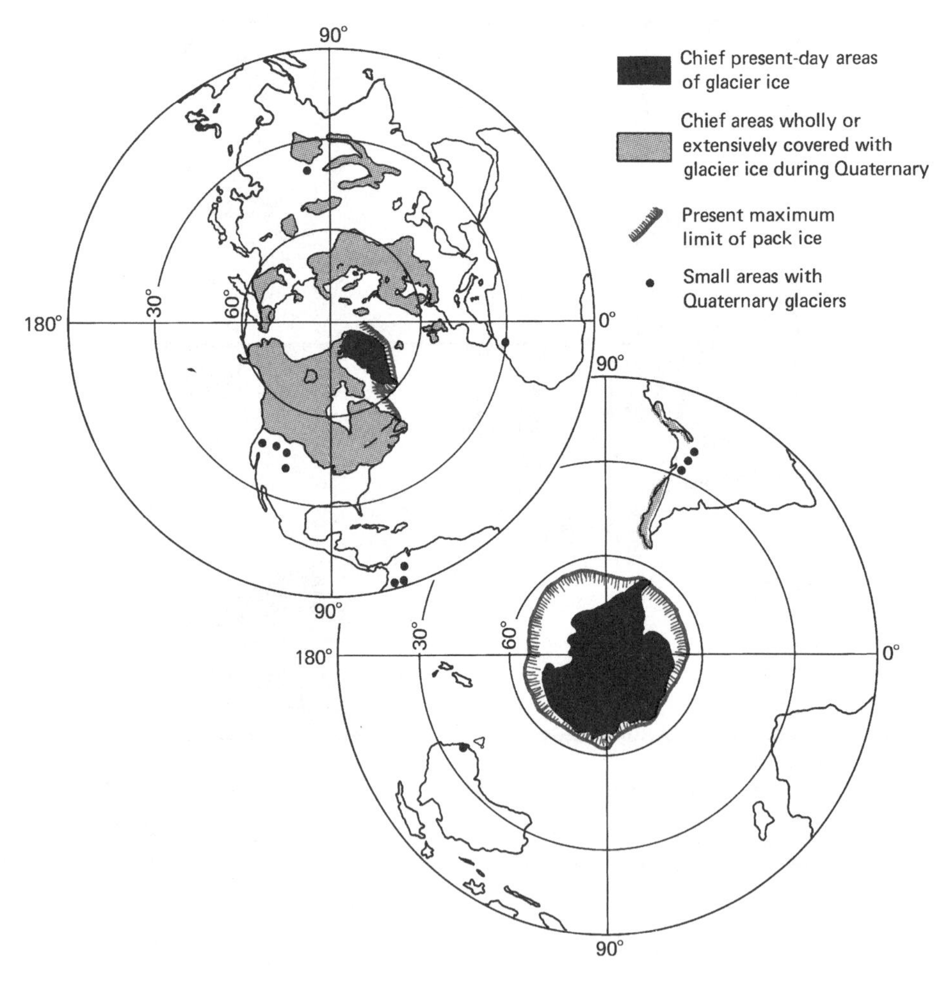

Figure 24-1. Quaternary ice sheets have repeatedly occupied much of North America and Europe, but only isolated parts of Siberia. Present-day glaciation in Africa and Australia is trivial. An overspreading ice sheet makes Antarctica the most elevated of the continents today. Glaciers in Antarctica and Greenland discharge icebergs directly into the ocean; consequently these ice sheets were never much larger than they are now. Rather, the icebergs simply broke off more frequently. [*After J. R. L. Allen,* Physical Processes of Sedimentation, *American Elsevier Publishing Company, Inc., New York, 1970.*]

both of these hostile planets having very little water. Approximately 80 calories of heat energy must be added to one gram of ice at 0°C to convert it to water at the same temperature. This energy is used to break chemical bonds while converting the systematic atomic structure in an ice crystal into the disordered arrangement in a liquid. Conversely, 80 calories per gram must be removed in the transition from water to ice at 0°C. Approximately 600 calories must be added to a gram of water at 0°C to convert it into water vapor. H_2O is an excellent thermal "buffer" that absorbs or releases heat energy while changing amongst the solid, liquid, or gaseous states, thus helping to stabilize the temperature of an environment.

Another peculiarity is the open, rather loose crystal structure of ice, making it about 9 percent less dense than liquid water. Ice floats on water, whereas most solids are more dense and would sink through a liquid medium composed of that same material. If ice is near the freezing point, application of pressure forces it into becoming liquid water, the more dense state; the ice has melted while remaining at constant temperature (Figure 24-2). Skaters glide on a thin film of water that is pressure-generated beneath the skate blade.

GLACIER ICE: A METAMORPHIC ROCK

In some ways, a glacier is like a mechanically weak metamorphic rock kept near its melting point. Nourished by fallen snow (a sediment), the substance of a glacier continually recrystallizes while in the solid state (process of metamorphism), finally to be recycled by melting (becoming "magma"). Unlike ordinary metamorphic rock, glacier ice is plainly visible while all these processes are at work, though sampling the interior of a glacier presents a technical challenge. Gravity is the controlling force, causing the ice to compact and flow under its own weight. The behavior of glacier ice is the subject of elegant mathematical descriptions.

Cold and Warm Glaciers

Speaking of cold and warm (or temperate) glaciers may sound a little absurd. Of course, all ice is cold to the touch, but just as conditions of metamorphism deep in the earth may vary over a range of temperature and pressure, so it is with metamorphism of glacier ice. In glaciers the ice temperature is never warmer than the melting point at 0°C, nor colder than about 50°C below zero. Even this modest temperature range makes for considerable differences among glaciers from polar to temperate climatic zones.

How does snow transform into ice? Melting and re-freezing may seem the most obvious way, but in many glaciers, as in central Antarctica and Greenland, melting occurs only rarely. Instead, progressive changes occur with accumulation and burial of snow. The delicate lacework of a fresh snowflake [Figure

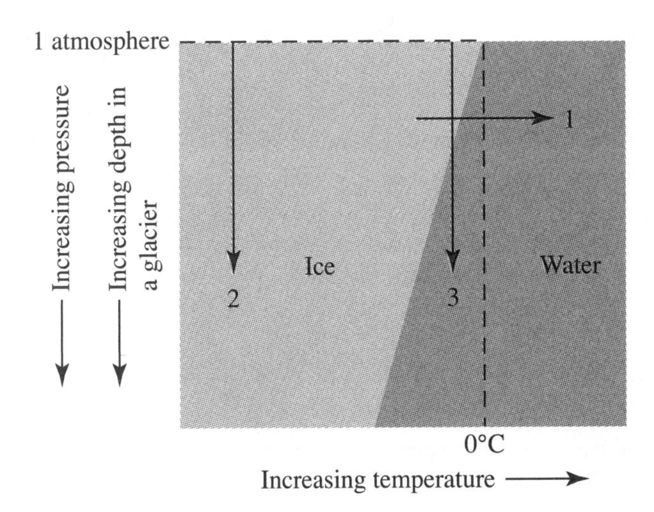

Figure 24-2. A diagram shows how temperature and pressure affect the stability of the solid and liquid phases of H_2O. Arrow 1 depicts the melting of ice at constant pressure. If the ice is quite cold, it remains solid when placed under higher pressure (arrow 2), but if the temperature is initially just below the melting point, raising the pressure will melt the ice even at constant temperature (arrow 3).

24-3(*a*)] is quickly destroyed not only because fragile points break off but also because the surface area of the crystal is so large relative to its volume. Always the tendency during compaction is to reduce the surface area by consolidating small particles into larger ones. Soon the dry, powdery snow converts into rounded grains of "old snow," or *firn* [(Figure 24-5(*e*)]. With deeper burial, the firn becomes less porous, and finally, when the connected air pockets are squeezed into isolated bubbles, the result is glacier ice.

Solid ice is first encountered at a shallow depth in temperate glaciers, but much deeper in cold glaciers (Figure 24-5). In cold glaciers, the transformation from fresh snow to firn to ice is accomplished entirely in the solid state. The situation is quite different in temperate glaciers where some of the surface melts each summer. We noted that as a gram of meltwater enters the body of the glacier and re-freezes, it transports 80 calories of heat energy into the glacier's interior. This is an effective way to bring the temperature throughout an entire warm glacier exactly to the melting point (Figure 24-4). As mentioned, water at 0°C is more dense than ice, and thus the high pressure at depth would favor the more dense (liquid) state. To say it another way, the deep ice would have to be colder than 0°C if it were to remain solid, as seen in Figure 24-4.

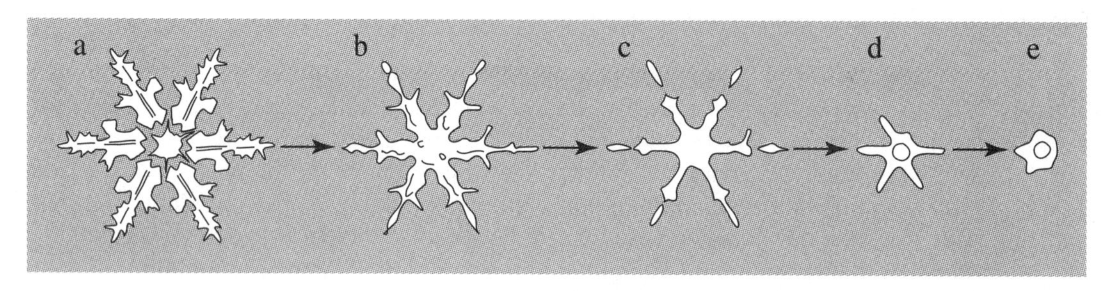

Figure 24-3. Transformation of fresh snow into firn takes but a few days or weeks in all but the coldest glaciers. Much of the change occurs by transfer of material from solid, directly to vapor, and back to solid, bypassing the liquid state. Sharp corners and edges disappear first as the particle becomes rounded, ever more approaching a spherical shape. A compact firn particle (*e*) may have as much volume as the original thin, delicate snowflake (*a*).

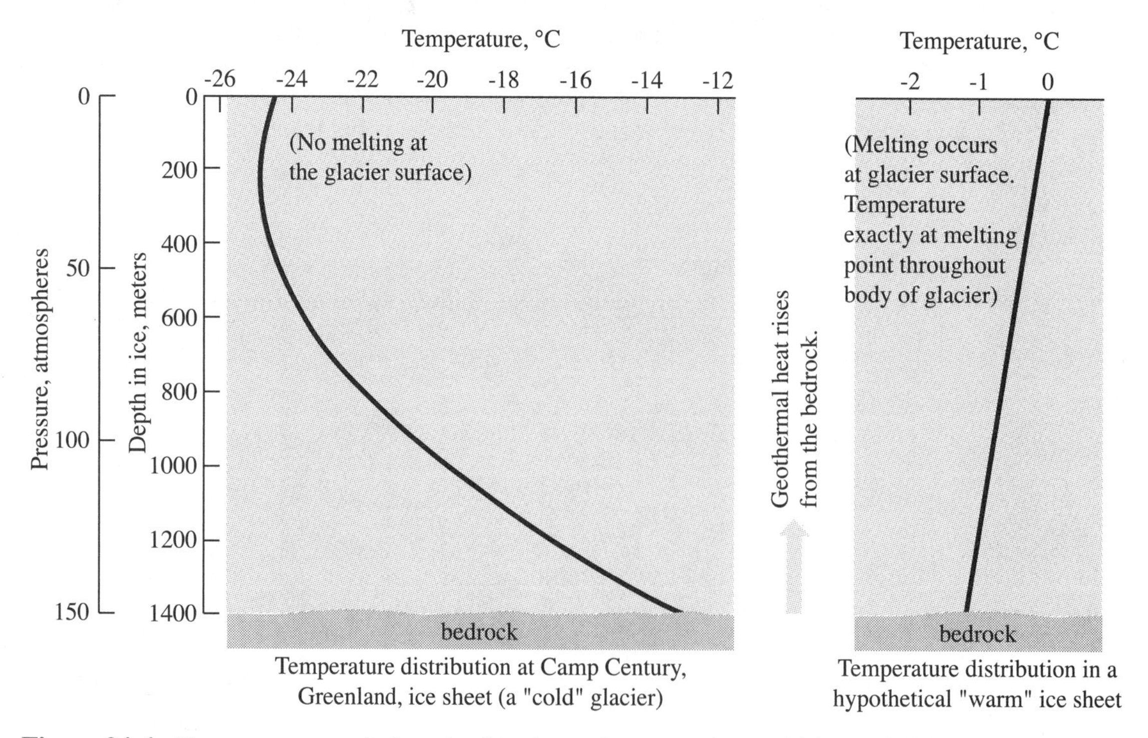

Figure 24-4. Temperatures are below the freezing point everywhere within a cold ice sheet, but the ice is warmest near its base, heated by geothermal energy flowing upward from the bedrock. In contrast, the temperature throughout the mass of a temperate glacier may be exactly at the freezing point (= melting point).

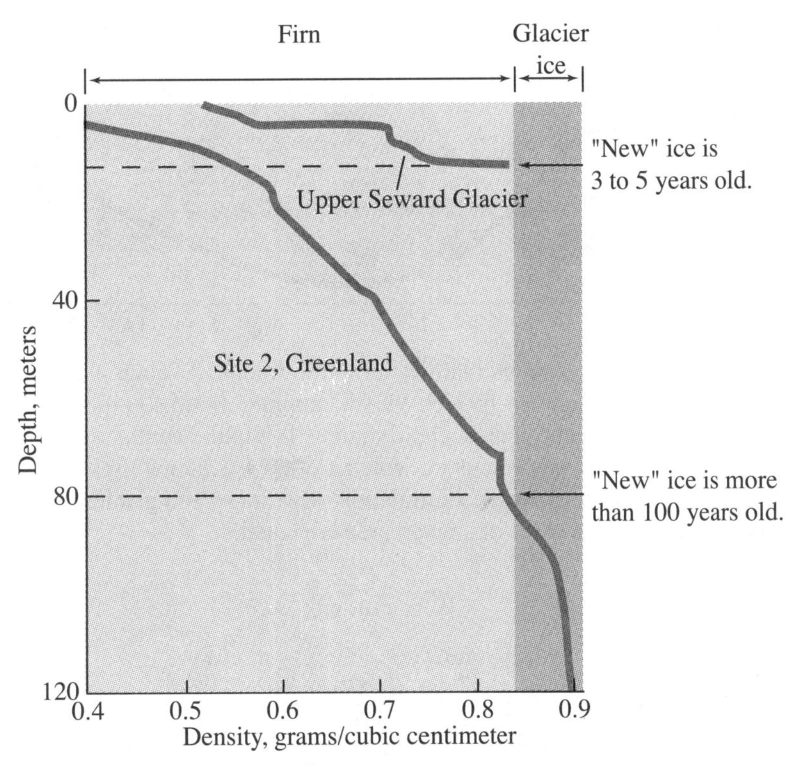

Figure 24-5. Firn has compacted into solid ice at a depth of about 13 meters on the temperate Upper Seward Glacier, Yukon, but not above a depth of about 80 meters at Site 2 in the Greenland ice sheet, a cold glacier. Snow accumulation rates differ greatly, as suggested by the age of the most recently formed ice in each glacier. Polar ice sheets are deceptive for, although they consist of nothing but H_2O, they are among the most arid regions on earth. Annual precipitation (liquid equivalent) at the South Pole is about 7 centimeters/year (less than 3 inches), 5 times less than at Site 2 and 50 times less than at the Upper Seward Glacier. [*After W. S. B. Paterson*, The Physics of Glaciers, *1969. Reprinted with the author's permission. Copyright 1969, Pergamon Press Ltd., Oxford.*]

Glacier Dynamics

Whether a glacier is warm or cold, whether it is a small tongue or the entire Antarctic ice sheet, its response to the force of gravity is basically the same. First, let us examine the behavior of alpine glaciers, so named after the Alps where they were first studied, in which the flowing ice is confined between valley walls. Every glacier operates on an annual budget in which the *accumulation* of ice at higher elevations is balanced by its *wastage* near the terminus (Figure 24-6). By drilling into glaciers and inserting flexible pipes, glaciologists have learned that there are several ways in which ice flows. The embedded pipe is wafted down the glacier as the ice slides over the bedrock as an entire coherent block, but the pipe also becomes distorted (Figure 24-7). That is, *internal deformation* makes an important contribution to the forward motion. In Chapter 16 we noted how varied circumstances cause a solid to behave in a ductile or brittle manner. Ice flows in a ductile manner when it is confined and placed under sustained stress; the strain (deformation) is permanent even after the stress is released. In contrast, the presence of deep open cracks, or *crevasses,* in many glaciers indicates that ice within 100 meters of the surface acts in a brittle manner, even while ductile flow is in progress at greater depth (Figure 24-8, plan view). The flow velocity of some alpine glaciers can approach zero (stagnation), but typically it lies between 10 and 200 meters per year.

How are small-scale internal adjustments accomplished in the moving ice? A tiny volume of ice could thaw, the liquid move a short distance, and then freeze again, repeatedly. This process does not occur at all in a cold glacier, and even in most temperate glaciers it is not considered to be important. Another possibility is that the ice crystals roll past one another like beans in a beanbag. In doing so, the crystals would become rounded into spheres, and pulverized into fine particles. Microscopic examination of thin sections of glacier ice reveals that exactly the opposite is occurring, that the maturing crystals

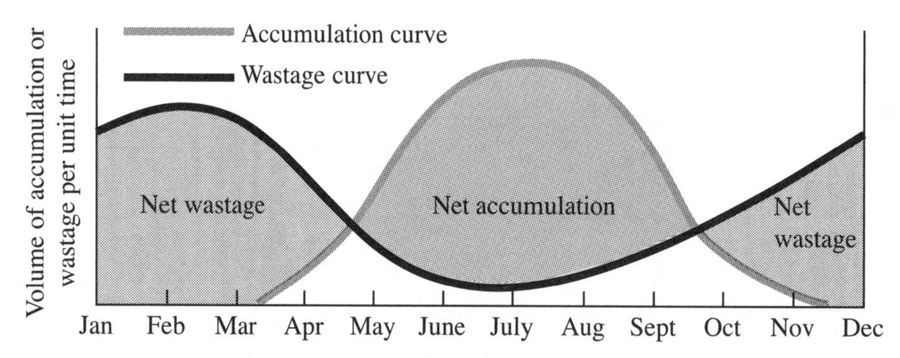

Figure 24-6. An annual budget for a temperate glacier in the Andes of Patagonia shows that accumulation ceases altogether during December through March, summer months in the Southern Hemisphere. Although wastage is continual, it greatly intensifies in the summer months. The area between a curve and the horizontal axis equals the volume of *total* accumulation or wastage (i.e., time x volume/time). Shaded areas represent *net* accumulation or wastage. If a glacier is in a steady-state condition, which is seldom, the two types of shaded area are equal.

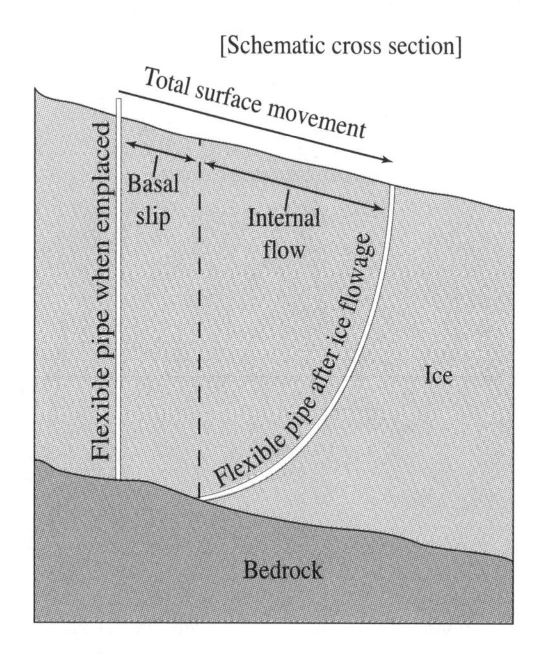

Figure 24-7. Basal sliding, lubricated by a film of water at the bottom of a glacier, may account for as little as 10 percent to as much as 90 percent of the total forward motion.

are growing larger and developing interlocking projections. Ultimately, a single crystal may grow to be a meter or so across, as in the lower end or "snout" of the old, far-traveled Malaspina Glacier, in Alaska. Ice textures indicate that motion is accommodated not *between* crystals as in a beanbag but *within* them. Crystals weld together, and they deform by slipping along planes of atoms while in the solid state.

In an overspreading ice sheet, the surface flow is not confined within rock walls, although the bottom ice may be forced to flow over or around buried mountainous topography. A schematic cross section through the Greenland ice sheet emphasizes the domelike profile of a continental glacier (Figure 24-9). As an annual deposit at the crest of the glacier subsides into the interior, and is progressively buried beneath later deposits, it becomes enormously thinned and stretched. Glaciologists have drilled entirely through the polar ice sheets in several localities, retrieving ice cores. Distinct annual layering is preserved through most of the core, but the ice record near the bottom becomes more and more condensed, revealing not so much the particular details of previous *weather* but more the sweeping generalities of changing *climate*. The oldest ice at the base of the Greenland sheet is estimated to be 250 thousand years old, and in Antarctica as much as 400 thousand years old.

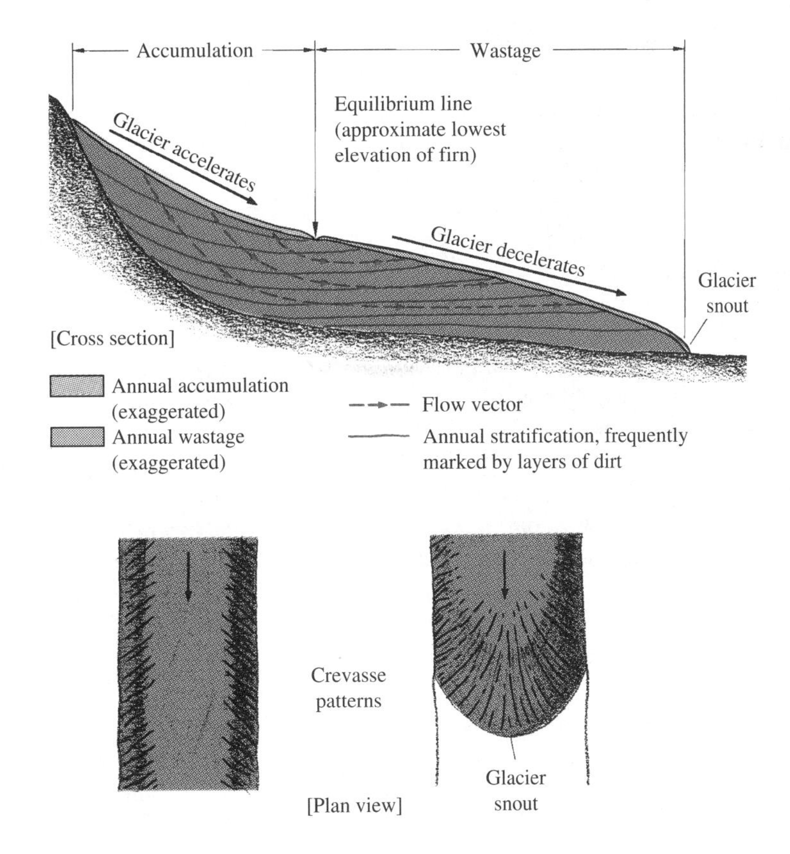

Figure 24-8. A steady-state glacier maintains a roughly constant shape and size. Since the rate of accumulation or wastage varies from point to point, the material balance is preserved only if velocity increases as the ice approaches the zone of wastage, then decreases as the ice nears the terminus. Flow vectors trace the paths taken by individual water molecules. Because burial occurs in the zone of accumulation, and exposure by melting occurs in the zone of wastage, it follows that a vector must plunge *into* the ice, then *emerge* down-glacier. Unlucky Alpine climbers, buried by an avalanche high up on a glacier, have unwittingly confirmed this flow pattern. Years later their frozen bodies reappeared at the surface at the snout, as predicted by this model.

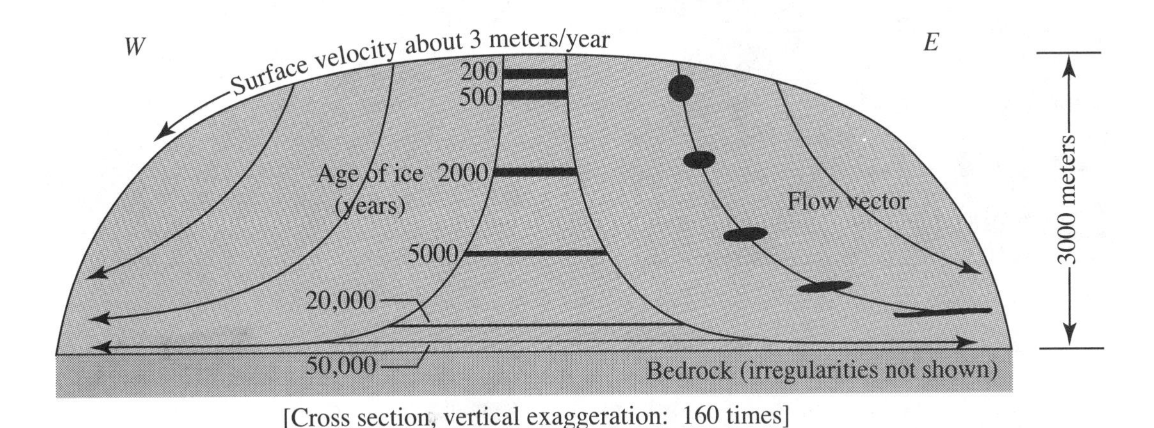

Figure 24-9. In this idealized cross section through the Greenland ice sheet, the flow vectors resemble those in an alpine glacier (Figure 24-8). Annual layers (black strips) deposited at the crest of the ice sheet will follow these flow lines, becoming stretched and thinned as they sink deeper into the body of the glacier. Near the base of the ice sheet, the annual layers become so highly condensed that a small thickness represents a long interval of accumulation. Progress of deformation may also be depicted by a sphere of ice (black circle) deforming into an ellipsoid, and eventually into a thin, somewhat warped wafer.

Most valley glaciers waste away by melting. In contrast, melting is minor in the great polar ice sheets that advance relentlessly until they enter the sea. Nearly all of the loss of mass from Antarctica and about half of the loss from Greenland come about by discharge of icebergs. Source areas for the largest icebergs are *ice shelves* fringing the land. These gigantic sheets are attached to land where the ice is fed into them, but their leading edges are afloat. On at least two recorded occasions, individual icebergs larger than Massachusetts have broken loose from the Ross Ice Shelf, in Antarctica.

The friction of ice sliding over the bedrock generates heat, to which is added geothermal heat ascending from the deep earth. These sources of energy may combine to melt the bottom ice, even in frigid Antarctica, thereby providing a thin lubricating film of water. At times, water confined at high pressure may spread across much of the base of the glacier, actually able to lift the ice off the bedrock. It is an unstable situation that is thought to trigger a *glacier surge*. A thickened bulge appears in the upper elevations, then migrates in a wave-like manner down the glacier, much faster than the ice itself is traveling. As the wave sweeps by, it leaves a chaotic jumble of pinnacles and crevasses in its wake. Upon reaching the snout, the traveling wave causes the glacier terminus to "jump" forward, and for two or three years the flow velocity increases to as much as 100 times the normal rate (Figure 24-10). Any glacier, whether warm or cold, alpine or a continental ice sheet, has the capacity to surge, and some of them have surged repeatedly. Although a stable, steady flow of ice is the norm, some glaciers seem never to "get it right."

a

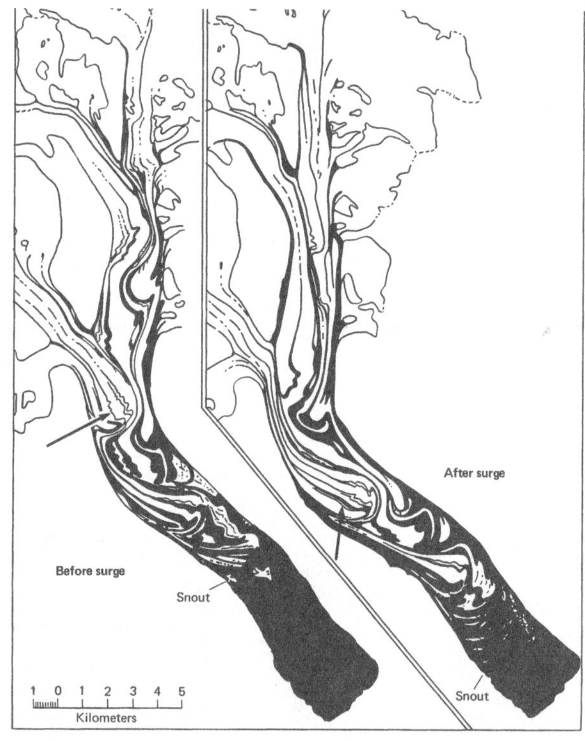

b

Figure 24-10. (*a*) An alpine-type glacier incorporates long strips of rubble, called *moraines*, that have been eroded off valley walls. Where two glaciers meet (arrows), a valley-side or *lateral* moraine of one glacier joins to the lateral moraine of the other, forming a *medial* moraine that is surrounded by ice on both sides. Contorted medial moraines, a hallmark of the Susitna Glacier, Alaska (pictured here), are a sign of glacier surging. [*Photo courtesy Bradford Washburn.*] (*b*) Before the 1952 surge of the Susitna Glacier, an active tributary glacier had pushed aside the moraines of the stagnant main stream (arrow on left). When the main glacier surged, it trimmed off the protrusion of tributary ice and carried it down-glacier (right arrow). At the same time, the glacier snout advanced several kilometers beyond its former position. [*Diagram after A. Post and E. R. LaChapelle,* Glacier Ice, *University of Washington Press, Seattle, 1971.*]

GLACIAL EROSION AND DEPOSITION

Small glaciers nestled in alpine valleys had been known for centuries, but it was not until the early 1800s that geologists began to realize that gigantic ice sheets must have once spread over northern Europe and most of North America. An acquaintance with modern ice sheets would have helped these geologists to accept this radical idea, but at the time Antarctica was unknown and Greenland unexplored. All of the available evidence for former continental glaciation was indirect, just the lingering effects of erosion or deposition by the vanished ice.

Pure ice is too easily deformed to be an effective agent of erosion, but ice that is armed with a few percent of rock debris is quite another matter. An embedded rock fragment scours the bedrock, which in turn grinds a smooth, flat face (a facet) into the fragment. Occasionally, the rasping tool is forced to rotate in its icy matrix, and more facets are abraded.

Debris left by a melted glacier is a highly distinctive terrigenous clastic sediment whose particles display the ultimate example of poor sorting, ranging from submicroscopic size up to boulders. Old Scottish farmers called this material *till,* and probably cursed the ground because it was so difficult for them to till. A fascinating assortment of cobbles and boulders, some of which could be car-size to house-size, may have been quarried from localities hundreds of kilometers distant. Mapping of distinctive rock types indicates that till is "sprayed out" over a fan-shaped area immediately down-glacier from the outcrop. What was to become the largest copper mine in Finland was discovered when glacial boulders containing ore were traced back to their source. Scores of excellent pebble-sized diamonds found in glacial till deposits from New York to the Midwest are assumed to have come from the Canadian Shield, but no one knows exactly where.

Near the border of a continental glacier, there is a transition between thick ice that is still moving and thin, brittle ice that has stagnated at the very edge (Figure 24-12). The flowing ice lifts a mass of debris up to the surface by shearing across and riding up over the stagnant fringe, then melting. So effectively has the coat of melted-out sediment insulated the stagnant ice of the Malaspina Glacier that a dense forest of century-old spruce trees has become established on top. During the retreat of the North American ice sheet, stagnant ice took as long as 3 thousand years to melt in some places. Meltwater pours forth from tunnels at the front of a wasting glacier, reworking much of the till downstream. Glacial streams promptly convert the unstratified debris into stratified deposits by means of the fluvial processes explored in Chapter 23.

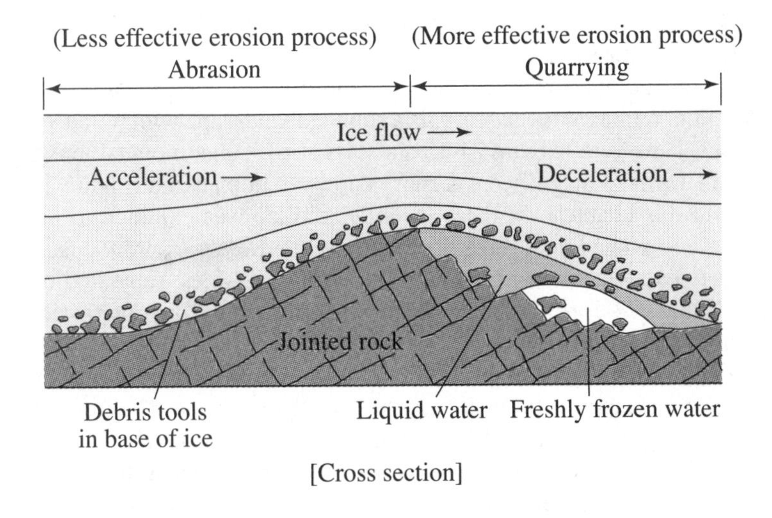

Figure 24-11. Debris embedded in the base of a glacier can abrade the bedrock. If the bedrock contains open cracks (joints), meltwater can penetrate them and expand as it freezes again, prying apart the rock so that it is easily dislodged. This "plucking" action requires an alternation between freezing (typically at night) and thawing (in the daytime), a situation common in the summer at the head of a temperate alpine glacier.

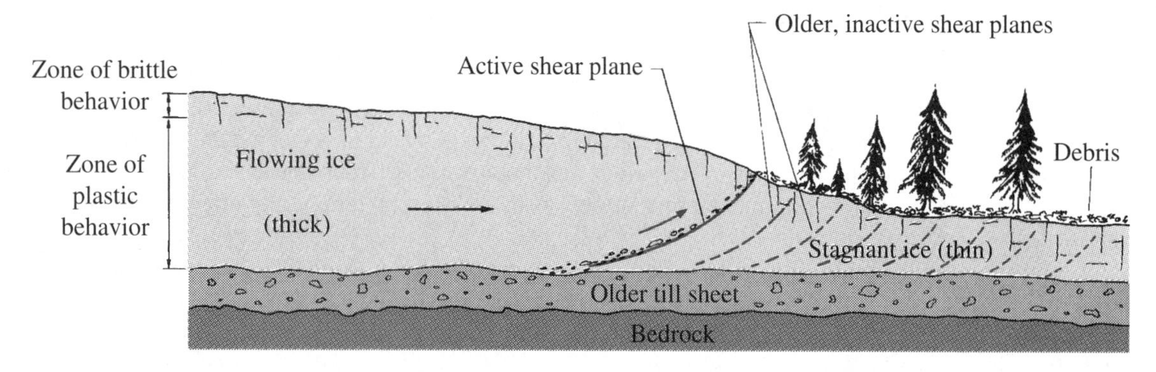

Figure 24-12. A shear plane marks the boundary between the region of ductile flow and the zone of brittle stagnation. Wastage causes the glacier to retreat, even though ice is continually moving forward. Ice moves up along only one shear plane at any one time. Ductile flow is possible only if the ice is at least approximately 100 meters thick.

Glaciated Landscapes

Most of the low-lying Precambrian shield areas of the world apparently have been glaciated at one time or another. Do these terrains owe their flat profile to glacial erosion, or did the glaciers do no more than remove an already crumbly soil zone? A rather modest volume of material scraped off the Canadian Shield suggests that erosion there was insignificant once the ice had scoured down to a cleaned and polished bedrock surface. The volume may be under-estimated if the Mississippi River, at that time a raging meltwater torrent, has carried much sediment to the Gulf of Mexico. In any case, glacial erosion is spectacular where an ice sheet takes advantage of a pre-existing valley or weakness in the underlying rock. A series of large freshwater lakes is arrayed along the boundary between Precambrian igneous-metamorphic basement in Canada, and its overlapping sedimentary cover (Figure 24-14). Glacier ice has scooped out the bottoms of some of these lakes well below sea level.

Deposition of a continental ice sheet places a massive load upon the earth's crust, causing it to become depressed by isostatic adjustment (discussed in Chapter 16). Today, the rock surface lies below sea level in Hudson Bay (central Canada), and beneath much of Antarctica and Greenland. At one time, the thickest part of the Canadian ice sheet lay over the site of Hudson Bay. After the ice melted away, the crust began to rebound, initially at a rate of several centimeters per year, then slowing down but still continuing (Figure 24-14). Isostatic rebound will have raised most of the shallow floor of Hudson Bay above sea level within a few more thousand years.

Glaciation of a highland may create a variety of landforms. If the ice was thick enough to overrun even the highest elevation, retreat of the ice reveals a subdued landscape with rounded contours, as in the Adirondack Mountains, New York [Figure 24-15 and 24-16(*a*)]. Other mountainous regions, eroded by alpine glaciers, contain the most magnificent scenery known to humankind [Figure 24-15 and 24-16(*b*), and lead photograph to this chapter]. In these localities the ice was confined to pre-existing valleys. Glaciers have carved steep-walled, bowl-like depressions called *cirques* (pronounced "serks") at heads of valleys. Cirques may encroach into a mountain from opposite sides, separated only by a towering, knife-sharp partition [Figure 24-16(*b*)], or after glaciers have attacked from several sides, a pyramid such as the Swiss Matterhorn may remain.

An alpine glacier commonly occupies a stream-eroded valley that has the familiar crooked or winding shape, and with a characteristic V-shape profile in cross section. The invading ice deepens and straightens the valley, modifying its profile into a U-shape in cross section (Figure 24-17). Cross sections through small and large alpine glaciers have similar shapes. Where a small tributary joins a larger glacier, their surfaces meet at the same elevation but the base of the master glacier has been excavated far deeper. Once the ice has melted, the valley of the tributary is left "hanging" high above the floor of the valley that contained the master. In Yosemite National Park, California, which is now deglaciated, streams cascade from hanging valleys over spectacular waterfalls into the main valley.

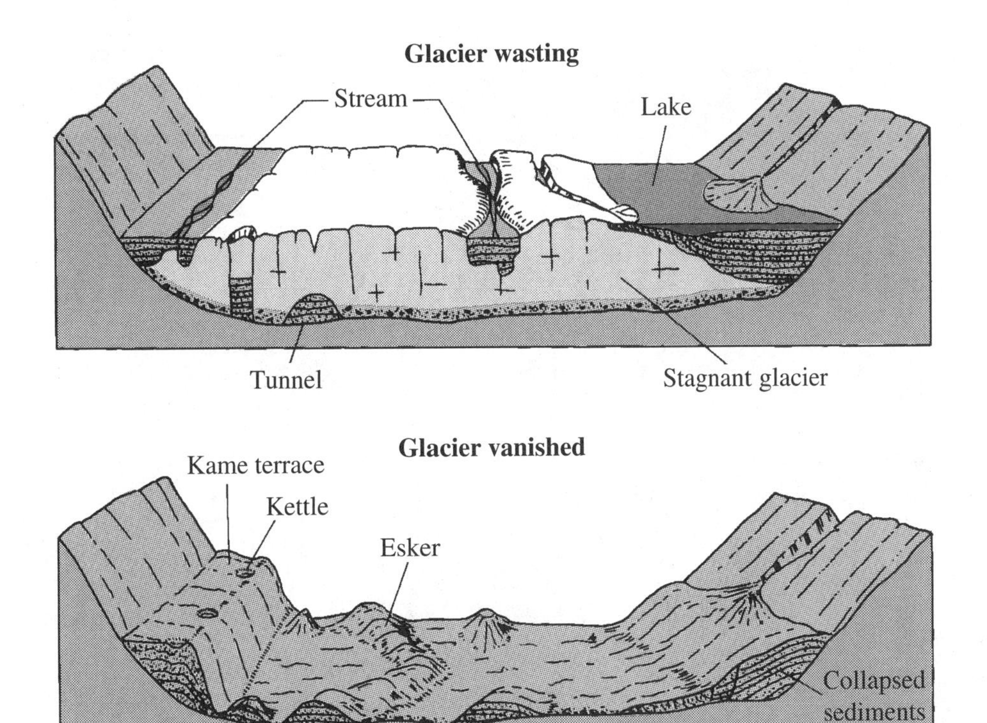

Figure 24-13. Meltwater cuts channels both on and below the surface of disintegrating ice. A *kame terrace* is a stratified deposit formed along the glacier edge. Melted blocks of stranded ice leave behind pockmarks, or *kettles*. An *esker* is a stratified, ridge-shaped deposit that may snake across the countryside for hundreds of kilometers. It may climb over low divides and creep down across valleys in complete disregard of existing topography. This peculiarity suggests that during deposition of the esker, the meltwater was confined to deep channels or to tunnels under the ice. Stratified glacial deposits are important sources of sand and gravel for the construction industry.

ICE AND ISOTOPES

Most of us live where vegetation and industry are continual sources of haze in the atmosphere. Only an occasional traveler has witnessed the extreme clarity of the air in a polar region, where one can usually see perfectly to the horizon no matter how distant. A polar ice sheet, especially the ice that pre-dates the industrial era, is extremely pure H_2O contaminated only by rare dust particles from some catastrophic windstorm or volcanic explosion. Though appearing to be a featureless mass, the ice consists of subtle winter and summer layers accumulated over thousands of centuries. It is a record of ancient climate, but how is it read? In fact, the H_2O contains its own record embodied in the stable isotopes of hydrogen and oxygen. Let's examine how to interpret this remarkable record, using oxygen isotopes to illustrate the process.

We are reminded (Table 1-2) that oxygen atoms are comprised of three stable isotopes: ^{16}O, ^{17}O, and ^{18}O. There is approximately one atom of ^{18}O for every 500 atoms of the most abundant isotope, ^{16}O, and these abundances are expressed as the ratio of ^{18}O to ^{16}O. In the deep ocean, the $^{18}O/^{16}O$ ratio is highly uniform as currents continually mix the water mass. Evaporation transfers water from the ocean into the atmosphere, and as moisture-laden air masses pass over an ice sheet, they nourish the ice by precipitation of snow. Ultimately, the source of glacier ice is ocean water.

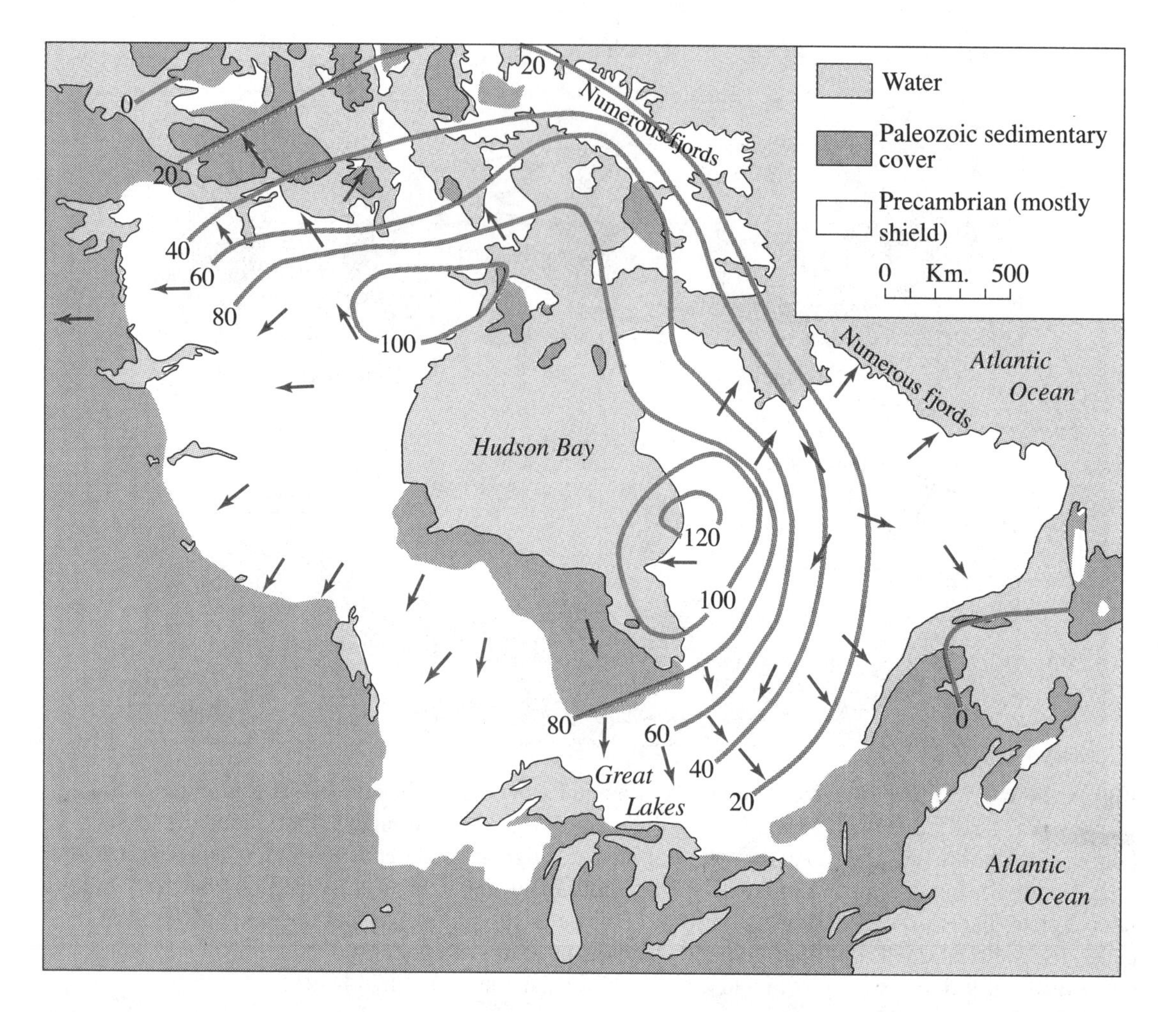

Figure 24-14. Erosion, deposition, and vertical movements of the earth's crust have operated on a grand scale in the glaciated expanses of Canada. Arrows indicate the directions of ice movement, as shown by striations, or grooves in the bedrock. Broadly speaking, they radiate here from two focal areas, one east and the other northwest of Hudson Bay, suggesting that the most recent ice sheet was thickest in these two places. Contours indicate the amount of isostatic uplift (in meters) during the past 8 thousand years. Till deposits and their stream-reworked equivalents are concentrated in the fringing one-third of the glaciated areas. Fertility of much of the soil in the Corn Belt of the U. S. is due to materials transported and deposited by glaciers. Along the eastern shores of Baffin Island and Labrador, the ice gouged numerous fjords.

H_2O molecules that contain the light oxygen isotope (^{16}O) are more active, evaporating slightly more readily than molecules that contain the heavy ^{18}O. Thus the $^{18}O/^{16}O$ ratio in water vapor is smaller than $^{18}O/^{16}O$ in ocean water; oxygen in water vapor is "light." As vapor is transferred onto a growing snowflake, more of the heavy isotope is precipitated onto the snowflake. It makes intuitive sense that the heavy isotope should be enriched in water or ice, which are condensed phases of H_2O, and depleted in the vapor phase.

Also important are the sizes of the ocean and atmospheric vapor reservoirs. By comparison, the ocean reservoir is almost of "infinite" size, too large for its composition to be affected by interchange with the atmospheric vapor reservoir. A humid air mass is a very small reservoir, becoming even smaller as it sweeps across an ice sheet, precipitating snow. As ^{18}O preferentially enters the snow, the remaining air-borne moisture is left depleted in the heavy isotope (Figure 24-18). Since this is a continuing process, both the vapor mass and precipitated snow become isotopically lighter and lighter as the snowstorm progresses inland. Light oxygen is characteristic of vapor, rain, snow, and other forms of *meteoric* water.

A cold glacier is fed by snow year round, summer as well as winter, but separation of isotopes is enhanced in the extreme cold of winter. Oxygen isotopes at an inland locality are not only light, but even lighter in winter ice than in summer ice. This is because, during the winter, the heavy isotope was

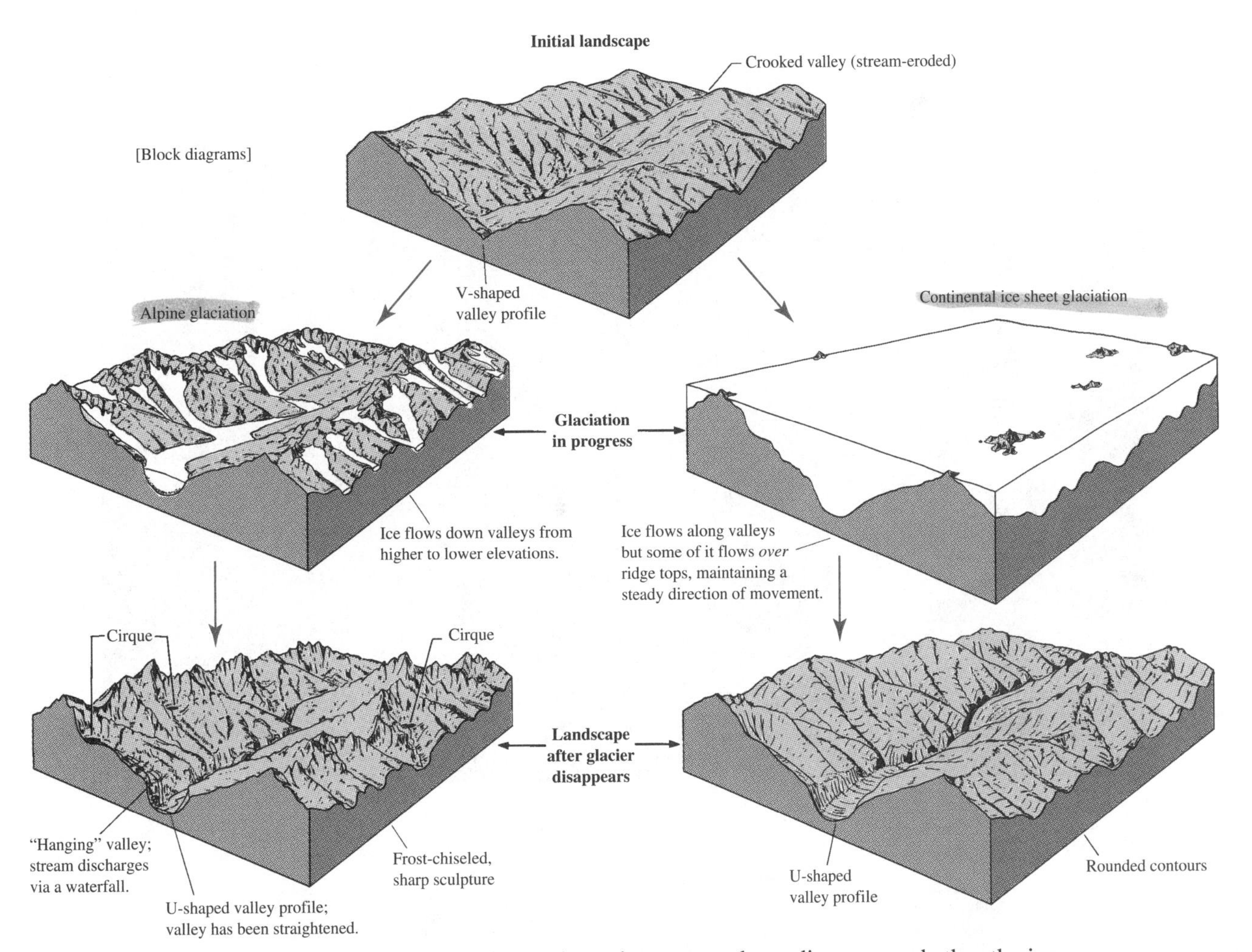

Figure 24-15. Glaciers modify a landscape in various ways, depending upon whether the ice was restricted (alpine type) or whether it blanketed the region. Unlike streams, an ice sheet attacks the entire landscape simultaneously. [*Diagram after R. F. Flint,* Glacial and Quaternary Geology, *copyright © 1970, by permission of John Wiley & Sons, Inc., New York.*]

precipitated more effectively while storms were yet in transit to a given spot on the glacier. Thus, we have layers of summer or winter ice that can be distinguished by isotopic composition. We can drill an ice core, make thousands of isotopic analyses along its length, and identify annual layers rather like counting tree rings. By combining data from ice sheets in both the northern and southern polar regions, we may assemble a picture of world climate through the ages.

Ice core records from several sites in the remote interior of the Greenland ice sheet illustrate some major features. Individual annual layers can be identified to a depth where the ice is about 40 thousand years old, perhaps back to 80 thousand years in the best case. The isotopic record of temperature confirms known historical events such as the Little Ice Age—several especially cold and stormy centuries responsible for famines—and even single episodes within the Little Ice Age such as the dreadful winter of AD 1694-95. Below a depth where the ice is 10 thousand years old, the oxygen isotopes shift sharply toward greater ^{18}O depletion, corresponding to lower temperatures down to ice that is about 75 thousand years ago. This was the time of the most recent full-scale Ice Age when continental glaciers were greatly expanded (Figure 24-1) and temperatures were 11 to 12°C colder than at present.

As the time of massive glaciation drew to a close, a several thousand year transition period followed with wild temperature swings. Within just a few decades, a warming of 6 or 7°C would occur as the climate became windy and very dusty, followed by centuries of slower cooling back to the previous state. Such climatic violence would be horrendous if it were to happen to us. Finally, the climate settled into the relative stability enjoyed for the past 10 thousand years (Figure 24-19). Near the base of the ice sheet where the ice is about 100 thousand years old, there is an isotopic record of the preceding warm period with evidence of similar sudden climatic changes. Why should world climate become so unstable, and what of our own immediate future? A favorite saying of geologists is: "Whatever *did* happen,

a

b

Figure 24-16. (*a*) Contours of the landscape in this part of the Adirondack Mountains, New York, have become smoothed and rounded by an ice sheet that once completely buried it. [*Courtesy Jerome Wyckoff.*] (*b*) When valley glaciers retreated in the Sierra Nevada, California, they left behind a rugged landscape. [*U. S. Forest Service photograph.*]

Figure 24-17. The classic U-shape cross sectional profile is magnificently developed in this valley in Canada formerly occupied by a glacier. [*Geological Survey of Canada photograph.*]

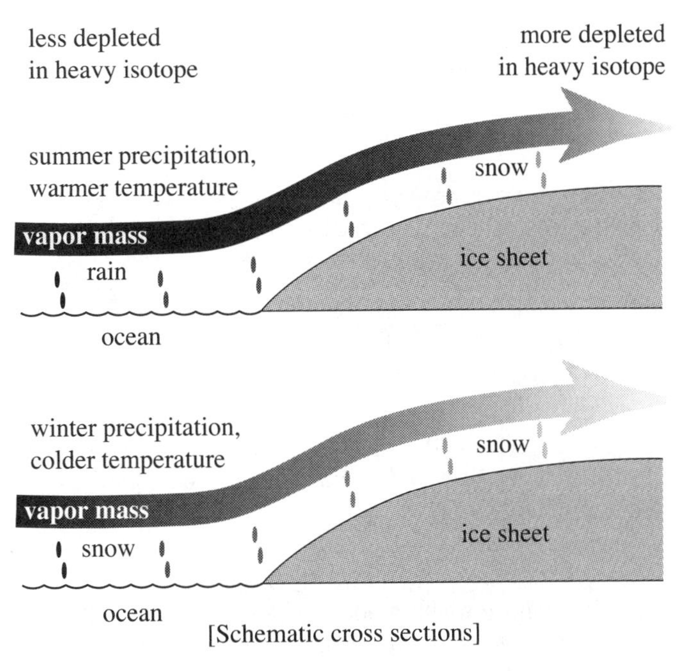

Figure 24-18. During precipitation, the heavy isotope (^{18}O) is concentrated in the rain or snow, leaving the vapor mass, a small reservoir, depleted in ^{18}O. While crossing the ice sheet, both the vapor and local precipitation become isotopically lighter. The depletion process is even more effective at lower temperature, making winter snow isotopically lighter than summer snow.

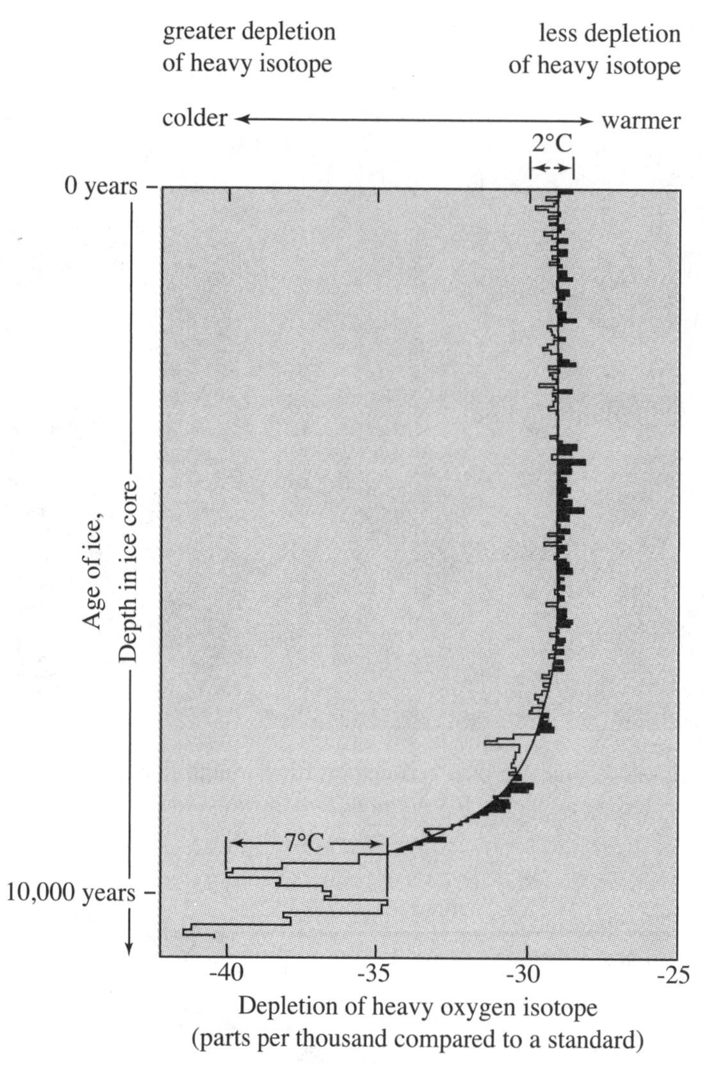

Figure 24-19. In this oxygen isotope record in the Greenland ice sheet, more negative compositions correspond to greater depletion of the heavy isotope, and thus to colder climate. Large, rapid fluctuations occurred immediately preceding the most recent 10 thousand years of stable, warm climate.

can happen." In reference to climate, it could happen *again*. Predictions of future climate must be firmly based in an understanding of past climates viewed on long and short timescales. Let's expand the climatic time scale to include millions of years.

Pleistocene Climates

We noted that a storm front contains a trivial amount of water compared to that in the ocean, but ice sheets are of substantial mass today, and they were much larger at the height of the Ice Ages. As H_2O was evaporated from the ocean and became stored in continental ice, sea level dropped as much as 120 meters (nearly 400 feet). Isotopically light oxygen deposited in the ice was balanced by the heavy isotope left behind in the ocean. Bottom-dwelling foraminifera in contact with ocean water (Figure 7-7) were building their tiny shells of calcium carbonate, and as the water became isotopically heavier, so did the oxygen in shell material. In fact, the concentration of the heavy isotope in shell material depends also upon the temperature of surrounding ocean water, which must have been colder during the Ice Ages. Whichever the cause, whether it was the effect of changing water isotopic composition, or the effect of temperature, the isotope record in foraminifera varied between heavier as the ice sheets expanded to lighter as the ice wasted away. Isotopic analyses of glacier ice and of microfossils in ocean-floor sediment are proxies (indirect indicators) for climate. A core of ocean sediment spans much farther back in geologic time, but it does not contain the fine details preserved in glacier ice.

By 1.4 million years ago, glaciation had already locked both of the polar regions in its icy grip. Oscillations in the oxygen isotope pattern in foraminifera faithfully record the expanding and shrinking ice volume (Figure 24-20). At around 650 thousand years ago, the climatic pattern suddenly changed from shorter, weaker glacial cycles, to ones that were longer and deeper. In the latter cycles, the ice typically accumulated gradually for about 100 thousand years, then melted back catastrophically, as shown by the sawtooth pattern in Figure 24-20. Superimposed smaller climatic wiggles are recorded in each major sawtooth. The maximum ice volume (top of the sawtooth) was similar from cycle to cycle. Clues to the magnitude of the most recent several cycles are preserved as extensive glacial moraines (described in Figure 24-10) in North America and Europe. North American ice spread from its Canadian zone of accumulation to the Midwestern states as far south as Iowa, Illinois, and Indiana. On the northern side, ice extended to the Arctic Ocean. After each melt-back, Europe and mainland North America became virtually ice-free, like they are today. Pulsating continental glaciations were the hallmark of the Pleistocene Epoch (Figure 13-13), and in fact the Recent Epoch, the past 10 thousand years, is but an undistinguished "blip" within the larger pattern.

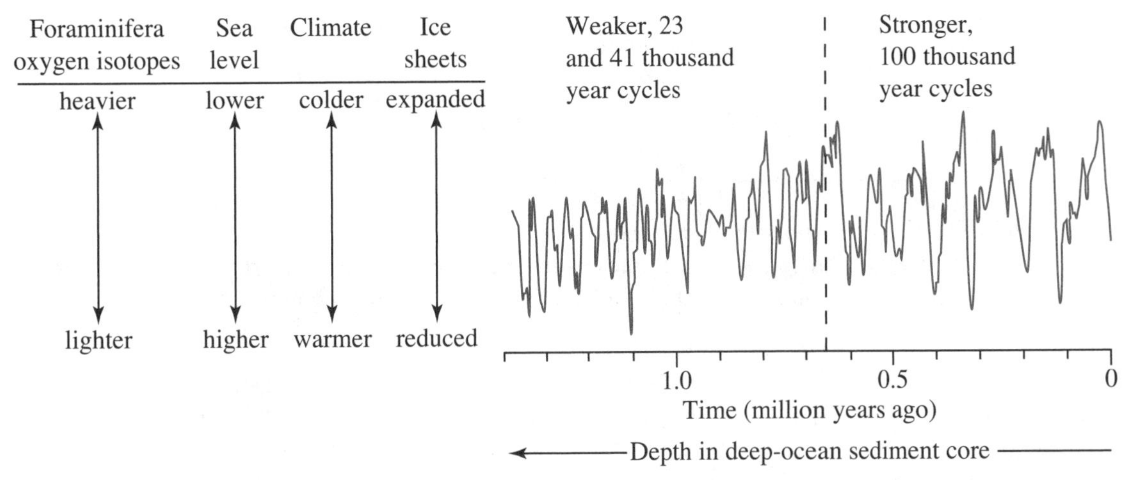

Figure 24-20. Heavier or lighter oxygen isotopes in foraminifera are a proxy for changing temperature and isotopic composition of the ocean, which in turn is related to expansion and decline of ice sheets. Sediment in deep-ocean core no. 677, from the equatorial Pacific, was deposited over the last 1.4 million years. Many cycles are evident, culminating in 100,000-year-long, intense cycles in which the ice volume characteristically grew slowly, then melted back abruptly.

Ancient Glaciations

Dinosaurs, early mammals, and their contemporaries flourished even in polar regions, not glaciated during the Mesozoic Era, and lived in a "greenhouse" environment that was about 10°C warmer than today. Dust hurled aloft by the catastrophic meteorite impact that terminated the era (Chapter 15) seemingly had no enduring effect on climate. Temperature did gradually decline through the early Cenozoic Era (Figure 24-21), and dipped sharply about 35 million years ago when ice possibly first appeared in Antarctica. Temperature dropped further about 14 million years ago, and yet further 2 to 3 million years ago, plunging the earth into the modern Ice Ages with its 40 to 50 complex cycles.

In the more distant past, Paleozoic glacial episodes had continued sporadically for 200 million years in Gondwana, the southern supercontinent. Deposits of till, and glacially scratched and polished bedrock pavement are famous in Africa, Australia, and elsewhere. At least within broad limits, the timing of these deposits can be known through their association with fossil-containing sediments, or with volcanic strata that can be dated by isotopic age methods. Even more ancient (Precambrian) glaciations have been identified, including a very long interval from 0.9 to 0.6 billion years ago. Another glaciation occurred about 2.3 billion years ago, but whether there were glaciations during the first half of earth history is conjectural, the evidence obscured by recycling of the geologic record.

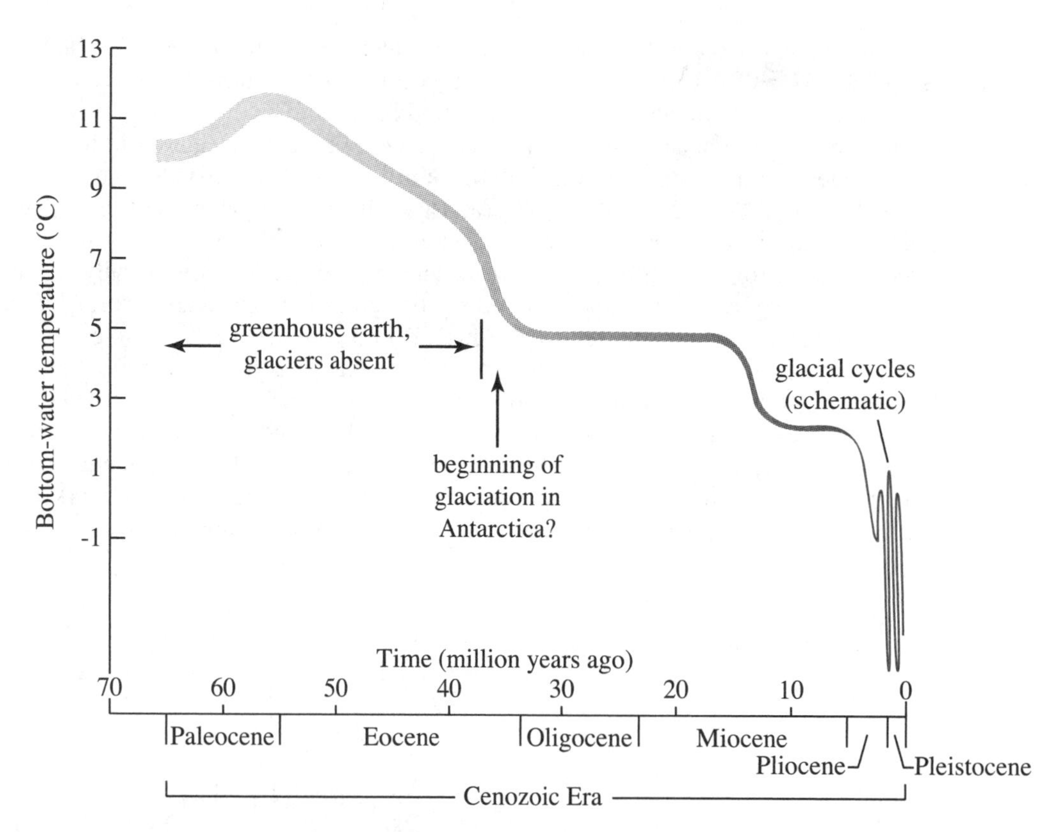

Figure 24-21. Oxygen isotope data from Cenozoic bottom-dwelling foraminifera, recovered from many samples of deep-ocean core sediment, reflect water temperature, itself a proxy for air temperature. The more recent the geologic record of climate, the better defined and more reliable it is.

CAUSES OF THE ICE AGES

To understand the causes of Ice Ages is one of the most daunting challenges of earth science, yet this knowledge is of practical importance because we appear to be living in a period of rapid climatic change. Time scales are diverse, from hundreds of millions of years (duration of Paleozoic and late Precambrian Ice Ages), to 100 thousand years (a late Pleistocene glacial cycle), to centuries (Little Ice Age), to one season's snowfall, to the hour or so of a single storm event. In all of this complexity, which phenomenon is the *cause* and which other phenomenon is the *effect*, or are the two possibly not related? Geologists believe they can answer some questions about Ice Ages quite well, but for other questions they haven't a clue. Changes can be so rapid as to suggest that earth climate is teetering toward instability, prone to switch abruptly and unpredictably between different climatic states. Let's examine some of the factors responsible for climate change.

Continental Drift, and Distribution of Land and Sea

Ocean currents transport heat energy between tropical and polar latitudes, thereby modulating the climate. For example, warm surface currents enter the North Atlantic, and some of their heat makes Europe habitable year round in spite of its far-northern location. Frigid Arctic air cools the Atlantic water, and loss of vapor increases its salt content, both processes making the water more dense. As the water sinks into the depths and flows southward, an enormous "conveyor belt" circulation is set up, delivering a volume of water 20 times the rate of flow of all the world's rivers combined. Transport of heat would be far more efficient if the polar regions were not so thermally isolated. Powerful ocean currents cannot reach the North Pole, which lies within the nearly landlocked Arctic Ocean, nor is heat readily transported across the Antarctic continent that contains the South Pole.

In past geologic times, world geography was different from today almost beyond recognition. We saw (Chapter 22) that as landmasses drifted apart, or slid laterally, or collided head-on, their distribution changed both relative to one another and to the earth's polar regions. A cold ocean current could begin to circumnavigate Antarctica only after that continent had split off from the Gondwana supercontinent. The narrow Isthmus of Panama is a barricade where Atlantic and Pacific waters had once mingled. When tectonic plate collisions uplifted the Andes Mountains of South America and the Tibetan Plateau of Asia, weather patterns were altered locally and even worldwide. Plate tectonic activity was responsible for all these examples, taking place within just the most recent millions of years.

Climatic consequences of the ancient, prolonged drift of Gondwana were spectacular. During the early Paleozoic, North Africa lay over the South Pole, as abundant glacial features in the Sahara Desert attest (Figure 24-22). Mid-Paleozoic glaciation shifted to southern Brazil, and in the late Paleozoic to southern Africa and Antarctica. During Mesozoic and early Cenozoic time, landmasses were situated nearer the Equator, and continental glaciation was unknown. Continued stately drift of landmasses explains the Ice Ages (or their absence) on the longest time scale of tens to hundreds of millions of years.

Milankovitch Cycles

Subtle motions are superimposed upon the familiar daily rotation of the earth, and its annual orbit around the sun. Jupiter and Saturn, which are massive planets, exert a gravitational influence upon the

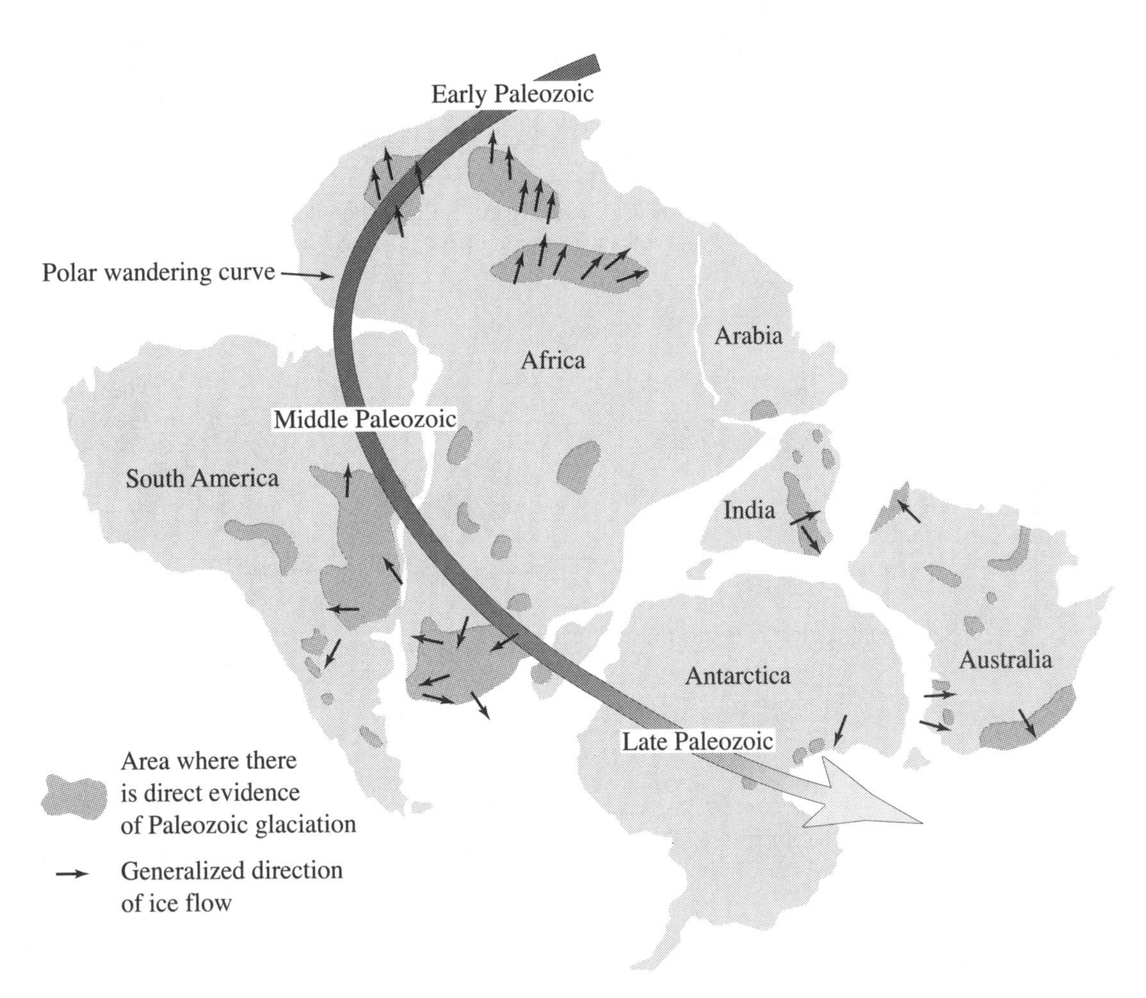

Figure 24-22. A curve traces the Paleozoic wanderings of the South Pole. Its path, obtained from paleomagnetic measurements (Chapter 22), is equivalent to a drift of the Gondwana supercontinent over a fixed pole position, or to a combination of continental drift and polar wandering. Glaciation may have continued during intervals over a period as long as 400 million years. In fact, this episode may have been a continuation of the latest Precambrian ice age evidenced in Britain, Scandinavia, and Greenland. Note that ice flowed *inland* onto what is now Brazil and southern Australia. This pattern makes sense only if the coasts of South America and Australia were attached to other landmasses at the time.

earth's orbit, and there is also a gravitational attraction between the earth's equatorial bulge (Chapter 16) and the sun and moon. In the early part of the 20th Century, the Serbian mathematician M. Milankovitch exhaustively described the following interactions ("Milankovitch cycles").

Tilt of the earth's spin axis with respect to the plane of its orbit around the sun is the well-known cause of the seasons [Figure 24-23(*a*)]. During a Northern Hemisphere summer, the axis at the North Pole points toward the sun, whereas the axis at the South Pole points toward the sun six months later.

[Schematic drawings, not to scale]

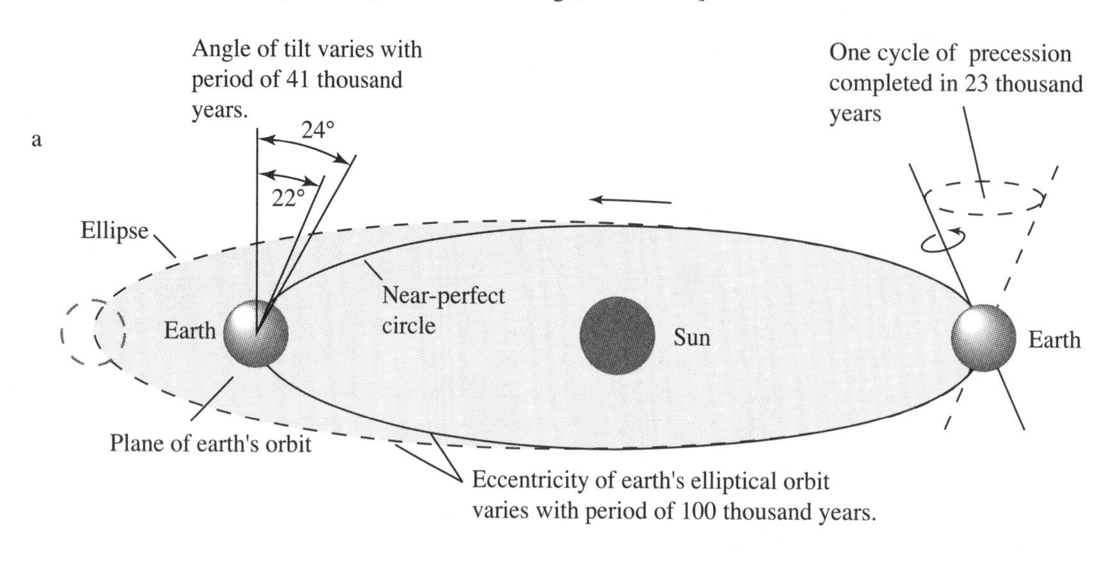

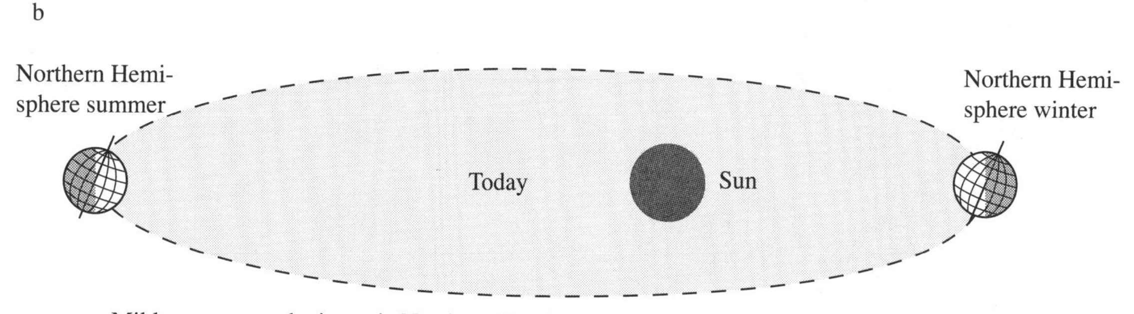

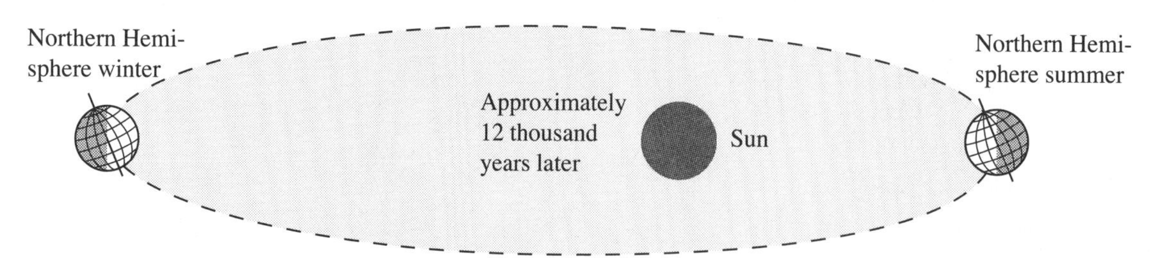

Figure 24-23. (*a*) Variations in tilt and precession of the earth's spin axis, and in the eccentricity of its orbit around the sun, appear to control the cyclical expansion and recession of ice sheets during the current Ice Age. (*b*) Orbiting the sun in an ellipse, the earth is nearest the sun during a given season, and farthest from the sun six months later. If, for example, the earth is nearest when the spin axis in the Northern Hemisphere is pointing away from the sun (i.e., in winter), the seasonal harshness is softened. After this Milankovitch cycle continues for a few thousand years, the Northern Hemisphere winter will coincide with greatest distance from the sun, and both winters and summers will be very severe. Milankovitch effects in the Southern Hemisphere are opposite to those in the Northern Hemisphere.

Currently, the angle of tilt is 23.4°, but it varies between approximately 22° and 24° over a 41 thousand year cycle. Increasing the tilt would enhance the seasonal contrast (hotter summers, colder winters). A second type of motion is *precession*, whereby the spin axis wobbles, a behavior familiar in a spinning top or gyroscope. Precession causes the direction of the spin axis to draw a circle in the sky, completing one cycle in about 23 thousand years. Precession is caused by the sun's pull on the equatorial bulge of the earth. Finally, the *eccentricity* of the earth's orbit around the sun continually changes. The orbit is an ellipse in which the sun is located at a focus, a somewhat off-center position. Eccentricity varies in a 100 thousand year cycle between 0.0 (a nearly perfect circle) and 0.05 (noticeably elliptical).

Variations of tilt, precession, and eccentricity, each with a different length of cycle, combine to exert a profound influence upon climate. Over the course of one year, the *amount* of heat energy received from the sun is the same, but the *distribution* of the heat varies with the effect of the Milankovitch cycle. For example, consider the climate of Anchorage, Alaska, which is at latitude 61° north. Because Anchorage lies not far from the Arctic Circle, it experiences long summer days and long winter nights, which would be expected to produce great seasonal contrast. However, the eccentricity of the earth's orbit places Anchorage closer to the sun's warmth in the winter than in the summer, which softens the severity of the seasons [Figure 24-23(*b*)]. Approximately 12 thousand years from now, precession will have "wobbled" the spin axis into the opposite direction, and of course the orbital eccentricity will have varied, too, on a much slower time scale. At this future time, the site of Anchorage will have long winter nights while at a maximum distance from the sun, thus increasing the severity of seasonal contrast. Changing the degree of tilt further modifies these influences. Earth's orbital characteristics are so well known that their combined effect can be calculated accurately for any time up to several million years into the past or into the future.

As mentioned above, polar ice sheets receive both summer and winter snow, but melting occurs only during summer. When summers are mild, the ice survives to grow yet more the next year. When cold winters are matched with hot summers, the ice cannot survive. Glacial cycles correlate extremely well with Milankovitch cycles, as seen in Figure 24-20. Apparently the orbital eccentricity factor has dominated for the past 650 thousand years, before which the 41 thousand year tilt cycle and 23 thousand year precession cycle predominated, and the smaller bumps on the sawtooth curve can also be explained by Milankovitch cycles.

Puzzles remain, however. For any given Milankovitch influence in the Northern Hemisphere, there should be an opposite influence in the Southern Hemisphere, yet the ice sheets in both polar regions have expanded and declined together on a schedule that is controlled by Northern Hemisphere events. Milankovitch cycles are manifested in ice, and also in sedimentary rocks of many geologic ages from recent to very ancient. If varying tilt, precession, and eccentricity have always moderated the climate, why did polar glaciation not begin until 2 or 3 million years ago? Milankovitch cycles are symmetrical, and so why do the ice sheets grow slowly, then melt back suddenly? Yet other factors must be influencing the earth's climate on a time scale of decades to millennia.

The Radiocarbon Clock

We shall need a suitable geologic timepiece in order to study events over the past few thousands of years. You recall that the potassium-argon method, uranium-lead method, and others (Chapter 11) are based upon the decay of radioactive isotopes into stable daughter isotopes. Half-lives are billions of years, with the result that radioactive decay and accumulation of daughter are very slow. If the dated geologic event were recent, not enough daughter would be present to measure accurately. Another radioactive isotope, carbon-14 (^{14}C), is an ideal tool because its 5730-year half-life matches the ages of recent climatic events rather well. Carbon-14 is also widely used to date archeological remains, and in other applications.

With such a short half-life, all of the ^{14}C inherited by the early earth decayed away long ago. Natural carbon-14 exists today only because, although it is decaying, it is continually being replenished as *cosmic rays* bombard the atmosphere. Cosmic rays are not like light rays; rather, they are particles (mostly protons) with mass and very high energy, created in the depths of outer space by supernova explosions among other things. When a cosmic-ray particle slams into an atomic nucleus high in the earth's atmosphere, the target nucleus disintegrates into a variety of smaller particles including neutrons that undergo further reaction producing atoms of carbon-14. These atoms promptly combine with oxygen, forming $^{14}CO_2$, carbon dioxide that is "labeled" with radioactivity. In a simple situation without interference by human activity, the rate of decay would be in approximate balance with the rate of production.

This "live" (i.e., radioactive) carbon mixes rapidly throughout the atmosphere in a steady-state concentration of one atom of ^{14}C for every 800 billion stable isotope carbon atoms.

As plants and other photosynthesizers utilize CO_2 in their life processes, carbon-14 becomes incorporated into their tissues, and into the tissues of animals farther along the food chain. Consider a tree that is adding a new annual growth ring. Only the outermost ring is biologically alive, its substance in communication with the external environment. Meanwhile, ^{14}C in the dead interior rings is decaying away and not being replenished by exchange with the environment. A tree ring that was deposited 5730 years (one half-life) ago would contain one-half of its original concentration of ^{14}C, and after 11,460 years (2 half-lives) one-fourth of the original would remain, and so on (Figure 24-24). By measuring the remaining ^{14}C, we date some event (such as death) that removed the sample from communication with the external reservoir of "live" carbon.

Tree rings are useful in studies of ancient climate for several reasons. With rare exceptions, a tree ring represents one year of growth, and so the age of a particular ring can be pinpointed by counting back through the sequence. Species such as the bristlecone pine, which live in high arid country, have deposited thick tree rings during rainy years and thin rings during years of harsh drought. The distinctive thick-and-thin pattern of rings in a living tree is matched with the ring pattern in an older tree with an overlapping lifetime, to establish the ages of inner rings of the older tree (Figure 24-25). A "tree ring stratigraphy" has been compiled back to 11.5 thousand years ago (two half-lives of ^{14}C), which was when the great ice sheets were in pell-mell retreat.

Moreover, carbon-14 analysis of ancient tree rings of known age can serve as an independent check on the accuracy of the dating method. The carbon-14 age of a given ring should be the same as the age obtained through tree-ring stratigraphy. An important assumption is that ^{14}C was always manufactured at the same rate as it is today. To no one's surprise, this assumption is not fulfilled perfectly, but comparison with the tree-ring chronology permits us to apply refined corrections to the carbon-14 ages of older material.

An advancing glacier may bury a forest, incorporating it into glacial till, or plant material may be lodged in outwash sediment deposited by meltwater. In these situations, a carbon-14 age of the sample can be related to glacier activity. Carbon-14 ages have documented the retreat of the latest ice sheet that covered northern North America (Figure 24-26). As the ice melted back, large lakes formed along its margin, temporarily restrained behind fragile ice dams. Gigantic lakes may also have formed *under* the ice and, indeed, a body of water estimated to be the size of Lake Erie has been detected by geophysical methods beneath the Antarctic ice sheet. Occasionally, the dams gave way, draining the lakes in a series of mind-boggling floods far exceeding anything in modern experience. For years, researchers in Washington State overlooked the evidence for such a flood there because of its magnitude. It deposited sedimentary ripples, normally millimeters to centimeters high, that are the size of small hills. At peak flow, water rushed out of the impounded lake at a rate that would have drained Lake Michigan, second largest of the Great Lakes, in less than three days! New exits were uncovered as the ice front retreated.

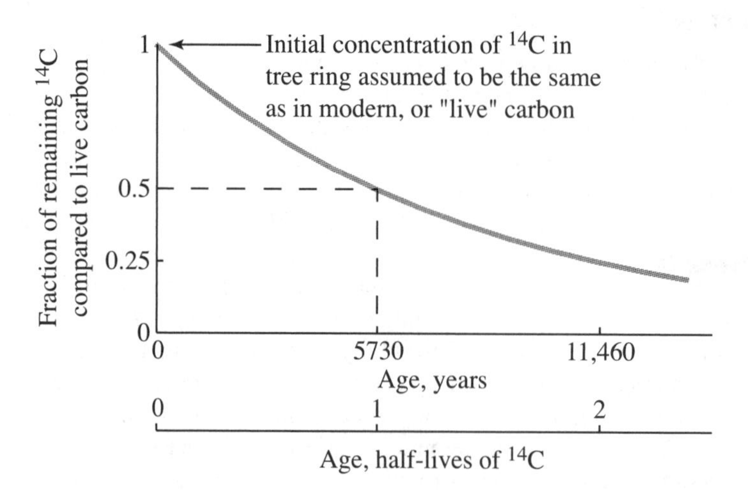

Figure 24-24. Carbon-14 in a tree ring, or other local reservoir that has become isolated from the atmospheric "live" reservoir, continues to diminish according to the radioactivity decay curve (compare with Figure 11-5).

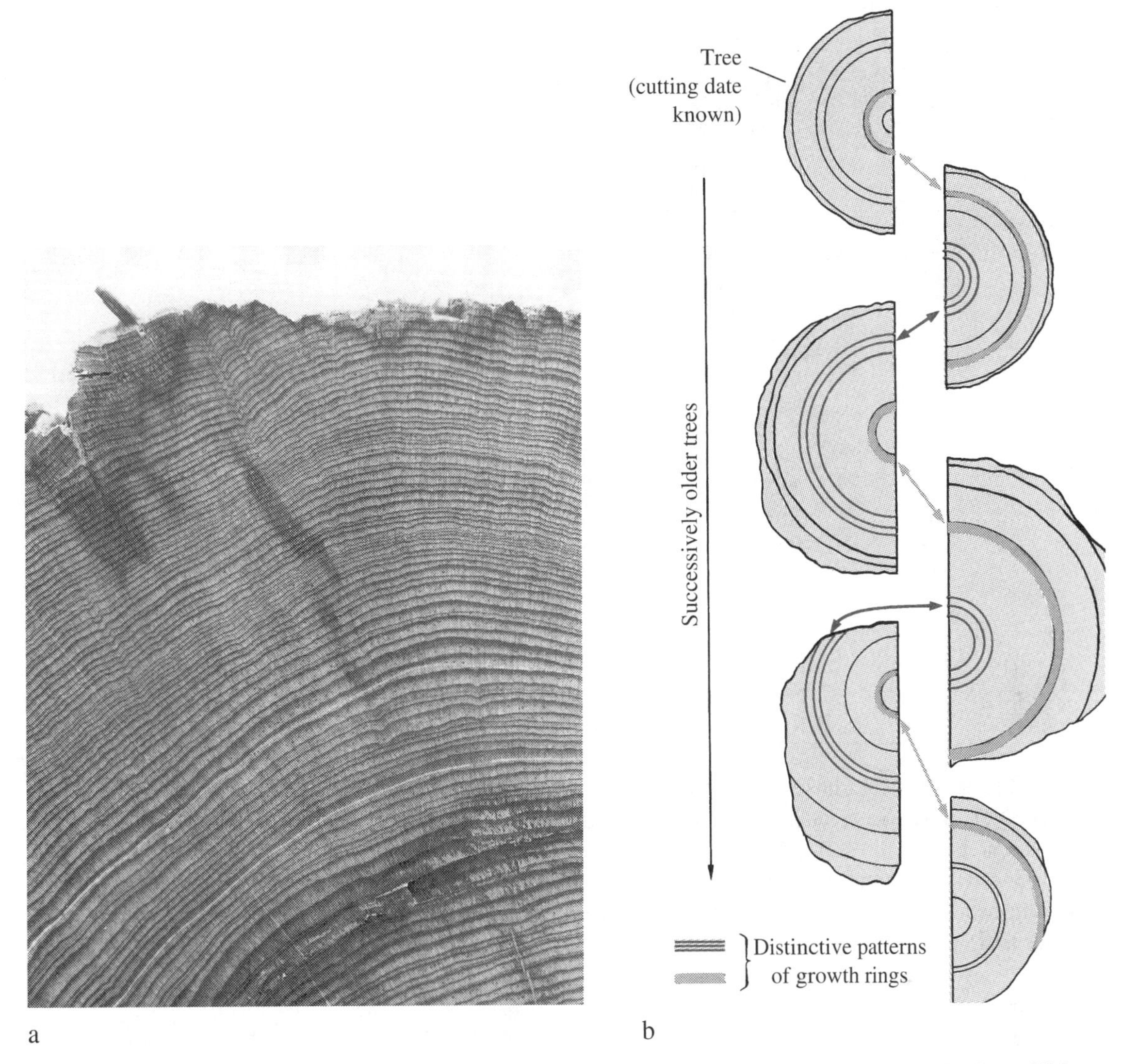

Figure 24-25. (*a*) Annual layers in gnarled, stunted bristlecone pine trees on the ragged edge of life vary greatly in width, depending upon the whims of the weather prior to and during a particular growing season. Each growth ring is a reservoir of carbon-14 that is isolated from further exchange with atmospheric CO_2 when the wood dies at the end of the season. [*Courtesy of H. C. Fritts and Laboratory of Tree-Ring Research, University of Arizona, Tucson.*] (*b*) Growth-ring patterns can be correlated from a modern tree back through successively more ancient trees whose lifetimes overlapped. Since occasionally a year may be represented by two rings, or no ring, entire sequences must be cross-correlated. In this manner, an independent chronology has been assembled back to 11.5 thousand years ago, against which carbon-14 ages can be compared.

Lake Agassiz, which once straddled the Canada-U. S. border, discharged down the Mississippi to the Gulf of Mexico, then north into the Arctic Ocean for a few centuries, then eastward via the Great Lakes and St. Lawrence Seaway. A vast sheet of fresh meltwater spread out over the surface of the North Atlantic, disrupting the "conveyor belt" flow of deep water discussed above.

Greenhouse Gases

Atmospheric carbon dioxide, the basis of the ^{14}C method, may also play a role in governing climate. Water vapor, carbon dioxide, methane (CH_4), and certain artificial substances including fluorocarbons (refrigerants) act as *greenhouse gases*. On a bitterly cold but sunny day in Ohio, tomatoes are basking in a greenhouse whose warmth is maintained without any apparent source of heat. This occurs because the

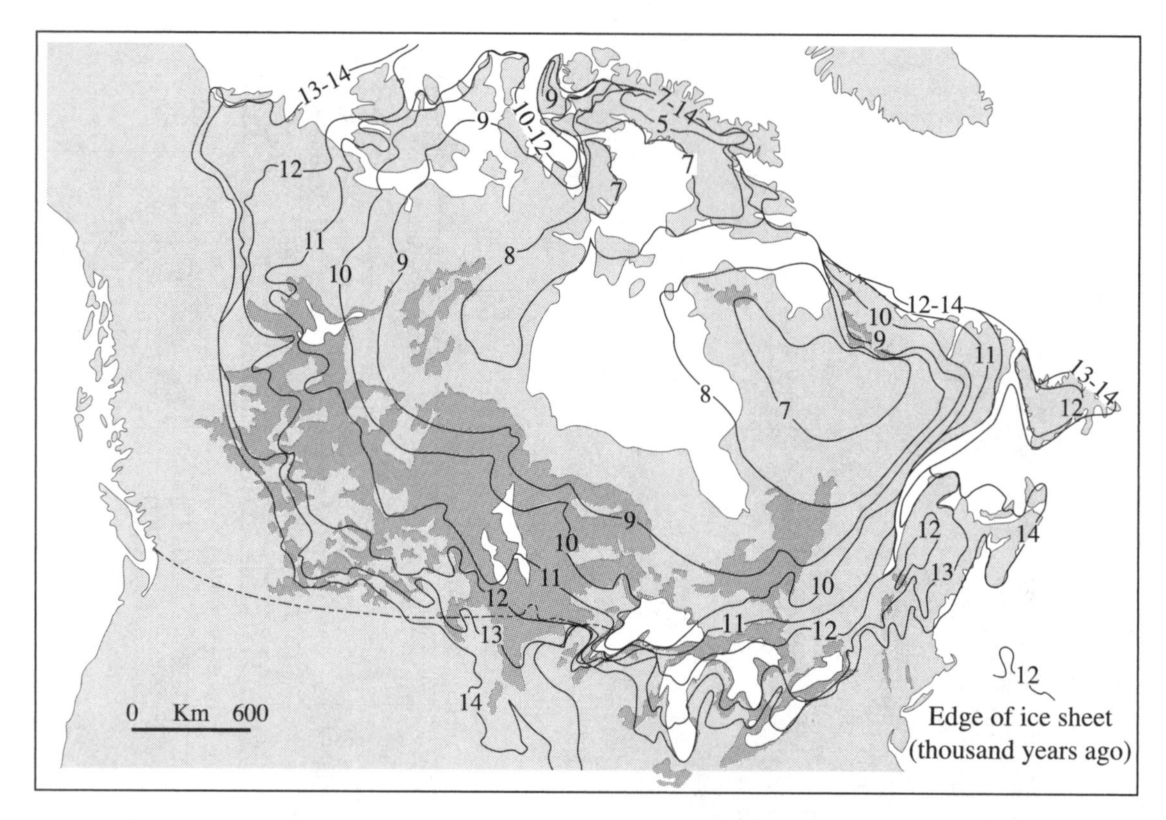

Figure 24-26. Contours based upon radiocarbon ages, glacial moraine directions, and other evidence trace the headlong (occasionally catastrophic) retreat of the Canadian ice sheet a few thousand years ago. Ice persisted longest in precisely those areas where it originally was thickest (compare with Figure 24-14). Sediment (colored area) was deposited in vast lakes that were ponded against the retreating ice front. This region was never occupied by a single lake, but rather it was covered by smaller lakes present in different places at different times.

greenhouse glass is transparent to visible light whose wavelengths are short. Upon striking objects below, the light energy is partly transformed into longer (infra-red) wavelengths unable to escape back out through the glass. Heat is trapped beneath the greenhouse glass, and on a larger scale trapped in the atmosphere whose greenhouse gases also block the outward passage of infra-red energy. As concentrations of greenhouse gases increase, so does the atmosphere's heat-trapping capacity. We are rapidly adding CO_2 into the atmosphere as a by-product of burning fossil fuel as well as by burning of grasslands and rain forest, so there is (vigorously debated) concern about global warming with fear of agricultural havoc, melting glaciers, rising sea level, flooded coastal cities. . . .

It is difficult to judge the importance of greenhouse gases in moderating Ice Age climates. These gases comprise only a tiny part of the atmosphere relative to nitrogen (78%) and oxygen (21%). The concentration of water vapor varies daily and from place to place in a complex manner. CO_2 and CH_4 do not precipitate out, but the atmospheric concentrations of these potent greenhouse gases are low. Analyses of air trapped in bubbles in glacier ice (Figure 24-27) show that concentrations of greenhouse gases have varied through time, in a manner that correlates with former climate. Did greenhouse gases force climatic change, or were both the gases and climate responding to some more fundamental control? Only 1/60th as much CO_2 is present in the atmosphere as that dissolved in ocean water. What happens to this balance, and to climate, when the oceanic conveyor belt turns on or off? Why do glacial cycles sink slowly into deep refrigeration, and suddenly snap into a melting phase? Why are there violent climate oscillations on a millennium timescale during waning stages of deglaciation? Will global warming due to increased greenhouse gases be a serious threat in our lifetime? Geologic studies, which tell us *what* has happened and *when* it happened, are important to understanding climatic complexities.

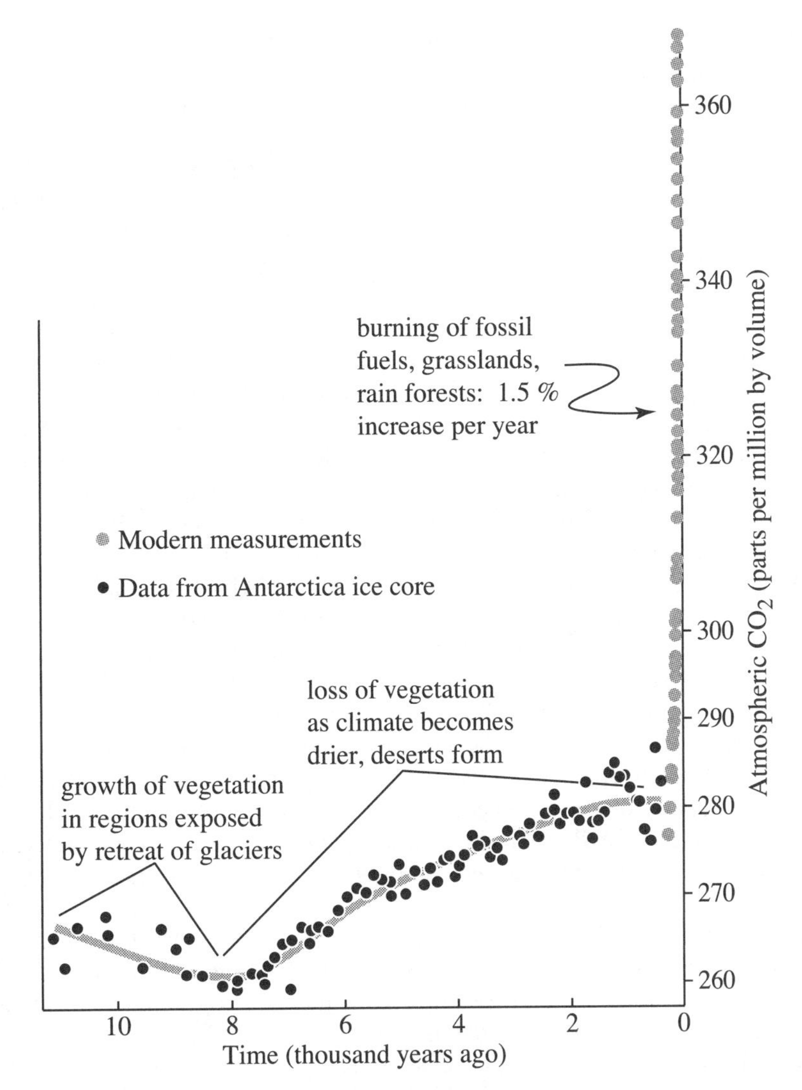

Figure 24-27. World climate has varied somewhat during the past 10 thousand years, much of this documented by written records and findings at archeological sites. These variations correlate well with abundances of CO_2, a greenhouse gas, measured in air trapped in bubbles in Antarctic ice. Earlier variations, of natural origin, were related to vegetative cover of the land surface. Growing plants extract CO_2 from the atmosphere, and decay releases it back into the atmosphere. Beginning recently, during the Industrial Age, the concentration of atmospheric CO_2 has shot upwards as a by-product of combustion, at a rate unprecedented by anything known in the geologic record.

SUMMARY

Modern world climate is highly stratified in contrasting zones. Although glaciers cover 10 percent of the land surface today, ice sheets occupied three times more area at the height of the Ice Ages. H_2O reduces the climatic extremes of temperature by absorbing or releasing heat energy during transitions amongst its solid, liquid, or vapor states, and ice is less dense than (and floats upon) liquid water, with profound consequences for climate.

Nourished by fallen snow, glacier ice behaves like a mechanically weak metamorphic rock kept near its melting point. Under low pressure near the surface of a glacier, ice behaves in a brittle manner by shattering and by developing open crevasses. Under higher pressure at depth, ice flows in a ductile manner under its own weight. The temperature of ice in "cold" glaciers, most of them in polar regions, is below the melting point throughout; melting occurs never or very rarely. Cold glaciers are nourished by snowfall in summer as well as winter. Melting is common in a "warm" glacier; temperature may be at the melting point throughout. As fresh snow matures, it recrystallizes into firn (granular snow) and then, by further compaction, into glacier ice.

Net accumulation of ice in the upper elevations of a glacier is balanced by downhill flow, with net wastage of the ice at lower elevations. Glaciers advance, typically at a rate between 10 and 200 meters/year, by sliding bodily over the bedrock and through internal deformation. In the process, many small ice crystals coalesce into fewer, larger crystals that deform while in the solid state by slippage along planes of atoms. A mountain, or alpine glacier is confined between valley walls, whereas an ice sheet overspreads the topography. As an annual ice layer is buried beneath later deposits, it becomes stretched and thinned. Most alpine glaciers waste by melting, but great ice sheets, especially in Antarctica, waste along extensive floating ice shelves that discharge icebergs. Liquid water lubricates the base of many glaciers, a condition that may create instability and sudden surging of the glacier, causing it to advance for several years at as much as 100 times its normal flow rate.

Flowing ice erodes chiefly through scouring using embedded rock fragments. Glacial debris left by a formerly widespread ice sheet consists of till (an unstratified, chaotic jumble of clastic particles ranging from microscopic clay to giant boulders). The till may be reworked by flowing meltwater to become a stratified outwash deposit. Glacial moraine is a landform, a heap composed of till, deposited at the terminus of a glacier or laterally along valley walls.

The weight of a thick ice sheet depresses the earth's crust, which rebounds isostatically after the ice has melted away. Alpine glaciers that occupy formerly stream-carved valleys tend to straighten their crookedness, and modify the original V-shape cross-sectional profile into a glacial U-shape profile. A cirque, a bowl-shape excavation, lies at the head of the valley, and tributary valleys that were formerly occupied by glaciers are left hanging high above the master valley after melt-back.

When ocean water evaporates, the light stable isotope of oxygen (^{16}O) is preferentially incorporated into the vapor while the heavy isotope (^{18}O) remains concentrated in the liquid. As vapor in a storm front precipitates, the heavy isotope is concentrated into the rain or snow, leaving the vapor mass isotopically lighter (depleted in ^{18}O). Because this is a continuing process as the storm front moves inland across the ice sheet, remote interior ice is especially light isotopically, and winter ice deposited at colder temperatures is even lighter than summer ice deposited at warmer temperatures. Thus, annual summer-winter layers in an ice core from Greenland or Antarctica may be distinguished isotopically, and counted down the core, and ancient temperatures may be evaluated both on the year-to-year scale (weather) and century-to-century scale (climate). These ice cores indicate changing climate, including the modern warm period, back to 10 thousand years ago, the most recent full-scale Ice Age back to 75 thousand years ago, and the warm period that preceded it. The ice record also indicates intervals of great climatic instability, sudden fluctuations both during the height of a glacial advance but especially during a several-thousand-year period at its conclusion.

Sea level dropped as much as 120 meters at the climax of the most recent Ice Age, and ocean water became isotopically heavier as more of the light oxygen isotope was locked into ice. Isotopic fluctuations, recorded in shells of foraminifera in seafloor sediment, are a proxy for advances and recessions of continental ice sheets. During the repeated cycles characteristic of the Pleistocene Epoch, ice sheets grew slowly, then melted back catastrophically. In the Cenozoic Era, world climate cooled by a series of small steps; Antarctica became glaciated first, and later the Northern Hemisphere, and both polar regions have experienced 40 to 50 glacial cycles during the past 2 to 3 million years.

Prolonged Ice Ages occurred in Gondwana during much of the Paleozoic Era, preceded by major glaciation between 0.9 and 0.6 billion years ago, another at about 2.3 billion years ago, and possibly at more ancient times. Continental drift causes the distribution of land and sea to change, thus determining whether or not land is situated in polar regions, and whether ocean currents can readily transport heat energy from the tropics into high latitudes. This plate tectonic phenomenon explains the presence or absence of widespread glaciation on a long time scale of millions to billions of years.

Orbital motions including precession (wobbling) of the earth's spin axis, degree of tilt of the axis, and eccentricity of the earth's orbit around the sun vary with a different lengths of cycle, and together cause variations of the distribution of heat energy received from the sun during one year. These Milankovitch cycles result in periods of relatively mild summers and winters, during which the continental ice sheets may grow, and other periods of severely cold winters and hot summers, the latter causing the ice sheets to waste away. Milankovitch cycles adequately explain the timing, duration, and intensity of major Pleistocene glacial cycles, but they do not explain the abrupt melt-backs or other instabilities on a shorter time scale.

Glacial events within the past tens of thousands of years can be dated by analysis of carbon-14 (^{14}C), a radioactive isotope whose half-life is 5730 years, that is replenished by being continually created in the upper atmosphere by cosmic-ray bombardment. Plants incorporate atmospheric carbon dioxide labeled with ^{14}C, which becomes emplaced into their tissues. After a plant dies (or an individual tree ring, which dies after one year), the carbon-14 continues to decay and is not replaced by life processes. A carbon-14 age is calculated by comparing the original concentration of ^{14}C to the remaining concentration, which has been reduced to 1/2 of the original after one half-life. A tree-ring "stratigraphy" is established by counting rings of living trees, with correlations continued to older trees whose lifetimes had overlapped, and this chronology is used to apply corrections to old carbon-14 ages. In turn, these ages spell out details of the modern warm period and final stages of the preceding deglaciation. The latter was marked by buildup of huge freshwater lakes, both adjacent to and underneath the waning ice, whose waters were released in prodigious floods.

Greenhouse gases (notably H_2O vapor, CO_2, and CH_4) allow the passage inward of visible light that, upon striking the earth's surface, is partly reflected back as longer-wavelength (infra-red) radiation. The greenhouse gases block in the infra-red, thereby trapping heat energy in the atmosphere. Climate responds to variations in the concentration of these gases. CO_2 is currently increasing rapidly as a product of the burning of fossil fuel and of land being claimed for agriculture. Analysis of bubbles trapped in ice cores reveals that the concentrations of greenhouse gases correlate with ancient climatic temperatures, but cause-and-effect relationships are obscure.

25
Dilemma

Spaceship Earth—mankind's only habitation. [*National Aeronautics and Space Administration photograph*]

Photographs from space, such as the one on the preceding page, vividly remind us of what we have always known. It is the finiteness of our wonderful earth and of its potential to sustain life. We face a frightening dilemma, for our awareness of the earth's limitations is tempered by another, more sinister awareness that ever more people are present, consuming its resources. Clearly, neither the size of the population nor the rate of consumption can increase indefinitely. You recall the conclusion of Thomas Malthus that "the power of population is indefinitely greater than the power in the earth to produce subsistence for man. . . . Population, when unchecked, increases in a geometrical ratio. Subsistence increases only in an arithmetical ratio."

Was Malthus correct? Is an exploding human population on a collision course with scarcity and pollution? These are not easy questions, for our ability to obtain needed material and energy depends upon complex national and international relationships as well as the generosity of Nature. The world community of have and have-not nations, peaceable and belligerent, Western, Communist, Third-World countries all must work together to obtain the resources that are lacking within their own borders. Technological consumer societies such as ours are the most vulnerable to disruption of the supply lines. Wise political decisions must be based upon geological reality. Where and how did earth resources form? How abundant are they and where do we look for more? These issues are the subject of this chapter.

One of the most urgent requirements in the short term is to stabilize human population. Demographers, population analysts, have estimated that world population grew slowly for many thousands of years, increasing to a few hundred million persons by the beginning of the Industrial Revolution about 1700 A.D. Since that time, improvement of health and living conditions has extended life expectancies, allowing the world population to expand at a rate of up to 2% or more per year. And because one year's gain is compounded with the gain experienced the previous year, the result was a geometrical increase similar to what Malthus had predicted. World population doubled in a period of 130 years, then doubled again in half of that time, and it will double yet again in half of the previous doubling period (Figure 25-1). It is a cause for alarm!

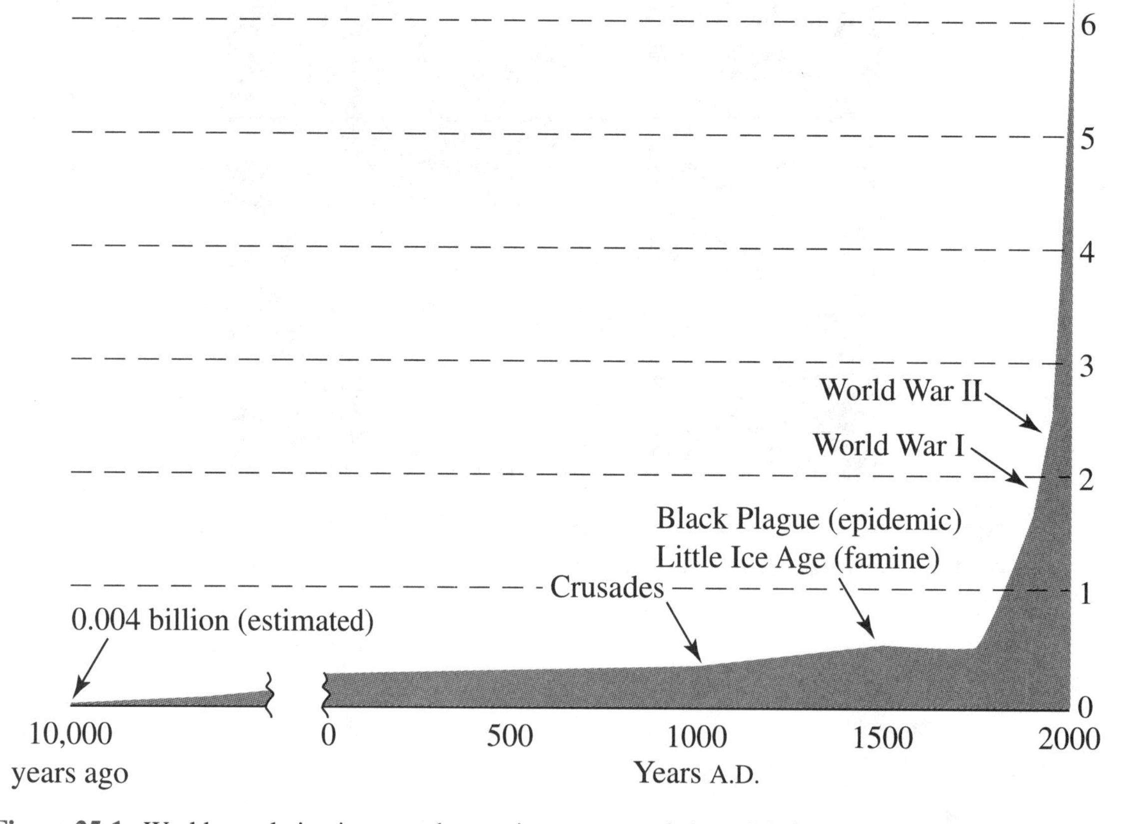

Figure 25-1. World population is currently growing at a rate of about 1.2% per year, but this is "compound interest" inasmuch as the population in each succeeding year builds upon the increase of its preceding year. Compounded at this rate, world population would double in about 35 years. Fortunately, the percent rate of increase is itself steadily declining. Wars, famine, and disease have done little to slow the rate of population growth. Since the beginning of the Industrial Revolution, at about A.D. 1700, the rate of population growth has been spectacular.

As population grew, the world's standard of living generally improved. People owned more stuff whose ultimate source is the earth. Thus the use of resources increased even more rapidly than population did. While world population grew 8-fold, its use of energy resources grew 80-fold. Of course, these changes have been extremely uneven; for example, a typical American uses 70 times more water than does a citizen of Ghana. But all of us are subject to the limitations of the earth.

Although our planet is finite, it is nevertheless a place whose substance, as we have learned, is continually being recycled. Nothing is ultimately consumed. As fabricated metals serve their various purposes, they become widely dispersed or changed in form, by rusting, for example. Burning of hydrocarbons and coal releases water and carbon dioxide into the atmosphere. Why not recycle the products of combustion back into useful fuel? Here also is a dilemma, as more energy would go into recycling than the reconstructed fuel would provide in return. Recycling of metals and water will become routine in the future, but at high cost in energy. Current economics are such that Americans, the foremost consumers, recycle less than 2% of their solid waste materials.

Natural recycling processes in the earth are much too slow. Some 1000 tons of the evaporite mineral trona ($Na_2CO_3 \cdot NaHCO_3 \cdot 2H_2O$) are mined daily from Lake Magadi, Kenya, for manufacturing of washing soda, etc. About 5 times that much trona is deposited in the lake each day. Lake Magadi is probably the only place on earth where nature is replenishing a deposit faster than it is being mined. Water pumped from the ground may be replaced in some areas in a matter of years. Most other valuable substances are being extracted thousands to millions of times faster than new concentrations are being created. Certain minerals such as diamond are considered to be abundant in principle, but they occur so deeply buried that most diamonds are forever out of reach. Practically speaking, earth resources are *exhaustible*; there is no second crop of minerals!

Plentiful resources such as coal and iron will remain abundant for another century or so at present rates of consumption. Other commodities such as silver and mercury are being consumed faster than they are mined. Within decades the natural reserves and the strategic stockpile may be used up. If a source of superabundant cheap power were found, it could alleviate the impending mineral shortage by permitting us to extract metals that occur in low abundance in ordinary rock. But such enormous volumes would have to be processed that further unacceptable "insults" would be delivered to the environment in the form of pollution.

If these comments sound both gloomy and hopeful, they only reflect the uncertainty of our future. It is a future whose more somber prospects can be averted only at great cost. An important task of geologists will be to search out and evaluate how the world's resources were formed and distributed, the subject to which we now turn.

GROUNDWATER

A fundamental characteristic of all natural resources, even the most plentiful, is their *sporadic distribution*. There is more than 30 times as much salt water in the ocean than water on land. Three-quarters of the continental water is either too salty to use, or frozen in glaciers far from the centers of population. The distribution of the remaining fresh water is also sporadic. In the United States, 95% is withdrawn from streams and lakes even though the volume stored in the ground is more than 40 times larger. Numerous but small rural villages of the Ganges Valley, India, obtain most of their water from shallow wells. Water is by far the cheapest commodity except for the air which, if not pure, is at least free.

Ancient philosophers had many oddly mistaken notions about the flow of H_2O among various natural reservoirs. Fascinated by springs, the ancients believed that water is fed to them through subterranean channels directly from the sea. (Supposedly the soil filters out the sea salt.) Atmospheric precipitation was considered to be a source insufficient to supply the springs, much less entire rivers. But in the late 1600s, measurements by the Frenchmen P. Perrault and E. Mariotte established that rainfall over the drainage basin of the Seine River, which flows through Paris, is more than 6 times greater than stream discharge. Availability of precipitation as a source of stream water is actually in excess, not deficiency. Figure 25-2 summarizes the various pathways that describe the *hydrologic cycle.*

In fact, what happens to all that excess precipitation? Normal yearly precipitation varies widely throughout the world, ranging from nearly zero to more than 26 meters (85 *feet*). In the relatively well watered United States it averages about 76 centimeters (30 inches), but even in the humid East or Pacific Northwest, most of the water is not available for use. Nearly 55 centimeters (72%) of the precipitation

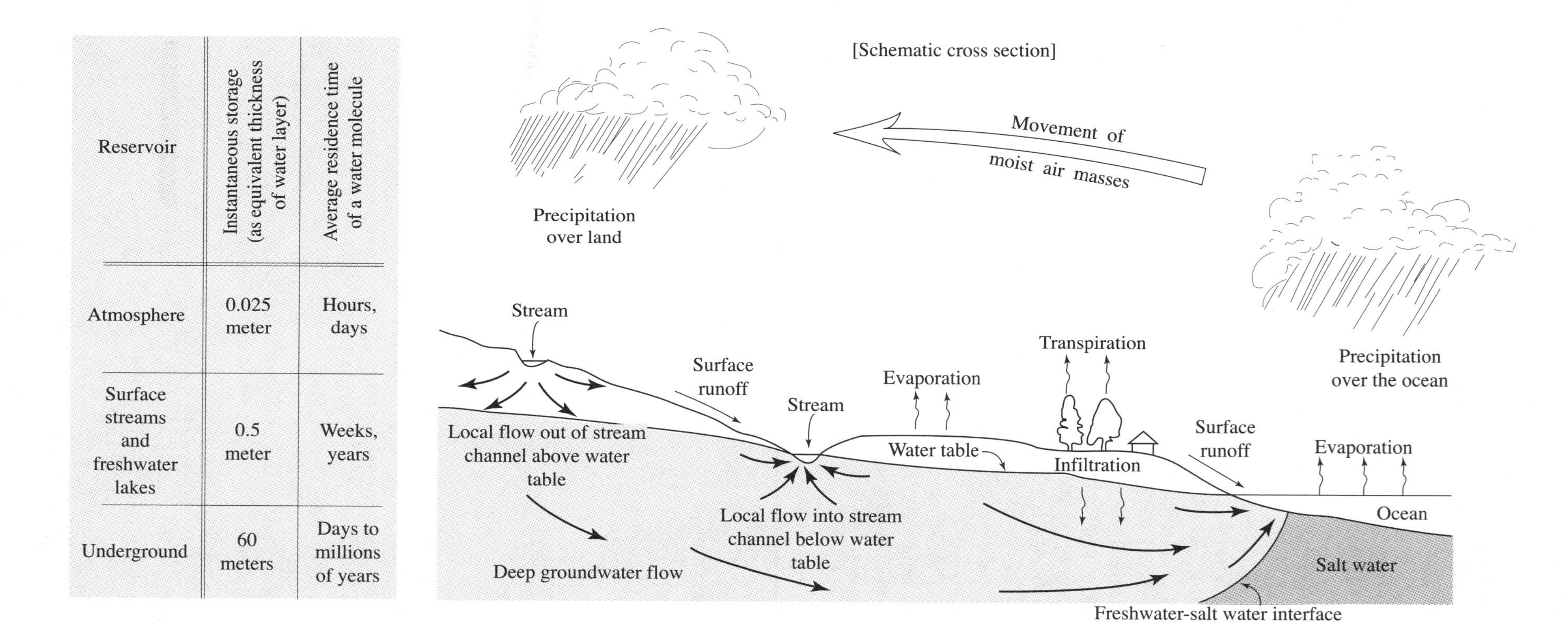

Reservoir	Instantaneous storage (as equivalent thickness of water layer)	Average residence time of a water molecule
Atmosphere	0.025 meter	Hours, days
Surface streams and freshwater lakes	0.5 meter	Weeks, years
Underground	60 meters	Days to millions of years

Figure 25-2. Only 20 percent of the water vapor transported over a continent is actually precipitated while the remainder sweeps out to sea again. A large mass of water passes into and out of the atmosphere quickly, thousands or millions of times more rapidly than the residence time of a water molecule in the ground.

promptly evaporates or re-enters the atmosphere by passing through the leaves of vegetation in the process of *transpiration*. Americans withdraw one-third of the remaining 28% of the precipitation that becomes runoff. They use half of it for industry and the other half for irrigation, drinking, bathing, etc., then return part of it to streams while most of it evaporates.

Some of the water travels through the ground on its way to eventual discharge into a stream. Water flow may be rapid through limestone full of caverns and passageways, or through granite or strata of basalt containing open joints. Rapidly flowing groundwater easily transmits pollution, but inflowing clean water flushes it out quickly. Groundwater passes very slowly indeed through most other types of rock. Estimates are that a typical water molecule spends several hundred years in transit through the underground reservoir, but some groundwater may have been trapped for millions of years, having been buried ever since the sediment was deposited. Generally the deeply buried water is transformed into a strong brine (salt solution) by chemical reaction with the sediment.

Geology of Groundwater

Open voids must be present for material to contain a fluid. The *porosity*, or fraction of the volume that is occupied by pore space, varies considerably according to rock type (Figure 25-3). For example, the porosity of most granite or metamorphic rock is not even a meager 1% unless there are open fractures. Porosity of a coarse gravel is around 20 to 30% and, surprisingly, the porosity of soupy mud may be as high as 80% even though we would expect the microscopic clay particles to be tightly packed. Each particle is coated by layers of water molecules.

Water can percolate through the pores of the material only if they are connected together; the rock must be not only porous, but *permeable*. When soupy mud is buried and compacted, the loosely bound water is squeezed out, leaving only the more tightly adhering water molecules in the resultant mudstone which is quite impermeable. The ease of travel of a fluid depends upon permeability of the rock, and also upon the density and viscosity of the fluid. A petroleum engineer who wishes to drive more oil and gas out of a reservoir rock by injecting water must keep in mind that high-viscosity petroleum flows sluggishly whereas low-viscosity natural gas moves readily. The *hydraulic conductivity* summarizes the combined effect of permeability and other factors that govern the flow of the fluid.

Any material that is both porous and permeable to water is called an *aquifer*, after the Latin *aqua*: "water," and *ferre*: "to bear." Only an aquifer can sustain a useful flow, though water may be withdrawn from other porous materials. For example, much of the water for Houston, Texas is pumped from buried delta deposits—sand aquifers amongst bodies of clay. Some 20% of the total supply comes out of the

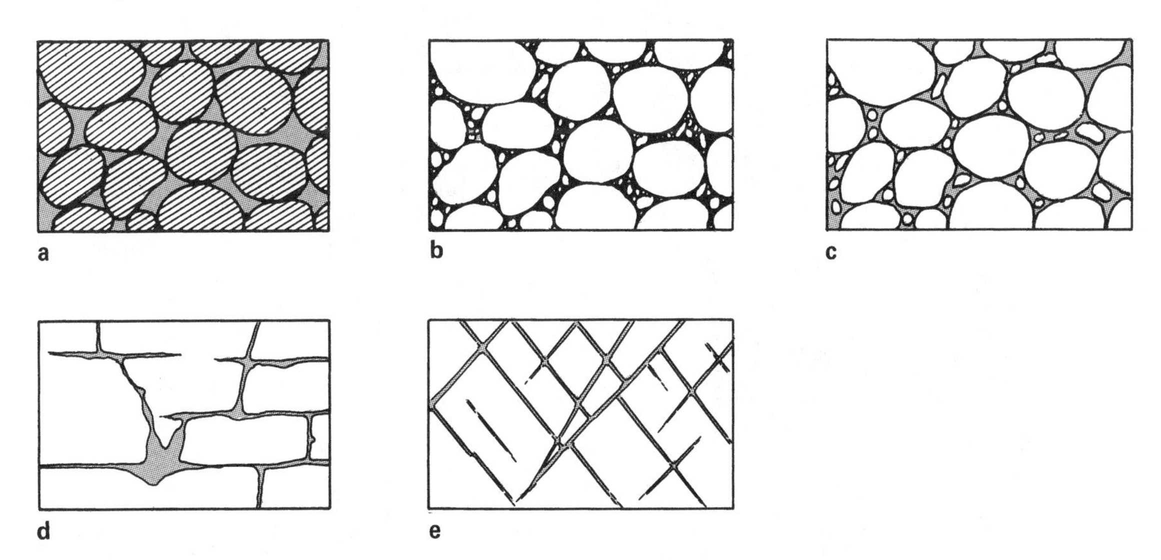

Figure 25-3. Porosity is a characteristic feature of the texture of a rock. High porosity of a well-sorted sandstone (*a*) is diminished if the spaces among large grains are filled by smaller particles (*b*), or by cement precipitated from solution (*c*). Porosity of limestone (*d*) is largely due to solution of channelways, and in a variety of igneous and metamorphic rocks (e), fractures are responsible for what little porosity there is. [*After O. E. Meinzer, "Ground Water,"* Physics of the Earth—IX: Hydrology, *Dover Publications, Inc., New York, 1942.*]

clay which then becomes more compacted. Clay is a "once only" supplier and because of this, compaction has caused areas in the Greater Houston region to sink below sea level. Parts of Long Beach, California subsided into the Pacific as petroleum was withdrawn from beneath the harbor. Eventually the rate of subsidence was reduced by introduction of salt water into the strata beneath.

Darcy's law Modern studies of groundwater began in 1856 with the work of Henri Darcy, an engineer who was commissioned to develop a water-purification system for the city of Dijon, France. Darcy constructed a simple apparatus (Figure 25-4) to determine how water flows through a sand filter.

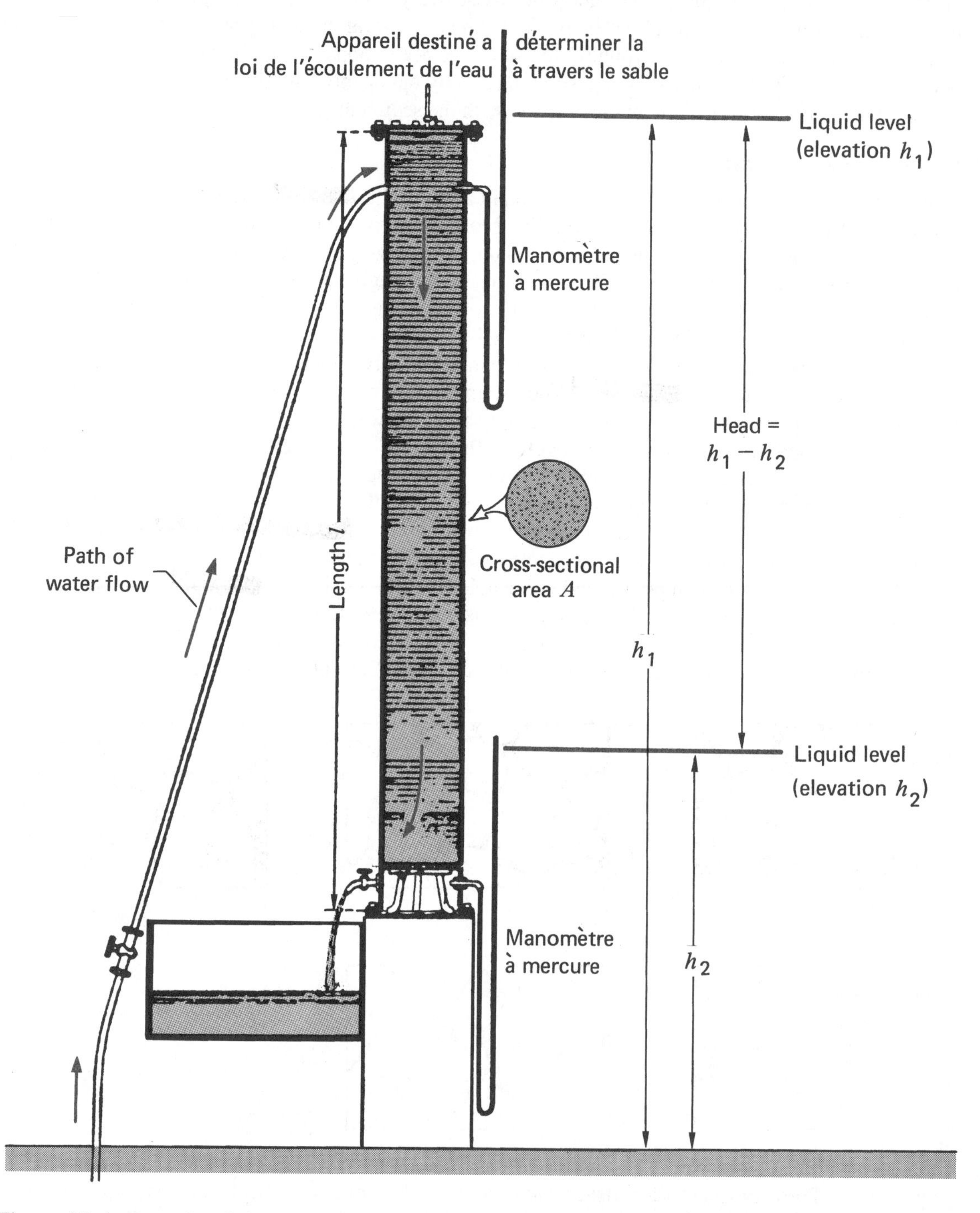

Figure 25-4. Darcy's original drawing (with added explanation) shows what a simple device was needed to establish the most fundamental law of groundwater hydrology. Translated, Darcy's caption reads: "Apparatus designed to determine the law of leakage of water across the sand." [*After M. K. Hubbert, "Darcy's Law and the Field Equations of the Flow of Underground Fluids,"* Transactions, American Institute of Mining, Metallurgical, and Petroleum Engineers, *vol. 207, 1956.*]

He filled a tube, whose cross-sectional area was A, with a length of sand l. A term K, called the coefficient of hydraulic conductivity, takes into account the permeability of the sand. Water introduced at the top of the tube seeped down into a measurement pan at the base at a rate of flow, Q. Connected at the top and bottom were open-ended, U-shaped tubes called manometers, partly filled with mercury. The pressure of the water forced the mercury up in the two tubes to elevations h_1 and h_2 (see figure). By making adjustments with a valve, Darcy could vary the "head" of water which is equal to the difference in elevation $(h_1 - h_2)$ multiplied by a factor to correct for the different densities of water and mercury. Darcy's observations are described by a formula:

$$Q = KA\frac{h_1 - h_2}{l} \tag{25-1}$$

A bit of intuition will help us to understand this equation. If the sand were more permeable, then K would be larger and the rate of flow (Q) would increase. Increasing the area of the cross-section A provides more pathways for flow, whereas an increase in length l results in more friction. Thus the flow rate Q increases with larger A and decreases with larger l. Or, to look at the formula another way, we may think of the quantity $(h_1 - h_2)/l$ as a slope or hydraulic gradient. As the gradient increases, the flow rate of groundwater also increases just as the velocity of a river would. Darcy formulated a relationship of hydraulic conductivity, gradient, etc. which are quantities that can be measured. This relationship has enabled hydrologists to understand the behavior of groundwater in many situations that bear little resemblance to a bed of sand in a pipe.

Unconfined aquifers Suppose that Darcy's apparatus were simply allowed to drain. Gravity would pull most of the water out, but a thin film would remain behind, adhering tightly to each sand grain (Figure 25-5). *Specific yield*, which refers to the fraction of the volume of rock occupied by *drainable*

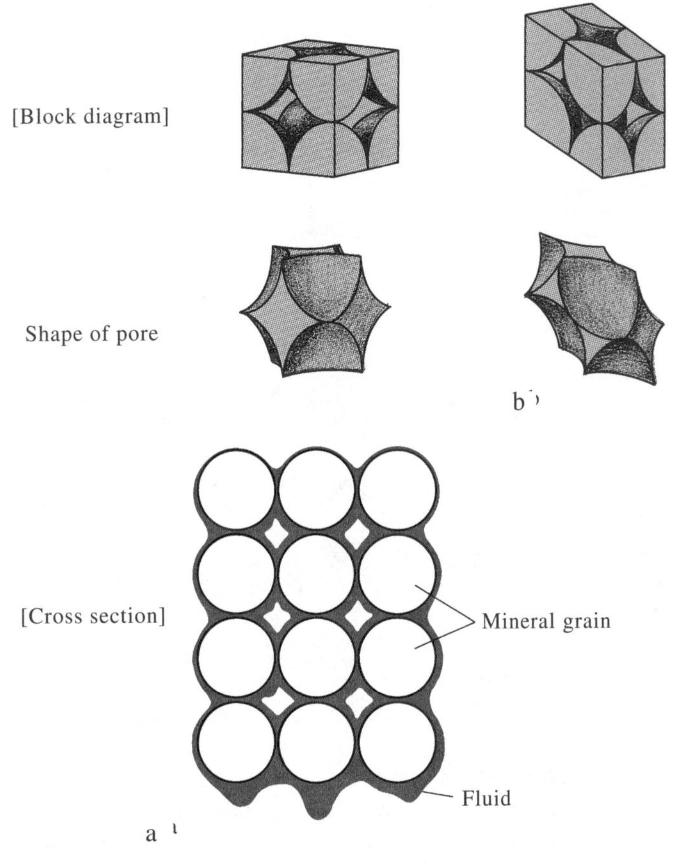

Figure 25-5. Total recovery of a fluid is never possible because some of it clings to the mineral grains in the reservoir rock. These drawings show two ways to pack together equal-sized spherical particles. Even with simple grain textures, the pores may assume a variety of sizes and shapes. If the open packing (a) were reorganized into a more compact arrangement (b), the porosity would decrease.

fluid, may range from nearly zero to has high as 40%. (Contrast this with porosity, which refers to total void space whether drainable or not.) Draining all of the water from an aquifer may not be desirable, but enhancing the recovery of valuable petroleum from a reservoir rock is an important subject of research in the oil industry. Specific yield depends upon the shape and packing of grains, the ability of the fluid to wet the rock, and other factors.

Water in an *unconfined* aquifer can move freely in any direction. In the moist but unsaturated region just beneath the land surface, water is clinging to surfaces of the pores, or seeping downward. At the base of this zone is the *water table*, a surface below which the aquifer is water-saturated. In a humid area, the water table ascends beneath hills and descends beneath valleys in a sort of subdued "topography" that mimics the land surface above (Figure 25-6). A permanent stream or a body of standing water commonly marks a point where the water table intersects the land surface and lies above it (see figure). As groundwater flows through the saturated zone into the stream channel, the high spots in the water table subside and become flattened, but the next rainstorm elevates the water table and restores its irregularities. In an arid region the water table lies deep, possibly even beneath the base of a stream channel. Stream water leaks downward to feed the saturated zone, not the other way around, and soon after a cloudburst the stream goes dry.

As water is pumped from an unconfined aquifer, the water table is drawn down into a "cone of depression" centered about the well (Figure 25-6). Pumping from a well near a stream may cause the local direction of groundwater flow to reverse. Instead of receiving groundwater through its channel bottom, the stream would lose water to the well. If the stream were contaminated, say, with toxic bacteria from pasture runoff, the result would be bad for both the stream and the owner of the well. Where numerous wells have been steadily pumped for a long period, the cones of depression merge together into a regional depression that may assume giant proportions.

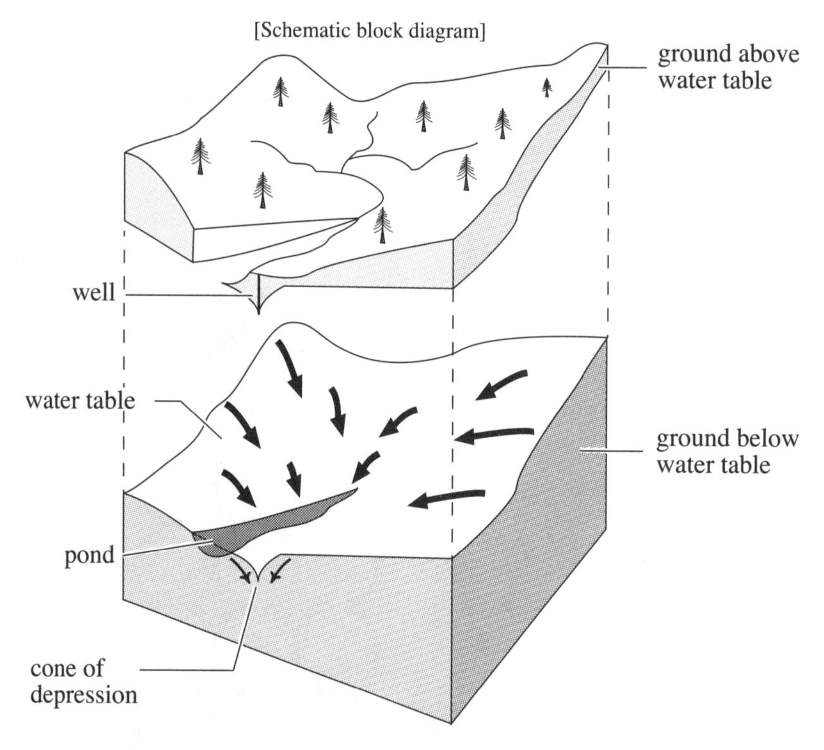

Figure 25-6. In this block diagram, the unsaturated earth is shown lifted up to reveal the water table. Just as water flows down a hillslope, it also flows underground down the slope of the water table at a speed proportional to the steepness of the slope (arrows of different lengths). Permanent streams and standing water occur where the water table is locally higher than the surface of the land. A groundwater "drainage basin" generally coincides with the outlines of the surface-water runoff basin lying overhead. After sustained pumping has lowered the water table in the vicinity of a well, the flow of water, normally from the ground into a permanent stream, may be reversed.

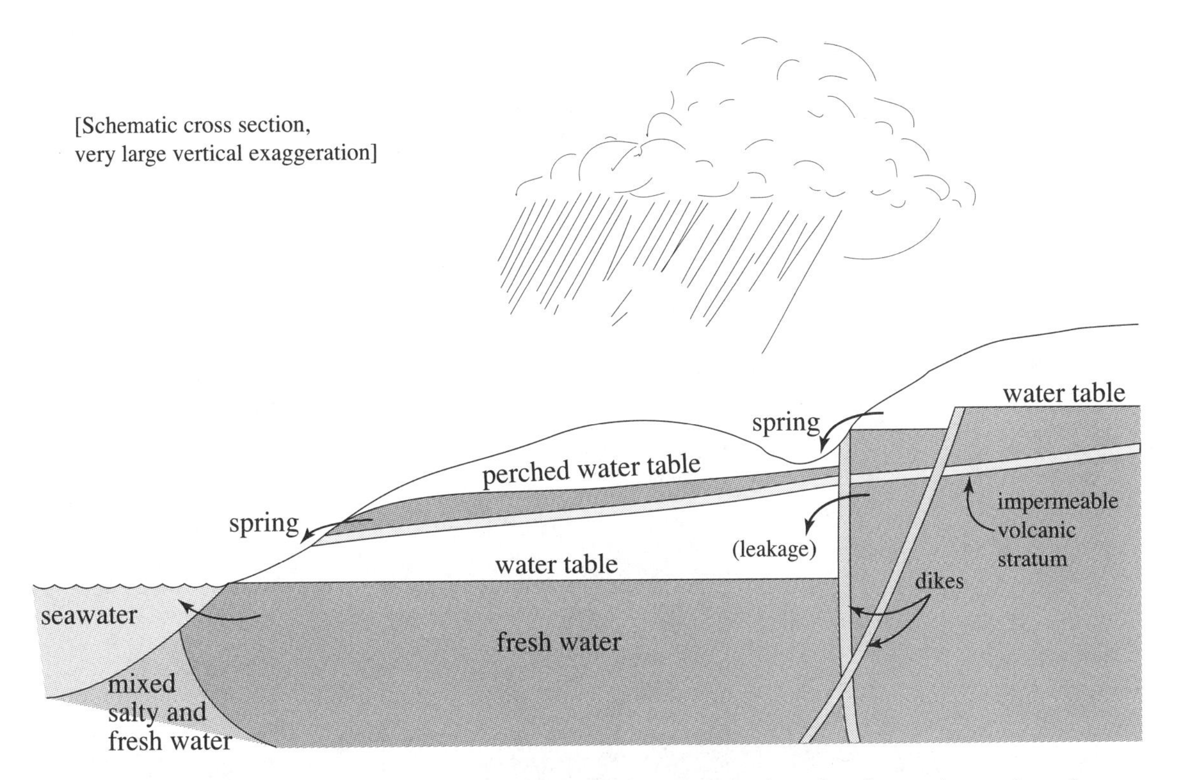

Figure 25-7. Aquifer "plumbing systems" may be highly complex in volcanic terrains such as the Hawaiian Islands. Fractured basalt is highly permeable, an excellent aquifer. Impermeable dikes and volcanic strata seal off local compartments of basalt, forcing the groundwater to flow over or around. "Perched" water may flow laterally upon an impermeable horizon. At the coast, fresh groundwater encounters saline sea water. A tongue of less-dense fresh water runs out under the sea bottom above a lens of more-dense salt water that encroaches beneath the dry land. After overpumping has depleted a coastal well of fresh water, the well begins to yield undesirable salty water.

The southern High Plains of the Texas Panhandle (Figure 25-8) have become the site of a famous example of depletion by overpumping. In Late Tertiary times a vast sheet of clastic debris, the Ogallala Formation, was shed from the Rocky Mountains across this area. Later, the Pecos and Canadian Rivers became established. As they lengthened headward toward the north and west, they cut valley systems that nearly encircled the High Plains, leaving them as an isolated, perched tableland capped by the Ogallala sand and gravel (see figure). Early settlers discovered that although no permanent streams cross this semiarid region, abundant fresh water was available stored in the Ogallala. More than 250 billion cubic meters (nearly 25% of the original water content) have already been pumped for irrigation, at a rate that in some areas exceeds 100 times the rate of natural recharge.

Is it wrong to mine this water or any other exhaustible resource, thereby denying it to future generations? Should we *preserve* a resource (leave it untouched), or *conserve* it (use it up cautiously, with an eye to environmental impact and future supply)? Correct decisions regarding these difficult moral and political problems must depend in part on an understanding of geology. Farmers in the High Plains, having convinced the government that their water asset is disappearing, were permitted a depletion allowance (a tax deduction) on their earnings.

Confined aquifers Many aquifers are permeable strata that are confined above and below by more impermeable beds. Groundwater can recharge a confined aquifer only where it is exposed at the surface, or through leakage across the enclosing strata (Figure 25-9). Water that has migrated down a dipping stratum will be under high pressure at depth. The concept of a water table, a surface whose shape and position may freely change, has no meaning for a confined aquifer. Nevertheless, just as a well in an unconfined aquifer is filled to the level of the water table, water also rises up in a well drilled into a

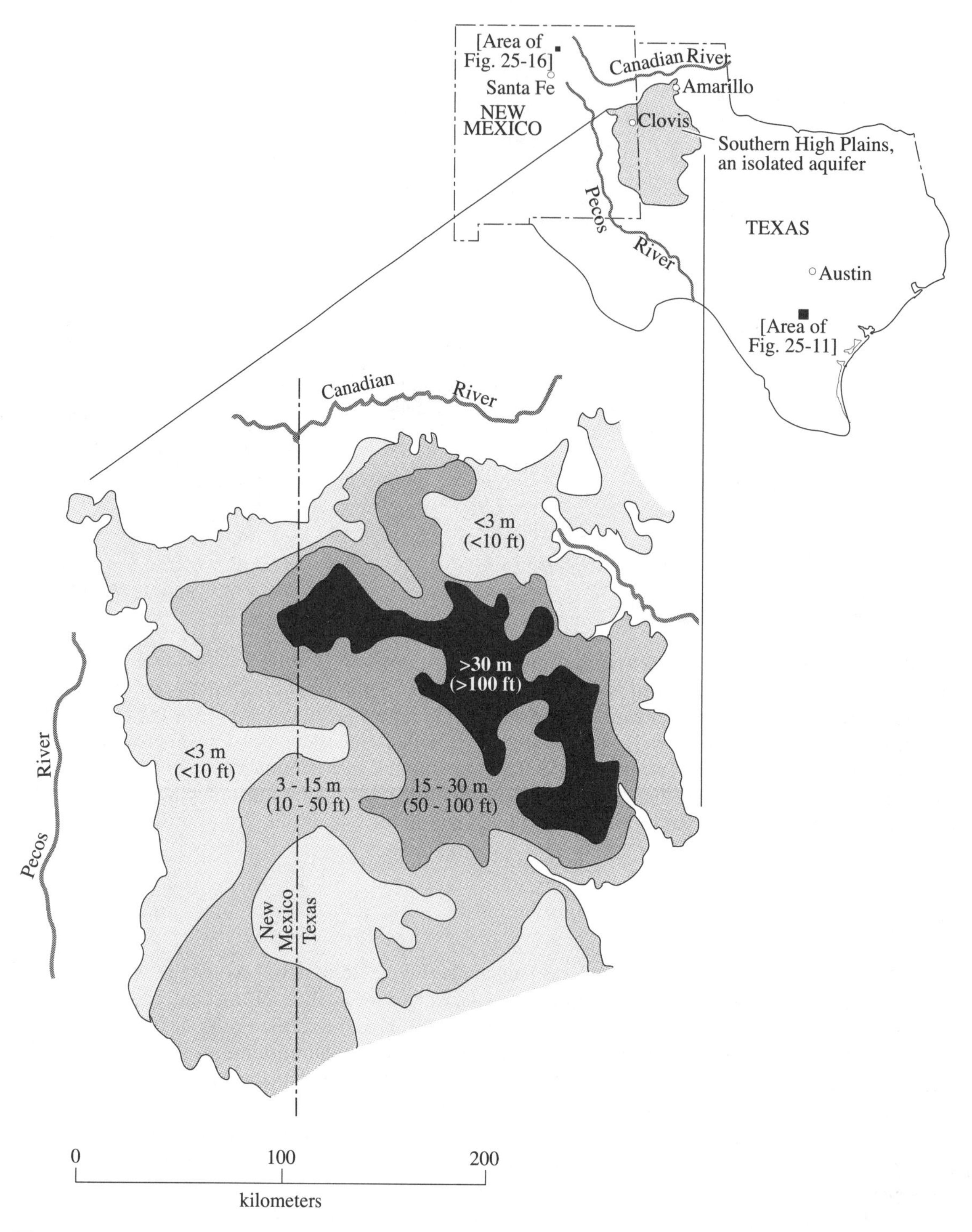

Figure 25-8. In four decades of heavy pumping between 1940 and 1980, the water table in the Ogallala aquifer dropped as much as 60 meters (200 feet) in places. As more than 50,000 wells are busy lowering the water table, the thickness of saturated aquifer also diminishes. Consequently it takes twice as many wells to do the same job today as at the beginning. [*After J. B. Weeks and others, "Summary of the High Plains Regional Aquifer-System Analysis in parts of Colorado, Kansas, Nebraska, New Mexico, Oklahoma, South Dakota, Texas, and Wyoming,"* U.S. Geological Survey Professional Paper 1400-A, 1988.]

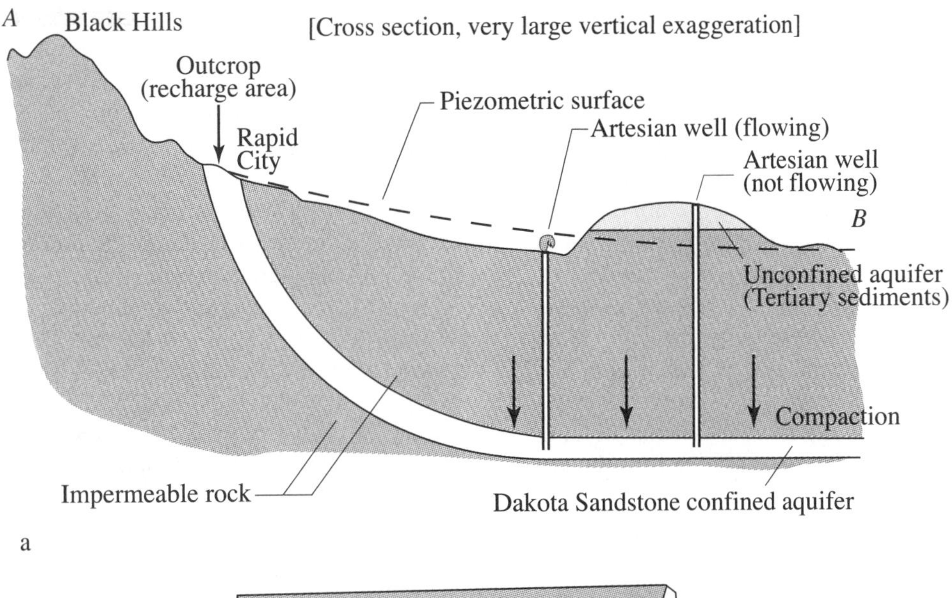

a

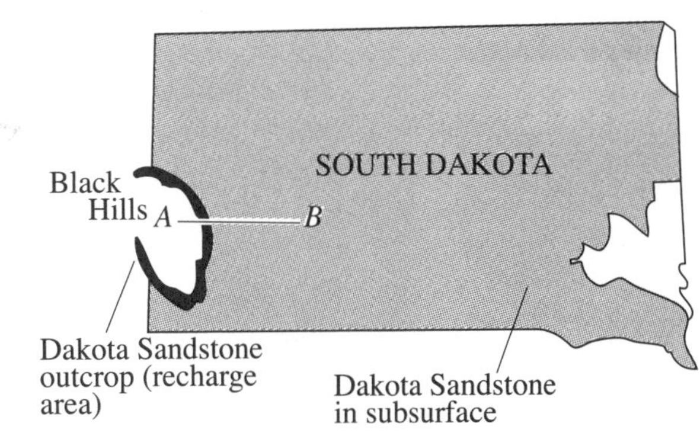

b

Figure 25-9. Most of South Dakota is underlain by the Cretaceous Dakota Sandstone (*a*), a highly prolific aquifer that is recharged where upturned strata are exposed in the Black Hills (*b*). Water descending eastward under the Great Plains is confined under high pressure where the Dakota aquifer is sealed off above and below by impervious beds. Here the aquifer yields artesian water, so named after Artois, the northern French province where deep wells first encountered pressurized water. Water is forced up into the artesian wells by compaction, not in the short term by flowage from the Black Hills recharge area which would take many thousands of years. An unconfined aquifer in superficial Tertiary sediments is independent of the confined water system of the Dakota Sandstone.

confined aquifer. If hypothetical wells were to be drilled at numerous points into a confined aquifer, the tops of the water columns could be mapped as a pressure surface, or *piezometric surface*.

Note that the landscape may actually lie below the piezometric surface in some places (see figure). This was the situation in the plains of South Dakota around the turn of the 20th Century. A confined aquifer, the Dakota Sandstone, extends from a region of outcrop in the Black Hills, and into the subsurface beneath the plains to the east. Water spurted high into the air from some of the first wells as though they were geysers. After a number of years the piezometric surface dropped, making it necessary to pump these wells.

Other fluids contained in underground reservoirs behave similarly. Most oil and gas reservoirs are confined, else the hydrocarbons would have leaked away long ago. In deep sedimentary basins, masses of shale (the source rock for hydrocarbons) have settled and compacted, encasing bodies of sand (the reservoir rock) that compact only a little. Fluids in the sand reservoir are typically under high pressure. *Primary* recovery includes the oil that is driven to the surface under pressure, or that can be lifted out by pumping.

A yield of 20% from primary recovery can be increased to as much as 50% by *secondary* recovery, accomplished by forcing in water or CO_2 which flushes the oil from the reservoir (Figure 25-10). In the 1990s, secondary recovery accounted for close to half of the oil production in the United States.

Flow velocities Water seeps through most aquifers at speeds ranging from a meter or so per day to a few meters per year. For example, the rate is about one foot (0.3 meter) per day through the Ogallala Formation in the High Plains. Hydrologists have devised a clever application of the carbon-14 method to date groundwater. Before entering the aquifer, the water passes through a surface zone rich in carbon dioxide from the decay of plants and the activity of soil bacteria. As we have seen in the preceding chapter, some of this carbon consists of radioactive ^{14}C which is present in all living things. After the groundwater has descended into the aquifer, its dissolved CO_2 is no longer able to exchange with carbon in the biosphere. Carbon-14 initially present in the water continues to decay with a half-life of 5730 years (see Chapter 11 for a review of half-life). The "age" of the water is simply the length of time that it has been in transit from the recharge zone to a given point down-aquifer. Its velocity is equal to the distance traveled, divided by age. Flow velocities obtained by radiocarbon ages from the Carrizo Sand aquifer, in South Texas, are in good agreement with results calculated from Darcy's law (Figure 25-11).

ORE DEPOSITS

Despite the amazingly diverse composition of the earth's crust, from an economic standpoint all but a very small part of it is "ordinary useless rock." It is the rare circumstance, the unusual environment in which nature has concentrated some valuable metal, gemstone, or fuel resource. An *ore* is a rock whose metal content can be recovered at a profit. Sometimes non-metals (for example, sulfur) are called ore,

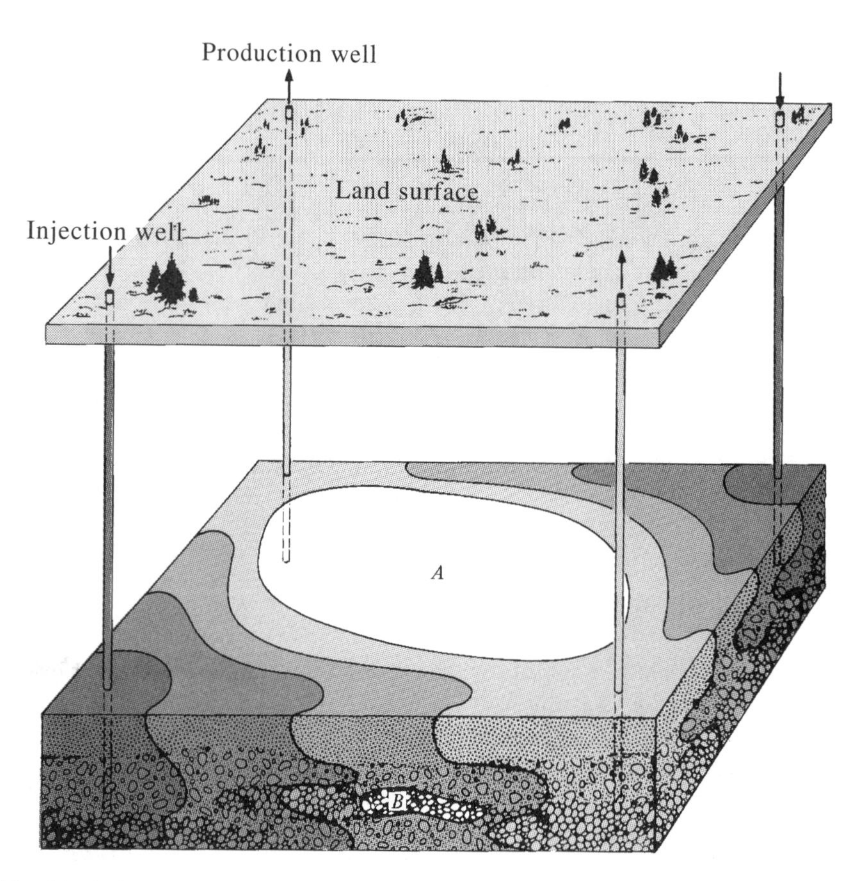

Figure 25-10. Shaded contours trace the annual advance of the contact between oil and the water that is being injected into the reservoir rock. Because water is less viscous than oil, tongues of water tend to break through the oil and bypass regions such as *A* and *B*, which remain stranded. [*After N. de Nevers, "The Secondary Recovery of Petroleum,"* Scientific American, *vol. 213, no. 1, 1965. Copyright ©1965 by Scientific American, Inc. All rights reserved.*]

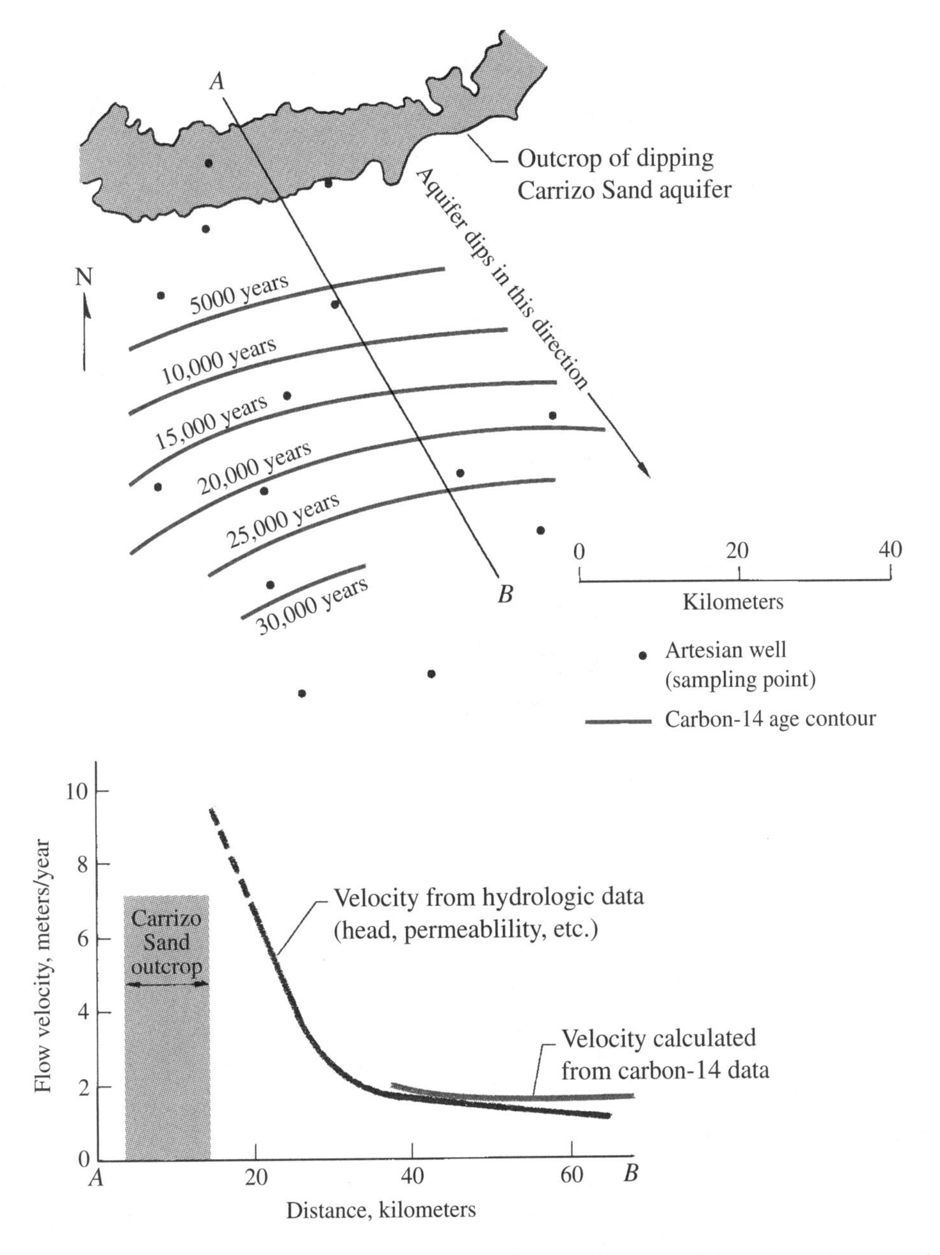

Figure 25-11. The Carrizo Sand, a confined aquifer, dips southeastward from its outcrop recharge area. Contours depict increasing carbon-14 ages as the water descends downdip. [*After F. J. Pearson and D. E. White, "Carbon 14 Ages and Flow Rates of Water in Carrizo Sand, Atascosa County, Texas,"* Water Resources Research, *vol. 3, no. 1, pp. 260, 261, 1967. Copyright by American Geophysical Union.*]

but never stone, salt, coal, or petroleum. A rich deposit is highly profitable to mine, but the decision whether to mine a rock body of marginal quality would depend upon fluctuations in the market. Such a deposit may be an orebody one day but not the next. Definitely an either-ore situation! During some of the early mining operations, diamonds, copper, or gold were not completely extracted and went onto the refuse heap. Improved technology of recovery, and increased value of these commodities, has made it profitable to recycle old mine tailings that formerly were waste, but today are ore.

For major elements such as iron and aluminum, a deposit qualifies as ore if the metal is about 4 times more abundant than in ordinary rock (Figure 25-12). Metals that are generally present in trace quantities can be mined profitably only if they are enriched hundreds or thousands of times above the

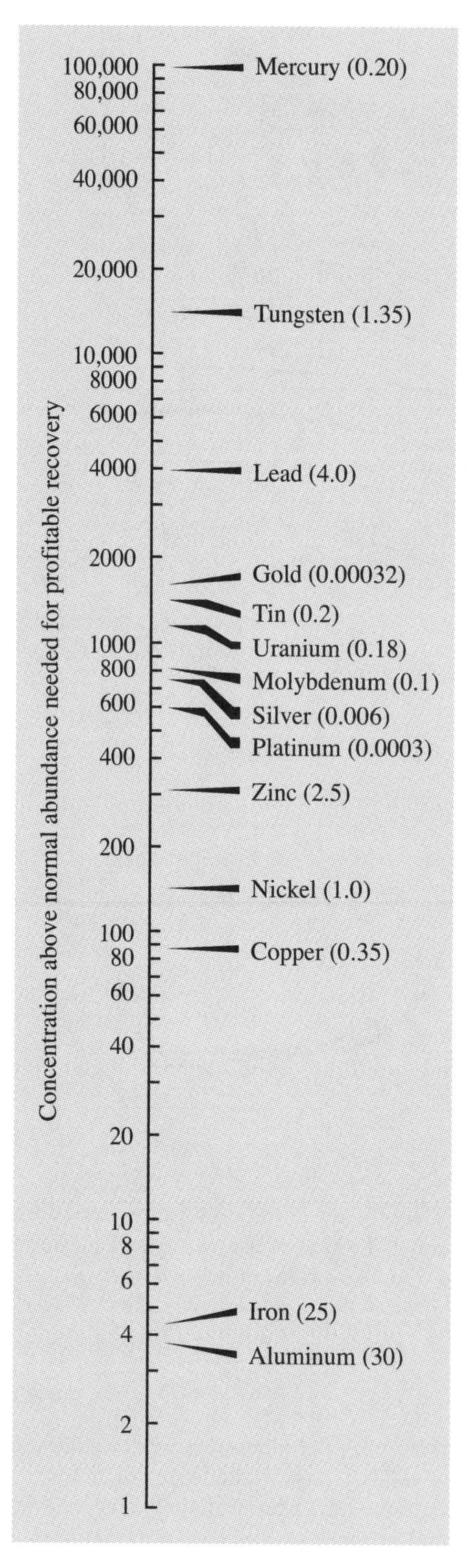

Figure 25-12. Numbers in parentheses are minimum, or cutoff, percentages of metal that can be profitably mined. For example, if mercury is enriched by a factor of 100,000 times, it forms an orebody in which the concentration is 0.2 percent. [*After Brian J. Skinner,* Earth Resources, *3d., 1986. Reprinted by permission of Prentice-Hall, Inc., Englewood Cliffs, New Jersey.*]

norm. Even at that, the amount of recovered metal may be minuscule. All of the platinum that has ever been mined would fit into a cube only 14 feet on a side!

Nevertheless, the amount of common rock is so vast that the quantity of many trace metals is also staggering. For example, average granitic crust contains about 15 parts per million of lead (Pb). Only about 25 cubic kilometers of such material—a modest-sized mountain—contains as much lead as one of the world's largest lead-zinc deposits at Broken Hill, Australia. Valuable material in an ore zone may have been concentrated from a very large but diffuse volume of source rock, not possible to pinpoint. Only natural processes, operating at unhurried pace on an immense scale, are able to create these precious deposits.

Although ore deposits have been essential to civilization for thousands of years, the question of origin remains one of the most frustrating and controversial in geology. This is partly because orebodies are "freaks." For some types of orebody, perhaps a half-dozen, or perhaps only one, are known in the entire world. Because of their uniqueness, they are cited in every textbook on the subject. Geologists disagree about the origin of even the largest and most intensively studied ore deposits. Ancient conglomerate of the Witwatersrand district, near Johannesburg, Republic of South Africa, has provided more than half of all the gold ever mined worldwide. Some geologists believe that the tiny flecks of gold were simply laid down as sedimentary particles along with the quartzite pebbles that make up the conglomerate. Others insist that hot aqueous solutions introduced the gold at a much later time. A third group combines these ideas; they say that the gold, originally deposited as clastic particles, was later dissolved and reprecipitated after moving some distance. A major puzzle is seen in the great Vaal Reef Mine where the gold is confined to just a thin horizon that is centimeters to meters thick, in the midst of thousands of meters of other conglomerate that looks just the same.

What difference does it make whether or not we know the origin of an ore deposit? After all, gold is where you find it according to the old proverb, and indeed, a task of junior geologists at the Vaal Reef Mine is to make certain that mining operations stay on that thin gold-rich horizon. Searching for a new deposit is a more sophisticated matter, demanding an artistic synthesis of data, experience, and geological intuition. However romantic it may seem to strike a bonanza by luck or persistence, it very seldom happens now that most of the obvious deposits have already been discovered. Old self-taught prospectors, who had experience and intuition (though not very scientific) knew that coal, which is sedimentary, is not associated with diamonds which originate deep in the earth's mantle. Even this trivial fact can be the basis of a simple strategy to guide exploration. Much greater ingenuity will be demanded as the search for resources is extended into the more inaccessible deep underground, the ocean, or under ice sheets. Today we also have the aid of powerful theories. For example, we know that along a boundary where tectonic plates are spreading apart, the ore deposits differ from those situated on a boundary where plates collide and subduct, and that deposits formed far from a plate boundary are different still. Moreover, the plate boundary may be a modern one that is active, or a fossil boundary along which plates had been assembled and "welded" together long ago.

Table 25-1. *Classification of Earth Resources*

Metallic	Nonmetallic
Abundant metals: iron, aluminum, nickel, manganese, chromium	Fresh water
Scarce metals: copper, zinc, cobalt, lead, uranium, titanium, magnesium	Building materials: sand, gravel, gypsum, cut stone, etc.
Trace metals: silver, gold, tin, beryllium, molybdenum, platinum, etc.	Fossil fuel: coal, crude oil, natural gas, oil shale (undeveloped)
	Specialty products: salt, phosphate rock, sulfur, mica, diamond, fluorspar, potash, etc.

Economic Geology

Study of these valuable deposits is the concern of a diverse subject known as *economic geology* (Table 25-1). Most exploration geologists work for the petroleum industry (Chapter 23), but many others are prospecting for copper, molybdenum, etc. using such clues as the presence of abnormally high concentrations of trace metal dissolved in local stream water. Even some very large deposits of abundant metals have long escaped notice. Not until 1963 was the Hamersley Range, Western Australia, recognized as containing one of the world's largest reserves of iron ore. Other bulky commodities are fresh water, fertilizer, salt, and construction materials including cement, gypsum, and sand. So much material is processed that it is important to find a deposit close to the population center where the resource is used. Transporting a carload of crushed limestone to the cement factory may cost more than mining the rock. Another necessary expense is restoring the land scarred by the mining operation.

Sedimentary ores Why are 90% of all economic resources located in sedimentary rocks? For one thing, sediments are relatively accessible near the surface, whether on land or the ocean floor. We have also noted that sediment is commonly sorted into bodies consisting of just one substance, for example sandstone composed only of quartz, or limestone consisting of nearly pure calcite. The sedimentary processes that make these rocks can also sort and concentrate the minerals that are of economic importance.

One variety called *placer* (PLASS-er) ore contains clastic particles of heavy metals such as gold or platinum. Released from the bedrock by weathering, these tiny grains are washed into a stream system. Because of their high density, they work down to the base of the sediment that fills the channel. Their resistance to abrasion protects them from being shattered by impact as the stream picks up and deposits its bedload again and again. Because the bedload is transported by turbulent water, rich "ore streaks" are left stranded where stream turbulence was least, on the inside banks of old abandoned meander loops (Figure 25-13). Upon arriving at a coast, the river sediment is redistributed along the shore where pounding waves substitute for the flowing stream as a source of energy. Prominent in beach placers are other dense minerals such as cassiterite (tin oxide: SnO_2), rutile (titanium oxide: TiO_2), and diamonds.

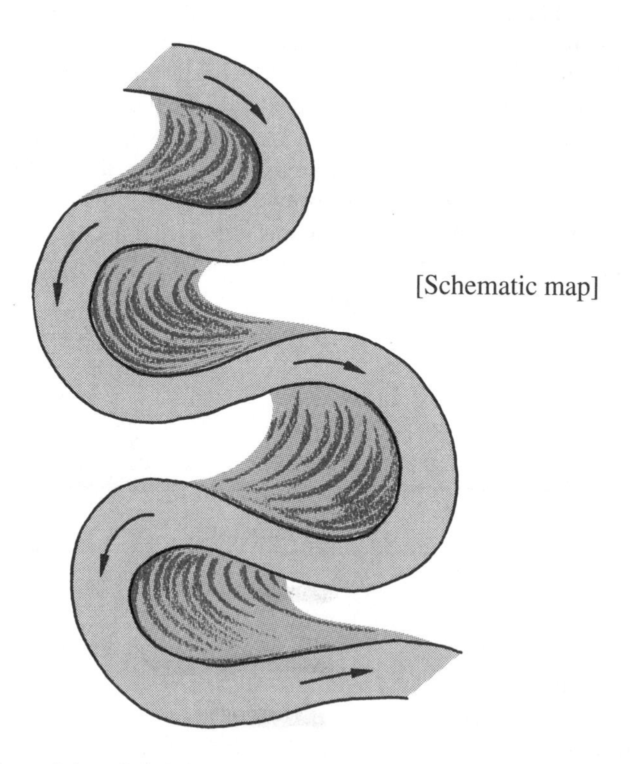

[Schematic map]

Figure 25-13. Knowledge of depositional processes in a meandering stream (Chapter 23) is important in the search for placer gold. Heavy, sandsized particles of gold may be concentrated not only in active meanders, but also in abandoned meander belts that may be distant from the modern stream. Placer bonanzas were the objects of a fervent search during the Gold Rush days in California and Alaska.

At most mines there is an ore processing mill. If the orebody consists of "hard rock," it is drilled and blasted. Then it is taken to the mill where it is crushed finely enough to free the mineral grains from one another, and finally the ore minerals are separated from quartz, feldspar, calcite, etc. that have no economic value. Uncemented placer ores are easily scooped up or dislodged by a high-pressure water jet, and crushing is not needed because the grains are already loose. Since less energy and machinery are required to process the placer ore, quite lean concentrations can be mined profitably.

Vast sedimentary iron ore deposits, at least 150 thousand million tons, are distributed in all of the continents. These distinctive rocks consist of layers of silica alternating with layers of hematite (Fe_2O_3) and magnetite (Fe_3O_4) (Figure 25-14). Their origin is controversial; most geologists agree that the ore originated as dissolved ions that became precipitated as solid material, but the sources and environments of deposition of the iron are in dispute. It is significant that these great iron deposits formed during the interval between 3.2 and 1.9 billion years ago, when the atmosphere contained little or no free oxygen (see Chapter 12). This permitted ions of ferr*ous* iron (Fe^{+2}), which are soluble in water, to be transported long distances to form large accumulations. No such deposits can form in the presence of today's oxygen-rich atmosphere. Oxygen dissolved in the water transforms soluble Fe^{+2} into the insoluble ferr*ic* ion (Fe^{+3}) that precipitates as iron oxide. Iron released by modern weathering of ferromagnesian minerals, or spewed out of an undersea volcanic vent, is promptly precipitated in the near vicinity.

In the early years of iron mining in the Upper Great Lakes district, the only material considered to be an ore was iron oxide from which most of the silica had been leached away. Fortunately, by the time the high-grade ores were depleted, new technology made it possible to use the low-grade (30% Fe) ore containing silica. In fact, the low-grade ore, after treatment to enrich the iron content somewhat, was found actually to make a superior feed for blast furnaces.

Weathering is responsible for concentrating the ores of aluminum. You recall that aluminum, the third most abundant element in the earth's crust, is a prominent constituent of feldspar. Weathering in the wet tropics may go far beyond the point of making clay minerals out of feldspar. Severe weathering

Figure 25-14. This photograph of ancient sedimentary iron ore from Africa shows contorted layers of iron oxide finely interbedded with chert (microcrystalline silica). [*Courtesy Charles F. Park.*]

attack can decompose even the clay minerals. Silica is dissolved, leaving only hydrated oxides of aluminum, the most insoluble materials of all. Because these aluminum-rich *bauxite* deposits are residues left upon the earth's surface, they are highly vulnerable to erosion. Most of them formed no earlier than a few tens of millions of years ago.

Brazil contains large deposits of manganese oxide released by deep weathering of metamorphic rock. Initially the manganese was contained in the metamorphic mineral, garnet. In New Caledonia, a Pacific island near Australia, the collision of tectonic plates has caused a slab of oceanic crust to be thrusted above sea level. Chapter 5 notes that oceanic crust is largely composed of ferromagnesian minerals such as olivine and pyroxene. Minor amounts of nickel can substitute for iron and magnesium in these minerals. When the oceanic rock in New Caledonia was exposed to chemical weathering, the iron and magnesium were leached away, leaving concentrated deposits of nickel silicate.

Let us summarize a few of the numerous processes that create ore deposits in the surface environment. Intense weathering can break down feldspar into an accumulation of aluminum oxide minerals (bauxite). Or weathering may simply prepare the way, for example in freeing diamonds by decomposing a matrix of hard rock. Once the clastic particles are separated, flowing water can sort them further according to size, shape, and density, concentrating the heavy minerals in placer deposits. More quiet environments may receive depositions of chemical sediment, for example sedimentary iron ore. With sustained evaporation, gypsum and halite (Chapter 7) will precipitate first from seawater, then more water-soluble salts containing potassium, a raw material useful for industry or fertilizer. In places, cobbles of manganese oxide litter the floor of the Pacific. Technology for deep-ocean mining of these slowly accumulated deposits is not yet well developed. Environments of sedimentary ores range from high to low energy, from mountain streams to the ocean abyss.

Sedimentary-volcanic ores An interesting class of ore deposits, not understood until recently, is of combined sedimentary and igneous origin. As geologists were mapping the rocks in certain regions of the Precambrian shield of Canada (see Chapter 11), they became aware that in walking across a succession of different rock types, they were advancing down the flank of an ancient submarine volcano, across sediment that had accumulated upon and buried the volcano, and onto sediment of more deep-water origin including iron formation. This is a subtle interpretation, not immediately obvious because these rocks have been deeply buried, metamorphosed, deformed, invaded by other igneous bodies, then uplifted and deeply eroded. Commonly the volcanic-sedimentary pile contains a spectacular bonanza, thick masses of little else than minerals in which copper, zinc, or lead are chemically combined with sulfur. How did these *massive sulfide deposits* form?

Answers to this question were possible only after exploration of very remote parts of the world: the East Pacific Rise and central rift of the Red Sea. Tectonic plates in these localities are pulling apart, permitting magma to rise up toward the ocean bottom. The magma energizes a "plumbing system" in which cold seawater descends through fractured oceanic crust where it becomes heated, then ascends to the ocean floor. As the hot water jets out of a vent, heavily laden with dissolved material, it is abruptly chilled by contact with the cold ocean. Instantly a fine cloud of microscopic crystals of sulfide minerals precipitates in the water, like smoke. Discovery of these underwater "black smokers" helps to explain the origin of massive sulfide deposits. Incidentally, bizarre and previously unknown species of worms, clams, and other animals were found to be congregated around black smokers. The animals feed upon bacteria that in turn obtain their energy from reactions involving the sulfide minerals.

Magmatic ores Experiments provide insight into the formation of ore from a magma. During cooling and crystallization of a melt, the different minerals generally do not all appear at the same temperature. If high-temperature, early-formed crystals are more dense than the remaining liquid, the crystals will sink toward the base of the magma chamber. In 1915 the American petrologist N. L. Bowen demonstrated this process in a classic experiment. After keeping a silicate melt containing a few crystals of olivine at high temperature for a few minutes, he suddenly congealed the melt by chilling it. By this point, much of the dense olivine had sunk to the bottom of the crucible [Figure 25-15(*left*)].

Nature has performed the same operation on a gigantic scale in the Bushveld Igneous Complex, in the Republic of South Africa. When emplaced 1.9 billion years ago, the Bushveld magma formed a complexly shaped "puddle" of basaltic composition, several kilometers thick and occupying an area equivalent to that of Ireland. It is difficult to imagine the source of heat to accomplish such a prodigious amount of melting. Some geologists believe that the energy was supplied extraterrestrially by impact of a large meteorite.

Figure 25-15. (*left*) Bowen cut three slices of the quenched silicate melt which consisted of crystals of olivine embedded in clear glass. Photographs of the slices are shown as originally positioned inside the crucible. [*After N. L. Bowen, "Crystallization-Differentiation in Silicate Liquids,"* American Journal of Science, *vol. 189, no. 230, 1915.*] (*right*) Lower parts of the Bushveld Intrusion contain black, chromite-rich layers interbedded with light-colored, feldspar-rich strata. [*Courtesy Stephen Clabaugh.*]

At various times during solidification, dense chromite grains ($FeCr_2O_4$, a valuable source of chromium) separated from the magma, often accompanied by sulfide minerals containing precious metals of the platinum group. Astonishingly uniform layers of chromite rained down upon the bottom of the magma chamber [Figure 25-15 (*right*)]; one stratum of igneous "sediment" about 15 centimeters thick has been traced for a distance of 250 kilometers! Resemblance between these igneous layers and deep-ocean sediments is uncanny, even to existence of graded bedding and other evidence for turbidity currents.

As layers of crystals built upward from the base of the magma body, the first to settle were dense ferromagnesian minerals. Iron and magnesium were thus removed from the magma, leaving the remaining melt enriched in other constituent elements such as potassium and sodium. Throughout this process of separation, the composition of the remaining melt continued to change, ultimately to make the Bushveld Complex resemble a layer cake in which dark, dense rocks at the base grade upwards into rocks that are more like granite. It was a process of igneous differentiation, a natural sorting rather like the differentiation that separated the entire earth into a core, mantle, and crust (Chapter 2).

Granitic magma cannot differentiate into a layered intrusion like the Bushveld Complex. For one thing, the magma becomes fully solid with only a slight drop in temperature. Granite does not contain much iron and magnesium, and early-formed crystals, even if they were dense biotite or hornblende, could not settle through the highly viscous magma. Important in the crystallization of granitic magma is the role of dissolved water, as discussed in Chapter 5. Crystal structures of feldspar and quartz, the major minerals, do not incorporate H_2O which becomes concentrated more and more into the melt as the crystals grow. The last dregs of melt are likely to be very water-rich and crystallize as a *pegmatite*. Whereas granite is coarse-grained, the crystals in pegmatite may be enormous. Masses of pure quartz the size of a large house and sheets of muscovite a meter or two across are commonly encountered. Some pegmatites contain minerals with the rare elements lithium, beryllium, or tantalum, to name a few. For example, the Harding pegmatite, in northern New Mexico, is studded with huge crystals of spodumene [$LiAl(SiO_3)_2$], a source of lithium (Figure 25-16).

Hydrothermal ores So far, we have seen how well-understood sedimentary or igneous processes can create ore deposits. Another class of mineral resources that includes the biggest reserves of silver, copper, lead, and zinc is of more uncertain, and controversial, origin. Seemingly the variations of composition and form of these ores are endless, but they share several important features in common. In some deposits the rock is peppered with tiny specks or shot through with countless small veins and stringers of metal sulfide. Along these channelways the shattered, mineralized rock may be intensely

Figure 25-16. Big "logs" of spodumene, a lithium-bearing mineral of the pyroxene family, are embedded in a wall at the mine pit at the Harding Pegmatite. Natural cleavage of spodumene even mimics the splintery appearance of wood. The largest single crystal ever discovered measured about 12.7 by 1.7 meters (42 by 5.6 feet), and weighed more than 16 metric tons. Crystals of other pegmatitic minerals are of similar gigantic size. [*Courtesy William Muehlberger.*]

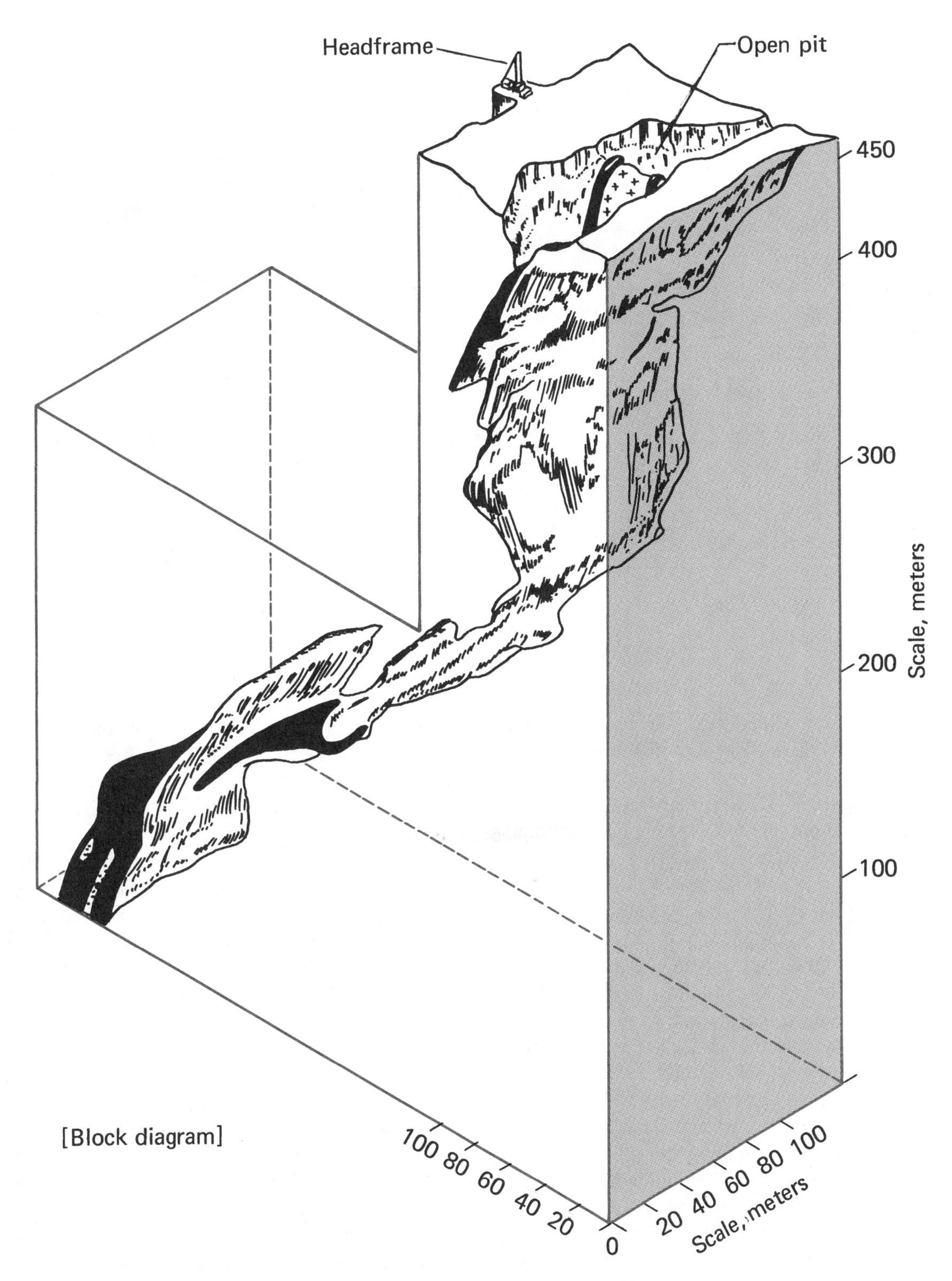

Figure 25-17. Ascending hydrothermal fluids deposited the complexly shaped orebody of the Tsumeb lead-zinc-copper mine, Namibia, Africa. This and many other mines began as an open pit, later extended by underground workings. A scale drawing of the headframe, a building several stories tall that houses a cable drum and lift machinery, emphasizes the impressive size of the mine. Mineral deposits are a source of unceasing legal disputes over ownership. Is the landowner entitled to surface rights only, or to everything beneath the surface? Who owns the portion of an orebody that extends beneath an adjacent property, or is offset by a fault? [*After H. Schneiderhöhn, "Das Otavi-Bergland und seine Erzlagerstätten,"* Zeitschrift für Praktische Geologie, *vol. 37, Sonderheft zum XV Internationalen Geologen-Kongress in Südafrika, 1929.*]

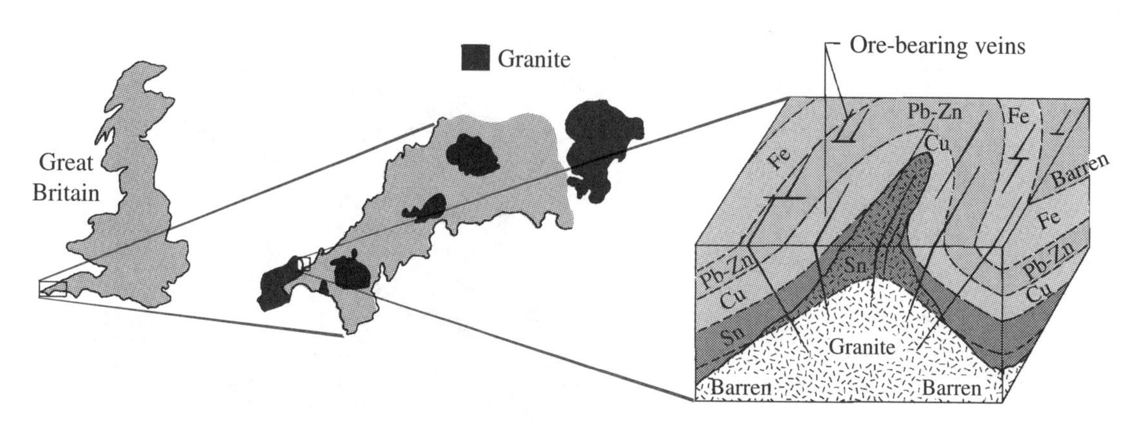

Figure 25-18. A granite batholith (Chapter 5) underlies southwest England. Upward projections of granite intersect the surface, forming a string of outcrops (middle drawing). Hydrothermal fluids have deposited metals in concentric zones from the granite outward into the host rock (right-hand drawing). From the inner to outer zone, the economic minerals are tin oxide, then copper sulfide, then lead and zinc sulfide, and finally iron oxide. These zones have provided an obvious guide to further exploration for ore. Mining in this region has continued ever since 600 B.C.

altered—impregnated with silica or its feldspar transformed into clay. Complex textures indicate that early mineral grains had been dissolved and replaced, perhaps again and again, by fresh surges of incoming material. On a larger scale, mineralization in an entire mining district may be arranged in definite zones (Figure 25-18). These observations are best explained if we postulate that hot water had introduced the material into the rock; the ore is of *hydrothermal* origin.

Sources of the metal ions, the hydrothermal fluid, and the heat energy may be far from obvious. There are no igneous rocks anywhere near some of the largest hydrothermal deposits, and even where there is a mineralized igneous intrusion, the origin of the orebody may not be clear. This is seen, for example, in the large porphyry copper deposits that are common in western North America. (Porphyry refers to an igneous texture in which coarse crystals are set in a fine-grained matrix.) Were the hydrothermal fluids brought in with the magma, or did they penetrate into the igneous rock from the host rock? Was the source of copper in the igneous intrusion or its host?

Evidence from stable isotopes has suggested a partial answer to this difficult question. In Chapter 24 we saw that as storm clouds sweep inland, the hydrogen and oxygen in precipitated rain and snow may become quite enriched in the light isotopes, ^{1}H and ^{16}O. If water with this distinctive isotopic "label" were to react with feldspar, transforming it into muscovite in a porphyry copper deposit, then oxygen and hydrogen in the muscovite would also become labeled isotopically. This has been found to be the case. Isotope data from the deposit at Butte, Montana, demand that some 50 to 90 percent of the hydrothermal fluid be of groundwater origin, not water brought up in the granitic magma.

With the benefit of these findings, we may postulate how hydrothermal deposits form. Today, about 40 major geothermal areas are scattered about in active volcanic regions, many of them near the edges of the great tectonic plates (Chapter 22). Examples are the hot springs and geysers in Iceland, New Zealand, and Yellowstone National Park. A large igneous intrusion, very slowly cooled, may lie hidden at depth, as at Steamboat Springs, Nevada, where boiling water has been discharged for a least a million years. We surmise that near a cooling intrusion, groundwater slowly descends on a journey that may take as long as 100 thousand years to complete (Figure 25-19). Water approaching the intrusion is strongly heated, and its ability to dissolve metal ions out of the host rock or the intrusion is increased. As the brine ascends from the intrusion, it precipitates ore minerals in a series of zones as temperature continues to decrease. The most volatile metal compounds are not precipitated until the fluid emerges in hot springs. For example, about 5 metric tons of arsenic and 1 ton of antimony are brought to the surface at Steamboat Springs each year. Other hot springs, modern and long inactive, are prominent sources of mercury minerals.

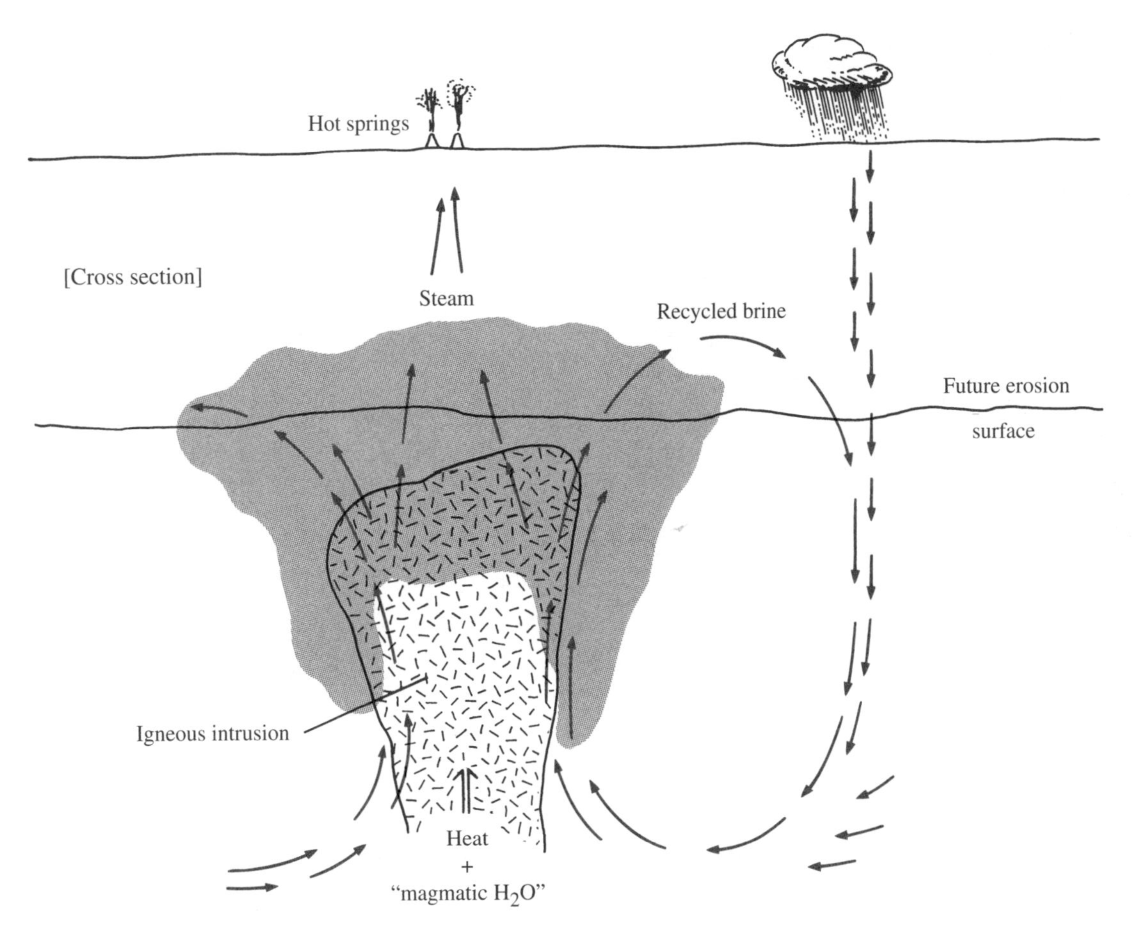

Figure 25-19. During the waning stages of cooling, hot copper-bearing brines moved upward through a highly fractured igneous intrusion. Copper sulfide minerals were precipitated through chemical reactions between the solutions and the rocks. Millions of years later, after considerable erosion had taken place, the deposit was exposed to surface weathering. Copper sulfide was oxidized to soluble copper sulfate, which seeped down to the water table, there to precipitate as insoluble secondary sulfide. During the second stage of the process, a large but diffuse ore deposit became concentrated into a smaller, highly enriched deposit.

ECONOMICS OF GEOLOGY

Processed mineral and energy resources account for roughly 7 percent of the Gross National Product (GNP) of the United States. In importance, however, earth resources far exceed this rather modest fraction of the GNP, for without them our civilization would immediately collapse. Economic health varies greatly among the nations of our small planet, from vigorous to wretched. For example, between 1960 and 1982, per person income in Korea quadrupled while in Ghana, although a land of generous natural resources, income fell by 25%. Geologic endowment of course plays a role in this, and so do climate, population patterns, and government policy which may be enlightened, or riddled with greed and ineptness.

All the nations come to depend more upon one another for resources, and as a commodity nears depletion, its price may go into abnormally violent fluctuations. An association of producer nations may set up a cartel to assure themselves of stable profits. Cartels fix the prices of petroleum and diamonds, and with less success, the prices of copper and mercury (Figure 25-20). A powerful cartel is the Organization of Petroleum Exporting Countries (OPEC), which combined to limit production in the

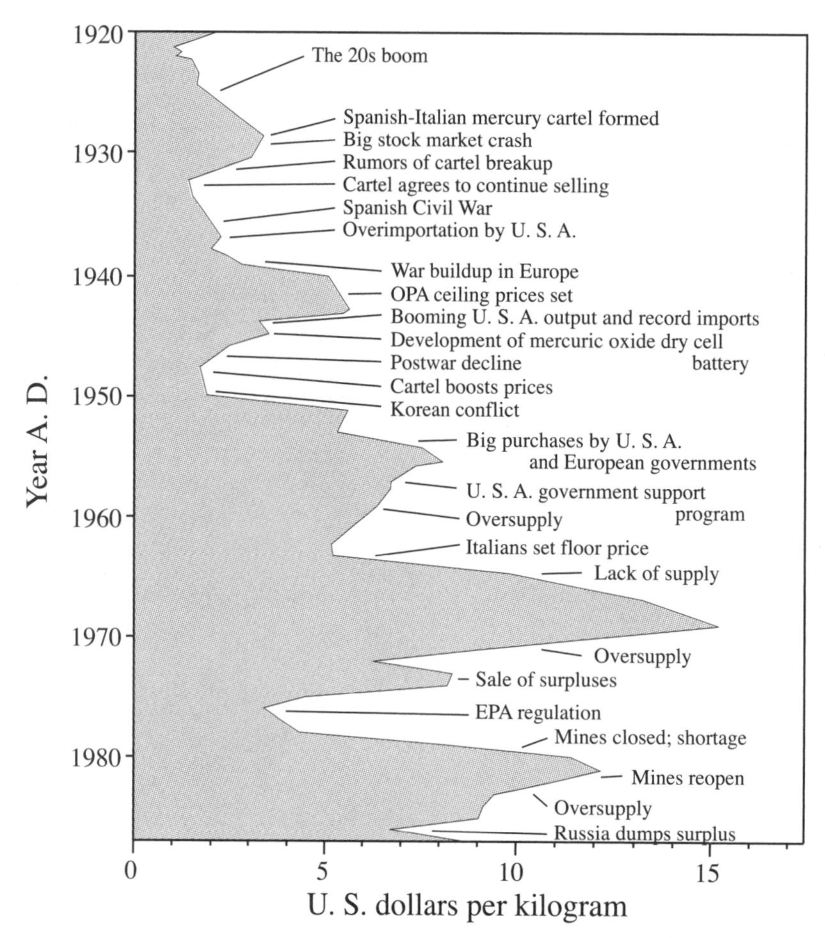

Figure 25-20. "Mercurial," meaning quick and changeable in character, aptly describes the behavior of liquid mercury (quicksilver) and its market price. Fluctuations of price have grown more violent during the past several decades.

early 1970s. Oil-importing Western nations experienced a six-fold increase in price. An effect of this economic shock was to limit consumption, at a cost of considerable hardship to the consumer nations (Figure 25-21). In some ways the victims ultimately benefited from this trauma, which resulted in smaller cars, more efficient construction, and generally heightened cost awareness. It takes a country about a decade to adjust to a revolution in its accustomed ways of thinking and doing.

Will the ingenuity of the engineers and exploration geologists continue, as always, to provide the necessary materials as we have need of them? After all, new discoveries are made nearly every day, while lower and lower grades of ore are mined at a profit. Development of huge earth-moving equipment has made it profitable to mine ore in which copper is only 0.35% of the rock. A rise in the price may also cause a low-grade mass of rock to be reclassified as an orebody. Even as ore becomes more abundant (through new definition), the mineral industries remain in a peculiar jeopardy. First, they must discover a deposit, then drill it extensively to determine its boundaries and economic potential, then secure legal rights to the land, then demonstrate how the environment will be protected, then construct an ore-processing mill, all before digging can commence. By this point, typically many millions of dollars and maybe 15 years have gone by without a single ounce of production. Who could have predicted today's economic conditions 15 years ago?

Could we mine some unconventional deposits, for example in the ocean that occupies 70 percent of the earth's surface? With few exceptions, geologic data from both the water and oceanic crust are not encouraging. Already, seawater is a major source of magnesium, bromine, and common salt, but other substances, except for the nodules of manganese oxide, are in abundances too low to exploit. Nor will it always help to drill or dig deeper. Volatile compounds of the scarce metals zinc, lead, cadmium, and

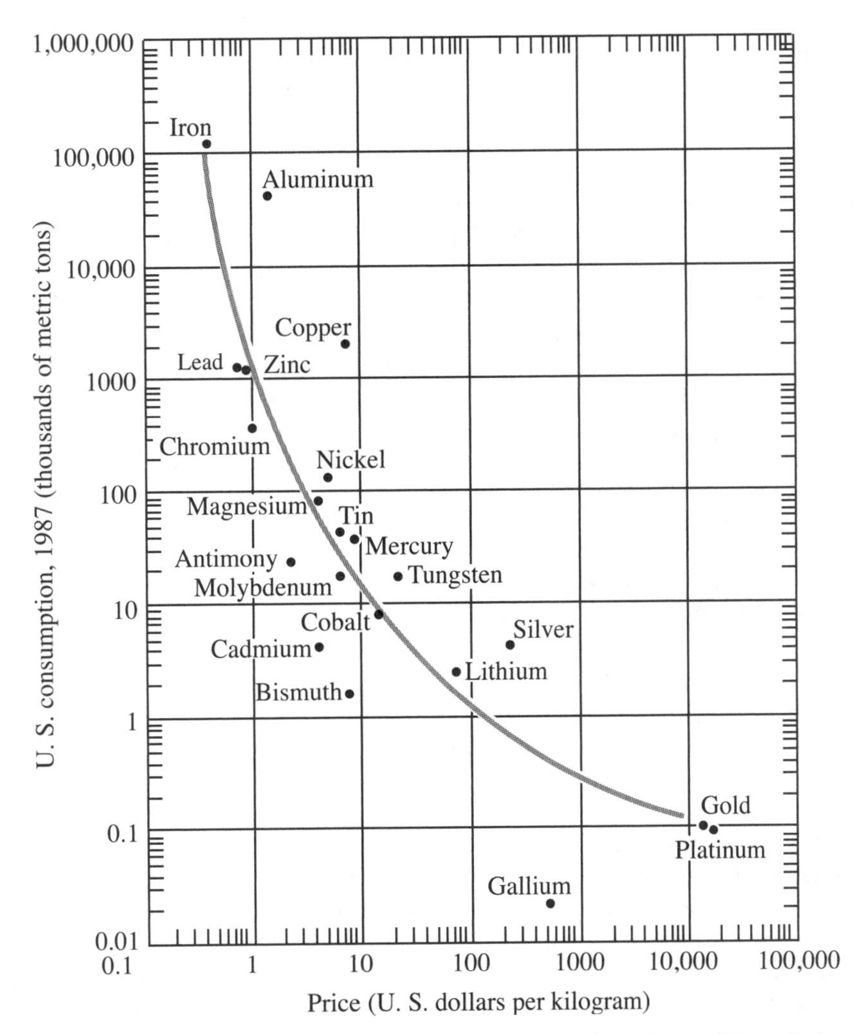

Figure 25-21. The United States consumes a million times more iron than gold or platinum. Price is determined by availability of a commodity, its uses, and other factors. [*Source:* Mineral Yearbook, Vol. 1, Metals and Minerals, *U.S. Government Printing Office, 1987.*]

mercury travel upward; these mineral deposits are to be found near the earth's surface, or not at all. At depth, geothermal heat decomposes the hydrocarbon fuels into a useless residue, and the weight of overlying rock reduces the porosity, hence the capacity to store hydrocarbons. Very deeply buried sediment might yield natural gas, but not petroleum.

Behind all of these considerations is an incessant rising demand for the resources of the earth. In 1962, President John Kennedy sobered the nation by reporting to Congress that in the preceding 30 years the people of the United States had consumed more mineral products than all the world's peoples had previously consumed since the dawn of history. Production of many commodities that we now consider necessary has risen spectacularly. Compared to production in 1882, when the United States first began to report statistics, domestic production of cement in the late 1980s was up by a factor of 5100, and for sulfur it was up 18,500 times. Not only that, but today we are making use of argon, dysprosium, europium, fluorine, germanium, hafnium, helium, krypton, lutetium, neon, radium, radon, rhenium, and xenon, none of which was even known in 1882, and using perhaps 40 other chemical elements that were regarded then as mere laboratory curiosities.

As we grow more sensitive to the ultimate exhaustion of these precious mineral and energy resources, we will conserve them better. Conservation cannot mean replacement, but only more protracted, efficient usage. It is accomplished by *substituting* fiber optics for copper wires in telephone lines, *stockpiling* of tin and silver, *recycling* aluminum cans and car bodies, and by the *efficient extraction* of rare cadmium from zinc ore. Long ago, the petroleum industry learned that slow, methodical pumping yields more oil than unregulated pumping from a "jungle" of wells crowded together.

A WORLD VIEW

Because mineral distribution is so sporadic, very large nations are more likely to have inherited the mixture of resources necessary for economic development. Even so, not the biggest country, nor even an entire continent, is self-sufficient. North America is rich in molybdenum but poor in tin, tungsten, and manganese; Asia is the opposite. More than 85 percent of the world's accessible coal is located in the Northern Hemisphere. For every one unit of coal allotted to an inhabitant of Latin America, Africa, and Australia, the quota for each U.S. or Russian citizen is 20 units (Figure 25-22). Our southern neighbors must regard such an unequal distribution as one of nature's cruelest ironies.

Each country's development is a product of its own history, culture, and natural endowment. Comments about selected countries are offered here to illustrate the global economics of geology.

The United States and Canada benefit from the most vigorous and unrestricted trade of any two countries in the world. Both are wealthy, technologically advanced, Western nations, sharing the same language and an undefended border. Vast in size and small in population, Canada can supply internal needs and export a surplus of many products. The United States exports only a few products such as coal, while importing nearly 50% of its oil and more than 50% of 20 important minerals. Most of the richest deposits in the United States have been mined or pumped out; Canada will follow within a generation. Australia, like Canada, is a large treasure house with a small population.

Because of its colossal size (encompassing 11 time zones) Russia, second largest industrial power in the world, is the most nearly self-sufficient. Mineral wealth is concentrated in Asia in which a crazy-quilt patchwork of tectonic plates have been joined together. Russia suffers from poor roads, vast distances, and an economy that encourages waste and inefficiency. It and Brazil, another huge country, are "sleeping giants" yet to realize their potential.

Resource-poor Japan is half the size of Texas, with a population more than half that of the United States. Japan must import nearly all resources, including virtually 100% of energy products. The country is thus in such a precarious position that it maintains by being friendly to everyone. Tightly knit in culture and infrastructure, Japan is the world's "middleman"—importing raw goods and exporting high-technology finished products. Korea and Taiwan are strong competitors, similarly situated.

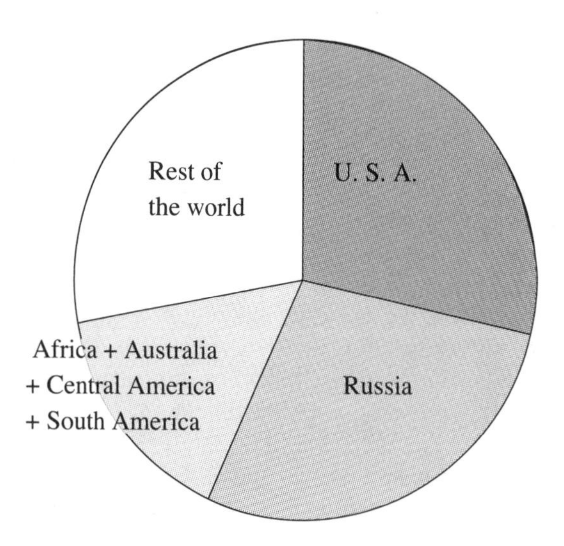

Figure 25-22. Together the United States and Russia own more than half of the world's known reserves of coal. [*Source:* Annual Energy Review, *Energy Information Administration, U.S. Government Printing Office, 1987.*]

The Republic of South Africa, a medium-sized country, is endowed with unbelievable mineral wealth, a rail network, harbors, everything but abundant rainfall. Exports include gold, platinum, diamonds, chromium, manganese, and much else. Argentina is another medium-sized country with extraordinary natural wealth, yet poorly known.

Guyana, on the northern coast of South America, exemplifies a small country with one product, bauxite. Plagued with poverty, inflation, and negative growth, Guyana can retaliate against a drop in world demand for aluminum only by withholding production at further peril to itself. Other countries with "one-crop" economies are Zaire (copper), Bolivia (tin), and Saudi Arabia (oil).

All of the other countries have their own stories, each unique and complex, and each interwoven with the others. What of mankind's future? Can we cope with the common enemies of overpopulation, pollution, and scarcity? Not even the wise sages know the answers, but we are assured that whatever is the future, it will be interesting!

SUMMARY

After millenniums of slow growth, world population has risen spectacularly during the past two centuries, doubling every few decades. Rates of consumption of resources have grown even faster, with ominous portent of scarcity. It takes more energy to recombine the products of combustion back into fuel than the energy to be gained by burning fossil fuel. Natural recycling of mineral and energy resources is slow, hence these resources are exhaustible. Plentiful iron, aluminum, and coal will last for the next century or more, but scarce resources (for example, silver and mercury) face impending depletion. Mining of ordinary rock would consume enormous energy and further imperil the environment.

Groundwater and all other resources are sporadically distributed over the earth. The hydrologic cycle describes the pathways by which H_2O moves through the atmosphere, surface waters, and underground. Groundwater is replenished by precipitation, not by subterranean flow from the ocean. Even in humid areas, most of the precipitation either evaporates or transpires through leaves of vegetation. The ability of a material to transmit groundwater depends upon porosity (fraction of the volume consisting of open voids) and permeability (a measure of the connectedness of the pores). An aquifer is sufficiently porous and permeable to yield a usable flow of water. Darcy's law relates the rate of fluid flow to the physical properties of the fluid and its transmitting medium.

Specific yield refers to the fraction of fluid that can be drained from a porous medium. Water may freely seep downward into an unconfined aquifer, whereas a confined aquifer is sealed off above and below by impermeable material. In an unconfined aquifer, the water table is a surface below which the ground is saturated, and above which it is unsaturated. For a confined aquifer, the piezometric surface signifies the height to which water would rise in a well drilled at that point. Heavy pumping draws down the water table or piezometric surface, creating a cone of depression that could even cause the local flow of groundwater to reverse direction. After pumping has exhausted the primary recovery of oil, flooding the reservoir rock with water or CO_2 under pressure can produce further secondary recovery. The carbon-14 method can be used to date how long groundwater has been traveling from the recharge zone to a given point down-aquifer; this information and the distance traveled provide the speed of flow.

An ore is material from which a mineral of economic value can be recovered at a profit. Ore deposits are very small compared to the volume of ordinary rock. To qualify as ore, an abundant metal (for example, iron) needs to be concentrated only several times above the abundance in ordinary rock, but a rare metal (for example, gold) must be concentrated at least thousands of times. Origins of many orebodies are not well understood.

In placer deposits, clastic particles of dense minerals have been concentrated by stream flow or wave action. Large sedimentary deposits of hematite and magnetite formed in Precambrian times before the atmosphere contained much free oxygen (O_2). Intense humid tropical weathering can concentrate bauxite consisting of aluminum oxides.

Massive deposits of the sulfides of copper, lead, and zinc have precipitated where hot springs vented onto the sea floor. Layers of early-formed, dense crystals of chromite or platinum minerals have settled out during crystallization of large magma chambers of basaltic composition. Water-rich granitic magma may solidify as pegmatite which contains giant crystals of minerals with lithium and other rare metals. As groundwater circulates through an already solidified but very hot igneous intrusion, the water may dissolve and transport material that precipitates as a hydrothermal deposit when the water ascends and cools.

An association of producer nations may set up a cartel (for example, OPEC) to control the price of a scarce resource (petroleum). Typically, much time and money are spent between the discovery of a new mineral deposit and the beginning of production. New deposits will be discovered beneath ice, tundra, sedimentary cover, etc., but recovery of wealth from extreme depth in the earth, or dissolved in ocean water, is not likely to be cost-effective. No country, nor even an entire continent, contains the mix of all the resources necessary to self-sustain modern civilization.

26

Geology of Texas

INTRODUCTION

Texas, being the size of a small country, is large enough to contain an interesting variety of distinct geologic provinces, each with a unique geologic history. Thus the geology of Texas may be described by its development in time and space. Let's look first at the spatial aspect (Figure 26-1).

PHYSIOGRAPHY

To a first approximation, the land surface is a gradual ramp rising steadily from sea level at the Gulf Coast, to the highest elevation at approximately 4000 feet in the far northwestern corner of the state: the Texas Panhandle. The Rio Grande, Nueces, Guadalupe, Colorado, Brazos, Trinity, and Sabine Rivers flow southeast across the state, draining the Texas ramp. There is evidence that these rivers were established immediately when the land surface first rose above the sea some 60 million years ago. Thus the rivers of Texas, though relatively small, are indeed ancient.

An exception to the simple ramp pattern is present in Trans-Pecos Texas (west of the Pecos River), where large-scale fault movements and vigorous Tertiary volcanism have created sizable mountain ranges separated by intermontane valleys. Streams dead-end into salt flats in some of these valleys (interior drainage). The highest point in Texas is Guadalupe Peak, near El Paso, which rises to nearly 9000 feet.

GEOLOGIC PROVINCES AND HISTORY

Among the more important geologic provinces of Texas (Figure 26-1) are the Coastal Plain bordering the Gulf of Mexico, the Llano Uplift, the Edwards Plateau, a North-Central province, the High Plains of the Panhandle, and the Trans-Pecos region. A fundamental dividing line *B* (Figure 26-1) separates these provinces into two major groups. Line *B* pertains to structures in rocks that in many places lie buried, but

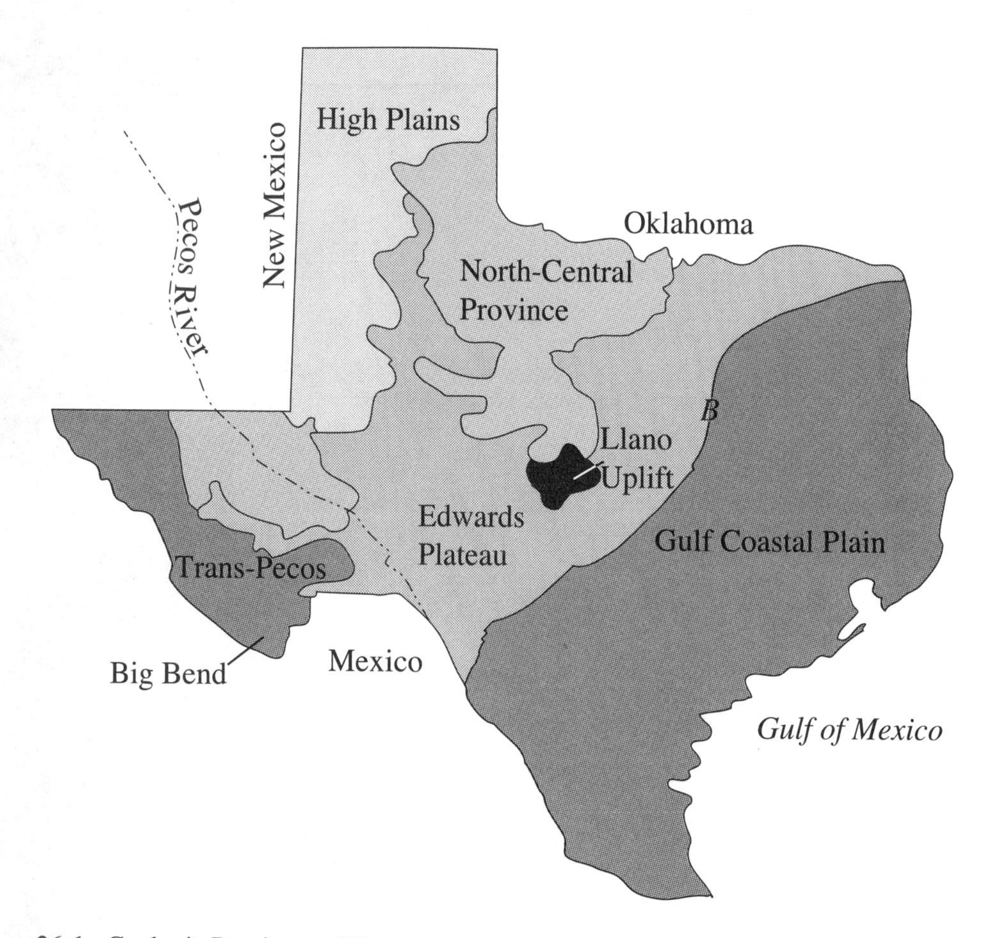

Figure 26-1. Geologic Provinces of Texas

manifestations of the line are prominent at the earth's surface from near the Dallas-Fort Worth area, south through Waco, Austin, San Antonio, thence trending more westerly into Mexico. It was a geologic boundary important at three different times in earth history.

First, this line marks the *edge of the ancient North American continent.* Basement rocks are Precambrian to the north and west of line *B*, consisting of thick, rigid continental crust of granite (felsic) composition. To the east, under the Gulf Coastal Plain, the character of the deep crust is not well known because it lies inaccessible beneath a thick sequence of sedimentary rocks. This region had formerly been the site of the ancestral Gulf of Mexico, and geophysical evidence suggests that basaltic (mafic) oceanic crust, or perhaps crust of transitional nature is present.

- *Precambrian igneous and metamorphic basement* is exposed in the Llano Uplift in the center of the state, and in scattered exposures in far West Texas. Rocks of the Llano Uplift have been uplifted into a gentle dome. Superficial strata were eroded from the top of the dome, exposing an oval patch of more ancient rocks rimmed by younger strata in an escarpment that continues to retreat by erosion. Basement rocks in the Llano Uplift were intensely deformed and metamorphosed between 1.2 and 1.3 billion years ago. About 1.1 billion years ago they were invaded by major batholiths of granite, following which there was a long period of stability, and deep erosion to a plain with moderate hilly relief. In the subsurface of North Texas, basement rocks are older—1.5 to 1.6 billion years.
- *Paleozoic sedimentary rocks* are exposed chiefly in a broad band that trends northward from the Llano Uplift into Oklahoma (the North-Central Province, Figure 26-1). During the early to middle Paleozoic Era, much of Texas was occasionally flooded by shallow seas, in which thin sediment was deposited. At other times the land lay barely above sea level, and was eroded. Late in the Paleozoic, the North American tectonic plate collided with another land mass (perhaps a volcanic arc). The resulting crumpled crust became the second geologic feature to occupy line *B*, the *Ouachita Mountains.* (Today the Ouachita Mountains are still a prominent highland in Arkansas and Oklahoma, though eroded away in Texas). Pennsylvanian and Permian rivers in Texas drained westward from the Ouachita barrier, whereas the modern streams flow to the east. These late Paleozoic streams built systems of deltas toward the west while still farther west, in a region astride the Texas-New Mexico boundary, lay a deep inland sea. Eventually the sea was entirely filled, first by deposition of clastic sediments and in the end stages by evaporite sediment (gypsum, salt).
- *Cretaceous shallow marine sediments* are exposed in a broad band adjacent to line *B* along its west side. The early Gulf of Mexico was beginning to rift apart, and for an interval there was deposition of thick salt accumulations under the Coastal Plain. During the early Mesozoic Era, Texas elsewhere had been above sea level, experiencing erosion. In the Cretaceous Period the sea once again transgressed across the low-lying continental surface, depositing an extensive but thin sheet of limestone unconformably upon older, deeper rocks. In West Texas this sheet is known as the Edwards Plateau (Figure 26-1); where the plateau is dissected by streams it is called the Texas Hill Country.
- *Tertiary clastic sediments* were deposited in the Gulf Coastal Plain after the Cretaceous sea had retreated. Stream systems became established, bringing sand and mud to prodigious delta systems on the coast. As the deltas prograded (advanced due to build-out of sediment into the sea), the land surface grew as the Gulf of Mexico basin was filled in. The process continues today. These Tertiary sediments increase in thickness, from zero where they pinch out along the inner boundary of the Coastal Plain, to about 15 kilometers (10 miles) near the coast. Local regions are rich in oil, gas, or lignite.

  Depression of the earth's crust under the load of sediment likely helped to establish the third geologic feature along line *B*. Previous events had already made it a zone of crustal weakness, in late Tertiary time to be further broken by the *Balcones Fault System* of normal faults.
- *Tertiary sedimentary and volcanic rocks* comprise the Basin-and-Range Province in Trans-Pecos Texas. These were created during a period of stretching, thinning, and faulting of the crust accompanied by volcanic outpourings. Paleozoic and Precambrian rocks were also involved in structural dislocation.
- *Miocene and Pliocene alluvium* was shed off mountains to the west in New Mexico, and spread as a sheet of clastic debris, the Ogallala Formation which caps the High Plains in the Panhandle. In late Cenozoic time, as the Pecos River extended itself headward up through eastern New Mexico, it diverted the eastward-flowing streams coming out of the mountains, leaving the Ogallala Formation perched high and dry, devoid of through-going streams.

Geology of Texas

Six Distinct Geologic Provinces

- High Plains
- North-Central Province
- Edwards Plateau
- Llano Uplift
- Trans-Pecos Texas
- Gulf Coastal Plain

Precambrian

- Edge of the North American continent along line *B*
- North and west of line *B*, basement rocks are of Precambrian age and composed of continental crust of granitic composition.
- To the east, under the Gulf Coastal Plain, the character of the basement is not well known as it lies buried beneath a thick sequence of sedimentary rocks. The basement is composed at least partly of basaltic oceanic crust.
- Llano Uplift: Precambrian igneous and metamorphic basement
- Deformation and metamorphism occurred between 1.2 and 1.3 billion years (b.y.) ago.
- Intrusion of granitic batholiths occurred 1.1 b.y. ago.

Paleozoic Era

- Early to middle Paleozoic Era
  - Much of Texas was occasionally flooded by shallow seas and at other times the land lay barely above sea level.
- Late Paleozoic Era
  - Collision of North America tectonic plate with another land mass formed the Ouachita Mountains.
  - During the Pennsylvanian and Permian Periods, rivers drained westward from the Ouachita barrier, in a direction opposite to the present drainage direction.

Mesozoic Era

- Early Mesozoic Era
  - Early formation of the Gulf of Mexico
  - Thick salt deposition under the coastal plain
- Late Mesozoic Era
  - Marine transgression resulting in deposition of a sheet of limestone unconformably over older rocks
  - Edwards Plateau in West Texas

Cenozoic Era

- Early Cenozoic Era (Tertiary Period)
  - The sea retreated, and the current drainage system (toward the southeast) became established.
  - Thick sediment, chiefly of delta origin, was deposited in the Coastal Plain.
  - Depression of the earth's crust resulted from the load of sediment, initiating the Balcones Fault System.
  - Widespread volcanism and faulting occurred in Trans-Pecos region where the crust was stretched and thinned.
- Late Cenozoic Era (Tertiary/Quaternary Period)
  - Ogallala Formation in the High Plains - alluvium shed off mountains that lay to the west in New Mexico

Hydrogeology

- Aquifer: a rock body that has the capacity to transmit "usable" quantities of water to a well
  - Rock types that are good aquifers: sandstone (if weakly cemented), conglomerate, fractured limestone
- Aquitard: A rock body that does NOT transmit "usable" quantities of water over a reasonably short period of time
  - Example of aquitard: shale
- Water table: a level below which the ground is saturated with water, and above which it is not saturated (although moisture may be present)

Porosity and Permeability

- Porosity: fraction of a rock body consisting of void spaces (example: 20% porosity)
  - Primary porosity - present initially in a rock body when created
  - Secondary porosity - created later by processes such as fracturing or dissolution
- Permeability: a measure of how well inter-connected the pores are, hence how easily the material can transmit fluids

Types of Aquifers

- Alluvial aquifer: sandstone, conglomerate
  - High primary porosity and permeability
  - Diffuse flow (slow), providing time for breakdown of contaminants
  - Serves as a natural filter for contaminants.
- Karst aquifer: fractured limestone
  - Limestone may have low primary porosity or permeability
  - but, fracturing and dissolution can create secondary porosity/permeability.
  - Discrete (rapid) flow: little or no filtering or breakdown of contaminants

---

- Recharge: the process of surface water entering an aquifer
  - Infiltration: water soaks into the ground over a large area. Recharge of alluvial aquifers.
  - Focused recharge: along narrow zones of interconnected fractures exposed at the surface. Recharge of karst aquifers.
- Discharge: the process by which groundwater exits an aquifer and enters a body of surface water
- Problems with increased impervious cover (material such as asphalt and concrete):
  - concentrates pollutants on top of the cover.
  - increases rate of runoff and worsens floods.
  - inhibits recharge.

Important Texas Aquifers

- Tertiary Ogallala Aquifer - alluvial aquifer
  - Semi-arid region with low rate of recharge
  - Overpumping, resulting in lowering of the water table
- Cretaceous Edwards Aquifer - karst aquifer
  - Vulnerable to contamination
  - Focused recharge. Hence construction, which disturbs the earth's surface, must be regulated stringently along the fault zone.

27

Hydrogeology in Texas

INTRODUCTION

Average annual precipitation varies dramatically across Texas, from 50 inches per year along the eastern border to less than 10 inches per year at El Paso (Figure 27-1). In much of the state the chief source of income is through agriculture in an arid to semi-arid environment. Local rainfall is inadequate and must be supplemented by irrigation. Large cites (for example, San Antonio) do not have sufficient nearby surface water to meet their needs. Whether in a rural or urban setting, *groundwater* is commonly the source of local supply. Obtaining water, ever an important environmental problem in Texas, will become more serious as population grows. This chapter discusses *hydrogeology*—the geologic factors that control the occurrence and flow of water through the earth.

An *aquifer* is a rock body (not necessarily solid rock) that has the capacity to transmit "usable" quantities of water to a well. The opposite is an *aquitard*, a rock body that does *not* transmit usable water. Almost any earth material can transmit fluid at least very slowly. Notice the emphasis in these definitions on practical useful delivery.

Open voids, or pores, must be present to contain the water, and these voids must be connected together if water is to flow through the aquifer. *Porosity* is the fraction of the volume of rock occupied by void spaces, and *permeability* is a measure of interconnectedness of the pores, allowing water to be transmitted. A good aquifer must have both high porosity and permeability. Examples include fractured limestone, and uncemented sandstone or conglomerate in which porosity may be 20 percent or greater. Typical shale is an aquitard.

TYPES OF AQUIFER

In some aquifers the porosity is *primary*, having been present in the material from the beginning. *Secondary* porosity may develop in an aquifer during a later geologic event. For example, countless large and small channelways have been dissolved out of the famous Edwards Limestone aquifer (in the Edwards Plateau, Figure 26-1). Along line *B* (Figure 26-1) the Edwards Limestone was shattered by faults of the Balcones Fault System, and the resultant secondary porosity can originate by physical means (faulting) or chemical means (dissolution).

In general, if compact hard rock has porosity, it was of secondary origin. Rainwater with natural slight acidity attacks carbonate rocks (limestone or marble) but its attack is not very effective on silicate rocks (granite, most metamorphic rocks). The latter *crystalline* rocks contain almost no porosity or permeability, except to yield small amounts of water from fractures.

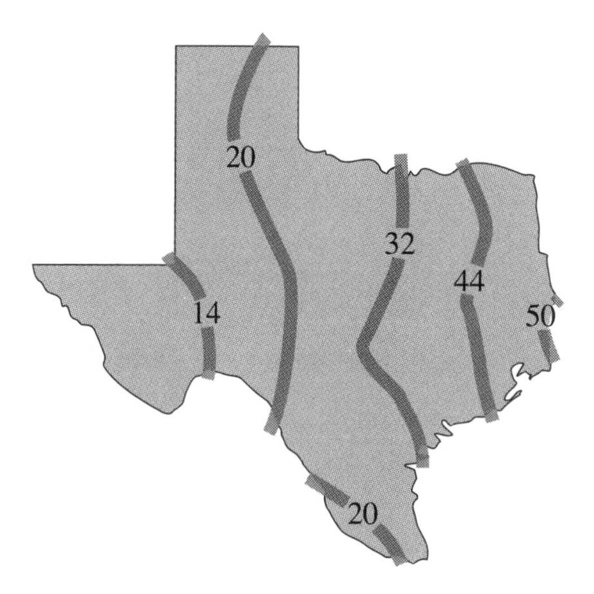

Figure 27-1. Average Annual Precipitation (in./year)

Dissolution is the most important agent of change in a limestone landscape such as the Edwards Plateau or Texas Hill Country. Porosity is evident everywhere, from large caverns to hairline fissures. During normal flow a stream may lose as much as 75 percent of its water through the channel bottom. Sinkholes and underground streams are common, and so are springs where the water emerges back to the surface. This type of terrain is named *karst*, after a region of the former Yugoslavia.

Processes of flow may be diverse. Flow in a karst aquifer tends to be concentrated along irregular networks of solution-enlarged fractures that act almost as pipelines. Water flow is rapid and *discrete* (highly focused) in the channelways [Figure 27-2(*a*)], but they are so irregular that often one cannot be certain that water from "this" spring had any connection with "that" sinkhole.

In an alluvial aquifer, such as sandstone or conglomerate, the tortuous pathway of flow takes place on a smaller scale around and amongst individual mineral grains. It is *diffuse* flow that fans out along a broad front as it travels through the aquifer [Figure 27-2(*b*)].

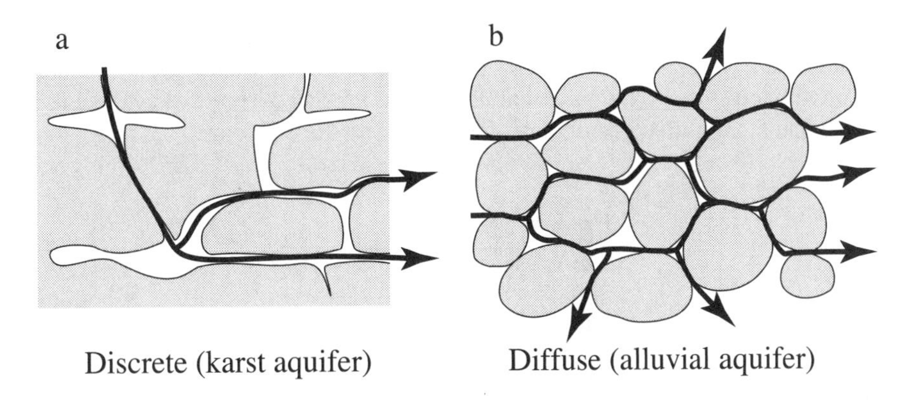

Figure 27-2. Discrete Flow and Diffuse Flow

RECHARGE AND DISCHARGE

Water *recharges* (enters) an aquifer, travels, and *discharges* (exits) from it. Recharge to alluvial aquifers is typically by a diffuse process of *infiltration* of rain or surface water (lakes, rivers, etc.) over a widespread area. Recharge and discharge of a karst aquifer are more focused. Discharge may be through a spring, or under a river or lake bottom—any local low spot. Depending upon circumstances, surface water can be a site of either recharge or discharge.

CONTAMINATION OF AQUIFERS

Contamination of aquifers is another major environmental concern in Texas. Ideally, contaminants should travel slowly, taking time to degrade, flowing along diffuse pathways that cause contaminants to disperse. Of the two aquifer types, alluvial aquifers are more easily cleansed because very slow flow of water (a long time scale) encourages entrapment of impurities in the pores, or absorption on their walls. Tiny but numerous pores would have a large internal surface area. Micro-organisms have opportunity to decompose polluting organic molecules.

Contamination could be sudden and catastrophic, for example from a spill at a refinery or chemical manufacturing plant. It could be a low-level but chronic result of urbanization, especially from creation of *impervious cover* such as roofing, roads, parking lots. Increasing the impervious cover has these bad effects:

- Pollutants such as drippings of oil from car engines concentrate on top. There is little opportunity for them to degrade before the next storm washes them into bodies of surface water.
- The rate of runoff increases, and with it the potential for damaging floods.
- Aquifers are robbed of potential recharge.

CASE EXAMPLES: IMPORTANT AQUIFERS IN TEXAS

The *Tertiary Ogallala Formation* is a productive *alluvial aquifer*, the primary source of water in the High Plains of Texas (Figure 27-3). Most of the water is used for livestock and to irrigate crops (early in the 20th century, the High Plains supplied 3% of the food production of the entire world). Because the High Plains is a semi-arid region, recharge to the Ogallala *is limited* while *irrigation is prevalent*. High Plains farmers are mining groundwater, for which recharge is so slow that on the time scale of human generations, the groundwater is an irreplaceable resource. As a net effect, the water level in the aquifer has declined. Now pumps must work harder, at greater expense, to produce less water. In some places the fresh groundwater is depleted and the pumps yield saline water extracted from deeper evaporite deposits.

As mentioned, the *Cretaceous Edwards Limestone* is a productive *karst aquifer*. It is so porous and permeable, with such rapid flow-through, that the water level rises and falls on a time scale of a few weeks. When the next prolonged drought comes, San Antonio and other municipalities situated on the Balcones Fault Zone, for which the Edwards is the water source, will be placed in serious jeopardy.

The Edwards is also *vulnerable to contamination* because recharge is rapid, and in discrete zones. Pollutants may enter the aquifer in concentrated plumes. Currently the quality of water in the Edwards Aquifer is quite good. However, by the time that degradation is discovered and evaluated, it is usually too late to avert the damage. So in this case, prevention may be the only cure.

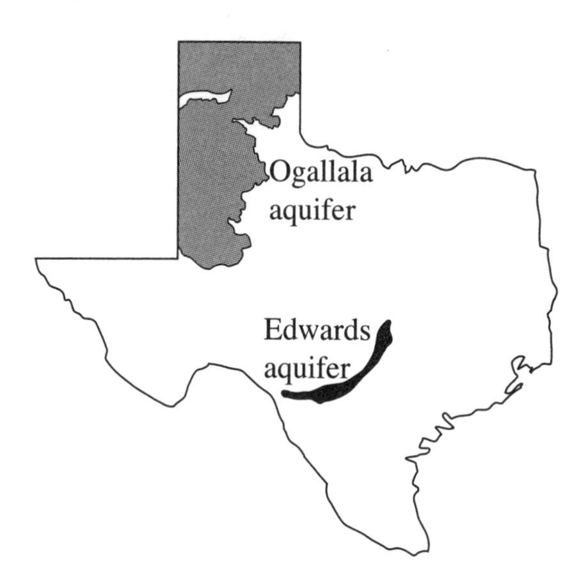

Figure 27-3. Ogallala and Edwards Aquifers

Fossil Record of Animal Phyla

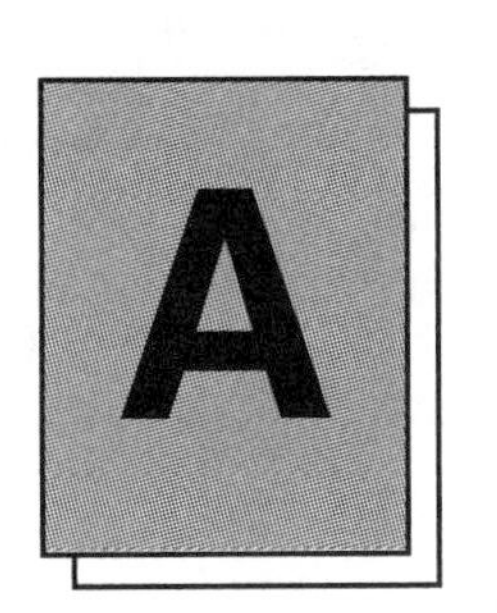

PORIFERA

Sponges are such a short step beyond single-celled organisms that it could be argued that they are not animals. At best, the porifers are an evolutionary dead end. They are more like cell colonies exhibiting just a hint of specialization of functions among different cell types. Nutrition, respiration, and excretion of waste products are performed individually, cell by cell, but water is circulated through the pores of a sponge along well-directed pathways. Hence the name *porifera*.

Porifers first appeared before the Cambrian Period. Modern species may be freshwater or marine. Sponges may be bowl-shaped or cup-shaped, or irregular. Their hard parts (if there are any) consist of tiny spines, or spicules, of calcium carbonate or silica (Figure A-1). Glassy sponge spicules are probably a major source of silica that can readily dissolve and reprecipitate as chert.

CNIDARIA

Cnidarians have three distinct types of tissue that are much more highly diversified than that of sponges. Many of them have a rather complex life cycle. At one stage, the animal is a polyp, an attached form. The polyp is essentially a tube, closed off at the attached end and surrounded by an array of stinging tentacles at the open mouth. Food and waste material proceed in and out through the same opening. A polyp may develop a bud that breaks off to become a medusa, or free-floating individual. A medusa can release eggs or sperm (never both) which unite to form a larva that grows into a new polyp. Many cnidarians skip either the polyp or medusa stage.

Jellyfish are an exclusively marine class of cnidarians in which the medusa form of the animal is the more important stage. A jellyfish is hardly more than a gelatinous, umbrella-shaped body fitted with

Figure A-1. (*a*) These vase-shaped fossil sponges from the Burgess Shale are exceptionally well preserved. [*American Museum of Natural History photograph.*] (*b*) Tiny sponge spicules may assume a variety of shapes.

tentacles and rudimentary sensory and digestive systems. Adults may be from 1 centimeter to 2 meters across, with tentacles up to 10 meters long. Though we would hardly expect to find many jellyfish in fossil form, there do exist some impressions made by jellyfish, as at the Ediacara site (see Chapter 12). Jellyfish were among the first true animals to appear, some time before the Cambrian Period.

A vastly more important fossil is *coral*, another class of marine cnidarians. Coral never produces a medusa. Varieties of soft coral—polyps with no hard parts, or with flesh reinforced by spicules—are little known from fossils. Stony corals, that build a rigid skeleton of calcium carbonate, are a major constituent of many limestones, and are a familiar sight in modern shallow tropical waters (Figure A-2). (A few species can tolerate deep, frigid water.) Coral grows today in only a few localities, but in past times, when there were widespread shallow seas, this animal was both abundant and represented by more species than are living today.

Some "solitary" corals, now extinct, built cone-shaped skeletons resembling a horn of plenty (see Figure 2-20). Other corals reproduced asexually by developing buds that grew into new adults. The colonies thus formed could accumulate into giant reefs featuring all manner of fantastic shapes: fans, compact masses, treelike branches, and others.

BRACHIOPODA

Most brachiopods are attached filter-feeders that superficially resemble clams, and indeed were once classified in the same phylum with clams. Both organisms have bilateral symmetry, but the line dividing the equal halves is different in each case [(Figure A-3(*a*)]. The valves (shells) of a brachiopod, composed of calcium carbonate or calcium phosphate, are bound together, and attached to the sea bottom via a muscular stalk. Inside is a complicated set of fleshy coils coated with tiny beating filaments. This feeding structure traps food particles as water is moved along by the filaments waving to and fro. Sometimes details of the calcified support of the feeding structure are preserved [(Figure A-3(*b*)]. Every so often, the animal clears itself of sediment and waste material by clapping its valves violently together. The valves of fossil species range in size from 1 millimeter to almost 40 centimeters in some gigantic forms.

Figure A-2. This scene in Heron Island, in Australia's Great Barrier, the world's mightiest living reef (see Figure 7-8), shows masses of colonial coral. Each colony contains hundreds to thousands of tiny individual animals. [*Courtesy Judy Lang.*]

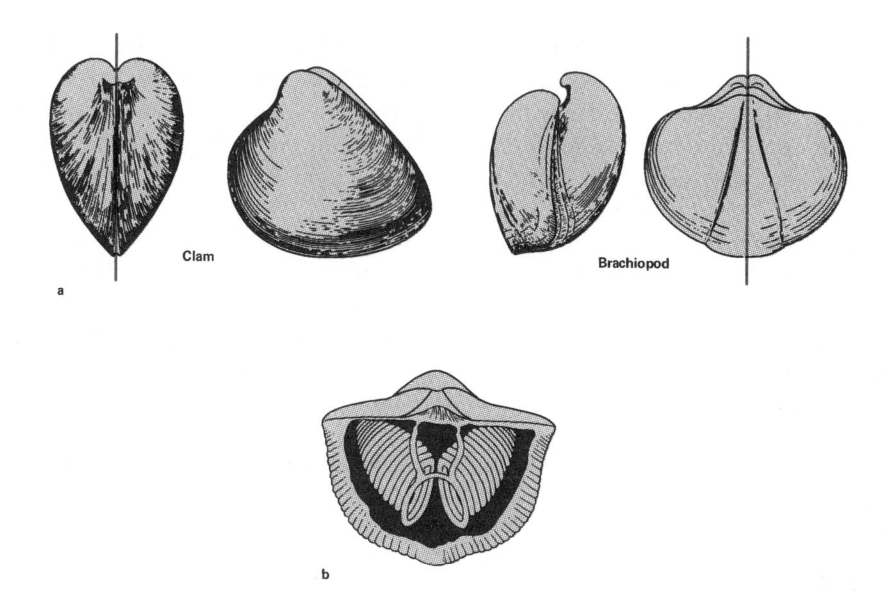

Figure A-3. (*a*) The symmetry of clams is *between* the valves. The line of symmetry of brachiopods lies *across* the valves. (*b*) The ciliated feeding structure inside many brachiopods is arranged in a complicated series of loops. The literature describing fossil brachiopods has grown to bewildering size; about 700 terms have been used just to describe the shape of the shell.

Brachiopods are marine organisms that can tolerate brackish (somewhat freshened) water only for short periods.

Obscure and little understood, the modern brachiopods have definitely been displaced by a more successful group of animals, the mollusks. Brachiopods are the only phylum for which the known fossil species (30,000) far exceed the number of modern, living species (220).

ANNELIDA

About half the 20 or so animal phyla can be broadly described as worms. The worm phyla are distinguished from one another entirely upon the basis of soft parts, hence the fossil record is absent aside from a few impressions, horny jaws, and trails, tracks, and burrows.

Most significant geologically is the phylum of annelid worms, which are segmented into a number of similar sections terminated at the front end by a head region containing specialized sensory organs. Annelids range in length from a few millimeters to about 3 meters. Although annelid worms appeared before the Cambrian period, the most celebrated collection site is the Middle Cambrian Burgess Shale.

MOLLUSCA

From general appearance, mollusks do not seem to be related to annelid worms, and for that matter, neither do snails, clams, or octopuses (all mollusks) resemble one another closely. The correct assignment of the relationship of these diverse organisms has been a small triumph of taxonomy. What do the mollusks share in common? These animals (excepting clams) possess a well-developed head with tentacles and eyes. A mollusk also has a single muscular foot (in some cases greatly modified) that enables it to "spud into" soft sediment and to creep or glide along. In addition, mollusks have a sheety tissue called a mantle that drapes downward to enclose the animal's guts. One of the several functions of the mantle is to secrete a protective shell of calcium carbonate or of chitin (a flexible horny substance). The octopus has an internal shell, and in certain rare species, shells are entirely lacking.

The origin of mollusks was debated for many years. And then, in 1957, several living specimens of a primitive mollusk (*Neopilina*), dredged from 3500 meters depth in the East Pacific, shed new light on the question. The soft parts of these living fossils (their nearest relatives had become extinct about 400 million years ago) are definitely arranged in segments. Although most of the mollusks have lost their segmentation, it appears likely that long ago this phylum split off from the annelid worms.

Gastropods—snails and their kin—are the most diverse mollusks; they live in all types of water from marine to fresh, and they are the only group of mollusks to have invaded the dry land. Different species graze upon algae, scavenge dead organisms, or actively pursue a carnivorous diet. Meat-eating snails can bore through the shell of an unlucky clam or some other supposedly secure victim. The body of a snail becomes severely twisted as it matures toward adulthood, and usually so does its shell. An astonishing variety of snail-shell shapes are preserved in the fossil record, but unfortunately they tell us little about the life habits of the animal.

Bivalves, another class of mollusks, include oysters, clams, and scallops. Species of these animals are adapted to life in almost any aqueous environment, where they may crawl, or swim, or burrow through loose sand and mud, or even bore a living space out of solid rocks (Figure A-4). Most bivalves are filter-feeders that strain out microscopic bits of food with tiny beating hairs (cilia). Their shells may be from 1 millimeter long to as much as 1.5 meters across. The largest modern clam weighs more than 270 kilograms, of which 95 percent is shell material.

The *cephalopods*, a marine class, probably represent the highest evolutionary potentiality of any unsegmented organism. These animals evolved more rapidly, and in more directions, than almost any other group. Cephalopods are represented today by octopuses (umbrella-like), squids and cuttlefish (cigar-

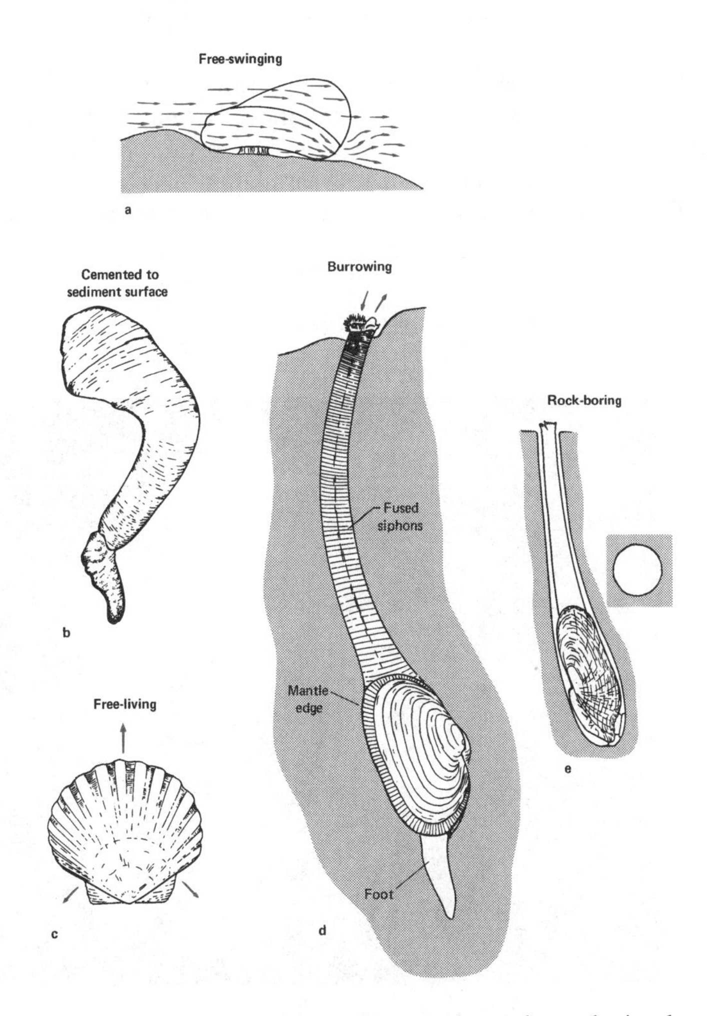

Figure A-4. By making careful comparisons with modern species, paleontologists have been highly successful in interpreting the living habits of extinct species of marine bivalves from the form of the fossil shell.

shape), and by a single coiled-shell genus, *Nautilus*. The deep-ocean squid is undoubtedly the largest of all animals that have no backbone. An individual 16 meters long, including tentacles, was once caught.

The fossil record suggests that primitive cephalopods began as a snail-like animal that deposited, not a single chamber as snails do, but a series of chambers separated by thin partitions. If extinct species were like the modern pearly nautilus, only the most forward of these chambers was occupied by the fleshy part of the animal (Figure A-5). Compare with the exterior of a coiled cephalopod (Figure 13-17). Pearly nautilus is a swimming carnivore, but extinct species probably were filter-feeders, grazers, floaters, bottom-dwelling forms, etc., in various combinations.

ARTHROPODA

The arthropod ("jointed feet") phylum accommodates far more living species (perhaps more than 8 million) than all other phyla combined. Actually, not only the feet, but the entire body of an arthropod, are divided into many jointed segments. An affinity of arthropods to their probable ancestors, the annelid worms, is thus obvious. One of the Burgess Shale fossils is an impression of an organism that looks strikingly like both segmented worms and certain arthropods such as the millipede. Arthropods evolved early in the Cambrian Period, and in fact some geologists use the appearance of the trilobite genus *Olenellus* to define the base of the Cambrian System.

The arthropod skeleton, an external, tough, laminated crust secreted by skin cells, serves both as support for the soft tissue inside and as protective armor. However, the platy covering of an arthropod cannot grow along with the rest of the individual. Arthropods solve the space problem by molting, or shedding off their armor from time to time. Until they grow new protection, they are quite vulnerable to being eaten.

An extinct class of arthropods, the *trilobites*, is exceedingly abundant in the Paleozoic record. The name trilobite, or "three-lobed one," refers not to the animal's segments (which were numerous in some species), but rather to its division lengthwise into three parts separated by grooves (Figure A-6). Basically, trilobites were marine scavengers that swam, skimmed through the surface of the mud, or burrowed into it. Adults of various species were as little as 0.5 centimeter to as much as 75 centimeters long.

Figure A-5. A nautilus shell sliced parallel to the plane of symmetry reveals a succession of more than 30 chambers culminated by the large end chamber currently occupied by the soft parts of the animal at the time of death. [*Judy Camps.*]

Figure A-6. The three-part plan, one central and two side sections (all segmented), is evident in these fossil trilobites from eastern Nevada. [*Courtesy James Sprinkle.*]

Another arthropod class represented by abundant fossils is composed of the *crustaceans* (lobsters, crabs, shrimp, and barnacles). Crustaceans populate the ocean by the uncounted trillions; they are the most abundant animals on earth on the basis of number of individuals. Adult crustaceans may be as much as 3.5 meters across, but most species are an inconspicuous 0.5 millimeter or so in length. The 40,000 species of these animals have adapted to land habitats and to all types of water from concentrated brine to fresh water.

Insects are enormously successful arthropods that have invaded a great variety of environments, but regrettably their fragile skeletons made of chitin do not fossilize readily. Insect fossils may be flattened impressions in fine-grained sediment, or delicately preserved entire bodies trapped in lumps of amber—fossil tree resin (Figure A-7).

ECHINODERMATA

The echinoderms are a large and important marine phylum, so plentiful that thick layers of some limestones are composed of echinoderm skeletal fragments. Echinoderm fossils first appeared in Cambrian rocks. Here we have the only phylum whose adult symmetry is five-sided, like a pentagon. The skin of most of these animals is a tough, leathery covering in which just a few to as many as hundreds of calcium carbonate plates are embedded. Since the plates are not fused together, each plate can enlarge quite simply as the animals grows. The disconnected plates do, however, tend to get scattered after the animal dies.

Another structure common to this phylum is a set of canals (tubes or grooves) called the water vascular system. The animal uses its hydraulic network to inflate one area while relaxing another to accomplish a rather stiff and awkward movement.

Most adult *crinoids* and *blastoids* are attached forms of echinoderms, and extremely abundant as fossils. A typical crinoid is fastened to the sea bottom by a long stalk consisting of little disks attached like buttons on a string (Figure A-8). At its base are hold-fasts that in some species even developed into a system of plantlike rootlets. At the top is a cup from which there sprouts a thick sheaf of waving arms. The arms are not tentacles—they do not seize large prey that is forcibly shoved into the mouth. Instead,

Figure A-7. This primitive ant, preserved in amber, is the most ancient known fossil of a "social insect." Features of its anatomy strongly indicate that ants and wasps had a common ancestry. The specimen was discovered in Cretaceous sediments on the New Jersey coast in 1965. [*From E. O. Wilson and others, "The First Menozoic Ants,"* Science, *vol. 157, no. 3729,* 1967. *Copyright 1967 by the American Association for the Advancement of Science.*]

the arms are outfitted with beating cilia that waft microscopic particles down to the digestive system located in the central cup.

If the dense beds of extinct crinoids were anything like their brilliantly colored modern descendants, they must have looked just like animated underwater flower gardens. Fossil crinoid heads are a rarity compared to the abundance of stalks. Perhaps the great number of flattened, crushing-type sharks' teeth in crinoid beds is a clue that the fish considered crinoid heads (hard plates and all) to be a tempting meal.

Starfish and *sea urchins* are mobile echinoderms. Some starfish are filter-feeders, like the crinoids, but a number are voracious carnivores that devour clams, coral, and other prey. Fossil starfish are rare but instructive [Figure A-9(*a*)]. Sometimes hollow molds are found into which the paleontologist can pour a preparation of latex. The rubber cast that comes out is a perfect replica; it can even be flexed gently to show how the hard parts of the starfish mesh together.

The sea urchin, or spiny echinoid, is the porcupine of the marine world. Its central body, which may be anything from spherical to a flattened disk, is armored with an imposing set of sharp-pointed spines. Not only are the spines protection against predators, but they help the animal shift about, dig burrows (even in rock), and collect food. Fossil sea urchins are only occasionally accompanied by their spines, which are easily loosed and scattered [Figure A-9(*b*)].

CHORDATA

Every individual in the chordates has a rod called a notochord running along its back (at least during the embryo stage of development). A subphylum called *vertebrata* includes species in which the embryonic notochord is later replaced by a jointed structure, the backbone. Chapter 15 takes a detailed look at vertebrate evolution.

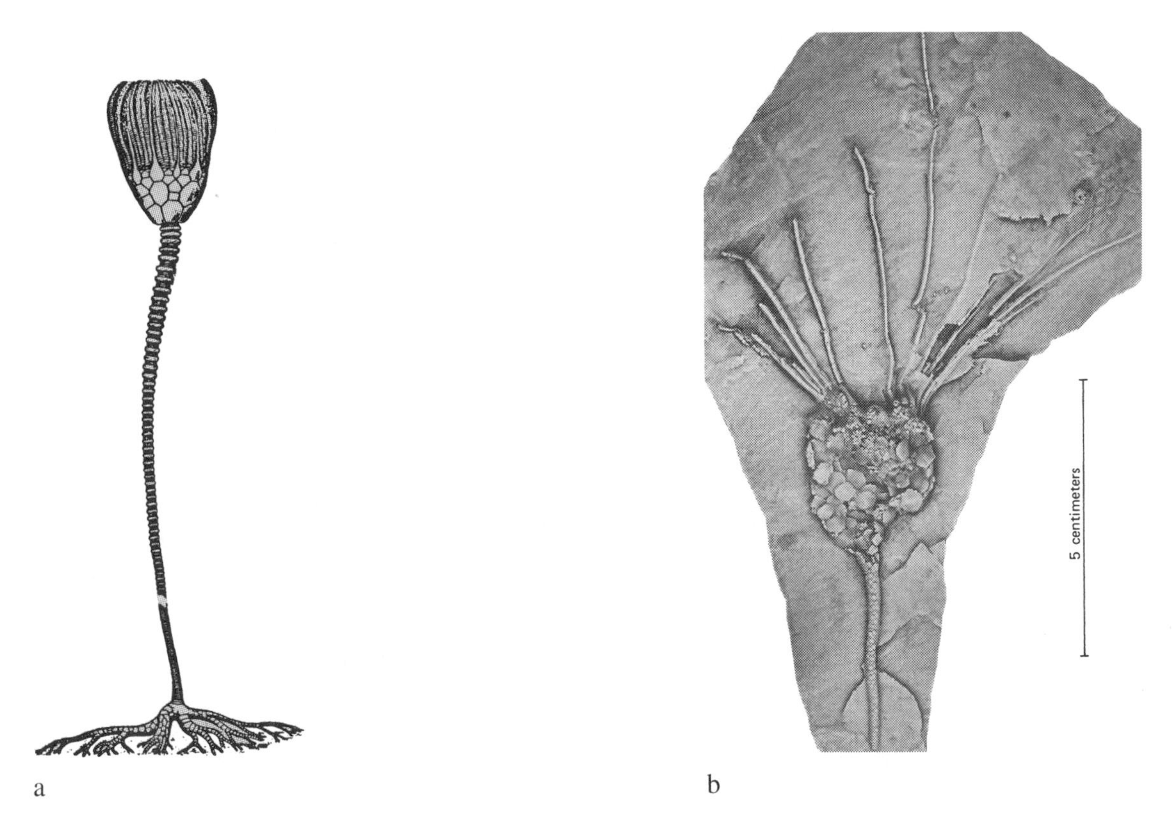

a b

Figure A-8. (*a*) An attached, mid-Paleozoic crinoid. (*b*) An early, primitive eocrinoid ("dawn crinoid"), from Middle Cambrian strata near the Burgess Shale locality, shows little of the organization of symmetrical body structures exhibited by specimen (*a*) [*Courtesy James Sprinkle.*]

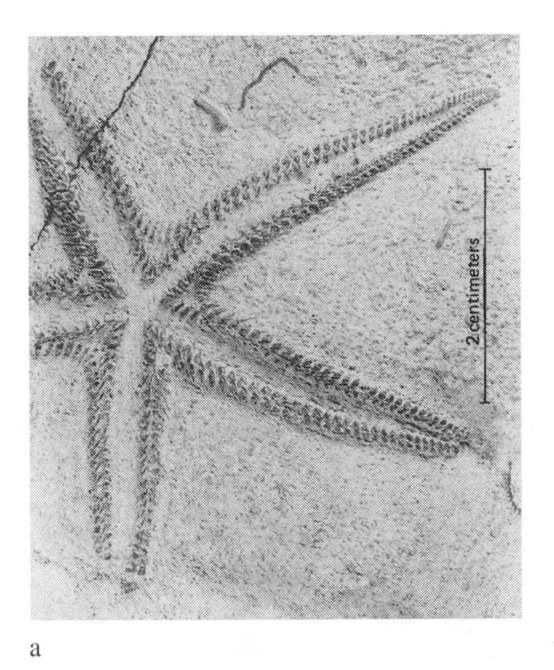

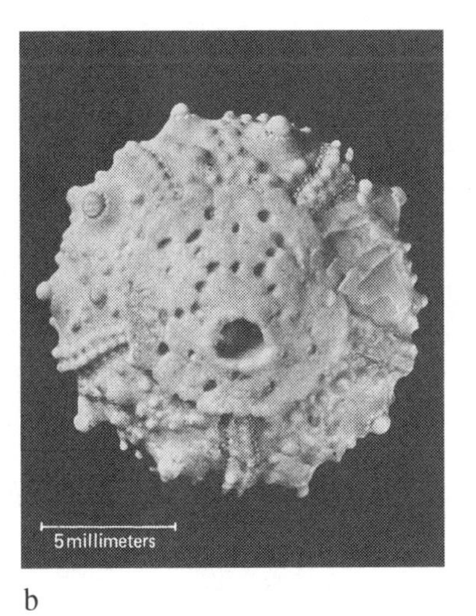

a b

Figure A-9. (*a*) This slab of limestone from a locality in Austin, Texas, contains an exceptional, nearly intact fossil starfish. (*b*) Spines are generally not found associated with the central body of a fossilized spiny echinoid. They were formerly attached to the many small knobs that adorn the surface of this specimen. Note the echinoid's five-fold symmetry. [*Courtesy James Sprinkle.*]

Fossil Record of Plant Divisions

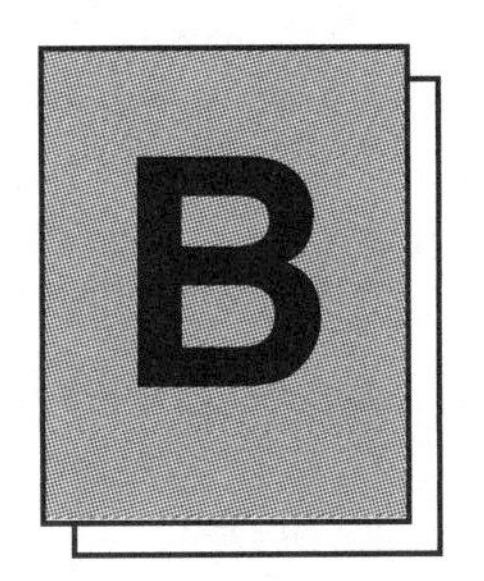

PSILOPHYTA

Psilophytes are unquestionably the most primitive plants, though not necessarily ancestral to other groups. Psilophytes are, in fact, about as simple as vascular plants can be. The most famous, and one of the oldest, psilophyte fossil localities is a Devonian chert bed (a former peat bog) near the village of Rhynie, in eastern Scotland.

A restoration of the petrified Rhynie psilophytes (Figure B-1) shows naked upright stems connected to short horizontal stems that crept along at the ground level or slightly below it. Nutrients and water entered the horizontal stem through tiny hairs. The plant stems divided by branching into two equal-sized parts. This style, called dichotomous branching, is considered to be a primitive attribute.

MICROPHYLLOPHYTA

Numerous, but tiny and simple, nonvascular, leaflike structures are the distinguishing feature of this plant division. Club mosses and spike mosses (technically not true mosses) are modern creeping forms of microphyllophyta, but extinct representatives reached tree size, approaching 50-meter heights on occasion. This division appeared in the Devonian Period but attained fullest development during the Mississippian and Pennsylvanian Periods, when it was prominent in extensive coastal swamplands of the Northern Hemisphere. Entire logs of the genus *Lepidodendron* are often encountered in coal mines. The microphyllophytes were probably the first to experiment (so to speak) with the production of roots, "leaves," and a treelike growth habit (Figure B-2).

ARTHROPHYTA

The arthrophytes, represented today by horsetails (branched species) and scouring rushes (unbranched), provide an interesting variation on the plant theme. In this division, the stems, both above and below ground, completely dominate the structure. They are hollow and interrupted by many joints, and their cell walls are heavily charged with gritty silica. In most species the leaves, of minor importance at best, are attached at intervals along the branches as radiating leaf-bursts, or "whorls" (Figure B-3). The arthrophytes also made their first appearance in the Devonian, reaching full climax late in the Paleozoic Era.

PTEROPHYTA

The highly successful ferns took the opposite track — they developed leaves as the dominant organ. The lovely fern leaves, familiar to most people, are complexly branched with generally a large number of leaflets [see Figure 13-4(*b*)]. Unlike the plant divisions mentioned above, ferns have continued to flourish as a large number of species to this day.

Figure B-1. Stems of some species of the Rhynie flora (above) were naked: stems of other species were densely clothed with scalelike emergences (not true leaves). Knobs at the tips of the branches are spore-bearing reproductive organs. *[From "Reconstruction of Ancient Vegetation by the Late Professor Paul Bertrand,"* The Paleobotanist, *vol. 1, 1952.*]

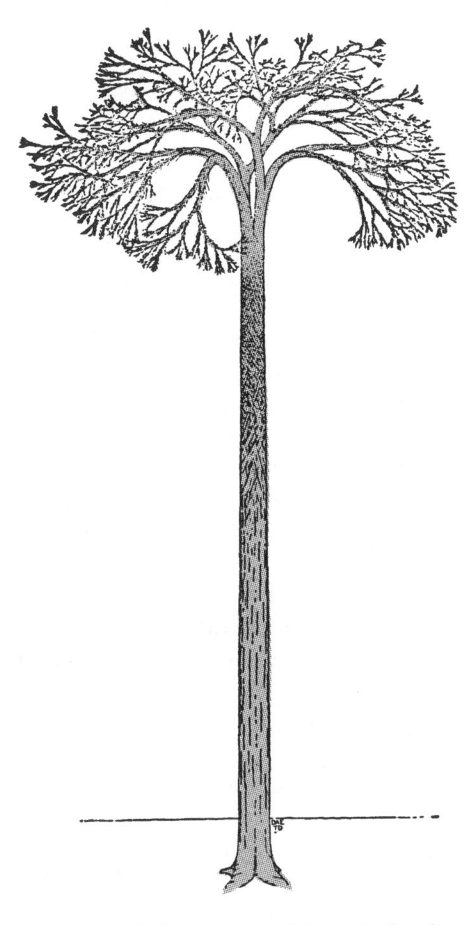

Figure B-2. Dichotomous branching of the crown of *Lepidodendron* caused its growth to be self-limiting. An analogy would be a thick bundle of wires that can be divided and divided until eventually the frayed ends of individual wires are separated. Similarly, the strands of vascular tissue in *Lepidodendron* divided until the tree was "used up." Spirally arranged rows of scars on the trunk are points of former attachment of leaves. [*After D. A. Eggert, "The Ontogeny of Carboniferous Arborescent Lycopsida."* Paleontographica, *Band 108, Abt. B., 1961.*]

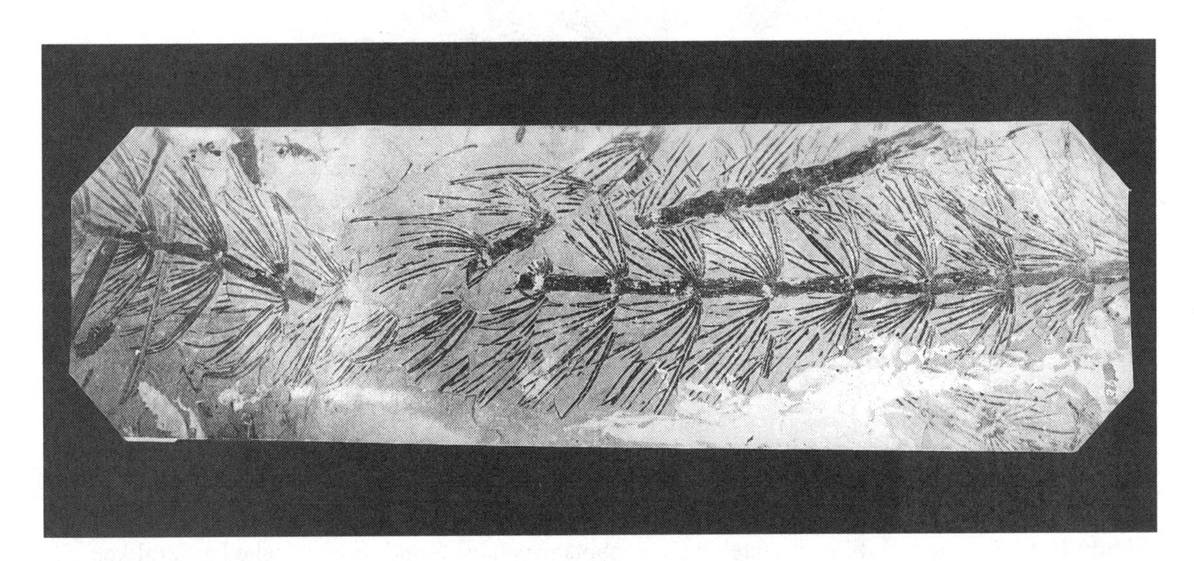

Figure B-3. Fossils of a Late Paleozoic treelike genus show the hollow, jointed stem and delicate leaf whorls typical of the arthrophytes. [*From H. N. Andrews,* Ancient Plants, *Comstock Publishing Associates, a division of Cornell University Press, Ithaca, N.Y., 1947.*]

CONIFEROPHYTA

The conifers are represented by pine, sequoia, cedar, yew, etc. These richly branched plants produce distinctive cones as part of the reproductive cycle, and are endowed with numerous needlelike or straplike leaves. Conifers and all the divisions described below are seed-bearing. Conifers appeared in the Paleozoic Era and probably reached their peak during the Mesozoic Era.

CYCADOPHYTA

Modern cycads (SIGH-cads) are a rather obscure group that look like a cross between ferns and palms, but cycads differ from both ferns and palms in the texture of the stem and mode of reproduction.

An extinct group of cycadophytes known as seed ferns points up one of the hazards of an attempt to imply too much from fragmentary fossils. For many years, species of supposed fern leaves were known which consistently failed to reveal any associated spore-bearing organs. Then, in 1905, seeds were discovered actually attached to unmistakable fernlike foliage (Figure B-4). Inasmuch as seeds are never produced by true ferns, these mysterious fossils had to be reassigned to another plant division, the cycadophytes.

Once it became apparent that the fernlike leaves are an important and recurring type, much interest was generated in learning their origin. One popular theory takes the simple, all-stem plants (such as psilophytes) as a starting point. As evolution continued, the stems became increasingly branched and flattened into a single plane (Figure B-5). Then a webbing of vegetation developed to connect the strands of vascular tissue, forming a fern-type leaf with branching veins. The extinct seed ferns support this theory (Figure B-6).

Figure B-4. In spite of a diligent searching, paleobotanists have found seeds attached to fernlike foliage only a dozen or so times. This Permian seed fern is actually allied more closely to cycads than to true ferns. [*After H. N. Andrews,* Ancient Plants, *Comstock Publishing Associates, a division of Cornell University Press, Ithaca, N.Y., 1947.*]

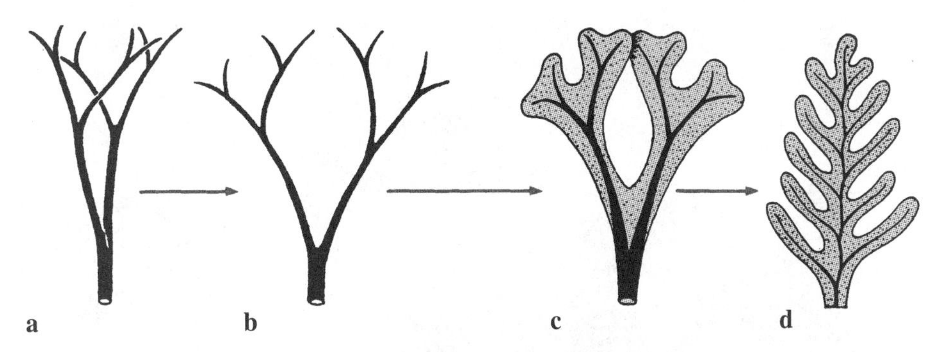

Figure B-5. The progression of forms, (*a*) to (*d*), represents the evolutionary development of leaves. [*After W. N. Stewart, "An Upward Look in Plant Morphology,"* Phytomorphology, *vol. 14., no. 1, 1964.*]

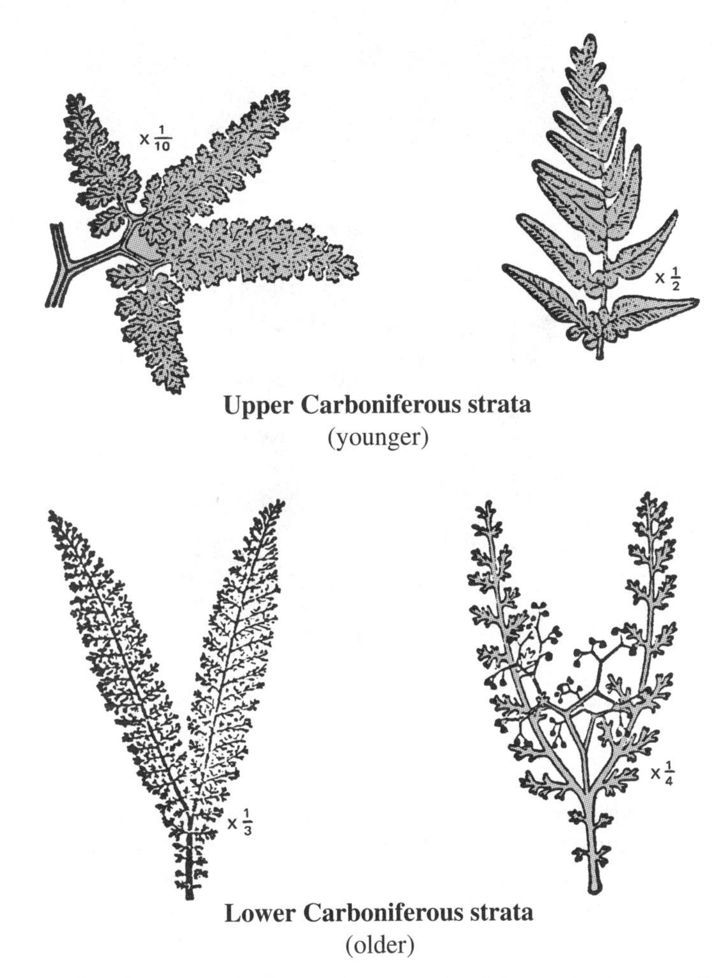

Figure B-6. In accord with theory, the lower (more ancient) leaves look more like stages (*a*) and (*b*) of Figure B-5, whereas the upper leaves look more like stages (*c*) and (*d*). [*After K. R. Sporne,* The Morphology of Gymnosperms, *Hutchinson & Co. (Publishers), Ltd., London, 1965.*]

GINKGOPHYTA

The modern ginkgo (hard "g") is truly a living fossil. Long thought to be extinct, a group of living ginkgo trees were discovered by Westerners in a small area of China in the late 1600s. The slow-growing ginkgo has been exported to many parts of the world where it survives handsomely. The one extant ginkgo species forms a stately tree covered by distinctive fan-shaped leaves (Figure B-7). Although it superfi-

a

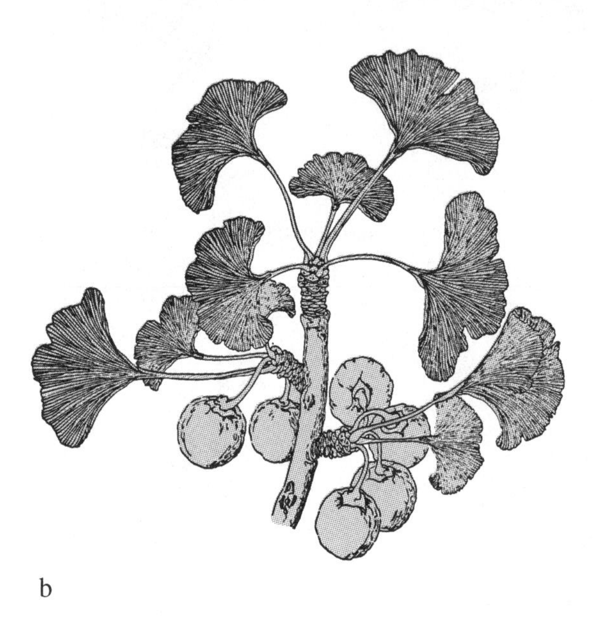

b

Figure B-7. (*a*) Leaves of a certain extinct ginkgo species are fan-shaped, like leaves of the modern plant (*b*), but the fossil leaves are more deeply indented. Thus it appears probable that the ginkgo leaf, like those of the ferns, gradually fused into more continuous bladelike forms. [(*a*) *from T. Delevoryas,* Plant Diversification, *Holt, Rinehart & Winston, Inc., New York, 1966.* (*b*) *after H. N. Andrews,* Ancient Plants, *Comstock Publishing Associates, a division of Cornell University Press, Ithaca, N.Y., 1947.*]

cially resembles the flowering trees, the ginkgo makeup differs from that of angiosperms in numerous technical details. Accordingly, ginkgo is placed in a separate division.

ANTHOPHYTA

The flowering plants beggar description because they are so abundant and diverse. Aside from the presence of flowers, other features that set angiosperms apart are well known to botanists but not apt to be fossilized. This enormous and successful division includes plant species that have invaded nearly every land environment in which life is possible.

Flowering plants have undoubtedly taken over some of the niches previously held by the still abundant but less widespread conifers. Two factors could contribute to the rapid evolution, hence relative success, of the anthophytes. Many of these plants have short reproductive cycles, in contrast with the long periods needed by most conifers to reach maturity. Another factor is that many anthophytes require insects to spread their pollen, whereas the pollen of conifers simply blows about indiscriminately. The evolution of insect-pollinated plants is firmly locked into the evolution of the insects themselves. This inter-dependence also caused rapid speciation.

Specialists have studied the tough, resistant fossil angiosperm pollen grains as sensitive indicators of ancient climate (Figure B-8). Extensive changes took place as a previously moderate world climate shifted into its present sharply stratified zonation in which polar ice sheets, temperate forests, deserts, and tropical rain forests are known. Pollen research has received great impetus from the invention of the scanning electron microscope. This instrument pictures the pollen surfaces in vivid detail never before witnessed.

Figure B-8. Details of angiosperm pollen are studied with the scanning electron microscope. Modern pollen, pictured here, are strikingly similar to their ancient fossil counterparts. [*Courtesy Thomas Taylor.*]

Index

M

N

O

S

T